nature

The Living Record of Science

《自然》 百年科学经典

英汉对照版　套装共十卷

第五卷

1966-1972

总顾问：李政道 （Tsung-Dao Lee）

英方主编：Sir John Maddox
Sir Philip Campbell

中方主编：路甬祥

外语教学与研究出版社 · 麦克米伦教育 · 自然科研

FOREIGN LANGUAGE TEACHING AND RESEARCH PRESS · MACMILLAN EDUCATION · NATURE RESEARCH

北京 BEIJING

图书在版编目（CIP）数据

《自然》百年科学经典：套装共十卷．第五卷：英汉对照／（英）约翰·马多克斯（John Maddox），（英）菲利普·坎贝尔（Philip Campbell），路甫祥主编．—— 北京：外语教学与研究出版社，2020.9
ISBN 978-7-5213-2021-3

Ⅰ．①自… Ⅱ．①约… ②菲… ③路… Ⅲ．①自然科学－文集－英、汉 Ⅳ．①N53

中国版本图书馆 CIP 数据核字（2020）第 155158 号

地图审图号：GS（2020）5244 号

出 版 人　徐建忠
项目统筹　章思英
项目负责　刘晓楠　黄小斌
责任编辑　王丽霞
责任校对　黄小斌
封面设计　高 蕾
版式设计　孙莉明
插图设计　麦克米伦提供原图扫描版
出版发行　外语教学与研究出版社
社　　址　北京市西三环北路 19 号（100089）
网　　址　http://www.fltrp.com
印　　刷　北京华联印刷有限公司
开　　本　787×1092　1/16
印　　张　76.5
版　　次　2021 年 1 月第 1 版 2021 年 1 月第 1 次印刷
书　　号　ISBN 978-7-5213-2021-3
定　　价　8000.00 元

购书咨询：（010）88819926　电子邮箱：club@fltrp.com
外研书店：https://waiyants.tmall.com
凡印刷、装订质量问题，请联系我社印制部
联系电话：（010）61207896　电子邮箱：zhijian@fltrp.com
凡侵权、盗版书籍线索，请联系我社法律事务部
举报电话：（010）88817519　电子邮箱：banquan@fltrp.com
物料号：320210001

记载人类文明
沟通世界文化
www.fltrp.com

《自然》百年科学经典（英汉对照版）

总顾问：李政道（Tsung-Dao Lee）

英方主编：Sir John Maddox　　　　　　中方主编：路甬祥

Sir Philip Campbell

编审委员会

英方编委　　　　　　　　**中方编委**（以姓氏笔画为序）

Philip Ball　　　　　　　许智宏

Vikram Savkar　　　　　赵忠贤

David Swinbanks　　　　滕吉文

本卷审稿专家（以姓氏笔画为序）

于 涌	王 昕	王晓晨	王敏康	邓祖淦	冯兴无	刘 力
刘佳佳	刘京国	孙 军	李三忠	李芝芬	李军刚	李素霞
杨 志	肖伟科	沈 杰	沈志侠	张元仲	张忠杰	张德兴
陈建国	陈继征	陈新文	武宝玕	林圣龙	尚仁成	昌增益
金 城	周 江	郑家驹	孟庆任	秦志海	袁 峥	莫 韫
顾孝诚	曹文广	崔 巍	梁前进	董 为	蒋世仰	

编译委员会

本卷翻译工作组稿人（以姓氏笔画为序）

王晓蕾　王耀杨　刘　明　刘晓楠　关秀清　李　琦　何　铭
沈乃澂　张　健　郭红锋　蔡则怡

本卷翻译人员（以姓氏笔画为序）

王耀杨　毛晨晖　邓铭瑞　冯　琛　冯　翀　吕　静　刘　霞
刘振明　刘皓芳　齐红艳　李　梅　吴　彦　何　钧　沈乃澂
张锦彬　岳友岭　金世超　周志华　郑建全　孟　洁　荆玉祥
钱　磊　黄　娆　彭丽霞　董培智　韩少卿　蔡则怡

本卷校对人员（以姓氏笔画为序）

王　迪　王　敏　王帅帅　王丽霞　王晓蕾　王德孚　孔凌楠
代　娟　刘　明　齐文静　闫　妍　阮玉辉　杜赛赛　李　四
李　琦　李　景　张文杰　陈思婧　周玉凤　周平博　郑期彤
宗伟凯　赵广宇　赵凤轩　胡婷婷　姜　薇　顾海成　黄小斌
韩玲俐　韩静文　曾芃斐　蔡　迪　潘卫东　潘承志

Contents
目录

Volume V

(1966-1972)

Stonehenge—An Eclipse Predictor

F. Hoyle

Editor's Note

During the 1960s there was considerable interest in, and debate about, the purpose of the ancient Stonehenge monument in western England. While British astronomer Fred Hoyle was not the first to suggest that Stonehenge was used to predict eclipses, he does demonstrate here how it could more accurately predict them if the "Aubrey circle" represents the ecliptic (the plane of the Solar System, in which the planets orbit the Sun).

THE suggestion that Stonehenge may have been constructed with a serious astronomical purpose has recently received support from Hawkins, who has shown[1] that many alignments of astronomical significance exist between different positions in the structure. Some workers have questioned whether, in an arrangement possessing so many positions, these alignments can be taken to be statistically significant. I have recently reworked all the alignments found by Hawkins. My opinion is that the arrangement is not random. As Hawkins points out, some positions are especially relevant in relation to the geometrical regularities of Stonehenge, and it is these particular positions which show the main alignments. Furthermore, I find these alignments are just the ones that could have served far-reaching astronomical purposes, as I shall show in this article. Thirdly, on more detailed investigation, the apparently small errors, of the order of $\pm 1°$, in the alignments turn out not to be errors at all.

In a second article[2] Hawkins goes on to investigate earlier proposals that Stonehenge may have operated as an eclipse predictor. The period of regression of the lunar nodes, 18.61 years, is of especial importance in the analysis of eclipses. Hawkins notes that a marker stone moved around the circle of fifty-six Aubrey holes at a rate of three holes per year completes a revolution of the circle in 18.67 years. This is close enough to 18.61 years to suggest a connexion between the period of regression of the nodes and the number of Aubrey holes. In this also I agree with Hawkins. I differ from him, however, in the manner in which he supposes the eclipse predictor to have worked. Explicitly, the following objections to his suggestions seem relevant:

(1) The assumption that the Aubrey holes served merely to count cycles of 56 years seems to me to be weak. There is no need to set out fifty-six holes at regular intervals on the circumference of a circle of such a great radius in order to count cycles of fifty-six.

(2) It is difficult to see how it would have been possible to calibrate the counting system proposed by Hawkins. He himself used tables of known eclipses in order to find it. The builders of Stonehenge were not equipped with such *post hoc* tables.

2

巨石阵——日月食的预报器

霍伊尔

编者按

在 20 世纪 60 年代，英格兰西部古老巨石阵的用途是大家非常关注和存在争议的问题。虽然第一个提出巨石阵是用于预测日月食的工具的人并非英国天文学家弗雷德·霍伊尔，但他在这里解释了在"奥布里环"代表黄道面（即太阳系的运行平面，所有行星都在这个平面内绕太阳运动）的前提下如何利用巨石阵更精确地预言日月食。

巨石阵可能是出于一个重要的天文目的而修建的，这一假设最近得到了霍金斯的支持。他指出 [1]，在该建筑的不同位置中存在着有天文学意义的准线。一些研究者曾质疑：在一个拥有如此多方位的布局中，这些准线是否应该被认为具有统计学上的显著性。最近我检验了霍金斯发现的所有准线。我认为这个布局不是随机的。正如霍金斯所指出的，有些位置与巨石阵的几何规律之间有特殊的关联，而主要的准线正是在这些特殊位置上发现的。其次，我还发现这些准线恰好就是能长期服务于天文学观测需要的准线，在本文中我会解释这一点。第三，根据更加细致的调查，在这些准线中看似存在的量级为 ±1° 的小偏差其实根本就算不上偏差。

在第二篇文章中 [2]，霍金斯又对早先的一个假说进行了研究，即认为巨石阵可能曾用于预报日月食。月球交点的回归周期为 18.61 年，这一周期在日月食分析中是非常重要的。霍金斯指出：有一个石标以每年 3 个洞的速率沿着由 56 个奥布里洞组成的圆周运动，旋转一周所用的时间恰好是 18.67 年。这和 18.61 年非常接近，因而说明月球交点的回归周期与奥布里洞的数量之间是存在相关性的。在这一点上我也同意霍金斯的观点。不过，我与他的分歧之处在于他所说的预测日月食的方式。显然，以下几条对其所持观点的反对意见看起来是合理的：

（1）在我看来，假设奥布里洞仅仅是被用于计算 56 年的循环未免有点站不住脚。没有必要为了表示出 56 年的循环，而在这么大半径的圆周上以一定的间距建造 56 个洞。

（2）很难解释古人是如何校准由霍金斯所提出的计算系统的。为了找到这一系统，他本人使用了已发生过的日月食的记录表。巨石阵的建造者们哪里会有这些在日月食发生之后才统计出的表格。

(3) The predictor gives only a small fraction of all eclipses. It is difficult to see what merit would have accrued to the builders from successful predictions at intervals as far apart as 10 years. What of all the eclipses the system failed to predict?

My suggestion is that the Aubrey circle represents the ecliptic. The situation shown in Fig. 1 corresponds to a moment when the Moon is full. The first point of Aries γ has been arbitrarily placed at hole 14. *S* is the position of the Sun, the angle ☉ is the solar longitude, *M* is the projection of the Moon on to the ecliptic, *N* is the ascending node of the lunar orbit, *N′* the descending node, and the centre *C* is the position of the observer. As time passes, the points *S*, *M*, *N* and *N′* move in the senses shown in Fig. 1. *S* makes one circuit a year. *M* moves more quickly, with one circuit in a lunar month. One rotation of the line of lunar nodes *NN′* is accomplished in 18.61 years. In Fig. 1, *S* and *M* are at the opposite ends of a diameter because the diagram represents the state of affairs at full Moon.

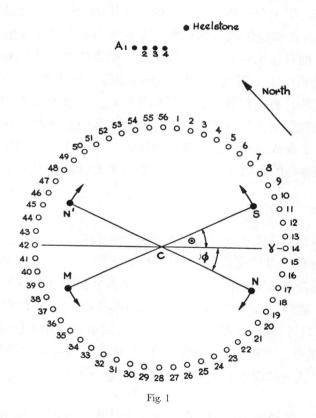

Fig. 1

If the Moon is at *N*, there is a solar eclipse if the Sun is within roughly ±15° of *N*, and a lunar eclipse if the Sun is within ±10° of *N′*. Similarly, if the Moon is at *N′*, there will be a solar eclipse if the Sun is within ±15° of coincidence with the Moon, and a lunar eclipse if it is within roughly ±10° of the opposite end of the line of lunar nodes. Evidently if we represent *S*, *M*, *N* and *N′* by markers, and if we know how to move the markers so as to

（3）这种预报方法只预测出了全部日月食中很小的一部分。很难理解这些建造者们会因为成功预言间隔可达 10 年之久的日月食而得到什么好处。怎么解释那么多该系统没有预言出来的日月食呢？

我的观点是奥布里环代表了黄道。图 1 所示的位置对应于满月时的位置。任意取白羊座 γ 作为第一个点放在第 14 号洞处。S 是太阳的位置，⊙ 角代表黄经，M 是月球在黄道面上的投影，N 是月球轨道的升交点，N' 为降交点，中心 C 是观测者所在的位置。随着时间的流逝，S、M、N 和 N' 点会按图 1 所示的方式运动。S 每年转一圈。M 运行得会更快一些，一个朔望月循环一周。两个月球交点所连成的直线 NN' 旋转一周的时间为 18.61 年。在图 1 中，S 和 M 位于一条直径的两端是因为这张图代表的是满月时的状态。

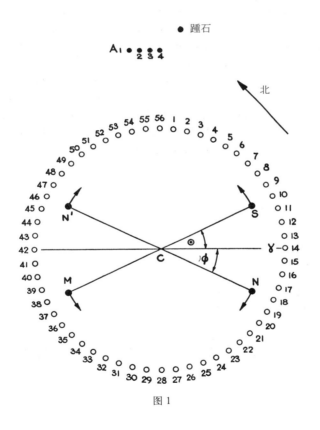

图 1

如果月球位于 N 点，那么当太阳在距离 N 点大致 ±15° 范围之内时就会发生一次日食；而当太阳在距离 N' 点 ±10° 范围之内时就会发生一次月食。同样，如果月球位于 N' 点，那么当太阳在距离月球位置 ±15° 范围之内时就会发生一次日食；而当太阳在距离两个月球交点连线的另外一端大致 ±10° 范围之内时就会发生一次月

represent the actual motions of the Sun and Moon with adequate accuracy, we can predict almost every eclipse, although roughly half of them will not be visible from the position of the observer. This is a great improvement on the widely scattered eclipses predictable by Hawkins's system. Eclipses can occur as many as seven times in a single year, although this would be an exceptional year.

The prescriptions for moving the markers are as follows: (1) Move S anticlockwise two holes every 13 days. (2) Move M anticlockwise two holes each day. (3) Move N and N' clockwise three holes each year.

We can reasonably assume that the builders of Stonehenge knew the approximate number of days in the year, the number of days in the month, and the period of regression of the nodes. The latter follows by observing the azimuth at which the Moon rises above the horizon. If in each lunar month we measure the least value of the azimuth (taken east of north), we find that the "least monthly values" change slowly, because the angle $\phi = NC\gamma$ changes. The behaviour of the "least monthly values" is shown in Fig. 2 for the range $-60° \le \phi \le 60°$. (The azimuthal values in Fig. 2 were worked out without including a refraction or a parallax correction. These small effects are irrelevant to the present discussion.) The least monthly values oscillate with the period of ϕ, 18.61 years. By observing the azimuthal cycle, the period of ϕ can be determined with high accuracy by observing many cycles. At Stonehenge sighting alignments exist that would have suited such observations. With the periods of S, M and N known with reasonable accuracy the prescriptions follow immediately as approximate working rules.

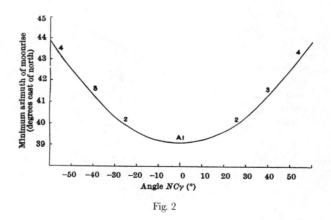

Fig. 2

Suppose an initially correct configuration for M, N and S is known. The prescriptions enable us to predict ahead what the positions of M, N and S are going to be, and thus to foresee coming events—but only for a while, because inaccuracies in our prescriptions will cause the markers to differ more and more from the true positions of the real Moon, Sun, and ascending node. The lunar marker will be the first to deviate seriously—the prescription

食。显然，假设我们用标记标出了 S、M、N 和 N' 的位置，并且假设我们知道如何通过移动这些标记来足够精确地表示太阳和月球的真实移动过程，那么我们就可以预言几乎所有的日月食，尽管有大约一半的日月食在观测者所在的位置上是看不到的。这在很大程度上优于利用霍金斯系统预测非常分散的日月食。在一年之中，日月食的发生次数可多达七次，不过这样的年头是很少见的。

移动这些标记的方法如下所述：（1）每 13 天将 S 点逆时针移动 2 个洞。（2）每天将 M 点逆时针移动 2 个洞。（3）每年将 N 点和 N' 点顺时针移动 3 个洞。

我们可以合理地认为巨石阵的建造者们知道一年中的大致天数、一个月的天数以及月球交点的回归周期。后者可以通过观测月球从地平线升起时的方位角求得。如果在每个朔望月我们都能测量出方位角的最小值（由北向东），我们就会发现"每月最小值"在缓慢变化，这是因为角 $\phi = NC\gamma$ 在不断变化。图 2 中显示出了当 ϕ 的范围处于 $-60° \leqslant \phi \leqslant 60°$ 时"每月最小值"的变化情况。（图 2 中的方位角值没有经过折射校正或视差校正。这些较小的效应与现在讨论的内容无关。）每月最小值在 ϕ 的周期——18.61 年内上下波动。通过观测方位角的周期变化，并根据多个周期的观测结果就可以精确地测算出 ϕ 的周期。巨石阵中有一些可用于瞄准的排列很适合进行这样的观测。只要知道具有合理精确度的 S、M 和 N 的周期，就可以马上把上述方法作为大体的工作流程。

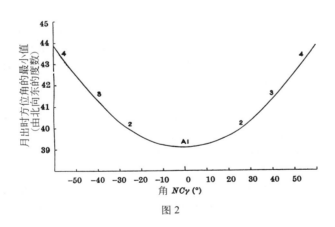

图 2

假设 M、N 和 S 的初始位置是已知的并且是正确的。利用上述方法可以使我们提前预测出 M、N 和 S 未来的位置，并由此预见到将要发生的日月食——但这只能维持很短的时间，因为上述方法中所存在的误差会使标记与真实月球、真实太阳和真实月球轨道升交点的实际位置之间的偏差越来越大。第一个发生显著偏离的将是

gives an orbital period of 28 days instead of 27.32 days. But we can make a correcting adjustment to the M marker twice every month, simply by aligning M opposite S at the time of full Moon, and by placing it coincident with S at new Moon. The prescription for S gives an orbital period of 364 days, which is near enough to the actual period because it is possible to correct the position of S four times every year, by suitable observations made with the midsummer, midwinter, and equinoctial sighting lines that are set up with such remarkable accuracy at Stonehenge.

Stonehenge is also constructed to determine the moment when $\phi=0$, that is, when N should be set at γ. The line C to A 1 of Fig. 1 is the azimuthal direction for the minimum point of Fig. 2. By placing N at γ when the Moon rises farthest to the north, the N marker can be calibrated once every 18.61 years. The prescription implies only a small error over one revolution of N. If N started correctly, it would be out of its true position by only 1° or so at the end of the first cycle. The tolerance for eclipse prediction is about 5°, so that if we were to adjust N every cycle, the predictor would continue to work indefinitely without appreciable inaccuracy. The same method also serves to place N at the beginning.

But now we encounter an apparent difficulty. The minimum of Fig. 2 is very shallow and cannot really be determined in the way I have just described. Angular errors cannot have been less than ±0.25°, and even this error, occurring at the minimum of Fig. 2, is sufficient to produce an error of as much as ±15° in ϕ.

The correct procedure is to determine the moment of the minimum by averaging the two sides of the symmetrical curve, by taking a mean between points 2, for example. The inaccuracy is then reduced to not more than a degree or two—well within the permitted tolerance.

What is needed is to set up sighting directions a little to the east of the most northerly direction. The plan of Stonehenge shows a line of post holes, A 1, 2, 3 and 4, placed regularly and with apparent purpose in exactly the appropriate places.

The same point applies to solsticial measurements of the Sun. In summer the sighting line should be slightly increased in azimuth, in winter it should be slightly decreased.

Hawkins[1] gives two tables in which he includes columns headed "Error Alt.". These altitude errors were calculated on the assumption that the builders of Stonehenge intended to sight exactly the azimuthal extremes. The test of the present ideas is whether the calculated "errors" have the appropriate sign—on the argument given here "errors" should be present and they should have the same sign as the declination. In ten out of twelve values which Hawkins gives in his Table 1 this is so. The direction from C to the Heelstone is one of the two outstanding cases. Here the "error" is zero, suggesting that this special direction

月球的标记 M——在该方法中所采用的运行周期为 28 天而非 27.32 天。但是我们可以每个月对标记 M 的位置进行两次校正，只需在满月时把 M 点调整到 S 点对面，而在新月时将其摆放到和 S 点重合即可。S 在该方法中的运行周期为 364 天，这已经非常接近真实的周期值了，因为每年都可以对 S 的位置进行四次校正，方法是在夏至点、冬至点、春分点和秋分点时刻正确地测量光线的位置，这些都可以在巨石阵中以很高的精度被测定。

巨石阵也可以用于测定 $\phi=0$ 的时刻，即当 N 被设定在 γ 点时。图 1 中从 C 到 $A1$ 的连线方向即是图 2 中最小值点的方位角方向。当月球在最靠北的角度升起的时候，需要将 N 定位于 γ 点，这样每 18.61 年就可以对标记 N 进行一次校准。上述方法要求 N 在循环一周后只能有很小的偏差。如果 N 的起始位置是正确的，那么它在环行一周结束时只会与真实位置偏离 1° 左右。日月食预测所允许的误差在大约 5° 的范围以内，所以如果我们每循环一周就对 N 点进行一次校准，那么这个预报器将会在误差很小的情况下无限期地发挥作用。还可以用同样的方法把 N 的初始位置确定下来。

但是现在我们遇到了一个明显的麻烦。图 2 中的最小值范围非常宽，用我刚刚描述的方法很难真正确定这个最小值点。角度误差不能小于 $\pm0.25°$，而在确定图 2 中的最小值时即便只存在这么大的误差，也足以使 ϕ 产生 $\pm15°$ 的误差。

正确的方法是通过在对称曲线的两边取平均来测定最小值的时刻，例如取图中两个点 2 之间的平均值。利用这种方法就可以把误差减小到不大于 1 度或 2 度——远低于误差允许的范围。

现在需要在最北边偏东一点的方向上设置视线方向。在巨石阵的平面图中有一条由柱坑 $A\,1$、$A\,2$、$A\,3$ 和 $A\,4$ 排成的直线，它们的排列很有规律，并且准确地摆放在了适当的位置上，这显然是有意安排的。

可以用同样的方法来测量太阳的二至点。在夏季，视线的方位角会略有增加；而在冬季，它应该略有减少。

霍金斯 [1] 给出了两张表格，表格中含有标题为"高度误差"的列。计算这些高度误差的前提是假设巨石阵的建造者想要精确地观测出最大方位角。检验上述观点的方法是要看计算出的"误差"是否具有正确的符号——这里给出的论点是应该存在"误差"，并且与偏角的符号一致。对于霍金斯在表 1 中所给出的 12 个值，有 10 个属于这种情况。从 C 点到那块踵石的方向是两个最突出的偏差点之一。在这里"误

was kept exactly at the direction of midsummer sunrise, perhaps for aesthetic or ritualistic reasons. The other discrepant case is 91→94. Here my own calculation gives only a very small discrepancy, suggesting that this direction was also kept at the appropriate azimuthal extreme.

Negative values of the altitude error correspond to cases where it would be necessary to observe below the horizontal plane, if the objects in question were sighted at their extreme azimuths. This is impossible at Stonehenge because the land slopes gently upward in all directions. Such sighting lines could not have been used at the extremes, a circumstance which also supports this point of view.

It is of interest to look for other ways of calibrating the N marker. A method, which at first sight looks promising, can be found using a special situation in which full Moon happens to occur exactly at an equinox. There is evidence that this method was tried at Stonehenge, but the necessary sighting lines are clearly peripheral to the main structure. Further investigation shows the method to be unworkable, however, because unavoidable errors in judging the exact moment of full Moon produce large errors in the positioning of N. The method is essentially unworkable because the inclination of the lunar orbit is small. Even so, the method may well have caused a furore in its day, as the emphasis it gives to a full Moon at the equinox could have been responsible for the dating of Easter.

An eclipse calibrator can be worked accurately almost by complete numerology, if the observer is aware of a curious near-commensurability. Because S and N move in opposite directions the Sun moves through N more frequently than once a year, in 346.6 days. Nineteen such revolutions is equal to 6,585.8 days, whereas 223 lunations is equal to 6,585.3 days. Thus after 223 lunations the N marker must bear almost exactly the same relation to S that it did before. If the correct relation of N to S is known at any one moment N can be reset every 223 lunations; that is, every 18 years 11 days. The near-commensurability is so good that this system would give satisfactory predictions for more than 500 years. It requires, of course, S to be set in the same way as before. The advantage is that in the case of N it obviates any need for the observational work described above. But without observations the correct initial situation cannot be determined unless the problem is inverted. By using observed eclipses the calibrator could be set up by trial and error. This is probably the method of the Saros used in the Near East. There is no evidence that it was used at Stonehenge. The whole structure of Stonehenge seems to have been dedicated to meticulous observation. The method of Stonehenge would have worked equally well even if the Saros had not existed.

Several interesting cultural points present themselves. Suppose this system was invented by a society with cultural beliefs associated with the Sun and Moon. If the Sun and Moon are given godlike qualities, what shall we say of N? Observation shows that whenever M and S are closely associated with N, eclipses occur. Our gods are temporarily eliminated. Evidently, then, N must be a still more powerful god. But N is unseen. Could this be the origin of the concept of an invisible, all-powerful god, the God of Isaiah? Could it have been the discovery of the

差"为零，说明这个特殊方向与夏至时太阳升起的方向保持精确一致，这也许是出于审美上的需要或者仪式上的要求吧。另一个偏差点是 91 → 94 方向。我通过计算发现这里只有很小的误差，说明这个方向也与最大方位角保持着相当的一致性。

高度误差中的负值对应于需要在地平面以下进行观测的情况，比如在只有这么做才能以最大方位角观察某些天体时。对巨石阵来说这是不可能的，因为在所有方向上地势都是微微向上倾斜的。这样的视线方向不可能用于观测出最大方位角，这一事实再次印证了上述观点。

人们对寻找其他方式校准标记 N 很感兴趣。有一种方法，初看起来前景还不错，但后来发现它用到了一个特殊条件，即要求满月刚好出现在春分点或秋分点。有证据表明，这种方法曾在巨石阵中被尝试过，但视线显然只能位于巨石阵主体结构的外部。然而，进一步的调查表明该方法行不通，这是因为在判断满月的具体时刻时会产生难以避免的误差，而这种误差又会使 N 的定位出现很大的偏差。由于月球轨道的倾角太小，所以这种方法从本质上讲是不可行的。即便如此，该方法很可能在当时曾造成过一时的轰动，因为它要观测在二分点时刻发生的满月，而春分见到的满月可能曾被用于确定复活节的日期。

如果观测者知道一种特殊的近似对等关系，那么几乎完全用数字学就能够准确地进行日月食的校准。因为 S 和 N 向相反的方向运动，所以太阳每次经过 N 所需的时间不到一年，为 346.6 天。19 个这样的循环等于 6,585.8 天，而 223 个朔望月等于 6,585.3 天。因此，在 223 个朔望月之后，标记 N 相对于 S 的位置就会与 223 个月前几乎完全一致。如果能了解到 N 和 S 在任意时刻的正确位置关系，那么每 223 个朔望月，也就是 18 年零 11 天，就可以把 N 的位置重新调整一次。这种近似对等关系非常绝妙，以至于该系统能够在 500 多年的时间里给出令人满意的预测结果。当然，设置 S 点位置的方法应该与以前相同。这种方法的优势在于不需要根据之前描述的观测过程来确定 N 的位置。但没有经过观测就不能确定正确的初始位置，除非这个问题是反过来问的。而利用已经观测到的日月食数据就可以反复地校正这个预报器。这种方法大概就是近东地区所采用的沙罗周期。没有证据能够证明在巨石阵中使用了这一方法。巨石阵的整体结构似乎曾被用于精确的观测。即使不存在沙罗周期，巨石阵的方法也同样可以很好地预报日月食。

以下是几个文化方面的有趣话题。假设巨石阵的建造者来自于一个崇尚与日月有关的文化的民族。如果太阳和月亮被赋予了类似神的特性，那么我们应该怎么看待 N？观测结果表明在 M 和 S 非常靠近 N 时总会有日月食现象发生。我们的神就会被暂时抛在一边。那么显然 N 一定是一个更加强有力的神。但 N 是不可见的。这

significance of N that destroyed sun-worship as a religion? Could M, N and S be the origin of the doctrine of the Trinity, the "three-in-one, the one-in-three"? It would indeed be ironic if it turned out that the roots of much of our present-day culture were determined by the lunar node.

(**211**, 454-456; 1966)

Fred Hoyle: University of Cambridge.

References:
1. Hawkins, G. S., *Nature*, **200**, 306 (1963).
2. Hawkins, G. S., *Nature*, **202**, 1258 (1964).

难道就是一个无形而全能的神——以赛亚神概念的起源吗？发现 N 的重要性会不会破坏了宗教中对太阳的崇拜？M、N 和 S 会不会就是三位一体教义，即"三中有一、一中有三"的起源呢？如果能够证明现今文明的根源主要来自于月球交点，这还真有点讽刺意味。

（孟洁 翻译；肖伟科 审稿）

Stonehenge—A Neolithic "Observatory"

C. A. Newham

Editor's Note

The astronomical function of the ancient monument of Stonehenge near Salisbury in England is also considered in this contribution by astronomer C. A. ("Peter") Newham. He proposes that the post holes of the stone circle were used to mark the bearing of moonrise, which would be used to help predict eclipses. Archaeologists, however, have remained somewhat sceptical of such speculative interpretations by astronomers.

PROF. G. S. Hawkins[1] has shown how Stonehenge could be regarded as a "computer" to predict the time when eclipses of the Sun and Moon were due, though not always visible at Stonehenge. He ingeniously relates the fifty-six Aubrey holes with a 56-year eclipse cycle. The principle is valid, but there is no evidence to support the idea that Stonehenge was intended to be a "computer" other than that the majority of main features embodied in the "monument" unquestionably have some astronomical connexion. There are, however, a number of "post holes"; however, no satisfactory explanation has so far been put forward to explain their purpose.

An analysis of the position and number of post holes prompts a suggestion as to their purpose, and may well provide the clue to the method by which the builders of Stonehenge acquired elementary knowledge of Moon cycles, possibly including the approximate 56-year eclipse cycle.

Stonehenge post holes. Of the many post holes found in and around Stonehenge, there is one group of about forty holes situated in the "causeway" near the northeast entrance (Fig. 1). The holes seem to radiate from the centre of the Aubrey circle, and lie within a 10-degree arc north of the heelstone or solstice line. They are roughly arranged into six ranks crossing the line of the causeway.

巨石阵——一个新石器时代的"天文台"

纽汉

编者按

在这篇文章中，天文学家纽汉（"彼得"）也在思考英国索尔兹伯里附近的史前纪念碑——巨石阵的天文学功能，他提出石圈中的柱坑可以用于标志月亮升起的方位，这对日月食的预测是有帮助的。然而，考古学家们仍然对这些天文学家的试探性解释持怀疑态度。

霍金斯教授[1]曾解释过如何把巨石阵看作"计算工具"来预言日月食的发生时间，虽然在巨石阵的位置上未必能观测到所有的日月食。他巧妙地将56个奥布里洞与56年的日月食周期联系起来。虽然他提出的原理具有可行性，但是现在还没有证据能证明巨石阵原本是被设计为一种"计算工具"，而不是大部分主体结构无疑与天文学有一定联系的"纪念碑"。然而，这里存在很多"柱坑"；迄今为止还没有令人满意的解释能够说明这些柱坑的用途。

本文根据对柱坑位置和数目的分析得出了一个有关其用途的假设，该假设很可能提供了有关巨石阵建造者如何获取月球周期基础知识方面的线索，其中或许包括约为56年的日月食周期。

巨石阵的柱坑。在巨石阵之内和周围发现的很多柱坑中，有一组柱坑位于"长堤"上靠近东北入口的地方，数量大约有40个（图1）。这些柱坑似乎是从奥布里环的中心延伸出来的，并且分布在从奥布里环中心到踵石或至日点的连线以北10度的范围之内。它们在垂直于长堤的延伸方向上大致排成6行。

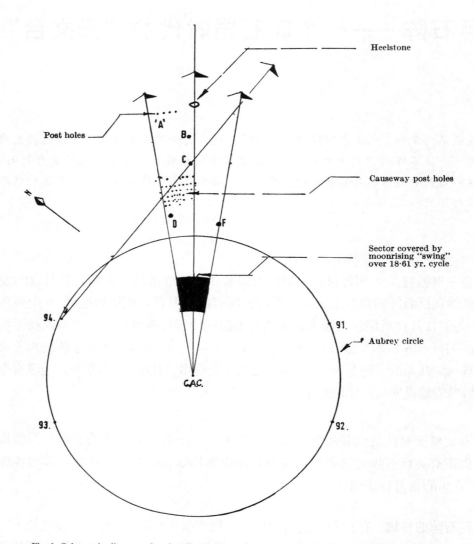

Fig. 1. Schematic diagram showing the position of post holes in relation to other main features

A fairly reliable record of the behaviour of the Moon could be obtained by planting a temporary marker (wooden stake) to align on the point where the winter full-moon appeared above the horizon each year. The indications are such that this was done over a large number of years covering several 18.61-year cycles. Such a period would be sufficient to ascertain a 19-year phase or metonic cycle and possibly the approximate 56-year eclipse cycle as suggested by Hawkins (that is, $3 \times 18.61 = 55.83$). It should be appreciated, however, that they would have considerable difficulty in defining this eclipse cycle by their crude methods.

Starting from the premise that the post holes were used for the purpose suggested, the azimuth bearing of each post hole was first ascertained in rank order, numbered 1 to 6 counting in a north-easterly direction.

16

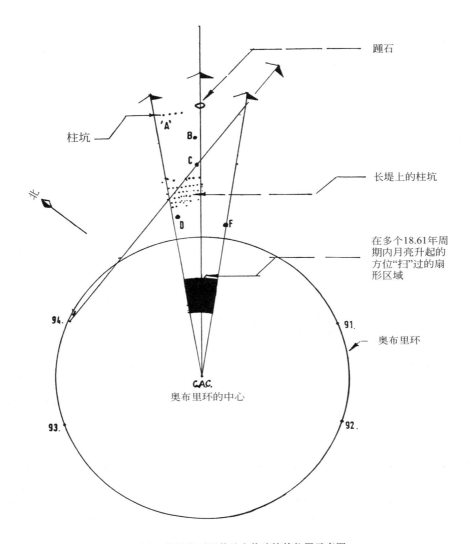

图 1. 柱坑相对于其他主体建筑的位置示意图。

通过在每年冬季满月初升出地平线时的方向点上植入一个临时的标志（木桩）就可以非常可靠地记录月球的活动。一些迹象表明这样的观测记录工作持续了涵盖多个 18.61 年周期的时间。这么长的时间足以使测定者发现 19 年的太阴周期或称默冬章，还可能发现霍金斯所指出的约 56 年的日月食周期（即：3×18.61=55.83）。然而，可以想象当时人们用如此粗糙的方法来确定这个日月食周期势必会遇到相当大的困难。

假设这些柱坑就是为了达到上述目的而留下的，以此为前提，先将每个柱坑的方位按行的顺序编号，沿着东北方向依次为 1 到 6。

The number of holes attributed to each rank and their azimuth bearings taken from the centre of the Aubrey circle are given in Table 1.

Table 1

Rank No.	1	2	3	4	5	6
	–	–	(40.4)	(40.7)	–	(40.3)
	41.9	41.9	–	–	41.8	–
	43.1	43.0	43.0	42.9	42.9	42.7
	–	44.1	44.0	43.8	44.0	–
Azimuth	–	45.3	45.3	45.5	45.6	–
bearings	–	45.6	45.6	–	–	–
degrees	46.3	46.4	46.5	46.3	46.4	46.4
E. of N.	–	– *47.4	–	–	–	46.7
	–	47.8	47.5	47.2	47.6	47.5
	–	49.3	49.4	49.0	48.9	49.1
	–	49.8	–	–	49.8	–
	–	–	50.4	50.2	50.8	50.3

The figures in parentheses refer to holes beyond the line of full orb but are reached by the line of first gleam of moonrise.
*This hole is situated between ranks No. 2 and No. 3 and cannot be allocated to either rank.

Preliminary calculations reveal that the causeway post holes lie within the arc or sector of the most northerly limits of winter full-moon rise as seen from the centre of the Aubrey circle (C.A.C.); also, the number of holes in any one rank did not exceed the number of risings that could appear north of the heelstone or solstice line in any one cycle.

If individual bearings of moonrise in a sequence of cycles were found to agree with the "hole alignments", any doubt as to their significance would be eliminated; furthermore, dating of the post holes would be feasible. Unfortunately, the necessary data concerning the Moon are not available; to obtain such information would severely tax the ability of the most expert celestial mechanician.

However, computed moonrise bearings covering the period of 2000–1000 B.C. were first used in an attempt to determine whether any similarity existed between general grouping of the post holes and a sequence of moonrisings. The data used were kindly supplied by Prof. G. S. Hawkins. His calculations are based on first-order terms and refer to the full-moon nearest the winter solstice and also require that the instant of moonrise should coincide with the time when the Moon reaches its appropriate maximum declination. This particular feature seldom applies (see Fig. 2).

每一行中柱坑的数量以及它们相对于奥布里环中心的方位角列于表1。

表1

行号	1	2	3	4	5	6
	–	–	(40.4)	(40.7)	–	(40.3)
	41.9	41.9	–		41.8	
	43.1	43.0	43.0	42.9	42.9	42.7
		44.1	44.0	43.8	44.0	
		45.3	45.3	45.5	45.6	
方位角度数 由北向东		45.6	45.6	–		
	46.3	46.4	46.5	46.3	46.4	46.4
		– *47.4	–	–	–	46.7
		47.8	47.5	47.2	47.6	47.5
		49.3	49.4	49.0	48.9	49.1
		49.8			49.8	
		–	50.4	50.2	50.8	50.3

圆括号中的数字指的是满月线以外的柱坑，但月亮升起时的第一道光线可以照到这些柱坑。
* 这个柱坑位于第 2 行和第 3 行之间，并且无法把它归到这两行的任意一行中去。

初步的计算结果显示：长堤上的这些柱坑是排列在一个圆弧或扇形区域内的，而这个扇形区域对应的是从奥布里环中心（C.A.C）观测冬季满月升起的最靠北的极限；同时，任何一行中柱坑的数目都没有超过在任何一个周期内所能看到的月亮从奥布里环中心与踵石或至日点连线以北升起的次数。

如果在一个周期序列中，每次月亮升起的方位角都与"柱坑的排列"相符，那么所有对这些柱坑重要性的怀疑都将烟消云散；此外，测定这些柱坑的年代也将是可行的。不幸的是，我们没有与月球活动相关的必要数据；即使是最内行的天体力学专家，想要获得这样的信息也要经受得起对其能力的严峻考验。

不过，计算得到的从公元前 2000 年到公元前 1000 年的月亮升起方位角的数据，被首次用于确定柱坑的分组和月出时间序列之间是否存在某种相似性。该数据是由霍金斯教授热心提供的。他的计算基于一阶近似数据，并且参考了最靠近冬至点的满月，还要求月出的同时月球也应当达到其相应的最大赤纬值。这样特殊的条件很少能得到满足（见图 2）。

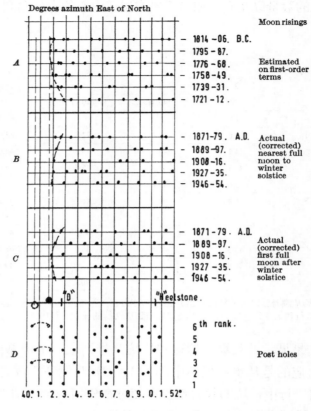

Fig. 2. Comparable azimuth bearings of winter full-moon risings (Full-orb tangent to horizon) and post hole
alignments

Group "*A*": Six cycles of moonrisings based on first-order terms as supplied by Hawkins for period 1814–1712
B.C.
Group "*B*": Similar to "*A*" but the "Moons" correspond to the known rising position covering the period
A.D. 1871–1954 after correction to allow for the change in the angle to the ecliptic of the
Earth–Moon system over the past 3,800 years
Group "*C*": Basically similar to "*B*", but here it applies to the first full-moon after the winter solstice
Group "*D*": Depicts the post holes arranged according to their azimuth bearings

The data connected by broken lines are all separated by a period of 6,940 days or exactly 19 years within a few
hours, and differ from other similar Moons in that their rising positions are practically the same. The broken
lines in group "*D*" merely indicate the position the three holes would occupy if they were aligned on full orb.
The two larger circles immediately above represent the most northerly position of first gleam and full orb of
moonrise. The positions of stone "*D*" and the heelstone are indicated on the same line

The pattern of risings that would apply to the early Stonehenge period is more truly
represented in groups "*B*" and "*C*". Even so, their arrangements could be subject to slight
variations as many individual moons have possible alternative rising positions. This applies in
those cases when the Moon reaches "full" during the daytime, for example, on December 12,
1875, the Moon was full at 0745 h (shortly before setting). In similar circumstances, would they
regard the critical Moon as being that which rose on the afternoon of December 12, or that of

20

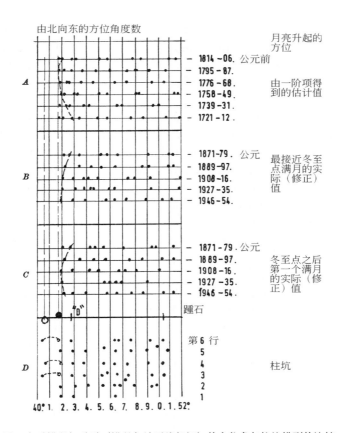

图 2. 冬季满月初升时（满月与地平线相切）的方位角与柱坑排列的比较。

"A"组：月亮在 6 个周期中的升起位置，基于霍金斯所提供的公元前 1814 年至公元前 1712 年数据的
      一阶项。

"B"组：与"A"组类似，但"月亮"的升起位置是公元 1871 年至公元 1954 年间实际测定的位置，并
      针对地月系统经过 3,800 年之后与黄道面夹角的变化进行了一定的修正。

"C"组：与"B"组大体上一致，但在此用到的是冬至点之后的第一次满月。

"D"组：描绘了柱坑按照方位角排列的情况。

由虚线连接起来的数据都相隔 6,940 天或者恰好 19 年，误差在几个小时以内，它们与其他类似数据的
不同之处在于月亮升起的位置基本相同。"D"组中的虚线只是为了说明这三个柱坑应该占据的位置，
如果它们在发生满月的时候能排成一条直线的话。在它们上边的两个稍大一点的圆代表了满月初升时
第一缕光线最北端的位置。在同一条水平线上还标有"D"号石和踵石的位置。

    这种适用于巨石阵时代早期的月升模式在"B"组和"C"组中得到了更真实的体现。
即使如此，它们的排列仍有可能会出现一些微小的变化，因为在很多情况下月亮升起
的位置可能会有两种选择。这种情况通常出现在当月亮在白天达到"满"月的时候，
例如：1875 年 12 月 12 日，月亮于早上 7 点 45 分达到满月（月落前不久）。在类似的情
况下，他们会把临界的月亮看作是 12 月 12 日的下午（译者注：原稿可能有误，此处

the following day? If midnight was their datum, the former Moon would apply. On the other hand, it would be the latter if the critical time was on its rising. A similar condition arises in respect of those Moons which are full 14 or 15 days before the solstice and would be followed by the next Moon 14 or 15 days after the solstice.

There is no question that people of early civilizations had to contend with the same difficulty which was partly obviated by choosing the critical Moon as the one which was full after a specified time, such as the day of the winter solstice or equinox. In the second millennium B.C. the Delians regarded the critical Moon as the first one that was full after the winter solstice, and the possibility that such was the case with the Stonehenge people cannot be overlooked. However, the remarkably close relationship of the moonrise sequences and hole patterns must surely be more than a coincidence. If this suggested method of observation had been carried out by the Stonehenge people, they would have had little difficulty in recognizing the 19-year phase or metonic cycle.

It seems fair to assume that these and other post holes served a purpose in obtaining preliminary information of the behaviour of the Sun and Moon. Once satisfactory alignments had been established, markers of a more permanent kind would be installed. If the foregoing assumptions were correct, then the long period of time that elapsed between the inception of the bank, etc., and the building of the first major stone structures would be accounted for.

The position and spacing of the four large post holes near the heelstone indicate a relationship with the causeway holes, especially so in conjunction with stone "*D*" and the heelstone. The size of the holes indicates that the posts were much larger than the causeway posts and, presumably, more permanent. If stone "*B*" were also included, then the seven markers which could be observed would act as a crude "vernier". When correlated with the setting Sun seen in the reverse direction, it would provide a means of defining the time when an eclipse of the Moon was probable.

Whether or not Stonehenge people discovered the 56-year cycle is a matter for conjecture, but their ability to predict pending eclipses after a crude fashion was certainly possible.

It can be shown that a person assisted by nothing more than the crudest equipment in the form of a peg and line and a few stakes could acquire the necessary information. The observer, however, would have to have the necessary tenacity of purpose to undertake systematic observations over a long period of time and a simple method of recording numbers by means of tokens, for example, notches on a stick or pebbles in a bag.

Doubtless, several generations of observers were involved, and if we are to believe that the writings of Diodorus referred to Stonehenge, then the position of supervisor of the "Spherical*" Temple" was held by a member of the same family from one generation to another.

---

* Early Greek term for "Astronomical". Heath: History of Greek Mathematics.

似应为 12 月 11 日下午）升起的月亮，还是接下来的一天呢？如果他们的数据以午夜为起止时刻，那么应该以前一天的月亮为准。另一方面，如果临界时间是在上升过程中的月亮，那么就应该以后一天的月亮为准。就至日点前 14 或 15 天发生的满月和至日点之后 14 或 15 天发生的下一个满月来说，情况是相同的。

毫无疑问，在文明的早期，人类不得不去面对同样的难题。通过选择临界时刻的月亮就可以在一定程度上回避这个难题，比如选择某个特定时间，如冬至点或者春/秋分点，之后的满月时刻。在公元前两千年，得洛斯人认为临界时刻的月亮是冬至点之后的第一次满月，巨石阵的建造者很可能也注意到了这一点。无论如何，月亮升起方位与柱坑排列之间显然存在的密切联系绝不仅仅是一种巧合。如果巨石阵的建造者们所采用的就是上面提到的观测方法，那么他们就会毫不费力地发现 19 年的周期或称默冬章。

似乎可以合理地假设留下这些以及其他柱坑的目的就是为了获得与太阳和月亮活动有关的初步知识。一旦找到了令人满意的排列方式，就可以建立更为耐久的标志。如果前面的假设是正确的，那么从筑堤等的开工到第一个主体石结构建成之间为什么需要花费那么长时间就可以得到解释了。

踵石附近四个大柱坑的位置和间距表明它们与长堤上的柱坑是有关联的，特别是与"D"号石和踵石有关联。从坑的大小来看，踵石附近的四个大柱坑显然比长堤上的柱坑大很多，而且可能更加固定。如果把"B"号石也包括在内，那么这七个被用于观测的标志就可以作为一个粗制的"游标尺"。当与从相反方向观察到的落日相联系时，它就可以被作为一种确定月食可能发生时刻的方式了。

关于巨石阵的建造者们是否发现了 56 年的周期这个问题还停留在猜测层面，但利用一种粗糙的方式预测出即将发生的月食是他们绝对可以做到的。

可以证明：一个人仅借助一些最原始的工具，如木钉和线以及几个木桩就可以得到所需的信息。然而，观测者还必须具有长期坚持进行系统观测的毅力，并会用一种简单的方法通过作记号来记录数字，比如在一根小棍上刻痕或者在一个袋子里装鹅卵石。

毫无疑问，这个过程需要好几代观测者才能完成，并且假如我们相信狄奥多在他的著作中所提到的就是巨石阵，那么坐在执掌这个"球形 *庙宇"宝座上的人必定出自于同一个家族，并且一代一代世袭下去。

---

*在早期希腊语中就是"天文"的意思。希思：希腊数学史。

The strong lunar influence with which Stonehenge must now be associated necessitates revision of hitherto accepted explanations of some salient features. Until new evidence is found pointing to the contrary, it is more logical to conclude:

(*a*) That the small stone (No. 11) in the sarsen circle was intentional, and that the circle represented the 29.5 days of the lunar month.

(*b*) The double circle or spiral[2] of the "*Y*" and "*Z*" holes represented the 59 days of two lunar months. The strong possibility that there were fifty-nine blue stones inside the sarsen circle would provide a more suitable means of representing the same thing.

(*c*) The 19-year phase or metonic cycle was represented by the nineteen blue stones inside the trilithon "horse shoe".

All things considered, including other similar post holes, there seems little doubt that Stonehenge, in its early stages, was a kind of "observatory". It provided a suitable site wherein systematic observations of "Soluna" (Sun and Moon) phenomena were carried out by these neolithic peoples.

(**211**, 456-458; 1966)

C. A. Newham: 5 Sedge Rise, Tadcaster, Yorkshire.

References:
1. Hawkins, G. S., *Nature*, **200**, 306 (1963); **202**, 1258 (1964).
2. Sale, J. L., *The Secrets of Stonehenge* (private publication, 1965).

从现在来看，巨石阵的建造显然与月球活动有很密切的关联，这使我们必须对迄今为止人们所接受的巨石阵主要结构的解释进行修正。在能找到与此相反的新证据之前，我认为以下这些结论更合乎逻辑：

（*a*）在砂岩漂砾圈中的小石头（11 号石）是被有意放在那里的，这个圈代表的是 29.5 天的朔望月周期。

（*b*）双圈或螺旋形[2]的"*Y*"和"*Z*"柱坑代表的是两个朔望月即 59 天。很有可能在砂岩漂砾圈内部曾摆放过 59 块蓝色的石头，这是代表两个朔望月 59 天的一个更为合适的方法。

（*c*）位于"马蹄"形巨石牌坊内部的 19 块蓝色石头代表了 19 年的周期或称默冬章。

在考虑到包括其他类似柱坑在内的所有因素之后，几乎可以肯定巨石阵在建成之初时就是一座"天文台"。它为新石器时代的古人系统观测与日月有关的现象提供了一个合适的场所。

（孟洁 翻译；肖伟科 审稿）

UGA: A Third Nonsense Triplet in the Genetic Code

S. Brenner *et al.*

Editor's Note

Proteins are assembled by the ribosome using a template of RNA, on which each triplet of nucleotide bases (codon) in the template sequence encodes an amino acid in the protein. South African biologist Sidney Brenner, working with Francis Crick in Cambridge, played a key role in deducing the genetic code that related RNA codons to amino acids. By 1967 the role of almost all the 64 codons was known; here Brenner, Crick and their coworkers elucidate the function of the only codon still outstanding, designated UGA. They find that, like the codons UAA and UAG, it is a "nonsense" triplet, encoding no amino acid at all. It is now known to be a "stop" codon, signalling termination of protein synthesis.

MOST of the sixty-four triplets of the genetic code[1] have been allocated to one or other of the twenty amino-acids. The two known nonsense triplets (UAA, *ochre* and UAG, *amber*) are believed to signal the termination of the polypeptide chain. The only other triplet so far unallocated is UGA, for which binding experiments give uncertain or negative results.

In this article we show that UGA is "unacceptable" in our system (*Escherichia coli* infected with bacteriophage *T*4) and present suggestive evidence that it is nonsense; that is, that it does not stand for any amino-acid. Theoretical arguments make it likely that there is no transfer RNA (*t*RNA) to recognize it. The reason for this apparent absence of function is not yet known. Neither is it known whether UGA is nonsense in other organisms.

Evidence that UGA may be nonsense in *E. coli* has also been presented by Garen *et al.*[2]. They investigated the reversion of *amber* and *ochre* mutants in the alkaline phosphatase gene of *E. coli*. *Amber* mutants (UAG) reverted, as expected, to seven different amino-acids including tryptophan which is coded by UGG. *Ochre* mutants (UAA) reverted to six of these amino-acids, but not to tryptophan. This negative result makes it unlikely that UGA stands for tryptophan (see also Sarabhai and Brenner[3]) and suggests that it might be a nonsense codon.

Mutant X655 contains UGA. Much of our genetic work has been concerned with the left-hand end of the B cistron of the *r*II region of bacteriophage *T*4. We have made extensive and detailed investigations of this region which are being reported elsewhere[4]. The mutant *X*655 occurs in the middle of this region. In brief our proof that *X*655 contains the triplet UGA consists in converting it to an *ochre* (UAA), using mutagens the behaviour of which is already known.

UGA：遗传密码中的第三个无义三联密码子

布伦纳等

编者按

蛋白质是由核糖体按照 RNA 模板装配而成的，在模板序列的核苷酸碱基中，每个三联体（密码子）编码蛋白质中的一个氨基酸。与弗朗西斯·克里克一同在剑桥大学工作的南非生物学家悉尼·布伦纳在推测与氨基酸对应的 RNA 密码子的遗传密码方面作出了重大贡献。到 1967 年时，人们已经破译了几乎全部的 64 个密码子；在本文中，布伦纳、克里克及其同事们阐明了唯一一个尚有争议的密码子——UGA 的功能。他们发现：与密码子 UAA 和 UAG 一样，UGA 是一个"无义"三联密码子，不编码任何氨基酸。现在我们知道它是一个"终止"密码子，标志着蛋白质合成的终止。

在遗传密码 [1] 的 64 个三联密码子中，可以与 20 种氨基酸一一对应的占大多数。两种已知的无义密码子（赭石密码子 UAA 和琥珀密码子 UAG）被人们看作是多肽链终止的信号。到目前为止，唯一一个尚未确定的密码子就是 UGA，因为由结合实验给出的结果要么是不确定的，要么是阴性的。

在本文中我们要证明 UGA 在我们的系统(被噬菌体 T4 感染的大肠杆菌)中是"不可被接受"的。这可以作为它是无义密码子的证据，也就是说，它不编码任何氨基酸。理论上的说法是，有可能没有能识别它的转运 RNA（tRNA）。目前人们还不知道为什么这种功能会明显缺失，更不清楚 UGA 在其他生物体中是否也是无义的。

加伦等人也举出了能证明 UGA 在大肠杆菌中有可能是无义的证据 [2]。他们对大肠杆菌的碱性磷酸酶基因中琥珀突变体和赭石突变体的回复突变产物进行了研究。正如预期的那样，琥珀突变体（UAG）可以回复成 7 个不同的氨基酸，其中包括由 UGG 编码的色氨酸。而赭石突变体（UAA）则只能回复成除色氨酸以外的其他 6 个氨基酸。上述阴性结果说明 UGA 编码色氨酸的可能性不大（参见萨拉巴伊和布伦纳的文章 [3]），并且暗示着它有可能是一个无义密码子。

突变体 X655 含有 UGA。我们在基因研究方面的大部分工作涉及噬菌体 T4 rII 区域的 B 顺反子的左手末端。我们已对该区域进行了广泛而细致的研究，研究结果即将在其他出版物上发表 [4]。突变体 X655 出现在该区域的中间。简言之，我们认为 X655 含有三联密码子 UGA 的证据是可以利用性能已知的诱变剂使之转变成赭石密码子（UAA）。

$X655$ was induced from wild type by 2-aminopurine, and identical mutants are also found after treatment of wild type phage with hydroxylamine. This shows that it differs from an acceptable triplet by a G–C to A–T base pair change in the DNA. It is not suppressed by any *amber* or *ochre* suppressor (Table 1) and is therefore neither UAG nor UAA. The reversion properties of $X655$ are shown in Table 2. It is strongly induced to revert to r^+ by 2-aminopurine, as is expected, but there is no induction to r^+ by hydroxylamine. Thus the triplet in the DNA either contains no G–C pairs or, if it does contain one, it is connected to another unacceptable triplet by a G–C to A–T transition.

Table 1. Suppression Properties of $X655$ and Its Derivatives

Mutant	Triplet	su^-	Amber suppressors			Ochre suppressors		
			su_I^+	su_{II}^+	su_{III}^+	su_B^+	su_C^+	su_D^+
$X655$	UGA	0	0	0	0	0	0	0
$X655$ *ochre*	UAA	0	0	0	0	+	+	+
$X655$ *amber*	UAG	0	+	+	+	+	+	+

Phage stocks were plated on the following strains[9]: su^-, CA244; su_I^+, CA266; su_{II}^+, CA180; su_{III}^+, CA265; su_B^+, CA165; su_C^+, CA167; and su_D^+, CA248.

Table 2. Reversion of $X655$

	Reversion index (in units of 10^{-7})			
	Spontaneous	2-Aminopurine	Hydroxylamine direct	Hydroxylamine after growth
to r^+	4	312	5	6
to *ochre*	4	51	1,090	533

$X655$ was treated with 2-aminopurine and hydroxylamine as previously described[4,5]. Total phage was assayed on *E. coli* B and r^+ revertants on CA244 (su^-). *Ochre* revertants were selected on CA248 (su_D^+) and distinguished from r^+ revertants by picking and stabbing about 300 plaques into CA248 and CA244.

The triplet is in fact connected to UAA by a transition, because $X655$ can be converted to an *ochre* and this change is induced by 2-aminopurine (Table 2). The nature of the transition is more precisely specified by the finding that the conversion to an *ochre* is induced by hydroxylamine and that the *ochre* triplet produced does not require any replication for expression. Using a previous argument[5] this result suggests that the change arises from a G→A change in the messenger RNA. Because $X655$ is not an *amber*, this proves that it contains the triplet UGA. To confirm that an *amber* at the site of $X655$ would be suppressed by *amber* suppressors the $X655$ *ochre* has been converted to an *amber* by mutation and its properties tested (Table 1).

Other occurrences of UGA. In three cases we have been able to produce the triplet UGA by selected phase shifts in our region. When (+ –) phase shifts are made over the first part of the B cistron, the two phase shift mutants frequently do not suppress each other. We have shown[4] that these barriers to mutual suppression are due to the generation of unacceptable triplets in the shifted frame. One of these barriers, b_9, has been identified as an *amber* and two others,

X655 是用 2- 氨基嘌呤诱导野生型产生的，在用羟胺处理野生型噬菌体后也能得到完全相同的突变体。这说明该密码子不同于 DNA 中由 G–C 到 A–T 的碱基对替换产生的可接受密码子，它不会被任何琥珀抑制基因或赭石抑制基因所抑制（表 1），因此不可能是 UAG 或者 UAA。X655 的回复性质示于表 2。正如所预计的，它很容易被 2- 氨基嘌呤诱导从而回复成 r^+，但用羟胺诱导就不能使其回复成 r^+。因此，DNA 中的这个三联密码子或者不含 G–C 碱基对，或者只含有一个 G–C 碱基对，而且这个碱基对是通过 G–C 到 A–T 的转换连接到另一个不可接受的三联密码子上的。

表 1. X655 及其衍生物的抑制特性

突变体	三联密码子	su^-	琥珀抑制基因			赭石抑制基因		
			su_I^+	su_{II}^+	su_{III}^+	su_B^+	su_C^+	su_D^+
X655	UGA	0	0	0	0	0	0	0
X655 赭石型	UAA	0	0	0	0	+	+	+
X655 琥珀型	UAG	0	+	+	+	+	+	+

将噬菌体液加到下面这些菌株 [9] 中：su^-，CA244；su_I^+，CA266；su_{II}^+，CA180；su_{III}^+，CA265；su_B^+，CA165；su_C^+，CA167；su_D^+，CA248。

表 2. X655 的回复性质

回复指数（单位是 10^{-7}）				
	自发	2- 氨基嘌呤	羟胺直接	羟胺培养后
回复成 r^+	4	312	5	6
回复成赭石密码子	4	51	1,090	533

和以前描述过的方法一样，X655 都用 2- 氨基嘌呤和羟胺处理的 [4,5]。总噬菌体在大肠杆菌 B 中进行实验，而 r^+ 回复子在 CA244（su^-）菌株中进行。赭石回复子在 CA248（su_D^+）菌株中进行选择，并通过在 CA248 和 CA244 菌株中挑选 300 个噬菌斑和 r^+ 回复子进行鉴别。

事实上，该三联密码子就是通过转换连接到 UAA 上的，因为 X655 能被 2- 氨基嘌呤诱导转换成赭石密码子（表 2）。根据以下发现可以更加确切地判断转换的本质，即羟胺能够诱导其转换成赭石密码子，而且产生的密码子不需要进行复制就可以表达。由之前的讨论可知 [5]：上述结果说明该转换是由信使 RNA 中发生了 G → A 的替换而引起。因为 X655 不是琥珀密码子，所以由此可以证明它含有 UGA 三联密码子。为了进一步证实 X655 位置上的琥珀密码子能够被琥珀抑制基因所抑制，我们通过突变将 X655 赭石密码子转换成了琥珀密码子，并检测了它的性质（表 1）。

出现 UGA 的其他情况。 在三次实验中，我们已经通过在一定区域内进行的特定相位移动产生了 UGA 三联密码子。当在 B 顺反子的第一部分进行（+ −）相位移动时，这两个相位移动突变体很少会相互抑制。我们曾指出 [4]：相互抑制受到阻碍的原因是在移动的读码框内产生了不可接受的密码子。其中一个障碍物 b_9 已被确定

b_3 and b_4, as *ochres*. Three barriers, b_2, b_5 and b_6, have now been identified as UGA by their base-analogue induced reversion to *ochres*. In each case the identification has been checked by converting the *ochre* to an *amber* at the same site.

Tryptophan is represented by the single codon UGG. It would therefore be expected to mutate by transitions to both UAG (*amber*) and UGA, and thus in such cases *amber* and UGA mutants should occur in close pairs. The *amber* mutant, *HB*74, which maps close to *X*655, is an example of this. Genetic crosses between it, *X*655, and the *ochre* and *amber* derived from *X*655, show that *HB*74 maps identically to the *amber* derived from *X*655, as expected (Table 3).

Table 3. Recombination between Various Mutants

	*X*655	*X*655 *ochre*	*X*655 *amber*	*HB*74	Triplet
*X*655	0				UGA
*X*655 *ochre*	0	0			UAA
*X*655 *amber*	+	0	0		UAG
*HB*74	+	0	0	0	UAG

The phages were crossed in *E. coli* B and the complexes irradiated with ultra-violet light to stimulate recombination (see ref. 4). In the Table, 0 means that r^+ recombinants were not significantly above the reversion rate, which was between 2 and 9×10^{-7}; in those experiments where positive results were obtained (+), the frequency was between 2 and 6×10^{-5}.

So far we have found the expected pairs consisting of UGA and an *amber* in two other cases. In the A cistron, a mutant *X*665[*] is found with the *amber* mutant *N*97, and in the B cistron, *N*65 is paired with the *amber* mutant *X*237. Both *N*97 and *X*237 are likely to have arisen from UGG (tryptophan) which is confirmed by the finding that they respond only poorly to the *amber* suppressor su_{II}^+ which inserts glutamine[5]. Both *X*665 and *N*65 have been converted into *ochre* mutants, showing that they contain the triplet UGA. These *ochres* have also been converted to *ambers* at the same site. Mapping investigations, analogous to those in Table 3, are consistent with these allocations.

Unacceptability of UGA. There is very good evidence that the amino-acid sequence coded by the first part of the B cistron is not critical for the function of the gene[4]. It can be replaced by varying lengths of the A cistron using deletions that join the two genes. Moreover, an extensive (− +) frame shift can be made without noticeable effect on the function. Of the fifteen known base-analogue mutants in the region, thirteen are either *ochres* or *ambers*; one, *HD*263, is temperature sensitive and *X*655 is UGA. The extreme bias towards *amber* and *ochre* chain-terminating mutants confirms the dispensability of the region[4]. These results make it unlikely that the unacceptability of UGA in *X*655 and the three barriers results from the insertion of an amino-acid, and strongly suggest that it is nonsense.

---

* This is not a misprint for X655.

是琥珀密码子，而另外两个，即 b_3 和 b_4，则被鉴定为赭石密码子。还有三个障碍物 b_2、b_5 和 b_6 暂时被看作是 UGA，因为它们能够在碱基类似物的诱导下回复成赭石密码子。在每次实验中，我们都会通过将同一位点的赭石密码子转变为琥珀密码子来验证密码鉴定的准确性。

编码色氨酸的唯一密码子是 UGG。因而它应该可以通过转换突变成 UAG（琥珀密码子）和 UGA，所以在这种情况下，琥珀密码子和 UGA 突变体应该会成对出现。与 X655 配对的琥珀突变体 HB74 就是一个琥珀密码子。将它与 X655 以及 X655 的赭石和琥珀突变体进行基因交配，结果发现：和预期一样，HB74 的基因图谱与来自 X655 的琥珀突变体完全相同（表 3）。

表 3. 不同突变体之间的重组

	X655	X655 赭石型	X655 琥珀型	HB74	三联密码子
X655	0				UGA
X655 赭石型	0	0			UAA
X655 琥珀型	+	0	0		UAG
HB74	+	0	0	0	UAG

使噬菌体在大肠杆菌 B 中发生基因交配，并用紫外光照射复合物以便刺激重组（见参考文献 4）。在上表中，0 代表 r^+ 重组子并没有显著高于回复突变率 $2 \times 10^{-7} \sim 9 \times 10^{-7}$。在那些结果为阳性（+）的实验中，频率都介于 $2 \times 10^{-5} \sim 6 \times 10^{-5}$ 之间。

到目前为止，我们已经根据预期在另外两个实验中找到了由 UGA 和琥珀密码子组成的密码对。我们发现在 A 顺反子中，突变体 X665* 和琥珀突变体 N97 是同时存在的，而在 B 顺反子中，N65 和琥珀突变体 X237 会配对。N97 和 X237 很有可能都来源于 UGG（色氨酸），以下发现可以证实这一点，即它们仅对插入谷氨酰胺的琥珀密码子抑制基因 su_{II}^+ 反应不敏感 [5]。X665 和 N65 都能被转变成赭石突变体，这说明它们含有 UGA 三联密码子。这些赭石密码子也都能在同一位点处被转变成琥珀密码子。这些定位结果与通过类似于表 3 的基因图谱研究所得到的结果相符。

UGA 的不可接受性。我们有足够充分的证据可以证明：由 B 顺反子第一部分编码的氨基酸序列不会对该基因的功能产生至关重要的影响 [4]。通过能够连接两个基因的缺失序列，B 顺反子第一部分编码的氨基酸序列可以被长度不同的 A 顺反子片段所替换。此外，还可以进行读码框的（−+）移动而不会显著地影响到基因的功能。在该区域 15 个已知的碱基类似突变体中，有 13 个不是赭石突变体就是琥珀突变体；另外一个，HD263，属于温度敏感型，而 X655 是 UGA。这种对琥珀或者赭石链终止突变体的极端倾向性足以证明该区域是可有可无的 [4]。这些结果说明 X655 中的 UGA 和三个障碍物的不可接受性不太可能源自于一个氨基酸的插入，从而强烈地支持了 UGA 是无义密码子的观点。

---

* 此处并非 X655 的误印。

In addition, the UGA mutant X665 in the A cistron has been combined with the deletion r1589 and has been found to remove the B activity of this phage. This is the test for nonsense originally used by Benzer and Champe[6].

In all these cases, however, it could be argued that UGA might code cysteine, especially as the two known triplets for cysteine are UGU and UGC. If the B protein already contained a cysteine essential for its function the effect of UGA elsewhere might be to produce an S–S bridge between the cysteine inserted by UGA and the (hypothetical) essential one, and thus inactivate the protein. Nevertheless we regard this as unlikely for two reasons, one genetic and one chemical.

The genetic evidence concerns the anomalous minutes produced by certain (++) combinations in the B cistron[4]. In some regions of the first part of the B cistron combinations of two (+) phase shift mutants are able to grow to some extent on the restrictive host, *E. coli* K12. The plaques produced are minute, however, showing that the wild type phenotype is very far from being completely restored. A detailed analysis of one set of these combinations showed that minutes are obtained only from pairs of (+) mutants which straddle barrier b_6. The presence of the barrier is obligatory because, if it is removed by mutation, the (++) doubles are unable to grow at all on *E. coli* K12. The minutes are clearly due to a phase error of one sort of another and the phase error is dependent on the barrier b_6 which we now know to be UGA. This result shows that UGA cannot be associated with any normal amino-acid reading and points strongly to the conclusion that it is nonsense.

The chemical reason for UGA not coding for cysteine comes from the work of Khorana *et al.*[7]. They have shown that poly (UGA)$_n$ when used as a messenger in a cell-free system derived from *E. coli* induces the production of poly methionine (corresponding to AUG) and also poly aspartic acid (corresponding to GAU). No other amino-acid appears to be incorporated. In particular, no poly cysteine was found. For various reasons this evidence is not completely decisive, but it at least makes it unlikely that UGA is cysteine.

Function of UGA. It might be thought that the sequence containing UGA was nonsense because it was the signal for the beginning or ending of a gene (or operon). In other words, that it produced its effect during the synthesis of the messenger RNA on the DNA template of the gene. This explanation is highly unlikely because the effects of UGA depend on it being read in phase. The phenotypic effect of X655 can be removed when the mutant is placed in a (− +) shifted frame[4], and the barriers b_2, b_5 and b_6 are of course produced by phase shifts. That is, the base sequence UGA actually occurs at these places in the wild type messenger RNA but in such a way that it is out of phase when the message is read correctly. Because we have no reason to suspect that RNA polymerase synthesizes messenger RNA in groups of three bases at a time these results imply that the phenotypic effects of UGA must occur during protein synthesis.

It thus seems unlikely that UGA codes for any amino-acid, and in particular it does not appear

此外，已发现 A 顺反子中的 UGA 突变体 *X*665 可以和缺失子 *r*1589 重组，我们还发现它能够去除该噬菌体的 B 活性。这就是本则尔和钱普起先用来检测无义密码子的方法 [6]。

但是针对所有这些实验，有人提出 UGA 或许可以编码半胱氨酸，尤其是因为人们已经知道半胱氨酸的两个三联密码子是 UGU 和 UGC。如果 B 蛋白已经含有一个对其功能有重要影响的半胱氨酸，那么 UGA 在其他位置处的功能也许就是在 UGA 插入的半胱氨酸和（假定存在的）基本半胱氨酸之间形成一个 S–S 键，以便使蛋白质失活。尽管如此，我们还是可以举出两方面的理由来驳斥这一点，一方面是基因上的，另一方面是化学上的。

在基因上的证据与由 B 顺反子中某些（++）重组产生的反常菌斑有关 [4]。在 B 顺反子第一部分的某些区域中，两个（+）相位移动突变体的重组子能够在限制性宿主大肠杆菌 *K*12 中生长到一定程度。但产生的菌斑非常小，这说明野生表型还远远没有得到完全恢复。在对其中一组重组子进行深入研究后发现：只有跨过障碍物 *b*₆ 的（+）突变体对才能生成菌斑。这种障碍物的存在是必不可少的。因为，如果它被突变移除，那么（++）突变体对将完全不能在大肠杆菌 *K*12 中生长。菌斑的产生显然是由某种相位误差造成的，而相位误差又是由障碍物 *b*₆ 决定的，我们现在知道障碍物 *b*₆ 就是 UGA。这一结果说明 UGA 不可能与任何正常氨基酸的编码密码相关，并可以使我们明确地得到 UGA 是无义密码子的结论。

在化学上证明 UGA 不能编码半胱氨酸的证据源自霍拉纳等人的工作 [7]。他们发现：当多聚 (UGA)$_n$ 在大肠杆菌来源的无细胞系统中被用作信使时，它会诱导生成多聚甲硫氨酸（密码子是 AUG）以及多聚天冬氨酸（密码子是 GAU）。此外别无其他的氨基酸产生。尤其是没有发现多聚半胱氨酸。虽然可以列出多种原因来证明该结果并不具备完全确定性，但它至少可以用于否定 UGA 编码半胱氨酸的可能性。

UGA 的功能。 有人可能会认为含有 UGA 的序列是无义的，因为它是一个基因（或者操纵子）开始或者终止的信号。换句话说，只有在基因的 DNA 模板上合成信使 RNA 时它才发挥作用。这个解释不可能成立，因为 UGA 的功能取决于它的同相读取。当突变体被置于（–+）移动的读码框中时，*X*655 的表型效应就会丧失 [4]，而且障碍物 *b*₂、*b*₅ 和 *b*₆ 显然是由相位移动产生的。也就是说，碱基序列 UGA 确实存在于野生型信使 RNA 的这些位点上，但是当信息被正确读取时，它们会因此而处在相位不符合的状态。因为我们没有理由怀疑 RNA 聚合酶是以三个碱基为单位同时合成信使 RNA 的，所以这些结果暗示着 UGA 的表型效应只会出现在蛋白质的合成过程之中。

因此，这样看起来 UGA 编码任何氨基酸都不太可能，尤其是不会编码半胱氨

to code for either cysteine (UGU and UGC) or tryptophan (UGG). The wobble theory of codon-anticodon interaction developed by one of us[8] makes the prediction that because of a wobble in the recognition mechanism at the third place of the codon no *t*RNA molecule can recognize XYA alone without at the same time recognizing either XYG or both XYU and XYC. Such theoretical arguments cannot be considered conclusive, but they certainly suggest that UGA is a triplet for which no *t*RNA exists. For this reason we think it unlikely that UGA produces the efficient termination of the polypeptide chain, but more direct evidence will be needed to establish this point.

Conclusion. We have thus established that in the phage-infected cell UGA is certainly "unacceptable" in the *r*II cistrons, although it remains to be seen whether this is true for other species. We have produced reasons why it is unlikely to code for any amino-acid. We are confident that there must be weighty reasons if even a single triplet is not used in the genetic code, because otherwise natural selection would have certainly allocated it to an amino-acid. At the moment we are inclined to believe that UGA may be necessary as a "space" to separate genes in a polycistronic message. It is possible to make a plausible theory for *E. coli* along these lines, but we prefer to leave the discussion of this until we have more experimental evidence to support it. This we are at present attempting to obtain.

We thank Drs. A. Garen, H. G. Khorana and A. Sarabhai for interesting discussions and for showing us their papers in advance of publication. One of the authors (E. R. K.) is a holder of a United States Churchill Foundation scholarship.

(**213**, 449-450; 1967)

S. Brenner, L. Barnett, E. R. Katz and F. H. C. Crick: M.R.C. Laboratory of Molecular Biology, Hills Road, Cambridge.

Received December 22, 1966.

References:

1. For the structure of the genetic code and the evidence for nonsense triplets see the papers in the Cold Spring Harbor Symposium XXXI on "The Genetic Code", 1966 (in the press).

2. Weigert, M. G., Lanka, E., and Garen, A., *J. Mol. Biol.*, **23**, 391 (1967).

3. Sarabhai, A., and Brenner, S., in preparation.

4. Barnett, L., Brenner, S., Crick, F. H. C., Shulman, R. G., and Watts-Tobin, R. J., *Phil. Trans. Roy. Soc.* (in the press).

5. Brenner, S., Stretton, A. O. W., and Kaplan, S., *Nature*, **206**, 994 (1965).

6. Benzer, S., and Champe, S. P., *Proc. U.S. Nat. Acad. Sci.*, **48**, 1114 (1962).

7. Morgan, A. R., Wells, R. D., and Khorana, H. G., *Proc. U.S. Nat. Acad. Sci.* (in the press).

8. Crick, F. H. C., *J. Mol. Biol.*, **19**, 548 (1966).

9. Brenner, S., and Beckwith, J. R., *J. Mol. Biol.*, **13**, 629 (1965).

酸（UGU 和 UGC）或者色氨酸（UGG）。我们中的一位作者提出过密码子 – 反密码子相互作用的摆动理论[8]，该理论预言，由于密码子的第三位识别是可以发生摆动的，因而所有能够识别 XYA 的 tRNA 分子都能同时识别 XYG 或者 XYU 和 XYC。虽然这一理论依据不能被认为是绝对正确的，但确实可以说明 UGA 是一种不对应于任何 tRNA 的三联密码子。基于这个原因，我们认为 UGA 不太可能会有效地终止多肽链，不过这一点还需要更多直接的证据来证明。

结论。我们已经证实在噬菌体感染的细胞中，UGA 在 rII 区顺反子中确实是"不可被接受"的。然而，在其他物种中它是否也会如此还有待于进一步的研究。我们提出了几个它不可能编码任何氨基酸的理由。我们相信：即便只有一个三联密码子未被用于基因编码中，也一定有不同凡响的原因，否则的话自然选择必然会将其分配给某一个氨基酸。目前我们倾向于认为在多顺反子的序列中或许需要用 UGA 作为一个"空格"来分隔基因。根据这些结果我们完全可以提出一套似乎适用于大肠杆菌的理论，但我们宁愿暂时不去讨论它，直到我们有更多的实验证据来验证。这就是我们目前正在努力去获得的。

感谢加伦、霍拉纳和萨拉巴伊博士对我们的工作进行了饶有兴致的讨论，还要感谢他们能在自己的论文发表之前先拿给我们看。我们中的一位作者（卡茨）得到了由美国丘吉尔基金会授予的奖学金的资助。

（毛晨晖 翻译；陈新文 陈继征 审稿）

Specific Binding of the λ Phage Repressor to λ DNA

M. Ptashne

Editor's Note

In 1961, French biologists François Jacob and Jacques Monod described a negative form of gene regulation whereby so-called repressor proteins switch off target genes. But the underlying molecular mechanism was unclear. Here molecular biologist Mark Ptashne solves the problem by showing that a protein called the λ repressor protein binds directly to specific DNA sequences, suggesting that repressors exert their effects by blocking the transcription of DNA to RNA. Although the protein was originally isolated from a virus, Ptashne and others went on to show that the same mechanism occurs in yeast, plants, fruit flies and humans, and is a key form of gene regulation.

THERE are many examples, in bacteria and their phages, of a group of genes controlled by the product of another gene—a regulator gene. In the classical cases discussed by Jacob and Monod[1], the control is negative and the product of the regulator gene is called a repressor. Repressors act by switching off their target genes; in order to activate these genes the repressor itself must be inactivated. These facts were learned from genetic experiments which do not reveal how repressors work at the molecular level.

The isolation in recent months of two repressors[2,3] makes possible biochemical experiments exploring the mechanism of repression. Many of the models for this mechanism propose different sites for the action of the repressor. According to the simplest model, the repressor binds to a site on the DNA, directly preventing the transcription from DNA to RNA. According to other models the repressor interacts with mRNA or sRNA to block translation of the genetic message from RNA to protein. A prediction of the first model is that an isolated repressor will bind *in vitro* to DNA containing the receptor site for that particular repressor, but not to DNA lacking this site. The experiments reported here confirm this expectation.

The Genetic System

The protein made by the C_1 gene of phage λ, called the λ phage repressor, is used in these experiments. This repressor blocks the expression of the other phage genes, keeping the phage chromosome dormant within its host, *E. coli*. Only a very short segment of the phage genome is involved in this control[4,5], a region including the C_1 gene and the sites which determine the sensitivity of the phage to the repressor. Two phages which differ only in this segment are λ and λ*imm*[434] (see ref. 4). Phage λ*imm*[434], which contains almost all the other known genes of phage λ, makes and is sensitive to the 434 phage repressor only. Therefore, a critical test of specificity is that the isolated λ repressor should bind to λ DNA but not to λ*imm*[434] DNA.

λ噬菌体阻遏物与λ DNA的特异性结合

普塔什尼

编者按

1961年，法国生物学家弗朗索瓦·雅各布和雅克·莫诺描述了一种负向的基因调节作用，被称为阻遏物的蛋白可以借此关闭靶基因。但能够解释上述现象的分子作用机制尚不明晰。在本文中，分子生物学家马克·普塔什尼指出，用一种被称为λ阻遏物的蛋白直接与特殊DNA序列结合即可解释上述作用，他认为阻遏物发挥作用的方式是阻断由DNA向RNA的转录过程。尽管这种蛋白最初是从病毒中分离出来的，但普塔什尼和其他研究者随后发现在酵母、植物、果蝇和人类中都存在同样的机制，而且这种机制还是基因调节的主要形式。

在细菌和它们的噬菌体中有很多这样的例子：一组基因被另外某个基因——调节基因的产物所调控。在雅各布和莫诺[1]讨论过的那些经典例子中，调控都是负向的，所以调节基因的产物被称为阻遏物。阻遏物的作用是关闭靶基因；为了激活这些靶基因，就必须使阻遏物自身失活。上述结论可以从遗传学实验中得到，但遗传学实验并不能揭示在分子水平上阻遏物是如何起作用的。

在最近几个月中分离出了两种阻遏物[2,3]，这使得通过生物化学实验来研究阻遏机制成为可能。在为解释这一机制而提出的多种模型中，阻遏物的作用位点并不相同。根据最简单的模型，阻遏物结合于DNA上的某个位点并直接阻止了从DNA到RNA的转录过程。而根据其他一些模型，阻遏物通过与信使RNA（$mRNA$）或小的非编码RNA（$sRNA$）的相互作用阻止了遗传信息从RNA到蛋白质的翻译过程。由第一个模型可以预测：在体外条件下，一个分离出来的阻遏物能够结合含这一阻遏物特异结合位点的DNA，而不能结合缺乏这种位点的DNA。本文报道的实验证实了这一预测。

遗 传 系 统

由λ噬菌体 C_1 基因编码的蛋白质被称为λ噬菌体阻遏物，我们在下述实验中使用的就是这种蛋白质。该阻遏物能够阻断其他噬菌体基因的表达，使噬菌体的染色体在它的宿主大肠杆菌内只能处于休眠状态。在噬菌体的基因组中只有一个非常短的DNA片段参与了这一调控过程[4,5]，该区域包括 C_1 基因和若干能决定噬菌体对阻遏物敏感程度的位点。仅在这个片段上有所不同的两种噬菌体是λ噬菌体和λimm^{434}噬菌体（见参考文献4）。λimm^{434}噬菌体含有λ噬菌体中几乎所有的其他已知基因，唯一的不同就在于它只能合成434噬菌体阻遏物并只对434噬菌体阻遏物敏感。因此，对于阻遏物特异性来说，决定性的检验标准就是：分离出来的λ阻遏物应该与λ DNA结合，而不是与λimm^{434} DNA结合。

Characterization of the λ Phage Repressor

The isolation of the λ phage repressor was achieved by destroying the host DNA with ultra-violet light, thereby drastically decreasing cellular protein synthesis[3]. These irradiated cells were infected with many λ phages which, under the conditions of the experiment, synthesized little or no phage protein except repressor. The infected cells were fed radioactive amino-acids, and a single labelled protein was separated from the background label on a DEAE-cellulose column. This protein was identified as the product of the C_1 gene by two criteria: first, it was missing from cells infected with phages bearing amber mutations in the C_1 gene, and second, it was made in modified form by phages which produce temperature sensitive repressors as a result of mutation in the C_1 gene. Electrophoresis and sedimentation of the repressor indicate that it is an acidic protein with a sedimentation coefficient of about 2.8S, which corresponds to a molecular weight of approximately 30,000.

The binding experiments to be described were performed mainly with the repressor made by the mutant phage λ*ind*⁻. The *ind*⁻ mutation renders the repressor insensitive *in vivo* to many conditions which inactivate the wild type repressor[6]. For example, a small dose of ultra-violet light delivered to a λ-lysogen will inactivate the wild type but not the *ind*⁻ repressor. The *ind*⁻ repressor can be isolated in the same way as the wild type and has approximately the same sedimentation coefficient, but it chromatographs separately from wild type on DEAE-cellulose columns (Fig. 1). The altered chromatographic behaviour may be due to a charge or a conformational change. However, the fact the this mutation in the C_1 gene, from wild type to *ind*⁻, also changes the behaviour of the protein on DEAE provides further proof that this protein is coded for by the C_1 gene.

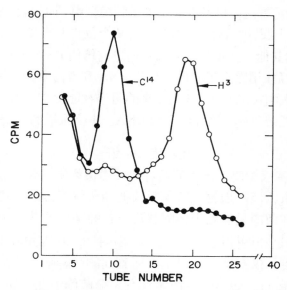

Fig. 1. DEAE-cellulose chromatography of λ*ind*⁻ and λ wild type repressors. Extracts of *E. coli* phage-infected cells containing ¹⁴C-labelled λ*ind*⁻ repressor in one case and ³H-labelled λ wild type repressor in the other were applied to a DEAE-cellulose column. Fractions from a salt gradient were collected and assayed as described previously[3]. The label used in this and the other experiments reported in this paper was ¹⁴C or ³H labelled reconstituted protein hydrolysate.

λ 噬菌体阻遏物的特性

对 λ 噬菌体阻遏物的分离可以通过用紫外光破坏宿主 DNA 来实现，因而大大减少了胞内蛋白质的合成 [3]。我们用大量 λ 噬菌体侵染这些被辐射过的细胞，在我们的实验条件下，λ 噬菌体几乎不能合成除阻遏物之外的其他噬菌体蛋白。在这些被感染的细胞中加入放射性标记的氨基酸，最后用二乙氨基乙基纤维素（DEAE-纤维素）柱层析就可以从背景标记中分离出一种单标蛋白。根据以下两点即可确定这种蛋白就是 C_1 基因编码的产物：第一，在用 C_1 基因中发生琥珀突变的噬菌体侵染过的细胞内并不存在这种蛋白；第二，在 C_1 基因中突变的作用下生成温度敏感型阻遏物的噬菌体将使这种蛋白以被修饰的形式存在。由阻遏物的电泳和沉降实验可知，该阻遏物是一种酸性蛋白，其沉降系数约为 $2.8S$，与此对应的分子量在 30,000 上下。

在下文要描述的阻遏物结合实验中，我们主要用到的是由 λind^- 突变型噬菌体合成的阻遏物。由 ind^- 突变体合成的阻遏物在体内对许多能使野生型阻遏物失活的条件均不敏感 [6]。例如，用小剂量紫外光照射 λ 溶原菌能使野生型阻遏物失活，但不能使 ind^- 突变型阻遏物失活。用分离野生型阻遏物的方法同样可以分离 ind^- 突变型阻遏物，两者的沉降系数也大致相同，但是利用 DEAE-纤维素柱层析即可将 ind^- 突变型阻遏物与野生型阻遏物分开（图 1）。这种在层析时特性发生改变的现象可能是由于电荷或者构象的变化造成的。不过，C_1 基因从野生型向 ind^- 型的突变也能改变蛋白质在 DEAE 柱层析时的行为，这一事实为证明这种蛋白是由 C_1 基因编码产生提供了进一步的证据。

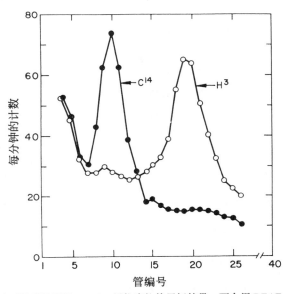

图 1. λind^- 型和 λ 野生型阻遏物通过 DEAE-纤维素柱的层析结果。两个用 DEAE-纤维素柱进行分析的样品都是大肠杆菌噬菌体感染过的细胞的提取物，其中一个含有 ^{14}C 标记的 λind^- 型阻遏物，另一个含有 ^{3}H 标记的 λ 野生型阻遏物。收集用盐梯度洗脱下来的组分并按以前描述过的方法进行检测 [3]。在这个实验和本文报道的其他实验中所用的标记物都是 ^{14}C 或 ^{3}H 标记的重组蛋白的水解产物。

Binding of the Repressor to DNA

The labelled λ*ind⁻* repressor was mixed with λ DNA and sedimented through a sucrose gradient. Fig. 2 shows that some of the label sedimented with the DNA, indicating that the λ*ind⁻* repressor binds to DNA. Fig. 2 also shows that this binding is specific: when the repressor was mixed with DNA from phage λ*imm*⁴³⁴, no binding was observed. This experiment has been performed with several different preparations of repressor and phage DNA.

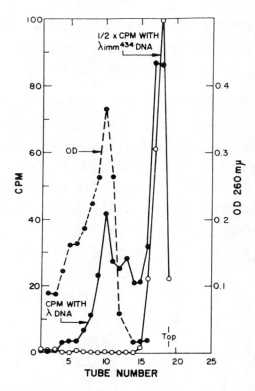

Fig. 2. Specific binding of the λ*ind⁻* repressor to λ DNA. A portion of ¹⁴C-labelled λ*ind⁻* repressor, pooled and concentrated from the peak fractions of a DEAE column run, was mixed with 100 μg of λ or λ*imm*⁴³⁴ DNA. The DNA was preheated at 70°C for 15 min. to minimize aggregation. The solutions were made 0.01 M EDTA, 0.1 M KCl, and 10⁻⁴ M Cleland's reagent, and 5 μg of commercial *s*RNA was added as an additional inhibitor of possible endonuclease activity. After 5 min. incubation at 37°C, the final volume of 0.7 ml. was layered on a 5–25 percent sucrose gradient containing 0.05 M KCl, 10⁻⁴ M Cleland's reagent, and 0.5 mg/ml. BSA as carrier. The gradients were spun at 41,000 r.p.m. for 5 h in an *SB*269 rotor in an IEC centrifuge. Fractions were collected and the DNA peak located by absorbance at 260 mμ. Each fraction was then precipitated on a Millipore filter with TCA and counted in a gas flow counter. The optical density profiles at 260 mμ from the tubes containing λ and λ*imm*⁴³⁴ DNA are essentially identical. Phages λ and λ*imm*⁴³⁴ were purified by several bandings in CsCl according to the method of Thomas and Abelson[9], and DNA was then extracted and purified from the two phage preparations using the same phenol and buffer solutions.

阻遏物与 DNA 的结合

　　将标记的 λ*ind*⁻ 阻遏物与 λ DNA 混合并通过蔗糖密度梯度进行沉淀。由图 2 可知：有一部分带有标记的阻遏物会与 DNA 一起沉降，这说明 λ*ind*⁻ 阻遏物结合了 DNA。图 2 还表明这种结合具有特异性：当阻遏物与 λ*imm*⁴³⁴ 噬菌体的 DNA 混合时是观察不到结合现象的。在这个实验中，我们采用了几种不同的阻遏物和噬菌体 DNA 样品。

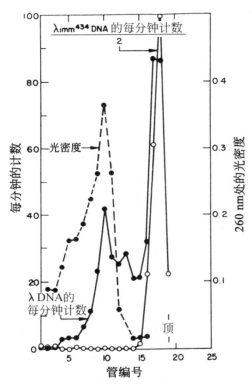

图 2. λ*ind*⁻ 阻遏物与 λ DNA 的特异性结合。用 DEAE– 纤维素柱分离 ¹⁴C 标记的 λ*ind*⁻ 阻遏物，先收集峰位洗脱部分并浓缩，然后与 100 μg 的 λ DNA 或 λ*imm*⁴³⁴ DNA 混合。将所用 DNA 在 70℃ 下预热 15 min 以减少 DNA 的聚集。溶液中包括 0.01 M EDTA（译者注：乙二胺四乙酸）、0.1 M KCl 和 10⁻⁴ M 克莱兰氏试剂，然后再加入 5 μg 商业 *s*RNA 作为一种抑制核酸内切酶活性的附加抑制剂。在 37℃ 下孵育 5 min 后，将终体积为 0.7 ml 的样品铺展到 5%~25% 的蔗糖密度梯度上，该蔗糖密度梯度中还含有 0.05 M KCl、10⁻⁴ M 克莱兰氏试剂以及作为载体的 0.5 mg/ml 牛血清白蛋白。将梯度样品置于一台 IEC 离心机的 *SB*269 转子中以每分钟 41,000 转的速度离心 5 h。收集分离出的组分，DNA 峰的位置是在光吸收为 260 nm 处。然后在密理博滤膜上对每一组分进行 TCA（译者注：三氯乙酸）沉淀，并用气流式计数器对沉淀物进行放射性计数。含 λ DNA 的组分管与含 λ*imm*⁴³⁴ DNA 的组分管在 260 nm 处的光密度分布图基本一致。按照托马斯和埃布尔森提出的方法 [9]，我们用几轮 CsCl 沉降来纯化 λ 噬菌体和 λ*imm*⁴³⁴ 噬菌体，然后用同样的苯酚和缓冲液从这两个噬菌体样品中提取并纯化 DNA。

The repressor used in the binding experiments was not isotopically pure. Depending on the fractions pooled from a DEAE column run, as much as 50 percent of the label might be present in impurities other than the repressor. In order to guarantee that the label sedimenting with the DNA was in the repressor and not in some contaminant, a double label binding experiment was performed. ^{14}C-labelled λ*ind⁻* repressor was isolated on a DEAE column from a mixture of extracts which included the ^{3}H-labelled products of cells infected with the phage λC₁*sus*34. This phage bears in its C₁ gene the amber mutation *sus*34 which blocks production of the repressor[7]. Therefore the ^{3}H will have labelled all the proteins made except the repressor. Fig. 3 shows that about half the ^{14}C label but none of the ^{3}H label sedimented with the DNA.

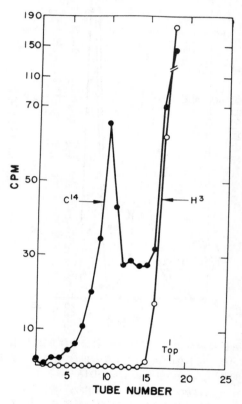

Fig. 3. Selective binding of the λ C₁ product to λ DNA. ^{14}C-labelled λ*ind⁻* repressor was isolated on a DEAE column from an extract which also contained the ^{3}H-labelled gene products of the phage λC₁*sus*34. This mixture was then tested for binding to λ DNA as described in Fig. 2. The 260 mμ *OD* profile of the λ DNA is essentially identical to that shown in Fig. 2. The fractions were precipitated with TCA, dissolved in 1/2 ml. 0.1 M NaOH, and counted in 10 ml. of scintillation fluid containing toluene and Triton X-100 in the ratio 3:1 plus 0.4 percent PPO and 0.005 percent POPOP[10].

The repressor does not bind to denatured DNA. Fig. 4 shows that no counts were displaced from the top of the tube when a mixture of denatured DNA and labelled λ*ind⁻* repressor was

结合实验中所用的阻遏物并不是纯的同位素标记。由于在收集从 DEAE 柱流出的组分时存在误差，所以有时可能会有高达 50% 的标记出现在杂质中而不是阻遏物中。为了保证与 DNA 一起沉降的标记在阻遏物中而不是在杂质中，我们进行了一次双标结合实验。利用 DEAE 柱，我们从含有 λC₁sus34 噬菌体侵染细胞的 ³H 标记产物的混合提取物中分离出了 ¹⁴C 标记的 λind⁻ 阻遏物。λC₁sus34 噬菌体的 C₁ 基因发生了 sus34 琥珀突变，这一突变可以阻断该噬菌体中阻遏物的产生 [7]。因此，³H 将能够标记除阻遏物之外的所有蛋白。从图 3 中可以看出：与 DNA 一起沉降的有大约一半的 ¹⁴C 标记，但没有 ³H 标记。

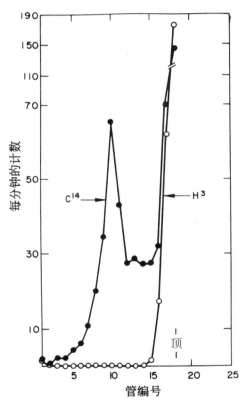

图 3. λ C₁ 产物与 λ DNA 的选择性结合。利用 DEAE 柱从同时含有 ³H 标记的 λ C₁sus34 噬菌体基因产物的抽提物中分离出 ¹⁴C 标记的 λind⁻ 阻遏物。然后按照图 2 中所描述的方法检测所得混合物与 λ DNA 的结合情况。λ DNA 在 260 nm 处的光密度分布图与图 2 中所示的结果基本一致。对收集的组分进行 TCA 沉淀，然后在 1/2 ml 0.1 M 的 NaOH 溶液中溶解沉淀，最后将其加入到 10 ml 闪烁液中进行放射性计数，闪烁液的成分是：比例为 3:1 的甲苯和曲拉通 X-100（译者注：化学名称为聚乙二醇辛基苯基醚，是一种优异的表面活化剂）、0.4% 的 2,5- 二苯基恶唑和 0.005% 的 1,4-双 [2-(5-苯基) 恶唑基] 苯 [10]。

阻遏物并不结合变性的 DNA。图 4 表明：当变性 DNA 与标记的 λind⁻ 阻遏物的混合物在蔗糖梯度中沉降时，管子顶部的放射性计数并没有转移到别的地方。上

sedimented through a sucrose gradient. The repressor preparation used in this experiment was found to bind efficiently to native DNA, hence its failure to bind here must have been due to the changed configuration of the DNA.

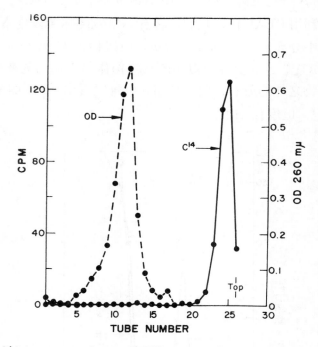

Fig. 4. Binding of λ*ind⁻* repressor to denatured λ DNA. 100 μg of λ DNA was denatured in 0.1 M NaOH and then neutralized with HCl. The salt concentration was adjusted to 0.1 M KCl and a binding experiment was performed using ¹⁴C-labelled λ*ind⁻* repressor as described in Fig. 2. The gradient was spun for only 2.5 h because of the increased sedimentation coefficient of denatured λ DNA in 0.05 M KCl[11].

In several experiments, the wild type repressor was tested for binding to DNA. Some binding was detected, but the results were not as striking as with the λ*ind⁻* repressor. It is possible that the *ind⁻* form is less susceptible to inactivation during the isolation procedure or that it binds more tightly to DNA.

Nature of the Binding

In order of binding to have been detected under the experimental conditions used, the repressor must bind very tightly to DNA. A close examination of Figs. 2 and 3 shows that some of the bound repressor washes off the DNA as it sediments. This suggests that the dissociation constant is of the same order of magnitude as the concentration of DNA binding sites (called operators) in the peak tubes. Assuming a small number of operators per phage genome (there are probably one or two), this value is roughly 10^{-9}–10^{-10} M. A repressor-operator affinity in this range *in vivo* is suggested by the magnitude of derepression observed with the *lac* operon. Since a 1,000-fold increase in β-galactosidase synthesis occurs on induction, the dissociation constant of the repressor–operator complex should be 1,000-fold less than the concentration

述实验所用的阻遏物曾被发现能够有效结合天然状态的 DNA，因此，该阻遏物在此不能结合变性 DNA 的原因一定是 DNA 的构型发生了改变。

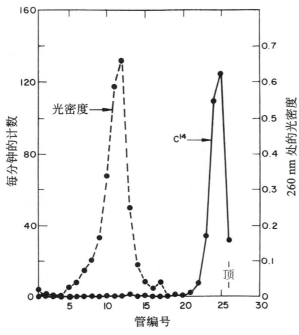

图 4. λ*ind*⁻ 阻遏物与变性 λ DNA 的结合。使 100 μg λ DNA 在 0.1 M NaOH 中变性，然后用 HCl 中和。
将盐浓度调整到 0.1 M KCl，然后按照图 2 中所描述的方法用 ¹⁴C 标记的 λ*ind*⁻ 阻遏物进行结合实验。
因为变性的 λ DNA 在 0.05 M KCl 中的沉降系数变大，所以将样品铺到梯度上后只离心 2.5 h 即可 [11]。

我们通过几次实验检测了野生型阻遏物与 DNA 的结合情况。有些情况下可以检测到这种结合，但是效果不及用 λ*ind*⁻ 阻遏物时那么明显。这可能是因为 *ind*⁻ 形式在分离过程中更不容易失活，或者它与 DNA 的结合更加紧密。

结合的特性

为了得到在所用实验条件下已经检测到的结合效果，阻遏物就必须与 DNA 结合得十分紧密。仔细观察图 2 和图 3 后发现，在沉降过程中一些本来与 DNA 结合的阻遏物脱离下来了。这表明：在与峰位对应的收集管中，解离常数与 DNA 结合位点（被称为操纵基因）的浓度具有相同的数量级。假设在每个噬菌体的基组中只有少数几个操纵基因（可能是一个或者两个），那么该浓度值大致为 10^{-9} M 至 10^{-10} M。在浓度处于这一范围内的体内条件下，阻遏物与操纵基因之间的亲和力可以通过用乳糖操纵子进行实验得到的去阻遏作用幅度来推断。因为诱导后 β– 半乳糖苷酶的合成

of free repressor in the cell[8]. The concentration of free *lac* repressor has been estimated at 10^{-7} M (ref. 2), implying that the dissociation constant is of the order of 10^{-10} M.

The finding of the λ*ind⁻* repressor to λ DNA was noticeably weaker when the complex was sedimented through a sucrose gradient containing 0.1 M KCl instead of the 0.05 M KCl used in the experiments described here. In a gradient containing 0.15 M KCl, no binding was detected. This observation suggests that the binding is partly electrostatic.

The finding that the λ repressor binds specifically and with high affinity to λ DNA strongly suggests that the simplest model for the mechanism of action of the repressor is correct—namely, that the repressor blocks transcription from DNA to RNA by directly binding to DNA. This conclusion is further supported by the recent observation of Dr. W. Gilbert that the *lac* repressor binds specifically to *lac* DNA and is removed by IPTG (W. Gilbert, to be published).

I thank Nancy Hopkins for technical assistance, and also Drs. W. Gilbert, J. D. Watson and S. E. Luria for help. The work was supported by grants from the U.S. National Science Foundation and the U.S. National Institutes of Health.

(**214**, 232-234; 1967)

Mark Ptashne: Department of Biology, Harvard University.

Received April 9, 1967.

References:

1. Jacob, F., and Monod, J., *J. Mol. Biol.*, **3**, 318 (1961).
2. Gilbert, W., and Mueller-Hill, B., *Proc. U.S. Nat. Acad. Sci.*, **56**, 1891 (1966).
3. Ptashne, M., *Proc. U.S. Nat. Acad. Sci.*, **57**, 306 (1967).
4. Kaiser, A. D., and Jacob, F., *Virology*, **4**, 509 (1957).
5. Isaacs, L. N., Echols, H., and Sly, W. S., *J. Mol. Biol.*, **13**, 963 (1965).
6. Jacob, F., and Campbell, A., *C.R. Acad. Sci., Paris*, **248**, 3219 (1959).
7. Jacob, F., Sussman, R., and Monod, J., *C.R. Acad. Sci., Paris*, **254**, 4214 (1962).
8. Sadler, J. R., and Novick, A., *J. Mol. Biol.*, **12**, 305 (1965).
9. Thomas, jun., C. A., and Abelson, J., *Procedures in Nucleic Acid Research*, edited by Cantoni, G. L., and Davies, D. R., 553 (Harper and Row, New York, 1966).
10. Modified according to E. Kennedy, pers. comm., from Patterson, M. S., and Greene, R. C., *Ann. Chem.*, **37**, 854 (1965).
11. Studier, F. W., *J. Mol. Biol.*, **11**, 373 (1965).

增加了 1,000 倍，所以阻遏物 – 操纵基因复合物的解离常数应该是胞内游离阻遏物浓度的 1/1,000[8]。游离乳糖操纵子阻遏物的浓度估计值是 10^{-7} M（参考文献 2），这意味着解离常数的数量级应为 10^{-10} M。

如果让复合物在含 0.1 M KCl 的蔗糖梯度中，而不是在本文所述实验中所用的含 0.05 M KCl 的蔗糖梯度中沉降，则会发现 λind⁻ 阻遏物与 λ DNA 的结合明显变弱。而如果用含 0.15 M KCl 的蔗糖梯度，则检测不到结合现象。上述结果表明这种结合有一部分是通过静电作用完成的。

λ 阻遏物与 λ DNA 的结合具有特异性和很高亲和力这一发现显然说明：解释阻遏物作用机制的最简单模型是正确的，即阻遏物通过直接与 DNA 结合而阻断了从 DNA 到 RNA 的转录过程。吉尔伯特博士最近的观察结果进一步证实了上述结论，他发现乳糖操纵子阻遏物能够特异地结合乳糖操纵子 DNA，并且这种结合作用可以被异丙基 –β–D– 硫代半乳糖苷消除（吉尔伯特即将发表的结果）。

感谢南希·霍普金斯在技术上给了我帮助，还要感谢吉尔伯特博士、沃森博士和卢里亚博士的帮助。此项研究受到了美国国家科学基金会和美国国立卫生研究院的资助。

（吕静 翻译；陈新文 陈继征 审稿）

The North Pacific:
An Example of Tectonics on a Sphere

D. P. McKenzie and R. L. Parker

Editor's Note

Although the discovery of seafloor spreading by Fred Vine and Drummond Matthews in 1963 confirmed the theory of plate tectonics—the idea that the Earth's crust consists of rigid plates moving on a mobile bed of molten rock—this paper by geophysicists Dan McKenzie and Robert Parker at the University of California was one of the two that truly marked the birth of the idea. They show how these "paving slab" plates, moving on the spherical planetary surface, can account geometrically for the behaviour of observed geological faults that mark the boundaries of plates, where volcanic activity and earthquakes are commonly observed. The paper stimulated many later studies that mapped plate movements from fault movements during earthquakes.

THE linear magnetic anomalies[1,2] which parallel all active ridges can only be produced by reversals of the Earth's magnetic field[1] if the oceanic crust is formed close to the ridge axis[3]. Models[4] have shown that the anomalies cannot be observed in the North Atlantic unless most dyke intrusion, and hence crustal production, occurs within 5 km of the ridge axis. The spreading sea floor[3] then carries these anomalies for great horizontal distances with little if any deformation. The epicentres of earthquakes also accurately follow the axis and are offset with it by transform faults[5,6]. The structure of island arcs is less clear, though the narrow band of shallow earthquakes suggests that crust is consumed along a linear feature. These observations are explained if the sea floor spreads as a rigid plate, and interacts with other plates in seismically active regions which also show recent tectonic activity. For the purposes of this article, ridges and trenches are respectively defined as lines along which crust is produced and destroyed. They need not also be topographic features. Transform faults conserve crust and are lines of pure slip. They are always parallel, therefore, to the relative velocity vector between two plates—a most useful property. We have tested this paving stone theory of world tectonics in the North Pacific, where it works well. Less detailed studies of other regions also support the theory.

The movement of blocks on the surface of a sphere is easiest to understand in terms of rotations. Any plate can clearly be moved to a given position and orientation on a sphere by two successive rotations, one of which carries one point to its final position, a second about an axis through this point then produces the required orientation. These two rotations are equivalent to a single rotation about a different axis, and therefore any relative motion of two plates on the surface of a sphere is a rotation about some axis. This is Euler's theorem, and has been used to fit together the continents surrounding the Atlantic[7]. If one of two plates is taken to be fixed, the movement of the other corresponds to a rotation about some pole, and

北太平洋：一个球体上的板块构造实例

麦肯齐，帕克

编者按

虽然弗雷德·瓦因和德拉蒙德·马修斯于 1963 年发现了海底扩张从而证实了板块构造理论，即地壳是由运动在流动熔岩层上的刚性板块组成，但这篇由加利福尼亚大学地球物理学家丹·麦肯齐和罗伯特·帕克撰写的文章才是真正标志板块构造理论形成的两篇文章之一。对于这些在球状行星表面运动的"铺石板"状板块，他们在文中阐述了如何能够从几何学上解释观测到的地质断层的特征。这些断层代表了板块的边界，在那里常常可以观测到火山活动和地震。由本文引发了很多根据地震期间的断层运动来描绘板块运动的后续研究。

如果洋壳紧邻洋脊轴形成，那么与所有活动洋脊平行的线状磁异常 [1,2] 就只能由地磁场的反转 [1] 产生 [3]。许多模型 [4] 显示：当在北大西洋中距洋脊轴 5 千米的范围之内有许多岩墙侵入并形成新的地壳时，便可观测到这种异常。不断扩张的海底 [3] 将这些异常沿水平方向携带出很远的距离，并且几乎不发生变形。地震震中也紧临洋脊轴，并与其一起被转换断层错开 [5,6]。虽然浅源地震发生在一个狭窄的地带说明地壳沿线性构造消减，但人们对岛弧构造的认识仍不清晰。假如海底作为一个刚性板块发生扩张，并且与其他板块在地震活动区或新构造活动区相互作用，那么上述观测到的结果就可以得到解释。为方便起见，本文把洋脊和海沟分别定义为地壳沿其形成和消减的线条。它们不一定具备地貌特征。转换断层并不破坏地壳，它们仅仅是滑移线。因此，转换断层总是与两个板块之间的相对速度矢量相平行——这是一个非常有用的特性。我们在北太平洋对大地构造的铺石板理论进行了验证，结果吻合得很好。对其他地区的研究虽不是很详细，但得到的结果也与上述理论相符。

根据旋转来理解块状物体在一个球体表面上的运动是最容易的。显然，任何板块都可以通过两次连续的旋转而被移动到球面上一个给定的位置和方位上，其中一次旋转将一个点带到它最终的位置，而另一次则是围绕着通过该点的轴旋转而达到所需的方位。这两次旋转与沿环绕另一个轴的单次旋转相当，因此，球面上两个板块之间的所有相对运动都可以被视为是沿着某个轴的旋转。这就是欧拉定理，该定理已被用于拼接大西洋周围的大陆 [7]。如果把两个板块中的一个看作是静止的，则另一个板块的运动就表现为绕某个极点的旋转，并且两个板块之间的所有相对速度

all relative velocity vectors between the two plates must lie along small circles or latitudes with respect to that pole. If these small circles cross the line of contact between the two plates, the line must be either a ridge or a trench depending on the sense of rotation. Neither of these structures conserves crust. If the line of contact is itself a small circle, then it is a transform fault. This property of transform faults is very useful in finding the pole position and is a consequence of the conservation of crust across them. There is no geometric reason why ridges or trenches should lie along longitudes with respect to the rotational pole and in general they do not do so. The pole position itself has no significance, it is merely a construction point. These remarks extend Wilson's[8] concept of transform faults to motions on a sphere, the essential additional hypothesis being that individual aseismic areas move as rigid plates on the surface of a sphere.

There are several points on the surface of the Earth where three plates meet. At such points the relative motion of the plates is not completely arbitrary, because, given any two velocity vectors, the third can be determined. The method is easier to understand on a plane than on a sphere, and can be derived from the plane circuit in Fig. 1. Starting from a point x on A and moving clockwise, the relative velocity of B, $_Av_B$ is in the direction AB in the vector diagram. Similarly the relative velocities $_Bv_C$ and $_Cv_A$ are represented by BC and CA. The vector diagram must close because the circuit returns to x. Thus:

$$_Av_B + {}_Bv_C + {}_Cv_A = 0 \qquad (1)$$

The usual rules for the construction of such triangles require three parameters to be known, of which at least one must be the length of a side, or spreading rate. Transform faults on both ridges and trenches are easy to recognize, and they determine the direction, but not the magnitude, of the relative velocities. The magnetic lineations are one method of obtaining $_Bv_C$, though this value must be corrected for orientation unless the spreading is at right angles to the ridge. Then the triangle in Fig. 1 determines both $_Av_B$ and $_Cv_A$. This method is probably most useful to determine the rate of crustal consumption by trenches. Equation (1) must be used with care, because it only applies rigorously to an infinitesimal circuit round a point where three (or more) plates meet. If the circuit is finite, the rotation of the plates also contributes to their relative velocity, and therefore these simple rules no longer apply.

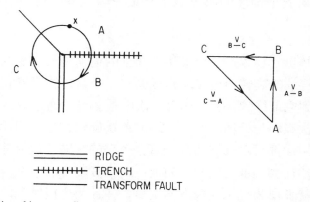

RIDGE
TRENCH
TRANSFORM FAULT

Fig. 1. The circuit and its vector diagram show how a ridge and a trench can meet to form a transform fault.

50

矢量必然在以该极点为圆心的小圆或称纬线上。倘若这些小圆与两板块之间的边界线相交，那么该边界线肯定是洋脊或海沟，具体是哪一个将取决于旋转的方向。这两种构造都可导致地壳发生变化。倘若边界线本身就是一个小圆，那么它就是一个转换断层。转换断层的这一特性在寻找极点位置时非常有用，并且也是其两侧地壳维持不变的结果。没有任何几何学上的原因要求洋脊或者海沟必须相对于旋转极沿着经线分布，而且从总体上看情况也并非如此。极点位置本身并不重要，它仅仅是一个构造点。上述讨论将威尔逊[8]提出的转换断层概念扩展到了在球体上的运动，其重要的补充设想是把单个无震区作为在球体表面上运动的刚性板块。

地球表面存在数个三个板块的交界点。在这些点上，板块的相对运动不是完全任意的，因为如果已知任意两个速度矢量，就可以确定第三个。在一个平面上理解这种方法比在一个球面上更容易，该方法可从图1的平面环路中推导出来。从板块 A 上的一个点 x 出发沿顺时针运动，则在矢量图上，板块 B 的相对速度 $_Av_B$ 将沿 AB 方向。同样，相对速度 $_Bv_C$ 和 $_Cv_A$ 将分别沿 BC 和 CA 方向。矢量图必须是封闭的，因为环形路线会返回到 x 点。因此：

$$_Av_B + {}_Bv_C + {}_Cv_A = 0 \tag{1}$$

建立此类三角形的一般法则要求已知三个参数，并且其中至少有一个必须是三角形中某个边的长度或者扩张速率。与洋脊和海沟相关的转换断层很容易辨认，它们确定了相对速度的方向，但不能确定其大小。利用磁线理是获得 $_Bv_C$ 的一种方法，但在扩张方向与洋脊不成直角的情况下必须对数据进行方向校正。因此，根据图1中的三角形可以确定 $_Av_B$ 和 $_Cv_A$。该方法在确定海沟处地壳的消减速率时可能非常有用。必须谨慎使用公式(1)，因为它仅适用于以三个（或更多）板块相遇点为圆心的一个无限小的圆上。如果该小圆是有限的，则板块的旋转也会对其相对速度产生影响，因此，上述简单法则就不再适用了。

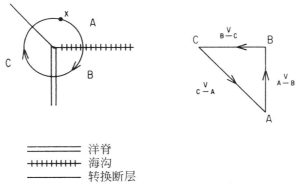

========== 洋脊
++++++++++ 海沟
————————— 转换断层

图 1. 表示洋脊和海沟可以相遇并形成一个转换断层的环路图和矢量图。

Equation (1) is easily extended to the corresponding problem on a spherical surface because angular velocities behave like vectors[9]:

$$_A\omega_B + _B\omega_C + _C\omega_A = 0 \tag{2}$$

The sign convention takes a rotation which is clockwise when looked at from the centre of the sphere to be a positive vector which is pointing outward along the rotation axis. By adding more terms, equation (2) can be extended to circuits crossing more than three plates and applies to all possible circuits on the surface. ω diagrams for three plates are no more difficult to construct than those for v, because the third vector must lie in the plane containing the other two. This result does not apply to diagrams for four or more plates, which are three dimensional and therefore less easy to draw.

These geometrical ideas can now be applied to the North Pacific. There are many fault plane solutions for earthquakes in the area, and these are used in a new way in order to determine the direction of the horizontal projection of the slip vector. Unlike the projection of the principal stress axes, that of the slip vector varies in a systematic manner over the entire region. This is clearly a consequence of spreading of the sea floor, which determines the relative motion, not the stress field.

The North Pacific was chosen for several reasons. The spreading rate from the East Pacific rise is the most rapid yet measured[2], and should therefore dominate any slight movements within the plate containing North America and Kamchatka[10]. The belt of earthquake epicentres which extends from the Gulf of California to Central Japan without any major branches[10] suggests that the area contains only two principal plates. Also, the belt of seismic activity between them is one of the most active in the world and many fault plane solutions are available[6,11-17]. It is an advantage that the trend of the belt which joins the two plates varies rapidly over short distances, because this illustrates the large variety of earthquake mechanisms which can result from a simple rotation (Fig. 2). It is also helpful that the outlines of the geology and topography of the sea floor are known.

因为角速度具有类似矢量的特征[9]，所以可以很容易把公式（1）扩展为球体表面的相应问题：

$$_A\omega_B + {}_B\omega_C + {}_C\omega_A = 0 \tag{2}$$

符号法则约定：从球心向外看，顺时针旋转为正矢量，它沿旋转轴向外指。通过增加更多的项，可以将公式（2）扩展到穿越三个以上板块的环线，进而应用于球面上所有可能的环线。建立三个板块的 ω 图并不比建立 υ 图更难，因为第三个矢量一定位于包含另外两个矢量的平面之内。这一结果不适用于四个或更多板块的图，因为它们是三维的，所以不容易绘制。

现在可以把这些几何概念应用到北太平洋。在北太平洋地区有许多为了解地震而获得的断层面解，这些资料可根据新的思路来应用，从而确定滑移向量水平投影的方向。与主应力轴的投影不同，滑移向量的投影在整个区域内存在系统变化。这显然是海底扩张的结果，它决定的是相对运动而不是应力场。

选择北太平洋有以下几方面的原因。东太平洋海隆的扩张速率在迄今为止测量到的扩张速率中是最快的[2]，因而与包含北美和堪察加半岛的板块内的任何轻微运动相比应占主要地位[10]。地震中心带从加利福尼亚湾一直延伸至日本中部，并且没有任何大的分支[10]，这种现象指示该地区仅存在两个主要板块。另外，这两个板块之间的地震活动带也是世界上最活跃的地震带之一，并且有许多可用的断层面解资料[6,11-17]。一个有利条件是，连接这两个板块的地震带走向在短距离内发生了快速的变化，因为这说明用简单的旋转就可以解释各种地震机制（图 2）。另外，我们对这一区域的海底地质和地形概况都已了解，这也很有帮助。

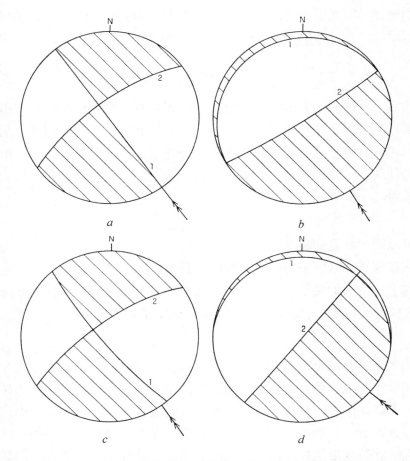

Fig. 2. Mechanism diagrams for four circum-pacific earthquakes. The lower half of the focal sphere is projected stereographically on to a horizontal surface, and the rare-fraction quadrants are shaded. The horizontal projection of the slip vector in plane 1 is marked with a double arrow. (a) June 28, 1966, Parkfield[15], strike slip. (b) September 4, 1964, Alaska[16], overthrust. (c) June 14, 1962, Near and Aleutian Islands[14], strike slip. (d) October 20, 1963, Kurile Islands[17], overthrust.

Fault plane solutions which were obtained from the records of the world-wide network of standardized stations now give excellent and consistent results[6,16]. The directions of principal stress axes, however, which were determined from first motions, vary widely over short distances (Fig. 2) and are therefore difficult to use directly. The concept of spreading of the sea floor suggests that the horizontal projection of the slip vector is more important than that of any of the stress axes, and Fig. 2 shows that this is indeed the case. The examples which are illustrated are stereographic projections of the radiation field in the lower hemisphere on to a horizontal plane[16]. The direction of the projection of the slip vector in plane one is obtained by adding or subtracting 90° from the strike of plane two if the planes one and two are orthogonal. The slip directions which are shown give the motion of the oceanic plate relative to the plate containing North America and Kamchatka. For each case in Fig. 2 there are two possible slip directions, but, whereas one changes in direction slowly and systematically between Baja California and

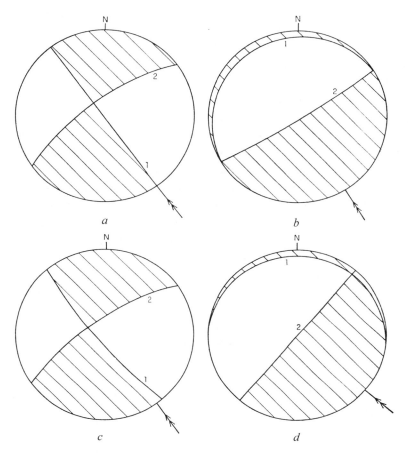

图 2. 四个环太平洋的地震机制图。将震源球的下半部分以赤平投影的方式投射到一个水平面上，稀疏区以阴影表示。滑移向量在平面 1 中的水平投影以双箭头表示。(a)1966 年 6 月 28 日，帕克菲尔德 [15]，走向滑移。(b) 1964 年 9 月 4 日，阿拉斯加 [16]，逆冲推覆。(c) 1962 年 6 月 14 日，阿留申群岛及附近 [14]，走向滑移。(d) 1963 年 10 月 20 日，千岛群岛 [17]，逆冲推覆。

目前，由世界标准台网的记录所得到的断层面解给出了极好且一致的结果 [6,16]。然而，由第一次运动决定的主应力轴的方向，由于其在短距离内的变化很大（图 2），因而很难被直接采用。海底扩张观点认为：滑移向量的水平投影较所有应力轴的水平投影更重要，图 2 说明事实的确如此。所举的例子是下半球辐射场在一个水平面上的赤平投影图 [16]。如果平面 1 和平面 2 相互垂直，则滑移向量在平面 1 上的投影方向可通过将平面 2 的走向加上或减去 90 度而得到。图中所示的滑移方向反映出大洋板块相对于包括北美和堪察加半岛在内的板块的运动。在图 2 所示的每一种情况下，都存在两个可能的滑移方向。然而，在下加利福尼亚和日本之间，当一个滑移方向发生缓慢且系统的变化时，另一个并没有表现出相应的变化，即使对同一地区

Japan, the other shows no consistency even for earthquakes in the same area. The ambiguity is therefore unimportant in this case. If all the earthquakes between the Gulf of California and Japan are produced by a rotation of the Pacific plate relative to the continental one, any pair of widely spaced slip directions can be used to determine the pole of relative rotation. The two which are used here are the strike of the San Andreas between Parkfield and San Francisco, and the average slip vector of all the aftershocks in the Kodiak Island region[16] of the 1964 Alaskan earthquake. A pole position of 50°N., 85°W. was obtained by construction on a sphere. If the paving stone theory applies, all slip vectors must be parallel to the latitudes which can be drawn with respect to this pole. Though this prediction could be tested by tabulating the disagreement with the observations, a simpler and more obvious test is to plot the slip vectors on a map of the world in Mercator projection, taking the projection pole to be the rotation axis (Fig. 3). The Mercator projection has two advantages; it is conformal, which means that angles are locally preserved and slip vectors can be plotted directly, and also all small circles centred on the projection pole are parallel. Because the upper and lower boundaries of Fig. 3 are themselves small circles, the theory requires all slip vectors to be parallel both to each other and to the top and bottom. This prediction was tested on eighty published[6,11-17] fault plane solutions for shallow earthquakes during and after 1957. Of these, about 80 percent had slip vectors with the correct sense of motion and within ±20° of the direction required by Fig. 3. Most of the fault plane solutions for earthquakes before this date also agreed with the sense and direction of motion. Representative slip vectors in Fig. 3 show the motion of the Pacific plate relative to the continental one, which is taken to be fixed. The rotation vector is therefore negative and points inward at 50°N., 85°W. The agreement with theory is remarkable over the entire region. It shows that the paving stone theory is essentially correct and applies to about a quarter of the Earth's surface.

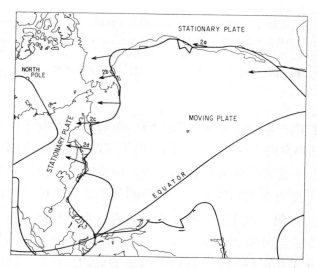

Fig. 3. A Mercator projection of the Pacific with a pole at 50°N., 85°W. The arrows show the direction of motion of the Pacific plate relative to that containing North America and Kamchatka. If both plates are rigid all slip vectors must be parallel with each other and with the upper and lower boundaries of the figure. Possible boundaries of other plates are sketched.

的地震来讲也是如此。因此模糊性在这种情况下并不重要。如果加利福尼亚湾和日本之间所有的地震都是由太平洋板块相对于大陆板块的旋转造成的，那么任何一对相距较远的滑移方向都可以用来确定相对旋转的极点。本文所用的两个滑移方向分别是：圣弗朗西斯科和帕克菲尔德之间的圣安德烈亚斯断层的走向以及在 1964 年阿拉斯加大地震中科迪亚克岛地区[16] 所有余震的平均滑移向量方向。由此，我们在球体上得到了一个位于北纬 50 度西经 85 度的极点。如果应用铺石板理论，那么所有滑移向量都应该与相对于该极点所画的纬线平行。虽然上述预测可以通过把与观测结果不一致的地方列成表格来检验，但一个更简单和更直观的检测方法是：采用墨卡托投影法将滑移向量投射到世界地图上，并把投影极点作为旋转轴（图 3）。采用墨卡托投影有两个优点：其一，它是正形投影，这就意味着角度在局部保持不变，滑移向量可以直接画出；其二，所有以投影极点为中心的小圆都是平行的。因为图 3 的上边界和下边界本身就是小圆，所以该理论要求所有滑移向量不仅要相互平行，而且还要平行于图的顶边和底边。1957 年以来，该预测已得到 80 个已发表的[6,11-17]浅源地震断层面解的验证。其中大约 80% 的滑移向量显示出正确的运动方向，误差范围在 ±20 度以内，与图 3 所要求的一致。在 1957 年之前，多数地震的断层面解也与所要求的运动方向一致。图 3 中代表性的滑移向量指示太平洋板块相对于大陆板块的运动，而大陆板块被认为是静止的。因此，旋转向量为负值，并且向内指向北纬 50 度西经 85 度处。在整个区域内，观测与理论的一致性是显而易见的。这说明铺石板理论基本上是正确的，并且可应用于约四分之一的地球表面。

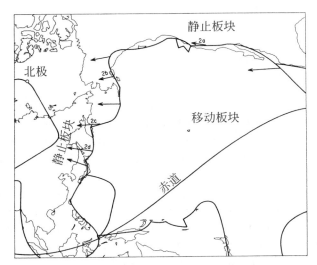

图 3. 以北纬 50 度西经 85 度为极点的太平洋墨卡托投影图。箭头表示太平洋板块相对于包括北美和堪察加半岛在内的大陆板块的运动方向。如果两个板块都是刚性的，那么所有滑移向量都必须相互平行，并且还要平行于图的上下边界。其他板块的可能边界也被示意性地画出。

The disadvantage of the Mercator projection is the distortion it introduces around the poles. It is therefore difficult to use Fig. 3 to estimate spreading velocities. For this purpose an orthonormal projection is more useful (Fig. 4), for the spreading rate is then proportional to distance from the centre if this is taken at the pole of rotation. In this projection, which is simply a vertical projection on to a plane at right angles to the rotation axis, rigid rotations of the two plates on a sphere become rigid body rotations on the plane, and all slip vectors must be tangents to concentric circles about the centre of projection (Fig. 4). This projection is useful if spreading rates, rather than angles, are known. There are as yet few such measurements in the North Pacific.

Fig. 4. An orthonormal projection of the North Pacific centred on the Mercator Pole. Slip vectors are tangents to concentric circles about the centre.

The large active tectonic areas of the North Pacific are now clear from Fig. 3. The fault systems of the San Andreas, Queen Charlotte Islands and Fairweather form a dextral transform fault joining the East Pacific rise to the Aleutian trench. The strike slip nature of these faults is clear from field observations[18-20] and from the fault plane solutions (for example, Fig. 2a). In Alaska the epicentral belt of earthquakes changes direction[10] (Fig. 3) and follows the Aleutian arc. The fault solutions also change from strike slip to overthrust[16] (for example, Fig. 2b), and require that the islands and Alaska should override the Pacific on low angle (~7°) faults. Though the direction of slip remains the same along the entire Aleutian arc, the change in strike changes the fault plane solutions from overthrusting in the east to strike slip in the west (Fig. 2c). A sharp bend occurs between the Aleutians and Kamchatka (Fig. 3). Here the fault plane solutions change back to overthrust (Fig. 2d). This motion continues as far as Central Japan, where the active belt divides (Fig. 3) and the present study stops. Thus the North Pacific contains the two types of transform faults

墨卡托投影的缺点是它会使极点周围地区发生变形。因此很难用图3来估算扩张速度。若要估算扩张速度，正交投影更为实用（图4），因为扩张速率与其到作为旋转极点中心的距离成正比。正交投影是一种简单的向平面上的垂直投影，该平面与旋转轴成直角。在这种情况下，两个板块在球面上的刚性旋转变成了刚性体在平面上的旋转，并且所有滑移向量都必须是围绕投影中心的同心圆的切线（图4）。如果已知扩张速率而不是角度，这种投影方法是很有用的。迄今为止，在北太平洋地区的此类测量结果还很少。

图 4. 以墨卡托投影极为中心的北太平洋地区正交投影。滑移向量都是围绕中心的同心圆的切线。

现在可以从图3中清楚地看到北太平洋的大型活动构造区。圣安德烈亚斯、夏洛特皇后群岛和费尔韦瑟断层体系形成了一个连接东太平洋海隆和阿留申海沟的右旋转换断层。根据野外观测[18-20]和断层面解（例如图2a），这些断层的走滑性质非常明显。在阿拉斯加，地震中心带的方向发生改变[10]（图3），变为沿阿留申岛弧的走向。断层类型也由走滑断层转变为逆冲断层[16]（例如图2b），这就要求阿留申群岛和阿拉斯加必须以低角度（约7度）推覆在太平洋板块之上。虽然滑移方向沿整个阿留申岛弧是一致的，但其走向的变化导致断层性质由东部的逆冲断层变为西部的走滑断层（图2c）。在阿留申群岛与堪察加半岛之间有一个急弯（图3），在这里断层又变为逆冲断层（图2d）。这种运动一直延伸到日本中部，活动带在那里出现分支（图3），而该研究也到此为止。因此，北太平洋包含两类与海沟相关的转换断

which require trenches[8], and clearly shows the dependence of the fault plane solutions on the trend of the fault concerned.

The variation of trend also controls the distribution of trenches, active andesite volcanoes, intermediate and deep focus earthquakes[10]. All these phenomena occur in Mexico, Alaska, the Eastern Aleutians, and from Kamchatka to Japan, but are absent where the faults are of a strike slip transform nature. This correlation is particularly obvious along the Aleutian arc, where all these features become steadily less important as Kamchatka is approached[10], then suddenly reappear when the trend of the earthquake belt changes. Though it is clear from these remarks that the paving stone theory applies to the North Pacific region as a whole, there are some small areas which at first sight are exceptions.

The most obvious of these is the complicated region of the ocean floor off the coast between northern California and the Canadian border[21]. The difficulties begin where the San Andreas fault turns into the Mendocino fault. Fig. 5 shows that the change in trend of the epicentres is possible only if crust is consumed between C and A (or created in B, which is unlikely). The earthquakes along the coast of Oregon[22] and the presence of the volcanoes of the Cascade range, one of which has recently been active and all of which contain andesites, support the idea that crust is destroyed in this area. In the same area two remarkable seismic station corrections which possess a large azimuthal variation[23] also suggest that there is a high velocity region extending deep into the mantle similar to that in the Tonga–Kermadec[24] region. These complications disappear when the ridge and trench structures join again and become the Queen Charlotte Islands fault.

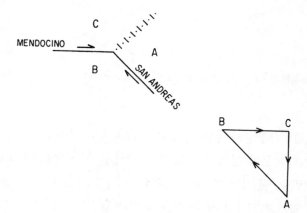

Fig. 5. Both the Mendocino and San Andreas faults can be strike slip if there is a trench to the north or east.

Another complicated area is in Alaska between 147.5°W. and the north end of the Fairweather fault[16]. In this same area the local uplift after the 1964 earthquake suggested that several faults were active[16], and therefore the tectonics cannot be understood without more fault plane solutions.

The third area is in the Kurile Islands where two fault plane solutions (Fig. 6a and b) require

层[8]，并且可以清楚地看出，断层的性质取决于相应断层的走向。

断层走向的变化也控制着海沟、活动的安山岩火山以及中源和深源地震的分布[10]。所有这些现象都出现在墨西哥、阿拉斯加、阿留申东部以及从堪察加半岛到日本一带，但当断层具有走滑转换断层特性时，上述现象便消失了。这种相关性在沿阿留申岛弧一带尤为明显，而随着向堪察加半岛的靠近，所有这些特征逐渐变得不明显了[10]。然而当地震带的走向发生变化时，这些特征又会突然再现。虽然铺石板理论从整体上明显适用于北太平洋地区，但还有一些小的区域乍看起来与该理论不相符。

其中最明显的就是加利福尼亚北部和加拿大边界之间海岸线外的复杂洋底[21]。难题出现在圣安德烈亚斯断层与门多西诺断层相接的地方。图 5 显示：只有当 C 与 A 之间的地壳消减时（或 B 处有地壳形成时，但这是不可能的），震中走向才有可能会发生变化。沿俄勒冈海岸的地震[22]以及喀斯喀特山脉火山群（均包含安山岩，其中一座最近刚刚喷发过）都支持地壳在该区遭到毁坏的观点。在同一地区，地震台所作的两次较大的校正指示很大的方位变化[23]，表明那里存在一个一直延伸到地幔深处的高速区，与汤加–克马德克地区[24]类似。而当洋脊和海沟构造再次连接而形成夏洛特皇后群岛断层时，上述复杂性就消失了。

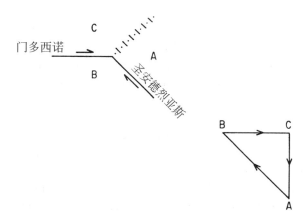

图 5. 如果在北边或东边存在一个海沟，则门多西诺和圣安德烈亚斯断层都可以是走滑断层。

另一个复杂地区位于阿拉斯加，在西经 147.5 度和费尔韦瑟断层北端之间[16]。该区在 1964 年地震之后发生了局部的隆升，说明那里存在多个活动断层[16]，因此如果没有更多的断层面解资料，将无法了解其构造特征。

第三个地区位于千岛群岛，在那里有两个断层面解（图 6a 和 b）证明曾发生过

dip slip faulting and crustal extension. This motion is completely different from most of the solutions in the area, which agree well with the rest of the North Pacific. Both earthquakes occurred beneath the steep wall of the Kurile trench on the island arc side, and are consistent with gravity slides down into the trench. The terraces which would result from such slides are common features of the trenches of both Japan and the Aleutians[25,26]. There is also one fault plane solution which requires that the Pacific should be overthrusting the Kurile Islands (Fig. 6c), though the crustal shortening is consistent with the regional pattern.

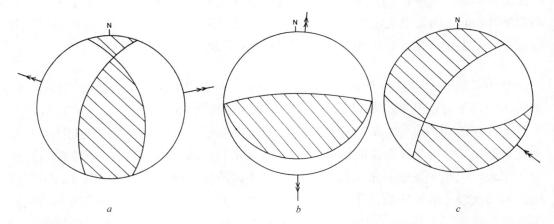

Fig. 6. Mechanism diagrams drawn as in Fig. 2 for three earthquakes in the Kurile Islands. (a) September 15, 1962 (ref. 14), extension by normal faulting. (b) November 15, 1963 (ref. 17), extension by normal faulting. (c) May 22, 1963 (ref. 17), island arc overthrust from the Pacific side.

The two ends of the North Pacific belt may also be discussed with the help of vector circuits. The end in Central Japan gives the trivial result that two trenches can join to give a third. The other end at the entrance to the Gulf of California is the circuit in Fig. 1, and shows how the East Pacific rise and the Middle America trench combine to become the San Andreas transform fault.

The North Pacific shows the remarkable success of the paving stone theory over a quarter of the Earth's surface, and it is therefore expected to apply to the other three-quarters. It is, however, only an instantaneous phenomenological theory, and also does not apply to intermediate or deep focus earthquakes. The evolution of the plates as they are created and consumed on their boundaries is not properly understood at present, though it should be possible to use the magnetic anomalies for this purpose. The other problem is the nature of the mechanism driving the spreading. It is difficult to believe that the convection cells which drive the motion are closely related to the boundaries of the plates.

One area where the evolution is apparent lies between the plate containing the Western Atlantic, North and South America[10] and the main Pacific plate. The transform faults in the South-East Pacific are east–west; therefore the ocean floor between the rise and South America is moving almost due east relative to the main Pacific plate. The motion of the Atlantic plate

倾滑断裂和地壳伸展。这种运动完全不同于该区域内的绝大多数与北太平洋其他地区一致的断层面解。两次地震均发生于岛弧一侧的千岛海沟的陡壁下，并且与进入海沟的重力滑坡体一致。由这些滑动体形成的阶地具有与日本海沟和阿留申海沟相同的特征 [25,26]。虽然地壳的缩短与区域变形类型一致，但仍然有一个可以推断出太平洋应该逆冲于千岛群岛之上的断层面解（图 6c）。

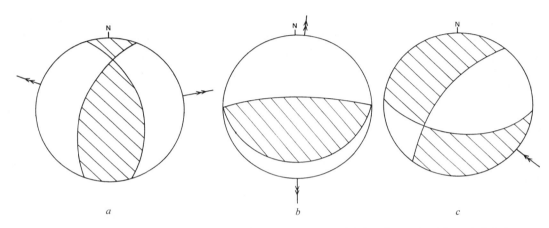

图 6. 图 2 所示的千岛群岛三次地震的机制图。(a)1962 年 9 月 15 日(参考文献 14)，由正断层引起的扩张。(b) 1963 年 11 月 15 日 (参考文献 17)，由正断层引起的扩张。(c) 1963 年 5 月 22 日 (参考文献 17)，来自太平洋一侧的岛弧逆冲断层。

北太平洋带的两端也可以用矢量环路来讨论。根据位于日本中部的一端可以得出一个不重要的结论，即两个海沟可相连形成第三个海沟。位于加利福尼亚湾入口处的另一端就是图 1 中的环路，它说明了东太平洋海隆和中美洲海沟是如何联合在一起并形成了圣安德烈亚斯转换断层。

铺石板理论对占地球表面四分之一的北太平洋的解释非常成功，因此我们也希望它能应用于地球表面的另外四分之三。然而，这只是一个反映瞬间现象的理论，并且也不适用于中源或深源地震。我们目前还不十分了解板块在其边界处形成和消减的演化过程，不过利用磁异常进行这方面的研究应该是可行的。另一个问题是扩张驱动机制的性质。很难相信驱动该运动的对流环与板块边界之间存在着密切的关系。

明显具有这种演化的一个区域位于包含大西洋西部和南、北美洲的板块 [10] 与太平洋主板块之间的区域。东南太平洋地区的转换断层均为东西走向，因而东南太平洋海隆与南美洲之间的洋底相对于太平洋主板块来说几乎是向正东方向运动的。大西洋板块相对于太平洋的运动可根据圣安德烈亚斯断层确定，其运动方向

relative to the Pacific is given by the San Andreas, and is towards the south-east. If the motion of the Atlantic plate is less rapid than that of the South-Eastern Pacific north of the Chile ridge, then the crust must be consumed along the Chile trench. The faults involved must have both over thrustand right-handed strike slip components. The present motion on the San Andreas is not in conflict with the east–west transform faults of the North-Eastern Pacific if there was originally a plate of ocean floor between North America and the main Pacific plate joined to that which still exists to the west of Chile. This piece of ocean floor has since been consumed, and therefore the direction of spreading in the Pacific appears to have changed in the north but not in the south. This explanation requires changes in the shape of the plates but not in their relative motion, and therefore differs from those previously suggested[2,6]. This study suggests that a belief in uniformity and the existence of magnetic anomalies will permit at least the younger tectonic events in the Earth's history to be understood in terms of sea floor spreading.

We thank H. W. Menard for his help.

This research was supported by the US Air Force Office of Scientific Research, Office of Aerospace Research.

(**216**, 1276-1280; 1967)

D. P. McKenzie and R. L. Parker: Institute of Geophysics and Planetary Physics, University of California at San Diego.

Received November 14, 1967.

References:
1. Vine, F. J., and Matthews, D. H., *Nature*, **199**, 947 (1963).
2. Vine, F. J., *Science*, **154**, 1405 (1966).
3. Hess, H. H., in *Petrologic Studies* (edit. by Engel, A. E. J., James, H. L., and Leonard, B. F.) (Geol. Soc. Amer., New York, 1962).
4. Matthews, D. H., and Bath, J., *Geophys. J.*, **13**, 349 (1967).
5. Sykes, L. R., *J. Geophys. Res.*, **68**, 5999 (1963).
6. Sykes, L. R., *J. Geophys. Res.*, **72**, 2131 (1967).
7. Bullard, E. C., Everett, J. E., and Smith, A. G., *Phil. Trans. Roy. Soc.*, A, **258**, 41 (1965).
8. Wilson, J. T., *Nature*, **207**, 343 (1965).
9. Goldstein, H., *Classical Mechanics* (Addison-Wesley, 1950).
10. Gutenberg, B., and Richter, C. F., *Seismicity of the Earth and Associated Phenomena* (Princeton University Press, 1954).
11. Stauder, W., *Bull. Seism. Soc. Amer.*, **50**, 293 (1960).
12. Stauder, W., and Udias, A., *Bull. Seism. Soc. Amer.*, **53**, 59 (1963).
13. Udias, A., and Stauder, W., *Bull. Seism. Soc. Amer.*, **54**, 2049 (1964).
14. Stauder, W., and Bollinger, G. A., *Bull. Seism. Soc. Amer.*, **54**, 2198 (1964).
15. McEvilly, T. V., *Bull. Seism. Soc. Amer.*, **56**, 967 (1966).
16. Stauder, W., and Bollinger, G. A., *J. Geophys. Res.*, **71**, 5283 (1966).
17. Stauder, W., and Bollinger, G. A., *Bull. Seism. Soc. Amer.*, **56**, 1363 (1966).
18. Tocher, D., *Bull. Seism. Soc. Amer.*, **50**, 267 (1960).
19. Hill, M. L., and Dibblee, jun., T. W., *Bull. Geol. Soc. Amer.*, **64**, 443 (1953).
20. Allen, C. R., *Phil. Trans. Roy. Soc.*, A, **258**, 82 (1965).

为东南。如果大西洋板块的运动速度比智利洋脊北侧的东南太平洋板块的运动速度慢，那么沿智利海沟一线的地壳应该是消减的。其中所有相关断层必定有逆冲和右旋走滑两种分量。假设原先在北美板块和仍位于智利西侧并与北美板块相连的太平洋主板块之间曾存在过一个大洋板块，那么圣安德烈亚斯断层当前的运动与太平洋东北部的东西向转换断层就是不矛盾的。这块洋壳一直在消减，因而太平洋的扩张方向似乎在北部发生了变化，而在南部没有改变。这种解释要求发生变化的是板块的形状而非其相对运动，这不同于前人提出的观点[2,6]。这项研究表明：相信均一性和磁异常的存在至少可使我们根据海底扩张理论来理解地球历史上较新的构造事件。

感谢梅纳德对我们的帮助。

本研究得到了美国空军科学研究办公室航空航天研究室的支持。

（齐红艳 翻译；孟庆任 审稿）

21. Wilson, J. T., *Science*, **150**, 482 (1965).

22. Berg, J. W., and Baker, C. D., *Bull. Seism. Soc. Amer.*, **53**, 95 (1963).

23. Bolt, B. A., and Nuttli, O. W., *J. Geophys. Res.*, **71**, 5977 (1966).

24. Oliver, J., and Isacks, B., *J. Geophys. Res.*, **72**, 4259 (1967).

25. Ludwig, W. J., Ewing, J. I., Ewing, M., Murauchi, S., Den, N., Asano, S., Hotta, H., Hayakawa, M., Ichikawa, K., and Noguchi, I., *J. Geophys. Res.*, **71**, 2121 (1966).

26. Gates, O., and Gibson, W., *Bull. Geol. Soc. Amer.*, **67**, 127 (1956).

Observation of a Rapidly Pulsating Radio Source

A. Hewish *et al.*

Editor's Note

A survey of radio emission in the sky revealed a curiously periodic source, as reported here by Anthony Hewish and his colleagues (the actual discovery was made by Jocelyn Bell, who was at that time Hewish's graduate student). The period was determined to be stable to one part in ten million, and the source showed no parallax, so it could not originate within the Solar System. The researchers also found three other sources with similar properties. Hewish speculated that they might arise from radial (in and out) pulsations of white dwarf stars or neutron stars. We now know that they arise from beams on rapidly rotating neutron stars (called pulsars), but the precise mechanism for generating the beams is still controversial. For this discovery, in 1974 Hewish became the first astronomer to be awarded the Nobel Prize in physics.

IN July 1967, a large radio telescope operating at a frequency of 81.5 MHz was brought into use at the Mullard Radio Astronomy Observatory. This instrument was designed to investigate the angular structure of compact radio sources by observing the scintillation caused by the irregular structure of the interplanetary medium[1]. The initial survey includes the whole sky in the declination range $-08° < \delta < 44°$ and this area is scanned once a week. A large fraction of the sky is thus under regular surveillance. Soon after the instrument was brought into operation it was noticed that signals which appeared at first to be weak sporadic interference were repeatedly observed at a fixed declination and right ascension; this result showed that the source could not be terrestrial in origin.

Systematic investigations were started in November and high speed records showed that the signals, when present, consisted of a series of pulses each lasting ~0.3 s and with a repetition period of about 1.337 s which was soon found to be maintained with extreme accuracy. Further observations have shown that the true period is constant to better than 1 part in 10^7 although there is a systematic variation which can be ascribed to the orbital motion of the Earth. The impulsive nature of the recorded signals is caused by the periodic passage of a signal of descending frequency through the 1 MHz pass band of the receiver.

The remarkable nature of these signals at first suggested an origin in terms of man-made transmissions which might arise from deep space probes, planetary radar or the reflexion of terrestrial signals from the Moon. None of these interpretations can, however, be accepted because the absence of any parallax shows that the source lies far outside the solar system. A preliminary search for further pulsating sources has already revealed the presence of three others having remarkably similar properties which suggests that this type of source may be relatively common at a low flux density. A tentative explanation of these unusual sources in terms of the stable oscillations of white dwarf or neutron stars is proposed.

快速脉动射电源的观测

休伊什等

编者按

正如安东尼·休伊什及其同事在本文中所报道的，对天空中射电辐射的探测揭示出了一个奇特周期性源的存在（实际上真正的发现者是乔斯琳·贝尔，那时她还是休伊什的研究生）。经测定，周期稳定在 10^{-7} 的误差内，并且该源没有视差，所以它不可能来自太阳系内部。研究人员还发现了另外三个具有同样特性的射电源。休伊什推测它们可能来自于白矮星或中子星的径向（胀缩）脉动。现在我们知道它们是由快速旋转的中子星（被称为脉冲星）所发射的辐射造成的，但人们对产生这种辐射束的确切机制尚存争议。因为上述发现，休伊什在 1974 年成为了第一位获得诺贝尔物理学奖的天文学家。

1967 年 7 月，一台工作频率是 81.5 MHz 的大型射电望远镜在玛拉德射电天文台投入使用。有了这台仪器，研究人员就可以通过观测由行星际介质不规则结构造成的闪烁来研究致密射电源的角结构[1]。最初的观测范围覆盖了赤纬 δ 为 $-08° < \delta < 44°$ 的全部天区，并且这一区域每周都会被扫描一次。因此大部分天区落在研究人员的定期监测之中。在这台仪器投入运行后不久，研究人员发现：一些起先看上去微弱而零星的干扰信号会在一个固定的赤经和赤纬上被反复观测到。上述结果说明该信号不可能来源于地球。

系统探测从 11 月开始进行。高速记录的结果表明：当这种信号出现的时候，它们总是由一系列脉冲组成，每个脉冲的持续时间约为 0.3 s，而重复周期约为 1.337 s，研究人员很快发现这一周期的稳定性很高。尽管地球的轨道运动可能导致了一定的系统变化，但进一步的观测结果表明，真实周期是一个误差不超过 10^{-7} 的常数。被记录信号的脉冲特性是由一个信号的周期部分产生的，该信号的频率在接收机的整个 1 MHz 通带内递减。

最开始，研究人员认为这些信号的不寻常特性源自于一些人造的信号传输装置，比如或许源自深空探测器、行星雷达或者从月球上反射回来的地球信号。但这些解释都不能为人们所接受，因为：没有视差足以说明信号源远在太阳系之外。在对更多的脉动源进行初步探测之后，研究人员发现还有三个源也具有非常类似的性质。这表明此类低流量密度的源在宇宙中可能还是比较常见的。本文提出了一个尝试性的解释，即认为这些不寻常的信号源来自于白矮星或者中子星的稳定振荡。

Position and Flux Density

The aerial consists of a rectangular array containing 2,048 full-wave dipoles arranged in sixteen rows of 128 elements. Each row is 470 m long in an E.–W. direction and the N.–S. extent of the array is 45 m. Phase-scanning is employed to direct the reception pattern in declination and four receivers are used so that four different declinations may be observed simultaneously. Phase-switching receivers are employed and the two halves of the aerial are combined as an E.–W. interferometer. Each row of dipole elements is backed by a tilted reflecting screen so that maximum sensitivity is obtained at a declination of approximately +30°, the overall sensitivity being reduced by more than one-half when the beam is scanned to declinations above +90° and below −5°. The beamwidth of the array to half intensity is about $\pm\frac{1}{2}°$ in right ascension and $\pm3°$ in declination; the phasing arrangement is designed to produce beams at roughly 3° intervals in declination. The receivers have a bandwidth of 1 MHz centred at frequency of 81.5 MHz and routine recordings are made with a time constant of 0.1 s; the r.m.s. noise fluctuations correspond to a flux density of 0.5×10^{-25} W m^{-2} Hz^{-1}. For detailed studies of the pulsating source a time constant of 0.05 s was usually employed and the signals were displayed on a multi-channel "Rapidgraph" pen recorder with a time constant of 0.03 s. Accurate timing of the pulses was achieved by recording second pips derived from the *MSF* Rugby time transmissions.

A record obtained when the pulsating source was unusually strong is shown in Fig. 1*a*. This clearly displays the regular periodicity and also the characteristic irregular variation of pulse amplitude. On this occasion the largest pulses approached a peak flux density (averaged over the 1 MHz pass band) of 20×10^{-26} W m^{-2} Hz^{-1}, although the mean flux density integrated over one minute only amounted to approximately 1.0×10^{-26} W m^{-2} Hz^{-1}. On a more typical occasion the integrated flux density would be several times smaller than this value. It is therefore not surprising that the source has not been detected in the past, for the integrated flux density falls well below the limit of previous surveys at metre wavelengths.

位置和流量密度

天线中包含着一个由 2,048 个全波段偶极子组成的矩形阵列，这些偶极子排成 16 行，每行 128 个。每一行在该阵列东西方向的长度为 470 m，南北方向的宽度为 45 m。用位相扫描来确定在赤纬方向的接收模式，使用四个接收机使得可以同时观测四个不同赤纬的目标。利用位相转换接收机，再加上两个半天线阵，就可以组成一台东西方向的干涉仪。每行偶极子单元都被置于一个倾斜的反射屏前面，因而在赤纬 +30° 附近灵敏度最高。当波束扫描到赤纬 +90° 以上或者 -5° 以下时，总灵敏度会降低一半以上。当达到一半强度时，该阵列的波束宽度在赤经和赤纬上分别为 $\pm\frac{1}{2}°$ 和 $\pm 3°$；而相位匹配被设定为在赤纬方向间隔大约 3° 产生波束。接收机的带宽是 1 MHz，中心频率为 81.5 MHz，通常以 0.1 s 的时间常数进行记录；其中噪声波动的均方根值相当于一个 0.5×10^{-25} W m^{-2} Hz^{-1} 的流量密度。在对脉动源进行更细致的研究时，通常会采用 0.05 s 的时间常数，并且这些信号在多通道"快速绘图"笔式记录仪上记录时所用的时间常数为 0.03 s。通过记录来自英国小镇拉格比的 *MSF*（译者注：英国的长波授时编码标准为 *MSF*）秒信号可以精确测量脉冲时间。

当脉动源非常强的时候测得的结果见图 1*a*。从图中可以清晰地看到规则的周期和脉冲幅度所特有的不规则变化。在这种情况下，尽管对 1 分钟内数据进行积分得到的平均流量密度只能达到 1.0×10^{-26} W m^{-2} Hz^{-1} 左右，但最大脉冲达到了流量密度（在 1 MHz 通带内的平均值）的峰值，即 20×10^{-26} W m^{-2} Hz^{-1}。在更典型的情况下，该值会是积分流量密度的数倍。由此可见，以前没有探测到这种源也在情理之中，因为积分流量密度要远小于过去在米波长情况下能够检测到的极限。

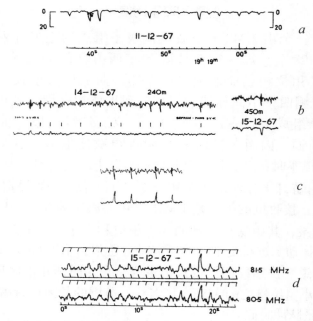

Fig. 1. *a*, A record of the pulsating radio source in strong signal conditions (receiver time constant 0.1 s). Full scale deflexion corresponds to 20×10^{-26} W m^{-2} Hz^{-1}. *b*, Upper trace: records obtained with additional paths (240 m and 450 m) in one side of the interferometer. Lower trace: normal interferometer records. (The pulses are small for $l=240$ m because they occurred near a null in the interference pattern; this modifies the phase but not the amplitude of the oscillatory response on the upper trace.) *c*, Simulated pulses obtained using a signal generator. *d*, Simultaneous reception of pulses using identical receivers tuned to different frequencies. Pulses at the lower frequency are delayed by about 0.2 s.

The position of the source in right ascension is readily obtained from an accurate measurement of the "crossover" points of the interference pattern on those occasions when the pulses were strong throughout an interval embracing such a point. The collimation error of the instrument was determined from a similar measurement on the neighbouring source 3C 409 which transits about 52 min later. On the routine recordings which first revealed the source the reading accuracy was only ±10 s and the earliest record suitable for position measurement was obtained on August 13, 1967. This and all subsequent measurements agree within the error limits. The position in declination is not so well determined and relies on the relative amplitudes of the signals obtained when the reception pattern is centred on declinations of 20°, 23° and 26°. Combining the measurements yields a position

$$\alpha_{1950}=19h \; 19m \; 38s \pm 3s$$

$$\delta_{1950}=22°00' \pm 30'$$

As discussed here, the measurement of the Doppler shift in the observed frequency of the pulses due to the Earth's orbital motion provides an alternative estimate of the declination. Observations throughout one year should yield an accuracy ±1'. The value currently attained from observations during December–January is $\delta=21°58'\pm30'$, a figure consistent with the previous measurement.

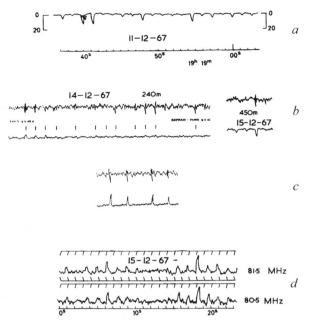

图 1. *a*. 在信号很强的情况下所记录的脉动射电源（接收机的时间常数为 0.1 s）。满刻度的偏转可以达到 20×10^{-26} W m^{-2} Hz^{-1}。*b*. 上半部分曲线：在干涉仪一侧增加了额外路径（240 m 和 450 m）后的记录。下半部分曲线：由正常干涉仪得到的记录。（当 *l*=240 m 时得到的脉冲很小，因为在干涉图形中这些脉冲都发生在零值附近；通过这种方式只能修正位相，而不会改变上半部分曲线的响应幅度。）*c*. 从信号发生器得到的模拟脉冲。*d*. 使用同样的接收机但在不同频率下得到的同步脉冲记录。频率较低时的脉冲延迟了大约 0.2 s。

当对应于干涉图样中某个"交叉"点的脉冲在整个时间间隔内达到很强时，只要我们对这个点进行精确测定就可以很容易地得到脉动源在赤经方向上的位置。对约 52 min 后出现的邻近源 3*C* 409 进行类似测量即可得到该仪器的瞄准误差。最早用于探测该源的仪器的读数精度通常只有 ±10 s，第一个可用于位置测量的记录是在 1967 年 8 月 13 日得到的。这一次以及之后的所有测量结果都在误差范围内相互吻合。赤纬方向的位置不太好确定，且赤纬的确定依赖于当接收模式以赤纬 20°、23° 和 26° 为中心时所得信号的相对幅度。结合已有的测量结果可以得到具体位置是：

$$\alpha_{1950} = 19h\ 19m\ 38s \pm 3s$$

$$\delta_{1950} = 22°00' \pm 30'$$

正如这里所讨论的，由于地球的轨道运动，在脉冲的观测频率上测量多普勒频移可以为我们提供一种新的赤纬估计方法。经过一年的观测，结果的精确度应该能达到 ±1′。目前由 12 月到 1 月的观测数据所得的结果为 δ=21°58′±30′，该值与之前的测量结果是一致的。

Time Variations

It was mentioned earlier that the signals vary considerably in strength from day to day and, typically, they are only present for about 1 min, which may occur quite randomly within the 4 min interval permitted by the reception pattern. In addition, as shown in Fig. 1*a*, the pulse amplitude may vary considerably on a time-scale of seconds. The pulse to pulse variations may possibly be explained in terms of interplanetary scintillation[1], but this cannot account for the minute to minute variation of mean pulse amplitude. Continuous observations over periods of 30 min have been made by tracking the source with an E–W. phased array in a 470 m × 20 m reflector normally used for a lunar occultation programme. The peak pulse amplitude averaged over ten successive pulses for a period of 30 min is shown in Fig. 2*a*. This plot suggests the possibility of periodicities of a few minutes duration, but a correlation analysis yields no significant result. If the signals were linearly polarized, Faraday rotation in the ionosphere might cause the random variations, but the form of the curve does not seem compatible with this mechanism. The day to day variations since the source was first detected are shown in Fig. 2*b*. In this analysis the daily value plotted is the peak flux density of the greatest pulse. Again the variation from day to day is irregular and no systematic changes are clearly evident, although there is a suggestion that the source was significantly weaker during October to November. It therefore appears that, despite the regular occurrence of the pulses, the magnitude of the power emitted exhibits variations over long and short periods.

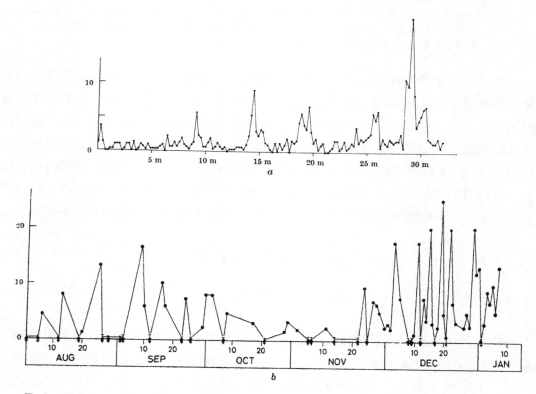

Fig. 2. *a*, The time variation of the smoothed (over ten pulses) pulse amplitude. *b*, Daily variation of peak pulse amplitude. (Ordinates are in units of W m^{-2} Hz^{-1} × 10^{-26}.)

随时间的变化

早先曾提到，这些信号的强度从一天到另一天的变化很大，它们在通常情况下只会在接收模式所允许的 4 min 间隔内随机出现 1 min 左右的时间。另外，正如图 1a 所示，脉冲幅度在以秒为单位的时标下有可能会有显著的变化。脉冲与脉冲之间的变化或许可以用行星际闪烁来解释 [1]，但这不能说明平均脉冲的幅度从一分钟到另一分钟的变化。利用在观测月掩星时通常所采用的 470 m × 20 m 反射器组成一个东西方向的相控阵，根据这个相控阵对脉冲源的追踪可以得到时间长达 30 min 的连续观测记录。在图 2a 中绘出了时长 30 min 内 10 个连续脉冲的峰值脉冲幅度的平均值。这张图说明有可能存在持续几分钟的周期，但是从相关分析中并没有得到有价值的结论。如果这些信号是线偏振的，则电离层中的法拉第旋转就会产生随机的变化，但是该曲线的形状似乎与这种机制并不相符。该脉动源在首次被发现后的每日变化情况示于图 2b。在这张分析图中，每天的数据都是以最大脉冲的峰值流量密度来表示的。另外，虽然该源在 10 月到 11 月期间有明显变弱的迹象，但每天的变化仍是不规则的，而且也没有明显的证据表明存在系统性的变化。因此，尽管这些脉冲的出现是规则的，但是其发射能量的大小在或长或短的时间段内都表现出了一定的波动性。

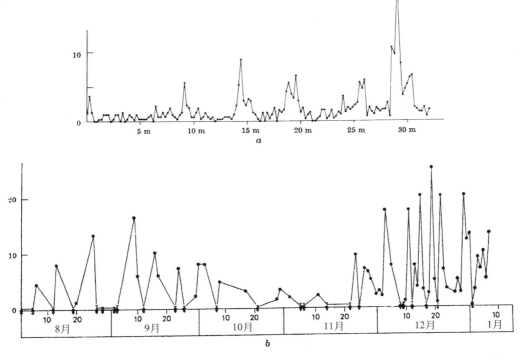

图 2. a. 平滑了（10 个脉冲）的脉冲幅度随时间的变化。b. 峰值脉冲幅度的逐日变化。（纵坐标的单位是 W m^{-2} Hz^{-1} × 10^{-26}。）

Instantaneous Bandwidth and Frequency Drift

Two different experiments have shown that the pulses are caused by a narrow-band signal of descending frequency sweeping through the 1 MHz band of the receiver. In the first, two identical receivers were used, tuned to frequencies of 80.5 MHz and 81.5 MHz. Fig. 1*d*, which illustrates a record made with this system, shows that the lower frequency pulses are delayed by about 0.2 s. This corresponds to a frequency drift of ~ −5 MHz s^{-1}. In the second method a time delay was introduced into the signals reaching the receiver from one-half of the aerial by incorporating an extra cable of known length *l*. This cable introduces a phase shift proportional to frequency so that, for a signal the coherence length of which exceeds *l*, the output of the receiver will oscillate with period

$$ t_0 = \frac{c}{l}\left(\frac{\mathrm{d}v}{\mathrm{d}t}\right)^{-1} $$

where dv/dt is the rate of change of signal frequency. Records obtained with *l*=240 m and 450 m are shown in Fig. 1*b* together with a simultaneous record of the pulses derived from a separate phase-switching receiver operating with equal cables in the usual fashion. Also shown, in Fig. 1*c*, is a simulated record obtained with exactly the same arrangement but using a signal generator, instead of the source, to provide the swept frequency. For observation with *l*>450 m the periodic oscillations were slowed down to a low frequency by an additional phase shifting device in order to prevent severe attenuation of the output signal by the time constant of the receiver. The rate of change of signal frequency has been deduced from the additional phase shift required and is dv/dt =−4.9±0.5 MHz s^{-1}. The direction of the frequency drift can be obtained from the phase of the oscillation on the record and is found to be from high to low frequency in agreement with the first result.

The instantaneous bandwidth of the signal may also be obtained from records of the type shown in Fig. 1*b* because the oscillatory response as a function of delay is a measure of the autocorrelation function, and hence of the Fourier transform, of the power spectrum of the radiation. The results of the measurements are displayed in Fig. 3 from which the instantaneous bandwidth of the signal to exp (−1), assuming a Gaussian energy spectrum, is estimated to be 80±20 kHz.

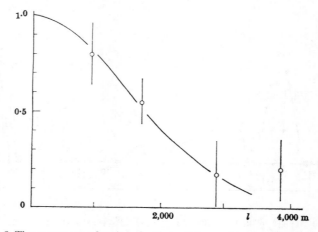

Fig. 3. The response as a function of added path in one side of the interferometer.

瞬时带宽和频率漂移

两个不同的实验都表明，这些脉冲是由一个在接收机的 1 MHz 带宽内频率逐渐下降的窄带信号导致的。在第一个实验中使用了两个同样的接收机，它们的频率分别被设定为 80.5 MHz 和 81.5 MHz。在图 1d 中显示的就是用这种系统得到的结果，从图中可以看出频率较低时的脉冲比频率较高时的脉冲延迟了大约 0.2 s，这与 ~ -5 MHz s^{-1} 的频率漂移相对应。在第二个实验中，将时间延迟引入从一半天线到达接收机的信号的方法是另外加入一截已知长度为 l 的电缆。由这截电缆导致的相位位移与频率成正比，所以对于相干长度超过 l 的信号，接收机的输出会以 t_0 为周期发生振荡：

$$t_0 = \frac{c}{l}\left(\frac{\mathrm{d}v}{\mathrm{d}t}\right)^{-1}$$

其中 $\mathrm{d}v/\mathrm{d}t$ 是信号频率的变化率。图 1b 给出的是当 l=240 m 和 450 m 时所获得的记录，此外还给出了脉冲同时记录，它是通过一个独立的位相转换接收机用同样的电缆在常规方式下得到的。在图 1c 中还有用完全相同的方法得到的模拟记录：其输入信号不是来自于脉动源，而是来自于一个能提供扫频的信号发生器。当在 l > 450 m 的情况下进行观测时，需要使用一个额外的移相器将周期振荡降至较低的频率，这样就可以避免由接收机时间常数对输出信号造成的严重衰减。由所需的额外相移可以推导出信号频率的变化率，其值为 $\mathrm{d}v/\mathrm{d}t = -4.9 \pm 0.5$ MHz s^{-1}。频率漂移的方向可以从记录下来的振动位相推算得到，结果表明从高频到低频的漂移与最初的结论相符。

从图 1b 所示类型的记录中还可以得到信号的瞬时带宽。因为作为延迟的函数的振荡响应就是辐射功率谱的自相关函数的量度，也相当于对其进行了傅里叶变换。这些测量结果绘于图 3 中，假设按高斯能谱分布，从图中可估计出降至 $\exp(-1)$ 处的信号瞬时带宽为 80 kHz $\pm$ 20 kHz。

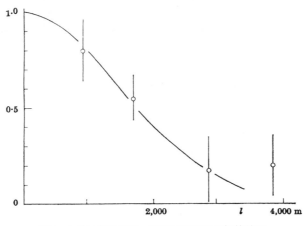

图 3. 响应与在干涉仪一侧增加的路径之间的关系。

Pulse Recurrence Frequency and Doppler Shift

By displaying the pulses and time pips from *MSF* Rugby on the same record the leading edge of a pulse of reasonable size may be timed to an accuracy of about 0.1 s. Observations over a period of 6 h taken with the tracking system mentioned earlier gave the period between pulses as $P_{obs}=1.33733\pm0.00001$ s. This represents a mean value centred on December 18, 1967, at 14 h 18 m UT. A study of the systematic shift in the frequency of the pulses was obtained from daily measurements of the time interval T between a standard time and the pulse immediately following it as shown in Fig. 4. The standard time was chosen to be 14 h 01 m 00 s UT on December 11 (corresponding to the centre of the reception pattern) and subsequent standard times were at intervals of 23 h 56 m 04 s (approximately one sidereal day). A plot of the variation of T from day to day is shown in Fig. 4. A constant pulse recurrence frequency would show a linear increase or decrease in T if care was taken to add or subtract one period where necessary. The observations, however, show a marked curvature in the sense of a steadily increasing frequency. If we assume a Doppler shift due to the Earth alone, then the number of pulses received per day is given by

$$N = N_0\left(1 + \frac{v}{c}\cos\varphi\,\sin\frac{2\pi n}{366.25}\right)$$

where N_0 is the number of pulses emitted per day at the source, v the orbital velocity of the Earth, φ the ecliptic latitude of the source and n an arbitrary day number obtained by putting $n=0$ on January 17, 1968, when the Earth has zero velocity along the line of sight to the source. This relation is approximate since it assumes a circular orbit for the Earth and the origin $n=0$ is not exact, but it serves to show that the increase of N observed can be explained by the Earth's motion alone within the accuracy currently attainable. For this purpose it is convenient to estimate the values of n for which $\delta T/\delta n = 0$, corresponding to an exactly integral value of N. These occur at $n_1=15.8\pm0.1$ and $n_2=28.7\pm0.1$, and since N is increased by exactly one pulse between these dates we have

$$1 = \frac{N_0 v}{c}\cos\varphi\left[\sin\frac{2\pi n_2}{366.25} - \sin\frac{2\pi n_1}{366.25}\right]$$

This yields $\varphi = 43°36'\pm30'$ which corresponds to a declination of $21°58'\pm30'$, a value consistent with the declination obtained directly. The true periodicity of the source, making allowance for the Doppler shift and using the integral condition to refine the calculation, is then

$$P_0 = 1.3372795\pm0.0000020 \text{ s}$$

脉冲重复频率和多普勒频移

在可以同时显示脉冲和拉格比 *MSF* 时间信号的记录中，对一个正常大小的脉冲前缘的计时也许能达到 0.1 s 左右的精确度。在利用上文中提到的跟踪系统进行长达 6 h 的观测之后可以得到脉冲的周期为 $P_{obs}=1.33733$ s ± 0.00001 s。这代表了以世界时 1967 年 12 月 18 日 14 时 18 分为中心的平均值。对脉冲频率系统性漂移的研究，可以通过每天测量某个标准时间与紧随其后出现的脉冲之间的时间间隔 T 得到，如图 4 所示。所选的标准时间是世界时 12 月 11 日 14 时 01 分 00 秒（对应于接收模式的中心），随后每隔 23 时 56 分 04 秒（大约为一个恒星日的长度）就会出现下一个标准时间。T 的每日变化示于图 4。如果在必要的时候增加或者减少一个周期，则在脉冲重复频率为常数的前提下就会出现 T 的线性增加或减少。然而，观测结果显示出明显的曲率，说明频率在稳步增长。如果我们假设多普勒频移仅归因于地球，那么每天接收到的脉冲个数可由下式得到：

$$N = N_0\left(1 + \frac{v}{c}\cos\varphi\,\sin\frac{2\pi n}{366.25}\right)$$

其中 N_0 是该源每天发射的脉冲个数，v 是地球的轨道速度，φ 是该源的黄纬，n 是任意指定的天数：在 1968 年 1 月 17 日，即地球沿着源的视向速度为 0 时，令 $n=0$。这种关系是近似的，因为它假设地球的运行轨道为圆形，而且原点 $n=0$ 也是不精确的。但是由此还是可以证明：在目前能够达到的精度上，观测到的 N 的增加可以仅由地球的运动来解释。为此，可以很方便地估算出当 $\delta T/\delta n = 0$ 时的 n 值，所对应的是一个确切的整数 N。它们会发生在 $n_1=15.8\pm0.1$ 和 $n_2=28.7\pm0.1$ 时，而且因为 N 在这些天内刚好增加了一个脉冲，所以：

$$1 = \frac{N_0 v}{c}\cos\varphi\left[\sin\frac{2\pi n_2}{366.25} - \sin\frac{2\pi n_1}{366.25}\right]$$

由上式可得 $\varphi=43°36'\pm30'$，所对应的赤纬为 $21°58'\pm30'$，这与通过观测直接得到的赤纬值相符。考虑到多普勒频移并使用整数条件对计算进行简化即可得到射电源的真实周期：

$$P_0 = 1.3372795 \text{ s} \pm 0.0000020 \text{ s}$$

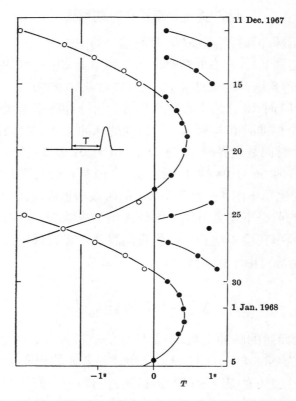

Fig. 4. The day to day variation of pulse arrival time.

By continuing observations of the time of occurrence of the pulses for a year it should be possible to establish the constancy of N_0 to about 1 part in 3×10^8. If N_0 is indeed constant, then the declination of the source may be estimated to an accuracy of $\pm 1'$; this result will not be affected by ionospheric refraction.

It is also interesting to note the possibility of detecting a variable Doppler shift caused by the motion of the source itself. Such an effect might arise if the source formed one component of a binary system, or if the signals were associated with a planet in orbit about some parent star. For the present, the systematic increase of N is regular to about 1 part in 2×10^7 so that there is no evidence for an additional orbital motion comparable with that of the Earth.

The Nature of the Radio Source

The lack of any parallax greater than about $2'$ places the source at a distance exceeding 10^3 A.U. The energy emitted by the source during a single pulse, integrated over 1 MHz at 81.5 MHz, therefore reaches a value which must exceed 10^{17} erg if the source radiates isotropically. It is also possible to derive an upper limit to the physical dimension of the source. The small instantaneous bandwidth of the signal (80 kHz) and the rate of sweep (-4.9 MHz s^{-1}) show that the duration of the emission at any given frequency does not exceed 0.016 s. The source size therefore cannot exceed 4.8×10^3 km.

80

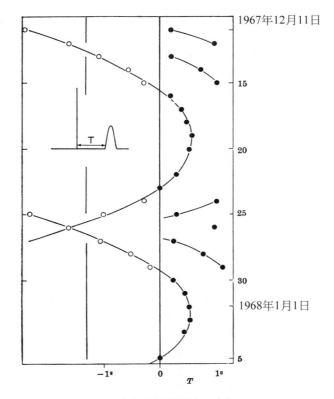

图 4. 脉冲到达时间的每日变化。

根据在一年内连续观测到的脉冲出现时间可以推出 N_0 是一个恒定的数，误差约为 $\frac{1}{3} \times 10^{-8}$。如果 N_0 真的是一个常数，那么对该脉动源赤纬的估计值就可以达到 $\pm 1'$ 的精度，这一结果是不会受到电离层折射影响的。

另一件值得一提的事是：我们可能会观测到由源自身运动所造成的多普勒频移的变化，这一效应在以下两种情况下或许有出现的可能性：或者脉动源是双星系统中的一个成员，或者该信号与在围绕某颗母恒星的轨道上运行的行星有关。就目前了解的情况而言，N 的系统性增长通常为 $\frac{1}{2} \times 10^{-7}$ 量级，所以可以证明：其他的轨道运动所造成的影响都无法与地球的轨道运动相比。

射电源的性质

观测视差不大于 $2'$ 说明源与地球的距离超过了 10^3 个天文单位。如果该源的辐射是各向同性的，那么它在一个脉冲间隔内释放的能量——在频率为 81.5 MHz 处的 1 MHz 带宽内进行积分——将会超过 10^{17} erg。还可以推算出该源物理尺寸的上限。信号的较窄瞬时带宽（80 kHz）和频率漂移速度（-4.9 MHz s^{-1}）表明，在任意给定频率上的能量释放时间都不会超过 0.016 s。因此，源的大小不可能超过 4.8×10^3 km。

An upper limit to the distance of the source may be derived from the observed rate of frequency sweep since impulsive radiation, whatever its origin, will be dispersed during its passage through the ionized hydrogen in interstellar space. For a uniform plasma the frequency drift caused by dispersion is given by

$$\frac{\mathrm{d}v}{\mathrm{d}t} = -\frac{c}{L}\frac{v^3}{v_p^2}$$

where L is the path and v_p the plasma frequency. Assuming a mean density of 0.2 electron cm^{-3} the observed frequency drift (−4.9 MHz s^{-1}) corresponds to $L\sim65$ parsec. Some frequency dispersion may, of course, arise in the source itself; in this case the dispersion in the interstellar medium must be smaller so that the value of L is an upper limit. While the interstellar electron density in the vicinity of the Sun is not well known, this result is important in showing that the pulsating radio sources so far detected must be local objects on a galactic distance scale.

The positional accuracy so far obtained does not permit any serious attempt at optical identification. The search area, which lies close to the galactic plane, includes two twelfth magnitude stars and a large number of weaker objects. In the absence of further data, only the most tentative suggestion to account for these remarkable sources can be made.

The most significant feature to be accounted for is the extreme regularity of the pulses. This suggests an origin in terms of the pulsation of an entire star, rather than some more localized disturbance in a stellar atmosphere. In this connexion it is interesting to note that it has already been suggested[2,3] that the radial pulsation of neutron stars may play an important part in the history of supernovae and supernova remnants.

A discussion of the normal modes of radial pulsation of compact stars has recently been given by Meltzer and Thorne[4], who calculated the periods for stars with central densities in the range 10^5 to 10^{19} g cm^{-3}. Fig. 4 of their paper indicates two possibilities which might account for the observed periods of the order 1 s. At a density of 10^7 g cm^{-3}, corresponding to a white dwarf star, the fundamental mode reaches a minimum period of about 8 s; at a slightly higher density the period increases again as the system tends towards gravitational collapse to a neutron star. While the fundamental period is not small enough to account for the observations the higher order modes have periods of the correct order of magnitude. If this model is adopted it is difficult to understand why the fundamental period is not dominant; such a period would have readily been detected in the present observations and its absence cannot be ascribed to observational effects. The alternative possibility occurs at a density of 10^{13} g cm^{-3}, corresponding to a neutron star; at this density the fundamental has a period of about 1 s, while for densities in excess of 10^{13} g cm^{-3} the period rapidly decreases to about 10^{-3} s.

If the radiation is to be associated with the radial pulsation of a white dwarf or neutron star there seem to be several mechanisms which could account for the radio emission. It has been suggested that radial pulsation would generate hydromagnetic shock fronts at the stellar surface which might be accompanied by bursts of X-rays and energetic electrons[2,3]. The radiation might then be likened to radio bursts from a solar flare occurring over the entire star during

因为所有的脉冲辐射，不论来源于哪里，都会在穿过星际空间中的电离氢时被色散，所以根据观测到的频率漂移速度就可以推导出该源与地球之间距离的上限。对于均匀的等离子体，由色散导致的频率漂移可由下式给出：

$$\frac{\mathrm{d}v}{\mathrm{d}t} = -\frac{c}{L}\frac{v^3}{v_p^2}$$

其中 L 是路径长度，v_p 是等离子体的频率。假设平均密度为每 cm³ 有 0.2 个电子，则观测到的频率漂移（$-4.9\ \mathrm{MHz\ s^{-1}}$）与 $L\sim 65$ 秒差距相当。当然，某些频散也可能来自于源本身，在这种情况下星际物质的色散作用肯定会更小，所以 L 的数值是上限。尽管我们对太阳附近的星际电子密度不甚清楚，但这一结果仍很重要，它表明迄今为止人们探测到的所有脉动射电源都一定来自于银河系内的天体。

就现在的定位精度而言，认真尝试进行光学证认是不可能的。现在人们搜索的区域距离银道面很近，在该区域中有两颗 12 等星和大量较暗的天体。由于缺乏更进一步的数据，所以只能对这些奇特的射电源作出可能性最大的解释。

需要解释的一个最显著的特征是这些脉冲的极端规律性。这表明源自一颗恒星整体脉动的可能性要大于恒星大气中的某种更为局部的扰动。就这一点来说，值得一提的是：已经有人提出 [2,3]，中子星的径向脉动可能在超新星和超新星遗迹演化史中起重要作用。

最近，梅尔策和索恩 [4] 对致密星径向脉动的几种标准模式进行了讨论，他们计算了中心密度在 10^5 g/cm³ 到 10^{19} g/cm³ 范围内的恒星所具有的脉动周期。他们论文中的图 4 表明，有以下两种可能性或许可以解释观测到的 1 s 量级的周期。当密度为 10^7 g/cm³——与白矮星的密度相当时，在基频模式下可以达到的最小周期值约为 8 s；当密度略微增加时，周期也会增加，因为系统有引力塌缩成一颗中子星的趋向。虽然由基频模式得到的周期值太大以至于不能解释观测到的结果，但高阶模式下的周期却具有合适的数量级。如果采纳了上述模型，那么我们就很难解释为什么基频模式下的周期不是主导周期。在目前的观测中应该很容易探测到基频模式下的周期，不能把没有探测到这样的周期归因于观测上的不得力。另一种可能性是：当密度为 10^{13} g/cm³——与中子星的密度相当时，基频模式在此密度下的周期值约为 1 s；当密度超过 10^{13} g/cm³ 时，周期迅速下降至 10^{-3} s 左右。

如果认为这种辐射与白矮星或中子星的径向脉动有关，那么就会有好几种机制可以解释这种射电发射。有人认为径向脉动将在恒星表面产生磁流体激波阵面，从而可能会伴随着 X 射线和高能电子的爆发 [2,3]。因而或许可以把这种辐射比作是在

each cycle of the oscillation. Such a model would be in fair agreement with the upper limit of $\sim 5 \times 10^3$ km for the dimension of the source, which compares with the mean value of 9×10^3 km quoted for white dwarf stars by Greenstein[5]. The energy requirement for this model may be roughly estimated by noting that the total energy emitted in a 1 MHz band by a type III solar burst would produce a radio flux of the right order if the source were at a distance of $\sim 10^3$ A.U. If it is assumed that the radio energy may be related to the total flare energy ($\sim 10^{32}$ erg)[6] in the same manner as for a solar flare and supposing that each pulse corresponds to one flare, the required energy would be $\sim 10^{39}$ erg yr^{-1}; at a distance of 65 pc the corresponding value would be $\sim 10^{47}$ erg yr^{-1}. It has been estimated that a neutron star may contain $\sim 10^{51}$ erg in vibrational modes so the energy requirement does not appear unreasonable, although other damping mechanisms are likely to be important when considering the lifetime of the source[4].

The swept frequency characteristic of the radiation is reminiscent of type II and type III solar bursts, but it seems unlikely that it is caused in the same way. For a white dwarf or neutron star the scale height of any atmosphere is small and a travelling disturbance would be expected to produce a much faster frequency drift than is actually observed. As has been mentioned, a more likely possibility is that the impulsive radiation suffers dispersion during its passage through the interstellar medium.

More observational evidence is clearly needed in order to gain a better understanding of this strange new class of radio source. If the suggested origin of the radiation is confirmed further study may be expected to throw valuable light on the behaviour of compact stars and also on the properties of matter at high density.

We thank Professor Sir Martin Ryle, Dr. J. E. Baldwin, Dr. P. A. G. Scheuer and Dr. J. R. Shakeshaft for helpful discussions and the Science Research Council who financed this work. One of us (S. J. B.) thanks the Ministry of Education of Northern Ireland and another (R. A. C.) the SRC for a maintenance award; J. D. H. P. thanks ICI for a research fellowship.

(**217**, 709-713; 1968)

A. Hewish, S. J. Bell, J. D. H. Pilkington, P. F. Scott and R. A. Collins: Mullard Radio Astronomy Observatory, Cavendish Laboratory, University of Cambridge.

Received February 9, 1968.

References:
1. Hewish, A., Scott, P. F., and Wills, D., *Nature*, **203**, 1214 (1964).
2. Cameron, A. G. W., *Nature*, **205**, 787 (1965).
3. Finzi, A., *Phys. Rev. Lett.*, **15**, 599 (1965).
4. Meltzer, D. W., and Thorne, K. S., *Ap. J.*, **145**, 514 (1966).
5. Greenstein, J. L., in *Handbuch der Physik, L.*, 161 (1958).
6. Fichtel, C. E., and McDonald, F. B., in *Annual Review of Astronomy and Astrophysics*, **5**, 351 (1967).

每个振荡周期内从一个贯穿恒星的耀斑发出的射电暴。这样一种模型与认为源的上限尺寸为 $\sim 5 \times 10^3$ km 的观点吻合得非常好，也与格林斯坦 [5] 提出的白矮星平均尺寸为 9×10^3 km 的论点相符。可以通过以下方式大致估计出该模型所需的能量：在 1 MHz 带宽内以第三类太阳暴形式发射的总能量将与在假设射电源位于 $\sim 10^3$ 个天文单位处的前提下得到的射电流量有相同的量级。如果假设射电能量和耀斑总能量（$\sim 10^{32}$ erg）[6] 之间的关系与和一个太阳耀斑的关系一样，并假设每个脉冲对应着一个耀斑，那么所需的能量将为 $\sim 10^{39}$ erg yr^{-1}，而在距离为 65 秒差距处的对应能量值将为 $\sim 10^{47}$ erg yr^{-1}。有人估计一颗中子星可用在振动模式中的能量为 $\sim 10^{51}$ erg，所以所需的能量值看起来还算合理，不过在考虑到脉动源的演化史时，其他阻尼机制也有能发挥重要作用的可能性 [4]。

尽管这种辐射的频率漂移特征会使人联想到第二类和第三类太阳暴，但它的产生机制似乎不太可能与这两类太阳暴相同。对于一颗白矮星或者中子星来说，其大气标高很小，预计扰动在传播时产生的频率漂移要比实际观测值高得多。正如上文所提到的，一种可能性更大的情况是脉冲辐射在穿过星际介质时被色散。

为了更好地理解这种奇特的新型射电源，显然还需要更多的观测证据。如果能够证明这种辐射的起源与本文中所设想的完全一致，那么经过进一步的研究人们或许可以了解到一些有关致密恒星行为以及高密度物质性质的重要线索。

我们要感谢马丁·赖尔爵士教授、鲍德温博士、朔伊尔博士和谢克沙夫特博士为此提出了有价值的意见，还要感谢科学研究理事会为此项研究提供了经费。我们中的一位作者（贝尔）要感谢北爱尔兰教育部，另一位作者（柯林斯）要感谢科学研究理事会提供了维持费用；皮尔金顿要感谢帝国化学工业公司提供研究基金。

（冯翀 翻译；蒋世仰 审稿）

Rotating Neutron Stars as the Origin of the Pulsating Radio Sources

T. Gold

Editor's Note

Three months after the publication above, Thomas Gold published his explanation of how pulsars function. The essential ingredients of his scheme are that pulsars are indeed neutron stars, that there must be intense magnetic fields associated with such structures and that the magnetic fields would generate intense radiation in the microwave (ultra-short radio waves) region of the spectrum. In Gold's view, the pulsation of these stars arose not from some kind of internal vibration as suggested by Hewish, but because the magnetic field generates "directional beams rotating like a lighthouse beacon". He made two predictions: the rate of rotation of a pulsar would decrease slowly but steadily with time and pulsars with a period of 1 second would be found to represent "the slow end of the distribution". Both predictions have been proved correct.

THE case that neutron stars are responsible for the recently discovered pulsating radio sources[1-6] appears to be a strong one. No other theoretically known astronomical object would possess such short and accurate periodicities as those observed, ranging from 1.33 to 0.25 s. Higher harmonics of a lower fundamental frequency that may be possessed by a white dwarf have been mentioned; but the detailed fine structure of several short pulses repeating in each repetition cycle makes any such explanation very unlikely. Since the distances are known approximately from interstellar dispersion of the different radio frequencies, it is clear that the emission per unit emitting volume must be very high; the size of the region emitting any one pulse can, after all, not be much larger than the distance light travels in the few milliseconds that represent the lengths of the individual pulses. No such concentrations of energy can be visualized except in the presence of an intense gravitational field.

The great precision of the constancy of the intrinsic period also suggests that we are dealing with a massive object, rather than merely with some plasma physical configuration. Accuracies of one part in 10^8 belong to the realm of celestial mechanics of massive objects, rather than to that of plasma physics.

It is a consequence of the virial theorem that the lowest mode of oscillation of a star must always have a period which is of the same order of magnitude as the period of the fastest rotation it may possess without rupture. The range of 1.5 s to 0.25 s represents periods that are all longer than the periods of the lowest modes of neutron stars. They would all be periods in which a neutron star could rotate without excessive flattening. It is doubtful that the fundamental frequency of pulsation of a neutron star could ever be so long (ref. 7 and unpublished work of A. G. W. Cameron). If the rotation period dictates the repetition rate, the fine structure of the observed pulses would represent directional beams rotating like a

旋转中子星作为脉动射电源的起源

戈尔德

编者按

在上一篇文章发表三个月后，托马斯·戈尔德发表了他对脉冲星工作原理的解释。他的模型包括三个要点：脉冲星实际上就是中子星；与此结构相关的是它一定具有很强的磁场；这种磁场会在光谱的微波（超短无线电波）波段产生很强的辐射。戈尔德认为：这些恒星的脉冲并不是由休伊什所假定的某种内部振荡产生的，而是因为磁场产生了"像灯塔中的信标一样不断旋转的定向波束"。他作了以下两项预言：脉冲星的旋转速率会随着时间的增长而有规律地缓慢下降；周期为 1 s 的那些脉冲星将代表着"分布范围中的慢端部分"。如今这两项预言都已被证实。

似乎有充足的理由相信，最近发现的脉动射电源 [1-6] 就是中子星。它们的脉动周期范围是 1.33 s 至 0.25 s，没有任何理论上已知的其他天体能有这样短而且精确的周期。有人曾指出，这是一颗白矮星所可能具有的较低基频的高次谐波；但是，在每个重复周期内的若干短脉冲存在复杂精细结构的事实使这类解释不太可能成立。源的距离可大致由不同射电频率的星际色散给出，很显然基于每单位发射体积的发射强度一定是非常高的；发出单个脉冲的发射区域大小无论如何也不可能远远超过光在几毫秒时间内所传播的距离，这个时间即单个脉冲的长度。这样高的能量聚集度是不可想象的，除非存在着一个强大的引力场。

高度稳定的内禀周期也表明：我们面对的是一个大质量的天体，而不仅仅是某种等离子体结构。一亿分之一的精度应归入大质量天体的天体力学领域，而非等离子体物理学。

由维里定理可以推出：一颗恒星的振荡有一个最低阶的模式，其周期通常与该恒星以最快速度转动而不致破裂的周期属于同一数量级。1.5 s 到 0.25 s 范围内的周期都要长于中子星的最低阶模式的周期。以这些周期旋转的中子星不会过度被压扁。而一颗中子星的脉动是否会有这样长的基频周期是值得怀疑的（参考文献 7 以及卡梅伦尚未发表的研究结果）。如果脉冲的重复频率是由转动周期决定的，那么观测到的脉冲的精细结构就代表了像灯塔中的信标一样不断旋转的定向波束。在不同的源中观测到了不同类型的精细结构，这只能归因于每颗恒星都各自有自己独

lighthouse beacon. The different types of fine structure observed in the different sources would then have to be attributed to the particular asymmetries of each star (the "sunspots", perhaps). In such a model, time variations in the intensity of emission will have no effect on the precise phase in the repetition period where each pulse appears; and this is indeed a striking observational fact. A fine structure of pulses could be generated within the repetition period, depending only on the distribution of emission regions around the circumference of the star. Similarly, a fine structure in polarization may be generated, for each region may produce a different polarization or be overlaid by a different Faraday-rotating medium. A single pulsating region, on the other hand, could scarcely generate a repetitive fine structure in polarization as seems to have been observed now[8].

There are as yet not really enough clues to identify the mechanism of radio emission. It could be a process deriving its energy from some source of internal energy of the star, and thus as difficult to analyse as solar activity. But there is another possibility, namely, that the emission derives its energy from the rotational energy of the star (very likely the principal remaining energy source), and is a result of relativistic effects in a co-rotating magnetosphere.

In the vicinity of a rotating star possessing a magnetic field there would normally be a co-rotating magnetosphere. Beyond some distance, external influences would dominate, and co-rotation would cease. In the case of a fast rotating neutron star with strong surface fields, the distance out to which co-rotation would be enforced may well be close to that at which co-rotation would imply motion at the speed of light. The mechanism by which the plasma will be restrained from reaching the velocity of light will be that of radiation of the relativistically moving plasma, creating a radiation reaction adequate to overcome the magnetic force. The properties of such a relativistic magnetosphere have not yet been explored, and indeed our understanding of relativistic magneto-hydrodynamics is very limited. In the present case the coupling to the electromagnetic radiation field would assume a major role in the bulk dynamical behaviour of the magnetosphere.

The evidence so far shows that pulses occupy about 1/30 of the time of each repetition period. This limits the region responsible to dimensions of the order of 1/30 of the circumference of the "velocity of light circle". In the radial direction equally, dimensions must be small; one would suspect small enough to make the pulse rise-times comparable with or larger than the flight time of light across the region that is responsible. This would imply that the radiation emanates from the plasma that is moving within 1 percent of the velocity of light. That is the region of velocity where radiation effects would in any case be expected to become important.

The axial asymmetry that is implied needs further comment. A magnetic field of a neutron star may well have a strength of 10^{12} gauss at the surface of the 10 km object. At the "velocity of light circle", the circumference of which for the observed periods would range from 4×10^{10} to 0.75×10^{10} cm, such a field will be down to values of the order of 10^3–10^4 gauss (decreasing with distance slower than the inverse cube law of an undisturbed dipole field. A field pulled out radially by the stress of the centrifugal force of a whirling plasma would decay as an inverse square law with radius). Asymmetries in the radiation could

特的非对称性（也许就像"太阳黑子"一样）。在这样的模型中，辐射强度随时间的变化将不会影响每个脉冲在重复周期内出现的精确相位——这确实是一个惊人的观测事实。一个重复周期内可能会出现由多个脉冲组成的精细结构，这只取决于该恒星周围的辐射区分布。同样，也可能会存在偏振的精细结构，因为每个区域都有可能产生不同偏振的辐射，或者被具有不同法拉第旋转的介质所覆盖。另一方面，单一的脉冲辐射区几乎不可能产生重复的偏振精细结构，目前的观测结果似乎与此相吻合 [8]。

至今还没有足够的线索以确定射电辐射的机制。它可能是一个通过提取某种恒星内部能量源来获取自身能量的过程，因此和太阳活动一样很难进行分析。但是还有另外一种可能性，即辐射的能量来自于恒星的转动能（转动能很可能是剩余能源中最主要的），而射电辐射是由共转磁层中的相对论效应产生的。

在一颗有磁场的旋转恒星周围，通常会形成共转的磁层。在一定距离之外，外部影响将占主导地位，因而共转会停止。对于一颗表面有强磁场并且旋转速度很高的中子星，其共转延伸的距离很可能会接近于共转速度为光速时的距离。磁层内等离子体不能达到光速的原因在于，以接近光速运动的等离子体所发出的辐射会产生足以抵抗磁力的辐射反作用力。这种相对论性磁层的性质还没有被研究过；实际上我们对相对论磁流体动力学的理解也是非常有限的。照现在的情况来看，等离子体与电磁辐射场的耦合可能是磁层动力学行为的主要根源。

从目前的证据来看，脉冲在每个重复周期内占大约 1/30 的时间。这使电磁辐射区域大小的数量级被限制在"光速圆周"周长的 1/30 左右。同样，在径向方向上尺寸也一定很小。我们可以认为要小到足以使脉冲上升时间等于或大于光穿过辐射区的时间。这意味着，产生辐射的等离子体的运动速度小于光速的 1%。对于有这样速度的区域，预计其辐射效应在任何情况下都会变得很重要。

这里暗含的轴向不对称性有待进一步讨论。一颗半径为 10 km 的中子星的表面磁场很可能会达到 10^{12} 高斯。对应于已观测到周期的"光速圆周"，其周长在 4×10^{10} cm 至 0.75×10^{10} cm 之间。在上述"光速圆周"处，磁场会降至 10^3 高斯～10^4 高斯的量级（对于标准的偶极磁场，场强随距离的负 3 次方的减小而下降。此处场强随距离的下降要慢于 –3 次方，因为一个旋转的等离子体在离心力的作用下会拖曳磁场沿径向向外运动，所以场强随半径的负 2 次方的减小而下降。）。辐射的非对称

arise either through the field or the plasma content being non-axially symmetric. A skew and non-dipole field may well result from the explosive event that gave rise to the neutron star; and the access to plasma of certain tubes of force may be dependent on surface inhomogeneities of the star where sufficiently hot or energetic plasma can be produced to lift itself away from the intense gravitational field (10–100 MeV for protons; much less for space charge neutralized electron-positron beams).

The observed distribution of amplitudes of pulses makes it very unlikely that a modulation mechanism can be responsible for the variability (unpublished results of P. A. G. Scheuer and observations made at Cornell's Arecibo Ionospheric Observatory) but rather the effect has to be understood in a variability of the emission mechanism. In that case the observed very sharp dependence of the instantaneous intensity on frequency (1 MHz change in the observation band gives a substantially different pulse amplitude) represents a very narrow-band emission mechanism, much narrower than synchrotron emission, for example. A coherent mechanism is then indicated, as is also necessary to account for the intensity of the emission per unit area that can be estimated from the lengths of the sub-pulses. Such a coherent mechanism would represent non-uniform static configurations of charges in the relativistically rotating region. Non-uniform distributions at rest in a magnetic field are more readily set up and maintained than in the case of high individual speeds of charges, and thus the configuration discussed here may be particularly favourable for the generation of a coherent radiation mechanism.

If this basic picture is the correct one it may be possible to find a slight, but steady, slowing down of the observed repetition frequencies. Also, one would then suspect that more sources exist with higher rather than lower repetition frequency, because the rotation rates of neutron stars are capable of going up to more than 100/s, and the observed periods would seem to represent the slow end of the distribution.

Work in this subject at Cornell is supported by a contract from the US Office of Naval Research.

(**218**, 731-732; 1968)

T. Gold: Center for Radiophysics and Space Research, Cornell University, Ithaca, New York.

Received May 20, 1968.

References:

1. Hewish, A., Bell, S. J., Pilkington, J. D. H., Scott, P. F., and Collins, R. A., *Nature*, **217**, 709 (1968).

2. Pilkington, J. D. H., Hewish, A., Bell, S. J., and Cole, T. W., *Nature*, **218**, 126 (1968).

3. Drake, F. D., Gundermann, E. J., Jauncey, D. L., Comella, J. M., Zeissig, G. A., and Craft, jun., H. D., *Science*, **160**, 503 (1968).

4. Drake, F. D., *Science* (in the press).

5. Drake, F. D., and Craft, jun., H. D., *Science*, **160**, 758 (1968).

6. Tanenbaum, B. S., Zeissig, G. A., and Drake, F. D., *Science* (in the press).

7. Thorne, K. S., and Ipser, J. R., *Ap. J.* (in the press).

8. Lyne, A. G., and Smith, F. G., *Nature*, 218, 124 (1968).

现象可能源自于磁场或者等离子体的非轴对称性。倾斜的非偶极场极有可能是在产生中子星的超新星爆发过程中形成的；恒星表面的非均匀性或许就是出现特定力线束的等离子体的原因，在恒星表面可能会产生温度或能量足够高的等离子体，这些等离子体可以从表面的强引力场中逃逸（质子需要 10 MeV ~ 100 MeV；而空间电荷为中性的正负电子束所需要的能量则要低很多）。

观测到的脉冲幅度分布表明，幅度的变化不太可能由一种调制机制来解释（根据朔伊尔尚未公布的研究结果和康奈尔大学阿雷西博电离层天文台的观测结果），而必须用可变的发射机制理解这一效应。如果事实确实如此，那么所观察到的瞬时强度对频率的强烈依赖（观测频带发生 1 MHz 的改变会导致出现完全不同的脉冲幅度）就预示了一种非常窄频带的辐射机制，例如要比同步辐射窄很多。因为还必须符合能够从子脉冲长度估计得到的单位面积辐射强度，所以这应是一种相干辐射机制。这种相干机制将描绘出相对论性旋转区域内的非均匀静态电荷分布。因为磁场中静态电荷的非均匀分布比以不同速度高速运动的电荷的分布更容易建立和保持，所以这里讨论的非均匀分布也许对建立相干辐射机制非常有利。

如果上述基本构想是正确的话，就有可能发现观测到的重复频率会稳定地一点一点变慢。还可以由此猜测，具有较高频率的源要多于具有较低频率的源，因为中子星的旋转速度可以高达 100/s 以上。看来观测到的周期代表的是分布范围中的慢端部分。

在康奈尔大学进行的这项研究是与美国海军研究办公室签有协议的。

（岳友岭 翻译；于涌 审稿）

Absorption Spectrum of Rhodopsin: 500 nm Absorption Band

R. Hubbard

Editor's Note

Ruth Hubbard at Harvard University was the wife of George Wald who, among others, was awarded a Nobel Prize for the understanding of the absorption of light by the pigments in the human eye. Her individual work is illustrated by this account of the absorption of rhodopsin, the principle absorber of light energy in the retina at the extreme red end of the visible spectrum. In the same issue of *Nature* she published a second paper dealing with the absorption at the blue end of the spectrum. Taken together, these papers amounted to the identification of the optically active chemical responsible for human vision.

RHODOPSIN, the photosensitive pigment of vertebrate rods and of a number of invertebrate photoreceptors, consists of a colourless protein (opsin), which carries the 11-*cis* isomer of retinal (retinaldehyde, vitamin A aldehyde) as chromophore. Bownds[1] showed that in cattle rhodopsin the chromophore is bound in Schiff base linkage to the ε–amino-group of an internal lysine residue in opsin.

Collins[2] and Morton, Pitt, and their co-workers[3] first demonstrated that retinaldehyde forms a Schiff base with an aliphatic amino-group on opsin[3]. This raises the question of how the absorption properties of rhodopsin arise from this type of attachment, for in aqueous solution λ_{max} of 11-*cis* retinal is at 380 nm, that of the Schiff bases at about 363 nm, and that of rhodopsin near 500 nm. (The precise position of λ_{max} in rhodopsins from various animals differs somewhat, presumably because of species differences in the opsins.)

To explain these absorption characteristics, Kropf and Hubbard[4] started with the observation first made by Ball *et al.*[5], that although the formation of a Schiff base of retinal with an aliphatic amine,

$$\overset{\text{H}}{C_{19}H_{27} \cdot C = O} + H_2N \cdot R \qquad \overset{\text{H}}{C_{19}H_{27} \cdot C = N \cdot R} + H_2O,$$

retinal   Schiff base

视紫红质的吸收光谱：500 nm吸收带

哈伯德

编者按

哈佛大学的露丝·哈伯德是乔治·沃尔德的妻子，后者因为发现人类视网膜中色素的光吸收而与其他人一起共同获得了诺贝尔奖。这篇关于视紫红质吸收的报道是由哈伯德独立完成的，视紫红质是视网膜中主要吸收可见光谱红端光能的吸收剂。在同一期《自然》杂志上，她发表了另一篇与可见光谱蓝端的吸收有关的论文。总的来说，这两篇论文加深了人们对形成人类视觉的光学活性物质的认识。

视紫红质，即脊椎动物视杆细胞和很多无脊椎动物光感受细胞中的光敏色素，是由一种无色的蛋白质（视蛋白）构成的，视蛋白上含有作为生色团的视网膜醛（视黄醛，维生素 A 醛）的 11– 顺式异构体。鲍恩兹[1]指出：在牛的视紫红质中，生色团被限于与视蛋白内一个赖氨酸残基的 ε– 氨基相连的席夫碱中。

柯林斯[2]以及莫顿、皮特及其同事[3]首先证明，视黄醛与视蛋白上的一个脂肪族氨基形成了一种席夫碱[3]。这引出了下面的问题，即这种类型的连接如何使视紫红质具有吸收性质，因为在水溶液中 11– 顺式视网膜醛的 λ_{max} 位于 380 nm 处，席夫碱的 λ_{max} 位于 363 nm 附近，而视紫红质的 λ_{max} 则位于接近 500 nm 处。（不同动物视紫红质 λ_{max} 的准确位置会略有差异，也许是因为视蛋白的种类有所不同吧。）

为了解释这些吸收特性，克罗普夫与哈伯德[4]从由鲍尔等人[5]最先进行的观测入手，即尽管视网膜醛与脂肪胺可以生成一种席夫碱：

$$C_{19}H_{27} \cdot \overset{H}{C} = O + H_2N \cdot R \qquad C_{19}H_{27} \cdot \overset{H}{C} = N \cdot R + H_2O,$$

视网膜醛   席夫碱

is accompanied by a shift in λ_{max} toward shorter wavelengths, the protonation of the imino group,

$$\overset{H}{C_{19}H_{27} \cdot C} = N \cdot R + H^+ \quad \overset{H}{C_{19}H_{27} \cdot C} = \overset{+}{N} \cdot R.$$
$$\phantom{C_{19}H_{27} \cdot C = N \cdot R + H^+ \quad C_{19}H_{27} \cdot C = N \cdot} \underset{H}{}$$

shifts λ_{max} to approximately 440 nm.

The hypothesis assumes that the chromophores of the visual pigments are derived from the protonated Schiff base of 11-*cis* retinal by secondary interactions with reactive groups on opsin, which increase the mobility of electrons within the molecular orbitals of the chromophore and so shift λ_{max} to longer wavelengths (compare ref. 6). The triad of wavelengths that is therefore significant for this formulation are the absorption maximum of the Schiff base in its free and protonated forms and that of rhodopsin—approximately 363, 440 and 500 nm.

A direct experimental test of this hypothesis will have to wait until more is known about the amino-acid sequence and the three-dimensional structure of rhodopsin. Indirect support comes, however, from the observation that the absorption maxima of all the visual pigments that are known to have 11-*cis* retinal as chromophore—by now rather a large number—span more than 100 nm (approximately 440 to 565 nm). Yet they all lie at λ_{max} of the protonated Schiff base, or at longer wavelengths.

I report here observations concerning the denaturation of cattle rhodopsin which support the protonated Schiff base hypothesis.

All known chemical and physical protein denaturants denature opsin more readily than rhodopsin[7,8]. The denaturation of opsin is usually measured by its loss of the ability to regenerate rhodopsin; that of rhodopsin, by its bleaching in the dark to 11-*cis* retinal and denatured opsin[8].

Cattle rhodopsin is stable in 8 M urea, though this reagent denatures opsin in much lower concentrations (Fig. 1, also ref. 9). Guanidine hydrochloride (Gu-HCl), which is usually a more effective protein denaturant than urea, denatures cattle rhodopsin, but again in much higher concentrations than those required to denature opsin (Fig. 1). The logarithm of the rate at which rhodopsin is denatured increases proportionately with the logarithm of the Gu-HCl concentration (Fig. 2): more precisely, doubling the Gu-HCl concentration increases the rate constant (k) by a factor of ten.

94

其间会伴随着 λ_{max} 向短波方向的位移，但亚氨基的质子化反应：

$$C_{19}H_{27} \cdot \overset{H}{C} = N \cdot R + H^+ \qquad C_{19}H_{27} \cdot \overset{H}{C} = \overset{+}{N} \cdot R$$
$$\underset{H}{}$$

却使 λ_{max} 移至大约 440 nm 处。

该假说认为视色素中的生色团是由 11- 顺式视网膜醛的质子化席夫碱通过与视蛋白上的反应基团发生次级相互作用得到的，从而增加了电子在生色团分子轨道内部的活动性，因此使 λ_{max} 发生红移（对比参考文献 6 中的结果）。因而对该假说而言，三个重要的波长是游离态和质子化态席夫碱的最大吸收以及视紫红质的最大吸收——大致位于 363 nm、440 nm 和 500 nm。

我们将不得不等到对视紫红质中氨基酸序列和三维结构有更多了解的时候，再用实验直接验证这一假说。但是对所有视色素最大吸收值的观察可以提供间接的证据：目前已知有相当大数量的视色素含有 11- 顺式视网膜醛生色团，它们的 λ_{max} 跨度超过 100 nm（大约从 440 nm 到 565 nm）。不过它们都位于质子化席夫碱的 λ_{max} 附近或更长的波长处。

这里我报道的是对牛视紫红质变性的观测结果，由此可以证实质子化席夫碱的假说。

与使视紫红质发生变性相比，所有已知的化学蛋白质变性剂和物理蛋白质变性剂都更容易使视蛋白发生变性 [7,8]。视蛋白的变性通常是用丧失视紫红质再生能力的程度来衡量的；而视紫红质的变性则是由它在黑暗中褪色变成 11- 顺式视网膜醛和变性视蛋白而测定的 [8]。

牛视紫红质在 8 M 尿素溶液中很稳定；但在浓度大幅降低的情况下，尿素仍可使视蛋白发生变性（参见图 1，另见参考文献 9）。在通常情况下，盐酸胍（Gu-HCl）是一种比尿素更为有效的蛋白质变性剂，它能使牛视紫红质变性，但所需浓度同样要比使视蛋白变性的浓度高很多（图 1）。视紫红质变性速率的对数随 Gu-HCl 浓度对数的增加而成比例地增加（图 2）：更确切地说，Gu-HCl 浓度加倍会使速率常数（k）增大至 10 倍。

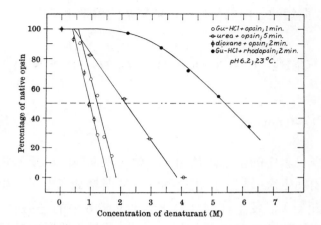

Fig. 1. Denaturation of opsin and rhodopsin as a function of the concentrations of several denaturants. The denaturation of opsin was measured as loss in its ability to form rhodopsin when incubated with excess 11-*cis* retinal in the dark. This assay took about 10 min, during which the denaturation continued. Estimates of native opsin therefore were too low and progressively more so as the concentration of denaturant increased. The lines therefore descend somewhat too steeply. Also the periods of incubation before the addition of 11-*cis* retinal differ for the three denaturants. The comparison therefore is only qualitative. The denaturation of rhodopsin was measured as irreversible bleaching in the dark. This involved only the measurement of the absorption spectrum in the presence of 0.07 M hydroxylamine, and entailed no systematic errors.

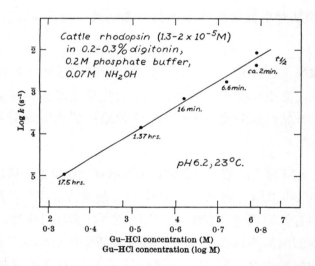

Fig. 2. The rate of denaturation of rhodopsin as a function of Gu-HCl concentration. Each point represents a separate experiment in which the unimolecular rate constant (k) for the denaturation was measured for a given Gu-HCl concentration. The half-times of denaturation ($t_{1/2}$) for each experiment are shown.

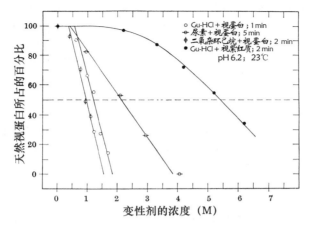

图 1. 视蛋白和视紫红质变性与几种变性剂浓度的关系曲线。视蛋白变性是由用过量 11- 顺式视网膜醛
在黑暗中培养时形成视紫红质能力的丧失程度来衡量的。该实验过程大约需要 10 min，其间一直
在发生变性反应。这样天然视蛋白所占百分比的估值就会偏低，而且当变性剂浓度增加时情况更
是如此。因此曲线的下降有点过于陡峭。另外，三种变性剂在加入 11- 顺式视网膜醛之前的培养
时间也各不相同。因此这只是定性的对比。视紫红质的变性由它在黑暗中的不可逆褪色来衡量。
本结果只涉及存在 0.07 M 羟胺时测定的吸收光谱，因此不会产生系统误差。

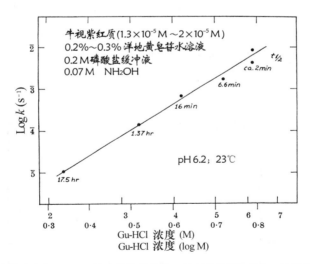

图 2. 视紫红质的变性速率与 Gu-HCl 浓度的关系曲线。每个点对应的是由一次单独实验得到的结果，
在这些实验中测定了给定 Gu-HCl 浓度下变性反应的单分子速率常数 (k)。由每次实验得到的变性
反应半衰期 ($t_{1/2}$) 均示于图中。

A closer examination reveals that Gu-HC1 exerts two effects on cattle rhodopsin, one rapid and reversible, the other slower and irreversible. The reversible interaction results in a shift in λ_{max} from 499 nm to shorter wave lengths, in the limit to 495.5 nm, without change in the half band width (Fig. 3), and is reversed rapidly by decreasing the concentration of Gu-HC1. I shall refer to the molecule with λ_{max} 495.5 nm as altered rhodopsin. It is not clear whether this shift in λ_{max} involves a series of intermediate compounds each with its own λ_{max} or a mixture of native rhodopsin (λ_{max} 499 nm) with increasing proportions of the altered pigment. Fig. 4 shows that the entire shift occurs within a rather narrow range of Gu-HC1 concentrations, suggesting that what is being dealt with is probably one transition from the native to the altered state rather than smaller sequential steps.

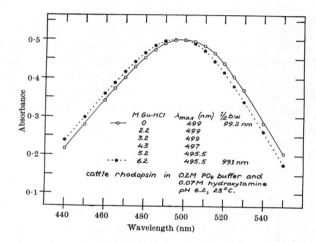

Fig. 3. The wavelength position of the absorption band of cattle rhodopsin as a function of Gu-HC1 concentration. As the concentration of Gu-HC1 increased, λ_{max} shifted to shorter wavelengths, with no change in half band width (1/2 bw). The shift in λ_{max} was reversed when the Gu-HC1 concentration was lowered.

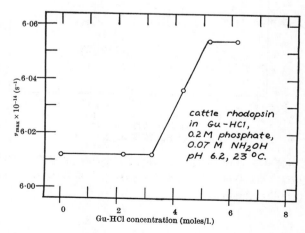

Fig. 4. Position of the absorption maximum (λ_{max}) of native and altered rhodopsin as a function of the Gu-HC1 concentration.

98

　　进一步检验发现 Gu-HCl 可以对牛视紫红质产生两种效应：一种是快速而可逆的，另一种则较慢且不可逆。可逆的相互作用使 λ_{max} 从 499 nm 位移到较短波长处而不会改变半峰宽（图 3），极限情况下可以达到 495.5 nm，且随着 Gu-HCl 浓度的降低上述效应会快速逆转。我在下文中将说明这种 λ_{max} 为 495.5 nm 的分子就是发生可逆变性的视紫红质。现在仍不清楚 λ_{max} 从 499 nm 位移至 495.5 nm 到底是与一系列具有自身 λ_{max} 的中间化合物有关，还是与随着发生可逆变性色素比例的增加天然视紫红质（λ_{max} 为 499 nm）组成的变化有关。从图 4 中可以看出整个位移发生在一段相当窄的 Gu-HCl 浓度区间内，这意味着我们正在研究的可能是一种从天然状态到可逆变性状态的质变，而非一些较小的连续量变。

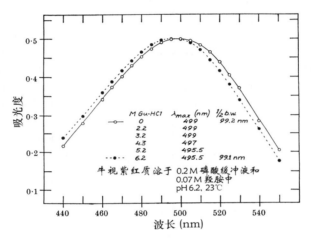

图 3. 牛视紫红质吸收带中波长的位置与 Gu-HCl 浓度的关系曲线。随着 Gu-HCl 浓度的增加，λ_{max} 位移到了较短波长处，而半峰宽（1/2 bw）并没有发生变化。当 Gu-HCl 浓度减少时，λ_{max} 又会向相反方向移动。

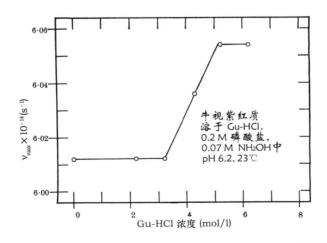

图 4. 天然和可逆变性视紫红质最大吸收的位置（λ_{max}）与 Gu-HCl 浓度的关系曲线。

Either interpretation presupposes that Gu-HC1 shifts the absorption spectrum of rhodopsin by altering the conformation of opsin. Gu-HC1, however, carries a positive charge, localized primarily on the central carbon atom of the symmetrical guanidinium ion, $\overset{+}{C} \cdot (NH_2)_3$. At the high concentrations at which Gu-HC1 affects the absorption spectrum of rhodopsin there could perhaps be a direct interaction between the charged guanidinium ion and the molecular orbitals of the retinyledene chromophore. But the abruptness with which λ_{max} of rhodopsin shifts with increasing Gu-HC1 concentration (Fig. 4) argues against a non-specific solvent effect on the chromophore and in favour of a conformational attack on opsin.

The irreversible denaturation of rhodopsin by Gu-HC1 is slower. Its first product is a pigment with λ_{max} 445 nm (Fig. 5, III), which is slowly converted to a pigment with λ_{max} 362.5 nm (Fig. 5, III and IV). There is no way to decide from there experiments whether the reversible alteration of rhodopsin to the pigment with λ_{max} 495.5 nm precedes the irreversible formation of the 445 nm pigment, or whether the two are parallel and independent processes. All concentrations of Gu-HC1 which alter rhodopsin also denature it (compare Figs. 2 and 4). The 495.5 nm pigment is never stable therefore and its absorption spectrum must be measured while it disappears. This is done in the presence of hydroxylamine, which in sufficiently low concentrations does not decrease the stability of the 495.5 nm pigment, while converting the 445 nm pigment rapidly to 11-*cis* retinaldehyde oxime (λ_{max} 362.5 nm) and denatured opsin (Figs. 4 and 5). This is the only way to measure the absorption spectra of the 495.5 and 445 nm pigments, for they overlap too extensively to permit of more direct resolution (compare Fig. 5, I, II and III).

两种解释都需要预先假定 Gu-HCl 是通过改变视蛋白的构象而使视紫红质的吸收光谱发生位移的。但是，Gu-HCl 所带的一个正电荷主要定域在对称胍离子（$\overset{+}{C} \cdot (NH_2)_3$）的中心碳原子上。当高浓度的 Gu-HCl 影响到视紫红质的吸收光谱时，在带电胍离子与视黄基生色团分子轨道之间有可能会存在着一种直接的相互作用。但视紫红质 λ_{max} 随 Gu-HCl 浓度增加而发生突然性变化的现象（图 4）说明并非来自非特异性溶剂对生色团的影响，而倾向于视蛋白构象发生了变化。

视紫红质在 Gu-HCl 作用下发生不可逆变性的速度是比较慢的。它的第一个产物是 λ_{max} 为 445 nm 的色素（图 5，III），这种色素会慢慢地转化成另一种 λ_{max} 为 362.5 nm 的色素（图 5，III 和 IV）。从这些实验中无法判断视紫红质可逆转化成 λ_{max} 为 495.5 nm 色素的过程是否要先于不可逆生成 445 nm 色素的过程，也不能说明这两个过程是否相互平行且互不影响。所有会使视紫红质发生可逆变性的 Gu-HCl 浓度也会使其发生不可逆变性（对比图 2 和 4）。因此 λ_{max} 为 495.5 nm 的色素并不是稳定的，我们只能在它消失的瞬间测量它的吸收光谱。实验中需要用到羟胺，但羟胺的浓度很低，不会降低 495.5 nm 色素的稳定性，但 445 nm 色素会快速转化为 11– 顺式视黄醛肟（λ_{max} 为 362.5 nm），并使视蛋白变性（图 4 和 5）。以下是测定 495.5 nm 和 445 nm 色素吸收光谱的唯一方法，因为它们的重叠部分太多以至于不能用更为直接的方法进行分析（比较图 5，I、II 和 III）。

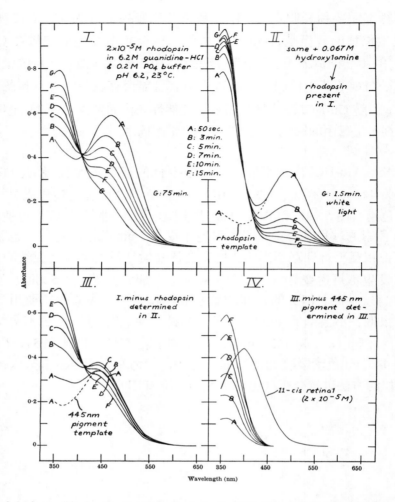

Fig. 5. Analysis of the irreversible denaturation of rhodopsin by Gu-HCl. Upper left (I), successive absorption spectra (*A* to *G*) recorded with a Cary model 14 spectrophotometer, after adding a small volume of a concentrated rhodopsin solution in 2 percent aqueous digitonin to buffered 6.2 M Gu-HCl. Upper right (II), the experiment was repeated with another aliquot of the same rhodopsin solution in the presence of 0.067 M hydroxylamine. This concentration of hydroxylamine does not labilize altered rhodopsin, so that the absorption spectra in (II) show the amounts of altered rhodopsin present in the experiment in (I). The dotted portion of curve II*A* is the absorption spectrum of this rhodopsin preparation below 450 nm, corrected to the appropriate absorbance at λ_{max}. Similar template spectra have been constructed for curves II*B*, *C* and so on. The relative absorbance and λ_{max} (362.5 nm) of the ultraviolet absorption band in spectra II*A* to *F* identify the product of the denaturation as 11-*cis* retinaldehyde oxime. Lower left (III), differences between successive absorption spectra in (I) and the corresponding template spectra in (II) (that is, curves I*A* minus II*A*, I*B* minus II*B* and so on). This yields the combined absorption spectra of the 445 and 362.5 nm pigments present in the experiment in (I). The dotted portion of curve III*A* was obtained by estimating the absorption of the 362.5 nm pigment present in the solidly drawn spectrum III*A* from the initial absorption of rhodopsin before denaturation (determined separately) and the amounts of the 362.5 and 445 nm pigments formed when a given amount of rhodopsin is denatured (that is, by comparing the differences between successive spectra in (II) and (III)). The absorption spectra of the 362.5 nm pigment shown at the lower right (IV) were obtained by subtracting successive 445 nm pigment template spectra obtained by scaling template III*A* to the successive absorbances at 445 nm, from the solidly drawn spectra in (III) (that is, curves III*A* minus template III*A*, III*B* minus template III*B*, etc.). (IV) Also shows the absorption spectrum of 11-*cis* retinal at the initial rhodopsin concentration in this solvent system. It has λ_{max} at 400 nm, a surprisingly long wavelength, and a specific absorbance at λ_{max} about 0.6 that of the Schiff base and of 11-*cis* retinaldehyde oxime, both of which have λ_{max} at 362.5 nm (compare ultraviolet absorption bands in (I) and (II)).

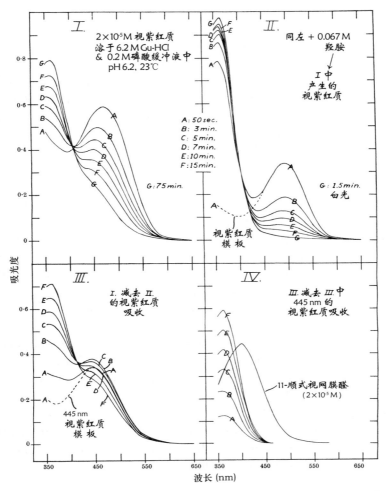

图 5. 视紫红质在 Gu-HCl 作用下发生不可逆变性的分析结果。左上图（I），将少量视紫红质浓缩液（2% 洋地黄皂苷水溶液）加入到 6.2 M Gu-HCl 缓冲液中，再用卡里 14 型分光光度计记录连续吸收光谱（A 到 G）。右上图（II），用另一份同样的视紫红质溶液在含有 0.067 M 羟胺的情况下重复该实验。因为该浓度的羟胺不会降低可逆变性视紫红质部分的稳定性，所以（II）中的吸收光谱能体现出由（I）中实验所产生的可逆变性视紫红质的量。曲线 IIA 中的虚线部分是这种视紫红质制剂在 450 nm 以下的吸收光谱，并根据 λ_{max} 处的吸光度进行过修正。用类似方法建立了曲线 IIB、C 等的模板光谱。谱线 IIA ~ F 中紫外吸收带的相对吸光度和 λ_{max}（362.5 nm）说明，不可逆变性产物就是 11– 顺式视黄醛肟。左下图（III）：（I）中连续吸收光谱与（II）中所对应的模板光谱的差谱（即，曲线 IA 减去 IIA，IB 减去 IIB，依此类推）。这样得到的是（I）中实验里色素表现出来的 445 nm 和 362.5 nm 的混合吸收光谱。曲线 IIIA 中的虚线部分，是通过估计光谱 IIIA（译者注：原稿可能有误，此处似应为 IIA）实线部分中 362.5 nm 色素吸收与视紫红质发生不可逆变性前初始吸收的差（单独测定），以及当给定量视紫红质发生变性时所形成的 362.5 nm 与 445 nm 色素的量而得到的（即，通过比较（II）与（III）中连续光谱的差异而得到）。显示于右下图（IV）中的 362.5 nm 色素的吸收光谱，是通过从（III）中光谱的实线部分里减去将色素模板 IIIA 与 445 nm 处连续吸收相对照而得到的连续 445 nm 色素模板而得到的（即，曲线 IIIA 减去模板 IIIA，IIIB 减去模板 IIIB，依此类推）。（IV）还显示出 11– 顺式视网膜醛在这一溶剂体系中于初始视紫红质浓度下的吸收光谱。它在波长非常长的 400 nm 处出现 λ_{max}，并且在 λ_{max} 处的比吸光度与席夫碱和 11–顺式视黄醛肟相比约为 0.6，后两者在 362.5 nm 处出现 λ_{max}（对比（I）和（II）中的紫外吸收带）。

103

The absorption spectra of the two consecutive products of the irreversible denaturation (with λ_{max} 445 and 362.5 nm) strongly suggest that they are the protonated and free forms of a Schiff base of 11-*cis* retinal. The way in which they arise in the experiment shown in Fig. 5 further suggests that the retinal is still attached at the chromophoric site on opsin for the following reasons. At the pH of this experiment (6.2) essentially all the amino-groups on opsin are protonated, for even the most conservative estimates place the pKs of the various classes of amino-groups in proteins well above pH 7. Retinal, however, forms Schiff bases only with unprotonated amino-groups[3] (see the first equation in this article). The very fact that the denatured product is a Schiff base therefore implies that retinal is attached at the same site as in native rhodopsin.

Furthermore, the pK of the Schiff bases of retinal (that is, of the imino-group) is considerably lower than that of the amino groups from which they arise[3], so that whereas at pH 6.2 all the amino-groups of opsin are protonated, the imino-group of the Schiff base of retinal should not be. The fact that at this pH the initial product of denaturation is protonated and gradually loses its proton as shown in Fig. 5, III, strongly suggests that the rhodopsin chromophore itself is protonated. Gu-HCl, so to speak, peels the opsin away from the chromophore and so reveals the unenhanced absorption spectrum of the protonated Schiff base.

This raises the question as to why the protonated Schiff base has not been seen as an intermediate in other types of denaturation of rhodopsin[7,8] except, of course, by strong acid[3]. The answer probably lies in the extraordinary stability of the unprotonated Schiff base in concentrated Gu-HCl. Fig. 5, I, II and IV, shows that λ_{max} of the unprotonated imine at 362.5 nm is unchanged throughout (that is, for 75 min at 23°C) whereas Schiff bases of retinal usually hydrolyse within about 15 min at this pH, as evidenced by a shift in λ_{max} to that of free retinaldehyde[3]. It must therefore be assumed that high concentrations of Gu-HCl so lower the activity of water that a 6 M solution behaves like a non-aqueous system.

This research was supported by a grant from the US Public Health Service.

(**221**, 432-435; 1969)

Ruth Hubbard: Biological Laboratories, Harvard University, Cambridge, Massachusetts.

Received November 6, 1968.

References:
1. Bownds, D., *Nature*, **216**, 1178 (1967).
2. Collins, F. D., *Nature*, **171**, 469 (1953).
3. Pitt, G. A. J., Collins, F. D., Morton, R. A., and Stok, P., *Biochem. J.*, **59**, 122 (1955); Morton, R. A., and Pitt, G. A. J., *ibid.*, **59**, 128 (1955).
4. Kropf, A., and Hubbard, R., *Ann. NY Acad. Sci.*, **74**, 266 (1958).
5. Ball, S., Collins, F. D., Dalvi, P. D., and Morton, R. A., *Biochem. J.*, **45**, 304 (1949).
6. Hubbard, R., and Kropf, A., *J. Gen. Physiol.*, **49**, 381 (1965-66).

　　不可逆变性的两种连续产物的吸收光谱（λ_{max} 为 445 nm 和 362.5 nm）显然说明，它们分别是 11- 顺式视网膜醛的一种席夫碱的两种形态——质子化态和游离态。图 5 显示出它们出现于实验中的方式，这种方式进一步说明视网膜醛仍然连接在视蛋白的生色团位置上，原因有以下几点。在这次实验的 pH 值（6.2）下，视蛋白中几乎所有的氨基都会被质子化，因为即使按照最保守的估计，蛋白质中各种氨基基团的 pK 值也会远远高于 pH 值 7；但是，视网膜醛只与未质子化的氨基基团形成席夫碱 [3]（参见本文中第一个反应式）。因此，变性产物是一种席夫碱这一事实说明视网膜醛的连接位置与在天然视紫红质中相同。

　　此外，视网膜醛席夫碱（也就是亚氨基）的 pK 值比生成它们的氨基所具有的 pK 值要低很多 [3]，因此，尽管在 pH 值 6.2 时视蛋白的所有氨基都被质子化，但视网膜醛席夫碱的亚氨基却不会完全被质子化。在这个 pH 值下，初始的变性产物是质子化的，并会逐渐失去质子，如图 5，III 所示，这显然说明视紫红质生色团本身是质子化的。可以这样讲，Gu-HCl 的作用是将视蛋白与生色团剥离，因而表现为质子化席夫碱吸收光谱未出现增强的现象。

　　这样就引出了以下这个问题，即为什么在其他类型视紫红质的变性过程中从未看到过质子化席夫碱作为中间产物出现 [7,8]，当然，在强酸条件下 [3] 除外。答案可能就在于未质子化席夫碱在高浓度 Gu-HCl 中的超常稳定性。图 5 中的 I、II、IV 表明，未质子化亚胺在 362.5 nm 的 λ_{max} 始终没有发生变化（即在 23℃下长达 75 min 的时间内），但视网膜醛席夫碱在这个 pH 值下通常会在约 15 min 之内水解，证据是 λ_{max} 位移到了自由视黄醛的位置 [3]。因此我们必须假定，高浓度的 Gu-HCl 显著降低了水的活性，以至于浓度为 6 M 的溶液就像不含水的体系一样。

　　本研究得到了美国公共卫生署提供的一项基金的资助。

（王耀杨 翻译；杨志 审稿）

7. Radding, C. M., and Wald, G., *J. Gen. Physiol.*, **39**, 923 (1955-56).

8. Hubbard, R., *J. Gen. Physiol.*, **42**, 259 (1958-59).

9. Abrahamson, F. W., and Ostroy, S. E., *Prog. Biophys. and Mol. Biol.*, **17**, 181 (1967).

10. Hubbard, R., and St George, R. C. C., *J. Gen. Physiol.*, **41**, 501 (1957-58).

Evidence in Support of a Rotational Model for the Pulsar *PSR* 0833–45

V. Radhakrishnan *et al.*

Editor's Note

This paper, appearing within a few months of the discovery of pulsating stars (pulsars), is an almost immediate confirmation of Gold's theory that the apparent pulsation is caused by rapid rotation, sending a beam of radiation across the sky much as a lighthouse announces its presence. Radhakrishnan was trained as a radioastronomer in India and Australia; he was a son of the Nobel-Prize-winning scientist C. V. Raman and succeeded him as Director of the physical laboratory in Bangalore.

THE pulsar *PSR* 0833–45, discovered at the Molonglo Radio Observatory[1] and tentatively identified with the supernova remnant Vela *X*, has been observed with the Parkes 210 foot reflector at frequencies of 2,700 MHz and 1,720 MHz. We find that this pulsar is remarkable for its short pulse width, high and constant intensity, complete linear polarization and changing periodicity. Our observations of this object seem to rule out radial pulsations as the source of the radio emission and support a rotational hypothesis along the lines suggested by Gold[2] and discussed by Goldreich[3] as the most likely model.

The first observations were made on December 8, 9 and 10 using the wideband correlation receiver[4] operating at 2,700 MHz. The pulse energy, linear polarization and an accurate period were measured and are listed in Table 1. Attempts to obtain a pulse shape, however, soon indicated that the drift time of ~ 10 ms through the 500 MHz effective passband of the receiver was smoothing out the natural pulse beyond recognition. It seemed probable that the polarization characteristics of the pulse were also being smeared by the passband. Observations of the pulsar were therefore repeated on the nights of December 11, 12, 13 and 20 at 1,720 MHz with narrower bandwidths. The fast rise and short duration of the pulse as recorded by a 400 channel integrator[5] are illustrated in Fig. 1. Apart from occasional pulses of extraordinary strength, the amplitude variations were so low that an average of 100 pulses taken at any time during the several days this pulsar was observed on either frequency showed less than 10 percent variation in amplitude and even less in pulse shape. Large *et al.*[6] have remarked on similar behaviour at 408 MHz. Table 1 lists various parameters obtained from measurements at either one or both of the observing frequencies.

支持脉冲星*PSR* 0833-45的旋转模型的证据

拉达克里希南等

编者按

这篇文章发表于发现脉动星（现称脉冲星）之后的几个月内，它使戈尔德的理论立即得到印证，该理论认为脉动是由快速旋转引起的，脉冲星在旋转时发射出一束穿越空间的辐射，就像灯塔一样显示着自己的存在。本文的作者拉达克里希南曾在印度和澳大利亚接受过射电天文学的培训；他是诺贝尔奖获得者著名科学家拉曼的儿子，后来他继承父业成为班加罗尔物理实验室的负责人。

我们用帕克斯 210 英尺反射望远镜在 2,700 MHz 和 1,720 MHz 频率下对莫隆格勒射电天文台发现的脉冲星 *PSR* 0833-45[1]——现在暂时被证认为船帆座 − *X* 的超新星遗迹——进行了观测。我们发现这颗脉冲星具有脉冲宽度窄、强度高且稳定、完全线偏振和周期变动等值得注意的特征。我们对该天体的观测结果似乎排除了径向脉动是射电辐射起源的可能性，而支持由戈尔德提出 [2] 并被戈德赖希讨论过 [3] 的旋转模型。

最初的观测是在 12 月 8 日、9 日和 10 日用工作于 2,700 MHz 的宽带相关接收机 [4] 进行的。由测量得到的脉冲能量、线偏振和精确周期列于表 1 中。然而我们在试图获得脉冲波形的过程中很快发现：在通过接收机的 500 MHz 有效通带时，∼ 10 ms 的漂移时间会将天然脉冲平滑到无法识别的程度。脉冲的偏振特征似乎也可能会被通带抹去。因此我们在 12 月 11 日、12 日、13 日和 20 日的夜晚用更窄的带宽在 1,720 MHz 频率下进行了重复的观测。用 400 通道积分器 [5] 记录脉冲的快速上升和短暂持续并示于图 1 中。除去偶然出现的强度异常的脉冲，在一般情况下振幅变动非常低：在我们用两种频率对该脉冲星进行观测的这几天中的任何时间里，取 100 个脉冲信号的平均值的结果显示仅有不到 10% 的振幅变动，更不用说脉冲波形了。拉奇等人 [6] 曾讨论过在频率为 408 MHz 时也有类似情况。表 1 中列出了由在一种或两种频率下进行观测所得到的几个参数。

Table 1. Characteristics of *PSR* 0833–45

Heliocentric period (December 8–9, 1968)	$0.089208370 \pm 4 \times 10^{-9}$ s
Pulse width	~ 2 ms
Drift rate at 1,720 MHz	$-9{,}280 \pm 50$ MHz s^{-1}
∫*nedl*	63 cm^{-3} pc
Pulse energy at 1,720 MHz (both polarizations)	$(0.038 \pm 0.004) \times 10^{-26}$ J m^{-2} Hz^{-1}
Pulse energy at 2,700 MHz (both polarizations)	$(0.023 \pm 0.003) \times 10^{-26}$ J m^{-2} Hz^{-1}
Energy spectral index 1,720–2,700 MHz	-0.93
Percentage linear polarization 1,720 MHz	> 95 percent
Percentage linear polarization 2,700 MHz	> 60 percent (see text)
Percentage circular polarization 1,720 MHz	< 3 percent
Position angle of mean polarization 1,720 MHz	$115° \pm 5°$
Position angle of mean polarization 2,700 MHz	$77° \pm 7°$
Rotation measure	$+ 38 \pm 10$ rad m^{-2}
Intrinsic plane of polarization	$\approx 50°$
Mean longitudinal galactic field	≈ 0.8 μgauss

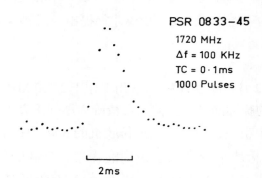

PSR 0833–45
1720 MHz
Δf = 100 KHz
TC = 0·1ms
1000 Pulses

2ms

Fig. 1. A 1,000 pulse integration at 1,720 MHz of *PSR* 0833–45. The channel separation is approximately 0.22 ms.

The drift rate of the pulse at 1,720 MHz was measured by timing the arrival of the pulses in 100 kHz filters separated by 6 MHz. The interstellar dispersion derived from this measurement is somewhat higher than the value quoted by Large *et al.*[6] but not significantly so. The pulse energy at 1,720 MHz was obtained by integrating the observed pulses in two opposite polarizations. This is plotted in Fig. 2 together with the 2,700 MHz value and the 408 MHz energy[6]. The spectrum shows no break at the higher frequencies and in this respect *PSR* 0833–45 resembles *CP* 1133 (ref. 7).

表 1. *PSR* 0833–45 的特性

日心参照系中的周期（1968 年 12 月 8 日～9 日）	$0.089208370 \pm 4 \times 10^{-9}$ s
脉冲宽度	~ 2 ms
1,720 MHz 时的漂移率	$-9,280 \pm 50$ MHz s^{-1}
$\int nedl$	63 cm^{-3} pc
1,720 MHz 时的脉冲能量（两种偏振态）	$(0.038 \pm 0.004) \times 10^{-26}$ J m^{-2} Hz^{-1}
2,700 MHz 时的脉冲能量（两种偏振态）	$(0.023 \pm 0.003) \times 10^{-26}$ J m^{-2} Hz^{-1}
1,720 MHz ~ 2,700 MHz 的能谱指数	−0.93
1,720 MHz 时线偏振的百分比	>95%
2,700 MHz 时线偏振的百分比	>60%（参见正文）
1,720 MHz 时圆偏振的百分比	<3%
1,720 MHz 时平均偏振面的位置角	$115° \pm 5°$
2,700 MHz 时平均偏振面的位置角	$77° \pm 7°$
（法拉第）旋转量	$+ 38 \pm 10$ rad m^{-2}
固有偏振面	$\approx 50°$
星系场的平均纵向分量	≈ 0.8 μgauss

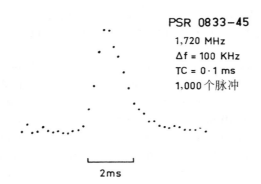

图 1. 在 1,720 MHz 下对 *PSR* 0833-45 的 1,000 个脉冲信号进行积分所得的结果。通道间隔约
为 0.22 ms。

    1,720 MHz 时的脉冲漂移率是用间隔为 6 MHz 的 100 kHz 滤波器记录脉冲到达时间测得的。从这一观测所推出的星际色散要比拉奇等人 [6] 提供的数值略微高一点，但差别不大。通过对观测到的两个相反偏振的脉冲进行积分可以得到 1,720 MHz 时的脉冲能量。所得结果与 2,700 MHz 和 408 MHz 时的能量值 [6] 一起示于图 2 中。能谱结果表明在较高频率处没有出现拐折，在这方面，*PSR* 0833-45 类似于 *CP* 1133（参考文献 7）。

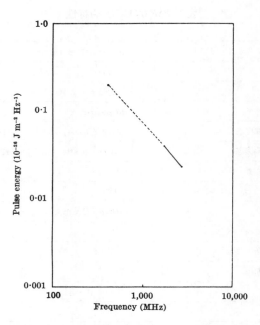

Fig. 2. The high frequency energy spectrum of *PSR* 0833–45. The spectral index is essentially constant at −0.9 between 408 MHz and 2,700 MHz.

The position angle at 1,720 MHz of the mean plane of linear polarization over the pulse was measured on the four nights of observation at this frequency and found to be the same. The internal agreement was considerably better than the error of 5 percent quoted in Table 1 for the absolute value of the position angle. The measurements of the position angle at 2,700 MHz on the previous three nights were also found to have remarkable internal consistency. Combining these two measurements on the assumption that the plane of polarization at these frequencies is indeed constant in time, and the same at the source, we have obtained a rotation of $38° \pm n180°$ between these two frequencies. For $n = 0$ the corresponding rotation measure is $+38 \pm 10$ rad m^{-2}. The mean value for the rotation measure in the region of Vela X obtained by Milne[8] is $+46$ rad m^{-2}. In view of the variations of rotation measure within the region the agreement is reasonable and provides strong support for the identification[1] of this pulsar with the supernova remnant. The average longitudinal component of the galactic magnetic field in this direction was then derived from the dispersion and the rotation measure[9]. A value of 0.8 μgauss was obtained which is intermediate between the values obtained by Smith[9,10] for three other pulsars in different directions in the galaxy.

The distribution of polarization across the pulse at 1,720 MHz is illustrated in Fig. 3. The Stokes parameter V has not been shown, for the circular polarization was found to be less than 3 percent. The whole pulse is almost completely linearly polarized (>95 percent) with the direction of the plane of polarization varying systematically across the main peak of the pulse. The Q axis was chosen as 115° to coincide with the polarization of the peak of the pulse. The plane of polarization rotates uniformly from a polarization angle (PA) near 140° on one edge of the pulse to less than PA 90° on the other, as sketched in Fig. 4. The

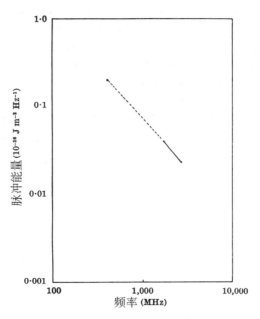

图 2. *PSR* 0833-45 的高频能谱。当频率在 408 MHz 到 2,700 MHz 之间时能谱指数基本上保持在常数 -0.9。

　　我们在 1,720 MHz 频率下观测了四个晚上，得到了对每个脉冲平均的线偏振面位置角，并发现数值是相同的。其内在一致性要比表 1 中所示的位置角绝对值的误差范围 5% 好很多。前三个夜晚在 2,700 MHz 频率下对位置角进行观测所得的结果也具有很高的内在一致性。假定在上述频率下偏振面不随时间变化且源也不随时间变化，综合这两次观测的结果，我们得出在这两个频率之间有 $38° \pm n180°$ 的转角。当 $n = 0$ 时，相应的旋转量为 $+38 \pm 10 \ \mathrm{rad \ m^{-2}}$。米尔恩[8]得到的船帆座 -X 区旋转量的平均值为 $+46 \ \mathrm{rad \ m^{-2}}$。考虑到在该区内旋转量存在变化，所以这两个结果之间的吻合还是比较好的，并且强有力地支持了这种脉冲星被证认为超新星遗迹的观点[1]。因此，根据色散和旋转量就可以推导出在这一方向上星系磁场的平均纵向分量[9]。得出的结果是 0.8 µgauss，此结果介于史密斯[9,10]由银河系中不同方向上的另外三颗脉冲星所得到的数值之间。

　　在 1,720 MHz 频率下脉冲中的偏振分布如图 3 所示。在图 3 中没有给出斯托克斯参数 *V*，因为我们发现圆偏振还不足 3%。整个脉冲几乎完全（>95%）是线偏振的，偏振面的方向从脉冲主峰的一侧到另一侧发生了系统的变化。*Q* 轴选取为 115° 以便与脉冲峰值处的偏振方向一致。偏振面从脉冲的一侧约 140° 偏振角（PA）处均匀地旋转到另一侧的小于 90° 偏振角处，如图 4 所示。因为辐射的振幅是从零开始增

113

magnetic field lines responsible for the polarization must vary smoothly over a similar range, for the amplitude of the radiation builds up from zero to a maximum and then falls off again. Detailed measurements across the pulse were not possible with the 2,700 MHz receiver because of the wide bandwidth as mentioned earlier. There were clear indications that the plane of polarization did change by about 40°–60° across the pulse, however. The smoothed pulse shapes obtained on different polarizations were consistent with the assumption that the polarization structure of the pulse was similar to that found at 1,720 MHz.

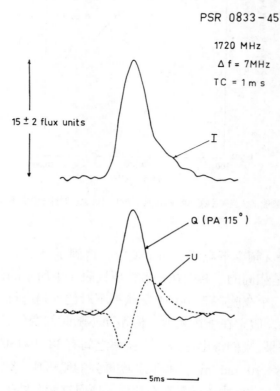

Fig. 3. The distribution of linear polarization across the pulse at 1,720 MHz. The distribution of Q and $-U$ represents a gradual change of approximately 45° in the position angle of polarization across the pulse. Within the errors of measurement the pulse is completely polarized.

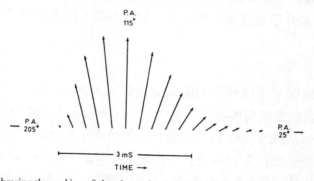

Fig. 4. Sketch showing the rocking of the plane of polarization during the pulse from *PSR* 0833–45.

加到最大值然后再次下降的，所以与偏振对应的磁力线也必然在类似的范围内平滑地变化。用 2,700 MHz 接收机不可能对脉冲进行更仔细的测量，原因在于前面已经提到过的带宽过大问题。然而仍然可以清晰地显示出偏振面在从脉冲一侧到另一侧时确实发生了约 40°～60° 的变化。在不同偏振下都得到了平滑的脉冲波形，这与 2,700 MHz 频率下的脉冲偏振结构类似于 1,720 MHz 下脉冲偏振结构的假定相吻合。

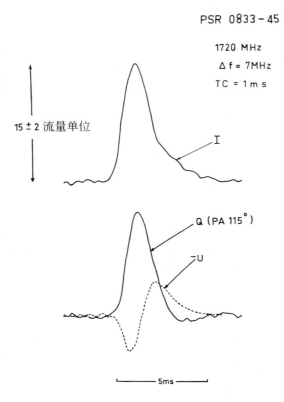

图 3. 在 1,720 MHz 下一个脉冲期间的线偏振分布。*Q* 和 -*U* 的分布状态表示出在一个脉冲期间偏振位置角逐渐改变了约 45°。在测量误差范围之内该脉冲是完全偏振的。

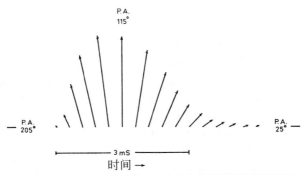

图 4. 表示在 *PSR* 0833-45 的脉冲中存在偏振面摆动的示意图。

Mills[11] reports that the pulsar in the Crab nebula has been observed at Arecibo and found to be slowing down in periodicity by one part in 2,400 yr^{-1}. He further suggested that as *PSR* 0833–45 has the next shortest period known, it might also exhibit the same characteristic. Following up his suggestion we made several other measurements of the period and the results are illustrated in Fig. 5.

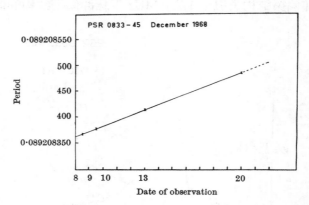

Fig. 5. The variation of the period of *PSR* 0833–45 over the 12 day observing span. The slope corresponds to an increase in the period of 10 ns or 1 part in 10^7 day^{-1}.

The period of *PSR* 0833–45 is increasing at the rate of 10 ns day^{-1}, or one part in 24,000 yr^{-1}. Assuming the position for the pulsar given by Large *et al.*[6] we have used all our measurements to give the heliocentric period $P = 0^s{\cdot}089208483 \pm 2 \times 10^{-9} + R$ (Julian date = 2440210.0) where the rate of increase $R = (10 \pm 0.4) \times 10^{-9}$ s. In the notation of Moffet and Ekers[7] the stability $\Delta P/P \approx 1.2 \times 10^{-13}$.

It seems reasonable to assume that the polarization of the radiation from pulsars reflects the magnetic field in the region of generation. A very highly linearly polarized pulse must then imply that all of the radiation in the pulse was generated in, or modified in, passage through a small region where the field was essentially homogeneous. If successive pulses all have exactly the same polarization, then it must mean that the same locality in the magneto-sphere of the pulsar remains in view for as long as the polarization remains constant. We have observed *PSR* 0833–45 on December 11, 12, 13 and 20 at 1,720 MHz for many hours each night and never detected any measurable change in either the degree or plane of polarization. It must follow that either a pulsating source of radiation or a "window" through which we periodically glimpse a steady source of radiation is permanently linked to one region in the magnetic field of the star. All of the observed characteristics of the pulse can be reasonably understood by assuming a rotating neutron star model as suggested by Gold[2]. Any hypothesis associating the radio pulses with radial oscillations of the star must invoke one of three special conditions: (*a*) the magnetic field is stationary as viewed from our frame of reference, (*b*) the rotation of the pulsar is synchronous with its pulsation, or (*c*) the rotational and magnetic axes of the star are aligned. (*a*) is extremely unlikely, (*b*) is unlikely in general and particularly so on the basis of our observations which show a slowing down of the pulse rate but no change in the polarization, and (*c*) can be dismissed from symmetry considerations in view of the observed systematic sweeping of the plane of polarization across the pulse.

116

　　米尔斯[11] 报道了他在阿雷西博观测到的蟹状星云脉冲星，他发现其周期在以每年 1 / 2,400 的速率加长。他进一步指出：由于 *PSR* 0833–45 具有目前已知的次短周期，或许它也会呈现出相同的特性。受其观点启示，我们又对 *PSR* 0833–45 的周期进行了几次观测，观测结果示于图 5 中。

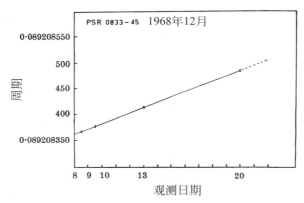

图 5. *PSR* 0833–45 的周期在 12 天观测期内显示出的变化。斜率所对应的周期增长为每天 10 ns 或 1 / 10⁷。

　　PSR 0833–45 的周期在以每天 10 ns 的速率增加，即每年 1 / 24,000。假设该脉冲星位于拉奇等人 [6] 所给出的位置，则利用我们的全部观测数据可以得出：日心参照系中的周期 $P = 0^s \cdot 089208483 \pm 2 \times 10^{-9} + R$（儒略日期 = 2440210.0）。其中，周期增长率 $R = (10 \pm 0.4) \times 10^{-9}$ s。根据莫菲特和埃克斯 [7] 的记号，稳定度 $\Delta P / P \approx 1.2 \times 10^{-13}$。

　　假定脉冲星辐射的偏振能反映其产生区域的磁场是合理的。那么脉冲的高度线偏振必定意味着脉冲中的所有辐射都产生自一个磁场基本均匀的小区域，或者在经过这样的区域时受到其影响。如果随后的脉冲都具有完全相同的偏振状态，那只能说明在偏振保持不变期间脉冲应该来自磁层中的同一部位。我们分别于 12 月 11日、12 日、13 日和 20 日每晚在 1,720 MHz 下对 *PSR* 0833–45 进行了好几个小时的观测，未曾发现偏振度或偏振面有任何可观测到的变化。由此可以推定：辐射的脉动源，或者在我们周期性观测到稳定辐射源时所通过的"窗口"，是与恒星磁场的某个区域恒定地联系在一起的。利用戈尔德[2] 提出的旋转中子星模型就可以合理地解释脉冲的所有观测特征。任何一种将射电脉冲与恒星径向振荡联系起来的假说都必须借助以下三个特殊条件中的一个：(*a*) 从我们的参照系看来该磁场是恒定的，(*b*) 脉冲星的旋转与它的脉动是同步的，或者 (*c*) 恒星的旋转轴和磁轴是在同一条直线上的。(*a*) 基本上没有成立的可能性；(*b*) 在一般情况下也不大可能成立，尤其是当我们在观测中发现脉冲速率在减慢而偏振状态并不改变时；基于对称性的要求 (*c*) 也可以被排除，因为已经观测到了偏振面从脉冲主峰一侧到另一侧的系统变化。

That the two most rapidly pulsating sources have shown an increase in period with time as predicted on Gold's model adds further support to the rotation hypothesis. Goldreich[3] has developed a simple axisymmetric version and shown that relativistic particles must be carried out along the field lines which extend beyond the velocity of light cylinder. If a pulsar is a non-axisymmetric version of this model as suggested, the beaming of the radiation in any given direction will be governed by the geometry linking the line of sight with the magnetic and rotational axes of the star. If this were indeed the case the average pulse shape would represent the profile of the magnetic "window" through which radiation can escape in a given direction, and the polarization of the pulse would be independent of frequency. Such a model would justify the tacit assumption in Faraday rotation interpretations that different frequencies are generated with the same polarization at the source. Any change of polarization across the pulse would then correspond to the rotation of the field lines in the duration of the pulse. A change of more the 45° in the plane of polarization such as seen in *PSR* 0833–45 implies that the radiation must emanate from a region close to the magnetic pole with the magnetic axis inclined at a considerable angle to the rotational axis.

We consider it relevant to draw attention to certain similarities between Jupiter and the pulsars. The low frequency radiation from both is characterized chiefly by unpredictability and fantastic complexity in structure and polarization. At the higher frequencies the polarization of Jupiter's radiation is chiefly linear, periodic and highly predictable. Over 180° of rotation the total intensity rises and falls due to beaming while the plane of polarization rocks[12] with the magnetic field. It is conceivable that at a high enough frequency the pulses from any pulsar will be as repetitive in character as they are in time.

If pulsars have satellites, and the satellites influence the activity of the pulsar in the manner of Io's influence on Jupiter[13], the radiation would exhibit many of the characteristics that are found at low frequencies. In spite of Jupiter's proximity and the time over which the low frequency radiation had been studied, it was only a statistical approach combined with a knowledge of Io's movements which finally led to the discovery of the modulation.

Goldreich[3] predicts a rate of change of period inversely proportional to the square of the period. The ratio of the rates of change of the Crab pulsar to the Vela pulsar is 10, in reasonable agreement with the predicted value of 7.5. The age of the Vela supernova on his model would then be $\sim 10^4$ yr.

We thank Dr. R. N. Manchester for help with the 1,720 MHz observations and Miss P. Beswick for help in the preparation of the manuscript.

(**221**, 443-446; 1969)

V. Radhakrishnan, D. J. Cooke, M. M. Komesaroff and D. Morris: Radiophysics Laboratory, CSIRO, Sydney, Australia.

正如戈尔德的模型所预言的那样，两个最快的脉动源都显示出周期随时间而增加的现象，这就为旋转假说提供了进一步的支持。戈德赖希 [3] 详尽阐述了一种简单的轴对称形式，并证明相对论性粒子一定是沿着延伸出光速圆柱面之外的磁力线运动的。如果一颗脉冲星被认为是处于此模型的非轴对称形式，那么在任意给定方向上的辐射束流都将由视线、该星体的磁轴及旋转轴这三者的几何关系所决定。如果事实确实如此，那么用平均脉冲波形将可以代表给定方向辐射逃逸时通过的磁"窗口"的轮廓，而脉冲的偏振状态将与频率无关。这一模型将证实在解释法拉第旋转时默认的假定，即认为不同的频率在源处以同一偏振产生。因此，偏振从脉冲主峰一侧到另一侧的任何变化都将与脉冲过程中磁力线的旋转相关联。如果偏振面的变化超过了 45°，例如在 *PSR* 0833−45 中观察到的情况，则意味着辐射必定来自于靠近磁极的区域，并且磁轴相对于旋转轴的倾斜角度不会太小。

我们认为有必要提请注意一下木星与脉冲星之间的某些相似之处。来自木星和脉冲星的低频辐射都以结构及偏振状态的不可预见性和高度复杂性为主要特征。而在较高频率下，木星辐射的偏振状态则基本上是线性的、周期性的和高度可预测的。在 180° 的转动中，总强度因束流而升高和降低，而偏振面会随着磁场的变化而摆动 [12]。可以设想：当频率足够高时，来自任何脉冲星的脉冲在性质上和时间上都将是可重复的。

假设脉冲星有卫星，而且这个卫星能够像木卫一影响木星 [13] 那样影响脉冲星的活动，那么辐射就将呈现出在低频时观察到的许多特征。尽管木星近在咫尺，并且人们对其低频辐射的研究也已经经历了很长时间，但也只有在将统计方法与木卫一的运动知识相结合之后才最终导致了调制现象的发现。

戈德赖希 [3] 预言周期的变化率反比于周期的平方。蟹状星云脉冲星与船帆座脉冲星的变化率之比为 10，与预估值 7.5 的吻合情况还是不错的。因此，根据他的模型，船帆座超新星的年龄为 $\sim 10^4$ 年。

感谢曼彻斯特博士帮助我们进行 1,720 MHz 频率下的观测，还要感谢贝斯威克小姐在准备手稿的过程中所提供的帮助。

（王耀杨 翻译；邓祖淦 审稿）

Received December 30, 1968.

References:

1. Large, M. I., Vaughan, A. E., and Mills, B. Y., *Nature*, **220**, 340 (1968).
2. Gold, T., *Nature*, **218**, 731 (1968).
3. Goldreich, P., *Proc. Ast. Soc. Austral.*, **1**, No. 5 (1969).
4. Batchelor, R. A., Brooks, J. W., and Cooper, B. F. C., *IEEE Trans. Antennas and Propagation*, **AP-16**, 228 (1968).
5. Radhakrishnan, V., Komesaroff, M. M., and Cooke, D. J., *Nature*, **218**, 229 (1968).
6. Large, M. I., Vaughan, A. E., and Wielebinski, R., *Nature*, **220**, 753 (1968).
7. Moffet, A. T., and Ekers, R. D., *Nature*, **218**, 227 (1968).
8. Milne, D. K., *Austral. J. Phys.*, **21**, 201 (1968).
9. Smith, F. G., *Nature*, **218**, 325 (1968).
10. Smith, F. G., *Nature*, **220**, 891 (1968).
11. Mills, B. Y., *Proc. Astro. Soc. Austral.*, **1**, No. 5 (1969).
12. Morris, D., and Berge, G. L., *Astrophys. J.*, **136**, 276 (1962).
13. Bigg, E. K., *Nature*, **203**, 1008 (1964).

Detection of Water in Interstellar Regions by Its Microwave Radiation

A. C. Cheung *et al.*

Editor's Note

As radio receivers became capable of observations at ever shorter wavelengths, new molecules were detected in space. A. C. Cheung and colleagues here report the discovery of radio emission from water in three regions in the sky. The brightness temperature of the emission from the Orion Nebula and the *W*49 region was surprisingly high, which puzzles the authors because the energetically excited state of the molecules they observed has a natural lifetime of just 10 seconds. The observations therefore implied that the water molecules were being constantly excited. It turns out that collisions with molecular hydrogen cause this excitation—but molecular hydrogen had not yet been discovered in space.

MICROWAVE emission from the $6_{16} \rightarrow 5_{23}$ rotational transition of H_2O has been observed from the directions of Sgr *B*2, the Orion Nebula and the *W*49 source. This radiation, at 1.35 cm wavelength, was detected with the twenty foot radio telescope at the Hat Creek Observatory using techniques described earlier for the detection of the NH_3 spectrum[1]. In the case of Sgr *B*2, the H_2O emission is from the same direction in which considerable NH_3 is observed (unpublished work of A. C. C. *et al.*), although there is reason to believe the two molecular species may not be closely associated. Strong H_2O radiation producing an antenna temperature of $14°K$ is observed from the Orion Nebula (where no NH_3 was detected), and an antenna temperature at least as high as $55°$ was found for H_2O radiation from *W*49.

Fig. 1 shows the spectral intensity near the H_2O resonance in the approximate direction of Sgr *B*2, the antenna being pointed at the position $\alpha_{1950} = 17$ h 44 m 23 s. $\delta_{1950} = -28°25'$. The observed antenna temperature is plotted as a function of Doppler velocity. The mean Doppler velocity of about 70 km s^{-1} for the spectral line observed is not very different from the 68 km s^{-1} mean velocity found for one of the OH emission and broad OH absorption features observed in this region[2], the 62 km s^{-1} Doppler velocify of a small nearly HII region[3], and the velocity of about 58 km s^{-1} found for NH_3 (unpublished work of A. C. C. *et al.*) observed in this direction. The results shown in Fig. 1 were obtained with filters producing a spectral resolution of about 1.3 MHz.

通过微波辐射探测到星际空间中存在水分子

Cheung 等

编者按

随着射电接收机能够观测的波长越来越短，星际空间中不断有新的分子被发现。在本文中，Cheung 及其同事在三个天区探测到了水的射电辐射。猎户座星云和 W49 辐射源的亮温度高得惊人，这使本文的作者们感到非常困惑，因为他们观测到的分子的能量激发态仅有 10 s 的自然寿命。因此，这些观测结果表明水分子是在不断地被激发。后来人们发现是氢分子的碰撞引发了这种激发过程——但当时人们还没有发现在星际空间中存在氢分子。

在人马座 B2、猎户座星云和 W49 源的方向上观测到了由水分子 $6_{16} \rightarrow 5_{23}$ 转动跃迁产生的微波辐射。这种波长为 1.35 cm 的射电辐射是在哈特克里克天文台用 20 英尺的射电望远镜观测到的，采用的技术与早先探测氨分子光谱的方法 [1] 相同。尽管有理由相信这两种分子之间并不存在密切的联系，但在人马座 B2 方向上，水分子的辐射和以前发现的大量氨分子的辐射（Cheung 等人尚未发表的研究结果）都来自同一个方向。从猎户座星云（在其中并未探测到氨分子）中观测到水分子强辐射产生的天线温度为 14 K；而从 W49 方向上观察到水分子辐射产生的天线温度至少可以达到 55 K。

图 1 展示出大致在人马座 B2 方向上水分子共振线附近的光谱强度。天线所指的位置是 $\alpha_{1950} = 17$ h 44 m 23 s，$\delta_{1950} = -28°25'$。图中给出了观测到的天线温度随多普勒速度变化的关系。被观测到的光谱线的平均多普勒速度约为 70 km/s，与在羟基发射线和在该区域宽广的羟基吸收特征中发现的平均多普勒速度 68 km/s[2]、在附近的一小块 HII 区（译者注：即电离氢区）内发现的多普勒速度 62 km/s[3] 以及在该方向上观测到的氨分子的多普勒速度 58 km/s（Cheung 等人尚未发表的研究结果）相比，并没有很大的差异。图 1 所示的结果是经过了能使光谱分辨率达到 1.3 MHz 左右的滤波器后得出的。

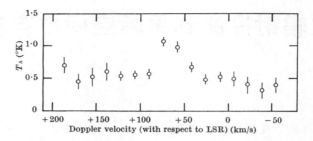

Fig. 1. Observed spectral intensity of $6_{16} \rightarrow 5_{23}$ H_2O rotational transition in the direction of Sgr $B2$ at $\alpha_{1950.0} =$ 17 h 44 m 23 s $\pm$ 6 s, $\delta_{1950.0} = 28°$ 24.9' $\pm$ 1'.

Fig. 2 shows the antenna temperature as a function of Doppler velocities observed in the Orion Nebula at $\alpha_{1950} = 5$ h 32 m 57 s $\pm$ 4 s and $\delta_{1950} = -5°$ 25.5'$\pm$1.0'. In Orion, the radiation intensity was sufficiently high to make practical the use of filters producing a spectral resolution of about 350 kHz. In Fig. 2 the solid line represents the continuum temperature as it was measured with filters of width 2 MHz; the plotted points represent observations made with the filters having bandwidths of 350 kHz. These points are, in some places, closer together than the filter widths of 350 kHz because measurements were made during different runs in which the central frequencies of the filters were displaced in order to examine the structure of the spectral line, which is composite, representing at least two distinct Doppler velocities. The mean Doppler velocity of about +7 km s^{-1} found for the water line is somewhat different from the HII Doppler shifts in the range of −2 to −6 km s^{-1} found in the same direction[3,4]. OH radiation from this direction shows Doppler velocities near 20 km s^{-1} and 7 km s^{-1} (ref. 2); the latter coincides more closely with the H_2O velocity.

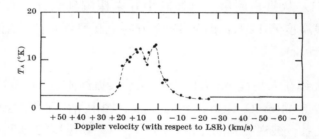

Fig. 2. Observed spectral intensity of $6_{16} \rightarrow 5_{23}$ H_2O rotational transition in the direction of the Orion Nebula. The position of peak emission is $\alpha_{1950.0} = 5$ h 32 m 57 s $\pm$ 4 s, $\delta_{1950.0} = -5°$ 25.5'$\pm$1.0'.

Fig. 3 shows similar data for the still more intense source $W49$, at $\alpha_{1950} = 19$ h 7 m 55 s$\pm$4 s and $\delta_{1950} = 9°$ 0.4'$\pm$1'. Over most of the spectral line, the narrow filters of width 350 kHz were used and several narrow and intense features were revealed. The measured antenna temperature was as high as 55° K, but allowance for atmospheric attenuation of this source, which was rather low in the sky during the observations, raises its effective antenna temperature to somewhat more than 70°. Presumably, narrower filters would give still higher antenna temperatures at some frequencies. The solid lines on either side of the diagram show the radiation intensity observed with filters about 2 MHz wide. Radiation present on the extreme right of Fig. 3 seems to be above the continuum level, showing that H_2O radiation also occurs

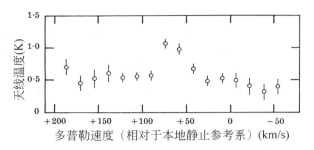

图 1. 在人马座 *B*2 方向（$\alpha_{1950.0}$ = 17 h 44 m 23 s±6 s，$\delta_{1950.0}$=−28° 24.9′±1′）上观测到的水分子 $6_{16} \to 5_{23}$ 转动跃迁的光谱强度。

图 2 展示出在猎户座星云方向（α_{1950} = 5 h 32 m 57 s±4 s，δ_{1950} = −5° 25.5′ ±1.0′）上观测到的天线温度随多普勒速度变化的关系曲线。在猎户星座，射电辐射的强度高到足以使用能使光谱分辨率达到约 350 kHz 的滤波器。在图 2 中，实线代表由带宽 2 MHz 的滤波器测得的连续谱温度；黑点则表示用带宽 350 kHz 的滤波器得到的观测值。黑点之间的距离在有些地方比滤波器的带宽 350 kHz 还小，这是因为为了探测光谱结构进行了多次测量，而在每次测量中滤波器的中心频率都会有所偏移的缘故。光谱结构表明它至少有两种不同的多普勒速度成分存在。从水分子谱线中观察到的平均多普勒速度约为 +7 km/s；它与在同一方向测得的 −2 km/s~−6 km/s 的 H II 区多普勒速度 [3,4] 有所不同。从这个方向上的羟基辐射测得的多普勒速度接近 20 km/s 和 7 km/s（参考文献 2）；后者更接近于水分子的多普勒速度。

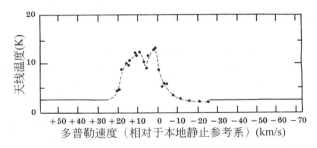

图 2. 在猎户座星云方向上观测到的水分子 $6_{16} \to 5_{23}$ 转动跃迁的光谱强度。辐射峰值的方位是 $\alpha_{1950.0}$ = 5 h 32 m 57 s±4 s，$\delta_{1950.0}$ = −5°25.5′±1.0′。

图 3 中展示的是更强的 *W*49 源的类似数据，观测方向是 α_{1950} =19 h 7 m 55 s±4 s，δ_{1950} = 9° 0.4′±1′。带宽为 350 kHz 的窄频带滤波器覆盖了谱线的大部分区域，揭示出一些很强的窄带特征。实际测出的天线温度为 55 K，但在补偿了该源的大气衰减（在观测时的夜空中非常低）之后，有效天线温度增加至稍稍大于 70 K。可以推测：在某些频率上，更窄的滤波器将给出更高的天线温度。位于这幅图两侧的实线所表示的是由带宽约为 2 MHz 的滤波器得到的辐射强度。图 3 中最右侧的辐射似乎高于连续谱，说明水分子的辐射也同样发生在宽频带滤波器的这一波段。在 *W*49 源中，羟

within the band of this last wide filter. The Doppler shift of OH in W49 ranges from -2 km s^{-1} to $+23$ km s^{-1} (ref. 2) and that of the HII region is $+6$ km s^{-1} (ref. 3). These are in the same general range, but by no means similar to the dominant values of Doppler shifts shown in Fig. 3.

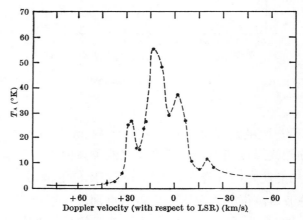

Fig. 3. Observed spectral intensity of H_2O transition in the direction of W49. The position of peak emission is $\alpha_{1950.0} = 19$ h 07 m 55 s$\pm$5 s, and $\delta_{1950.0} = +09°$ 0.4$'\pm$1$'$.

In all three figures, the continuum temperatures should be scaled down by a factor of two, because the heterodyne detection system received continuum radiation in both side bands.

The Orion and W49 sources were not large enough in angular size noticeably to broaden the beam width of 8.8$'$ in drift scans across the sources. Thus we conclude that these radiating sources are not larger in angular diameter than 3$'$.

The radiation found is attributed to H_2O because its frequency coincides very closely to that found for H_2O in the laboratory, and no other known atomic or molecular species can explain the observations. The Doppler shifts plotted in the figures represent small departures from the laboratory frequency of 22,235.22 MHz for H_2O, for which 10 km s^{-1} corresponds to a frequency shift of 0.75 MHz. No other simple molecular of atomic species which can be expected in interstellar space is known to produce a line within several tens of MHz of this frequency except NH_3, the (3,1) inversion transition of which lies at 22,234.53 MHz. This is a rather weak NH_3 transition, but it is still important to examine carefully the possibility that the observed radiation might be caused by NH_3. A search was therefore made for other stronger transitions of NH_3. The (3,3) transition is somewhat more than an order of magnitude stronger than this (3,1) transition at excitation temperatures above 50° K, while the (1,1) transition is similarly more intense at temperatures below 50° K. Even at excitation temperatures considerably above 50°K, the (1,1) transition is always more than twice as intense as the (3,1) transition. A search for these two NH_3 transitions in the Orion Nebula was made. They were not found, with the upper detection limit of antenna temperature being set at less than 0.07°K for both the (1,1) and the (3,3) inversion transition. This limit is almost two orders of magnitude less than the intensity of radiation found at about 22,235 MHz, and hence we

基的多普勒速度在 –2 km/s ~ +23 km/s 之间（参考文献 2）；而 HII 区的多普勒速度为 +6 km/s（参考文献 3）。这些数值处于相同的范围内，但与图 3 中所示的多普勒速度的显著值并不相符。

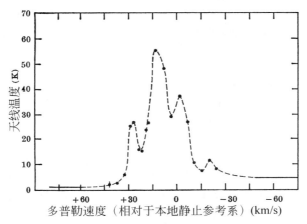

图 3. 在 W49 方向上观测到的水分子跃迁的光谱强度。辐射峰值的方位是 $\alpha_{1950.0} = 19$ h 07 m 55 s±5 s，$\delta_{1950.0} = 09° \; 0.4'±1'$。

因为外差式检波系统在波段的两侧都接受连续辐射，所以在这三幅图中，连续谱的温度都应下降为原来的一半。

由于猎户座星云和 W49 源的角直径不足够大，以致无法在对整个源的漂移扫描过程中将宽度为 8.8' 的光束显著加宽。因此我们可以下结论认为这两个辐射源的角直径都不大于 3'。

认为被发现的辐射与水分子有关是因为其频率与实验室中的水分子频率非常接近，并且用其他已知原子或分子都解释不了这些观测现象。对水分子来说，10 km/s 的速度对应于 0.75 MHz 的频移，所以这些图中显示的多普勒位移与水分子在实验室中的频率 22,235.22 MHz 有小小的偏差。除位于 22,234.53 MHz 的氨分子（3,1）反演跃迁以外，在星际空间中再也没有其他简单分子能产生与这个频率相差几十兆赫之内的谱线了。虽然氨的这种跃迁很微弱，但仔细检查观测到的辐射是否有可能来自于氨分子仍然很重要。因此需要搜索氨分子的其他一些较强的跃迁。当激发温度高于 50 K 时，（3,3）跃迁比（3,1）跃迁大致强一个量级以上；而在激发温度低于 50 K 时，（1,1）跃迁同样会更强。即使在激发温度远高于 50 K 时，（1,1）跃迁的发生概率也常常是(3,1)跃迁的两倍以上。我们在猎户座星云中搜索了氨的这两种跃迁。结果表明：直至天线温度的检测上限被设在小于 0.07 K 时，（1,1）和（3,3）反演跃迁都始终没有被探测到。这种限制条件比在 22,235 MHz 附近发现的辐射强度低大约两个量级，因此我们可以断定：我们已观测到的辐射并非由氨的（3,1）跃迁所引起，

conclude that the radiation we have observed cannot be caused by the (3,1) transition of NH_3, and can be explained only by H_2O.

In the case of Sgr $B2$, the situation is more complex. Rather strong NH_3 radiation was, in fact, observed from the same (or nearly the same) direction as the H_2O radiation. The (1,1), (2,2), (3,3) and (4,4) inversion transitions of NH_3 were all found with antenna temperatures between 0.5° K and 1.5° K (unpublished work of A. C. C. *et al.*). The possibility that the line observed at 22,235 MHz is caused by NH_3 may be ruled out by the following argument, however. The NH_3 rotational states (1,1), (2,2), (3,3) and (4,4) can be excited by collision, but are metastable, with exceedingly long radiation lifetimes. The (3,1) state can radiate in the infrared, however, by making a transition to the (2,1) state. The mean radiation lifetime of the upper state is about 50 s; thus unless the state is excited in a comparable time, it should be very much less populated than any of the states which were observed. The (4,3) state also radiates with a lifetime comparable with that of the (3,1) state. Thus a search was made for (4,3) level inversion radiation to find out whether or not some excitation mechanism was producing a significant population in the (4,3) level and, by inference, also producing an appreciable number of NH_3 molecules in the (3,1) state. The (4,3) inversion radiation was not observed, the limit of detection being an antenna temperature of 0.07° K. The (4,3) transition searched for is about an order of magnitude more intense than the (3,1) transition. If the observed antenna temperature of 1° K in Sgr $B2$ at 22,235 MHz were caused by the (3,1) transition, the (4,3) transition would have an antenna temperature of 10° K. No such temperature is observed, so we conclude that the observed radiation at 22,235 MHz must be caused by H_2O rather than this weak NH_3 transition.

In the case of $W49$, a search was made for the NH_3 (1,1) inversion transition. It was not found, and an upper limit of 0.5° could be established for the antenna temperature at its frequency.

There is, of course, H_2O in the Earth's atmosphere. One might wonder if it could produce the observed radiation. It can be eliminated as a possible source for several reasons. One is that the antenna beam is switched from one part of the sky to a neighbouring part, so that only radiation which varies very rapidly with angle is detected. A second reason is that the microwave resonant line was detected in the three particular fixed directions in space, and not nearby. Still a third is that an atmospheric water line would have occurred at the laboratory frequency, which corresponds to a Doppler shift of +15 km s^{-1} in Fig. 1 and −30 km s^{-1} in Fig. 2.

It has previously been suggested that the $6_{16} \rightarrow 5_{23}$ transition of H_2O could be of interest to radio astronomy[5], and recently a substantial proposal for its detection has been made by Snyder and Buhl at the AAS meeting, Dallas, December 1968. But it is surprising that the transition is as strong as observed, because it involves levels of rotational energy of 456 cm^{-1} which can radiate to lower states in about 10 s. They require moderately high temperatures and frequent excitations, either by collisions or by radiation. Rotational states of NH_3 which can similarly radiate have not been found, indicating that the NH_3 and H_2O have been detected in rather

它只能用水分子的存在来解释。

人马座 $B2$ 的情况要复杂得多。事实上，在观测到水分子辐射的同一方向（或接近这一方向）上也发现了很强的氨分子辐射。在天线温度介于 0.5 K ~ 1.5 K 之间时，氨的四种反演跃迁（1,1）、（2,2）、（3,3）和（4,4）都被探测到了（Cheung 等人尚未发表的研究结果）。然而，根据下述讨论也许可以排除在 22,235 MHz 观测到的谱线来源于氨分子的可能性。氨分子的转动态（1,1）、（2,2）、（3,3）和（4,4）会因为碰撞而激发，但它们在很长的辐射寿命之内是处于亚稳态的。氨分子可以从（3,1）态跃迁到（2,1）态并发出红外波段的辐射。其中高能态的平均辐射寿命约为 50 s。因此，除非该能态在 50 s 左右的时间内被激发，否则处于该能态的粒子数量会比处于观测到的任何其他能态的粒子数量少很多。（4,3）态的辐射寿命也与（3,1）态近似。因此有人对（4,3）能级的反演跃迁辐射进行了探测，力图判断是否存在某种可以产生大量（4,3）能级粒子的激发机制，并且还可以推知由这种机制同样会产生可观数量的（3,1）态氨分子。当天线温度的探测极限为 0.07 K 时，（4,3）态下的反演跃迁辐射并没有被观测到。所搜寻的（4,3）跃迁比（3,1）跃迁强大约一个数量级。如果在人马座 $B2$ 方向上 22,235 MHz 处观测到的 1 K 天线温度是由（3,1）跃迁造成的，那么从（4,3）跃迁得到的天线温度将达到 10 K。鉴于人们从未观测到过如此高的温度，所以我们可以得出结论：在 22,235 MHz 处观测到的辐射一定来自于水分子，而不可能来自微弱的氨分子跃迁。

人们在 $W49$ 方向上对氨分子（1,1）的反演跃迁进行了搜索。但当在该频率处将天线温度的上限设定为 0.5 K 时，仍没有探测到这种跃迁。

当然，水分子在地球的大气中确实存在。有人怀疑可能是地球大气中的水分子产生了观测到的辐射。以下几条理由可以排除这种来源的可能性。原因一，因为天线射束从天空中的一个区域转向另一个邻近区域，所以只有随角度不同而迅速发生变化的辐射才会被探测到。原因二，微波共振线是在太空中的三个固定方向上探测到的，在这三个特殊方向附近并没有发现。原因三，大气中水分子谱线的出现位置应与实验室中水分子的频率相同，对应于图 1 中多普勒速度 +15 km/s 处和图 2 中多普勒速度 –30 km/s 处。

之前曾有人提出水分子的 $6_{16} \rightarrow 5_{23}$ 跃迁在射电天文学方面很有研究价值 [5]，最近在 1968 年 12 月于达拉斯举行的美国科学院会议上，斯奈德和布尔提出了一个与这项探测相关的实质性计划。观测到的跃迁出人意料地强，因为它涉及位于 456 cm^{-1} 处的转动能级，在大约 10 s 内即可实现向较低能级的跃迁并发出辐射。它们需要被较高的温度和频率所激发，通过碰撞或者辐射的方式。未曾探测到可发出类似辐射的氨分子转动态，这表明氨分子和水分子是在完全不同的区域内被检测到

different regions. Presumably the H_2O is present in rather special regions of higher than normal excitation. The matrix element for this H_2O line is appreciably less than that for the NH_3 inversion levels. Thus if there is thermal equilibrium between the 6_{16} and 5_{23} states, the population in these two levels, rather high above the ground state, must have a column density greater than that found for NH_3 (ref. 1), or about 10^{17} cm^{-2} in the Sgr $B2$ cloud.

In Orion, the actual microwave brightness temperature of the source would have to be at least as high as a few hundred degrees, and in $W49$ at least as great as about one thousand degrees. The actual temperatures may be much higher if these sources are smaller than the upper limit of $3'$ of arc given, or if they are optically thin. The high intensity, very narrow, lines suggest that perhaps thermal equilibrium does not occur and that there may even be maser action. Further study of the distribution and condition of H_2O in interstellar space is clearly needed. If thermal equilibrium does in fact apply, this intense microwave radiation from H_2O and the existence of strong HDO transitions in the radio region should allow an interesting measurement of the hydrogen–deuterium abundance ratio.

We thank Professor Harold Weaver for giving us his positions of OH clouds in the Sagittarius region and for discussions, and Paul Rhodes for his help with the observations. This work is supported in part by NASA, the US Office of Naval Research and the US National Science Foundation.

(**221**, 626-628; 1969)

A. C. Cheung, D. M. Rank and C. H. Townes: Department of Physics, University of California, Berkeley.

D. D. Thornton and W. J. Welch: Radio Astronomy Laboratory and Department of Electrical Engineering, University of California, Berkeley.

Received January 13, 1969.

References:

1. Cheung, A. C., Rank, D. M., Townes, C. H., Thornton, D. D., and Welch, W. J., *Phys. Rev. Lett.*, **21**, 1701 (1968).

2. Weaver, H. F., Dieter, N. H., and Williams, D. R. W., *Ap. J. Suppl.*, **16**, 219 (1968).

3. Mezger, P. G., and Höglund, B., *Ap. J.*, **147**, 490 (1967).

4. Gordon, M. A., and Meeks, M. L., *Ap. J.*, **152**, 417 (1968).

5. Townes, C. H., in *Fourth IAU Symp., Manchester, 1955* (edit. by van de Hulst, H. C.) (Cambridge Univ. Press, 1957).

的。据推测，水分子存在于高于正常激发的特殊区域。导致出现水谱线的分子显然要少于对应氨反演能级的分子。因此，如果在 6_{16} 态和 5_{23} 态之间可以达到热平衡，那么在这两个比基态能量高很多的能态上的粒子数柱密度一定会高于氨分子的密度（参考文献 1），或者说在人马座 $B2$ 云中约为 10^{17} cm^{-2}。

在猎户座星云中，源的实际微波亮温度至少可以达到几百度；而在 $W49$ 中至少可以达到 1,000 度左右。如果这两个源的角直径比所给的上限 3′ 小，或者当它们为光学薄时，实际温度可能还会高出很多。这种强度很高并且宽度极窄的谱线说明可能没有达到热平衡，甚至还可能发生脉泽。进一步研究星际空间中水分子的分布和状态显然是有必要的。如果确实达到了热平衡，那么根据水分子的强微波辐射和存在于射电波段的强氘化水（HDO）跃迁就可以使我们进行一次关于氢 – 氘丰度比的有趣测量。

在此感谢哈罗德·韦弗教授为我们提供了人马座天区羟基云的具体位置并和我们进行讨论，还要感谢保罗·罗德为我们提供了观测上的帮助。美国国家航空航天局、美国海军研究办公室和美国国家科学基金会为这项工作提供了一定的支持。

（冯翀 翻译；沈志侠 审稿）

Early Stages of Fertilization *in vitro* of Human Oocytes Matured *in vitro*

R. G. Edwards *et al.*

Editor's Note

Robert Edwards worked at the University of Cambridge for most of his career. His goal was to develop means of producing human embryos by *in vitro* fertilization in cases where the union of sperm and ovum is difficult or impossible within the female body. Artificial fertilization is now widely practised throughout the world, and stems uniquely from Edwards' pioneering work with surgeon Patrick Steptoe. Here Edwards and his student Barry Bavister, working with Steptoe, report the first evidence of fertilization of a human egg *in vitro*.

THE technique of maturing human oocytes *in vitro* after their removal from follicles provides many eggs for studies on fertilization[1]. Their fertilization *in vitro* would yield a supply of embryos for research or clinical use, but in previous attempts the incidence of fertilization was too low to be useful[2].

A possible solution to the problem of obtaining "capacitated" spermatozoa has recently emerged from experiments on hamster eggs, where the addition of epididymal spermatozoa to eggs in tubal[3] or follicular[4] secretions can lead to a high incidence of fertilization. Study of the conditions leading to capacitation of hamster spermatozoa and fertilization *in vitro*[5] has led to the use of a medium based on Tyrode's solution, but with extra bicarbonate (final concentration 3 mg/ml.); also added were sodium pyruvate (9.0 µg/ml.), bovine serum albumin (2.5 mg/ml.), phenol red (20 µg/ml.) and penicillin (100 IU/ml.)[5] . After equilibration with 5 percent CO_2 in air, the pH of this medium was 7.6. Bicarbonate has been shown to stimulate the respiration and motility of rabbit spermatozoa *in vivo* and *in vitro*[6].

We have adapted the conditions found successful in the hamster for work on the human oocyte. The preliminary results reported in this article indicate that human eggs can be fertilized in conditions similar to those found most suitable for the fertilization of hamster eggs *in vitro*.

Maturation of Eggs and Insemination

Oocytes were released from Graafian and smaller follicles into a medium composed of equal amounts of Hank's solution containing heparin, and medium 199 (Microbiological Associates, Inc.) supplemented with 15 percent foetal calf serum (Microbiological Associates, Inc.) and buffered (pH 7.2) with phosphate buffer. Penicillin (100 IU/ml.) was added to these media. Some oocytes were transported from Oldham to Cambridge (a journey taking about 4 h), in medium 199 supplemented with 15 percent foetal calf serum.

体外成熟后的人类卵母细胞体外受精的早期阶段

爱德华兹等

编者按

罗伯特·爱德华兹的绝大部分职业生涯是在剑桥大学度过的。他的目标是为那些难以或不能在自身体内实现精子和卵子结合的女性患者找到通过体外受精产生人类胚胎的途径。目前，人工授精技术已经在全世界得到了广泛的应用，这类技术毫无例外地来源于爱德华兹和外科医生斯特普托的开创性研究。在本文中，爱德华兹和他的学生巴里·巴维斯特与斯特普托合作，第一次报道了可证明人类卵子能在体外受精的证据。

可使从卵泡中分离出来的人类卵母细胞在体外发育成熟的技术为受精研究提供了大量的卵子 [1]。它们的体外受精将会为研究或临床应用提供胚胎，但是在先前的实验中卵子的受精率非常低以至无法使用 [2]。

最近在对仓鼠卵子进行实验时发现，将仓鼠附睾的精子添加到输卵管 [3] 或卵泡 [4] 的分泌液中可使其中的卵子达到很高的受精率，这为解决如何获得"获能"精子这一难题提供了一种可能的解决途径。在研究使仓鼠精子在体外条件下获能并受精的条件时发现 [5]，应使用一种基于台罗德溶液的培养基，不过还需在培养基中另外添加碳酸氢盐（终浓度为 3 mg/ml）以及丙酮酸钠（9.0 μg/ml）、牛血清白蛋白（2.5 mg/ml）、酚红（20 μg/ml）和青霉素（100 IU/ml）[5]。用含 5% CO_2 的空气平衡后，这种培养基的 pH 值为 7.6。体内和体外的研究结果都表明，碳酸氢盐能够刺激兔精子的呼吸作用和运动能力 [6]。

我们已经把这种在仓鼠身上实验成功的条件应用到人类卵母细胞上。由本文中报道的初步结果可知，人的卵子在类似于最适合仓鼠卵子体外受精的条件下也可以成功受精。

卵子的成熟和人工授精

将卵母细胞从格拉夫卵泡和小卵泡中分离，并放入含有等量的以下两种成分的培养基中：含肝素的汉克氏溶液和加入 15% 胎牛血清（微生物联合有限公司）并用磷酸缓冲溶液缓冲（pH 值为 7.2）的 M199 培养基（微生物联合有限公司）。将青霉素（100 IU/ml）加入到上述培养基中。有些卵母细胞是从奥尔德姆运送到剑桥的（路上大约需要 4 h），运送过程中卵母细胞一直被保存在添加了 15% 胎牛血清的 M199 培养基中。

The oocytes were cultured soon after liberation from their follicles, or after transport to Cambridge, in follicular fluid obtained from the same or different ovaries. Where follicular fluid was in short supply it was supplemented by Hank's, Brinster's[7] or Bavister's[5] medium. Oocytes were cultured under a gas phase of 5 percent CO_2 in air, in droplets of medium under liquid paraffin previously equilibrated with medium 199 containing 15 percent foetal calf serum, and with the same gas mixture. After 38 h in culture many of the oocytes had extruded their first polar body and reached metaphase of the second meiotic division (metaphase-II).

Ejaculated spermatozoa were washed once with Bavister's medium to remove seminal plasma, and were then re-suspended at a concentration of 10^6/ml. in more of the same medium. Human follicular fluid was added to some samples of spermatozoa before they were added to the oocytes. Oocytes were washed through one or two droplets of Bavister's medium and then pipetted into the sperm suspension. At different intervals after insemination, living eggs were examined by phase contrast microscopy, and then fixed in acetic-saline (20 percent acetic acid in normal saline solution) or acetic-alcohol (1:3), stained with aceto-orcein, and re-examined. In one-celled eggs, the occurrence of penetration was inferred from the presence of spermatozoa in the zona pellucida or in the perivitelline space; the presence in the vitellus of pronuclei, with mid-pieces or tails of spermatozoa, and the extrusion of the second polar body, were regarded as evidence of fertilization.

Fertilization

Fifty-six human eggs were inseminated. When examined for evidence of fertilization, twenty of them were found still to be in dictyotene, having failed to mature *in vitro*. In one of these eggs, a spermatozoon was seen in the perivitelline space. Two other eggs were degenerate.

The remaining thirty-four eggs had matured *in vitro*, as judged by the presence of chromosomes or polar bodies. Many of these eggs were so heavily coated with spermatozoa attached to the zona pellucida that it was difficult to discern internal details. Sixteen of them were in metaphase-II, and showed no evidence of penetration.

In eleven eggs spermatozoa had begun to move through the zona pellucida. One or more spermatozoa were deeply embedded in the zona pellucida in six eggs (Fig. 1). When fixed and stained, each of these eggs was found to be at metaphase-II. Spermatozoa were seen in the perivitelline space of the other five eggs (Fig. 2), and in four of them the spermatozoa were motile. When fixed and stained, four of these eggs were seen to be in metaphase-II, and one had a small nucleus.

在将卵母细胞从卵泡中分离出来后，或者在将其置于从相同或不同卵巢中获取的卵泡液中并运送到剑桥后，即对其进行培养。如果卵泡液短缺，可以补充汉克氏溶液、布林斯特[7]培养基或巴维斯特[5]培养基。将培养基微滴中的卵母细胞培养于含 5% CO_2 的混合空气中，微滴表面覆盖着液体石蜡并且之前曾用相同空气条件、含 15% 胎牛血清的 M199 培养基平衡过。培养 38 h 后，许多卵母细胞已排出第一极体，并且进入第二次减数分裂的中期（中期 –II）。

将射出的精子用巴维斯特培养基洗涤一次以除去精浆，然后用更多的巴维斯特培养基重悬精子，使其浓度达到 10^6/ml。在将一些精子样品加入到卵母细胞中之前，要先向这些精子样品中加入人的卵泡液。用 1~2 滴巴维斯特培养基洗涤卵母细胞，再用微管将其吸取到精子悬液中。在人工授精后的不同时间点用相差显微镜观察存活的卵子，然后将其在醋酸 – 生理盐水（含 20% 醋酸的生理盐水）或醋酸 – 酒精混合液（1∶3）中固定，经醋酸地衣红染色后重新观察。对于单细胞期的卵子，有无发生穿卵可以通过观察在透明带或卵周隙中是否存在精子来判断。在原核卵黄处存在可观察到中部或者尾部的精子以及第二极体的排出都被认为是受精发生的证据。

受　　精

采取人工授精处理的共有 56 枚人类卵子。我们在检测受精是否发生时发现：有 20 枚卵子仍处在核网期，它们未能完成体外成熟。我们在其中 1 枚卵子的卵周隙中观察到了 1 个精子。另外还有 2 枚卵子发生了退化。

其余 34 枚卵子均出现了染色体或者极体，可以据此认为它们已完成体外成熟。这些卵子大多被附着在透明带上的精子紧紧包裹，以至于很难分辨其内部结构。其中有 16 枚卵子处在中期 –II 阶段，而且没有出现精子穿卵的迹象。

在 11 枚卵子中，精子已经开始穿过透明带。一个或多个精子深深地植入到其中 6 枚卵子的透明带中（图 1）。对其进行固定和染色后发现：这 6 枚卵子都处在中期 –II 阶段。我们在另外 5 枚卵子的卵周隙中发现了精子（图 2），而且其中 4 枚卵子中的精子仍能移动。在对这 5 枚卵子进行固定和染色后发现：其中 4 枚卵子正处于中期 –II 阶段，另外 1 枚卵子有一个小细胞核。

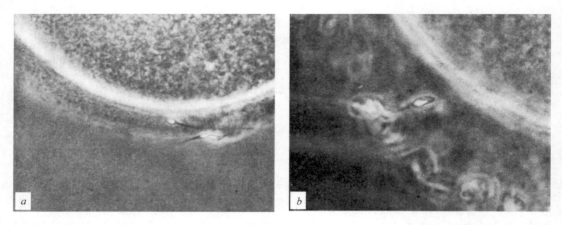

Fig. 1. Spermatozoa lying in the zona pellucida of living human eggs 24 h after insemination. (*a*, × 675; *b*, ×1,200.)

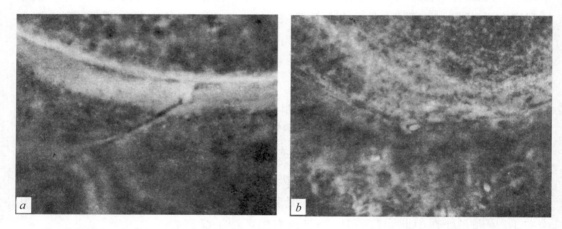

Fig. 2. Spermatozoa in the perivitelline space of human eggs. In *a*, the sperm head is lying in the vitellus, the mid-piece is still embedded in the zona pellucida, and the main piece lies outside the zona. This egg was examined 13 h after insemination; the spermatozoon was still active. (× 1,650.) In *b*, the whole of the spermatozoon was in the perivitelline space, although only the sperm head can be seen in the illustration. This spermatozoon was still active. (× 750.)

Seven eggs had well formed pronuclei. Two of them possessed two pronuclei each (Fig. 3), four had three pronuclei and one had five. Spermatozoa were seen in the zona pellucida or perivitelline space of three of these eggs.

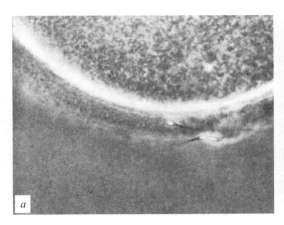 

图 1. 人工授精 24 h 后处于存活人卵透明带中的精子。（*a*，放大 675 倍；*b*，放大 1,200 倍）

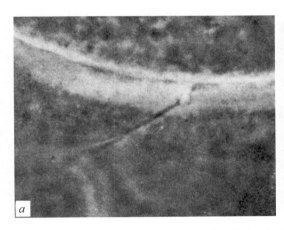 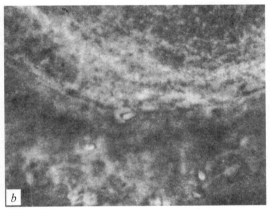

图 2. 处于人卵卵周隙中的精子。*a*，精子的头部位于卵黄中，中部仍嵌在透明带里，而主要部分则在透明带之外。这是在人工授精 13 h 后观察到的卵子的情况；其中的精子仍可移动（放大 1,650 倍）。*b*，整个精子都位于卵周隙中，不过我们只能在图里看到精子的头部。这个精子仍能移动（放大 750 倍）。

　　有 7 枚卵子已经很好地形成了原核。其中 2 枚卵子各有 2 个原核（图 3），4 枚卵子各有 3 个原核，另外 1 枚卵子有 5 个原核。其中 3 枚卵子的透明带或卵周隙中有精子存在。

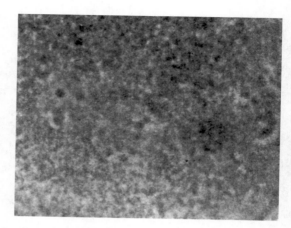

Fig. 3. Two pronuclei in a living human egg examined 22 h after insemination. Polar bodies were seen in this egg, but a sperm mid-piece could not be unequivocally identified. (× c. 675.)

These observations are related to the time after insemination in Table 1. Penetration of spermatozoa into the perivitelline space was first seen in eggs examined 7–7.25 h after insemination, and pronuclei at 11.5 h. Spermatozoa were found in the zona pellucida or perivitelline space of eggs in metaphase–II as late as 27 h after insemination. Many of these spermatozoa were immotile, and it is doubtful whether they would have penetrated further.

Table 1. Details of Human Oocytes Examined at Various Intervals after Insemination *in vitro*

Time after insemination (h)	1. Failed to mature *in vitro*		2. Matured *in vitro*			
	Germinal vesicle	Vacuolated or degenerate	Unpenetrated	Spermatozoa in zona pellucida	Spermatozoa in perivitelline space	Pronucleate
6–6.5	1		3			
7–7.5	1				3	
8–9	1	1	2	1	1†	
9.5–10.75	3		3			
11.5	5		1	1		1
12.5–13.5	6*				1	1
22–31	3	1	7	4		5
	20	2	16	6	5	7

* In one of these eggs, a spermatozoon was present in the perivitelline space.
† This egg may have been in metaphase of the first meiotic division.

Mid-pieces and tails of spermatozoa were not seen with certainty in any of the living eggs, but after fixation structures of a size similar to mid-pieces (as illustrated by other workers[8]) were recognizable in three eggs (Fig. 4). In two eggs, each with two pronuclei, the first and second polar bodies could be identified. In one of these eggs, the two pronuclei were lying close to each other (Fig. 3); on staining, a mass of coarser chromatin was observed in one pronucleus in

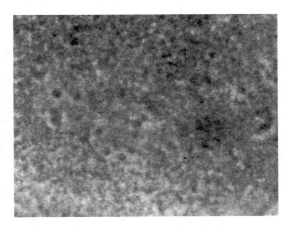

图 3. 人工授精 22 h 后在一存活人卵中观察到的 2 个原核。在这个卵子中可以看到极体，但不能明确地
分辨出精子的中部（放大约 675 倍）。

上述观察结果与人工授精后所经过的时间之间的关系示于表 1。最早发现精子穿过卵周隙的时间是在人工授精 7 h ～ 7.25 h 之后，而看到原核则是在 11.5 h 之后。人工授精 27 h 后可在处于中期 –II 阶段卵子的透明带或卵周隙中发现精子。这些精子中有不少已不能移动，我们很怀疑它们是否还会进一步穿卵。

表 1. 体外人工授精后在不同时间点观察到的人类卵母细胞的详细结果

人工授精后经过的时间（h）	1. 未能完成体外成熟的卵子		2. 完成体外成熟的卵子			
	生发泡	空泡化或退化	未穿卵	在透明带中的精子	在卵周隙中的精子	形成原核
6 ～ 6.5	1		3			
7 ～ 7.5	1				3	
8 ～ 9	1	1	2	1	1†	
9.5 ～ 10.75	3		3			
11.5	5		1	1		1
12.5 ～ 13.5	6*				1	1
22 ～ 31	3	1	7	4		5
	20	2	16	6	5	7

* 在其中 1 枚卵子的卵周隙中发现了 1 个精子。
† 该卵子可能已处于第一次减数分裂的中期。

在任何存活的卵子中都没有明确观察到精子的中部和尾部，但是经过固定后，我们在 3 枚卵子（图 4）中发现了大小类似于精子中部的结构（正如其他研究者所描述过的那样 [8]）。在 2 枚各有 2 个原核的卵子中可以分辨出第一极体和第二极体。在其中 1 枚卵子中，两个原核还相互靠得很近（图 3）；染色后，在两个原核相互靠

a region where the two pronuclei were apposed.

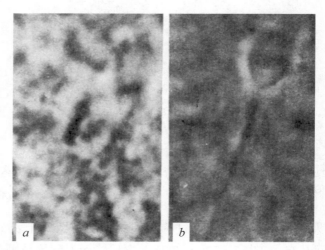

Fig. 4. In *a*, a small body resembling a sperm mid-piece was found in a stained egg which contained three pronuclei and at least one polar body. (× 3,300.) In *b*, a spermatozoon present in the perivitelline space of another egg has been photographed in a position illustrating the size of the mid-piece, for comparison with *a*. (× 3,300.)

As controls, seventeen eggs were cultured without the addition of spermatozoa. Eight of them failed to mature and displayed germinal vesicles. Of the remainder, one had a small mass of chromatin instead of metaphase chromosomes, seven had metaphase chromosomes, and in one the contents were obscured by overlying cumulus cells. Pronuclei were not seen in any of these eggs.

Of the seventy-three inseminated and control eggs, thirty-one failed to mature or degenerated. Thirteen of these failures occurred in one set of experiments involving a total of fifteen eggs. If this group of eggs is excluded, about 70 percent of the oocytes matured in culture. After insemination, eighteen of the thirty-four oocytes that had matured *in vitro* had spermatozoa in the zona pellucida, spermatozoa in the perivitelline space, or pronuclei. Judged on the criteria of fertilization given, it is highly probable that most of these eighteen eggs were undergoing fertilization.

Capacitation and Embryonic Development

The possible function of follicular fluid in the capacitation of spermatozoa and the fertilization of human eggs *in vitro* requires further examination. All eggs in the present series were matured in follicular fluid obtained from the same or a different ovary, and then washed in order to reduce any deleterious effect of follicular fluid on spermatozoa. We have found that spermatozoa of some animal species can be immobilized or agglutinated by follicular fluid, and heat treatment of the fluid does not necessarily abolish these effects. In some of the present experiments, however, we pre-incubated spermatozoa in follicular fluid before adding them to

近的区域中可以看到一个原核内有大量较粗大的染色质块。

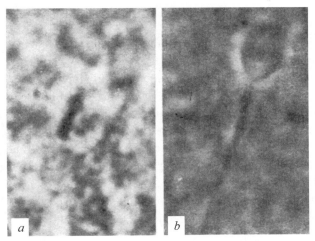

图 4. *a*，在 1 枚染色卵子中发现的 1 个类似于精子中部的小体，这枚被染色的卵子含有 3 个原核和至少
1 个极体（放大 3,300 倍）。*b*，为了与图 *a* 进行比较，我们在能说明精子中部尺寸的位置上拍摄了
位于另外 1 枚卵子卵周隙中的 1 个精子（放大 3,300 倍）。

作为对照，我们在没有加入精子的条件下培养了 17 枚卵子。其中 8 枚卵子未能
完成体外成熟，还呈生发泡样形态。在其余的卵子中，1 枚出现了一小团染色质而
非中期染色体，7 枚出现了中期染色体，另外 1 枚由于卵丘细胞覆盖于其上而无法
看清内部结构。在所有这些作为对照的卵子中都没有发现原核。

在 73 枚人工授精的和作为对照的卵子中，有 31 枚未能完成体外成熟或发生了
退化。其中 13 例失败发生在一组总共包括 15 枚卵子的实验中。如果将这组卵子排除，
则约有 70% 的卵母细胞能在体外培养时成熟。人工授精后，在 34 个完成体外成熟
的卵母细胞中有 18 个被发现在透明带、卵周隙里存在精子，或出现了原核。根据前
面给出的受精判断标准，这 18 枚卵子中的大多数很可能正在经历受精过程。

精子获能和胚胎发育

卵泡液在精子获能和人卵体外受精过程中可能发挥的作用还有待于进一步研究。
目前系列实验中所用的卵子都是在来自相同或不同卵巢的卵泡液中发育成熟的，随
后进行洗涤以减少卵泡液对精子的有害作用。我们曾发现卵泡液会使某些动物的精
子不能移动或者发生凝集，而对卵泡液进行加热处理不一定能起到消除这种有害效
应的作用。但是，在现在的一些实验中，我们是用卵泡液预孵育精子然后将其加入

the eggs. Our impression is that this pre-incubation led to the attachment of more spermatozoa to the zona pellucida, and to a higher incidence of penetrated and pronucleate eggs.

The failure of spermatozoa to pass completely through the zona pellucida or into the vitellus may reflect the existence of different layers in the zona with different requirements for penetration, or it may signify that the final movement of spermatozoa through the zona pellucida depends to a large extent on sperm/egg association. Complete penetration might be achieved by conferring greater activity on spermatozoa; mouse eggs can be fertilized *in vitro* by uterine spermatozoa[9] in a medium richer in pyruvate and albumin[10] than our media. Delayed fertilization may well have occurred in the conditions of our culture, and led to anomalies in the eggs. Thus the egg with a spermatozoon in the perivitelline space, polar bodies and a single small nucleus might have been activated parthenogenetically. The presence of several pronuclei in some eggs may have arisen through polyspermy, but is more probably due to the abnormal movement of chromosomes along the spindle or to fragmentation of the female pronucleus; multipronucleate eggs are common after delayed fertilization *in vivo* of eggs of various mammalian species[11].

Problems of embryonic development are likely to accompany the use of human oocytes matured and fertilized *in vitro*. When oocytes of the rabbit and other species were matured *in vitro* and fertilized *in vivo*, the pronuclear stages appeared normal but many of the resulting embryos had sub-nuclei in their blastomeres, and almost all of them died during the early cleavage stages (ref. 12 and unpublished work of R. G. E.). Abnormal development might have been the result of incomplete RNA synthesis when oocytes are removed from follicles for maturation *in vitro*; small amounts of RNA are synthesized by *Xenopus* oocytes in response to luteinizing hormone (LH) during the final period of maturation[13]. When maturation of rabbit oocytes was started *in vivo* by injecting gonadotrophins into the mother, and completed in the oviduct or *in vitro*, full term rabbit foetuses were obtained (ref. 12 and unpublished work of R. G. E.). Another developmental problem could be that some oocytes blocked during maturation at anaphase of the first meiotic division[1,14] could yield polyploid or heteroploid embryos at fertilization. Fortunately human oocytes in the present and earlier[1] work were rarely blocked at this stage.

Clinical Use of Human Embryos

These potential difficulties with human embryos may be solved when the conditions necessary for maturation *in vitro* are better understood, or, as in rabbits, by initiating maturation *in vivo* by administering gonadotrophins or clomiphene to the mother. When women were injected with gonadotrophins, maturing oocytes were recovered from excised pieces of ovary[15]. The timing of the stages of oocyte maturation in this work[15] was very similar to that exhibited by oocytes matured *in vitro*[1], and should indicate the appropriate moment to remove oocytes in preparation for fertilization *in vitro*.

Fertilized human eggs could be useful in treating some forms of infertility, and many infertile patients will probably be older women. If the "production line" of eggs in the ovary, inferred

到卵子中去的。我们感觉这种预孵育处理能使更多的精子黏附到卵子的透明带上，从而提高了穿卵和卵子原核形成的几率。

精子不能完全穿过透明带或到达卵黄也许意味着透明带中存在着不同的层，每一层都对精子穿卵有不同的要求，也可能意味着精子穿过透明带的最后过程在很大程度上取决于精子/卵子的相关性。通过使精子达到更高的活性或许可以实现完全穿卵；在比我们的培养基更富含丙酮酸盐和白蛋白的培养基 [10] 中，用从子宫内冲取的精子 [9] 能使小鼠卵子在体外完成受精。另外，在我们的培养条件下也很可能发生了延迟受精，从而使卵子出现异常。这样，那些已有一个精子进入卵周隙、出现极体以及单个的小细胞核的卵子可能已经被以孤雌生殖方式激活。某些卵子中存在好几个原核的原因可能与多精入卵有关，但可能性更大的原因是染色体沿着纺锤体的不规则移动，或者是源自雌性原核的碎片化；许多哺乳动物的卵子在体内发生延迟受精之后通常会出现多原核卵子 [11]。

胚胎发育中出现的问题很可能与实验时使用了在体外成熟并受精的人类卵母细胞有关。当兔子和其他动物的卵母细胞在体外成熟而在体内受精时，它们看起来都能正常地发育到原核阶段，但是许多由此得到的胚胎在形成卵裂球时出现了亚核，并且几乎所有这样的胚胎在分裂早期就会死亡（参考文献 12 和爱德华兹尚未发表的研究结果）。胚胎发育异常或许是因为当把将要在体外培养成熟的卵母细胞从卵泡中取出时，RNA 的合成还没有全部完成；处于成熟最后阶段的爪蟾卵母细胞会在促黄体生成激素（LH）的作用下合成一小部分 RNA[13]。如果我们通过给雌兔注射促性腺激素来促发兔卵母细胞在体内的成熟过程，那么不管后续的成熟过程是在输卵管中完成还是在体外完成，都能够得到足月的胎兔（参考文献 12 和爱德华兹尚未发表的研究结果）。胚胎发育中的另一个问题是：一些在成熟过程中受阻于第一次减数分裂后期的卵母细胞 [1,14] 可能在受精时会形成多倍体或异倍体胚胎。幸运的是，人类卵母细胞在目前和早先 [1] 的研究工作中极少在这个阶段发生阻滞。

人类胚胎的临床应用

如果我们能对卵母细胞体外成熟所需的条件了解得更为透彻，那么在人类胚胎发育过程中可能出现的困难或许就会迎刃而解。或者像在兔子中的情形一样，采用给供卵雌兔注射促性腺激素或克罗米酚从而在体内促发卵母细胞成熟的方法来解决上述问题。给妇女注射促性腺激素后，从卵巢被切除部分中可以分离出正在成熟的卵母细胞 [15]。这样得到的卵母细胞在成熟过程的时间进度上 [15] 非常类似于体外成熟的卵母细胞 [1]，这使我们可以推算出何时取出卵母细胞才能适合于对其进行体外受精。

受精的人类卵子或许能有助于治疗某些不孕症，而且许多不孕患者可能会是年龄较大的妇女。如果从研究小鼠卵母细胞 [16] 中推断出来的卵巢内卵子的"生产线"

from studies on mouse oocytes[16], also occurs in humans, the eggs of older women will have more anomalies of bivalent association than those of younger women. A higher incidence of trisomic and polysomic embryos, and hence of mongols and abortions, would thus be expected in these patients.

The clinical use of human embryos will require the development of operative techniques for the recovery of follicular oocytes and for the transfer of eggs into human oviducts and uteri. Preliminary work using laparoscopy has shown that oocytes can be recovered from ovaries by puncturing ripening follicles *in vivo*, and that a few of the eggs transferred into the oviducts can be recovered following salpingectomy (unpublished work of P. C. S. and R. G. E.). Improvements in equipment and techniques may give better results and avoid resorting to laparotomy.

We thank especially Professor C. R. Austin for his encouragement and advice, and Drs. C. Abberley, G. Garrett and L. Davies for their help. One of us (R. G. E.) is indebted to the Ford Foundation and another (B. D. B.) to the Medical Research Council for financial assistance. We thank Professor N. Morris and Drs. M. Rose, J. Bottomley and S. Markham for ovarian tissue.

(**221**, 632-635; 1969)

R. G. Edwards and B. D. Bavister: Physiological Laboratory, University of Cambridge.
P. C. Steptoe: Oldham General Hospital, Oldham.

Received December 13, 1968.

References:

1. Edwards, R. G., *Lancet*, ii, 926 (1965).

2. Edwards, R. G., Donahue, R. P., Baramki, T. A., and Jones, H. W., *Amer. J. Obstet. Gynec.*, **96**, 192 (1966).

3. Yanagimachi, R., and Chang, M. C., *J. Exp. Zool.*, **156**, 361 (1964).

4. Barros, C., and Austin, C. R., *J. Exp. Zool.*, **166**, 317 (1967).

5. Bavister, B. D., *J. Reprod. Fertil.* (in the press).

6. Williams, W. L., Weinman, D. E., and Hamner, C. E., *Fifth Intern. Cong. Anim. Reprod. A. I.*, Trento, 7, 288 (1964).

7. Brinster, R. L., *Exp. Cell Res.*, **32**, 205 (1963).

8. Dickmann, Z., Clewe, T. H., Bonney, W. A., and Noyes, R. W., *Anat. Rec.*, **152**, 293 (1965).

9. Whittingham, D. G., *Nature*, **220**, 592 (1968).

10. Whitten, W. K., and Biggers, J. D., *J. Reprod. Fertil.*, **17**, 399 (1968).

11. Austin, C. R., *The Mammalian Egg* (Blackwell, Oxford, 1961).

12. Chang, M. C., *J. Exp. Zool.*, **128**, 379 (1955).

13. Davidson, E., Allfrey, V. G., and Mirsky, A. E., *Proc. US Nat. Acad. Sci.*, **52**, 501 (1964).

14. Edwards, R. G., *Nature*, **208**, 349 (1965).

15. Jagiello, G., Karnicki, J., and Ryan, R. J., *Lancet*, i, 178 (1968).

16. Henderson, S. A., and Edwards, R. G., *Nature*, **218**, 22 (1968).

也适用于人类，那么和年龄较小的妇女相比，年龄较大的妇女的卵子会更容易出现与染色体二倍性相关的异常。由此可以推测，在年龄较大的妇女中出现三倍体和多倍体胚胎从而产生先天愚型后代和流产胎儿的可能性也会更大。

由体外受精得到的人类胚胎要在临床上得到应用尚需要以下两项相关技术的进一步发展，即获取卵泡卵母细胞的技术以及将受精卵重新植入人体内输卵管和子宫的技术。利用腹腔镜技术进行的初步研究表明，通过对体内正在成熟的卵泡进行穿刺可以从卵巢中获取卵母细胞，也可以通过输卵管切除术取出一些迁移到输卵管中的卵子（斯特普托和爱德华兹尚未发表的研究结果）。医疗设备和技术的进步或许会带来更好的结果，还能避免采用剖腹手术。

在此特别要感谢奥斯汀教授给我们的鼓励和建议，以及阿伯利博士、加勒特博士和戴维斯博士的帮助。我们中的一位作者（爱德华兹）受到了福特基金会的资助，另一位（巴维斯特）受到了医学研究理事会的资助。还要感谢莫里斯教授、罗斯博士、博顿利博士和马卡姆博士给我们提供了卵巢组织。

（彭丽霞 翻译；王敏康 审稿）

Galactic Nuclei as Collapsed Old Quasars

D. Lynden–Bell

Editor's Note

Shortly after the highly energetic and distant astrophysical objects called quasars were discovered, it was suggested that they might be powered somehow by gravitation, which ultimately is far more efficient at converting mass to energy than nuclear fusion. Here Donald Lynden–Bell develops this idea into what would eventually become the "standard model" of such active galactic nuclei. It is now generally accepted that all galaxies with central bulges (such as our own) contain supermassive black holes at their centres. When lots of gas is being fed into the black hole, it is known variously as a quasar, Seyfert or radio galaxy, depending on the total energy being generated and the wavelength of the peak radiation.

RYLE gives good evidence[1] that quasars evolve into powerful radio sources with two well separated radio components, one on each side of the dead or dying quasar. The energies involved in the total radio outbursts are calculated to be of the order of 10^{61} erg, and the optical variability of some quasars indicates that the outbursts probably originate in a volume no larger than the solar system. Now 10^{61} erg have a mass of 10^{40} g or nearly 10^7 Suns. If this were to come from the conversion of hydrogen into helium, it can only represent the nuclear binding energy, which is $3/400$ of the mass of hydrogen involved. Hence 10^9 solar masses would be needed within a volume the size of the solar system, which we take to be 10^{15} cm (10 light h). But the gravitational binding energy of 10^9 solar masses within 10^{15} cm is GM^2/r which is 10^{62} erg. Thus we are wrong to neglect gravity as an equal if not a dominant source of energy. This was suggested by Fowler and Hoyle[2], who at once asked whether the red-shifts can also have a gravitational origin. Greenstein and Schmidt[3], however, earlier showed that this is unlikely because the differential red-shift would wash out the lines. Attempts to avoid this difficulty have looked unconvincing, so I shall adopt the cosmological origin for quasar red-shifts. Even with this hypothesis the numbers of quasar-like objects are very large, or rather they were so in the past. I shall assume that the quasars were common for an initial epoch lasting 10^9 yr, but that each one only remained bright for 10^6 yr, and take Sandage's estimate (quoted in ref. 4) of 10^7 quasar-like objects in the sky down to magnitude 22. This must represent a snapshot of the quasar era, so only one in a thousand would be bright. If these represent all the quasar-like objects that there are, then the density of dead ones should be $10^7 \times 10^3$ $= 10^{10}$ per Hubble volume. The distance between neighbouring dead ones is then an average of 10^{-3} Hubble distances (10^{10} light yr) or 3 Mpc. From these statistics it seems probable that a dead quasar-like object inhabits the local group of galaxies and we must expect many nearer than the Virgo cluster and $M87$. If we restrict ourselves to old quasars bright at radio wavelengths, then Sandage reduces his estimate by a factor of

星系核是塌缩的老年类星体

林登－贝尔

编者按

在发现被叫做类星体的这种高能而遥远的天体后不久，就有人提出也许是引力在以某种方式为它们提供能量，在把质量转化为能量方面，从根本上说引力要比核聚变有效得多。在这里，唐纳德·林登－贝尔将这个想法发展到有可能最终成为这种活动星系核的"标准模型"的形式。现在大家普遍承认，所有中心有核球的星系（比如我们自己的星系）都会在它们的中心处包含超大质量的黑洞。当大量气体被摄入黑洞时，就会因其产生的总能量和辐射峰值波长的不同而被认为是类星体、塞弗特星系或射电星系等活动星系核。

赖尔给出了有力的证据[1]证明：类星体会演化为具有两个分得很开的射电子源的强射电源，它们分别位于这个死去或者正在死去的类星体的两侧。计算表明射电爆发的总能量为 10^{61} erg 量级，而一些类星体的光学光变表明这些爆发有可能源于一个不大于太阳系的空间体积中。10^{61} erg 的能量相当于 10^{40} g 或者将近 10^7 个太阳的质量。如果这些能量均来源于氢聚变为氦的反应，那么它就只能是原子核的结合能，其大小等于参加反应氢质量的 3/400。因而需要 10^9 倍太阳质量的物质处于和太阳系一样大的体积里，我们取太阳系的尺度为 10^{15} cm（10 光时）。但按公式 GM^2/r 计算，在 10^{15} cm 范围内，质量为 10^9 倍太阳的天体所具有的引力束缚能应该是 10^{62} erg。因此我们犯了忽视引力的错误——引力即使不是一个主要的能量来源，至少也是一个同等重要的能量来源。这一理论是由福勒和霍伊尔提出的[2]，他们还曾问过红移会不会也是由引力造成的。然而，在这之前，格林斯坦和施密特[3]就曾指出这是不大可能的，因为不同的红移会把谱线抹掉。为避免这个困难所作的尝试看起来并不令人信服，所以我将采用类星体红移的宇宙学起源。即使在上述假定下，类星体的数目还是非常巨大，或者更确切地说它们在过去是这样的。我将假设在最初的一个持续 10^9 年的时期里类星体是常见的，但是每个类星体只能在 10^6 年内保持明亮，采用桑德奇的估计（见参考文献 4 中的引述），天空中应有 10^7 个亮于 22 星等的类似类星体的天体。这应该代表了类星体时期的一个快照，因此只有千分之一会是明亮的。如果这些代表了所有类似于类星体的天体，那么死亡类星体的密度应为每哈勃体积 10^7 个 $\times 10^3 = 10^{10}$ 个。于是两个相邻的死亡类星体之间的平均距离就是 10^{-3} 哈勃距离（10^{10} 光年）或者 3 兆秒差距（Mpc）。从这些统计结果看来，很可能有一个死去的类似类星体的天体存在于本星系群中，并且我们必然可以预期有很多这样的天体距我们比室女座星系团和 $M87$ 还近。如果我们仅限于研究那些在射电波段明亮的老年类星体，那么桑德奇的估计值就会减

200 so the average distance between dead quasars is around 20 Mpc. This is typical of the distance between clusters of galaxies.

If some 10^7–10^9 solar masses were involved in the quasar, releasing 10^7 solar masses as energy, then the dead quasar is likely still to be in the range 10^7–10^9 solar masses and to be bound still within a radius of the size of the solar system. Such an object is unlikely to exist for 10^{10} yr without burning out its nuclear fuel. There are no equilibria for burnt-out bodies of masses considerably in excess of a solar mass, however. Even uniform rotation hardly increases Chandrasekhar's critical mass of about $1.4\,M_\odot$ and non-uniform rotation always leads to the generation of magnetic fields and to angular momentum transport. For masses already of the size of the solar system such periods of angular momentum transport will not be very long. In a few thousand years the outer parts acquire a large fraction of the angular momentum and slow down in circular orbit while the more massive inner portion contracts and spins faster. This central portion will collapse and finally fall within its Schwarzschild radius and be lost from view. Nothing can ever pass outwards through the Schwarzschild sphere of radius $r = 2\,GM/c^2$, which we shall call the Schwarzschild throat. We would be wrong to conclude that such massive objects in space-time should be unobservable, however. It is my thesis that we have been observing them indirectly for many years.

Effects of Collapsed Masses

As Schwarzschild throats are considerable centres of gravitation, we expect to find matter concentrated toward them. We therefore expect that the throats are to be found at the centres of massive aggregates of stars, and the centres of the nuclei of galaxies are the obvious choice. My first prediction is that when the light from the nucleus of a galaxy is predominantly starlight, the mass-to-light ratio of the nucleus should be anomalously large.

We may expect the collapsed bodies to have a broad spectrum of masses. True dead quasars may have 10^{10} or $10^{11}\,M_\odot$ while normal galaxies like ours may have only 10^7 – $10^8\,M_\odot$ down their throats. A simple calculation shows that the last stable circular orbit has a diameter of $12\,GM/c^2 = 12m$ so we shall call the sphere of this diameter the Schwarzschild mouth. Simple calculations on circular orbits yield the following results, where M_7 is the mass of the collapsed body in units of $10^7\,M_\odot$, so that M_7 ranges from 1 to 10^4.

Circular velocity

$$V_c = [GM / (r - 2m)]^{1/2} \quad \text{where } r > 3m \tag{1}$$

Binding energy of a mass m^* in circular orbit

$$m^*\varepsilon = m^*c^2 \left\{ 1 - (r - 2m) \left[r\,(r - 3m) \right]^{-1/2} \right\} \tag{2}$$

少到原来的 1/200，于是死亡类星体之间的平均距离将约为 20 Mpc。这是星系团之间距离的典型值。

如果类星体的质量约为太阳质量的 $10^7 \sim 10^9$ 倍，并且释放了太阳质量的 10^7 倍作为能量，那么死亡类星体的质量很可能仍能达到太阳质量的 10^7 倍 $\sim 10^9$ 倍，并且仍能被束缚于和太阳系同样半径大小的体积内。这样一个天体不大可能存在 10^{10} 年而不耗尽自身的核燃料。然而，一个质量远远超过太阳质量而耗尽了燃料的天体是没有平衡态的。即使均匀转动也很难增加量值约为 1.4 $M_\odot$（译者注：$M_\odot$ 代表太阳的质量）的钱德拉塞卡临界质量，而非均匀转动通常会导致磁场的产生以及角动量的转移。对于已经具有太阳系尺度的大质量天体，它们的角动量转移时间不会很长。在数千年期间，靠外的部分将获得角动量中的大部分并且减速为沿圆轨道运动；而质量较大的靠内的部分则会收缩并且旋转得更快。其中心部分将会塌缩并最终落到它的史瓦西半径之内而从视线中消失。任何物质都不能向外通过半径 $r = 2GM/c^2$ 的史瓦西球面，我们在下文中将称之为史瓦西喉。然而，如果我们认为在时空中不可能观测到如此大质量的天体，那就错了。我的论述就是要说明我们已经间接观测到它们很多年了。

质量塌缩效应

因为史瓦西喉被认为是引力中心，所以我们预测将发现物质向它们聚集。于是我们可以预期这些喉将在大量恒星聚集区的中心被发现，而星系核的中心显然是一个不错的选择。我的第一个预测是：当来自于一个星系核的光主要是星光时，这个星系核的质光比就会异常大。

我们可以预期那些塌缩后的天体会有很宽的质量范围。真正死亡的类星体可能有 10^{10} $M_\odot$ 或 10^{11} $M_\odot$ 的质量，而像银河系这样的普通星系在它们的喉内的质量可能只有 10^7 $M_\odot \sim 10^8$ $M_\odot$。简单的计算表明，最内面的稳定圆轨道的直径为 $12GM/c^2 = 12m$，因而我们将把直径这么大的一个球面称为史瓦西嘴。在对圆轨道进行简单的计算之后可以得到以下结果，如果 M_7 是以 10^7 $M_\odot$ 为单位的塌缩天体的质量，则 M_7 的取值范围是 $1 \sim 10^4$。

圆周速度为：

$$V_c = [GM / (r - 2m)]^{1/2}，其中 r > 3m \tag{1}$$

圆轨道中质量为 m^* 的质点的束缚能为：

$$m^*\varepsilon = m^*c^2 \{1 - (r - 2m) [r (r - 3m)]^{-1/2}\} \tag{2}$$

Angular momentum of circular orbit per unit mass

$$h = [mc^2r^2 / (r - 3m)]^{1/2} \qquad (3)$$

The maximum binding energy in circular orbit is

$$m^*c^2 (1 - 2\sqrt{2}/3) = 0.057\ m^*c^2 \sim m^*c^2/18 \qquad (4)$$

which occurs at $r = 6m$ and $h = \sqrt{12}\ mc$ (equation (5)). This orbit is also the circular orbit of least angular momentum. The period of the circular orbit as seen from infinity is $(2\pi r/ V_c)(1-[2m/r])^{-1/2} = 2\pi\ (r^3/GM)^{1/2}$ (equation (6)). The maximum wavelength change toward the blue visible from infinity is $\lambda_0/\lambda = 2^{1/2}$ for a stable circular orbit while for a stable parabolic orbit it is $\lambda_0/\lambda = 1+2^{-1/2}$. For parabolic orbits that will disappear down the Schwarzschild throat the greatest blueward change is seen from $r = 27m/8$ when $\lambda_0/\lambda = 1.77$. There is no possibility of synchrotron-like blue-shifts.

Numerical values are: $V_c = 200\ (M_7/r)^{1/2}$ km s^{-1} at r pc. $12m$ diameter of Schwarzschild mouth $= 1.6\times10^{13}\ M_7$ cm $\simeq M_7$, AU. Roche limit for a star of density ρ^* g cm^{-3} $(R) = 4.1\times10^{13}\ (M_7/\rho^*)^{1/3}$ cm $= 2.8\ (M_7/\rho^*)^{1/3}$ AU. Greatest swallowable angular momentum per unit mass $h_0=4mc=0.5\ M_7$ pc km s^{-1}. Once the initial very low angular momentum stars have been swallowed (those with $h < h_0$) the star swallowing rate rapidly declines to a negligible trickle of about 10^{-8} stars yr^{-1}. Because the Roche limit is near the Schwarzschild mouth we may likewise neglect the tearing apart of stars by tides. Spectroscopic velocity dispersion of the same energy as the circular orbit $\sigma^2 = \frac{1}{3} V_c^2$, that is, $\sigma=116\ (M_7/r)^{1/2}$ km s^{-1}. Period of circular orbit at r pc $= 3\times10^4\ (r^3/M_7)^{1/2}$ yr.

It is thus by no means impossible that there are collapsed masses in galactic nuclei. Considerable support for the notion comes from a detailed consideration of what happens when a cloud of gas collects in the galactic nucleus. (This was first considered by Salpeter, who also derived the 0.057 $F c^2$ power output[5] which is now described.)

Gas Swallowing

The total mass loss from all stars in a galaxy will be roughly 1 $M_\odot$ per year. A fraction of this accumulates in galactic nuclei, which are the centres of gravitational attraction. There is dissipation when gas clouds collide, due to shock waves that radiate the energy of collision. For a given angular momentum the orbit of least energy is circular, so we must expect gas to form a flat disk held out from the centre by circular motion. Such a differentially rotating system will evolve due to "friction" just as described earlier for a dying quasar. Nothing happens in the absence of friction so the energy is liberated via the friction. In the cosmic situation molecular viscosity is negligible and it is most probable that magnetic transport of angular momentum dominates over turbulent transport just as it does in Alfvén's theory of the primaeval solar nebula. To give a sensible model of the swallowing rate we must estimate the magnetic friction and investigate what happens to

圆轨道中单位质量的角动量为：

$$h = [mc^2r^2 / (r - 3m)]^{1/2} \qquad (3)$$

圆轨道的最大束缚能为：

$$m^*c^2 (1 - 2\sqrt{2}/3) = 0.057\ m^*c^2 \sim m^*c^2/18 \qquad (4)$$

这出现于 $r = 6m$ 和 $h = \sqrt{12}\ mc$（式（5））的情况下。这个轨道也是角动量最小的圆轨道。从无穷远处观察到这个圆轨道的周期是 $(2\pi r/V_c)(1-[2m/r])^{-1/2} = 2\pi\ (r^3/GM)^{1/2}$（式（6））。从无穷远处可看到的最大的波长蓝移，对于稳定的圆轨道为 $\lambda_0/\lambda = 2^{1/2}$，对于稳定的抛物线轨道为 $\lambda_0/\lambda = 1+2^{-1/2}$。对于在史瓦西喉以内将会消失的抛物线轨道，最大的向蓝改变是在 $r = 27m/8$ 处观察到的 $\lambda_0/\lambda = 1.77$。类似于同步辐射的蓝移是不可能出现的。

具体的数值是：在 r 秒差距（pc）处，$V_c = 200\ (M_7/r)^{1/2}$ km/s。史瓦西嘴的直径 $12m = 1.6 \times 10^{13}\ M_7$ cm $\approx M_7$ 个天文单位（AU）。对于密度为 ρ^* g/cm³ 的恒星，洛希极限 $(R) = 4.1 \times 10^{13}\ (M_7/\rho^*)^{1/3}$ cm $= 2.8\ (M_7/\rho^*)^{1/3}$ AU。每单位质量的最大可吞噬角动量 $h_0 = 4mc = 0.5\ M_7$ pc km s^{-1}。一旦初始角动量非常低的恒星（即 $h < h_0$ 的恒星）被吞噬了以后，恒星吞噬率就会迅速下降到一个非常低的值，只有约 10^{-8} 恒星 / 年。因为洛希极限靠近史瓦西嘴，所以我们同样可以忽略由潮汐产生的恒星撕裂。和圆轨道有相同能量的光谱速度弥散度 $\sigma^2 = \frac{1}{3} V_c^2$，也就是 $\sigma = 116\ (M_7/r)^{1/2}$ km/s。位于 r pc 处的圆轨道的周期为 $3 \times 10^4\ (r^3/M_7)^{1/2}$ 年。

因此，在星系核中存在塌缩了的质量并非不可能。详细地考虑当一团气体云在星系核中聚集时将发生什么会有力地支持这一说法。（上述说法由萨尔皮特最先提出，他也推导出了 $0.057\ Fc^2$ 的功率输出 [5]，这正是现在所描述的结果。）

气 体 吞 噬

一个星系中，所有恒星的总质量损失大约是 $1\ M_\odot$ / 年。其中的一部分质量积聚在引力中心的星系核中。在气体云碰撞时，由于激波辐射了碰撞的能量，因此会产生耗散。对于给定的角动量，最小能量的轨道是圆形轨道，因此我们只能期望气体将形成一个扁平的盘，靠圆周运动来维持与中心的距离。这样一个较差自转系统会由于"摩擦"而不断演化，正如人们早期对一个正在死去的类星体所描述的那样。因为在没有摩擦的情况下什么都不会发生，所以能量是通过摩擦释放的。在宇宙环境中，分子的黏性是可以忽略的，而角动量的磁输运极有可能比湍动输运更起支配作用，这恰与在阿耳文的原初太阳星云理论中所遇到的情况类似。为了给出一个合理的吞噬率模型，我们必须估计磁摩擦并研究磁场所获得的能量会发生什么样的变

the energy acquired by the magnetic field. Before doing this let us assume a conservative swallowing rate of 10^{-3} $M_\odot$ per year and work out the power available through magnetic friction. We assume that this mass flux is processed down through the circular orbits until it reaches the unstable orbit at $r = 6m$. We shall assume that the flux is swallowed by the throat without further energy loss. The power for a mass flow F is then 0.057 $F c^2 = 3.5 \times 10^{42}$ erg s^{-1} $\simeq 10^9$ $L_\odot$ where the values are for $F = 10^{-3}$ $M_\odot$ yr^{-1} and $L_\odot$ is the power of the energy output of the Sun. This sort of power emitted as light could just noticeably brighten a nucleus. If a fraction were emitted in the radio region the nucleus would be a radio source. Clearly it only requires a mass flux of 1 $M_\odot$ yr^{-1} and a conversion into light at 10 percent efficiency for the nucleus to equal the stellar light output from the whole galaxy. Can this be the explanation of the Seyfert galaxies?

We now return to the model for the magnetic transfer of angular momentum in a disk. As a magnetic field B is sheared by an initially perpendicular displacement. The component across the shear is left unchanged but the component down the shear is progressively amplified. We may therefore expect the magnetic field in a shearing medium to be progressively amplified until it somehow changes either the motion or its own configuration. The magnetic field first has a significant effect when it can bow upwards and downwards out of the differentially rotating disk leaving the material to flow down the field lines and so collect into clouds in the disk[6]. For significant cloudiness to result, the magnetic field pressure $B^2/8\pi$ must equal the turbulent and gas pressures ρc_s^2. Here ρ is the density and c_s^2 the combined velocity dispersion of microscopic and molecular motion. The thickness of the disk $2b$ is determined by the balance between the gravity of the central mass and the non-magnetic pressure, $GMr^{-3}z\rho = -c_s^2\,\partial\rho/\partial z$, which gives

$$\rho = \rho_0 \exp\left[-z^2/2b^2\right] \quad \text{where } b^2 = r^3 c_s^2/GM \tag{7}$$

The local shear rate is given by Oort's constant A

$$A = -\tfrac{1}{2} r\, \mathrm{d}(v/r)/\mathrm{d}r = \tfrac{3}{4}(GM/r^3)^{1/2} \tag{8}$$

Hence

$$\frac{B^2}{8\pi} \simeq \rho_0 c_s^2 = \frac{16}{9}A^2 b^2 \rho_0 = \left(\frac{16}{9\sqrt{2\pi}}\right)A^2 b\Sigma \tag{9}$$

Here Σ is the surface density of matter in the disk, $\Sigma = \sqrt{2\pi}\, b\,\rho_0$.

On multiplication by b^3, equation (9) tells us that the magnetic field energy in a volume b^3 is about equal to the kinetic energy of the shearing in the same region. Equation (9) may be obtained approximately from a dimensional analysis of a general shearing sheet of highly conducting material. As such, it claims general validity, so it is interesting to apply it to the gas in the neighbourhood of the Sun. The very reasonable result, $B = 4 \times 10^{-6}$ G, restores confidence in this rather inadequate treatment. We are now in a position to estimate the magnetic frictional force per unit length in a shearing disk. The Maxwell stress $B_x. B_y/(4\pi)$ acts over a thickness of about $2b$. Once the medium has broken up into clouds the magnetic field will be rather chaotic but the shearing will still give it some

化。在这之前，让我们先假设一个保守的吞噬率——$10^{-3} M_\odot$/年，并计算出通过磁摩擦可以产生的功率。我们假设这个质量流量沿着圆轨道不断流入，直到它到达 $r = 6m$ 处的不稳定轨道。我们假定这个质量流到史瓦西喉时被吞噬而没有进一步的能量损失。于是质量流量 F 产生的功率为 $0.057Fc^2 = 3.5 \times 10^{42}$ erg s$^{-1} \approx 10^9 L_\odot$，其中：$F = 10^{-3} M_\odot$/年，$L_\odot$ 是太阳能量输出的功率。这种能量如以光的形式发射出来则刚好能使星系核显著增亮。如果有一部分能量是在射电波段发出的，那么这个星系核就会成为一个射电源。显然，为了使星系核辐射的光和整个星系的星光同样明亮，只需要质量流量达到 $1 M_\odot$/年且转化为光的效率为 10% 就足够了。这是否可以作为对塞弗特星系的解释呢？

现在我们回到一个盘内角动量的磁转移模型中去。当磁场 B 被一个起初与之垂直的位移剪切时，垂直于剪切方向的分量保持不变而沿剪切方向的分量则逐渐放大。因此我们可以预期一个处于剪切介质中的磁场会被逐渐放大，直到它在某种程度上改变这种运动或者它自身的构型。在磁场可以向上和向下弯曲离开较差转动着的盘时，它会首先产生一个重要的效应使物质沿磁力线流动，从而在盘中聚集成云[6]。为产生大量的云，磁场压强 $B^2/8\pi$ 必须等于湍流和气体压强 ρc_s^2。这里 ρ 是密度，c_s^2 是微观运动和分子运动联合的速度弥散度。盘的厚度 $2b$ 由中心质量的引力和非磁场压强之间的平衡 $GMr^{-3}z\rho = -c_s^2 \, \partial\rho/\partial z$ 确定，由此得到：

$$\rho = \rho_0 \exp [-z^2/2b^2]，\text{其中 } b^2 = r^3c_s^2/GM \tag{7}$$

局域剪切率由奥尔特常数 A 给出：

$$A = -\tfrac{1}{2} r \, \mathrm{d}(v/r)/\mathrm{d}r = \tfrac{3}{4}(GM/r^3)^{1/2} \tag{8}$$

因此
$$\frac{B^2}{8\pi} \approx \rho_0 c_s^2 = \frac{16}{9}A^2b^2\rho_0 = \left(\frac{16}{9\sqrt{2\pi}}\right)A^2b\sum \tag{9}$$

这里 $\sum$ 是盘中物质的面密度，$\sum = \sqrt{2\pi}\, b \, \rho_0$。

乘以 b^3 后，由式（9）可知，在体积 b^3 内的磁场能量差不多等于同一区域中的剪切动能。从对高导电率材料的一般剪切层的量纲分析中就可以近似得到式（9）。就此而论，式（9）应该具有普遍的适用性，所以把它应用到太阳附近的气体中是很有意思的。由此得到了一个非常合理的结果：$B = 4 \times 10^{-6}$ 高斯（G），这使我们在这个不严格的处理中找回了信心。现在我们就可以估计一个剪切盘中每单位长度的磁摩擦了。麦克斯韦应力 $B_x \cdot B_y/(4\pi)$ 作用于大约 $2b$ 的厚度上。一旦介质碎裂为云块，磁场就会变得非常混乱，但剪切仍会赋予介质某种系统性的倾向以反抗剪切。对于给

systematic tendency to oppose the shear. The greatest possible value of B_xB_y for given $[\mathbf{B}]$ is $B^2/2$, so we estimate $B^2/4$ as a typical value in a sense directed to oppose the shear. The force per unit length is then

$$bB^2/8\pi = [16/(9\sqrt{2\pi})]A^2b^2\Sigma \tag{10}$$

Unlike a normal viscous drag, the force here depends on the square of A, the rate of shear. This is reasonable because the shear itself is needed to build up the magnetic field which eventually opposes it. We shall use this estimate of the friction to make a model of the disk, but it is important to consider first where the energy goes. We must consider why the field is not further amplified by further shearing once it has reached the value estimated. Once the medium has split into clouds each cloud acts like a magnet. As the medium is sheared these magnets try to re-align themselves to take up a configuration of minimum energy. The intercloud medium, although dominated by the magnetic field, is still a highly conducting medium, however. In free space re-alignment of the magnets involves reconnexion of magnetic field lines through neutral points. This cannot happen in a force-free, strictly perfect, conductor. Rather one may show that neutral sheets develop with large sheet currents flowing through them. This situation does not really happen; any small resistivity causes a return to the reconnecting case and it is of the greatest interest to see how a plasma of particles behaves near a neutral point at which reconnexion takes place. (In the frame in which the neutral point is fixed this involves an electric field E. The mechanism of acceleration is basically that of Syrovatskii[7].) Tritton at this observatory has been studying with me the details of an exact model. To reconnect a finite flux in a finite time through a point at which $B = 0$, it is clear that the lines of force much move infinitely fast at the neutral point. They are not material lines and there is nothing wrong with this; even the normal formula for their velocity $v = c\,(\mathbf{E}\times\mathbf{B}/B^2)$ gives superluminous velocities when $|\mathbf{E}\times\mathbf{B}| > B^2$ (that is, for $|E| > |B|$ in gaussion units assuming they are perpendicular). The particles gyrate about their field lines until the lines move with the velocity of light; thereafter the electric field predominates, the magnetic field is too weak to change anything significantly and the particles are electrostatically accelerated. The potential drop follows directly from Faraday's law

$$\Phi = -\frac{1}{c}\,\mathrm{d}N/\mathrm{d}t$$

where $\mathrm{d}N/\mathrm{d}t$ is the rate of flux reconnexion. To calculate this e.m.f. we estimate the reconnexion rate as a flux of $2b^2B$ in a time of $(2A)^{-1}$. This gives an e.m.f. of $4b^2AB/c$ (equation (11)). We shall see that these e.m.f.s are of the order of 10^{12} V. Because I believe that this can be the primary source of dissipation for the highly conducting disk I deduce that the energy of dissipation can be converted directly into cosmic rays in the GeV range. We have now good reason to believe that galactic nuclei ought to be radio sources because such cosmic rays will clearly radiate by the synchrotron mechanism in the magnetic field. In summary, we expect from a shear $2A$ the generation of a magnetic field given by equation (2), a shearing force given by equation (3), and a power p per unit area dissipated into cosmic rays of energy up to $4b^2AB/c$ given by $p = 2AbB^2/8\pi = (32/(9\sqrt{2\pi}))\,A^3b^2\Sigma$

定的 [**B**]，B_xB_y 的最大可能值是 $B^2/2$，所以我们估计直接反抗剪切的典型值应该是 $B^2/4$。于是，单位长度上的力为：

$$bB^2/8\pi = [16/(9\sqrt{2\pi})]A^2b^2\Sigma \tag{10}$$

和普通的黏滞阻力不同，这里的力取决于剪切率 A 的平方。这是合理的，因为磁场的建立需要剪切，而建立后的磁场最终又会反抗剪切。我们将使用上面这种对摩擦的估计来构造一个盘模型，但重要的是首先要考虑这些能量的去向。我们必须思考以下问题，即为什么一旦达到了所估计的值，磁场便不再会被进一步的剪切继续放大？一旦介质分裂为云块，每个云块就会表现得像一块磁体。当介质受到剪切时，这些磁体将会试图重新排列以便占据一个能量最小的位形。对于云际介质，虽然它们被磁场所支配，但仍然是高导电率的介质。在自由空间中，磁体的重新排列会导致磁力线通过中性点的重联。这种情况不可能在无阻力的严格理想导体中发生。虽然可以证明中性片会在流经它们的大的片电流中产生，但这种情况并不会真的发生；因为任何小的电阻率都会导致再回到重联的情况，而了解由粒子组成的等离子体在发生重联的中性点附近有什么样的行为是极其有趣的。（在中性点固定的参考系里，可以产生一个电场 E。加速机制基本上就是瑟罗瓦茨基提出的机制 [7]。）皇家格林尼治天文台的特里顿一直在和我一起研究一个精确模型的具体细节。为了在一个有限的时间内通过 $B = 0$ 的点使有限的磁通重联，显然需要磁力线在中性点处以无限快的速度移动。磁力线不是物质的线，因而以无限快的速度移动并没有什么不妥；甚至表征磁力线速度的标准公式 $v = c\,(\mathbf{E}\times\mathbf{B}/B^2)$ 也会在 $|\mathbf{E}\times\mathbf{B}| > B^2$（即，在高斯单位制中满足 $|E| > |B|$ 时，假设两者是垂直的）时给出视超光速的速度。粒子会一直绕着磁力线旋转直到磁力线的运动速度达到光速；随后电场开始起主导作用，而磁场变得很弱以至于不能使任何物理量发生显著的变化，这时粒子是通过静电场加速的。电位降可以直接由法拉第定律给出：

$$\Phi = -\frac{1}{c}\,\mathrm{d}N/\mathrm{d}t$$

其中 $\mathrm{d}N/\mathrm{d}t$ 是磁通的重联速率。为了计算这个电动势，我们可以根据在时间 $(2A)^{-1}$ 内重联的磁通为 $2b^2B$ 估算出重联速率。由此得到的电动势为 $4b^2AB/c$（式（11））。我们将会看到，这些电动势的级别为 10^{12} V。因为我认为这可能是高导电率盘能量的主要耗散源，所以推断耗散能量能够直接被转化为 GeV 量级的宇宙线。现在我们有充足的理由相信星系核应该是射电源，因为这些宇宙线显然将通过在磁场中的同步辐射机制进行辐射。综上所述，我们期望从剪切 $2A$ 将可以产生由式（2）给出的磁场，由式（3）给出的剪切力，和由 $p = 2AbB^2/8\pi = (32/(9\sqrt{2\pi}))\,A^3b^2\Sigma$（式（12））给出的每单位面积通过能量高达 $4b^2AB/c$ 的宇宙线耗散掉的功率 p。这些关系式在银

(equation (12)). These formulae have very general application in the astrophysics of the Galaxy, in the early history of the solar nebula and in the origin of peculiar A stars from binaries. There is, however, one caveat: the reconnexion energy only goes into cosmic rays if the density is low enough in the reconnecting region. If the particle being accelerated has a collision before it reaches the r.m.s. velocity, then it cannot run away to high energy; instead the reconnexion energy is dissipated by ohmic heating.

If m_A, m_p are the masses of the accelerated particle and the proton, then the condition for acceleration is

$$e\, m_A^{-1}\, E\, t_s > \left(\frac{3}{2} kT m_p^{-1} \right)^{1/2}$$

where t_s is the time between scatterings of the particles A. This time may be taken from Spitzer's book[8] to be approximately

$$t_s = m_A\ \rho^{-1}\ T^{3/2}\ m_A/(m_A + m_P) \text{ seconds}$$

T is the temperature and ρ is the density at the acceleration region. Putting in our expressions for the electric field $\Phi/2b$ we obtain for our disk in c.g.s. units the acceleration condition

$$\rho < 10^{-24} \left(\frac{2m_A}{m_A + m_p} \right) bABT$$

Notice the density for proton acceleration can be 918 times that for electron acceleration.

The Steady Model Disk

We look for a steady state of gas swallowing with a mass flux F. We shall assume that a small fraction of the rotational energy is converted into random motions so that $c_s \propto V_c$. Sensible values would be $c_s = 10$ km s^{-1} when $V_c = 200$ km s^{-1} so we write $c_s = (1/20)\, x\, V_c$, where x is of order unity but might be a weak function of r. The couple on the material inside r due to magnetic friction is from equations (10), (8) and (7)

$$g = 2\pi r^2 bB^2/8\pi = \sqrt{2}\, \pi\, c_s^2 r^2 \Sigma \tag{13}$$

Apart from the trickle of angular momentum $\sqrt{12}\, mcF$ into the singularity g must be balanced in a steady state by the inward flux of angular momentum carried by the material. Thus, using equations (3) and (5)

$$g = \sqrt{12}\, mcF + F\, [mc^2 r^2 (r{-}3m)^{-1}]^{1/2} \ \text{ for } r > 6m \tag{14}$$

that is $$g \simeq F (GM\, r)^{1/2} \tag{15}$$

河系天体物理学中、在太阳星云的早期历史中以及在双星系统内特殊 A 型星的起源问题中都有着非常广泛的应用。但有一点需要说明：如果重联区内的密度低到一定程度，那么重联能量就只会以宇宙线的形式释放。如果被加速的粒子在达到均方根速度之前发生了一次碰撞，那么它就不能以很高的能量逃逸出去；这时，重联能量会通过欧姆加热的方式被耗散掉。

如果 m_A、m_p 分别表示被加速粒子和质子的质量，那么加速的条件是：

$$e\, m_A^{-1} E\, t_s > \left(\frac{3}{2} kT m_p^{-1}\right)^{1/2}$$

其中，t_s 是 A 粒子两次散射之间的时间。从斯皮策的著作 [8] 中可以了解到这个时间间隔大致为：

$$t_s = m_A\, \rho^{-1}\, T^{3/2}\, m_A/(m_A+m_P)\ \text{s}$$

T 是温度，ρ 是加速区的密度。代入电场的表达式 $\Phi/2b$，则可以得到在我们的盘模型中，以厘米克秒单位表示的加速条件是：

$$\rho < 10^{-24} \left(\frac{2m_A}{m_A + m_p}\right) bABT$$

注意质子可加速的密度能达到电子可加速密度的 918 倍。

稳态模型盘

我们要寻求一个质量流量为 F 的气体吞噬的稳态。我们将假设转动能量中有一小部分转化成为随机运动，因而 $c_s \propto V_c$。当 $V_c = 200$ km/s 时，c_s 的合理取值为 $c_s = 10$ km/s，所以我们可以写出以下关系式：$c_s = (1/20)\, x\, V_c$，其中 x 的量级为 1，但有可能是微弱依赖于 r 的函数。由磁摩擦造成的 r 之内物质上的力偶可以从式（10）、（8）和（7）得到：

$$g = 2\pi r^2 b B^2/8\pi = \sqrt{2}\,\pi\, c_s^2 r^2 \sum \tag{13}$$

除了缓慢进入奇点的角动量流 $\sqrt{12}\,mcF$ 以外，在稳态中必须有被物质携带的角动量的内流来平衡 g。因此，根据式（3）和式（5）可得：

$$g = \sqrt{12}\, mcF + F\, [mc^2 r^2(r-3m)^{-1}]^{1/2}，\quad \text{其中 } r > 6m \tag{14}$$

即

$$g \approx F\,(GM\,r)^{1/2} \tag{15}$$

Because $g \propto r^{1/2}$ we see from equation (13) that $\sum \propto r^{-3/2} c_s^{-2} \propto r^{-3/2} V_c^{-2} \propto r^{-1/2}$ and that the radial velocity

$$V_r = F (2\pi r \sum)^{-1} \qquad (16)$$

The power $2\pi r p(r) \, \delta r$ liberated into heat or cosmic rays in the region between r and $r + \delta r$ is $-Fd\varepsilon/dr$ where $-d\varepsilon/dr$ is the derivative of the binding energy in circular orbit given by equation (2).

$$p(r) = \frac{Fc^2}{4\pi r} \frac{m(r - 6m)}{\left[r(r - 3m)\right]^{3/2}} \quad \text{for } r \geq 6m \qquad (17)$$

$$p(r) \simeq FGM/(4\pi r^3) \qquad \text{for } r \gg m \qquad (18)$$

For a given total mass and radius of the disk, a given Schwarzschild mass and choice of the parameter $x \simeq 1$, we have now a unique model of the disk including the cosmic ray power, the heating per unit area, the magnetic field and the mass flux. Rather than given the total mass and radius of the disk, we shall determine everything in terms of the mass flux. Any chosen maximum radius then determines the total mass within. We shall calculate two temperatures T_1 and T_2 as follows. T_1 is the temperature that the disk would have if it radiated as a black body just the power per unit area that is locally generated. Thus $T_1(r) = (P(r)/(2\sigma))^{1/4}$ where σ is Stefan's constant and the factor 2 arises because the disk has two sides. $T_2(r)$ is the ambient black body temperature at a distance r from a source the total power of which is the total power of one disk. Thus

$$T_2(r) = [P/(16\pi\sigma r^2)]^{1/4}$$

We now give the numerical values in terms of the following variables: F_{-3} the mass flux in units of $10^{-3} M_\odot$ per year, M_7 the Schwarzschild mass in units of $10^7 M_\odot$, x the ratio of the turbulent velocity to $1/20 \, V_c$. r_0, m_0 the running variable r in units of 1 pc and GM/c^2 respectively. From equation (15) couple $g = 4\times10^{48} r_0^{1/2} F_{-3} M_7^{1/2} = 2.6\times10^{45} m_0^{1/2} F_{-3} M_7$ g cm^2 s^{-1} $(m_0 \gg 6)$. From equation (13) surface density $\sum = 0.16 \, r_0^{-1/2} x^{-2} F_{-3} M_7^{-1/2} = 240 \, m_0^{-1/2}$ $x^{-2} F_{-3} M_7^{-1}$ g cm^{-2} $(m_0 \gg 6)$. $\int_0^r 2\pi r \sum dr = 6.7\times10^{36} r_0^{3/2} x^{-2} F_{-3} M_7^{-1/2}$ g $= 3.4\times10^3 r_0^{3/2}$ solar masses. From equation (7) $b/r = 0.05x$. $\rho_0 = (2\pi)^{-1/2} \sum /b = 4.6\times10^{-19} r_0^{-3/2} x^{-3} F_{-3} M_7^{-1/2} = 1.4\times10^{-9}$ $m_0^{-3/2} x^{-3} F_{-3} M_7^{-2}$ g cm^{-3} $(m_0 \gg 6)$. From equation (13), $B = 3\times10^{-3} r_0^{-5/4} x^{1/2} F_{-3}^{1/2} M_7^{1/4} = 2.7\times10^5 m_0^{-5/4} x^{-1/2} F_{-3}^{1/2} M_7^{-1}$ G $(m_0 \gg 6)$. From equation (18), $p(r) \simeq 0.22 r_0^{-3} F_{-3} M_7$ ergs cm^{-2} s^{-1}(r $\gg$ 6m). Notice that the power is strongly concentrated towards the centre, where we need the accurate relativistic formula (17)

$$p(r) = 0.22 \, r_0^{-3} \left[\frac{1 - 2.6 \times 10^{-6} M_7 r_0^{-1}}{\left(1 - 1.3 \times 10^{-6} M_7 r_0^{-1}\right)^{3/2}}\right] F_{-3} M_7$$

$$= 2.6\times10^{18} \left[\frac{1 - 6 \, m_0^{-1}}{\left(1 - 3 \, m_0^{-1}\right)^{3/2}}\right] m_0^{-3} F_{-3} \, M_7^{-2} \text{ erg cm}^{-2} \text{ s}^{-1}$$

因为 $g \propto r^{1/2}$，所以我们从式（13）中可以得出 $\sum \propto r^{-3/2} c_s^{-2} \propto r^{-3/2} V_c^{-2} \propto r^{-1/2}$ 以及径向速度：

$$V_r = F (2\pi r \textstyle\sum)^{-1} \tag{16}$$

在 r 和 $r+\delta r$ 之间的区域，以热或宇宙线形式释放掉的功率 $2\pi r p(r)\delta r$ 为 $-Fd\varepsilon/dr$，其中 $-d\varepsilon/dr$ 是由公式（2）给出的圆轨道束缚能的导数。

$$p(r) = \frac{Fc^2}{4\pi r}\frac{m(r-6m)}{\left[r(r-3m)\right]^{3/2}} \quad \text{其中 } r \geq 6m \tag{17}$$

$$p(r) \approx FGM/(4\pi r^3) \quad \text{其中 } r \gg m \tag{18}$$

对于一个给定的总质量和盘半径，在给定史瓦西质量并选定参数 $x \approx 1$ 的情况下，我们就会得到一个唯一的盘模型，其中包含宇宙线的功率、单位面积的加热、磁场以及质量流量。在没有给定总质量和盘半径的情况下，我们也可以根据质量流量得出所有其他的物理量。只要选定了最大半径就可以确定其内的总质量。下面我们将计算两个温度 T_1 和 T_2。T_1 是如果盘以黑体辐射释放出与局域单位面积产生的功率刚好相等时应该有的温度。于是 $T_1(r) = (P(r)/(2\sigma))^{1/4}$，其中 σ 是斯忒藩常数，出现因子 2 是因为盘有两个面。$T_2(r)$ 是总功率为一个盘的总功率而与源相距为 r 的周围黑体温度。所以：

$$T_2(r) = [P/(16\pi\sigma r^2)]^{1/4}$$

现在我们根据以下变量计算具体的数值：F_{-3} 是单位为 10^{-3} $M_\odot$ / 年的质量流量；史瓦西质量 M_7 的单位是 10^7 $M_\odot$；x 是湍流速度与 $1/20$ V_c 的比值；r_0 和 m_0 分别是以 1 pc 和 GM/c^2 为单位的移动变量 r。由式（15）可以得到：力偶 $g = 4\times10^{48} r_0^{1/2}$ $F_{-3} M_7^{1/2} = 2.6\times10^{45} m_0^{1/2} F_{-3} M_7$ g cm^2 s^{-1} $(m_0 \gg 6)$。由式（13）可以得到面密度 $\sum = 0.16$ $r_0^{-1/2} x^{-2} F_{-3} M_7^{-1/2} = 240$ $m_0^{-1/2} x^{-2} F_{-3} M_7^{-1}$ g cm^{-2} $(m_0 \gg 6)$，$\int_0 2\pi r \sum dr = 6.7\times10^{36} r_0^{3/2} x^{-2} F_{-3}$ $M_7^{-1/2}$ g $= 3.4\times10^3 r_0^{3/2}$ 太阳质量。由式（7）得到 $:b/r = 0.05x$; $\rho_0 = (2\pi)^{-1/2}\sum/b = 4.6\times10^{-19}$ $r_0^{-3/2} x^{-3} F_{-3} M_7^{-1/2} = 1.4\times10^{-9}$ $m_0^{-3/2} x^{-3} F_{-3} M_7^{-2}$ g cm^{-3} $(m_0 \gg 6)$。由式（13），$B = 3\times10^{-3} r_0^{-5/4} x^{-1/2}$ $F_{-3}^{1/2} M_7^{1/4} = 2.7\times10^5 m_0^{-5/4} x^{-1/2} F_{-3}^{1/2} M_7^{-1}$ G $(m_0 \gg 6)$。根据式（18），$p(r) \approx 0.22 r_0^{-3} F_{-3}$ M_7 erg cm^{-2} s$^{-1}(r \gg 6m)$。可以看出：功率具有向中心区高度聚集的趋势，在那里我们需要使用精确的相对论公式（17）：

$$p(r) = 0.22 \, r_0^{-3} \left[\frac{1-2.6\times10^{-6} M_7 r_0^{-1}}{(1-1.3\times10^{-6} M_7 r_0^{-1})^{3/2}}\right] F_{-3} M_7$$

$$= 2.6\times10^{18} \left[\frac{1-6 \, m_0^{-1}}{(1-3 \, m_0^{-1})^{3/2}}\right] m_0^{-3} F_{-3} \, M_7^{-2} \text{ erg cm}^{-2} \text{ s}^{-1}$$

Total power
$$P = 0.057 \, F \, c^2 = 3.2 \times 10^{42} \, F_{-3} \text{ erg s}^{-1} \sim 10^9 \, L_\odot$$

$$T_1(r) = 6.7 \; r_0^{-3/4} \left[\frac{1 - 2.6 \times 10^{-6} M_7 r_0^{-1}}{(1 - 1.3 \times 10^{-6} M_7 r_0^{-1})^{3/2}} \right]^{1/4} F_{-3}^{1/4} M_7^{1/4}$$

$$= 3.7 \times 10^5 \; m_0^{-3/4} \left[\frac{1 - 6 \, m_0^{-1}}{(1 - 3 \, m_0^{-1})^{3/2}} \right]^{1/4} F_{-3}^{1/4} \, M_7^{-1/2} \text{ K} \qquad\qquad (m_0 \geq 6)$$

$$T_2(r) = 100 \; r_0^{-1/2} F_{-3}^{1/4} = 1.6 \times 10^5 \; m_0^{-1/2} F_{-3}^{1/4} M_7^{-1/2} \text{ K}$$

Maximum cosmic ray energy $e\Phi = 1.5 \times 10^{13} \; r_0^{-3/4} x^{3/2} F_{-3}^{1/2} M_7^{3/4} = 10^{18} \; m_0^{-3/4} \, x^{3/2} \, F_{-3}^{1/2}$ eV. Period of circular orbit (seen from infinity) $3 \times 10^4 \; r_0^{3/2} \, M_7^{-1/2}$ yr $= 9.8 \times 10^{-6} \; m_0^{3/2} \, M_7$ yr. Circular velocity $V_c = 200 \; r_0^{-1/2} \; (1 - 9.7 \times 10^{-7} \, M_7 \, r_0^{-1})^{-1/2} = 3 \times 10^5 \; m_0^{-1/2} \; (1 - 2 \, m_0^{-1})^{-1/2}$ km s^{-1} ($m_0 > 6$). Radial velocity $V_r = 0.2 \; r_0^{-1/2} \, x^2 \, M_7^{1/2} = 3 \times 10^2 \; m_0^{-1/2} \, x^2$ km s^{-1} ($m_0 \gg 6$). Condition for electron acceleration is $\rho < 3 \times 10^{-20} \; T_4 \, r_0^{-7/4} \, x^{1/2} F_{-3}^{1/2} M_7^{3/4}$ and for proton acceleration $\rho < 3 \times 10^{-17} \, T_4$, etc., where T_4 is the temperature in the acceleration region in units of 10^4 K and ρ is the density. Acceleration will be between the clouds so at any region of the disk we should probably take $\rho_0/10$ for ρ (and $T_4 \sim 1$ unless the ambient temperature T_1 is greater.)

Diameter of Schwarzschild mouth $12m = 5.7 \times 10^{-6} \, M_7$ pc, that is, $m_0 = 12$. Diameter of region producing half the power $44m = 2.1 \times 10^{-5} \, M_7$ pc, that is, $m_0 = 44$. Rotational period at that radius $9 \times 10^{-4} \, M_7$ yr $= 0.32 \, M_7$ days. Inward movement time r/V_r at that radius $1.6 \times 10^{-1} \, M_7 \, x^{-2}$ yr $\sim 59 \, M_7$ days.

It should by now be clear that with different values of the parameters M_7 and F_{-3} these disks are capable of providing an explanation for a large fraction of the incredible phenomena of high energy astrophysics, including galactic nuclei, Seyfert galaxies, quasars and cosmic rays. The next section is therefore devoted to predicting the spectra.

Spectrum

The maximum temperature is at $m_0 = 7.05$ and is $T_1 = 6.6 \times 10^4 \; F_{-3}^{1/4} \, M_7^{-1/2}$ K. The medium will be optically thick for $\Sigma = 90 \; x^{-2} \, F_{-3} \, M_7^{-1}$ g cm^{-2}. The disk is in danger of becoming optically thin around $\Sigma = 1$, but there the temperature has fallen to $T_2 \sim 700$ K so dust will take over as a source of opacity (this may not happen for large M_7). Our standard model with the parameters all at unity will provide opacity out to about a parsec or so. Because all but the centre of our disk obeys a law $T = A r^{-2a}$ with $a = 4$ in the outer parts where T_2 is relevant and $a = 8/3$ in the inner parts where T_1 is relevant, we study the radiation from disks with such power law temperature distributions. The total emission at frequency ν is given by

$$S_\nu = \int_0^\infty \frac{c}{4} \, u_\nu \, (T(r)) \; 4\pi r \, dr = \frac{8\pi^2 \, h}{c^2} \int_0^\infty \frac{\nu^3 \, r \, dr}{\exp(h\nu/kT) - 1}$$

Writing $x = h\nu/kT = h\nu r^{2a}/(kA)$ we find

总功率 $\qquad P = 0.057\ F\ c^2 = 3.2\times10^{42}\ F_{-3}\ \text{erg s}^{-1} \sim 10^9\ L_\odot$

$$T_1(r) = 6.7\ r_0^{-3/4}\left[\frac{1-2.6\times10^{-6}\,M_7\,r_0^{-1}}{(1-1.3\times10^{-6}\,M_7\,r_0^{-1})^{3/2}}\right]^{1/4}F_{-3}^{1/4}\,M_7^{1/4}$$

$$= 3.7\times10^5\,m_0^{-3/4}\left[\frac{1-6\,m_0^{-1}}{(1-3\,m_0^{-1})^{3/2}}\right]^{1/4}F_{-3}^{1/4}\,M_7^{-1/2}\ \text{K} \qquad\qquad (m_0{\geq}6)$$

$$T_2(r) = 100\ r_0^{-1/2}F_{-3}^{1/4} = 1.6\times10^5\,m_0^{-1/2}F_{-3}^{1/4}M_7^{-1/2}\ \text{K}$$

宇宙线能量的最大值为 $e\Phi = 1.5\times10^{13}\ r_0^{-3/4}x^{3/2}F_{-3}^{1/2}M_7^{3/4} = 10^{18}\ m_0^{-3/4}\ x^{3/2}\ F_{-3}^{1/2}$ eV。圆轨道周期（在无穷远处看）为 $3\times10^4\ r_0^{3/2}\ M_7^{-1/2}$ 年 = $9.8\times10^{-6}\ m_0^{3/2}\ M_7$ 年。圆周速度为 $V_c = 200\ r_0^{-1/2}\ (1-9.7\times10^{-7}\ M_7\ r_0^{-1})^{-1/2} = 3\times10^5\ m_0^{-1/2}\ (1-2\ m_0^{-1})^{-1/2}$ km/s $(m_0{>}6)$。径向速度为 $V_r = 0.2\ r_0^{-1/2}\ x^2\ M_7^{1/2} = 3\times10^2\ m_0^{-1/2}\ x^2$ km/s $(m_0{\gg}6)$。电子加速的条件是 $\rho < 3\times10^{-20}\ T_4\ r_0^{-7/4}\ x^{1/2}F_{-3}^{1/2}M_7^{3/4}$；质子加速的条件是 $\rho < 3\times10^{-17}\ T_4$，等等。其中 T_4 是加速区的温度，单位是 10^4 K；ρ 代表密度。因为加速将发生在云之间，所以在盘中的任何区域我们或许应该把 ρ 的值取为 $\rho_0/10$（且 $T_4 \sim 1$，除非周围的温度 T_1 比较高。）

史瓦西嘴的直径为 $12m = 5.7\times10^{-6}\ M_7$ pc，即 $m_0 = 12$。产生一半功率的区域直径为 $44m = 2.1\times10^{-5}\ M_7$ pc，即 $m_0 = 44$。在该半径处的转动周期为 $9\times10^{-4}\ M_7$ 年 = $0.32\ M_7$ 天。由该半径处向内运动的时间 r/V_r 为 $1.6\times10^{-1}\ M_7\ x^{-2}$ 年 $\sim 59\ M_7$ 天。

现在应该已经很清楚：利用参数 M_7 和 F_{-3} 的不同取值，这些盘可以解释高能天体物理中的很多难以置信的现象，包括星系核、塞弗特星系、类星体和宇宙线。下一节将专门讨论对其光谱的预测。

光　谱

当 $m_0 = 7.05$ 时温度达到最大值，即 $T_1 = 6.6\times10^4\ F_{-3}^{1/4}\ M_7^{-1/2}$ K。当面密度 $\Sigma = 90\ x^{-2}\ F_{-3}\ M_7^{-1}$ g cm^{-2} 时，介质是光学厚的。当大致有 $\Sigma = 1$ 时，盘有变成光学薄的危险，但这时温度已经下降到 $T_2 \sim 700$ K，因而尘埃将代之成为不透明度的主要来源（如果 M_7 很大，这种情况可能不会发生）。在我们的标准模型中，如果取所有这些参数均为 1，根据我们的标准模型可以得出达到 1 pc 左右的不透明度。因为在我们的盘中，除中心以外的所有区域都服从 $T = Ar^{-2a}$ 的分布律，在与 T_2 相应的靠外区域，$a = 4$；在与 T_1 有关的靠内区域，$a = 8/3$。我们在研究来自盘的辐射时采用的就是这种幂律的温度分布。频率为 ν 的总辐射由下式给出：

$$S_\nu = \int_0^\infty \frac{c}{4}\ u_\nu\left(T(r)\right)\ 4\pi r\mathrm{d}r = \frac{8\pi^2 h}{c^2}\int_0^\infty \frac{\nu^3 r\mathrm{d}r}{\exp\left(h\nu/kT\right)-1}$$

令 $x = h\nu/kT = h\nu r^{2a}(kA)$，则有：

$$S_\nu = \frac{4\pi^2 h}{c^2}\left(\frac{kA}{h}\right)^a \int\limits_0^\infty \frac{a\,x^{a-1}}{e^x-1}\mathrm{d}x\; \nu^{3-a}$$

where

$$\int\limits_0^\infty \frac{a\,x^{a-1}}{e^x-1}\mathrm{d}x = a\,\Gamma(a)\zeta(a)$$

Thus for $a = 8/3$ we have $S_\nu \propto \nu^{1/3}$ while for $a = 4$ we have $S_\nu \propto \nu^{-1}$. Before trying to use these formulae it is important to find out at what radius the main contributions to S_ν arise. For $a < 1$ the main contributions come from radii close to those for which $h\nu \sim kT$. We may therefore deduce that for our standard model $S_\nu \propto \nu^{-1}$ when $100\ \mathrm{K} < h\nu/k < 3{,}000\ \mathrm{K}$ and $S_\nu \propto \nu^{1/3}$ when $3\times10^4\ \mathrm{K} < h\nu/k < 10^5\ \mathrm{K}$, and that for frequencies corresponding to temperatures of $10^5\ \mathrm{K}$ or greater the system shines like a black body of $10^5\ \mathrm{K}$. In practice it is known that at least for Seyfert galaxies the reddening by dust takes a large fraction of the energy out of the ultraviolet and replaces it in the infrared. Because I have no theory for the amount of dust at each radius I cannot predict the final optical spectrum in detail. But because dust evaporates at a thousand degrees or so it would seem likely that the radiation should be peaked on the red side of the corresponding frequency. Fig. 1 shows the details of the emitted "black body" radiation. It is clear that fluorescence from the ultraviolet will mean that the optical spectrum should be full of emission lines. Those arising from where the disk has ambient temperatures near $2\times10^3\ \mathrm{K}$ come from regions $r_0 \simeq 10^{-3}$ where the circular velocities are $V_c \simeq 6\times10^3\ \mathrm{km\ s^{-1}}$. These emission lines should therefore be very broad. We may expect that the real disk is not steady, although exact periodicity due to a source in orbit is unlikely. Rather, we should expect variations on a time scale given by $2r/V_r$ at $m = 22$ (120 days) because that is the time scale in which the material flux can vary over the region in which most of the flux is emitted. Using our theory in the most straight-forward way it is clear that more power is used in accelerating protons than is used in accelerating electrons. Protons can be accelerated in a density 918 times as great as that in which the electron acceleration can operate. Density in our model behaves like $r^{-3/2}$ while total power between $3/2\ r$ and $1/2\ r$ behaves like r^{-1}. We deduce that the proton power is about 10^2 times the electron power. The steady state spectrum is easily determined. From our accelerator we expect energy proportional to potential drop. Because particles start from all points the energy spectrum ejected by the accelerator is uniform up to the maximum energy, $e\Phi \sim 10^{13}\ \mathrm{eV}$.

$$S_v = \frac{4\pi^2 h}{c^2} \left(\frac{kA}{h}\right)^a \int_0^\infty \frac{a\,x^{a-1}}{e^x - 1} dx\,v^{3-a}$$

其中
$$\int_0^\infty \frac{a\,x^{a-1}}{e^x - 1} dx = a\,\Gamma(a)\zeta(a)。$$

于是，当 $a = 8/3$ 时，我们得到 $S_v \propto v^{1/3}$；而当 $a = 4$ 时，我们有 $S_v \propto v^{-1}$。在使用这些公式之前，找出对 S_v 的主要贡献到底出现在多大半径处是很重要的。当 $a < 1$ 时，主要贡献来自于满足条件 $hv \sim kT$ 的半径附近。于是我们可以推断出：在我们的标准模型中，当 100 K $< hv/k <$ 3,000 K 时，$S_v \propto v^{-1}$；而当 3×10^4 K $< hv/k < 10^5$ K 时，$S_v \propto v^{1/3}$。此外还可以得出：对于与 10^5 K 或更高温度相应的频率，这个系统的发光和一个 10^5 K 的黑体一样。实际上，人们已经知道至少在塞弗特星系中，尘埃造成的红化将很大一部分紫外的能量转移到了红外。因为我没有理论来描述每个半径处的尘埃数量，所以不能详细预言最终的光谱。不过因为尘埃会在 1,000 度左右蒸发，所以辐射很可能应在相应频率的红边达到峰值。图 1 给出了发射的"黑体"辐射的细节。显然来自紫外的荧光意味着光谱中充满了发射线。那些由盘周围温度接近 2×10^3 K 的区域发出的发射线来自于 $r_0 \approx 10^{-3}$ 处，其对应的圆周速度为 $V_c \approx 6\times10^3$ km/s。因而这些发射线会非常宽。我们可以预期真实的盘是不会处于稳态的，尽管一个在轨道里运动的源不大可能产生严格的周期性。更准确地说，我们预期会在 $m = 22$ 处发生时标为 $2r/V_r$（120 天）的光变，因为这刚好是物质流能够在其发射大部分流量的区域内发生变化的时标。应用我们的理论所得到的一个最直接的结果显然是：更多的能量被用于加速质子而不是电子。质子被加速所要求的密度是电子被加速所需密度的 918 倍。在我们的模型中，密度的变化如同 $r^{-3/2}$，而总功率在 3/2 r 和 1/2 r 之间的变化如同 r^{-1}。我们推测质子的功率大约是电子功率的 10^2 倍。稳态的谱容易被确定。从我们的加速器来看，我们期望能量与电位降成比例。因为粒子是从各个点开始运动的，所以被加速器喷射出的能谱在直到最高能量 $e\Phi \sim 10^{13}$ eV 的范围内都是均匀的。

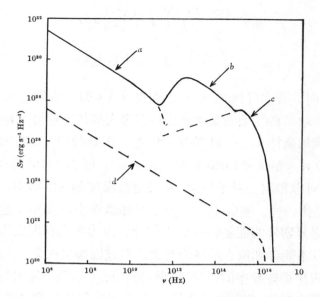

Fig. 1. The emitted spectrum of disk and synchrotron radiation for the standard model. The flux from Sagittarius *A* is weaker by a factor 100, indicating only 1 percent efficiency of the proton synchrotron. *a*, Proton synchrotron; *b*, outer disk; *c*, central disk; *d*, electron synchrotron.

Each particle of energy E radiates at a rate proportional to E^2. If there were constant monoenergetic injection into the medium, the flux of particles downwards in energy would be constant. Thus the number per unit area at any E less than the injection energy would follow the law $N(E) = KE^{-2}$ for $E < E_{max} \equiv E_m$. This law is only slightly modified by our uniform injection at all energies up to E_{max}. It is

$$N(E) = K\,(1 - E/E_m)E^{-2} \quad E < E_m$$

where K is related to the total power of injection power per unit area p by

$$K = \frac{2p}{E_m}\frac{9\,m_A^2\,c^7}{4e^2}\,B^{-2}$$

Because the power law is near E^{-2} except close to E_{max}, we expect the γ of synchrotron radiation theory to be close to two, and the corresponding spectrum to be close to $S_\nu \propto \nu^{-a}$ with $\alpha = \frac{1}{2}$. It is possible to work out a better approximation using the δ function approximation to the frequency spectrum of a single electron[9]. For our disk model the flux is

$$S_\nu = \int_{r_A}^{\infty}\int_{0}^{E_m}\frac{2p}{E_m}\,\delta\,(\nu - \nu_m)\left(1 - \frac{E}{E_m}\right)\,dE\,2\pi r\,dr$$

where r_A is the least radius at which the particles can be accelerated and

$$\nu_m = 0.07\left(\frac{2}{3}\right)^{1/2}\frac{e}{m_A^3 c^5}BE^2$$

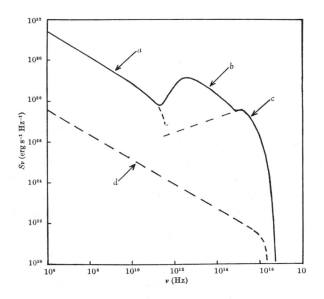

图 1. 标准模型中盘和同步辐射的发射谱。来自人马座 A 的流量减弱为原来的 1/100，表明质子同步辐射的效率只有 1%。a，质子同步辐射；b，外盘；c，中心盘；d，电子同步辐射。

每个能量为 E 的粒子都会以正比于 E^2 的速率发射辐射。如果有持续的单一能量注入介质中，那么能量更低的粒子的流量应该保持不变。因此，对于任何低于注入能量的能量 E，单位面积的粒子数都应遵循 $N(E) = KE^{-2}$ 的规律，其中 $E < E_{max} \equiv E_m$。在直到 E_{max} 的所有能量都均匀注入时，这个规律只需进行微小的修正，即：

$$N(E) = K\,(1 - E/E_m)E^{-2} \quad E < E_m$$

其中 K 与单位面积中注入的总功率 p 的关系是：

$$K = \frac{2p}{E_m}\frac{9\,m_A^2\,c^7}{4e^2}\,B^{-2}$$

因为除了在 E_{max} 附近以外，幂律都接近于 E^{-2}，所以我们可以预期同步辐射理论中的 γ 应该接近于 2，而相应的谱接近于 $S_v \propto v^{-a}$，其中 $\alpha = \frac{1}{2}$。用 δ 函数对单个电子频谱的近似很可能会是一种更好的近似 [9]。将其应用于我们的盘模型，得到的流量为：

$$S_v = \int_{r_A}^{\infty} \int_0^{E_m} \frac{2p}{E_m}\,\delta\,(v - v_m)\left(1 - \frac{E}{E_m}\right)\mathrm{d}E\,2\pi r\,\mathrm{d}r$$

其中 r_A 是粒子可以被加速的最小半径，且

$$v_m = 0.07\left(\frac{2}{3}\right)^{1/2}\frac{e}{m_A^3\,c^5}BE^2$$

165

Using our power laws for $p(r)$, $E_m(r) \equiv e\Phi$, $B(r)$, we obtain

$$S_\nu = 3.8 \times 10^{28} \left(\frac{m_A}{m_p}\right)^{12/11} \nu_9^{-7/11}$$

$$\left[1 - \frac{1}{11}\left(14 - 3\left(\frac{\nu_9}{\nu_A}\right)^{1/2}\right)\left(\frac{\nu_9}{\nu_A}\right)^{3/22}\right] x^{-10/11} F_{-3}^{5/11} M_7^{4/11}$$

where this formula holds for $\nu < \nu_A \equiv \nu_m (r_A)$ and ν_9 is ν in units of GHz. This formula has assumed that all the power dissipated goes into fast protons or electrons as the case may be. In regions where both electrons and protons are accelerated the power should obviously be divided by two. In practice it is probable that S_ν should be reduced by some efficiency factor because probably only a fraction of the total reconnexion energy really gets into fast particles. The radius of the source at frequency ν is about

$$r_0 = 0.7 \ \nu_9^{-4/11} \left(\frac{m_A}{m_p}\right)^{-12/11} x^{10/11} F_{-3}^{6/11} M_7^{7/11}, \ \nu < \nu_A$$

Notice that the fast electrons can only be produced much further out than the protons but that they nevertheless produce radiation to much higher frequencies.

Comparison with Observations

In the Galaxy it is not clear that the circular velocity near the centre falls below 200 km s^{-1}, but the OH observations do suggest velocities as low as 100 km s^{-1} within 70 pc of the centre. This indicates a nuclear mass of $M_7 \sim 3$ for the central singularity. The size and flux from Sagittarius A are in rough accord with our estimate of the synchrotron spectrum. An infrared flux found at 100 μm could be due to dust from an ultraviolet source radiating $10^9 \ L_\odot$, so the flux of mass into the throat must be around $F_{-3} = 1$. The general level of activity observed at radio wavelengths close to the nucleus indicates that high energy phenomena are involved[10].

The Magellanic clouds have no nucleus. $M31$ has a strong radio source rather larger but weaker than that found in the Galaxy[11]. Code has discovered strong ultraviolet emission from the nucleus, which Kinman finds to have a large mass-to-light ratio and to contain some 10^8 solar masses. This suggests a small mass flux into the centre of $M31$ and only a very small ultraviolet disk about the Schwarzschild mouth. $M32$ has a nucleus which is not a radio source but the system is very deficient in gas. We suggest that this system has a Schwarzschild mass but the Galaxy has run out of gas and left it hungry. $M82$ has had a recent violent radio explosion and an infrared nucleus with a small bright radio source in the centre. I suspect $M_7 \sim 3$ and $F_{-3} \sim 10$ but that F_{-3} was larger in the recent past. $M81$ has a very small flux but an intense radio source at its nucleus. I suggest that it is intermediate between the Galaxy and $M31$. $M87$ is the nearest really bright radio galaxy. Luckily the velocity dispersion in its nucleus has been measured[12]. We can therefore measure M_7 with some pretence of accuracy to be about $4 \times 10^{10} \ M_\odot$, that is, $M_7 = 4 \times 10^3$. Over 10^{10} yr it would take an F_{-3} of 4×10^3 to build such an object. This is probably the nearest old dead radio-bright quasar. It is only a shadow of its former self, as F_{-3} has declined severely as the gas has run out. Its electron synchrotron still produces copious

把我们的幂律代入 $p(r)$、$E_m(r) \equiv e\Phi$ 和 $B(r)$，得到：

$$S_v = 3.8 \times 10^{28} \left(\frac{m_A}{m_p}\right)^{12/11} v_9^{-7/11}$$

$$\left[1 - \frac{1}{11}\left(14 - 3\left(\frac{v_9}{v_A}\right)^{1/2}\right)\left(\frac{v_9}{v_A}\right)^{3/22}\right] x^{-10/11} F_{-3}^{5/11} M_7^{4/11}$$

上式的成立条件是 $v < v_A \equiv v_m(r_A)$，v_9 代表以 GHz 为单位的 v。该式假设所有耗散的功率都转移给了快质子或快电子。在电子和质子都被加速的区域，功率显然应该除以 2。实际上，S_v 的值很可能应乘以某个效率因子使其适当减小，因为在总的重联能量中很可能只有一部分真正转移到了快粒子中。频率为 v 的源的半径大约是：

$$r_0 = 0.7 \, v_9^{-4/11} \left(\frac{m_A}{m_p}\right)^{-12/11} x^{10/11} F_{-3}^{6/11} M_7^{7/11}, \quad v < v_A$$

注意：快电子只能在比产生快质子靠外很多的地方产生，但尽管如此，它们仍会产生频率高得多的辐射。

与观测结果的比较

在银河系中，中心附近的圆周速度是否会小于 200 km/s 尚不清楚，然而对羟基（OH）的观测结果确实表明：在距中心 70 pc 的范围之内，速度低至 100 km/s。这表明中心奇异性的核质量是 $M_7 \sim 3$。人马座 A 的尺度和辐射流量大致与我们对同步辐射谱的估计一致。100 μm 处观测到的红外流量可能来源于一个辐射功率为 10^9 $L_\odot$ 的紫外源中的尘埃，因此进入喉的质量流量应该大致为 $F_{-3}=1$。在射电波段观测到的星系核附近的整体活动性水平表明有高能现象产生 [10]。

麦哲伦云没有星系核。M31 有一个强射电源，比在银河系中发现的射电源更大但更弱 [11]。科德已经发现了来自这个星系核的强紫外辐射，欣曼发现它有大的质光比并且其质量约为太阳质量的 10^8 倍。这表明只有少量的质量流入了 M31 的中心，并且在史瓦西嘴周围只有一个非常小的紫外盘。M32 有一个不是射电源的星系核，但是这个系统十分缺乏气体。我们认为该系统有一个史瓦西黑洞，但是这个星系中的气体已经耗尽从而使它无气体可吞噬。最近，M82 发生了一次强烈的射电爆发，其中心有一个带有小而明亮的射电源的红外核。我认为 $M_7 \sim 3$ 以及 $F_{-3} \sim 10$，但 F_{-3} 在不久之前比现在还要大。M81 的流量非常小，但在其中心处有一个很强的射电源。我认为它介于银河系和 M31 之间。M87 是真正最近邻的亮射电星系。幸而其核的速度弥散度已经被测定出来了 [12]。因此我们可以假定其 M_7 的量值已经被精确测定为 $4 \times 10^{10} M_\odot$，即 $M_7 = 4 \times 10^3$。以 4×10^3 的 F_{-3} 构建这样一个天体需要超过 10^{10} 年的时间。这可能就是距离我们最近的老死了的射电亮类星体。它只是自己过去的一个影子，

X-rays[13], however. *NGC* 4151 is a Seyfert galaxy, and M_7 need not be greater than 3, or more likely 30, but F_{-3} is high because there is still much gas in the central regions. Seyfert galaxies that are active have $F_{-3} = 10^3$ but probably are only active at this flux level for one-hundredth of the time. The breadths of the wings of the Balmer lines are 6,000 km s^{-1}—I suggest that these are Doppler widths[14]. *NGC* 4151 is a strong infrared source.

Quasars

When F_{-3} achieves large values $\sim 10^6$ or 10^7 (that is, 10^{3-4} $M_\odot$ yr^{-1}) the mass of the Schwarzschild throat rapidly build up to 10^9–10^{10} $M_\odot$. When galaxies first formed there was this amount of gaseous material in them. Large proto-galaxies rapidly achieved large Schwarzschild throats and greedily swallowed gas. It is clear that the right energy is available and by making M close to 10^{10} $M_\odot$ we lower the densities close to the Schwarzschild throat. This allows the radio phenomena to occur closer to the singularity where more of the power is.

Note added in proof. Low's recent observations of the galactic centre at 100 μm (reported at the Cambridge conference on infrared astronomy, 1969) suggest that F_{-3} for the galaxy is nearer 10^{-2} than 1. A dust model by Rees can explain the infrared observations assuming a single central source of visible or ultraviolet light. The light pressure from such sources will expel dusty material from the nuclei of Seyfert galaxies causing the observed outflow as suggested by Weymann. Such a mechanism could cut off the flux F_{-3} and therefore produce the changes in the emitted flux. The light pressure may drive the dust out of the nucleus so that no dust is ever swallowed. This could leave a great enhancement of dust in the surroundings of the nucleus corresponding to the dust content of all material swallowed in the past. A violently active outburst of such a nucleus would then be associated with the expulsion of great swathes of dust such as those seen across several radio galaxies.

The proton synchrotron radiation discussed here is probably replaced in practice by synchrotron radiation from electron secondaries and X and γ-ray bremsstrahlung corresponding to a sizable fraction of the power input into fast protons.

I thank the Astronomer Royal for discussions, and Drs. Pagel, Bingham, Tritton, Rowan-Robinson, Weymann and Osterbrock for further help and encouragement.

(**223**, 690-694; 1969)

D. Lynden-Bell: Royal Greenwich Observatory, Herstmonceux Castle, Sussex.

Received July 8, 1969.

因为在其气体耗尽之后 F_{-3} 已经急剧减小。然而，它的电子同步辐射仍在产生大量的 X 射线 [13]。*NGC* 4151 是一个塞弗特星系，M_7 不一定要大于 3，或者可能性更大的 30，但 F_{-3} 很大，因为在中心区域仍存在着大量的气体。对于活动的塞弗特星系，有 $F_{-3}=10^3$，在这个流量水平保持活跃的时间很可能只占总时间的 1%。巴耳末线的线翼宽度为 6,000 km/s——我认为这正是多普勒宽度 [14]。*NGC* 4151 是一个强红外源。

类 星 体

当 F_{-3} 达到 $\sim 10^6$ 或 10^7（即 $10^3 \sim 10^4$ $M_\odot$/ 年）的高值时，史瓦西喉的质量就会迅速增大到 10^9 $M_\odot \sim 10^{10}$ $M_\odot$。在星系刚开始形成时，其中就有如此大量的气体。巨大的原初星系很快形成巨大的史瓦西喉并贪婪地吞噬着气体。显然该过程可以产生足够的能量，并且通过使 M 接近于 10^{10} $M_\odot$，我们可以降低史瓦西喉附近的密度。这使得射电现象能够发生在更靠近奇点的地方，那里也是有更高功率的地方。

附加说明。洛最近在 100 μm 波段对银河系中心进行了观测（报告于 1969 年的剑桥红外天文学会议），结果表明银河系的 F_{-3} 更接近于 10^{-2} 而不是 1。瑞斯提出的尘埃模型可以在假设存在单一的可见光或紫外光中心源的前提下来解释这些红外观测结果。来自这些源的光压将把含尘埃的物质从塞弗特星系的星系核中排出，导致观测到的外流，正如魏曼所提出的一样。这样一种机制可以截断质量流 F_{-3} 并因此产生辐射流量的变化。光压可能会驱使尘埃离开星系核，因此没有尘埃再被吞噬。这将导致星系核周围的尘埃相对于过去被吞噬的所有物质中的尘埃量而言大大增加。因此，这样一个星系核的剧烈爆发活动将伴随着大量尘埃的排出，正如人们在对几个射电星系进行观测时所看到的那样。

这里所讨论的质子同步辐射在实践中很可能被替换为来自电子的次级同步辐射，而 X 射线和 γ 射线波段的韧致辐射提供了相当一部分注入于快质子的功率。

我要感谢皇家天文学家们对此进行了多次讨论，也要感谢帕格尔博士、宾厄姆博士、特里顿博士、罗恩－鲁滨逊博士、魏曼博士和奥斯特布罗克博士给了我进一步的帮助和鼓励。

（钱磊 金世超 翻译；邓祖淦 审稿）

References:

1. Ryle, M., *Highlights of Astronomy* (edit. by Perek, L.) (D. Reidel, 1968).

2. Hoyle, F., Fowler, W. A., Burbidge, G., and Burbidge, E. M., *Astrophys. J.*, **139**, 909 (1964).

3. Greenstein, J. L., and Schmidt, M., *Astrophys. J.*, **140**, 1 (1964).

4. Schmidt, M., *Texas Conf. Relativistic Astrophys.* (edit. by Maran, S. P., and Cameron, A. G. W.) (1968).

5. Salpeter, E. E., *Astrophys. J.*, **140**, 796 (1964).

6. Parker, E. N., *Astrophys. J.*, **149**, 517 (1967).

7. Syrovatskii, S. I., *IAU Symp. No. 31, Radio Astronomy and the Galactic System* (edit. by Van Woerden, H.), 133 (Academic Press, 1967).

8. Spitzer, L., *Physics of Fully Ionised Gases* (Interscience, 1955).

9. Ginzburg, V. L., and Syrovatskii, S. I., *Ann. Rev. Astron. Astrophys.*, **3**, 297 (1965).

10. Lequeux, J., *Astrophys. J.*, **149**, 393 (1967).

11. Poolley, G. G., *Mon. Not. Roy. Astron. Soc.*, **144**, 101 (1969).

12. Brandt, J. C., and Rosen, R. G., *Astrophys. J. Lett.*, **156**, L59 (1969).

13. Byram, E. T., Chubb, T. A., and Friedman, H., *Science*, **152**, 66 (1966).

14. Woltjer, L., *Astrophys. J.*, **130**, 38 (1959).

Evidence for Extraterrestrial Life: Identity of Sporopollenin with the Insoluble Organic Matter Present in the Orgueil and Murray Meteorites and also in Some Terrestrial Microfossils[*]

J. Brooks and G. Shaw

Editor's Note

With the exception of lander missions on Mars, search for direct evidence of extraterrestrial life has been largely confined to the examination of the structure and composition of meteorites, which represent the chance arrival of material from elsewhere in the Solar System. This paper illustrates the kind of investigation undertaken some decades ago on carbon-containing material from two well-known meteorites. It reports the presence of organic material derived by the degradation of plant life, thus offering evidence of such life in the planetary sources of the meteorites. No such claims have yet stood the test of time: such complex organic matter in meteorites has turned out to be due to terrestrial contamination.

WITH very few exceptions[1] the insoluble organic matter present in both Pre-Cambrian sediments and carbonaceous chondrites has been neglected and organo-geochemical studies of these materials have been largely devoted to the readily solvent extractable soluble organic substances[2]. This is in some ways unfortunate, for by far the greater proportion of carbonaceous matter in both Pre-Cambrian sediments (up to 95 percent)[3] and in carbonaceous chondrites (up to 70 percent)[4] is insoluble and the soluble matter is frequently of a very minor nature. In addition, the soluble, and so potentially more mobile, organic chemicals are more likely to have moved in total or in part from their point of origin, and problems of rock contamination with such substances, either over long periods through seepage or, in the case of meteorites, at impact[5], are especially acute.

We have shown[6] that sporopollenin which forms a major part of pollen and spore exines is an oxidative polymer of carotenoids and carotenoid esters, and have suggested[7] that it is identical with older kerogen derived from terrestrial, especially Pre-Cambrian, sediments. We now present briefly some results of experiments carried out on the Orgueil and Murray meteorites which in our opinion clearly establish that the insoluble matter they contain is identical with sporopollenin.

---

[*] This article, received on June 20, 1969, is a much shortened version of a manuscript originally submitted in February 1969.

地外生命存在的证据：孢粉素与存在于奥盖尔陨星、默里陨星以及一些地球上微化石中的不溶有机质的同一性*

布鲁克斯，肖

编者按

除了依靠火星登陆任务以外，寻找地外生命存在的直接证据主要局限于对陨石结构和组成的检查，而陨石只是从太阳系中其他地方偶然降落到地球上的石块。这篇发表于几十年前的文章描述了人们对两颗著名陨星所含含碳物质的这类研究。文中报告称陨石中含有植物降解后产生的有机物质，从而提供了在陨石所来自的行星上有生命物质存在的证据。类似这样的证据都未能经得起时间的考验：陨石中的复杂有机物质最终被证明来源于地球上的污染。

除极少数例外[1]，绝大多数情况下存在于前寒武纪沉积物和碳质球粒陨石中的不溶有机质总是被忽略，人们对这些材料的有机地球化学研究主要集中在一些易于用溶剂萃取的可溶有机质[2]。这有些令人遗憾，因为前寒武纪沉积物及碳质球粒陨石中的含碳物质大多不溶于萃取剂（前者高达 95%[3]，后者高达 70%[4]），而可溶物通常都很次要。此外，可溶的、比较容易迁移的有机化学物质更有可能已经全部或部分地离开了它们的发源处。因而岩石遭到可溶物质污染的问题，不管是通过长时间渗漏还是通过撞击（后者指的是陨石）[5]，就显得尤为突出了。

我们曾指出[6]：用于构成花粉和孢子外膜主要部分的孢粉素，是类胡萝卜素和类胡萝卜素酯的氧化性聚合物；并且我们认为[7]，这种聚合物与从地球上、特别是前寒武纪沉积物中提取的早期油母质完全相同。现在简要介绍一下我们在对奥盖尔陨石和默里陨石进行实验后所得的一些结果。我们认为，这些结果确实可以证明其中的不溶物质就是孢粉素。

---

* 这篇文章是在 1969 年 6 月 20 日收到的，它是作者最初在 1969 年 2 月提交的手稿的一个精简版本。

The insoluble organic matter was isolated from samples of the Orgueil (0.1 g) and Murray (0.9 g) meteorites as brown amorphous solids by repeated digestion with hydrofluoric and nitric acids and potassium hydroxide in the usual manner, taking maximum care in manipulation. The relatively large amounts of organic matter (Orgueil 3.5 percent, Murray 4.4 percent) would make trace contamination of little or no consequence to our subsequent chemical studies. The solids were examined by infrared spectroscopy, pyrolysis gas chromatography, potash fusion followed by thin-layer chromatography of the products and by some elemental analyses[9], and results compared with similar examinations of sporopollenins from many modern pollen and spore exines, some synthetic analogues, some microfossils and artificially metamorphosed (by heating with sand) spore exines. The results clearly show that all these substances belong to the same class of polymeric material which we know as sporopollenins[8]. Their common identity rests chiefly on the following set of criteria. (a) They have stability to non-oxidative chemical reagents including those used to separate microfossil or insoluble organic material from their inorganic environment. (b) They are highly unsaturated and readily oxidized—the oxidation (especially ozonization) products from both modern[6] and fossil[7] spore exines are very similar both qualitatively and quantitatively and the limited evidence from related experiments with carbonaceous chondrites shows formation of typical and characteristic sporopollenin degradation products[1]. (c) They are stable to acetolysis. (d) They give a characteristic pattern of phenolic acids (ref. 6 and our unpublished results) (m and p-hydroxy benzoic acids and protocatechuic acid or mixtures thereof) after fusion with potassium hydroxide. (e) They have similar infrared spectra (Fig. 1 gives a few examples). (f) They give similar pyrolysis gas liquid chromatograms (Fig. 2 gives a few examples) and characteristic pattern changes occur with change of pyrolysis temperature (our unpublished results). It is especially noteworthy that the infrared spectra and the pyrolysis gas liquid chromatograms of the insoluble organic matter from both meteorites are virtually indistinguishable from each other and from those of the morphologically intact microfossil planktonic algal spore *Tasmanites punctatus* (3.5×10[8] yr old). Other microfossils examined (our unpublished results), including *T. huronensis* (Dawson), have almost identical infrared spectra and pyrolysis gas liquid chromatograms. (g) Fossil spore exines survive in morphologically intact form into the Pre-Cambrian. They are accompanied by amorphous insoluble organic material and the properties of this leave little doubt that it is also composed of sporopollenin and presumably derived from those exines which (in modern counterpart, for example, poplar pollen exine) readily lose their shape yet retain the typical chemical structure of sporopollenin (ref. 8 and our unpublished results).

从奥盖尔陨石样品（0.1 g）和默里陨石样品（0.9 g）中分离不溶有机质的方法是：将其与氢氟酸、硝酸和氢氧化钾以常规方式一起反复浸煮，最终得到棕色的非晶固体，整个操作过程需要尽最大努力做到细心。这么大量的有机物（奥盖尔陨石含 3.5%，默里陨石含 4.4%）即使受到轻微污染，也不会对我们后续的化学检测造成多大的影响或者根本没有影响。检测固体的手段包括红外光谱、裂解气相色谱和钾熔法，随后对产物进行薄层色谱分析和元素分析[9]。同时，我们对以下来源的孢粉素——许多现代的花粉和孢子外膜、某些人工合成的类似物、微化石和一些人工变质（与砂子一起加热）的孢子外膜——也进行了类似的检测，并与前者进行了比较。结果清楚地表明：上述所有物质都属于同一种类型的聚合物，我们确信是孢粉素[8]。它们的共性主要体现在以下几个方面：(a) 它们对于非氧化性化学试剂具有稳定性，其中包括用于分离微化石或从无机环境中提取不溶有机质的非氧化性试剂。(b) 它们都是高度不饱和的并且很容易被氧化——无论从定性角度还是从定量角度来看，现代孢子外膜[6] 和化石孢子外膜[7] 的氧化（尤其是臭氧化）产物都极其相似，同时源自若干碳质球粒陨石相关实验的有限证据也证明形成物具有孢粉素降解产物的典型特征[1]。(c) 它们在乙酸的作用下不发生水解。(d) 它们与氢氧化钾发生熔合后，给出的特征谱类似于酚酸（参考文献 6 和一些我们尚未发表的结果）（间羟基苯甲酸、对羟基苯甲酸和原儿茶酸，或者是它们的混合物）。(e) 它们具有相似的红外光谱（图1 中给出了几个例子）。(f) 它们具有相似的裂解气液色谱（图 2 中给出了几个例子），并且其特征谱随裂解温度的变化而变化。尤其值得注意的是，实际上很难区分出分别源自这两颗陨石的不溶有机质的红外光谱和裂解气液色谱，并且它们与一种形态上完整的微化石浮游藻孢子——塔斯曼藻（年龄为 3.5 亿年）的红外光谱和裂解气液色谱也非常相似。我们对包括另一种塔斯曼藻（道森）在内的其他微化石的检测（结果尚未发表）也得到了几乎相同的红外光谱和裂解气液色谱。(g) 化石孢子外膜可以形态完整地存活至前寒武纪，其中伴有非晶的不溶有机质；毫无疑问，这一性质说明它也是由孢粉素构成的，并且很可能就是源自于那些尽管很容易失去原有形状，但仍能保持孢粉素的典型化学结构[8] 的外膜（与现代的物质对应的有白杨的花粉外壁等）（参考文献 8 和一些我们尚未发表的结果）。

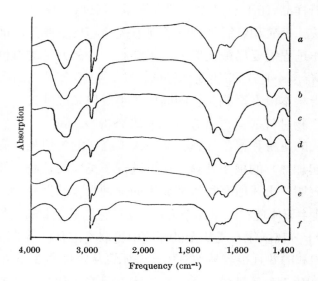

Fig. 1. Infrared spectra of some sporopollenins. *a*, *Lycopodium clavatum* spore exine after heat treatment; *b*, *Tasmanites punctatus* spore exine (a fossil planktonic alga); *c*, insoluble organic matter form the Orgueil meteorite; *d*, insoluble organic matter from the Murray meteorite; *e*, oxidative polymer of *β*-carotene; *f*, synthetic oxidative polymer from *Lilium henryii* carotenoids and carotenoid esters[6]. Each material (1–3 mg) was intimately ground with dry potassium bromide, the mixture compressed *in vacuo* to a disk (final weight about 0.1 g) at pressures up to 10 pounds per square inch for several minutes, and the infrared spectra measured on a Perkin-Elmer infrared spectrometer model 157.

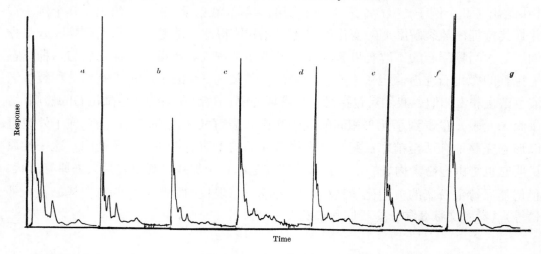

Fig. 2. Pyrolysis-gas chromatograms of some sporopollenins. *a*, *Lycopodium clavatum* spore exine with cellulose intine removed; *b*, *Lycopodium clavatum* spore exine with cellulose intine removed, after heat treatment; *c*, *Tasmanites punctatus* spore exine (a fossil planktonic alga); *d*, insoluble organic matter from the Orgueil meteorite; *e*, insoluble organic matter from the Murray meteorite; *f*, synthetic oxidative polymer from *Lilium henryii* carotenoids and carotenoid esters[6]; *g*, oxidative polymer of *β*-carotene[6]. A stainless steel column, 1/8 in.×5 ft., was packed with 5 percent SE 52 stationary phase on "Chromosorb W" (DMCS-treated, acid washed) support. A Varian-Aerograph 1520 gas chromatograph was used with flame ionization detectors. The N_2 carrier gas had a flow rate of 20 ml./min. The temperature of the column was 87°C. A Philips chromatography (P.V.4000 series) pyrolysis head and control units were used to give pyrolysis temperatures of the materials at 770°C. This temperature (770°C) was attained using the Curie temperature of a Fe (PV.4198) 0.5 mm filament wire.

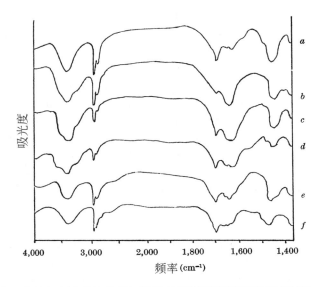

图 1. 几种孢粉素的红外光谱。(a) 加热处理后的石松孢子外膜 (b) 塔斯曼藻的孢子外膜（一种化石浮游藻）(c) 奥盖尔陨石中的不溶有机质 (d) 默里陨石中的不溶有机质 (e) β– 胡萝卜素的氧化性聚合物 (f) 由湖北百合的类胡萝卜素和类胡萝卜素酯人工合成的氧化性聚合物[6]。将每种物质（1 mg ~ 3 mg）与干燥的溴化钾混在一起充分研磨，混合物在真空中被施以每平方英寸可达 10 磅的压力，持续几分钟后被压制成一个圆形薄片（最终重量约为 0.1 g）。采用珀金 – 埃尔默公司的 157 型红外光谱仪对以上样品进行红外光谱测量。

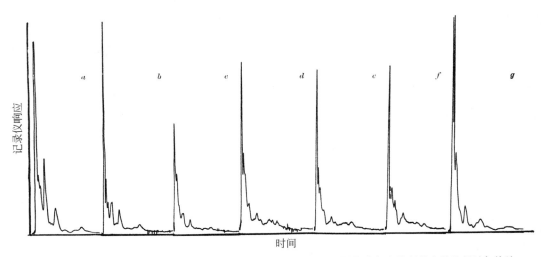

图 2. 几种孢粉素的裂解气相色谱。(a) 去除纤维内壁的石松孢子外膜 (b) 去除纤维内壁且经过加热处理的石松孢子外膜 (c) 塔斯曼藻的孢子外膜（一种化石浮游藻）(d) 奥盖尔陨石中的不溶有机质 (e) 默里陨石中的不溶有机质 (f) 由湖北百合的类胡萝卜素和类胡萝卜素酯人工合成的氧化性聚合物 [6] (g) β– 胡萝卜素的氧化性聚合物 [6]。色谱柱为一根 1/8 英寸 ×5 英尺的不锈钢柱，在硅烷化白色硅藻土（用二甲基二氯硅烷处理，并经过酸洗）上填充有 5% 的 SE 52 固定相。测试中使用带有火焰离子化检测器的瓦里安 – 埃罗格拉夫 1520 型气相色谱仪。所用载气 N₂ 的流速为 20 ml/min。色谱柱的温度为 87℃。采用飞利浦色谱仪（P.V. 4000 系列）裂解头和温控单元使样品的裂解温度达到 770℃。这一温度（770℃）是通过一根 0.5 mm 细铁丝（PV. 4198）的居里点温度实现的。

To our objective results must be added the earlier recorded subjective evidence which claimed the presence of spore-like bodies in both carbonaceous chondrites[9] and early terrestrial Pre-Cambrian sediments[10].

Our experimental results on the two meteorites, which are completely objective and readily repeatable on quite small amounts of material, provide, we believe, powerful evidence for the existence of extraterrestrial life. At the same time, because meteorites have consistently been shown to be $4.5-4.7\times10^9$ yr old[11] (at least as old as the Earth) our results imply that there was life in the Universe before the time of formation of the planet and certainly before probable reworking of the whole planet's surface occurred 4.0×10^9 yr ago[12], when the existence of life or even reasonably large organic nucleoproteins on Earth would have been most unlikely.

We hope that these results, which will be presented in much greater detail elsewhere, will help form a useful basis for future examinations of insoluble organic matter which might be present not only in Pre-Cambrian sediments and carbonaceous chondrites but also in lunar or other extraterrestrial rock samples.

We thank Mr. G. C. Speers, British Petroleum Co., and Professor G. Mueller for samples of the Murray (Smithsonian sample No. 1769) and Orgueil meteorites, Professor J. Sutton and Dr. M. D. Muir, Imperial College, London, for samples of Tasmanites species, A. B. Cernelle Ltd, Vegeholm, Sweden, for pollen samples, and Mr. D. Grant, Coal Tar Research Association, Cleckheaton, for loan of a pyrolysis unit.

(**223**, 754-756; 1969)

J. Brooks and G. Shaw: School of Chemistry, University of Bradford.

Received June 20, 1969.

References:

1. Bitz, M. O., and Nagy, B., *Proc. US Nat. Acad. Sci.*, **56**, 1323 (1966).

2. Calvin, M., in *Chemical Evolution* (Oxford University Press, 1969).

3. Schopf, J. S., *J. Paleontol.*, **42**, 651 (1968); Meinschein, W. G., *Space Science Rev.*, **2**, 480 (1963).

4. Hayes, J. M., *Geochim. Cosmochim. Acta*, **31**, 1395 (1967).

5. Han, J., Simoneit, B. R., Burlingame, A. L., and Calvin, M., *Nature*, **222**, 364 (1969).

6. Brooks, J., and Shaw, G., *Nature*, **219**, 532 (1968); *Grana Palynologica*, **8** (2-3), 227 (1968).

7. Brooks, J., and Shaw, G., *Nature*, **220**, 678 (1968).

8. Shaw, G., *Sporopollenin*, in *Phytochemical Phylogeny* (Academic Press, New York and London, in the press).

9. Nagy, B., and Claus, G., in *Advances in Organic Geochemistry*, 109 (Pergamon Press, London, 1964).

10. Barghoorn, E. S., and Schopf, J. W., *Science*, **152**, 758 (1956); Pflug, Hans D., *Rev. Paleobotan. Palynol.*, **5**, 9 (1967).

11. Anders, E., *Accounts of Chemical Research*, **1** (10), 289 (1968); Cameron, A. G. W., *Space Sci.*, **711** (Blackie Ltd, London, 1965).

12. Sutton, J., *Proc. Geol. Assoc.*, **78** (4), 493 (1967).

先前曾有人认为，在碳质球粒陨石 [9] 和地球上早期的前寒武纪沉积物中 [10] 均存在孢子状物质。我们应该把现在得到的客观结果加入到这一主观论断中去。

我们从这两种陨石样品中得到的实验结果是完全客观的，并且只要很少量的样品就可以轻易重复出这些结果。我们认为，这些结果足以证明地外生命的存在。同时，因为不断有证据证明陨石的年龄在 45 亿年到 47 亿年之间 [11]（至少相当于地球的年龄），所以我们的研究结果意味着宇宙在地球形成以前就已存在生命，并且无疑会出现在整个行星表面 40 亿年前可能曾发生过的重组之前 [12]，那时在地球上不大可能存在生命抑或一定大小的有机核蛋白。

我们将在其他场合更详细地公布这些结果，希望这些结果能有助于构筑进一步进行不溶有机质分析的有益基础。不溶有机质不仅可能会存在于前寒武纪沉积物和碳质球粒陨石中，还有可能存在于月球或其他来自地球以外的岩石样品中。

感谢英国石油公司的斯皮尔斯先生和米勒教授为我们提供默里陨石样品（史密森样本 1769 号）和奥盖尔陨石样品；感谢伦敦帝国学院的萨顿教授和缪尔博士为我们提供塔斯曼藻类样品；感谢瑞典韦耶霍尔姆的切尔内利公司提供花粉样品，同时还要感谢克莱克希顿煤焦油研究协会的格兰特先生将裂解设备借给我们。

（金世超 翻译；武宝玕 审稿）

Remains of Hominidae from Pliocene/ Pleistocene Formations in the Lower Omo Basin, Ethiopia

F. C. Howell

Editor's Note

The search for fossil hominids moved from Olduvai Gorge in the Rift Valley of East Africa to the Omo valley in Ethiopia—further north, and back in time. This is Clark Howell's field report on work by a team from the University of Chicago which, over two seasons, looked at sediments laid down between four and two million years ago, antedating Olduvai and with the potential to plumb further back in human evolution. Baldly, the report is a long list of teeth, tentatively assigned to one known form of australopithecine or another. There was little sign, as yet, of the palaeoanthropological revolution that finds from Ethiopia would spark in the 1970s and 1980s, with "Lucy" (*Australopithecus afarensis*) and still more ancient, primitive forms at humanity's root.

DURING two seasons of geological and palaeontological study in the lower Omo Basin, Ethiopia, a series of remains of Hominidae were recovered from deposits of Pliocene/Pleistocene age. These deposits are the Omo Beds (including the Shungura formation and the Usno formation) which are now known to range in age from >4.0 m.y. to <2.0 m.y. These discoveries have been made by an international expedition with a contingent from the University of Chicago under my leadership, and a contingent from the Museum National d'Histoire Naturel, Paris, under the leadership of C. Arambourg and Y. Coppens. The hominids are from a series of horizons rich in fossil vertebrates, especially mammals, and are of particular interest as they antedate those recovered from Olduvai Gorge, Tanzania. Hence the fossil record of Hominidae in eastern Africa is extended farther back through the earlier Pleistocene into the terminal Pliocene. This preliminary article records the specimens recovered by the Chicago contingent of the expedition.

Hominid remains have now been recovered from twelve localities in the lower Omo Valley. The temporal relationships of the hominid localities are set out in Table 1 and their positions keyed to a succession of volcanic tuffs which are useful and important marker horizons within the >500 m thick Omo Beds series. Radiometric (K/Ar) age determinations are available for: (*a*) three tuffs (*B, D, I*) in the main area of Omo Beds exposures[1]; (*b*) from a basalt underlying the fossiliferous sediments at two localities (Brown Sands and White Sands) north-east of that area (F. H. Brown, personal communication); and (*c*) from a basalt overlying fossiliferous sediments (seemingly without Hominidae) at the Yellow Sands locality situated at the south-western foot of Nkalabong Mountain at the northern end of the basin (F. H. Brown; and R. E. Leakey, K. W. Butzer, F. J. Fitch and J. A. Miller, personal communications).

在埃塞俄比亚奥莫下游盆地的上新世/更新世地层中发现的人科化石

豪厄尔

编者按

对原始人类化石的搜寻从位于东非大裂谷的奥杜威峡谷转移到了奥莫河谷——更靠北，年代也更古老。这篇由克拉克·豪厄尔撰写的调查报告记录了芝加哥大学探险队在两个季度的时间里对奥莫河谷400万年前到200万前的沉积物的考察结果，这些沉积物比奥杜威的年代更早并且有望由此进一步追溯人类的进化过程。坦率地说，这篇报告列举了大量的牙齿，作者暂时把它们分别归到了南方古猿的两个已知种类。到目前为止，来自埃塞俄比亚的发现还没有标引出远古人类的进化线，也再没有发现能够与20世纪七八十年代发现的"露西"（南方古猿阿法种）一样引人注目的更古老、更原始的人类祖先化石。

在对埃塞俄比亚奥莫下游盆地进行地质学和古生物学研究的两个季度的时间里，我们从上新世/更新世年代的堆积物中发掘出了一系列人科化石。这些堆积物就是现在已知距今400多万年前到不到200万年前的奥莫组（包括上古拉地层和乌斯诺地层）。发掘工作由我领导的芝加哥大学分队和阿朗堡、科庞领导的巴黎国立自然历史博物馆分队组成的国际探险队共同完成。这些原始人类是从一系列富含脊椎动物化石，尤其是哺乳动物化石的地层中发现的；因为它们比在坦桑尼亚的奥杜威峡谷发现的标本年代更久远，所以受到了特别的关注。由此，东非的人科化石记录可以向前提早到早更新世时期甚至延伸到上新世末期。这篇初步报告记录了由这支探险队的芝加哥分队发现的化石。

现在已经在奥莫下游河谷的12处地点发掘出了原始人类的化石。表1中标明了这些原始人类遗址的时间关系，它们的位置是揭开一系列火山凝灰岩之谜的钥匙；在500多米厚的奥莫层序列内，这些火山凝灰岩具有实用且重要的标志。我们将放射性（K/Ar）年代测定法应用于以下几种岩石：(*a*) 位于奥莫组暴露出来的主要区域的三层凝灰岩（*B*、*D*、*I*层）[1]；(*b*) 位于上述区域东北方向的两处地点（褐沙滩和白沙滩）、覆盖着含有化石的沉积物的一层玄武岩（布朗，个人交流）；(*c*) 位于盆地北端恩卡拉邦山脉西南山脚下的黄沙滩所在地、被含有化石的沉积物（看来似乎未见人科化石）所覆盖的一层玄武岩（布朗，利基、巴策、菲奇和米勒，个人交流）。

Table 1. Temporal Relations of the Pliocene/Pleistocene Hominidae Recovered from the Lower Omo Basin

Tuffs of main Omo Beds succession

Secondary	Primary	
	J	
	I	K/Ar age = 1·81–1·87 m.y. (I_2)
	H	
U	G	Hominid localities = *Locality 7; Locality 74*
T	F	Hominid locality = *Locality 28*
S	E	Hominid locality = *Locality 26*
R	D	Hominid localities = *Locality 9; Locality 64* K/Ar age = 2·37–2·56 m.y.
Q P		
	C	Hominid localities = *Localities 2, 45, 51, 54* White Sands and Brown Sands localities: K/Ar age = ≦3·1 m.y.
	B	K/Ar age = 3·75 m.y. (B_4)
	A	Yellow Sands locality: K/Ar age = > 4·0 m.y.

Brown Sands and White Sands Localities

Eight hominid teeth or parts thereof were recovered from the White Sands locality (Fig. 1). These represent a minimum of two, probably three, individuals. The series comprises the following (length and breadth in mm, and length/breadth or shape index in percent, are given successively where appropriate in parentheses)

White Sands.

W-23.	Left P_4 (11.8×10.5; 112)
W-508.	Right M_1 (13.25×12.2; 108)
W-749.	Right M^2 (13.2×14.6; 90.4)
W-752.	Right M_1 (14.1×13.0; 108.4)
W-578.	Mesial quadrant of crown of left M_1
W-750.	Fragment of P^3
W-751.	Disto-lingual quadrant of P_4 crown
W-753.	Right dm^1 (11.35×12.0; 94.5)

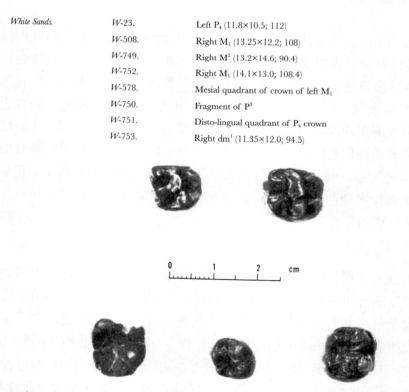

0   1   2 cm

Fig. 1. Hominid teeth from White Sands locality. Above, right dm^1 (*W*-753), right M^2 (*W*-749); below, left P_4 (*W*-23), right M_1 (*W*-752), right M_1 (*W*-508).

表 1. 从奥莫下游盆地发掘出的上新世／更新世人科化石的时间关系

主奥莫层序列的凝灰岩

第二	第一	
	J	K/Ar 年代 = 181万年 ～ 187万年 (I_2)
	H	
U	G	原始人类遗址 = 第 7 号地点；第74号地点
T	F	原始人类遗址 = 第28号地点
S	E	原始人类遗址 = 第26号地点
R	D	原始人类遗址 = 第 9 号地点；第64号地点
	D	K/Ar 年代 = 237万年 ～ 256万年
Q	C	原始人类遗址 = 第 2、45、51、54 号地点
		白沙滩和褐沙滩所在地：
	B	K/Ar 年代 = ≦310万年
		K/Ar 年代=375 万年(B_1)
	A	黄沙滩所在地：K/Ar 年代 = >400万年

褐沙滩和白沙滩所在地

从白沙滩所在地发掘出来了 8 枚原始人类的牙齿或其中的部分（图 1）。这些标本至少代表了 2 个或 3 个个体。该系列包括如下几部分（在对应位置的圆括号中依次给出用毫米表示的长度和宽度，以及用百分数表示的长宽比或称形状指数）：

白沙滩：	W-23.	左 P_4（11.8×10.5；112）
	W-508.	右 M_1（13.25×12.2；108）
	W-749.	右 M^2（13.2×14.6；90.4）
	W-752.	右 M_1（14.1×13.0；108.4）
	W-578.	左 M_1 近中侧的四分之一齿冠
	W-750.	P^3 碎片
	W-751.	P_4 远中舌侧的四分之一齿冠
	W-753.	右 dm^1（11.35×12.0；94.5）

0　　　1　　　2　　厘米

图 1. 在白沙滩所在地发现的原始人类牙齿。上排：右 dm^1（W-753），右 M^2（W-749）；下排：左 P_4（W-23），右 M_1（W-752），右 M_1（W-508）。

Eleven teeth or parts thereof were recovered from the Brown Sands locality (Fig. 2). These seem to represent a minimum of six individuals. The series comprises

Brown Sands.	*B*-27.	Right I^1
	B-14*a*.	Left P^4 (9.85×12.80; 75.4)
	B-14*b*.	Left P^4 (9.2×12.5; 73.6)
	B-4.	Left P^4 (9.0×12.5; 72. 0)
	B-23*a*.	Left P^4 (8.15×12.35; 65.9)
	B-23*b*.	Left M^1 (11.5×13.2; 87.1)
	B-39*a*.	Left P^3 (8.35×12.6; 66.2)
	B-39*b*.	Left P^4 (9.3×13.4; 60.9)
	B-39*c*.	Disto-buccal quadrant of M^1 crown
	B-20.	Lingual half of dm^2 crown
	B-28.	Distal half of dm$_2$ crown

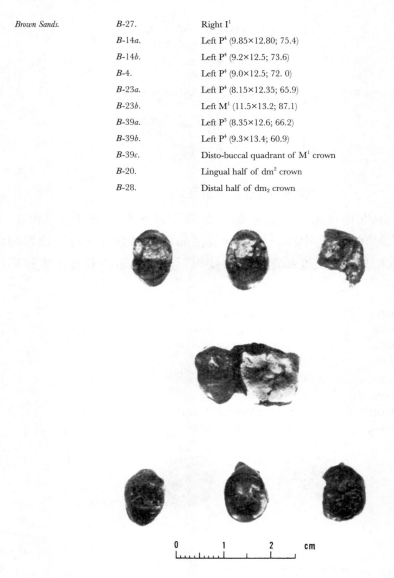

Fig. 2. Hominid teeth from Brown Sands locality. Above, left P^3, left P^4, inc. M^1 (*B*-39*a*, *b*, *c*); middle, left P^4, left M^1 (*B*-23*a*, *b*); below, left P^4 (*B*-4); left P^4 (*B*-14*b*); left P^4(?) (*B*-14*a*).

Except for several milk teeth and an upper incisor (from Brown Sands) the teeth from these two localities represent exclusively the permanent premolar and molar dentition. The complete dm^1 (*W*-753) is larger than the few known (and reported) specimens referred to either *Australopithecus africanus* (four specimens from two individuals) or to *A. robustus* (a single worn specimen). Its overall morphology and that of the incomplete dm^2 (*B*-20)

从褐沙滩所在地发掘出来了 11 枚牙齿或其中的部分（图 2）。这些标本似乎至少代表了 6 个个体。该系列包括：

褐沙滩：　　　　B-27.　　　　　右 I^1

　　　　　　　　B-14a.　　　　　左 P^4（9.85×12.80；75.4）

　　　　　　　　B-14b.　　　　　左 P^4（9.2×12.5；73.6）

　　　　　　　　B-4.　　　　　　左 P^4（9.0×12.5；72.0）

　　　　　　　　B-23a.　　　　　左 P^4（8.15×12.35；65.9）

　　　　　　　　B-23b.　　　　　左 M^1（11.5×13.2；87.1）

　　　　　　　　B-39a.　　　　　左 P^3（8.35×12.6；66.2）

　　　　　　　　B-39b.　　　　　左 P^4（9.3×13.4；60.9）

　　　　　　　　B-39c.　　　　　M^1 远中颊的四分之一齿冠

　　　　　　　　B-20.　　　　　　dm^2 齿冠的舌半侧

　　　　　　　　B-28.　　　　　　dm_2 齿冠的远舌侧

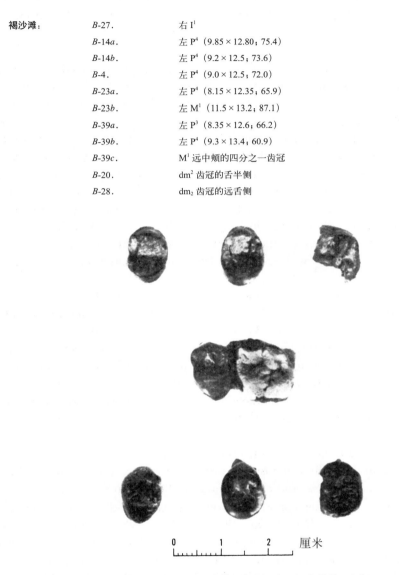

图 2. 在褐沙滩所在地发现的原始人类牙齿。上排：左 P^3、左 P^4、相关的 M^1（B-39a、b、c）；中央：左 P^4、左 M^1（B-23a、b）；下排：左 P^4（B-4），左 P^4（B-14b），左 P^4（?）（B-14a）。

除了几枚乳齿和一枚上门齿（来自褐沙滩）以外，从这两处地点得到的牙齿都属于恒前臼齿和恒臼齿。完整的乳齿 dm^1（W-753）比少数几个已知的（和已报道的）被认为是南方古猿非洲种（来自 2 个个体的 4 个标本）和南方古猿粗壮种（只有一个磨损的标本）的标本都要大。其整体形态和不完整的 dm^2（B-20）的形态都与南

resemble the australopithecines, while the incomplete dm_2 (*B*-28) has some morphological resemblance to samples from Swartkrans referred to *A. robustus*, as opposed to samples from Sterkfontein and Makapan Limeworks referred to *A. africanus*. The single upper incisor (*B*-27) has a mesiodistal length (9.2 mm) within the known australopithecine range.

The single P^3 (*B*-39*a*) is within the known size range of samples referred to *A. africanus*, but smaller than known homologues referred to *A. robustus* (or to *A. boisei*). Its shape index is within the lower range of samples from Sterkfontein and from Swartkrans. Two of the five complete P^4s from Brown Sands were associated with other teeth (see list earlier). All of these teeth fall within the known size range (based on eleven teeth) of samples referred to *A. africanus*, but are narrower than the known P^4s of samples referred to *A. robustus* (or to *A. boisei*). They are as short as, or shorter than, the smallest known specimens (of a sample of twenty teeth) of homologues referred to *A. robustus*. In the two associated specimens from Brown Sands, P^3 is smaller than P^4, not markedly so as in robust australopithecines, but more like the condition often found in *A. africanus*. The overall morphology of these teeth, particularly in the pattern of the primary fissure system and the lack of talon development, agrees most closely with specimens from Sterkfontein referred to *A. africanus*.

Only two complete upper molars are known, an M^1 (*B*-23*b*) from Brown Sands and an M^2 (*W*-749) from White Sands. The M^1 is within the known size range of homologues referred to *A. africanus*; it is shorter than known homologues referred to *A. robustus* (or to *A. boisei*), though barely within the known lower range in breadth and shape index. The M^2 is closer to the known size range of homologues referred to *A. africanus* than to those referred to *A. robustus* (or to *A. boisei*); its shape index falls within the ranges of both. The morphology of both teeth, and the incomplete M^1 (*B*-39*c*) as well, is broadly similar to that met within the Sterkfontein sample referred to *A. africanus*.

In the lower dentition only P_4 and M_1 are known. The White Sands P_4 (*W*-23) is unusually narrow. Its length and breadth dimensions and shape index diverge markedly from homologues referred to *A. robustus*, and also fall outside the known range of *A. africanus* (in which, however, only five specimens of P_4 are known). Its shape index even exceeds that of Olduvai hominid 7 (the type of "*Homo habilis*"). Both M_1s from White Sands (*W*-508, *W*-752) are within the range of variation of homologues referred to *A. africanus* for all dimensions. The former is smaller than the smallest known M_1 in the Swartkrans sample of *A. robustus*, while the latter is the same size as the smallest M_1 of that sample. The morphology of P_4 and of M_1 diverges from their homologues in the Swartkrans sample of *A. robustus* and approaches more closely the Sterkfontein sample of *A. africanus*.

In general, the teeth from these two localities suggest the presence of one hominid species which resembles the Sterkfontein sample referred to *A. africanus*. Most of the sample is therefore assigned to *A.* cf. *africanus*. An incomplete dm_2 (*B*-28) from Brown Sands and a complete dm^1 (*W*-753) from White Sands suggest that a second hominid, with resemblances in the deciduous dentition to known robust australopithecines, may also be represented.

186

方古猿很相像，而不完整的 dm_2（B-28）与来自斯瓦特克朗斯遗址的南方古猿粗壮种标本在形态上具有某种相似性，但与来自斯泰克方丹遗址和马卡潘石灰厂的南方古猿非洲种标本截然相反。唯一一枚上门齿（B-27）的近中远侧长度（9.2毫米）处于已知的南方古猿的范围之内。

唯一一枚 P^3（B-39a）的尺寸处于南方古猿非洲种标本的已知尺寸范围之内，但要小于已知的南方古猿粗壮种（或南方古猿鲍氏种）标本。其形状指数处于斯泰克方丹和斯瓦特克朗斯标本的下限范围。在褐沙滩发现的 5 枚完整 P^4 中，有 2 枚与其余牙齿有关联（见前面的列表）。所有这些牙齿的尺寸都处于南方古猿非洲种标本的已知尺寸范围之内（由 11 枚牙齿得到的范围），但是比南方古猿粗壮种（或南方古猿鲍氏种）的已知 P^4 标本要窄一些。它们与南方古猿粗壮种的最小已知标本（20 枚牙齿中的一个标本）一样短，甚至更短。在从褐沙滩发掘出来的两个关联标本中，P^3 比 P^4 小，不如粗壮南方古猿中那么明显，而与南方古猿非洲种中常见的情况更相似。这些牙齿的整体形态，尤其是最初裂隙系统的模式以及爪部发育的欠缺，都与在斯泰克方丹发现的南方古猿非洲种标本非常吻合。

现在人们只知道两枚完整的上臼齿，其中一枚是来自于褐沙滩的 M^1（B-23b），另一枚是来自于白沙滩的 M^2（W-749）。M^1 的长度落在南方古猿非洲种对应标本的已知尺寸范围之内，而比南方古猿粗壮种（或南方古猿鲍氏种）的已知标本要短一些，但是其宽度和形状指数仍落在已知的下限范围之内。与南方古猿粗壮种（或南方古猿鲍氏种）的同类标本相比，M^2 的大小更接近于南方古猿非洲种标本的已知尺寸范围；其形状指数落在二者的范围之内。这两枚牙齿的形态以及不完整的 M^1 都与属于南方古猿非洲种的斯泰克方丹标本非常相似。

在下齿系中，只有 P_4 和 M_1 已知。来自白沙滩的 P_4（W-23）异常狭窄。其长度、宽度和形状指数与南方古猿粗壮种的同类标本有很明显的差别，并且也落在了南方古猿非洲种（不过只有 5 个 P_4 标本是已知的）的已知范围之外。其形状指数甚至超过了 7 号奥杜威原始人类（即"能人"类型）的对应值。来自白沙滩的两枚 M_1（W-508、W-752）的所有尺寸都处于南方古猿非洲种标本的变异范围之内。前者的尺寸小于斯瓦特克朗斯南方古猿粗壮种标本中已知的最小 M_1，而后者与该标本的最小 M_1 大小相同。P_4 和 M_1 的形态与斯瓦特克朗斯南方古猿粗壮种的对应标本之间存在差异，而更接近于斯泰克方丹的南方古猿非洲种标本。

总之，在这两处地点发现的牙齿说明，存在着一种与斯泰克方丹南方古猿非洲种标本类似的原始人类。因此，大部分标本被归入南方古猿非洲种的名下。来自褐沙滩的一枚不完整的 dm_2（B-28）和来自白沙滩的一枚完整的 dm^1（W-753）表明：还可能存在着另外一种原始人类，它们具有与已知的粗壮南方古猿相似的乳齿齿系。

Localities below Omo Beds Tuff *D* and Tuff *C*

Arambourg and Coppens[2,3] have already reported a hominid mandible, without tooth crowns preserved, from a locality (their Omo 18) below Tuff *D*. Two K/Ar determinations on this tuff indicate an age of 2.37–2.56 m.y. (ref. 1). This fossiliferous zone thus seems to postdate the White Sands and Brown Sands localities, and it is certainly no older (this is also suggested by the faunal assemblages). A dozen isolated teeth have now been recovered by my contingent from one locality (2) below Tuff *C* and three localities below Tuff *D* (Fig. 3). These represent at least six or seven individuals. The series comprises

Omo Beds Locality 2.	2–79.	Incomplete $M_{2/3}$ (—; 13.8; —)
	2–89.	Left M_1 (13.7×11.5; 119.0)
Omo Beds Locality 45	45–2.	Right M_1 (12.9×12.0; 108.0)
Omo Beds Locality 54.	54–20.	Incomplete right dm_2
Omo Beds Locality 51.	†51–1.	Left M_2 (14.0×12.6; 111.0)
	*51–2.	Left M^1 (13.1×14.7; 89.0)
	†51–3.	Left M^1 (13.1×13.9; 94.2)
	‡51–4.	Left M^2 (or M^1?) (13.3×13.2; 100.7)
	*51–5.	Right I^1 (9×—; —)
	†51–6.	Incomplete right M^2
	*51–7.	Lingual half of right M (14.0×—; —)

* Younger individual.

† Older individual.

‡ Another younger individual, if 51–4 is an M^1.

Fig. 3. Hominid teeth from localities (51, 45, 2) below Tuff *D*, main Omo Beds. Above, left (?) M^2 (51–4); left M^1 (51–3); left M^1 (51–2); below, left M_2 (51–1); right M_1 (45–2); left M_1 (2–89).

Only the trigonid area is preserved in the single deciduous lower molar (*L*54–20) and it seems to have australopithecine affinities. The anterior dentition is represented only by

奥莫组凝灰岩 D 层和凝灰岩 C 层之下的地点

阿朗堡和科庞[2,3] 曾报道过一件原始人类的下颌骨，该下颌骨上没有保存下来任何齿冠，是在凝灰岩 D 层之下的一处地点（他们称之为奥莫第 18 号地点）发现的。对这种凝灰岩进行两次 K/Ar 测定的结果显示,其年龄在 237 万年 ~ 256 万年之间（参考文献 1）。因此这一含化石区的埋藏时间似乎晚于白沙滩和褐沙滩所在地的年代,并且其真实年代肯定不会比上述估计值更久远（动物区系的组成也暗示了这一点）。我的分队在 1 处位于凝灰岩 C 层之下的地点（第 2 号）以及 3 处位于凝灰岩 D 层之下的地点发现了 12 枚单独的牙齿（图 3）。这些牙齿代表了至少 6 个或 7 个个体。该系列包括：

奥莫第 2 号地点:	2–79.	不完整的 $M_{2/3}$（—；13.8；—）
	2–89.	左 M_1（13.7 × 11.5；119.0）
奥莫第 45 号地点:	45–2.	右 M_1（12.9 × 12.0；108.0）
奥莫第 54 号地点:	54–20.	不完整的右 dm_2
奥莫第 51 号地点:	†51–1.	左 M_2（14.0 × 12.6；111.0）
	*51–2.	左 M^1（13.1 × 14.7；89.0）
	†51–3.	左 M^1（13.1 × 13.9；94.2）
	‡51–4.	左 M^2（或 M^1？）（13.3 × 13.2；100.7）
	*51–5.	右 I^1（9 × —；—）
	†51–6.	不完整的右 M^2
	*51–7.	右 M 的舌半侧（14.0 × —；—）

* 年轻个体。

† 老年个体。

‡ 如果 51–4 是 1 枚 M^1，那么它就代表另一个年轻个体。

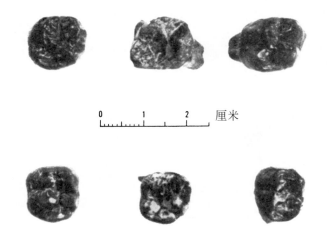

0　　　1　　　2　　厘米

图 3. 在主奥莫组凝灰岩 D 层之下地点（第 51 号、45 号、2 号）发现的原始人类牙齿。上排：左（?） M^2（51–4），左 M^1（51–3），左 M^1（51–2）；下排：左 M_2（51–1），右 M_1（45–2），左 M_1（2–89）。

唯一的一枚乳下白齿（L54–20）只保存下来了下三尖，看起来似乎与南方古猿具有亲缘关系。前面的齿系只有上中门齿作为代表（L51–5）。其大小与南方古猿粗

the upper medial incisor (*L*51–5). The size of this tooth is similar to both robust or gracile australopithecines; the morphology of its lingual surface, however, differs somewhat from both, and the morphology of the buccal surface is rather more like homologues referred to *A. africanus*.

The remaining teeth of this series represent upper molars (four) and lower molars (five). The first lower molars from Locality 2 (*L*2–89) and Locality 45 (*L*45–2) agree in size with homologues referred to *A. africanus*, and are as small as or smaller than the Swartkrans homologues referred to *A. robustus*. The second lower molar from Locality 51 (*L*51–1) is substantially smaller than its homologue in the Swartkrans sample of *A. robustus*, and slightly smaller than its homologue in the Sterkfontein and Makapan Limeworks samples referred to *A. africanus*. In respect to shape and particularly details of their fissure pattern and occlusal surface morphology these lower molars, and the incomplete specimens from Locality 2 (*L*2–79) and Locality 51 (*L*51–7) as well, have resemblances to lower molars from South African sites referred to *A. africanus*.

The first upper molars from Locality 51 are within the known size range of both *A. africanus* and *A. robustus*. The second upper molar (*L*51–4) from that locality is smaller than known homologues referred to *A. robustus*; its length falls within the known *A. africanus* range, though it is rather narrower. The morphology of these upper molars is clearly australopithecine, and there are some specific resemblances to the *A. africanus* sample from Sterkfontein. The sample from this horizon is therefore assigned to *A. cf. africanus*.

Localities below Omo Beds Tuff *E*

Hominid remains have been recovered from only two localities between Tuffs *D* and *E*. These represent only three isolated teeth (Fig. 4). They are

Omo Beds Locality 64.	64–2.	Left dm$_2$ (13.8×12.4; 111.2)
Omo Beds Locality 9.	9–11.	Incomplete right M$_3$ (>15.7×>14.0; >112.1)
	9–12.	Left M^3 (13.4×17.6; 76.1)

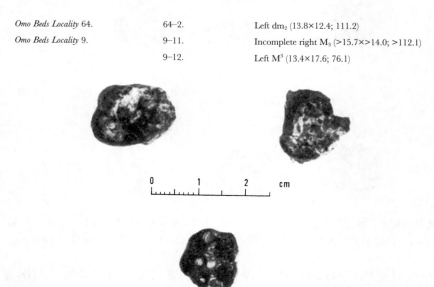

Fig. 4. Hominid teeth from localities (9, 64) below Tuff *E*, main Omo Beds. Above, left M^3 (9–12); right M$_3$ (9–11); below, left dm$_2$ (64–2).

壮种和纤细种都很相似；但其舌面形态与这两者稍有不同，颊面形态与南方古猿非洲种的同类标本更为相像。

该系列的其余牙齿还有上臼齿（4 枚）和下臼齿（5 枚）。在第 2 号地点（L2–89）和第 45 号地点（L45–2）发现的第一下臼齿的尺寸与南方古猿非洲种的同类标本一致，而与来自斯瓦特克朗斯的南方古猿粗壮种标本一样小，或者更小一些。来自第 51 号地点（L51–1）的第二下臼齿比来自斯瓦特克朗斯的南方古猿粗壮种标本小很多，而比来自斯泰克方丹和马卡潘石灰厂的南方古猿非洲种标本稍小一点。由形状，尤其是裂隙模式细微之处和咬合面形态，可以看出：这些下臼齿以及在第 2 号地点（L2–79）和第 51 号地点（L51–7）发现的不完整标本都与来自于南非遗址的南方古猿非洲种的下臼齿具有相像之处。

在第 51 号地点发现的第一上臼齿的大小与南方古猿非洲种和南方古猿粗壮种的已知尺寸范围均相符。来自于该地点的第二上臼齿（L51–4）比南方古猿粗壮种的已知标本小；其长度落在已知的南方古猿非洲种的范围之内，但是宽度要更小一些。这些上臼齿的形态显然对应于南方古猿，并与来自斯泰克方丹的南方古猿非洲种标本具有某些特定的相似性。因此从该地层得到的这一标本被归入南方古猿非洲种。

奥莫组凝灰岩 E 层之下的地点

仅在凝灰岩 D 层和 E 层之间的两处地点发现了原始人类的化石。这些标本只包括 3 枚单独的牙齿（图 4）。它们是：

奥莫第 64 号地点：	64–2.	左 dm_2（13.8 × 12.4；111.2）
奥莫第 9 号地点：	9–11.	不完整的右 M_3（>15.7 × >14.0；>112.1）
	9–12.	左 M^3（13.4 × 17.6；76.1）

0　　　1　　　2　　厘米

图 4. 在主奥莫组凝灰岩 E 层之下地点（第 9 号、64 号）发现的原始人类牙齿。上排：左 M^3（9–12），右 M_3（9–11）；下排：左 dm_2（64–2）。

The dm$_2$ is exceptionally large, whether comparison is made with other deciduous teeth from the Omo Beds series or with known australopithecines. It is as large as the largest dm$_2$s from the Swartkrans sample (thirteen teeth) referred to *A. robustus*, and larger than two specimens from Kromdraai. It is quite outside the known range of variation of samples referred to *A. africanus* (six teeth, two each from Sterkfontein, Makapan Limeworks, and Taungs, the last from a single individual). The tooth shows australopithecine affinities, with its general form like that of the Taungs child and most of its morphological details comparable with these described for the Swartkrans sample referred to *A. robustus*.

The upper and lower third molars from Locality 9 probably represent only one individual. Both teeth are large. The M^3 is in the range of samples referred to either *A. africanus* or *A. robustus*, though it is smaller than Olduvai hominid 5 referred to *A. boisei*. Its shape index and occlusal morphology agree best with specimens referred to *A. robustus* or *A. boisei*. The M$_3$, which lacks some enamel on its lingual and mesial margins, was also quite large. Its estimated dimensions are within the range for homologues referred to *A. robustus* and in the upper part of the range of specimens referred to *A. africanus*. Most of its morphological features can be seen in specimens of robust australopithecines from Swartkrans and from Peninj (Natron basin). The size of the deciduous molar and its morphology and the shape indices and morphological details of the two molars are similar to homologues which have been referred to the robust australopithecines *A. robustus* and *A. boisei*, but specific assignment of these specimens must wait pending results of studies by P. V. Tobias and others on the taxonomy of known robust australopithecines.

Locality below Omo Beds Tuff F

Two permanent teeth have been recovered from a locality (Locality 26) between Tuff *F* and Tuff *E* (Fig. 5), probably representing two different individuals. The specimens are

Omo Beds Locality 26.

26–1.   Right M$_2$ (15.5×13.0; 116.5)

26–59.   Incomplete left M^1 (14.5×—; —)

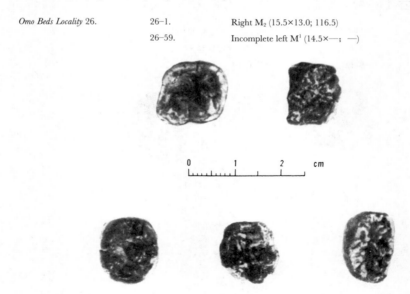

Fig. 5. Hominid teeth from localities below Tuff *F* (26) and below Tuff *G* (28), main Omo Beds. Above, right M^2 (28–58); left M^1 (26–59); below, right M$_2$ (26–1); right M$_2$ (28–31); right M$_2$ (28–30).

无论是与来自奥莫层序列的其他乳齿相比，还是与已知的南方古猿相比，这个 dm_2 都格外大。它同斯瓦特克朗斯南方古猿粗壮种标本（13 枚牙齿）中最大的那些 dm_2 一样大，比来自克罗姆德拉伊的两个标本要大一些。其大小与南方古猿非洲种标本（6 枚牙齿，两两分别来自斯泰克方丹、马卡潘石灰厂和汤恩，来自汤恩的标本属于同一个个体）的已知变异范围之间有很大的差距。这枚牙齿显示出与南方古猿具有亲缘关系，总体形状与在汤恩发现的幼儿标本类似，且大部分形态细节与对斯瓦特克朗斯南方古猿粗壮种标本的描述相符。

在第 9 号地点发现的上、下第三臼齿可能只代表一个个体。这两枚牙齿都很大。尽管 M^3 比归属于南方古猿鲍氏种的 5 号奥杜威原始人类小，但尚处于南方古猿非洲种或南方古猿粗壮种标本的范围之内。其形状指数和咬合形态与南方古猿粗壮种或鲍氏种标本非常吻合。在舌缘和近中缘缺少珐琅质的 M_3 也很大。估计其大小落在南方古猿粗壮种对应标本的范围之内，位于南方古猿非洲种标本的上限。其大部分形态特征与来自于斯瓦特克朗斯和佩宁伊(纳特龙盆地)的粗壮南方古猿标本一致。乳臼齿的大小和形态以及这两枚臼齿的形状指数和形态细节都与被归为粗壮南方古猿的南方古猿粗壮种和南方古猿鲍氏种相似，但是这些标本的具体分类要等到托拜厄斯等人对已知粗壮南方古猿的分类学研究有了结果之后才能定夺。

奥莫组凝灰岩 F 层之下的地点

在凝灰岩 F 层和凝灰岩 E 层之间的一处地点(第 26 号地点)发现的两枚臼齿(图 5)，很可能分属于两个不同的个体。这两个标本是：

奥莫第 26 号地点：　　26–1.　　　右 M_2（15.5 × 13.0；116.5）

26–59.　　右不完整的左 M^1（14.5 × —；—）

0   1   2   厘米

图 5. 在主奥莫组凝灰岩 F 层之下地点（第26号）和凝灰岩 G 层之下地点（第28号）发现的原始人类牙齿。上排：右 M^2（28–58），左 M^1（26–59）；下排：右 M_2（26–1），右 M_2（28–31），右 M_3（28–30）。

The complete M_2 crown is elongate, its length falling within the range of homologues referred to both *A. africanus* and *A. robustus*. It is slightly narrower, however, than homologues of either; its shape index is at the upper end of the *A. robustus* range, and is comparable with that of Olduvai hominid 7 (type of "*H. habilis*"). The morphology of this tooth resembles some specimens from the Sterkfontein sample referred to *A. africanus*. The incomplete M^1, which lacks small parts of the mesio-buccal and disto-lingual margins of the crown, is clearly australopithecine in its morphology. Both specimens are reasonably assigned to *A.* cf. *africanus*.

Locality below Omo Beds Tuff G

Three hominid teeth have been recovered from one locality (Locality 28) between Tuff *F* and Tuff *G* (Fig. 5). These seem to represent two individuals, one represented by an upper molar and the other by two lower molars. They are

Omo Beds Locality 28.	28–30.	Right M_3 (16.7×12.4; 135.0)
	28–31.	Right M_2 (ca. 15.0×13.0; ca. 115.0)
	28–58.	Worn right M^2 (15.5×14.0; 110.7)

The upper molar (*L28–58*), although very worn, is clearly australopithecine. This tooth has a very high length/breadth index, substantially above the range of teeth referred to *A. robustus* and even somewhat above the range of teeth referred to *A. africanus*. The M_2 (*L28–31*) has a shape index comparable with its homologue from Locality 26 (*L26–1*) and with Olduvai hominid 7. Its dimensions also accord well with the lower part of the known range of specimens referred to *A. africanus*. The M_3 (*L28–30*) is a long tooth, within the range of variation of specimens referred to both *A. africanus* and *A. robustus*. This tooth is very narrow, however, so that its shape (length/breadth) index is unusually high and outside the known range of specimens referred to either *A. africanus* or *A. robustus*. Olduvai hominid 7 (type of "*H. habilis*") lacks an M_3, but this tooth is preserved in a paratype specimen, Olduvai hominid 4 from site *MKI*. It is interesting to note that M_3 is shorter and slightly wider than the Locality 28 homologue, and its shape index is nearly twenty points lower. The morphology of both these lower molars from Locality 28 is similar to homologues from Sterkfontein referred to *A. africanus*. The specimens are therefore assigned to *A.* cf. *africanus*.

Localities above Omo Beds Tuff G

Hominid mandibles of australopithecine type have been recovered from two localities above Tuff *G* (and below Tuff *H*, although this tuff is hardly exposed in the northern sector of the main Omo Beds). Locality 7 (specimen No. *L7–125*) has yielded a complete mandibular corpus, lacking both ascending rami, with all permanent teeth except for three incisors. Locality 74 (specimen No. *L74–21*) has yielded a right mandibular corpus, without ascending ramus, preserving C, P_4 and the roots of P_3 and M_1. The second lower molar was evidently largely, or wholly, erupted to judge from the anterior part of its preserved socket.

这枚完整 M_2 的齿冠是细长的，其长度既落在南方古猿非洲种标本的范围之内，也落在南方古猿粗壮种标本的范围之内。不过其宽度比上述两者的同类标本略窄；其形状指数处于南方古猿粗壮种标本范围的上限，与 7 号奥杜威原始人类（"能人"类型）的相当。这枚牙齿的形态与来自斯泰克方丹的南方古猿非洲种标本中的某些标本很相像。另外一枚是缺少小部分近中颊侧和远中舌侧边缘齿冠的不完整 M^1，它在形态上显然应归属于南方古猿。有理由认为这两个标本都属于南方古猿非洲种。

奥莫组凝灰岩 G 层之下的地点

在凝灰岩 F 层和凝灰岩 G 层之间的一处地点（第 28 号地点）发现了 3 枚原始人类的牙齿（图 5）。这些牙看似代表两个个体，其中一枚上臼齿属于一个个体，另有两枚下臼齿属于另一个个体。它们是：

奥莫第 28 号地点：	28–30.	右 M_3（16.7×12.4；135.0）
	28–31.	右 M_2（约 15.0×13.0；约 115.0）
	28–58.	磨损的右 M^2（15.5×14.0；110.7）

虽然上臼齿（$L28$–58）磨损得很厉害，但是仍然可以清楚地判断出是南方古猿的。这枚牙齿的长宽比指数非常高，远远超出了南方古猿粗壮种的牙齿范围，甚至比南方古猿非洲种的牙齿范围还要略高一些。M_2（$L28$–31）的形状指数与在第 26 号地点发现的同类标本（$L26$–1）以及 7 号奥杜威原始人类的相当。它的尺寸也与南方古猿非洲种标本的已知范围的下半部分吻合得很好。M_3（$L28$–30）是一枚长牙，其大小既落在南方古猿非洲种标本的变异范围之内，也处于南方古猿粗壮种标本的变异范围之间。但是这枚牙齿宽度很小，所以它的形状指数（长宽比）特别高，落在了南方古猿非洲种或南方古猿粗壮种标本的已知范围之外。7 号奥杜威原始人类（"能人"类型）缺少一枚 M_3，但是在来自 MKI 遗址的 4 号奥杜威原始人类中，这枚牙齿以副模标本的形式被保存了下来。有趣的是：该 M_3 比在第 28 号地点发现的同类标本更短，并且还要略宽一些，其形状指数低了将近 20 个点。来自于第 28 号地点的这两枚下臼齿的形态都与斯泰克方丹的南方古猿非洲种标本类似。因此这些标本被归入南方古猿非洲种。

奥莫组凝灰岩 G 层之上的地点

在凝灰岩 G 层之上（位于凝灰岩 H 层之下，但在主奥莫组北部，这种凝灰岩很少会暴露出来）的两处地点发现了属于南方古猿类型的原始人类下颌骨。在第 7 号地点（标本编号 $L7$–125）出土了一件完整的下颌体，但缺少两侧的上升支，除 3 枚门齿以外其余所有恒齿都在。在第 74 号地点（标本编号 $L74$–21）发现了一件右下颌体，也缺少上升支，但 C、P_4 以及 P_3 的牙根和 M_1 的牙根被保存了下来。从其留存牙槽的前面部分判断，其第二下臼齿显然有很大一部分，甚至是全部都已经萌生出来了。

The hemimandible ($L74$–21) has a very deep, robust body (Figs. 6 and 7). The height of the body exceeds that of all previously known robust australopithecines, except for one value for the big adult $SK12$ specimen from Swartkrans. The thickness of the body is only exceeded in one dimension by that specimen and the Peninj (Natron basin) specimen. The symphysial height is great, at the upper end (or in excess of) the known robust australopith range, and this is equally true for the thickness values of this region. Both C and P_4 are large-crowned teeth. The length (8.8 mm) and breadth (9.7 mm) of C exceeds known values for the Swartkrans sample referred to *A. robustus* but is within the range of the Sterkfontein and Makapan Limeworks samples referred to *A. africanus*. The morphology of this tooth resembles fairly closely, however, that of the robust australopithecines. Only the roots of P_3 are preserved, but its length (approx. 12.8 mm) can be estimated from the contact facets on C and P_4. This value is greater than the known range of the Swartkrans sample referred to *A. robustus*, and that of the Peninj specimen, and also outside the 95 percent confidence limits of the former sample. This extreme elongation and apparent molarization of P_3 are the most distinctive and hitherto unknown features in such early hominids. The size of P_4 is within the upper part of the known range of homologues referred to *A. robustus*. Its length (13.0 mm) exceeds that of specimens referred to *A. africanus*, and its breadth (13.75 mm) is barely within that range. It has a higher shape index (94.4) than the range recorded for such homologues. The crown is strongly molarized, with expanded talonid, its overall morphology being similar to that of the Peninj individual or some specimens (for example, $SK9$) from Swartkrans.

Fig. 6. Superior (left) and inferior (right) views of hominid mandible ($L74$–21) from Locality 74, above Tuff G, main Omo Beds.

　　该半侧下颌骨（L74–21）具有一个很深且强壮的下颌体（图6和图7）。该下颌体的高度超过了除斯瓦特克朗斯的大型成年SK12标本之外其他所有之前已知的粗壮南方古猿的对应值。该下颌体的厚度只在一个方向上没有SK12标本和佩宁伊标本（纳特龙盆地）的大。其联合部高度很大，处于（或超过）已知粗壮南方古猿对应范围的上限；这一区域的厚度值也是如此。C和P₄都是大齿冠牙齿。C的长度（8.8毫米）和宽度（9.7毫米）均超过斯瓦特克朗斯南方古猿粗壮种标本的已知数值，但是落在了来自斯泰克方丹和马卡潘石灰厂的南方古猿非洲种标本的范围之内。然而，这枚牙齿的形态与粗壮南方古猿非常相像。虽然P₃只有根部被保存了下来，但是可以通过其与C和P₄的接触面来估计它的长度（约12.8毫米）。这个值高于斯瓦特克朗斯南方古猿粗壮种标本和佩宁伊标本的已知范围，并且还落在了前者的95%置信区间之外。P₃的极度伸长和明显的臼齿化特征非常显著，这是迄今在如此早期的原始人类中还未见到过的。P₄的尺寸处于南方古猿粗壮种标本的已知范围的上半部分。其长度（13.0毫米）超过了南方古猿非洲种标本，其宽度（13.75毫米）也几乎不在南方古猿非洲种的范围之内。它的形状指数（94.4）高于同类标本范围的已有记录。齿冠臼齿化严重，具有扩展的下臼齿远中部，其整体形态与佩宁伊个体或来自斯瓦特克朗斯的一些标本（例如SK9）相似。

图6. 在主奥莫组凝灰岩G层之上第74号地点发现的原始人类下颌骨（L74–21）的嚼面视（左图）和腹
　　面视（右图）。

0   1   2   3   4   5 cm

Fig. 7. Lateral (above) and lingual (below) views of hominid mandible (*L74–21*) from Locality 74, above Tuff *G*, main Omo Beds.

The Locality 7 mandible (Figs. 8, 9 and 10) clearly represents a very robust australopithecine. Compared with seven specimens from Swartkrans and that from Peninj, the Locality 7 individual exceeds all in most dimensions of the mandibular body, including height, thickness and overall robusticity, and in the size and robusticity of the symphysial region. The body is exceptionally deep and the roots of the canines, premolars and molars are very long and robust. The incisors, however, appear to have been shorter-rooted and less robust. The superior and inferior transverse symphysial tori are very robust, the latter exceptionally so, and the genioglossal fossa is extensive and deep. Mental spines are preserved on the postero-inferior surface of the inferior transverse torus. The alveolar planum exceeds far back to the midlevel of the last premolar. The digastric fossae are extensive and situated on the inner surfaces (rather than the inferior margin) of the body. The dental arcade is slightly parabolic with the premolar–molar series diverging slightly posteriorly from the nearly transversely aligned incisors and canines. The lingual surfaces of the mandibular bodies converge anteriorly to produce a A-shape to the inner mandibular contour, a consequence of the excessive thickening of their upper portion (comparable with the alveolar prominence) beginning just distal of the level of the second molar and continuous anteriorly as the alveolar planum.

0 1 2 3 4 5 厘米

图 7. 在主奥莫组凝灰岩 *G* 层之上第 74 号地点发现的原始人类下颌骨（*L*74–21）的侧面视（上图）和舌面视（下图）。

第 7 号地点的下颌骨（图 8、图 9 和图 10）显然代表了一个非常粗壮的南方古猿。与斯瓦特克朗斯的 7 个标本以及佩宁伊的标本相比，第 7 号地点处个体下颌体的大部分尺寸，包括高度、厚度和整体粗壮性以及联合区的大小和粗壮性，都超过了所有其他个体。下颌体格外深，犬齿、前白齿和白齿的齿根很长、很粗壮。但是门齿的根部似乎比较短，粗壮性也稍差些。上、下横向联合圆枕都很粗壮，尤其是后者，颏舌肌窝又宽又深。颏棘存于下横圆枕的后下方面上。牙槽平面远远超过了最后一枚前白齿的中间位置。二腹肌窝很宽阔，位于下颌体的内表面（而不是下缘）之上。齿弓略呈抛物线形，前白齿－白齿系列比几乎横向排列的门齿和犬齿稍微偏后一点儿。下颌体的舌面向前集中从而与下颌内廓形成一个 A 字形，这是它们的上半部分（相当于牙槽突出）发生大范围变厚的结果，这里的上半部分仅仅是从第二白齿水平的远端开始，然后继续向前而成为牙槽平面。

0 1 2 3 4 5 cm

Fig. 8. Right lateral view of hominid mandible (*L7–125*) from Locality 7, above Tuff *G*, main Omo Beds.

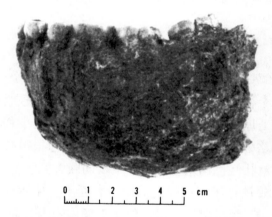

0 1 2 3 4 5 cm

Fig. 9. Left lateral view of hominid mandible (*L7–125*) from Locality 7, above Tuff *G*, main Omo Beds.

0　1　2　3　4　5　厘米

图 8. 在主奥莫组凝灰岩 G 层之上第 7 号地点发现的原始人类下颌骨（L7–125）的右侧视。

0　1　2　3　4　5　厘米

图 9. 在主奥莫组凝灰岩 G 层之上第 7 号地点发现的原始人类下颌骨（L7–125）的左侧视。

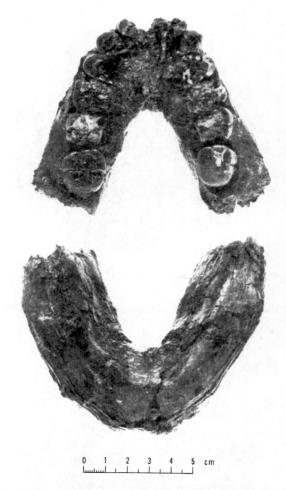

Fig. 10. Superior (above) and inferior (below) views of hominid mandible (*L7–125*) from Locality 7, above Tuff *G*, main Omo Beds.

The incisors are diminutive, the canines small, and the premolars and molars extremely large. The preserved right I_2 is smaller than that of any robust australopithecine yet known. The length (7.8 mm) of the left C is within the known robust australopithecine range, while its breadth (9.6 mm) is slightly above that range. The lengths of P_3 (10.4 and 11.2 mm) and of P_4 (11.7 mm) are within the known robust australopithecine range, but both teeth are exceptionally wide (P_3=approximately 17.5 mm, P_4=18.9 mm) and outside the known range of such samples. Hence these teeth have low shape indices, a condition also found in Olduvai hominid 5, referred to *A. boisei*. M_1 is both wider (18.7 mm) and longer (approximately 16.8 mm) than known homologues of robust australopithecines, and hence has a lower shape (length/breadth) index (approximately 89.8). The length (approximately 16.2 mm) of M_2 is within the range of robust australopithecine homologues, but the width (18.0 mm) exceeds that range, and the shape index (approximately 90.0) is correspondingly lower. The length (approximately 18.2 mm),

202

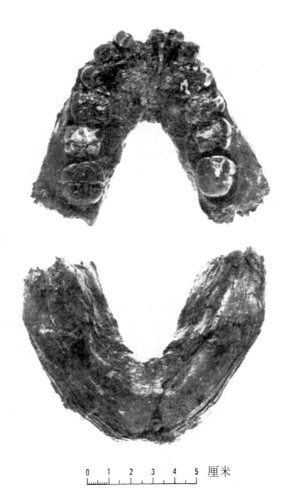

0 1 2 3 4 5 厘米

图 10. 在主奥莫组凝灰岩 *G* 层之上第 7 号地点发现的原始人类下颌骨（*L*7–125）的嚼面视（上图）和腹面视（下图）。

门齿小得出奇，犬齿也小，而前臼齿和臼齿却非常大。保存下来的右 I_2 比目前已知的所有粗壮南方古猿标本都要小。左 C 的长度（7.8 毫米）处于已知的粗壮南方古猿的范围之内，而其宽度（9.6 毫米）则略微超过了粗壮南方古猿的范围。P_3 的长度（10.4 毫米和 11.2 毫米）和 P_4 的长度（11.7 毫米）都处于已知的粗壮南方古猿的范围之内，但是这两枚牙齿格外宽（P_3 = 约 17.5 毫米，P_4 =18.9 毫米），这一数值落在了此类标本的已知范围之外。因此这些牙齿的形状指数偏低，该现象也会在属于南方古猿鲍氏种的 5 号奥杜威原始人类中被观察到。M_1 比粗壮南方古猿的已知标本更宽（18.7 毫米），也更长（约 16.8 毫米），因此形状指数（长宽比）（约 89.8）较低。M_2 的长度（约 16.2 毫米）处于粗壮南方古猿标本的范围之内，但是宽度（18.0 毫米）却超过了它的范围，所以形状指数（约 90.0）相应较低。M_3 的长度（约 18.2

breadth (14.8 mm) and shape index (approximately 123.6) of M_3 fall within the known range of robust australopithecine homologues. The details of the pattern of the occlusal surface of M_3 are sufficiently well preserved to indicate a close resemblance to homologues referred to robust australopithecines.

The crowns of the premolar and molar teeth are substantially worn. Dentine is exposed across the full width of P_3, and on the buccal side of P_4. The occlusal surfaces of M_1 and of M_2 have extensive dentine exposure except for the marginal rims of enamel. The surface of M_2 is worn deeply concave, even more so than that of M_1. The wear tends to be greatest on the lingual portion of the occlusal surface, as is frequently (but not invariably) so in individuals considered to represent robust australopiths. The mandible and dentition of this individual indicate that it represents a very robust variety of australopith in many respects comparable with hominid 5 recovered from Olduvai Bed I, site *FLK* I, and referred to *A. boisei*.

The Omo Beds of the lower Omo basin are now known to span a substantial range of Pliocene/Pleistocene time. Remains of Hominidae from a range of time hitherto largely unknown have now been recovered from a succession of fossiliferous horizons within this series of beds. Hominids known reasonably certainly from this general range of late Cenozoic time have included up to now a distal left humerus from Kanapoi, south-east Turkana[4], and a right temporal bone from the Upper Fish Beds of the Chemeron Beds series, Baringo basin[5]. In each case, the faunal evidence suggests broad equivalence with the earliest range of time represented in the oldest sediments of the Omo Beds Series, that is, probably between 3 and 4 million years.

A robust form of australopithecine, tentatively referred to *A.* cf. *boisei*, is known from the massive mandible from Locality 7 with a geological age of approximately 2.0 m.y. Another hemimandible from this same time range also has robust australopithecine affinities; but it is evidently unique in the extreme enlargement and presumably attendant molarization of the anterior premolar. For the moment, it is best treated as *Australopithecus* sp. Some teeth from earlier horizons, including specimens from Localities 9 and 64, as well as other localities worked by the French contingent of the expedition (Y. Coppens, personal communication), also have robust australopithecine resemblances. This suggests that antecedents of robust australopithecines extend back at least another half million, and probably more, years. The series of isolated teeth from nine other localities, ranging in age between about 3 and 2 million years, generally diverge dimensionally and/or morphologically from their homologues usually attributed to robust australopithecines. Their strongest resemblances are with specimens customarily referred to the small australopithecine, *A. africanus*. On the basis of present evidence it is not unreasonable to refer these specimens to *A.* cf. *africanus*.

If these attributions are confirmed, then the hominid samples from the Omo Beds would indicate the coexistence of (at least) two australopithecine taxa through much of the range of Pliocene/Pleistocene time. And this would have been the case not only in the Omo

毫米）、宽度（14.8 毫米）和形状指数（约 123.6）都落在粗壮南方古猿对应标本的已知范围之内。M_3 咬合面形式的细部保存状况非常好，足以表明其与粗壮南方古猿的同类标本非常相似。

前臼齿和臼齿的齿冠磨损得很严重。在 P_3 的整个宽度上以及 P_4 的颊侧都暴露出了牙本质。除了珐琅质边缘上的一圈以外，M_1 和 M_2 咬合面的其余部分都出现了牙本质的大面积暴露。M_2 的表面被磨蚀成很深的凹坑，甚至比 M_1 还要严重。在咬合面的舌侧部分，磨蚀似乎是最大的，这和被认为代表了粗壮南方古猿的个体经常（但并非必然）发生的情况一样。从这一个体的下颌骨和齿系可以看出：它代表的是一种非常粗壮的南方古猿类型，在很多方面类似于来自奥杜威第 I 层 *FLK* I 遗址的 5 号原始人类，并且被认为属于南方古猿鲍氏种。

现在人们已经知道奥莫下游盆地的奥莫组跨越了上新世 / 更新世时期的一段相当长的时间。现在已经从这组地层里的一系列化石层中发现了迄今为止鲜为人知的一段时期的人科化石。到目前为止，有理由认为肯定来自于新生代晚期这一大致范围的原始人类化石包括：来自图尔卡纳东南卡纳波伊的左肱骨远端 [4] 以及来自巴林戈盆地科莫龙地层序列的上菲什组的右颞骨 [5]。在每个例子中，来自动物群的证据都表明，其与奥莫层序列最古老沉积物所代表的最早的时间范围基本一致，也就是说，这些化石的年代可能介于 300 万年前到 400 万年前之间。

南方古猿中的一种粗壮类型，现在暂时被归为南方古猿鲍氏种，是根据在第 7 号地点发现的这件所处地质年代约为 200 万年前的巨型下颌骨得到的。另一件来自同一时间段的半侧颌骨也与粗壮南方古猿有亲缘关系；不过，第一前臼齿极度放大和可能与此相伴的臼齿化作用显然是它的独特之处。目前，最好的处理方法是把它归入南方古猿类。在早期地层中发现的牙齿，包括来自第 9 号地点和第 64 号地点的标本以及由本探险队法国分队（科庞，个人交流）从其作业的其他地点得到的标本，也都与粗壮南方古猿相近。这表明粗壮南方古猿祖先的出现年代至少还要再提前 50 万年，甚至还可能提前更长的时间。在其他 9 处地点发现的单独牙齿系列，年代介于约 300 万年前到 200 万年前之间，其大小和 / 或形态都与通常被归入粗壮南方古猿的同类标本迥然不同。与它们最相近的是习惯上被看作是小型南方古猿，即南方古猿非洲种的标本。从现有的证据来看，将这些标本暂时归入南方古猿非洲种并不是没有道理。

如果这些属性能够得以证实，那么在奥莫组发现的原始人类标本将表明：在上新世 / 更新世时代的大部分时间里，有（至少）两类南方古猿类群共存。不仅在奥

area, but even in broadly similar habitats, to judge from available palaeo-environmental data. The respective ecological niches of these creatures, however, remain essentially unknown.

The work of the Omo Research Expedition has been greatly helped by the full cooperation of the Governments of Ethiopia and Kenya. In particular, I thank Ato Kibbede Mikael, Minister of the Government of Ethiopia, for his interest and encouragement. In Nairobi, Dr. and Mrs. L. S. B. Leakey, and other members of the staff of the Centre for Prehistory and Palaeontology, have continually offered valuable assistance and hospitality. My work has been supported by grants-in-aid from the US National Science Foundation and from the Wenner–Gren Foundation for Anthropological Research.

(**223**, 1234-1239; 1969)

F. Clark Howell: Department of Anthropology, University of Chicago.

Received June 17, 1969.

References:

1. Howell, F. C., *Nature*, **219**, 567 (1968).

2. Arambourg, C., and Coppens, Y., *CR Acad. Sci. Paris*, **265**, 589 (1967).

3. Arambourg, C., and Coppens, Y., *S. Afr. J. Sci.*, **64**, 58 (1968).

4. Patterson, B., and Howells, W. W., *Science*, **156**, 64 (1967).

5. Martyn, J., and Tobias, P. V., *Nature*, **215**, 476 (1967).

莫地区如此，而且从可得到的古环境数据判断，甚至在与此大体相似的其他栖息地也是如此。然而，这些生物各自的生态位实质上还是未知的。

奥莫研究探险队的工作在埃塞俄比亚政府和肯尼亚政府的通力合作下得到了极大的帮助。特别是要感谢埃塞俄比亚政府大臣阿托·基比德·米卡埃尔对我们的关注和鼓励。在内罗毕，利基博士及其夫人以及史前考古学和古生物学中心的其他工作人员一直在为我们提供宝贵的支持和热情的款待。我的工作受到了来自美国国家科学基金会和来自温纳－格伦基金会人类学研究基金的资助。

（刘皓芳 翻译；冯兴无 审稿）

"Anomalous" Water

Editor's Note

Here two distinguished groups of scientists—J. Desmond Bernal and his collaborators in London, and colloid chemist Douglas Everett and colleagues at the University of Bristol—dismiss the earlier suggestion of F. J. Donahoe that polywater—an alleged new, highly viscous form of water—might be the most stable form of water, so that a tiny amount made in the laboratory might transform the Earth's hydrosphere into gum. Bernal was instrumental in popularizing the idea of polywater when he invited its "discoverer", Russian scientist Boris Deryagin, to visit his laboratory at Birkbeck College. But the researchers dismiss Donahoe's idea as "unduly alarmist", saying that the conditions for natural formation of polywater have existed for millennia without such a catastrophe occurring.

DR. Donahoe's unduly alarmist and misleading letter concerning anomalous water (*Nature*, **224**, 198; 1969) has come to our attention. As one of the groups currently trying to sort out the chaos surrounding this phenomenon, we feel a reply is called for, especially considering the alarming newspaper reports to which the letter has given rise.

Contrary to the data which Dr. Donahoe quotes as fact, remarkably little is still known about the precise properties of the substance, and it is still not certain that it even exists. Lippincott's polymeric structure, together with his binding energy figures, are still speculative and, in fact, contradictory stability figures have recently come from an independent theoretical investigation, suggesting the energy difference is not nearly so great.

One of the main reasons for there still being no coherent, self-consistent picture of anomalous water is the extreme difficulty of making it in quantities other than microlitres—and there is some suspicion that larger quantities are unstable. In the laboratory—where extreme care is taken—there is no evidence of its ability to grow at the expense of the normal phase (with which it is partially miscible) and in the absence of a quartz-like surface and without passing through the vapour phase; indeed, there is evidence of its gradual breakdown, especially upon heating and upon even small amounts of mechanical shearing. Although definite figures are impossible to give because of the quantities available, we are sure that not a single worker in the field shares Dr. Donahoe's science fiction worries.

There is still no adequate explanation of the phenomenon, and no coherent picture of its properties. One of the greatest difficulties in even accepting the existence of a more stable phase is its apparent absence in nature. Indeed, this is the most persuasive evidence of its inability to grow at ordinary water's expense, for it has stood the test of billions of years.

"反常"的水

编者按

在本文中，两位著名科学家所带领的团队——德斯蒙德·贝尔纳和他在伦敦的合作者以及胶体化学家道格拉斯·埃弗里特和他在布里斯托尔大学的同事——对多纳霍之前提出的论点表示反对。多纳霍认为聚合水（一种所谓的高黏度新型水）可能是水的一种最为稳定的存在形式，所以即使是在实验室中制备出的很少量的这种水也有可能会使地球表面的水变成胶体。当贝尔纳邀请它的"发现者"——俄罗斯科学家鲍里斯·杰里亚金造访他在伯克贝克学院的实验室时，他相当于帮助推广了聚合水的概念。但贝尔纳带领的研究小组并不同意多纳霍的观点，认为他"过分夸大其词"，他们指出：在自然界中形成聚合水的条件已经存在了数千年，却从未出现过那样的大灾难。

多纳霍博士所写的那篇关于反常水的快报（《自然》，第 224 卷，第 198 页；1969 年）过分夸大其词，容易使人产生误解，这引起了我们的注意。作为目前正致力于清理这类现象造成的混乱局面的小组之一，我们感到有必要作出回应，特别是考虑到由那篇快报所引发的一系列危言耸听的媒体报道。

与多纳霍博士引为事实的数据相反，目前人们对于该物质的确切性质所知甚少，甚至连它是否存在也不能确定。利平科特的聚合结构以及他的键能数据至今仍只是猜测性的；而事实上，最近一项独立的理论研究得出了与之矛盾的稳定性数据，认为能量差远没有那么大。

之所以还没有得到关于反常水的一致性自洽模型，其中一个重要的原因在于它非常难于大量制备，只能得到几微升的量——因而有人猜测它在量较大的情况下是不稳定的。在实验室中，无论操作多么精细，也不会在消耗大量正常相（反常水可以部分与之混溶）但没有石英状表面也不经过蒸汽相的情况下，发现反常水能够生长的证据；事实上，反而有证据表明它会逐渐分解，尤其是在加热和即使是很微弱的机械剪切力存在时。尽管由于所获得量的缘故而无法给出非常精确的数据，但我们仍可以肯定，本领域中的任何一位研究者都不会认同多纳霍博士营造的科幻小说式的忧虑。

目前尚没有令人满意的解释可以说明这一现象，也没有关于其性质的一致模型。哪怕只是承认有一个更稳定的相存在也是一个极大的难题，即这种相在自然界中显然不存在。毫无疑问，这是它不能通过消耗正常水而生长的最有力的证据，因为这

The classic conditions for its formation—a quartz surface and greater than 95 percent humidity—are very widespread in nature, yet no anomalous water has been detected. If it can grow at the expense of ordinary water, we should already be a completely dead planet.

Yet we are not, and totally unlikely to become so from this source. By all means draw the attention of scientists to the dangers of their work, but make sure it is a real danger before alarming everybody else.

J. D. Bernal
P. Barnes
I. A. Cherry
J. L. Finney

*   *   *

Donahoe's recent letter (*Nature*, **224**, 198; 1969) prompts us to draw attention to the present uncertainty concerning the nature and properties of "anomalous" water. First, it must be emphasized that, whatever the correct interpretation may be, several of Deryagin's experimental observations have been confirmed by recent work in several laboratories including our own. Anomalous properties are readily observed when saturated water vapour is allowed to condense in silica (or "Pyrex") capillaries with diameters less than 50 micrometres, and the bulk of the ordinary water removed by lowering the vapour pressure by about five percent. This is true even when the experiment is done in the presence of air and atmospheric pressure.

Because of the difficulty of making precise measurements on such small samples, some of the physical properties of "anomalous" water are still subject to some uncertainty. In particular, those listed by Donahoe cannot all be accepted without question. "Anomalous" water does not have negligible vapour pressure for it can be distilled; and although a density of 1.4 g/cm^3 has been reported, this value has been challenged recently by Mansfield[1]. Nor is there yet any conclusive evidence that "anomalous" water is more stable than ordinary water. The decreased vapour pressure of mixtures of "anomalous" and ordinary water is certainly no evidence for the greater stability of the anomalous species.

The mechanism by which "anomalous" water is formed is still not understood. The available evidence suggests that it forms only at the silica surface at the onset of condensation; subsequent condensation forms ordinary water which dilutes the anomalous species. There seems to be no evidence at all that, in solution in ordinary water, further "anomalous" water is formed spontaneously.

In view of the comparative ease with which "anomalous" water can be produced in the laboratory, it seems highly probable that it is also formed under terrestrial conditions, where suitable media and appropriate humidity fluctuations occur. Indeed, some of the

已历经了数十亿年时间的检验。形成反常水的典型条件——石英表面和95%以上的湿度——在自然界是非常容易满足的，但却没有人发现过反常水。如果它可以通过消耗正常水而生长，那我们现在应该已经处于一个彻底死亡的星球之中了。

但是我们还没有，而且也完全不可能因此而变成那样。尽一切可能让科学家们注意到自己的研究工作所具有的危险性是必要的，但是在向其他人报警之前就应该确保那的确是一种危险了。

贝尔纳
巴恩斯
谢里
芬尼

*   *   *

多纳霍最近的快报（《自然》，第 224 卷，第 198 页；1969 年）提醒我们关注当前与"反常"水的本质和性质相关的不确定性。首先，必须要强调的是：无论正确的解释可能是什么，杰里亚金的若干实验观测结果已经被几个实验室的最新研究工作所证实，其中也包括我们的实验室。将饱和水蒸气于直径不足 50 微米的石英（或"派莱克斯玻璃"）毛细管中液化，通过将蒸汽压降低约 5% 除去大量正常的水，这时就很容易观测到反常的性质。甚至在有空气存在和常压条件下进行实验也会出现这种现象。

由于用如此少量的样品难于进行精确的测定，"反常"水的某些物理性质到目前为止仍是不确定的。尤其是不能不加怀疑地全盘接受多纳霍列出的所有性质。"反常"水并不具有小到可以忽略不计的蒸汽压，因为它是可以蒸馏的；尽管有人报道说它的密度是 1.4 g/cm^3，但最近曼斯菲尔德对此提出了质疑[1]。而且目前也没有得到确凿的证据证明"反常"水比正常水更稳定。"反常"水与正常水的混合物的蒸汽压会下降无疑不能证明反常水具有更高的稳定性。

目前仍不清楚"反常"水的形成机制。已有的证据显示，它只能在冷凝开始时形成于二氧化硅的表面；在随后的冷凝过程中会形成正常水，从而稀释了最初形成的反常水。似乎完全没有任何证据可以表明，更多的"反常"水能在正常水的溶液中自发形成。

考虑到在实验室中制备"反常"水并非难事，它看来很有可能也会在地球上的自然环境中形成，只要有适当的介质和合适的湿度涨落出现。实际上，最早的一些

earliest suspicions of the existence of an anomalous form of water are to be found in work done thirty-five years ago on natural materials[2]. Ordinary and "anomalous" water must then surely have coexisted on Earth throughout geological time, without the kind of catastrophe envisaged by Donahoe. While, therefore, we respect Donahoe's concern that proper vigilance should be maintained in any research involving the preparation of new materials, we consider that none of the existing evidence warrants the pessimistic conclusions he reaches.

Robert Burns's affections were guaranteed to remain constant "till all the seas run dry". While he may not have envisaged the possibility that the oceans might instead become anomalous, we feel that his shade may derive some consolation from the fact that they have not already done so.

D. H. Everett
J. M. Haynes
P. J. McElroy

(**224**, 393-394; 1969)

J. D. Bernal, P. Barnes, I. A. Cherry and J. L. Finney: Department of Crystallography, Birkbeck College (University of London), Malet Street, London, WC1.

D. H. Everett, J. M. Haynes and P. J. McElroy: Department of Physical Chemistry, University of Bristol.

References:
1. Mansfield, W. W., *Abst. IUPAG Conf.* (Sydney, Australia, 1969).
2. Wilson, B. H., *J. Soc. Chem. Ind.*, 53, 397 (T) (1934).

关于水存在一种反常形式的猜测源于 35 年前人们对于天然物质的研究 [2]。那么，正常水和"反常"水必定曾一直共存于地球上的地质时期之中，却没有出现多纳霍所设想的大灾难。因此，虽然我们很重视多纳霍的担忧，即在任何涉及新物质制备的研究中都应保持适当的警惕性，但我们找不出任何证据可以支持他所得到的悲观结论。

罗伯特·彭斯（译者注：苏格兰诗人，1759 年～1796 年）的爱情誓言是：始终不变"直到所有的海洋都干涸"。尽管他可能想象不到所有海洋都变为反常水的这种可能性，但我们觉得，他的灵魂会因为海洋到现在为止还没有变成那种样子而感到一些安慰。

埃弗里特
海恩斯
麦克尔罗伊

（王耀杨 翻译；李芝芬 审稿）

Superfluidity in Neutron Stars

G. Baym *et al.*

Editor's Note

Physicists had come to understand that matter in neutron stars must exist at densities as high as 10^{15} grams per cubic cm. Some suggested that the interiors of such stars might well be superfluid (flowing without viscosity), and Gordon Baym and colleagues here comment on the likely consequences for these stars' properties. Superfluids, they note, tend to expel magnetic fields from their interiors, but their analyses suggested this could be so slow in stars as to be insignificant. The researchers suggest that interactions between superfluid neutrons and a star's surrounding magnetosphere might account for the observed slowing down of a number of pulsars—thought to be neutron stars—although more detailed calculations would be required to confirm that.

MATTER in the interior of a typical neutron star is a mixture of three degenerate interacting quantum liquids—neutrons, protons and electrons, the latter two having a density at most a few percent that of the neutrons[1]. The mixture, bounded on the inside by a superdense core of hadrons, muons and so on, and most likely by a solid mantle on the outside[2], is of density between 5×10^{13} and 10^{15} g cm^{-3}. As was first pointed out by Migdal[3], and more recently discussed by other[4-8], there are quite possibly superfluid states in this interior. Here we discuss certain general features of such states and the extent to which they influence the properties of the star.

As Ginzburg[7] has observed, the electrons are very unlikely to be superconducting, because they form a highly degenerate relativistic plasma in which effects of Coulomb interactions, relative to the kinetic energy, are of the order $e^2/\hbar c$. In particular, their superconducting transition temperature is vanishingly small on the scale of typical neutron star temperatures; the electrons are a weakly interacting normal system which can be treated microscopically by perturbation theory. On the other hand, strong interaction forces make neutron superfluidity and proton superconductivity serious possibilities. (Precise criteria for these possibilities, as well as their interrelation, can be furnished only on the basis of reliable microscopic calculations, which have yet to be performed.)

At first sight, one would expect that superconductivity of the protons would have a drastic effect on the magnetic properties of a neutron star, because superconductors exhibit some form of the Meissner effect—either a complete or an incomplete expulsion of magnetic flux from superconducting region[9]. As we shall now show, however, the enormous electrical conductivity of the normal state implies that the characteristic times for flux expulsion from macroscopic regions are typically comparable with the age of the universe.

中子星内部的超流

贝姆等

编者按

物理学家们逐渐认识到中子星内部的物质密度必须达到10^{15} g/cm³。有人认为，这类恒星的内部有可能会处于超流（无黏滞性流动）状态。戈登·贝姆和他的同事们在本文中讨论了超流对这些恒星的性质可能产生的影响。他们注意到超流体有将磁场排除出其内部的倾向，但他们通过分析表明这个过程是非常缓慢的，以至于对恒星而言并不重要。这几位研究者指出：超流中子与这类恒星周围磁层之间的相互作用也许能解释为什么会观测到若干脉冲星（被认为是中子星）的转速在减慢，尽管为确认这一点尚需要更详细的计算。

典型中子星的内部物质是三种相互作用的简并量子液体的混合物——中子、质子和电子。后两者的密度至多是中子密度的百分之几 [1]。该混合物被约束在由强子和 μ 介子等组成的高密度星体内核之中，其外部很可能有固态的幔 [2]，混合物的密度在 5×10^{13} g cm⁻³ $\sim 10^{15}$ g cm⁻³ 之间。米格达尔 [3] 最早提出在这种星体内部很可能存在超流态，最近有不少人对这种可能性进行了讨论 [4-8]。我们将在下文中论述这些超流态的一些基本特征，以及它们在何种程度上影响了中子星的性质。

正如京茨堡 [7] 所述，电子不太可能是超导的，因为电子形成了高度简并的相对论性等离子体，并且在等离子体中库仑相互作用与动能之比的量级是 $e^2/\hbar c$。尤其是，它们的超导转变温度与典型中子星的温度相比是极其小的；这些电子组成了一个正常的弱相互作用系统，在微观上可以用微扰理论进行处理。另一方面，强相互作用力使存在中子超流和质子超导的可能性变得非常大。（只有基于可靠的微观计算才能给出存在中子超流和质子超导的精确判据以及两者之间的相互关系，但至今还没有人进行过这样的计算。）

初看起来，我们会认为质子超导将对中子星的磁性质产生重大影响，因为超导体会表现出迈斯纳效应的某种形式——超导区域对磁场的完全排斥或部分排斥 [9]。然而，正如我们马上要说明的，因为正常态物质的电导率非常大，所以磁通量被排斥出宏观区域的特征时标通常会与宇宙年龄的量级相当。

215

The characteristic time, τ_D, for flux diffusion in normal, that is, non-superconducting, neutron star matter is $\sim 4\pi\sigma R^2/c^2$, where σ is the electrical conductivity of the normal state, R is the scale of variation of the magnetic field, typically the radius of the star, and c is the speed of light. Electrical conduction is primarily by the highly relativistic degenerate electrons, and thus $\sigma \approx n_e e^2 \tau_{tr} c/\hbar k_f$, where n_e is the electron number density, k_f the electron (and proton) Fermi wavenumber, and τ_{tr} is the transport relaxation time. From a detailed calculation, to be reported separately, we find that

$$\tau_{tr}^{-1} \approx \frac{\pi^2}{12}\left(\frac{e^2}{\hbar c}\right)^2\left(\frac{T}{T_p}\right)^2\frac{ck_f^2}{k_{FT}}$$

Here T_p is the proton Fermi Temperature, $k_{FT} \approx (4k_f m_n e^2/\pi\hbar^2)^{1/2}$ is the proton Fermi–Thomas wavenumber and m_n the nucleon mass. For $k_f \sim 0.7\times10^{13}$ cm^{-1} (corresponding to 2×10^{13} g of protons cm^{-3}) and $T \sim 10^8$ K, one has $T_p \sim 1.2\times10^{11}$ K, and $\tau_{tr} \sim 6\times10^{-14}$ s. Thus for $R \sim 10$ km the flux diffusion time is $\sim 10^{22}$ s (a striking manifestation of the proton degeneracy). In other words, the magnetic flux is rigidly tied to normal neutron star matter.

Suppose now it is energetically favourable for a given macroscopic region to become superconducting, with a condensation energy per unit volume $H_c^2/8\pi$, where H_c is the thermodynamic critical field. An elementary calculation shows that characteristic time to expel magnetic induction B from an initially normal region is $\tau_{nucl} \sim \tau_D(B^2/H_c^2)$; for typical values of B and H_c, τ_{nucl} is $\sim 10^{15}$ s. Nucleation of superconductivity thus cannot be accompanied by expulsion of flux. Superconductivity, if it occurs, occurs at constant B. Put another way, on a macroscopic scale, the magnetic flux at any point does not depend on whether the matter there is normal or superconducting.

There are two possible ways in which magnetic flux can penetrate superconductors[9]: in the mixed state in which one has a periodic array of quantified vortices of supercurrents, aligned parallel to the field; or in the intermediate state, where one has, on a fine scale, alternating regions of normal material containing flux, and superconducting material exhibiting a complete Meissner effect. Which of these two situations one expects depends on the ratio of the proton coherence length ξ_p to the penetration depth λ_p; for $\xi_p/\lambda_p < \sqrt{2}$ (Type II superconductivity) the vortex state is energetically preferable, while for $\xi_p/\lambda_p > \sqrt{2}$ (Type I) the intermediate state results. For s-state pairing the coherence length is given by $\xi_p \approx (2/\pi k_f)(\varepsilon_p/\Delta_p)$, where $\varepsilon_p = \hbar^2 k_f^2/2m_n$, and Δ_p is the proton superconducting energy gap. When $\lambda_p \gg \xi_p$, as we anticipate for proton superconductivity, λ_p is given by the London formula $\lambda_p^2 = m_n c^2/4\pi n_e e^2$, and

$$\frac{\xi_p}{\sqrt{2}\,\lambda_p} = \left(\frac{8}{3\pi^2}\frac{e^2 k_f}{m_n c^2}\right)^{1/2}\frac{\varepsilon_p}{\Delta_p} \sim n_c^{1/6}\frac{\varepsilon_p}{\Delta_p}$$

For $k_f = 0.7\times10^{13}$ cm^{-1} one finds $\lambda_p = 6.7\times10^{-12}$ cm, and $\xi_p/\sqrt{2}\,\lambda_p < 1$ for $\Delta_p/\varepsilon_p \geq 1.0\times10^{-2}$. Thus the protons are most likely a Type II superconductor, which, because of the finite B, will be in the vortex state. The magnetic flux associated with each vortex is

在正常的、或称非超导的中子星物质中，磁通量扩散的特征时标 τ_D 为 $\sim 4\pi\sigma R^2/c^2$。其中 σ 为正常态物质的电导率；R 为磁场的变化尺度，一般是指这类恒星的半径；c 为光速。因为导电主要依靠高度相对论性简并的电子，所以 $\sigma \approx n_e e^2 \tau_{tr} c/\hbar k_f$，其中 n_e 是电子数密度，k_f 是电子（也是质子）的费米波数，τ_{tr} 是输运弛豫时间。经过复杂的计算，具体过程将在其他论文中给出，我们得到：

$$\tau_{tr}^{-1} \approx \frac{\pi^2}{12}\left(\frac{e^2}{\hbar c}\right)^2\left(\frac{T}{T_p}\right)^2\frac{ck_f^2}{k_{FT}}$$

此处 T_p 是质子的费米温度，$k_{FT} \approx (4k_f m_n e^2/\pi\hbar^2)^{1/2}$ 是质子的费米 – 托马斯波数，m_n 是核子质量。由 $k_f \sim 0.7\times10^{13}$ cm^{-1}（对应于每 cm^3 2×10^{13} g 质子）和 $T \sim 10^8$ K 可以得到 $T_p \sim 1.2\times10^{11}$ K 和 $\tau_{tr} \sim 6\times10^{-14}$ s。对于 $R \sim 10$ km，磁通量扩散时标为 $\sim 10^{22}$ s（可以看出质子简并的显著影响）。换句话说，就是磁通量与正常态的中子星物质是严格绑定的。

现在假设一个每单位体积凝聚能为 $H_c^2/8\pi$ 的给定宏观区域（式中 H_c 是热力学临界场强）转变为超导态在能量上是有利的。初步的计算表明，从一个起先为正常的区域排斥出磁感应强度 B 的特征时标为 $\tau_{nucl} \sim \tau_D(B^2/H_c^2)$；代入 B 和 H_c 的典型值，得到 τ_{nucl} 为 $\sim 10^{15}$ s。因而超导成核过程不可能同时伴随着磁通量被排斥出超导区。如果超导能够产生，则一定是发生在 B 保持恒定的情况下。换一种说法就是：在宏观尺度上，任何一点的磁通量与该点处的物质是处于正常态还是处于超导态无关。

磁通量穿过超导体的可能方式有两种[9]：在混合态中，通过与磁场平行的超流量子涡旋的周期排列；在中间态中，通过小尺度上有磁通量的普通物质区和表现出完全迈斯纳效应的超导体区的交替出现。这两种情况中到底哪一种会发生取决于质子相干长度 ξ_p 与穿透深度 λ_p 的比值。当 $\xi_p/\lambda_p < \sqrt{2}$（II 型超导）时，涡旋态（译者注：即混合态）在能量上更有利；而当 $\xi_p/\lambda_p > \sqrt{2}$（I 型超导）时，中间态是有利的。对于 s 态配对超导态，相干长度由公式 $\xi_p \approx (2/\pi k_f)(\varepsilon_p/\Delta_p)$ 给出，其中 $\varepsilon_p = \hbar^2 k_f^2/2m_n$，$\Delta_p$ 是质子超导能隙。在 $\lambda_p \gg \xi_p$ 的情况下，当我们预期会发生质子超导时，λ_p 由伦敦公式 $\lambda_p^2 = m_n c^2/4\pi n_e e^2$ 和下式给出：

$$\frac{\xi_p}{\sqrt{2}\,\lambda_p} = \left(\frac{8}{3\pi^2}\frac{e^2 k_f}{m_n c^2}\right)^{1/2}\frac{\varepsilon_p}{\Delta_p} \sim n_c^{1/6}\frac{\varepsilon_p}{\Delta_p}$$

由 $k_f = 0.7\times10^{13}$ cm^{-1} 可以得到 $\lambda_p = 6.7\times10^{-12}$ cm；还可以得到：当 $\Delta_p/\varepsilon_p \geq 1.0\times10^{-2}$ 时，$\xi_p/\sqrt{2}\,\lambda_p < 1$。因而质子极有可能是 II 型超导体。由于 B 是有限的，所以这种超

$\varphi_0 = hc/2e \approx 2\times10^{-7}$ G cm^2 and the number of vortices per unit area is B/φ_0, where B is the locally averaged magnetic induction. For $B \sim 10^{12}$ G (ref. 10), the vortex lattice, which is triangular, has a lattice constant $\sim 5\times10^{-10}$ cm, large compared with the interparticle spacing. The vortices have normal cores of radius ξ_p, while the magnetic induction falls off in a distance λ_p from the core centre.

The critical magnetic fields (H, not B) between which the vortex state is thermodynamically stable are given by $H_{c1} \approx (\varphi_0/4\pi\lambda_p^2) \ln \lambda_p/\xi_p$ and $H_{c2} \approx \varphi_0/2\pi\xi_p^2$; for $\varepsilon_p/\Delta_p \sim 20$ and $k_f = 0.7\times10^{13}$ cm^{-1} one has $H_{c1}\sim10^{15}$ G and $H_{c2} \sim 3\times10^{16}$ G. We note further that the time for expulsion of flux from the vortex state is substantially greater than that for a normal region, τ_D.

In conditions of constant B, the transition from the normal to the superconducting state is first order. The maximum B for which the superconducting state is thermodynamically preferable to the normal state is that for which the free energy density of the vortices ($=BH_{c1}/4\pi$ for $B\ll H_{c1}$) is equal to the superconducting condensation energy density, $H_c^2/8\pi$ ($=m_n k_f \Delta_p^2/2\pi^2\hbar^2$). This critical B in fact equals H_{c2}; this is far greater than values of B one expects in neutron stars.

Because the flux in the superconducting regions is frozen, superconductivity in neutron stars is expected to have far less effect on magnetic properties of pulsars than previously believed[8]. We note also that in the rotation of a neutron star the electrons must corotate with the protons quite independently of whether the protons are superconducting or not, because any appreciable differential rotation would give rise to inordinately large magnetic fields.

Neutron superfluidity due to s-state pairing is expected[11,12] to occur for neutron densities between 0.6 and 2×10^{14} g cm^{-2}. In this regime the neutron Fermi wavenumber k_n varied from 1.0 to 1.5×10^{13} cm^{-1} and the neutron energy gap Δ_n is of the order of 1 MeV, falling with increasing density. The angular velocities of neutron stars lie well above Ω_{c1}, the minimum angular velocity at which it is energetically favourable to create vortices in the neutron superfluid, but well below Ω_{c2}, the angular velocity above which bulk superfluidity is destroyed by rotation. Thus, as Ginzburg and Kirzhnits[4] have noted, the neutron superfluid will contain an array of vortex lines parallel to the rotation axis, of sufficient number that on a macroscopic scale the neutrons will appear to be rotating as a rigid body and thus have their classical moment of inertia. The critical angular velocities are given by $\Omega_{c1} \approx (\hbar/2m_nR^2) \ln (R/\xi_n)$ and $\Omega_{c2} \sim \hbar/2m_n\xi_n^2$, where R is a typical dimension of the superfluid, and ξ_n, the neutron coherence length, is $\approx (2/\pi k_n)(\varepsilon_n/\Delta_n)$, where $\varepsilon_n= \hbar^2k_n^2/2m_n$. Taking $R \sim 10$ km, $k_n\sim1.4\times10^{13}$ cm and $\Delta_n=1$ MeV, one finds $\xi_n\sim1.6\times10^{-12}$ cm, $\Omega_{c1}\sim10^{-14}$ s^{-1} and $\Omega_{c2} \sim10^{20}$ s^{-1}. The angular momentum per neutron pair per vortex is $\hbar$, and thus the density of vortices per unit area is $\sim 2m_n\Omega/\pi\hbar \sim 2\times10^5$ cm^{-2} for $\Omega \sim 2 \times10^2$ s^{-1}, appropriate for the Crab pulsar *NP* 0532.

As pointed out by several authors[10,13,14], the slowing down of a neutron star results from the loss of energy via electromagnetic coupling of the charged particles in the star to the

导体将处于涡旋态。与每个涡旋相关联的磁通量为 $\varphi_0 = hc/2e \approx 2\times10^{-7}$ G cm^2，而每单位面积的涡旋数量为 B/φ_0，其中 B 是局域平均的磁感应强度。当 $B \sim 10^{12}$ G（参考文献 10）时，涡旋晶格呈三角形，晶格常数约为 5×10^{-10} cm，比粒子间隔要大。这种涡旋具有半径为 ξ_p 的正常核，同时磁感应强度在距离核中心 λ_p 处迅速降低。

涡旋态在两个临界磁场强度（H，而非 B）之间是热力学稳定的，它们分别是 $H_{c1} \approx (\varphi_0/4\pi\lambda_p^2) \ln \lambda_p/\xi_p$ 和 $H_{c2} \approx \varphi_0/2\pi\xi_p^2$；当 $\varepsilon_p/\Delta_p \sim 20$ 和 $k_f = 0.7\times10^{13}$ cm^{-1} 时，可得出 $H_{c1} \sim 10^{15}$ G 及 $H_{c2} \sim 3\times10^{16}$ G。我们还注意到，把磁通量排斥出涡旋态的时间要比排斥出正常态区域的时间 τ_D 长很多。

对于 B 保持不变的情况，从正常态到超导态的转变是一阶相变。使超导态在热力学上比正常态更稳定的 B 有一个上限，此时涡旋的自由能密度（$=BH_{c1}/4\pi$，当 $B\ll H_{c1}$ 时）应与超导态的凝聚能密度 $H_c^2/8\pi$（$=m_nk_f\Delta_p^2/2\pi^2\hbar^2$）相等。这个临界 B 值实际上就等于 H_{c2}，远高于预期的中子星中的 B 值。

由于在超导区磁通量是被冻结的，因而可以预测中子星内的超导对于脉冲星磁性质的影响要远远小于之前所认为的值 [8]。我们还注意到：当中子星旋转时，无论质子是否处于超导态，电子都必须与质子共转，因为任何明显的较差转动都会产生非常大的磁场。

可以预测由 s 态配对导致的中子超流 [11,12] 会发生在中子物质密度为 0.6×10^{14} g cm^{-2} $\sim 2\times10^{14}$ g cm^{-2} 时。在这个范围内，中子的费米波数 k_n 为 1.0×10^{13} cm^{-1} ～ 1.5×10^{13} cm^{-1}，而中子能隙 Δ_n 可达 1 MeV 量级并随密度的增加而降低。中子星转动的角速度应远大于 Ω_{c1}，Ω_{c1} 是使中子超流体产生涡旋在能量上更有利的最小角速度；同时中子星转动的角速度要远远小于 Ω_{c2}，大于此值时整体超流将会被旋转破坏。因此，正如京茨堡和基尔日尼茨 [4] 所指出的：中子超流体将包含与旋转轴平行的涡线阵列，因为涡线的数量足够多，所以在宏观尺度上中子物质将像刚体一样旋转，因而其转动惯量也具有经典的形式。这两个临界角速度可由 $\Omega_{c1} \approx (\hbar/2m_nR^2) \ln (R/\xi_n)$ 和 $\Omega_{c2} \sim \hbar/2m_n\xi_n^2$ 给出。其中 R 是超流体的典型尺度；ξ_n 是中子的相干长度，其值可由 $\xi_n \approx (2/\pi k_n)(\varepsilon_n/\Delta_n)$ 得到，上式中的 $\varepsilon_n = \hbar^2k_n^2/2m_n$。假设 $R \sim 10$ km、$k_n \sim 1.4\times10^{13}$ cm 和 $\Delta_n = 1$ MeV，则可以得到 $\xi_n \sim 1.6\times10^{-12}$ cm，$\Omega_{c1} \sim 10^{-14}$ s^{-1} 以及 $\Omega_{c2} \sim 10^{20}$ s^{-1}。每涡旋每中子对的角动量为 $\hbar$，所以当 $\Omega \sim 2\times10^2$ s^{-1} 时，单位面积上的涡旋密度为 $\sim 2m_n\Omega/\pi\hbar \sim 2\times10^5$ cm^{-2}，这对于蟹状星云脉冲星 NP 0532 来说是合适的。

正如一些作者所指出的 [10,13,14]，中子星转速的减慢是由这类恒星中带电粒子与周

surrounding magnetosphere; the pulsar clock is determined by the rotation of the charged particles in the star. The principal energy source, however, is the rotational energy of the neutrons. One is immediately led to ask how the neutrons can transfer their rotational energy to the charged particles. If both the neutron and proton fluids are normal, any relative motion is quickly damped out by strong interactions in a characteristic time $\tau \approx 9\hbar^3/[32\sigma_{np}m_n (k_B T)^2] \sim 10^{-17}$ s in bulk matter (σ_{np} is a typical neutron-proton scattering cross-section and k_B is Boltzmann's constant). Should the protons be superfluid, coupling between the charged particles and the neutrons is still provided by the interaction of the electrons with the neutron magnetic moments. Such processes cause charged particle–neutron relative motion in bulk to relax in a time $\sim 10^{-11}$ s, a factor 10^6 greater than when the protons are normal, but still microscopic.

If the neutrons are superfluid, the situation changes drastically. Now the only effective scattering of the charged particles by the neutrons takes place in the normal cores of the neutron vortices. This increases the relaxation times by a factor $\Omega_{c2}/\Omega \sim 10^{18}$, which is a measure of the relative volume of the vortex cores. In the case of simultaneous proton and neutron superfluidity the coupling time reaches years, not altogether negligible on the evolutionary time scale of a neutron star. Any change in the angular momentum of the neutron superfluid must occur via the creation or destruction of vortices, either in the bulk of the superfluid or at the interface of the superfluid and normal regions. Estimating the rates for these processes remains, as in the case of laboratory superfluid helium, an unsolved problem. The observed decrease in the slow-down rate of the Vela pulsar (*PSR 0833–45*), following its sudden speed-up, is conceivably due to such a relaxation between the solid crust and the fluid interior. (The details of the calculations will be published later.)

We thank Professor John Bardeen for useful comments and the Aspen Center for Physics for hospitality during the preparation of this communication. This research is supported by the US National Science Foundation, the Army Research Office (Durham), and the US Air Force Office of Scientific Research.

(**224**, 673-674; 1969)

Gordon Baym, Christopher Pethick[*] and David Pines: Department of Physics, University of Illinois, Urbana, Illinois 61801.

Received September 2, 1969.

References:

1. Nemeth, J., and Sprung, D. W. L., *Phys. Rev.*, **176**, 1496 (1968).
2. Ruderman, M., *Nature*, **218**, 1128 (1968).

* on leave of absence from Magdalen College, Oxford.

围磁层发生电磁耦合而导致的能量损失造成的；脉冲星的时钟取决于这类恒星中带电粒子的转动。但主要的能量来源仍是中子的转动能。于是我们马上会问：中子如何才能把转动能传递给带电粒子？如果中子流体和质子流体均处于正常态，那么任何相对运动都会因在大块物质中特征时标为 $\tau \approx 9\hbar^3/[32\sigma_{np}m_n(k_BT)^2] \sim 10^{-17}$ s（σ_{np} 是典型的中子－质子散射截面，k_B 为玻尔兹曼常数）的强相互作用而很快耗散掉。即使质子是超流体，带电粒子与中子的耦合仍由电子与中子磁矩的相互作用提供。这种作用使带电粒子与中子间大块相对运动的弛豫时间为 $\sim 10^{-11}$ s。这比质子处于正常态时大 6 个数量级，但仍然很小。

如果中子是超流体，情况就会发生显著的变化。此时，中子对带电粒子的有效散射仅发生在中子涡旋的正常态核心处。这将使弛豫时间增加 $\Omega_{c2}/\Omega \sim 10^{18}$ 倍，这个值也是涡旋核心相对体积的一种量度。在质子超流和中子超流同时存在的情况下，耦合时标将达到若干年，这相对于中子星演化的时间尺度来说是不能完全忽略不计的。中子超流体角动量的任何变化都必须通过生成或破坏涡旋来实现，无论是在超流体的内部还是在超流区与正常区的交界处。与在实验室超流氦研究中遇到的问题一样，怎样估计这些过程的速率也是一个尚未解决的问题。已经观测到船帆座脉冲星（*PSR* 0833–45）在突然加速之后慢下来的速率有所下降，这显然是由固体壳和液体核的弛豫过程造成的。（计算细节将在以后发表。）

感谢约翰·巴丁教授为我们提出了有价值的建议以及阿斯彭物理中心在准备此次会谈期间的热情招待。这项研究得到了以下单位的资助：美国国家科学基金会、陆军研究办公室（位于达勒姆）和美国空军科学研究办公室。

（岳友岭 翻译；蒋世仰 审稿）

3. Migdal, A. B., *Zh. Exp. Theor. Fiz.*, **37**, 249 (1959).

4. Ginzburg, V. L., and Kirzhnits, D. A., *Zh. Exp. Theor. Phys.*, **47**, 2006 (1964). English trans. in *Sov. Phys. JETP*, **20**, 1346 (1965).

5. Wolf, R. A., *Astrophys. J.*, **145**, 834 (1966).

6. Ruderman, M., in *Proc. Fifth Eastern Theor. Phys. Conf.* (edit. by Feldman, D.) (W. A. Benjamin, New York, 1967).

7. Ginzburg, V. L., *Uspekhi Fiz. Nauk*, **97**, 601 (1969).

8. Ginzburg, V. L., and Kirzhnits, D. A., *Nature*, **220**, 148 (1968).

9. De Gennes, P.-G., *Superconductivity of Metals and Alloys* (W. A. Benjamin, New York, 1966).

10. Gold, T., *Nature*, **218**, 731 (1968).

11. Ruderman, M., *J. de Physique* (in the press).

12. Kennedy, R., Wilets, L., and Henley, E. M., *Phys. Rev.*, **133**, B1131 (1964).

13. Pacini, F., *Nature*, **219**, 145 (1968).

14. Goldreich, P., and Julian, W. H., *Astrophys. J.*, **157**, 869 (1969).

New Finds at the Swartkrans Australopithecine Site

C. K. Brain

Editor's Note

The site of Swartkrans, near Sterkfontein, had been opened up by Broom and Robinson, who had discovered abundant remains of a robust australopithecine as well as a more advanced hominid, at first called *Telanthropus*, later referred to *Homo erectus*. This report from the site by C. K. Brain contains descriptions of stone tools similar to those found at Olduvai Gorge in East Africa, as well as a dramatic and grisly discovery—an australopithecine skull pierced by the canine teeth of a leopard. Brain re-interpreted at least some of the Swartkrans site not as a hominid living space, but the den of leopards, containing the remains of some of their meals.

SWARTKRANS, one of the five South African australopithecine cave sites, has produced remains of more than sixty individuals of the large hominid, *Paranthropus robustus*, and is the only cave site where fossils of *Homo* have been found in direct association with those of australopithecines.

The new investigations described here have clarified a number of the important Swartkrans issues. A new series of hominid fossils has been discovered (including two vertebrae which will be described in detail by Dr. J. T. Robinson[1]), and it has been possible to associate indisputable stone culture with the hominid remains. The tools have been critically examined by Dr. Mary Leakey, who has compared them with an equivalent series from Olduvai Gorge in Tanzania and has found striking similarities with the assemblage from Bed II of that site[2]. In the absence of absolute dating for the Swartkrans fossils, cultural comparisons of this sort assume particular significance. Unexpected new information has come to light on the nature of the second hominid at Swartkrans[3], while a study of the bone accumulation as a whole has led me to conclude that the australopithecine remains, together with many of the other fossils, probably represent food remains of carnivores, especially of leopards.

Swartkrans is situated in the Sterkfontein valley, approximately 8 miles north of Krugersdorp, Transvaal. It was first scientifically investigated in 1948 by the late Dr. Robert Broom and By Dr. J. T. Robinson, who transferred the Transvaal Museum's operations to the cave from Sterkfontein, on the opposite side of the valley. Excavation of *in situ* breccia continued throughout 1949 and resulted in the recovery of about 3,000 fossils, including numerous *Paranthropus* specimens and remains of a second hominid, named *Telanthropus capensis*[4], but subsequently reclassified as *Homo erectus*[5].

在斯瓦特克朗斯南方古猿遗址的新发现

布雷恩

编者按

靠近斯泰克方丹的斯瓦特克朗斯遗址是由布鲁姆和鲁滨逊发掘的，他们在那里发现了一种粗壮型南方古猿的大量化石以及一种更为高等的原始人类，这种原始人类起初被命名为远人，后来被归入直立人。布雷恩在这篇关于该遗址的报告中不仅谈到了一个不可思议的发现——一件曾被豹子的犬齿刺穿的南方古猿头骨，还论证了这里的石器与在东非奥杜威峡谷发现的类似。布雷恩的最新诠释是：在斯瓦特克朗斯遗址中至少有一部分并非原始人类的居住之所，而是豹的巢穴，里面有豹留下的食余垃圾。

斯瓦特克朗斯是南非的 5 个南方古猿洞穴遗址之一，在此出土了 60 多件大型原始人科——傍人粗壮种个体的标本，这里是唯一一处发现人属化石与南方古猿化石相伴生的洞穴遗址。

本文描述的新发现澄清了许多关于斯瓦特克朗斯的重要争议。在这里发现了一系列新的原始人类化石（包括两块脊椎骨，鲁滨逊博士 [1] 将对此进行详细记述），因而使我们有可能将无可置疑的石器文化与人科联系起来。玛丽·利基博士曾对这些石器进行过审慎的检查，她将这些石器和坦桑尼亚奥杜威峡谷相当的石器进行了比较，发现它们与在奥杜威遗址第 II 层发现的石器有着惊人的相似性 [2]。由于不知道斯瓦特克朗斯化石的绝对年代，所以这种文化比较就具有特别的意义。我们已经公布了一些关于斯瓦特克朗斯第二种人科标本特性的出人意料的新信息 [3]，而对堆积的骨骼化石进行的整体研究令我得出如下结论：南方古猿化石以及许多其他化石很可能是食肉动物的，尤其是豹的，食余垃圾。

斯瓦特克朗斯位于斯泰克方丹河谷，距离南非德兰士瓦省克鲁格斯多普北部约有 8 英里。1948 年，已故的罗伯特·布鲁姆博士和鲁滨逊博士最先对此地进行了科学考察，他们将德兰士瓦博物馆对斯泰克方丹的研究工作转移到了河谷对面的洞穴。现场角砾岩的挖掘工作一直持续到 1949 年年底，最终发现了约 3,000 件化石，包括数量众多的傍人标本和另一种人科的标本，后者被命名为开普远人 [4]，但是后来又被归入到直立人 [5] 中。

The palaeontological work of 1949 revealed a substantial seam of pure travertine along the north wall of the excavation, and this was exploited commercially by a lime-miner in 1950 and 1951, who left the site in a chaotic state. Robinson excavated the site again in 1952, but the cave was then abandoned until the new investigations, reported here, were started in April 1965.

New Investigations

The new fieldwork at Swartkrans has had two important achievements: first, order has been restored after the chaotic mining episode and excavation of undisturbed breccia is now possible; second, a large and representative sample of 14,000 bone fragments has been recovered.

Our first task was to sort through a substantial dump on the hillside below the cave. Unexpectedly, we found very numerous blocks of fossiliferous breccia, obviously not derived from the 1950–51 mining operations. In fact, more than 200 tons of breccia were recovered from the dump and stockpiled for subsequent attention. Enquiries among old residents of the area revealed[6] that Swartkrans had, in fact, been mined for lime on a previous occasion between 1930 and 1935. The miners had later refilled their excavations with rubble, thereby confusing the situation and leading Robinson[7] to believe that, unlike Sterkfontein, Swartkrans had not been modified by mining before its palaeontological exploration.

After working through the hillside dump, rubble was removed from the excavation and hand-sorted. This work is now almost complete and, after a grid over the excavation area has been erected, selected blocks of breccia from different stratigraphic levels will be removed for detailed comparative study of their fossil contents. It is fortunate that a substantial bank of *in situ* breccia survived the first mining operations and remains today as an inclined surface along the breadth of the cave's south wall. A profile is thus preserved of the whole thickness of the original breccia deposit.

Form of Original Cave

Clearing of the site has clarified the extent of the deposit and form of the original cave, and there will have to be some modification of the original interpretation[8]. In this interpretation, the cave was reconstructed as having comprised two filled chambers, an outer and an inner, with pink unstratified breccia in the former and a brown, stratified deposit in the latter. The two deposits were separated by an unconformable contact, the brown breccia proving to be younger than the pink. After our new investigations, separation into inner and outer chambers remains valid, but study of the east end of the deposit strongly suggests that the outer-cave breccia is not the oldest in the Swartkrans cave and that a still older breccia occupies the eastern extension of the site. This is separated from the normal australopithecine-bearing deposit by a steeply inclined unconformity. Each of the three unconformable contacts between the Swartkrans breccias seems to have resulted from progressive slumping into an underground, lower cavern system. Neither the oldest of the breccias, nor the underlying cavern, has yet been investigated.

1949 年的古生物学工作揭示出了沿着发掘地点的北墙有一大层纯石灰华基质，在 1950 年和 1951 年，一名石灰矿矿主对其进行了商业开采，将此地糟蹋得一片狼藉。鲁滨逊曾于 1952 年再度挖掘此地，但是自此之后这个洞穴一直处于被遗弃的状态，直到 1965 年 4 月重新开始研究，在本文中将报道一些最新的考察结果。

最新的考察结果

在斯瓦特克朗斯新开展的野外工作已经取得了两项重要的进展：首先，清理出胡乱开采期间搞乱的地层顺序，从而使对原状的角砾岩进行发掘成为可能；其次，出土了近 14,000 件有代表性的骨骼碎片标本。

我们的第一项任务就是筛选在山洞之下的山腰上的大量堆积物。出乎意料的是，我们发现了大量含有化石的角砾岩块，显然它们在 1950 年～ 1951 年的采矿作业中没有被动过。实际上，我们在这些堆积中清理出了 200 多吨角砾岩，并将它们储存起来以备后续的研究。对该地区老住户的调查结果显示 [6]：斯瓦特克朗斯其实在 1930 年到 1935 年间就曾有过一次石灰的开采经历。后来，开采者又用砾石将他们挖掘过的地方填满，因此混淆了视听，从而令鲁滨逊 [7] 相信：与斯泰克方丹不同，斯瓦特克朗斯的地层在进行古生物学发掘之前并没有受到过采矿事件的破坏。

在整理完山腰上的堆积之后，将砾石从发掘地点移走并对其进行人工分拣。目前该项工作基本完成，在发掘区安装好方格之后，我们就可以从不同的地层取出选中的角砾岩块以便对它们所含的化石进行详细的比较研究了。幸运的是，大量原位角砾岩在第一次采矿作业中并未受到破坏，目前它们沿着山洞南墙的宽度形成了一个斜面。因而原始的角砾岩沉积物在整个厚度上的剖面都被保存了下来。

洞穴的原始形状

对该处遗址的清理结果澄清了沉积物的范围和洞穴的原始形状，这就需要对最初的解释 [8] 进行一些修正。最初的解释认为：洞穴被重建成由两个充满堆积的洞室构成，包括一个外室和一个内室，外室填充的是粉色的非成层角砾岩，而内室填充的则是褐色的成层沉积物。这两种堆积物被一个不整合的接触面分开，研究表明粉色角砾岩的年代比褐色角砾岩更久远。我们的最新调查结果显示，内外室之间的分离仍然有效，但是对沉积物东端的研究强有力地证明：外洞的角砾岩并非斯瓦特克朗斯洞中最古老的，在该遗址向东延伸的地方还存在着更为古老的角砾岩。一个陡倾的不整合面将其与正常的含有南方古猿的沉积物分开。在斯瓦特克朗斯角砾岩之间的这三个不整合面似乎都是由渐进滑动进入地下的低地大洞穴系统引起的。现在还没有人研究过那些最古老的角砾岩和下面的大洞穴。

In 1958 (ref. 8), the entrance to the outer cave was interpreted as an incline, opening obliquely into the hillside. The walls of the cave can now be seen, however, on all sides except the south-east, where extensive decalcification has occurred. On the evidence of the new exposures, it seems very likely that the original entrance was a precipitous, shaft-like one, perhaps no more than 5 feet in cross-section, linking the cavern with the surface above. Such shaft-like entrances to caverns are a common feature on the undulating dolomite hillsides in the area today. Soil, rock and other debris are funnelled down a shaft of this sort during rain storms, to build up a talus cone in the cavern below the discharge point of the shaft. The discharge point itself is marked by a concentration of rocks and coarse particles in the sediment, while the finer fractions tend to be carried into the further recesses of the cave. It is likely that a vertical shaft discharged in this area, from a hillside depression perhaps 50 feet above it (Fig. 1).

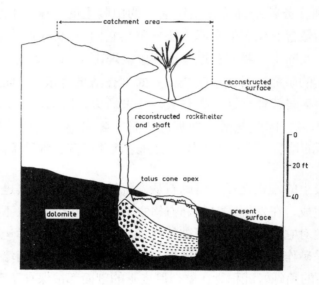

Fig. 1. Diagrammatic N–S section through the Swartkrans hillside. The upper reconstructed part has been removed by erosion since the accumulation of the fossiliferous deposit.

The Swartkrans cave system has developed at the intersection of two fault planes, clearly visible on an aerial photograph. They intersect at an angle of about 87 degrees and it is probable that a large rock-shelter may have existed on the surface in this area, with the shaft descending from it to the underground cavern. If this interpretation of cave form is correct, it is important to realize that the cavern containing the fossiliferous breccia would have been inaccessible to most animals, other than bats and owls. The deposit would, nevertheless, reflect events in the catchment area on the surface during the accumulation period. Relics left by animals or men in the upper rock shelter would ultimately find their way down to the subterranean fossilization site. Stratigraphy in a talus cone is difficult to follow because it is steeply inclined close to the apex, but becomes progressively flatter in those parts of the cave further from the shaft (see Fig. 1). Today, erosion has removed the overlying hillside with its shaft and rock shelter. The original form of these missing parts of the cave system is thus a matter for speculation, but it may be reconstructed on the

在 1958 年（参考文献 8）时，人们认为外洞的入口是一个斜坡，开口向山腰内部倾斜。但现在可以看到洞穴中除东南面以外的所有侧面。在东南面曾发生过大面积的脱钙作用。根据新清理出的露头判断，原来将大洞穴与其上表面相连接的入口很可能是一个陡峭的杆状通道，或许横截面还不足 5 英尺。目前，通往大洞穴的这种杆状入口在该地区连绵起伏的白云岩山腰区域已经成为一种很常见的现象。在下暴雨时，土壤、岩石和其他碎片从这种杆状通道漏下去，于是在大洞穴里杆状通道的排放点之下就形成了一个岩屑锥。排放点本身就是以沉积物中岩石和粗粒的丰度来确定的，较细的碎片倾向于被带到洞穴中更深的地方。很可能通过约 50 英尺以上的山腰凹陷处的一条垂直杆状通道可以排泄到这个区域（图 1）。

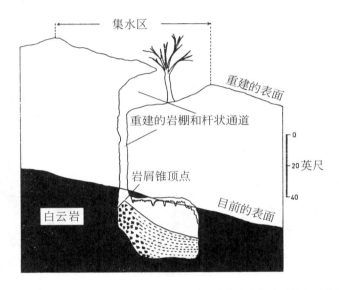

图 1. 穿过斯瓦特克朗斯山腰的南 – 北向剖面图。这里重建出来的上半部分已经在下部的含化石沉积物开始堆积时逐渐被剥蚀而不复存在了。

斯瓦特克朗斯洞穴系统形成于两个断层面的交汇处，这从航空照片上可以很清楚地看到。它们的交角约为 87 度，在该处的地表之上可能曾经有过一个巨大的岩棚，杆状通道就是从这里开始向下降至地面以下的大洞穴的。如果对洞穴形式的这种解释是正确的，那么意识到以下这一点就很重要，即除蝙蝠和猫头鹰以外的大部分动物很难进入到这个具有含化石角砾岩的大洞穴中。尽管如此，由沉积物也可以推断出岩屑积累时期地表集水区所发生的变迁。动物或人类在上方的岩棚上留下的遗骸最终会沿着伸入地下的通道下坠而堆积成化石。很难判断岩屑锥中的地层层序，因为在靠近顶点处它是陡峭倾斜的，而在洞穴中离杆状通道较远的部分它又逐渐变得平缓了（见图 1）。今天，侵蚀作用已经将覆盖于其上的山腰以及山腰上的杆状通道和岩棚一并剥蚀掉了。因此，该洞穴系统中这些缺失部分的原始形状就成为了我们

known geological conformation of the immediate area.

New Hominid Finds

The current fieldwork at Swartkrans has produced a little more than 11,000 bone fragments among which are seventeen recognizable hominid fossils. The hominids, which I shall describe briefly, are all presumed to represent *Paranthropus robustus*. It has been observed[6] that teeth in two of the mandible fragments (*SK* 1587 and *SK* 1588) were unusually small, with dimensions falling outside the observed range for *Paranthropus* from the site. At the time, it was suggested that these two mandibles may have represented a hominid other than *Paranthropus*, but this now seems unlikely—instead, the hominids probably extend the range of tooth dimensions for the Swartkrans *Paranthropus* sample. Measurements were taken on all teeth which had not suffered damage or undue wear. In the following descriptions mesio-distal length is quoted first, followed by bucco-lingual breadth, in millimetres.

Cranial and Vertebral Remains

SK 3978   Perfectly preserved and undistorted infant mandible lacking rami (see Fig. 2). Left dm_1 (10.2×7.8 mm) slightly worn, dm_2 (13.0×10.5 mm) unworn; right dm_1 (9.9×8.2 mm), dm_2 (12.9×10.7 mm). Sockets are present for deciduous incisors and canines while the unerupted left M_1 is visible in its crypt. Found August 8, 1967.

Fig. 2. An infant *Paranthropus* mandible (*SK* 3978) in superior (*a*), inferior (*b*) and lateral view (*c*).

SK 1585   A natural endocranial cast from a hominid, presumably *Paranthropus* (see Fig. 3). The skull was blasted out by lime miners in the early 1930s and was broken into several pieces before being dumped on the hillside. Two of the surrounding parts of the cranial vault have been recovered, but the face has not yet been found. It is clear that the skull originally came to rest in the cave on its right side and was filled with fine-grained sediment to the level of the top of the foramen magnum. The filling was subsequently hardened with calcium carbonate and is almost completely undistorted. The state of the sutures suggests that the individual was subadult. The endocast has recently been prepared and studied by Dr. R. Holloway, who estimates the capacity of the skull to have been 530 cc and whose detailed report will be published elsewhere. Found January 17, 1966.

需要推测的对象，不过根据邻近区域的已知地质构造还是有可能将其重建出来的。

新发现的人科化石

目前在斯瓦特克朗斯遗址出土的骨骼碎片略多于 11,000 件，其中包括 17 件可识别的人科化石。我在下文中简要记述的人科化石都权且属于傍人粗壮种。我曾经观察到 [6] 其中两件下颌骨碎片中的牙齿（SK 1587 和 SK 1588）小得异乎寻常，其尺寸落在来自该遗址的傍人的变异范围之外。当时，有人认为这两件下颌骨可能代表了一种不属于傍人属的人科化石，但是现在看来这似乎是不可能的——与此相反，其所代表的人科化石有可能扩大了斯瓦特克朗斯傍人标本的牙齿尺寸变异范围。我们测量了所有没有损坏或没有过度磨耗的牙齿。在下面的描述中，近中 – 远中长度在前，颊 – 舌宽度在后，单位都是 mm。

头骨和椎骨化石

SK 3978　保存完好且没有变形的幼年下颌骨，但下颌支缺损（见图 2）。左 dm_1（10.2 mm×7.8 mm）有轻微磨损，dm_2（13.0 mm×10.5 mm）未磨损；右 dm_1（9.9 mm×8.2 mm），dm_2（12.9 mm×10.7 mm）。乳门齿和犬齿的牙槽都保存下来了，可以看到未萌出的左 M_1 尚包埋于牙床中。发现于 1967 年 8 月 8 日。

a　　　　　　*b*　　　　　　*c*

图 2. 傍人幼年下颌骨（*SK* 3978）的嚼面视（*a*）、腹面视（*b*）及侧面视（*c*）。

SK 1585　人科天然颅内模标本，可能是傍人的（见图 3）。它的头骨是在 20 世纪 30 年代早期被石灰矿工爆破出来的，在被遗弃到山腰上之前就已经碎成了好几块。其中的两块头盖骨骨片已经找到，但还没有发现面部的骨片。显然该头骨最初在洞穴里埋藏时是向右侧侧卧的，而颅腔被细粒的沉积物填充至枕骨大孔顶部的水平。后来这些填充物被钙质胶结而硬化，几乎没有变形。骨缝愈合的状态表明该个体尚未成年。霍洛韦博士已于最近修理出了该颅内模并对其进行了研究，他估计这个头骨的颅容量可达 530 cc（译者注：即立方厘米），他的详细报告将另行发表。发现于 1966 年 1 月 17 日。

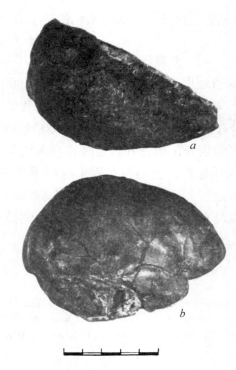

Fig. 3. A natural endocranial cast (*SK* 1585) from a Swartkrans hominid in superior (*a*) and right lateral view (*b*).

SK 3981   Two vertebrae, thought to belong to *Paranthropus*; (*a*) a last thoracic, (*b*) a last lumbar. These specimens have been described in detail by Dr. J. T. Robinson[1]. Found March 1968.

SK 1587   (*a*) Portion of the left corpus of a mandible with roots of P_2, complete P_4 (10.6×11.6 mm), M_1 (14.7×12.9 mm); (*b*) isolated right M_2 (15.2×12.9 mm) complete, from the same block and almost certainly from the same individual. Found July 19, 1966.

SK 1588   Part of a left corpus of a mandible with roots of P_3, complete P_4 (11.0×11.6 mm), M_1 (14.0×12.3 mm) and root of M_2. The specimen is of particular interest because the dimensions of M_1 are well below the hitherto observed range for *Paranthropus* from Swartkrans. Found October 6, 1966.

SK 1590   From an adult skull: two palatal fragments (*a*) and (*b*), with an incomplete right I^2, C, P^3 (9.25×13.3 mm), P^4 (10.2×14.5 mm) and M^1 (13.2×14.9 mm), all worn; crushed and distorted mandible (*c*) with parts of premolar and molar teeth. Associated were the head of a femur (*d*) and parts of an innominate bone in poor condition. Found April 13, 1965.

SK 1586   Almost complete adult mandible, severely shattered during fossilization, with right I_1, I_2, M_1 (broken), M_2 (15.0×14.9 mm) and M_2 (16.7×15.0 mm); also left I_1, M_1, M_2 (15.0×13.8 mm). One of the most robust mandibles from Swartkrans. Found September 1, 1965.

SK 1648   Anterior part of an adult mandible, severely distorted with worn right M_1 and M_2 (15.7×14.5 mm), left M_1 (incomplete) and roots of other teeth. Found November 4, 1966.

Isolated Teeth

SK 1593   Right P_3 (9.8×12.2 mm), well worn, with almost complete root system. Found March 24, 1966.

SK 3974   Right M_1 (14.9×13.4 mm), perfect crown, slightly worn, without roots. Found July 14, 1967.

SK 1594   Right M_1, moderately worn, most of the buccal half including the root. Found September 12. 1966.

SK 3976   Left M_2 (17.3×16.0 mm), complete and slightly worn. Found May 5, 1967.

SK 14001   Left P^3 (10.5×12.8 mm), complete crown but partly damaged root system. Found July 14, 1967.

SK 1589   Right P^4 (11.0×14.4 mm), complete crown of an unerupted tooth. Found October 14, 1966.

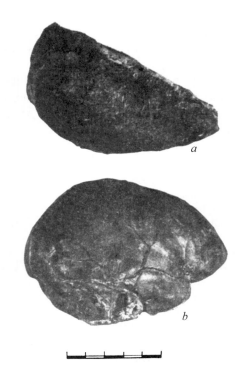

图 3. 斯瓦特克朗斯遗址出土的人科天然颅内模标本（SK 1585）的背侧视（a）及右侧视（b）。

SK 3981　被认为属于傍人的两块椎骨；（a）一块末尾的胸椎骨，（b）一块末尾的腰椎骨。鲁滨逊博士[1]已经描述过这些标本的细节。发现于 1968 年 3 月。

SK 1587　（a）带有 P_2、完整 P_4（10.6 mm × 11.6 mm）和 M_1（14.7 mm × 12.9 mm）牙根的左下颌体；（b）单独完整的右 M_2（15.2 mm × 12.9 mm），它们来自同一地点，并且几乎可以肯定属于同一个体。发现于 1966 年 7 月 19 日。

SK 1588　带有 P_3、完整 P_4（11.0 mm × 11.6 mm）和 M_1（14.0 × 12.3 mm）牙根以及 M_2 牙根的左下颌体。因为 M_1 的尺寸远远小于迄今为止观察到的斯瓦特克朗斯傍人的最小值，所以这件标本引起了人们特别的兴趣。发现于 1966 年 10 月 6 日。

SK 1590　来自于一个成人的头骨：两块上腭碎片（a）和（b），含不完整的右 I^2、C、P^3（9.25 mm × 13.3 mm）、P^4（10.2 mm × 14.5 mm）和 M^1（13.2 mm × 14.9 mm），所有这些牙齿都有磨损；压碎变形的下颌骨（c），含部分前臼齿和臼齿。与此相连的还有一块股骨头（d）和一些保存状况不佳且无法鉴定的骨骼碎块。发现于 1965 年 4 月 13 日。

SK 1586　几乎完整的成人下颌骨，在化石化过程中破碎严重，含右 I_1、I_2、M_1（断裂）、M_2（15.0 mm × 14.9 mm）和 M_3（16.7 mm × 15.0 mm）；还有左 I_1、M_1 和 M_2（15.0 mm × 13.8 mm）。这是在斯瓦特克朗斯发现的最粗壮的下颌骨之一。发现于 1965 年 9 月 1 日。

SK 1648　一件成人下颌骨的前部，变形严重，含磨损的右 M_1 和 M_2（15.7 mm × 14.5 mm）、左 M_1（不完整）以及其他牙齿的牙根。发现于 1966 年 11 月 4 日。

单独的牙齿

SK 1593　右 P_3（9.8 mm × 12.2 mm），磨损严重，牙根系统几乎完整。发现于 1966 年 3 月 24 日。

SK 3974　右 M_1（14.9 mm × 13.4 mm），牙冠完整，有轻微磨损，没有牙根。发现于 1967 年 7 月 14 日。

SK 1594　右 M_1，中度磨损，颊半侧的大部分带有牙根。发现于 1966 年 9 月 12 日。

SK 3976　左 M_2（17.3 mm × 16.0 mm），牙齿完整，有轻微磨损。发现于 1967 年 5 月 5 日。

SK 14001　左 P^3（10.5 mm × 12.8 mm），牙冠完整，但牙根系有部分损伤。发现于 1967 年 7 月 14 日。

SK 1589　右 P^4（11.0 mm × 14.4 mm），一颗未萌出的完整牙冠。发现于 1966 年 10 月 14 日。

233

SK 3977   Right M³ (15.5×17.9 mm), slightly worn. Found May 5, 1967.
SK 3975   Left M³ (14.6×16.7 mm), slightly worn. Found July 28, 1967.
SK 14000   Upper molar broken through middle, showing pulp cavity. Found November 11, 1967.

The following eight hominid fossils were recently found in blocks of breccia brought back to the Transvaal Museum during the Broom/Robinson operations at Swartkrans. They came to light when the breccia was processed in acetic acid. All are assigned to *Paranthropus robustus*.

SK 1596   Isolated upper canine, heavily worn, with almost complete root system.
SK 1591   Isolated left M¹ (13.0×14.4 mm), fairly worn with part of the root system.
SK 1524   Isolated left M³; most of the mesial portion of an unerupted and incompletely developed crown.
SK 1514   Mandibular fragment in very poor condition with roots of two molars and crown of one.
SK 1595   Fragment of a maxilla with slightly worn left dm² (11.5×12.4 mm) and pieces of erupting anterior teeth.
SK 1512   Palatal fragment with roots of several cheek teeth and part of a premolar.
SK 1592   Palatal fragment with broken right P⁴, M¹, M² and part of M³; also the root of one of the anterior teeth.
SK 14003   Part of a crushed skull with left M¹ (incomplete), part of right M¹, M² and complete M³ (15.0×16.2 mm).

Stone Culture

The presence of a stone culture at Swartkrans was first suspected in 1956 when several quartzite tools, encased in breccia, were found there[8]. Recent examination of breccia blocks, blasted from the outer cave by the lime miners, has led to further recovery of occasional pieces of rock, foreign to the immediate vicinity of the cave and, in some cases, artificially worked. To date, 195 foreign stones have been found, fifty-one of which show signs of artificial fracture. The whole collection has been studied in detail by Miss S. M. Johnston, who has very kindly made her results available to me (see Table 1).

Table 1

Rock type	No. of pieces	Percent of total foreign stones	Average wt (g)	No. of waterworn pieces	No. of worked pieces
Quartzite	148	75.9	507	87	33
Vein quartz	36	18.5	226	3	8
Diabase	6	3.1	450	1	5
Other	5	2.5	166	0	5
	195	100.0	337 (overall average)	91	51

The most numerous rock type present, quartzite, has its origin on the Witwatersrand escarpment a few miles to the south of Swartkrans; vein quartz occurs sporadically in the dolomite formation, while the closest outcrop of diabase is about 1 mile south-east of the cave, on the opposite side of the valley. Although fifty-one of the stones showed some signs of artificial fracture, only thirty of them could be termed artifacts and these have been studied and described in detail by Dr. Mary Leakey[2]. All the tools, with the exception of the two diabase bifaces and one quartzite chopper, have edges so sharp that they were clearly made close to the cave entrance shortly before their inclusion in the deposit. The

SK 3977   右 M^3（15.5 mm×17.9 mm），有轻微磨损。发现于 1967 年 5 月 5 日。

SK 3975   左 M^3（14.6 mm×16.7 mm），有轻微磨损。发现于 1967 年 7 月 28 日。

SK 14000   上臼齿，中间裂穿，露出髓腔。发现于 1967 年 11 月 11 日。

下面的 8 件人科化石标本是我们刚刚从布鲁姆／鲁滨逊在开采斯瓦特克朗斯期间带回到德兰士瓦博物馆的角砾岩块中发现的。它们是在用醋酸浸洗角砾岩时出现的。我们把它们归入傍人粗壮种。

SK 1596   单独的上犬齿，磨损严重，牙根系统几乎完整。

SK 1591   单独的左 M^1（13.0 mm×14.4 mm），有相当程度的磨损，牙根系统不完整。

SK 1524   单独的左 M^3；一颗未萌出且发育不完全的牙冠的大部分近中侧部分。

SK 1514   保存状况很差的下颌骨碎片，含两枚臼齿的牙根和一枚臼齿的牙冠。

SK 1595   上颌骨的碎片，含有轻微磨损的左 dm^2（11.5 mm×12.4 mm）和正在萌出的几颗前齿碎片。

SK 1512   上腭的碎片，含几枚颊齿的牙根和一枚前臼齿的一部分。

SK 1592   上腭的碎片，含断裂的右 P^4、M^1、M^2 和部分 M^3；还有一枚前齿的牙根。

SK 14003   一件被压碎的头骨的一部分，含左 M^1（不完整）、部分右 M^1、M^2 和完整的 M^3（15.0 mm×16.2 mm）。

石 器 文 化

对斯瓦特克朗斯遗址曾存在过石器文化的揣测始于 1956 年，当时在该遗址出土了几个包裹在角砾岩中的石英质石器 [8]。最近对石灰开采者从外洞爆破出来的角砾岩块的研究使我们发现了更多的特殊石块，这些石块的岩性与洞穴中的及近邻地区的迥然相异，其中有些石块有人工痕迹。到目前为止，我们已经找到了 195 块外来石块，其中有 51 块具有人工痕迹。约翰斯顿小姐对全部采集物都进行过详细的研究，她非常友好地把她的研究成果提供给我（见表 1）。

表 1

岩石类型	块数	占全部外来石块的百分比	平均重量 (g)	水蚀石块的数量	加工过的石块的数量
石英岩	148	75.9	507	87	33
脉石英	36	18.5	226	3	8
辉绿岩	6	3.1	450	1	5
其他	5	2.5	166	0	5
合计	195	100.0	337（总平均值）	91	51

存在数量最多的岩石类型是石英岩，这种岩石的来源地是距离斯瓦特克朗斯南部几英里处的威特沃特斯兰德悬崖；脉石英零星出现于白云岩地层中，而最近的辉绿岩露头是在离洞穴东南约 1 英里处的河谷对岸。尽管有 51 块石头显示出人工痕迹，但是其中只有 30 块可以被称作是人工制品，玛丽·利基博士 [2] 曾对它们进行过详细的研究和论述。除了两件辉绿岩两面器和一件石英岩单刃砍砸器外，所有工具都具有很锋利的边缘，所以它们显然是在被埋进沉积物之前不久才在洞穴入口附近制

diabase tools both have weathered cortices, but it is known that diabase weathers while it is enclosed in a damp breccia deposit. The one quartzite chopper had been waterworn after manufacture, but before fossilization. It was originally assumed that all the foreign stones must have been brought to Swartkrans by human (or proto-human) agency; it now seems likely, however, that an old river gravel may have existed on the Swartkrans hillside when the cave deposit was accumulating and that some of the pebbles found their way naturally into the cavern, together with the soil and debris which were washed down into it. Tools that were made at the cave entrance were presumably fashioned on pebbles which happened to be in the immediate vicinity.

In view of the possibility that the Swartkrans foreign stones may have originated in a river gravel, a detailed study of contemporary gravels in the area has been made. The cave is situated 700 feet from the present course of the Blaaubank River, but this stream does not normally flow except after heavy rain. Sparse river gravels occur along the sides of the valley and, from three separate localities within 1.5 miles of the cave, Miss Johnston was able to collect a sample of 152 foreign stones for comparison with the Swartkrans specimens. The results of this comparison indicate that the Swartkrans foreign stones are very similar to those associated with the stream course in the vicinity of the cave. Waterworn quartzite pebbles proved to be slightly more abundant in the Swartkrans sample than in the gravel, but the percentage abundance of vein quartz pieces did not differ significantly between the two. Weights of the pieces in the two samples were found to be almost exactly comparable. The stones in the gravel sample also did not differ significantly in shape from those in the Swartkrans collection.

On the basis of this study, it seems that the foreign stones at Swartkrans were almost certainly derived from an old gravel associated with the stream course. Artificial transportation need not be invoked because, if the gravel lay within the catchment area of the cave entrance, it would have been washed into the underground cavern together with other surface debris. The stone tools are nevertheless of special significance, because they are indicative of sporadic hominid activity near the cave entrance during the Swartkrans accumulation period. Two different hominids are known at the site, *Homo erectus* and *Paranthropus robustus*, but it is not certain which was responsible for the stone tools. Three of the stones in the collection show evidence of heat-spalding, suggesting that they had been in a fire shortly before inclusion in the deposit. On this slender, but interesting, evidence it would be premature to suggest that the Swartkrans hominids had mastered the deliberate use of fire. Grass fires, started by lightning, are a recurrent feature of the Transvaal highveld and, when sweeping through a leaf-strewn rock shelter, can generate a good deal of heat. Nothing resembling a bone tool has yet been found at Swartkrans, in spite of examination of every fragment in the collection.

Interpretation of the Bone Accumulation

In the interpretation of any bone accumulation preserved in a cave deposit, the original form of the cave is of crucial significance because it is this that determines the kinds of animals likely to have made use of the site. As already described, Swartkrans seems to have

造出来的。两件辉绿岩工具的外表都被风化了，但是我们知道当辉绿岩被封在潮湿的角砾岩沉积物中时也会发生风化。有一件石英岩单刃砍砸器在制造出来之后和埋藏之前受到了水的冲蚀。最初假定所有的外来石块都一定是被人类（或早期原始人）带到斯瓦特克朗斯的；但是现在看来在斯瓦特克朗斯的山腰上似乎存在过一层古老的河相砾石，在洞穴沉积物的堆积过程中，其中一些鹅卵石便自然而然地顺道掉进了洞穴中，同时被冲入其中的还有土壤和岩屑。在洞穴入口处出土的工具很可能取材于这些就近的鹅卵石。

考虑到斯瓦特克朗斯的外来石块可能来源于河相砾石，因而我们对这一区域目前的砾石进行了详细的研究。该洞穴位于距离布拉奥班克河现在的河道 700 英尺处，但是这条河通常不会有水流,除非是在暴雨之后。沿着河谷的两岸很少见到河相砾石，而约翰斯顿小姐从距离洞穴 1.5 英里以内的 3 处不同地点收集到了 152 块外来石块以便与斯瓦特克朗斯样本进行比较。比较结果显示：斯瓦特克朗斯的外来石块非常类似于在洞穴附近的那些与河道有关联的砾石。被水冲蚀的石英岩鹅卵石在斯瓦特克朗斯样本中确实比在砾石中略多一些，但是二者在脉石英岩块中的百分比丰度却没有明显的差异。两个样本中石块的重量也几乎完全相等。砾石样本中石块的形状也与在斯瓦特克朗斯收集到的石块的形状没有太大的差别。

基于此项研究，看来几乎可以肯定斯瓦特克朗斯的外来石块就是来自于与河道有关的古砾石。这个过程并不需要人工运输，因为：如果砾石位于洞口的集水区之内，那么它们早就会和地面的其他碎屑一起被冲到地下的洞穴里。不过出土的石器还是具有很重要的意义的，因为它们说明在斯瓦特克朗斯的堆积时期靠近洞口的地方曾存在过零星的原始人类活动。已知在该遗址曾有两种不同的人科成员——直立人和傍人粗壮种，但还不确定石器的制造者是其中的哪种。在出土的物品中有三件石器显示出受过热的迹象，说明它们在埋藏进沉积物之前刚刚被火灼烧过。用这个赢弱但又很有趣的证据来证明斯瓦特克朗斯的原始人类已经掌握了用火的技术还为时尚早。由闪电引发的草地着火是德兰士瓦高地频频发生的一种现象，当火苗横扫遍布树叶的岩棚时，就可以产生大量的热。尽管已检查过出土物品中的每一块碎片，但是到现在为止在斯瓦特克朗斯还未发现任何类似于骨制品的化石。

对骨骼堆积物的解释

在解释存于洞穴沉积物中的任何骨骼堆积物时，洞穴的原始形态具有至关重要的意义，因为它决定了可能利用过该处遗址的动物类型。如上所述，斯瓦特克朗斯

consisted of a hillside rock-shelter, probably supporting several large trees, but enclosing a vertical shaft which descended to an underground cavern, in which the fossiliferous deposit accumulated (Fig. 1). The latter cavern was simply a receptacle into which surface-derived debris was funnelled, while the nature of the rock-shelter on the surface was presumably such that it is likely to have been used by a wide variety of animals, as well as primitive man. The sample of 14,000 fossil bone fragments currently being analysed comes from a thickness of deposit which probably took several thousand years to accumulate. At Swartkrans we are not dealing with an impressive concentration of bones, but rather with a more or less even scatter throughout the calcified soil which originally filled the cave. It is probably not necessary to account for the collection of more than about ten bones per year and these could have found their way into the cave in a variety of ways. Some of the possibilities will be considered.

It is, for instance, known that many animals, when injured or sick, will retreat into caves to die. If unmolested, complete skeletons or scattered undamaged bones can be expected to result. Nothing approaching a complete or undamaged skeleton has been found in the Swartkrans breccia and natural deaths are not thought to have been important. The same is true of artificial burials which are unlikely to have occurred during the australopithecine period.

A recent study of important factors in Southern African bone accumulations (my work, in preparation) has shown that porcupines are of the greatest significance as collectors of bones in caves. They are known to horde large numbers of bones in their lairs, but all their collections so far studied have been characterized by a high percentage of gnawed bones on which the marks of the rodents' incisors are unmistakable. The final figure for the percentage of porcupine-gnawed bones in the Swartkrans sample has yet to be determined, but it will probably be less than 5. It is therefore concluded that, although porcupines almost certainly contributed to the Swartkrans bone collection, their influence was small.

Second to porcupines, primitive men rated high in importance as collectors of bone fragments in caves during the South African Stone Age. A detailed comparative study of human bony food remains from various Southern African caves has led me to conclude that these accumulations are characterized by the extreme fragmentation of the bones (my work, in preparation). A high percentage abundance of long-bone flakes and unrecognizable fragments is indicative of human activity, in which the bones are broken with stone tools for the extraction of marrow. As already mentioned, fifty-one stone artefacts have been recovered from the Swartkrans breccia, many of them chopping tools suited to the breaking of bones for the extraction of marrow. Bone flakes and fragments do occur in the accumulation but they are not abundant, suggesting that human feeding activity occurred sporadically within the catchment area of the Swartkrans cave but that this was not of major importance in the building up of the bone collection.

似乎曾有过一个位于山腰的岩棚，可能还长有几棵大树，不过这几棵大树包围着一条通往地下洞穴的垂直杆状通道，而含有化石的沉积物正是在这个洞穴里堆积起来的（图1）。这里所说的洞穴只是一个容纳地表岩屑的容器，而我们可以认为地面上岩棚的环境很可能不仅适合于原始人类，还适合于很多种动物的栖息。现在正在分析的标本包括 14,000 件骨头碎片化石，是从很厚的沉积物中出土的，这些沉积物的堆积可能经历了数千年。在斯瓦特克朗斯，我们研究的不仅是高度集中的化石，而且还有那些与化石同时堆积并填满洞穴的钙化土壤。也许无需解释每年约有 10 块以上的骨头会堆积到洞中，这些骨头可能通过很多种途径进入洞穴。对其中一些可能途径的探讨如下。

例如，我们都知道许多动物在受伤或生病之后会隐退至洞穴中苟延残喘至死。这些动物的尸体埋藏后如果未受干扰的话，完整的骨架或分散的未受损骨骼就有可能会被保存下来。在斯瓦特克朗斯的角砾岩中还从未发现过任何几近完整或未受损的骨架，因此它们是自然死亡的可能性不大。在南方古猿时代也不可能出现人为埋藏这些动物的现象。

一项对南非化石富集点的重要影响因素的最新研究结果（我的工作，完稿中）表明：豪猪对洞穴内骨骼的堆积贡献最大。我们知道它们会在自己巢穴中堆积大量的骨骼，但是从迄今为止的研究结果来看，它们的所有收集物都以高比例的啃咬过的骨头为特征，在这些骨头上的啮齿动物门齿痕迹清晰可辨。现在还未最终确定豪猪咬过的骨骼在斯瓦特克朗斯标本中所占的比例，不过这个值可能会小于 5%。因此可以得出如下结论：虽然几乎可以肯定豪猪对斯瓦特克朗斯的骨骼堆积有一定贡献，但是它们的影响并不大。

仅次于豪猪，在南非石器时代原始人类也是洞穴中骨骼碎片的主要堆积者。在对若干南非洞穴中人类骨质食余垃圾进行了详细的比较研究之后，我发现这些堆积物的特征是骨骼的破碎程度极高（我的工作，完稿中）。长骨的骨片和无法辨认的碎片所占比例很高说明有人类活动过，人类会用石器将骨骼打断以摄食其中的骨髓。正如前面已提到的那样，在斯瓦特克朗斯的角砾岩中曾发现了 51 件石器，其中有不少用于砍砸的工具适合用来剁碎骨头以吸取骨髓。骨片和骨渣在堆积物中的确存在，但是它们的数量并不是很多，这说明人类的摄食活动在斯瓦特克朗斯洞穴的集水区只是偶尔出现，因此人类活动在骨骼的堆积过程中也不起主要作用。

Carnivore Activity

The overall impression given by the Swartkrans bones is that they represent carnivore food remains; they come predominantly from antelope, baboons, australopithecines, hyraxes, and so forth, and are usually fragmentary, often showing damage apparently caused by carnivore teeth. Antelope are characteristically represented by a wide variety of damaged skeletal parts, but remains of many other animals are essentially cranial in origin, with very little else. The Swartkrans breccia has yielded an interesting series of carnivores, some of which were almost certainly involved in the collection of bones at the site. Forms identified to date are as follows (taxonomy according to Ewer[9-11]): hyaenids: *Crocuta crocuta venustula* (spotted hyaena), *Hyaena brunnea dispar* (brown hyaena), *Lycyaena silbergi nitidula*, *Leecyaena forfex*; sabre-toothed cats: *Therailurus* sp., *Megantereon* sp., *Nimravidae indet.*; felids: *Panthera pardus incurva* (leopard), *Panthera* sp. (lion); canids: *Canis mesomelas* (jackal), *Vulpes* sp. (fox); viverrids: *Cynictis penicillata* (mongoose).

Both the *Crocuta* and the *Hyaena* are regarded as early representatives of the extant spotted and brown hyaenas, while *Lycyaena* and *Leecyaena* represent extinct genera, the former showing characteristics which have been interpreted as "reflecting a secondary adaptation to a more predacious, less scavenging habit—a change presumably brought about under the selective pressure of competition with more efficient scavengers"[11]. *Leecyaena* is characterized by anterior cheek teeth resembling those of an advanced *Hyaena* and could possibly be ancestral to *H. bellax*, described from Kromdraai.

The three different sabre-toothed cats are represented by rather fragmentary material. Ewer has pointed out that, as a result of highly efficient carnassial shear, these carnivores were adapted to the slicing of meat and had premolars so reduced that they "must have been unable to deal with more than the very smallest bones"[11]. The conclusion that sabre-toothed cats left the skeletons of their prey almost intact has important implications, in that a niche was thus created for various species of hyaena, not necessarily capable of crushing the more resistant bones. Hyaenas like *Lycyaena* and *Leecyaena* may have owed their livelihood to the remains left by the abundant sabre-tooths of the day. As Ewer[11] has remarked: "The period of hyaena abundance in the Lower Pleistocene is thus also a period of abundant sabre-tooths and the disappearance of the latter during the Middle Pleistocene corresponds with the shrinkage of the hyaenid fauna to those few species which have succeeded in surviving today, in association with modern Felinae". Regrettably little is known about the behaviour of South African sabre-tooths and it is uncertain whether they were dominant to the associated hyaenas or whether they were forced to retreat with their prey into the seclusion of caves or trees. If so, it is likely that they would have contributed bones to the Swartkrans accumulation and that some of these may have been modified by the loss competent bone-crushing hyaenas, such as *Lycyaena* and *Leecyaena* before fossilization. (It is unlikely that the bones found today as fossils were ever thoroughly worked over by spotted or brown hyaenas; if they had, few would have remained to become fossilized.) Sabre-tooth involvement at Swartkrans can neither be demonstrated nor disproved, but it is very likely that the bone accumulation was added to by these cats and that the remains were modified by primitive hyaenas before being fossilized.

食肉动物的活动

斯瓦特克朗斯的骨骼化石给人留下的总体印象是：它们代表了食肉动物的食余垃圾；这些骨骼主要来源于羚羊、狒狒、南方古猿和蹄兔等，它们大多已成碎片，常常带有显然由食肉动物的牙齿所造成的损伤。羚羊的残骸主要是骨架上的不同部位，但是许多其他动物的残骸则主要是头骨，其他部位的几乎没有。在斯瓦特克朗斯角砾岩中已经出土了一系列有趣的食肉动物，几乎可以肯定其中的一些参与了该遗址内骨骼的堆积活动。迄今为止已经鉴定出来的动物种类如下（根据尤尔的分类方法[9-11]）。鬣狗类：斑鬣狗、棕鬣狗、狼鬣狗、李氏鬣狗；剑齿虎类：假剑齿虎、巨剑齿虎、猎猫；猫类：豹、狮；犬类：豺、狐狸；灵猫类：黄獴。

化石斑鬣狗和棕鬣狗被认为是现生斑鬣狗和棕鬣狗的早期代表者，而狼鬣狗和李氏鬣狗则代表已灭绝的属。狼鬣狗的特征被认为是"反映了对更多偏向食肉、更少偏向食腐的习性的一种次生适应性——这种变化可能是由与更强大的食腐动物进行竞争而产生的选择压力引起的"[11]。李氏鬣狗的特征是前面的颊齿与一种进步鬣狗的很像，所以李氏鬣狗可能是来自克罗姆德拉伊的贝拉斯鬣狗的祖先。

三种不同的剑齿虎标本均破损严重。尤尔指出：由于食肉动物可以用裂齿进行有效的撕裂，所以它们习惯于将肉切成薄片，并且前臼齿退化以至于它们"只能应付极其小的骨头"[11]。认为剑齿虎会将其猎物的骨架几乎完整地保留下来很有意义，因为各类鬣狗将各取所需，这样剑齿虎也就无需具有粉碎更具韧性的骨头的能力了。狼鬣狗和李氏鬣狗等鬣狗类动物当时也许可以靠大量剑齿虎留下的骨架残骸来维持生计。正如尤尔[11]曾指出的："因而早更新世时期的鬣狗繁盛阶段也是剑齿虎繁盛的时期，而剑齿虎在中更新世时期的灭绝也对应于鬣狗种群的缩减，幸存到今天的只有极少的几个与现代猫亚科有关的物种"。遗憾的是，对于南非剑齿虎的行为我们知之甚少，因而不确定它们是否支配着与之相关的鬣狗的数量，也不知道它们是否要将猎物带到洞穴或者密林深处才能进食。如果是这样的话，那么它们就有可能会对斯瓦特克朗斯的骨骼堆积有一定贡献，或许其中一部分骨骼在化石化之前曾被骨骼撕咬能力稍差的鬣狗啃过，例如狼鬣狗和李氏鬣狗等。（现今发现的骨骼化石不太可能曾被斑鬣狗或棕鬣狗彻底啃过；如果真的被它们啃过，就不会再有什么可以留下来变成化石了。）剑齿虎在斯瓦特克朗斯的存在既没有被证实也没有被证伪，但是这些猫科动物很有可能参与了骨骼的堆积活动，并且在这些残骸变成化石之前又经过了原始鬣狗的啃咬。

The Role of Leopards

Leopards are well represented among the Swartkrans fossils, where remains of at least thirteen individuals have been found. As *Panthera pardus incurva*[10], they differ from the living leopard on the subspecific level only, with an indication that the fossil form may have been a little smaller than its contemporary counterpart. It has already been noted that the presence of sabre-toothed cats could have been important to the survival of primitive hyaenas; in the same way, the direct association of leopards and spotted hyaenas was probably a crucial factor in the building up of the Swartkrans bone accumulation.

Where leopards share their hunting area with spotted hyaenas, it is well known that, if they are to retain their prey, they are obliged to feed in places inaccessible to the scavengers. I recently studied fifteen leopard kills in the Kruger National Park. Spotted hyaenas were attracted to all these kills, but in twelve cases the leopards took their prey into trees sufficiently promptly to avoid interference. In three they were not quick enough and, as a result, lost their prey to the hyaenas.

In a woodland habitat, leopards have little difficulty in finding suitable trees for storage of their prey, but the situation in open country is rather different. Swartkrans is situated today on the open highveld, an area of undulating grassland, almost devoid of trees except along the watercourses. Study of the composition of the antelope fauna from the Swartkrans deposit suggests that, during the infilling of the cave, open grassland conditions prevailed as they do today, the fossil fauna being dominated by gregarious plains-living species such as springbuck, gazelles and alcelaphines of various sizes. Leopards hunting on the open highveld have to make use of suitable cliffs, caves and the few available trees for the protection of their prey. An interesting and highly significant correlation is found to exist between the occurrence of large trees and caves in the dolomitic areas of the Transvaal highveld. In this gently undulating countryside, caves are typically of the shaft or sinkhole variety, with depressions surrounding their entrances. Whereas the hillsides themselves are devoid of trees, the cave entrances characteristically support several large stinkwood (*Celtis kraussiana*) or wild fig (*Ficus* spp.) trees, which flourish there as a result of protection afforded to them from frost and fire. Leopards are thus inevitably attracted to the dolomitic caves as places of safe retreat, while the associated trees are invaluable for the storage of their prey. Food remains of leopards are consequently introduced into the catchment areas of the cave entrances and some will ultimately find their way down to the subterranean fossilization sites. Assuming that the Swartkrans deposit accumulated during a period of perhaps 20,000 years, it would be surprising if the cave and its associated trees had not been used on innumerable occasions by leopards as a feeding place and lair. The cave was inhabited throughout its life by owls whose regurgitated pellets have built up a concentration of microfaunal remains in the deposit, to give a remarkably complete picture of the animals hunted by the owls in the vicinity of the cave. In the same way, the larger faunal remains at Swartkrans are very likely to contain evidence of the range of animals hunted by leopards in this particular area.

Studies on living leopards have made it clear that the nature of their food remains is

豹 的 角 色

在斯瓦特克朗斯的化石中有很多是来自豹的，目前已经发现了至少 13 头豹的个体残骸。作为弯豹亚种 [10]，它们仅在亚种水平上与现生的非洲豹有所不同，化石种可能比现生种略小一点。如前所述，剑齿虎的存在可能对于原始鬣狗的生存来说至关重要；同样，豹和斑鬣狗之间的直接关联也有可能是斯瓦特克朗斯骨骼堆积过程中的一个关键因素。

当豹与斑鬣狗同在一个狩猎区的时候，大家都知道，如果豹想保住自己的猎物，就必须在食腐动物难以到达的地方进食。最近，我研究了克鲁格国家公园中的 15 起豹捕猎行为。所有这些捕猎行为都引起了斑鬣狗的注意，但是豹能足够及时地把猎物带到树上以躲避鬣狗抢食的情况有 12 次。在其余的 3 次中，豹的动作不够迅速，结果使自己的猎物被鬣狗夺走。

在林地中，豹想找到适合挂放猎物的树并不困难，但是在旷野就很难办到了。今天的斯瓦特克朗斯位于开阔的高原之上，是一片波浪起伏的草原，除了水道沿岸以外几乎没有树木。对斯瓦特克朗斯沉积物中羚羊动物群的研究显示：在该山洞被填充期间，开阔的草原环境和现在没有什么两样，动物群的主要成员是生活在草原上的群居物种，如各种大小的跳羚、瞪羚和狷羚等。在开阔的高原上进行狩猎的豹不得不利用合适的悬崖、山洞和少数便于利用的树来保护它们的猎物。在德兰士瓦高原的白云岩地区，我们发现在出现大树和出现山洞之间存在着一种有趣且极其重要的相关性。在这片起伏不大的乡间，洞穴的类型多为杆状或形状不一的坑状，在它们的入口周围有洼地。虽然山腰上缺少树木，但在山洞的入口处通常有几棵大臭木或野生无花果树；这些大树在那里繁茂地生长着，因为受到的保护可以使它们躲开霜冻和火灾。因此豹被吸引到白云岩山洞并将此处作为安全庇护之所也在意料之中，因为洞口的树木非常适于储存它们的猎物。因此，豹的食余垃圾会落到洞口的集水区，其中有一部分还会最终掉到地下的化石堆积区。假设斯瓦特克朗斯的沉积物堆积了大约 20,000 年，那么如果说该洞穴和与之相关的树木未曾被豹无数次地用于进食或栖息的话就太令人惊奇了。洞穴里一直有猫头鹰居住，它们的吐余构成了沉积物中小动物化石的主要部分，由此可以非常全面地了解猫头鹰在洞穴附近曾捕食过哪些动物。同样，斯瓦特克朗斯化石中的大型动物很可能可以为我们提供在这一特定区域被豹捕食的动物种类的证据。

对现生豹的研究使我们很清楚地了解到豹的食余垃圾的性质在很大程度上受制

considerably influenced by the presence or absence of hyaenas (my work, in preparation). In the Kruger Park study area, where the leopards are constantly harried by hyaenas, they were found to do considerable damage to the skeletons of their prey (largely impala). They would typically return to the carcass in the tree during a period of 3–4 days, by which time most of the body had been consumed. The head and lower leg segments would invariably be left, usually hanging on strips of skin, but the rest of the skeleton generally disappeared. As part of this investigation, leopards were also studied in South West Africa, in an area where no hyaenas or other significant scavengers occur. Here the pattern of leopard food remains was completely different. The leopards made no attempt to drag their prey into inaccessible places, except where the kill had been made close to human habitation. They typically ate where they killed and did comparatively little damage to the prey skeletons, eating only a small quantity of meat before moving on to make another kill a few days later. It is consequently impossible to define the characteristics of "typical" leopard food remains. Their nature will depend on the availability of food and the pressure applied to the leopards by dominant scavengers such as spotted hyaenas.

The greater part of the Swartkrans bone accumulation shows characteristics consistent with those of leopard food remains, and suggests a situation where the leopards had been regularly harried by hyaenas. There are, however, several features of the bone collection which require special explanation. These involve the disproportions in the skeletal parts preserved. In the case of bovid skeletons, it has already been established that certain parts are more resistant to destruction than others and it is possible to predict which parts are likely to survive any particular treatment[12]. At Swartkrans, for instance, bovid distal humeri are almost five times as common as proximal ones. Such a disproportion is to be expected and means simply that the carnivore involved was able to chew away the relatively fragile proximal end of the humerus, but had trouble with the resistant distal one. The difficulty is encountered when we compare the recognizable remains of primate skeletons (such as of baboons and australopithecines) with those of bovids. The latter are typically represented by a wide variety of damaged skeletal parts, while the former are largely cranial in origin with very little else. In fact, the Swartkrans *Paranthropus* sample consists of 190 separate pieces, representing a minimum of at least sixty individuals. Of these fossils, only eleven are post-cranial bones.

The probable reasons for this remarkable state of affairs have been suggested by a series of feeding experiments with cheetahs that I have recently carried out. A natural group of five wild cheetahs was caught on Valencia Ranch in South West Africa and maintained in a large semi-natural enclosure there, through the cooperation of Mr. A. F. Port. Within a short period the cheetahs tolerated human observers and fed readily on the animals provided. Previous observations had indicated that cheetah damage to bovid skeletons, from animals in the 50–150 pound range, was minimal. It was restricted to fragile parts such as ribs, vertebral processes and scapulae. These observations were confirmed in the feeding experiments and, when the cheetahs had fed on a springbuck for instance, almost the whole skeleton remained. When a baboon of equivalent weight was eaten, however, a very different result was obtained. The cheetahs were able to consume the whole of the vertebral column, the hands and feet, as well as to do appreciable damage to the ends of

于鬣狗的存在与否（我的工作，完稿中）。在克鲁格公园研究区，豹经常遭到鬣狗的掠夺，而鬣狗对猎物（主要是黑斑羚）骨架的破坏相当严重。在 3 天~ 4 天之内，它们一定会回到树丛中的尸体那儿去，大部分尸体在这段时间里会被吃掉。剩下的一般是头部和小腿部分，通常连着丝丝缕缕的毛皮，但是骨架的其余部分在大多数情况下会消失不见。研究非洲西南部的豹也是本项课题中的一部分，在那里没有鬣狗或其他重要食腐动物的出没。豹的食余垃圾的形式在此处完全是另一番景象。除非捕杀行为是发生在靠近人类住所之处，否则豹根本不会将它们的猎物拖到其他动物难以接近的地方。它们一般会在捕杀动物的地方就地进食，对猎物骨架的破坏也很小，因为一次捕猎只吃掉猎物的一小部分肉，几天之后便进行一次新的捕杀。因此很难定义"有代表性"的豹子食余垃圾的特征。这些食余垃圾的性质将取决于食物的可利用率以及斑鬣狗等主要食腐动物给豹造成的压力。

斯瓦特克朗斯的大部分化石堆积所表现出来的特征与豹的食余垃圾相符，并且由此可以说明豹经常遭遇被鬣狗掠夺的处境。然而，这些骨骼堆积还有其他一些特征需要另行解释。例如为什么保存下来的骨骼部位不成比例。在牛科动物骨架的例子中，我们已经证明其中某些部位将比另一些部位更不容易被破坏，因而可以预测出哪些部位可能会在特定的环境中幸存[12]。例如在斯瓦特克朗斯，牛科动物肱骨远端的出现频率是近端部分的近 5 倍。上面提到的不成比例应该是预料之中的事情，这只不过说明相关的食肉动物只能咀嚼相对脆弱的肱骨近端，而对于有韧性的远端则比较吃力。在比较可识别的灵长类动物骨架残骸（例如狒狒和南方古猿）与牛科动物骨架残骸时，我们遇到了一些困难。后者通常包括各种受损的骨骼部位，而前者则主要是头盖骨，其他部位很少。事实上，斯瓦特克朗斯的傍人样本由 190 个单独的碎片组成，代表了至少 60 个个体。在这些化石中，只有 11 件是颅后骨骼。

我最近对猎豹的摄食行为进行了一系列实验，由此得到了这些不寻常事件的可能原因。我们在非洲西南部的巴伦西亚牧场捕获了一个由 5 只野生猎豹组成的自然豹群，并且在波特先生的配合下把它们关进了一个半自然的大型围场之内。在短时间内，这些猎豹接受了人类观察者，并且顺从地吃下了人类提供的动物。之前的观察表明：猎豹对牛科动物的骨架破坏很小，这些牛科动物的体重在 50 磅~150 磅之间。损伤部位局限于脆弱的部分，例如肋骨、椎突及肩胛骨。上述观察结果在喂食实验中得到了证实，例如当猎豹被喂以跳羚时，几乎会剩下整副骨架。然而，当喂以一只同等重量的狒狒时，就会得到完全不同的结果。猎豹除了会严重破坏狒狒的肢骨末端以外，还能吃掉其全部脊柱、前脚和后脚。造成这种差异的原因显然在于

the limb bones. The reason for this difference clearly lies in the fact that the construction of a baboon skeleton is considerably less robust than that of a bovid of equivalent live weight. The baboon vertebral column is fragile enough to be consumed, while the hands and feet are found to be fleshy and palatable.

It is not suggested that cheetahs were involved in the Swartkrans situation: they are simply amenable experimental animals. Nevertheless, conclusions drawn from them on the comparative robusticity of prey skeletons will be equally applicable to leopards, which are known to be capable of doing far more extensive damage to the skeletons of their prey. A leopard is potentially capable of eating virtually a whole baboon, with the exception of the skull, which is invariably left. Conclusions drawn about baboons will be equally applicable to hominids, built on the generalized primate pattern, provided that their larger size is taken into account. One of the reasons for the fact that so few primate limb bones have been recognized in the Swartkrans accumulation may lie in the fact that the diagnostic ends of such bones are typically chewed off by leopards, with the result that damaged and undiagnostic shaft pieces remain. Many of the indeterminate bone fragments at Swartkrans could well be of australopithecine origin.

One of the australopithecine skull pieces form Swartkrans appears to bear direct evidence of leopard activity. The specimen, *SK* 54, consists of much of the calvaria of a subadult hominid thought to have been a *Paranthropus*. It was found at the site in 1949 and subsequently prepared by Dr. Robinson in Wisconsin, using the acetic acid technique. As shown in Fig. 4, the fossil consists of left and right parietal bones, part of the occipital and much of the frontal. The frontal has been distorted downwards, approximately across the width of the coronal suture, while the whole specimen has been slightly flattened by pressure in the deposit. From a comparison of the size of the parietal bones with those of other Swartkrans specimens, it is estimated that the endocranial capacity of this skull was approximately 500 cm^3. The two holes in the back of the skull, one in each parietal bone, close to lambda (see Fig. 4), are particularly interesting. Each is slightly elongated in a lateral direction and is approximately 6 mm in its shortest diameter. It is clear that the holes were made by two pointed objects, whose tips diverged slightly. On the internal surface of the parietals, flakes of bone have been lifted in a characteristic manner, suggesting that the bone was fresh and pliable when the injury was inflicted. If the two holes were made simultaneously, the points of the two sharp objects responsible must have been approximately 33 mm apart.

狒狒骨架的结构远远不如同等重量牛科动物的骨架坚固。狒狒的脊柱软到足以能够被吃掉，而它的前脚和后脚既肥美又可口。

这不能说明猎豹参与了斯瓦特克朗斯的骨骼收集：它们只是受人摆布的实验动物。然而，根据猎豹的摄食行为而得到的关于猎物骨架相对强度的结论也能适用于豹，我们知道豹对猎物骨架的破坏程度远远高于猎豹。豹具有吃掉几乎整个狒狒的潜在能力，不过头骨通常是要被剩下来的。从狒狒中得到的结论也同样适用于具有普通灵长类动物结构的原始人类，但要考虑到它们的体型更大。在斯瓦特克朗斯的堆积物中极少能发现灵长类肢骨化石的原因之一可能在于以下事实：这些骨头的可鉴定部位通常会被豹嚼碎，剩下的只有不完整的无法鉴定的杆状碎片。斯瓦特克朗斯的许多无法鉴定的骨骼碎片很可能来自于南方古猿。

在斯瓦特克朗斯发现的南方古猿头骨碎片中有一块似乎能为我们提供豹活动的直接证据。该标本，即 SK 54，由一个接近成年的人科成员的大部分颅顶组成，这个人科成员被认为是傍人。该标本于 1949 年在斯瓦特克朗斯遗址被发现，随后威斯康星的鲁滨逊博士用醋酸浸洗法对其进行了处理。如图 4 所示，该化石包括左右顶骨、部分枕骨和大部分额骨。额骨已经向下扭曲，几乎贯穿了冠状缝的全部宽度，而整个标本由于在沉积物中受到压力而略微变平了。从比较该顶骨的大小和其他斯瓦特克朗斯标本顶骨大小的结果来看，这个头骨的颅腔容量约为 500 cm³。格外有意思的是：在头骨后面、靠近人字缝处有两个孔，每块顶骨上各有一个（见图 4）。每个孔在外侧方向上都有所拉长，最短直径约为 6 mm。这两个孔显然是由两个尖头物戳出来的，该尖头物的尖端略有一点分开。在顶骨的内表面，骨片以一种很有特色的方式被提高了，这说明顶骨在受到损伤时还是鲜嫩的。如果这两个孔是同时被戳出来的，那么两个尖头物的尖端之间必定相距 33 mm 左右。

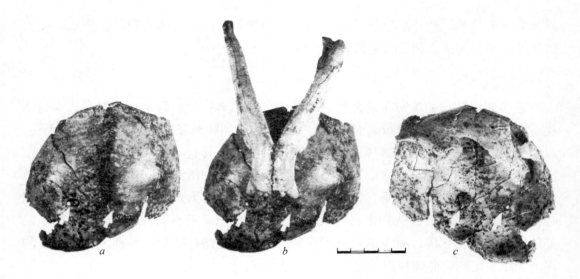

Fig. 4. Part of a hominid skull (*SK* 54) from Swartkrans showing holes thought to have been made by canine teeth. (*a*) Posterior view of left and right parietals and part of the occipital (arrows indicate position of holes on either side of lambda); (*b*) same view as in (*a*) to show how spacing of holes is matched by that of canine tips in the type mandible of the Swartkrans leopard; (*c*) internal view showing flakes of bone lifted when the parietals were pierced.

In a recent survey of the evidence for intrahuman killing in the Pleistocene, Roper[13] mentions this particular specimen and quotes Ardrey's argument[14] that the holes indicate that the australopithecine was struck twice on the back of the head with a pointed object. I believe that it is more likely that the two holes were made simultaneously by the canine teeth of a carnivore spaced about 33 mm apart. The question remains as to which species may have been involved and in what position the australopithecine's head could have been held when the damage was inflicted.

The Swartkrans fossils include remains of carnivores ranging in size from lion to mongoose. In many cases they represent forms closely related to living species so that, although the fossil material is fragmentary, modern skulls may be used to give an indication of typical canine spacings. Making use of the collection in the Transvaal Museum, distances between upper and lower canine tips have been measured on skulls of seven extant species (Table 2).

Table 2. Distances between Upper and Lower Canine Tips on Skulls of Seven Carnivores

Carnivore	*n*	Upper canine spacing, mm		Lower canine spacing, mm	
		Range	Mean	Range	Mean
Lion, *Panthera leo*	17	60–81	67	53–69	59
Brown hyaena, *H. brunnea*	17	44–57	52	43–57	52
Spotted hyaena, *Crocuta crocula*	8	49–57	54	42–54	46
Male leopard, *Panthera pardus*	10	33–47	39	31–41	36
Female leopard, *Panthera pardus*	14	33–42	38	30–38	33
Jackal, *Canis mesomelas*	20	21–28	25	21–26	23
Fox, *Vulpes chama*	11	14–19	16	11–16	13
Mongoose, *Cynictis penicillate*	25	10–13	11	9–13	10

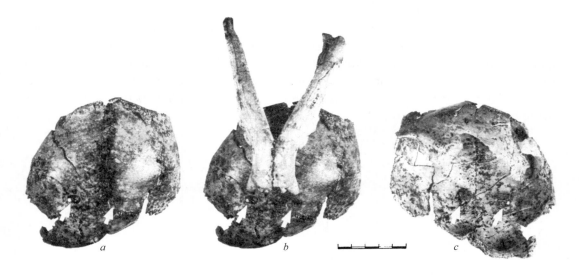

图 4. 一件斯瓦特克朗斯人科头骨（SK 54）的一部分，上面的孔被认为是犬齿造成的。（a）左右顶骨以及部分枕骨的后面观（箭头指向的是人字缝两边的孔的位置）；（b）与（a）相同的视图，目的是为了展示两个孔之间的间距与斯瓦特克朗斯豹典型下颌骨上的犬齿齿尖之间的间距相符；（c）显示出当顶骨被刺穿时骨片抬高的内侧面观。

　　在最近的一项对更新世时期人类之间相互杀戮证据的调查中，罗珀 [13] 提到了这个特殊标本，并且引用了阿德里的论据 [14]，阿德里认为这两个孔表明南方古猿的头后部曾被一个尖头物击中了两次。我相信更可能的情况是这两个孔是由某种食肉动物相距约 33 mm 的两枚犬齿同时造成的。那么这两个孔究竟是哪个物种造成的以及当损伤发生时南方古猿的头部处于什么位置，这些仍然是疑问。

　　斯瓦特克朗斯化石包括的食肉动物化石从狮子到黄鼬大小不等。这些化石所代表的动物类型大多与现生物种有很密切的关系，所以尽管化石化材料非常破碎，但是我们可以用现代头骨来说明典型的犬齿间距。利用德兰士瓦博物馆的收藏品，我们对 7 件现存物种头骨的上下犬齿齿尖之间的距离进行了测量（表 2）。

表 2. 7 件食肉动物头骨上的上、下犬齿齿尖之间的距离

食肉动物	n	上犬齿之间的间距，mm		下犬齿之间的间距，mm	
		范围	平均值	范围	平均值
狮子	17	60~81	67	53~69	59
棕鬣狗	17	44~57	52	43~57	52
斑鬣狗	8	49~57	54	42~54	46
雄豹	10	33~47	39	31~41	36
雌豹	14	33~42	38	30~38	33
胡狼	20	21~28	25	21~26	23
南非狐	11	14~19	16	11~16	13
黄鼬	25	10~13	11	9~13	10

Results are plotted in Fig. 5, where the estimated ranges for some of the extinct species are also shown. On the basis of rather inadequate material, it is concluded that the known Swartkrans sabre-toothed cats had canine spacings intermediate between those of lions and spotted hyaenas. The type skull of *Leecyaena forfex* (*SK* 314) is comparable in size with the skull of a *Crocuta* and had upper canines spaced about 46 mm apart. Specimens of *Lycyaena* from Swartkrans appear to have had spacings intermediate between those of the living hyaenas and leopards.

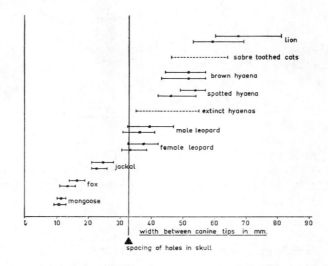

Fig. 5. Canine spacings in some South African carnivores. Observed ranges and means are plotted for upper and lower teeth while estimated ranges for Swartkrans sabre-tooths and extinct hyaenas are included.

It will be seen that the figure of 33 mm, representing the distance between the holes in the fossil skull, falls well within the leopard rang and coincides with the mean figure for lower canine spacings in the female skulls measured. It must be remembered, however, that the fossil leopards seem to have been a fraction smaller than their living counterparts. It can naturally not be proved that a leopard (or any other specific carnivore) was responsible for the damage to the fossil skull, but considering the various lines of evidence from Swartkrans, it is very probable that leopard canines did, in fact, produce the holes. Similar holes in the skulls of baboons eaten by leopards in the Suswa caves of Kenya have been reported by Simons[15]. A leopard typically kills its prey with a firm grip across the throat but, when subsequently dragging a dead animal to a protected feeding place, will often grip the head in its jaws. Fig. 6 shows how this may have been done in the case of the Swartkrans *Paranthropus* child. Under the weight of the child's body, the leopard's lower canines may have penetrated the rather thin parietal bones, while the upper canines were firmly embedded in the face.

250

图 5 中画出了所得的结果，某些已灭绝物种的估计范围也在图中标出。根据不太完整的材料推断：已知的斯瓦特克朗斯剑齿虎的犬齿间距介于狮子和斑鬣狗之间。李氏鬣狗的正型标本头骨（SK 314）在大小上与斑鬣狗的头骨相当，上犬齿之间的间距约为 46 mm。斯瓦特克朗斯狼鬣狗标本的犬齿间距似乎介于现生鬣狗和豹之间。

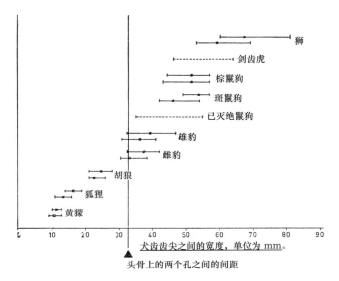

图 5. 几种南非食肉动物的犬齿间距。图中分别标出了上犬齿间距和下犬齿间距的范围和平均值，还包括斯瓦特克朗斯剑齿虎和已灭绝鬣狗的犬齿间距的估计范围。

从图中可以看到：头骨化石上两个孔之间的距离 33 mm 正好处于豹的范围之内，并与在雌豹头骨中测得的下犬齿间距的平均值相符合。但是，一定要记住，化石豹的个头似乎比现生豹小。虽然现在还无法证明是豹（或者某一种其他的食肉动物）对头骨化石造成了这一损伤，但是根据来自于斯瓦特克朗斯的各种证据，事实上这两个孔是由豹的犬齿造成的可能性还是很大的。西蒙斯[15] 曾报道过：在肯尼亚的苏苏瓦山洞穴，被豹吃掉的狒狒的头骨上也有类似的孔。一头豹通常会通过咬断猎物的喉咙来杀死它们，随后豹常常用自己的上下颌叼着死亡动物的头部以便把它拖到一个安全的进食场所。图 6 以斯瓦特克朗斯傍人小孩为例绘出了可能发生的过程。为了抵消小孩的体重，豹的下犬齿可能刺穿了非常薄的顶骨，而上犬齿则深深地嵌入面部。

Fig. 6. Reconstruction showing how the observed damage to the skull of a Swartkrans *Paranthropus* child could have been caused by a leopard. The leopard's lower canines are thought to have penetrated the parietals of the dead child while it was being dragged to a feeding place.

The evidence presented here suggests that *Paranthropus* individuals were preyed upon by leopards in the same way as were baboons, hyraxes and antelope. Leopard predation on humans still occurs today; such predation would presumably have been much more prevalent at a stage of human evolution when australopithecines were neither physically formidable nor protected by the weapons of an advanced technology.

The renewed work at Swartkrans would not have been possible without the support of the Wenner-Gren Foundation for Anthropological Research; in particular I wish to thank Mrs. L. Osmundsen for her interest in the project. I also thank the trustees of the Transvaal Museum and the South African CSIR for their support; the University of the Witwatersrand, present owners of Swartkrans, for help and permission to continue research there; Professor P. V. Tobias and Professor F. Clark Howell for helpful discussions; the South African National Parks Board for research facilities in the National Parks; Mr. and Mrs. A. F. Port for the opportunity to study living carnivores on Valencia Ranch, South West Africa; and my wife, Mr. A. C. Kemp and Mrs. E. A. Voigt for their help with the research.

(**225**, 1112-1119; 1970)

C. K. Brain: Transvaal Museum, Pretoria.

Received January 16, 1970.

References:
1. Robinson, J. T., *Nature* (in the press).

图 6. 示意斯瓦特克朗斯傍人小孩头骨上的损伤可能是由豹引起的情景复原图。在豹将死亡小孩拖到进
　　食之处的过程中，它的下犬齿刺穿了死亡小孩的顶骨。

　　这里列出的证据说明：豹捕食傍人个体的方式与捕食狒狒、蹄兔和羚羊是相同的。豹子捕食人类的现象至今仍有发生；在人类进化的早期，这种捕食行为想必远比现在普遍得多，那时的南方古猿既没有威慑的外形，也没有技术先进的武器用以保护自己。

　　如果没有温纳－格伦基金会人类学研究基金的支持，就很难在斯瓦特克朗斯再次开展研究；我要特别感谢奥斯姆德森夫人对本项目的关注。还要感谢德兰士瓦博物馆和南非科学及工业研究委员会的管理人员对我的支持；感谢斯瓦特克朗斯现在的所有者——南非威特沃特斯兰德大学（又名金山大学）支持我并允许我继续在那里开展研究；感谢托拜厄斯教授和克拉克·豪厄尔教授与我进行了很有意义的讨论；感谢南非国家公园管理局为我提供国家公园中的研究设备；感谢波特先生及夫人给了我在非洲西南部巴伦西亚牧场研究现生食肉动物的机会；还要感谢我的妻子、肯普先生和沃伊特夫人对本研究给予的帮助。

（刘皓芳 翻译；董为 审稿）

2. Leakey, M., *Nature* (in the press).

3. Clarke, R. J., Howell, F. C., and Brain, C. K., *Nature* (in the press).

4. Broom, R., and Robinson, J. T., *Nature*, **164**, 322 (1949).

5. Robinson, J. T., *S. Afric. J. Sci.*, **57**, 3 (1961).

6. Brain, C. K., *S. Afric. J. Sci.*, **63**, 378 (1967).

7. Robinson, J. T., *Ann. Transv. Mus.*, **22**, 1 (1952).

8. Brain, C. K., *Transv. Mus. Memoir*, No. 11 (1958).

9. Ewer, R. F., *Proc. Zool. Soc. Lond.*, **124**, 815 (1953); **124**, 839 (1953); **125**, 587 (1954).

10. Ewer, R. F., *Proc. Zool. Soc. Lond.*, **126**, 83 (1956).

11. Ewer, R. F., in *Background to Evolution in Africa* (edit. by Bishop, W. W., and Clark, J. D.), 109 (University of Chicago Press, 1967).

12. Brain, C. K., *Scient. Pap. Namib Desert Res. Stn.*, **32**, 1 (1967); **39**, 13 (1969).

13. Roper, M. K., *Current Anthrop.*, **10**, 427 (1969).

14. Ardrey, R., *African Genesis*, 300 (Collins, London, 1961).

15. Simons, J. W., *Bull. Cave Exploration Group E. Afric.*, **1**, 51 (1966).

RNA-dependent DNA Polymerase in Virions of RNA Tumour Viruses

D. Baltimore

Editor's Note

David Baltimore was a newly graduated PhD when he published this remarkable paper in 1970. Until then, molecular biologists had taken it as an article of faith that genetic information flowed from DNA to RNA to protein: this was known as "Crick's central dogma", but there was then mounting evidence that the genetic code for RNA viruses could be incorporated in the genomes of cells that they infected. Baltimore went on to become the first director of the Whitehead Institute at the Massachusetts Institute of Technology, president of the Rockefeller Institute (later university) in New York and president of the California Institute of Technology. He won a Nobel Prize for this work in 1975.

DNA seems to have a critical role in the multiplication and transforming ability of RNA tumour viruses[1]. Infection and transformation by these viruses can be prevented by inhibitors of DNA synthesis added during the first 8–12 h after exposure of cells to the virus[1-4]. The necessary DNA synthesis seems to involve the production of DNA which is genetically specific for the infecting virus[5,6], although hybridization studies intended to demonstrate virus-specific DNA have been inconclusive[1]. Also, the formation of virions by the RNA tumour viruses is sensitive to actinomycin D and therefore seems to involve DNA-dependent RNA synthesis[1-4,7]. One model which explains these data postulates the transfer of the information of the infecting RNA to a DNA copy which then serves as template for the synthesis of viral RNA[1,2,7]. This model requires a unique enzyme, an RNA-dependent DNA polymerase.

No enzyme which synthesizes DNA from an RNA template has been found in any type of cell. Unless such an enzyme exists in uninfected cells, the RNA tumour viruses must either induce its synthesis soon after infection or carry the enzyme into the cell as part of the virion. Precedents exist for the occurrence of nucleotide polymerases in the virions of animal viruses. Vaccinia[8,9]—a DNA virus, Reo[10,11]—a double-stranded RNA virus, and vesicular stomatitis virus (VSV)[12]—a single-stranded RNA virus, have all been shown to contain RNA polymerases. This study demonstrates that an RNA-dependent DNA polymerase is present in the virions of two RNA tumour viruses: Rauscher mouse leukaemia virus (R-MLV) and Rous sarcoma virus. Temin[13] has also identified this activity in Rous sarcoma virus.

Incorporation of Radioactivity from ³H-TTP by R-MLV

A preparation of purified R-MLV was incubated in conditions of DNA polymerase assay. The preparation incorporated radioactivity from ^{3}H-TTP into an acid-insoluble product

致癌RNA病毒粒子中的RNA依赖性DNA聚合酶

巴尔的摩

编者按

戴维·巴尔的摩于 1970 年发表这篇里程碑式的文章时，他还是个刚毕业的博士生。那时，遗传信息从 DNA 传递到 RNA 再传递到蛋白质已经被分子生物学家们奉为信条，这就是所谓的"克里克中心法则"。但此后越来越多的证据表明，RNA 病毒的遗传密码可以被整合到受其感染的细胞的基因组中。巴尔的摩后来成为麻省理工学院怀特黑德研究所的第一任所长、纽约洛克菲勒研究所（后来的洛克菲勒大学）的所（校）长以及加州理工学院的院长。他凭借本文所述的工作赢得了 1975 年的诺贝尔奖。

DNA 在致癌 RNA 病毒的复制和转化能力上似乎起到了关键作用 [1]。在病毒接触到细胞后最初的 8 小时 ～ 12 小时内，加入 DNA 合成的抑制剂可以阻止由这些病毒引起的感染和转化 [1-4]。虽然杂交研究的结果尚无法证明病毒特异性 DNA 的存在 [1]，但在必需的 DNA 合成过程中似乎产生了对感染病毒来说具有遗传特异性的 DNA[5,6]。另外，致癌 RNA 病毒粒子的形成对放线菌素 D 很敏感，因此病毒粒子的形成似乎包括了 DNA 依赖性 RNA 的合成过程 [1-4,7]。能够解释这些结果的一个模型是：遗传信息从感染 RNA 传递到一个 DNA 拷贝，然后以此 DNA 拷贝作为模板合成病毒 RNA[1,2,7]。这一模型需要一种特殊的酶，即 RNA 依赖性 DNA 聚合酶。

迄今为止，在任何类型的细胞中还从未发现过以 RNA 为模板合成 DNA 的酶。如果这种酶在未感染的细胞中不存在，那么它就一定是在致癌 RNA 病毒感染细胞后不久被诱导合成出来的，或者是作为病毒粒子的一部分被带入细胞的。有先例表明在动物病毒的病毒粒子中存在着核苷酸聚合酶。DNA 型牛痘病毒 [8,9]、双链 RNA 型呼肠孤病毒（Reo）[10,11] 和单链 RNA 型水泡性口炎病毒（VSV）[12] 都已被人们发现含有 RNA 聚合酶。本文所述的研究表明：RNA 依赖性 DNA 聚合酶存在于两种致癌 RNA 病毒粒子中——劳舍尔小鼠白血病病毒（R–MLV）和劳斯肉瘤病毒。特明 [13] 还鉴定过劳斯肉瘤病毒中这种酶的活性。

R–MLV 介导 ^{3}H– 胸苷三磷酸（^{3}H–TTP）的放射活性掺入

将纯化的 R–MLV 制剂在 DNA 聚合酶检测条件下进行孵育。在该制剂的制备过

(Table 1). The reaction required Mg^{2+}, although Mn^{2+} could partially substitute and each of the four deoxyribonucleoside triphosphates was necessary for activity. The reaction was stimulated strongly by dithiothreitol and weakly by NaCl (Table 1). The kinetics of incorporation of radioactivity from ^{3}H-TTP by R-MLV are shown in Fig. 1, curve 1. The reaction rate accelerates for about 1 h and then declines. This time-course may indicate the occurrence of a slow activation of the polymerase in the reaction mixture. The activity is approximately proportional to the amount of added virus.

Table 1. Properties of the Rauscher Mouse Leukaemia Virus DNA Polymerase

Reaction system	pmoles ^{3}H-TMP incorporated in 45 min
Complete	3.31
Without magnesium acetate	0.04
Without magnesium acetate + 6 mM $MnCl_2$	1.59
Without dithiothreitol	0.38
Without NaCl	2.18
Without dATP	<0.10
Without dCTP	0.12
Without dGTP	<0.10

A preparation of R-MLV was provided by the Viral Resources Program of the National Cancer Institute. The virus had been purified from the plasma of infected Swiss mice by differential centrifugation. The preparation had a titre of $10^{4.88}$ spleen enlarging doses (50 percent end point) per ml. Before use the preparation was centrifuged at 105,000g for 30 min and the pellet was suspended in 0.137 M NaC1–0.003 M KC1–0.01 M phosphate buffer (pH 7.4)–0.6 mM EDTA (PBS–EDTA) at 1/20 of the initial volume. The concentrated virus suspension contained 3.1 mg/ml. of protein. The assay mixture contained, in 0.1 ml., 5 μmoles Tris-HCl (pH 8.3) at 37°C, 0.6 μmole magnesium acetate, 6 μmoles NaCl, 2 μmoles dithiothreitol, 0.08 μmole each of dATP, dCTP and dGTP, 0.001 μmole [^{3}H-*methyl*]–TTP (708 c.p.m. per pmole) (New England Nuclear) and 15 μg viral protein. The reaction mixture was incubated for 45 min at 37°C. The acid-insoluble radioactivity in the sample was then determined by addition of sodium pyrophosphate, carrier yeast RNA and trichloroacetic acid followed by filtration through a membrane filter and counting in a scintillation spectrometer, all as previously described[12]. The radioactivity of an unincubated sample was subtracted from each value (less than 7 percent of the incorporation in the complete reaction mixture).

程中，^{3}H–TTP 的放射活性被掺入到一种不溶于酸的产物中（表 1）。这一反应需要 Mg^{2+}，不过 Mn^{2+} 也可以部分替代 Mg^{2+}，此外 4 种脱氧核苷三磷酸都是必需的。二硫苏糖醇可以在很大程度上影响反应，而 NaCl 对反应也有微弱的促进作用（表 1）。图 1 中的曲线 1 代表 R–MLV 掺入 ^{3}H–TTP 的放射活性的动力学曲线。反应速率在最初的 1 个小时左右不断加快，之后出现下降。这样的时间进程可能表明，在反应混合物中发生了缓慢的聚合酶激活。反应后产物的放射活性大致与加入的病毒量成正比。

表 1. 劳舍尔小鼠白血病病毒的 DNA 聚合酶的性质

反应系统	反应 45 分钟后掺入的 ^{3}H– 胸苷酸（^{3}H–TMP）的 pmol 数
完全的反应系统	3.31
无醋酸镁	0.04
无醋酸镁，但加入了 6 mM $MnCl_2$	1.59
无二硫苏糖醇	0.38
无 NaCl	2.18
无脱氧腺苷三磷酸（dATP）	<0.10
无脱氧胞苷三磷酸（dCTP）	0.12
无脱氧鸟苷三磷酸（dGTP）	<0.10

R–MLV 制剂由美国国家癌症研究所病毒资源组提供。通过差速离心法将病毒从受感染的瑞士小鼠血浆中纯化出来。每 ml 制剂的滴度为 $10^{4.88}$ 脾肿大剂量（终点值的 50%）。使用前，将制剂在 105,000 g 下离心 30 分钟，并将沉淀物悬浮于 0.137 M NaCl、0.003 M KCl、0.01 M 磷酸盐缓冲液（pH 值 7.4）、0.6 mM EDTA（PBS–EDTA）（译者注：PBS 为磷酸缓冲液，EDTA 为乙二胺四乙酸）中，使最终体积为初始体积的 1/20。浓缩的病毒悬浮液含有 3.1 mg/ml 蛋白。在 0.1 ml 反应混合物中含有 5 μmol Tris–HCl（pH 值 8.3，37℃）（译者注：Tris–HCl 为三羟甲基氨基甲烷盐酸盐）、0.6 μmol 醋酸镁、6 μmol NaCl、2 μmol 二硫苏糖醇以及 dATP、dCTP 和 dGTP 各 0.08 μmol，0.001 μmol [^{3}H–甲基]–TTP（每 pmol 为 708 次放射性计数 / 分钟）（新英格兰核公司）和 15 μg 病毒蛋白。反应混合物在 37℃ 下孵育 45 分钟。加入焦磷酸钠、载体酵母 RNA 和三氯乙酸，接着用滤膜过滤后再在闪烁谱仪上计数，由此测定样品中不溶于酸的物质的放射性，上述所有操作在我们以前发表的文章中均已涉及 [12]。测定得到的每个数值都要减去未孵育样品的放射活性（小于完全反应混合物中掺入程度的 7%）。

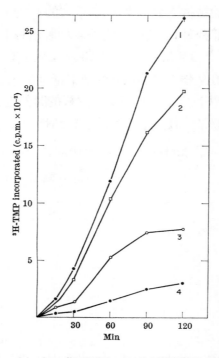

Fig. 1. Incorporation of radioactivity from ³H-TTP by the R-MLV DNA polymerase in the presence and absence of ribonuclease. A 1.5-fold standard reaction mixture was prepared with 30 μg of viral protein and ³H-TTP (specific activity 950 c.p.m. per pmole). At various times, 20 μl. aliquots were added to 0.5 ml. of non-radioactive 0.1 M sodium pyrophosphate and acid insoluble radioactivity was determined[12]. For the preincubated samples, 0.06 ml. of H₂O and 0.01 ml. of R-MLV (30 μg of protein) were incubated with or without 10 μg of pancreatic ribonuclease at 22°C for 20 min, chilled and brought to 0.15 ml. with a concentrated mixture of the components of the assay system. Curve 1, no treatment; curve 2, preincubated; curve 3, 10 μg ribonuclease added to the reaction mixture; curve 4, preincubated with 10 μg ribonuclease.

For other viruses which have nucleotide polymerases in their virions, there is little or no activity demonstrable unless the virions are activated by heat, proteolytic enzymes or detergents[8-12]. None of these treatments increased the activity of the R-MLV DNA polymerase. In fact, incubation at 50°C for 10 min totally inactivated the R-MLV enzyme as did inclusion of trypsin (50 μg/ml.) in the reaction mixture. Addition of as little as 0.01 percent "Triton N-101" (a non-ionic detergent) also markedly depressed activity.

Characterization of the Product

The nature of the reaction product was investigated by determining its sensitivity to various treatments. The product could be rendered acid-soluble by either pancreatic deoxyribonuclease or micrococcal nuclease but was unaffected by pancreatic ribonuclease or by alkaline hydrolysis (Table 2). The product therefore has the properties of DNA. If 50 μg/ml. of deoxyribonuclease was added to a reaction mixture there was no loss of

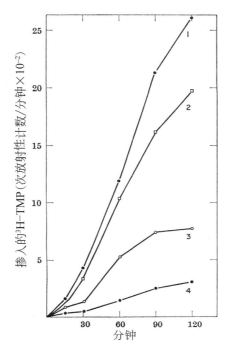

图 1. 在存在和不存在核糖核酸酶时，R–MLV 的 DNA 聚合酶催化掺入 ³H–TTP 的放射活性。用 30 μg 病毒蛋白和 ³H–TTP（比活度为每 pmol 950 次放射性计数 / 分钟）制备 1.5 倍的标准反应混合物。分别在不同时间点将 20 μl 的等分样品加入到 0.5 ml 非放射性的 0.1 M 焦磷酸钠中，然后测定酸不溶性物质的放射性[12]。预先孵育的样品指的是：将 0.06 ml 水和 0.01 ml R–MLV（30 μg 蛋白）分别在加入和不加入 10 μg 胰核糖核酸酶的条件下于 22℃ 下孵育 20 分钟，冷却后加入检测系统组分的浓缩混合物直至终体积达到 0.15 ml。曲线 1 代表没有进行过任何处理的实验组；曲线 2 代表预先孵育的实验组；曲线 3 代表在反应混合物中加入 10 μg 核糖核酸酶的实验组；曲线 4 代表用 10 μg 核糖核酸酶预先孵育的实验组。

对于病毒粒子中含核苷酸聚合酶的其他病毒，如果不提前用加热、加入蛋白水解酶或加入去垢剂来激活病毒粒子的话，就只能检测到很少的放射活性或根本检测不到放射活性[8-12]。所有这些处理均不会增加 R–MLV 的 DNA 聚合酶的活性。事实上，在 50℃ 下孵育 10 分钟就可以使 R–MLV 的酶完全失活，和向反应混合物中加入胰蛋白酶（50 μg/ml）的效果一样。添加浓度仅为 0.01% 的"曲拉通 N–101"（一种非离子型去垢剂）同样会使活性显著降低。

反应产物的特性

可以根据反应产物对各种处理的敏感性来研究它的特性。用胰脱氧核糖核酸酶或微球菌核酸酶处理该产物可使其溶于酸，但用胰核糖核酸酶处理或加碱水解并不能使该产物受到任何影响（表 2）。因此，该产物具有 DNA 的性质。如果向反应混合物中加入 50 μg/ml 的脱氧核糖核酸酶，不溶于酸的产物将不会有任何损失。因此，

acid-insoluble product. The product is therefore protected from the enzyme, probably by the envelope of the virion, although merely diluting the reaction mixture into 10 mM MgCl$_2$ enables the product to be digested by deoxyribonuclease (Table 2).

Table 2. Characterization of the Polymerase Product

Expt.	Treatment	Acid-insoluble radioactivity	Percentage undigested product
1	Untreated	1,425	(100)
	20 μg deoxyribonuclease	125	9
	20 μg micrococcal nuclease	69	5
	20 μg ribonuclease	1,361	96
2	Untreated	1,644	(100)
	NaOH hydrolysed	1,684	100

For experiment 1, 93 μg of viral protein was incubated for 2 h in a reaction mixture twice the size of that described in Table 1, with ^{3}H-TTP having a specific activity of 1,133 c.p.m. per pmole. A 50 μl. portion of the reaction mixture was diluted to 5 ml. with 10 mM MgCl$_2$ and 0.5 ml. aliquots were incubated for 1.5 h at 37˚C with the indicated enzymes. (The sample with micrococcal nuclease also contained 5 mM CaCl$_2$.) The samples were then chilled, precipitated with trichloroacetic acid radioactivity was counted. For experiment 2, two standard reaction mixtures were incubated for 45 min at 37˚C, then to one sample was added 0.1 ml. of 1 M NaOH and it was boiled for 5 min. It was then chilled and both samples were precipitated with trichloroacetic acid and counted. In a separate experiment (unpublished) it was shown that the alkaline hydrolysis conditions would completely degrade the RNA product of the VSV virion polymerase.

Localization of the Enzyme and Its Template

To investigate whether the DNA polymerase and its template were associated with the virions, a R-MLV suspension was centrifuged to equilibrium in a 15–50 percent sucrose gradient and fractions of the gradient were assayed for DNA polymerase activity. Most of the activity was found at the position of the visible band of virions (Fig. 2). The density at this band was 1.16 g/cm^3, in agreement with the known density of the virions[14]. The polymerase and its template therefore seem to be constituents of the virion.

上述产物未受酶破坏的原因很可能是由于病毒粒子的包封，不过只要用 10 mM 的 MgCl₂ 稀释反应混合物即可使产物被脱氧核糖核酸酶降解掉（表 2）。

表 2. 聚合酶产物的特性

实验	处理方法	不溶于酸的产物的放射活性	未被降解产物所占的百分比
1	未处理	1,425	(100)
	20 μg 脱氧核糖核酸酶	125	9
	20 μg 微球菌核酸酶	69	5
	20 μg 核糖核酸酶	1,361	96
2	未处理	1,644	(100)
	NaOH 水解	1,684	100

对于实验 1，取 93 μg 病毒蛋白孵育 2 小时，孵育所用的反应混合物的体积是表 1 中所述的 2 倍，其中 ³H-TTP 的放射性比活度为每 pmol 1,133 次放射性计数 / 分钟。用 10 mM MgCl₂ 将 50 μl 反应混合物稀释到 5 ml，然后等分成 0.5 ml 并分别加入表中所示的酶，再在 37℃ 下孵育 1.5 小时（加入微球菌核酸酶的样品中还含有 5 mM CaCl₂）。然后将样品冷却，用三氯乙酸沉淀后进行放射性计数。对于实验 2，取两份标准的反应混合物在 37℃ 下孵育 45 分钟，然后向其中一份样品中加入 0.1 ml 浓度为 1 M 的 NaOH 并煮沸 5 分钟。随后使其冷却，再将两个样品都用三氯乙酸沉淀并进行放射性计数。有一个独立实验（尚未发表）的结果可以说明，用碱水解能完全降解掉在 VSV 病毒粒子聚合酶作用下产生的 RNA 产物。

酶的定位及其模板

为了研究 DNA 聚合酶及其模板是否与病毒粒子有关，将 R–MLV 的悬浮液在 15% ～ 50% 的蔗糖梯度中进行离心，达到平衡后测定该梯度下各组分的 DNA 聚合酶活性。结果发现，大部分活性落在了病毒粒子的可见带部分（图 2）。此带处的密度为 1.16 g/cm³，与该病毒粒子的已知密度相符 [14]。这样看来聚合酶及其模板可能就是病毒粒子的组成部分。

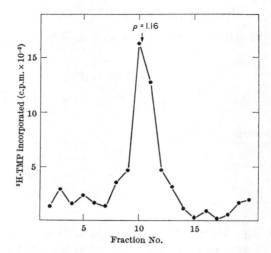

Fig. 2. Localization of DNA polymerase activity in R-MLV by isopycnic centrifugation. A preparation of R–MLV containing 150 μg of protein in 50 μl. was layered over a linear 5.2 ml. gradient of 15–50 percent sucrose in PBS–EDTA. After centrifugation for 2 h at 60,000 r.p.m. in the Spinco "SW65" rotor, 0.27 ml. fractions of the gradient were collected and 0.1 ml. portions of each fraction were incubated for 60 min in a standard reaction mixture. The acid-precipitable radioactivity was then collected and counted. The density of each fraction was determined from its refractive index. The arrow indicates the position of a sharp, visible band of light-scattering material which occurred at a density of 1.16.

The Template is RNA

Virions of the RNA tumour viruses contain RNA but no DNA[15,16]. The template for the virion DNA polymerase is therefore probably the viral RNA. To substantiate further that RNA is the template, the effect of ribonuclease on the reaction was investigated. When 50 μg/ml. of pancreatic ribonuclease was included in the reaction mixture, there was a 50 percent inhibition of activity during the first hour and more than 80 percent inhibition during the second hour of incubation (Fig. 1, curve 3). If the virions were preincubated with the enzyme in water at 22°C and the components of the reaction mixture were then added, an earlier and more extensive inhibition was evident (Fig. 1, curve 4). Preincubation in water without ribonuclease caused only a slight inactivation of the virion polymerase activity (Fig. 1, curve 2). Increasing the concentration of ribonuclease during preincubation could inhibit more than 95 percent of the DNA polymerase activity (Table 3). To ensure that the inhibition by ribonuclease was attributable to the enzymic activity of the added protein, two other basic proteins were preincubated with the virions. Only ribonuclease was able to inhibit the reaction (Table 3). These experiments substantiate the idea that RNA is the template for the reaction. Hybridization experiments are in progress to determine if the DNA is complementary in base sequence to the viral RNA.

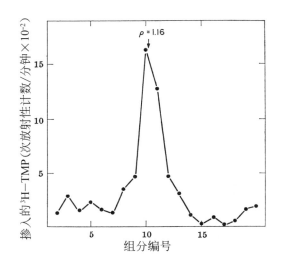

图 2. 用等密度梯度离心法对 R–MLV 中 DNA 聚合酶活性的定位。将 50 μl 含 150 μg 蛋白质的 R–MLV 样品铺在 5.2 ml 用 PBS–EDTA 配制的 15% ~ 50% 的蔗糖线性梯度上面。使用斯平科公司"SW65"型转头在 60,000 转 / 分钟的条件下离心 2 小时，然后按每份 0.27 ml 收集梯度组分，并从每个梯度组分中取出 0.1 ml 在标准反应混合物中孵育 60 分钟。随后收集酸不溶性物质并对其进行放射性计数。通过测定每个组分的折射率来确定其密度。箭头指示出了在密度为 1.16 处光散射物质的一个尖锐的可见条带。

模 板 是 RNA

致癌 RNA 病毒粒子中含有 RNA，但是没有 DNA[15,16]。因此，病毒粒子 DNA 聚合酶的模板很可能是病毒 RNA。为进一步证实 RNA 就是模板，研究了核糖核酸酶对反应的影响。当向反应混合物中加入 50 μg/ml 的胰核糖核酸酶时，在第 1 小时末有 50% 的活性被抑制，在第 2 小时末有超过 80% 的活性被抑制（图 1，曲线 3）。如果在 22℃的水中把病毒粒子与酶放在一起进行预孵育，然后再加入反应混合物的组分，那么抑制作用就会出现得更早而且更加严重（图 1，曲线 4）。如果是在没有核糖核酸酶的水中预孵育，那么病毒粒子的聚合酶活性只会发生轻微的失活（图 1，曲线 2）。在预孵育期间，增加核糖核酸酶的浓度能使 DNA 聚合酶的活性被抑制 95% 以上（表 3）。为了确认抑制作用源自于所加入蛋白质中的核糖核酸酶的活性，用另外两种碱性蛋白与病毒粒子一起进行了预孵育。结果只有核糖核酸酶能够抑制反应（表 3）。这些实验证实了 RNA 就是反应模板的设想。目前正在进行杂交实验以确定产生的 DNA 是否与病毒 RNA 的碱基序列互补。

Table 3. Effect of Ribonuclease on the DNA Polymerase Activity of Rauscher Mouse Leukaemia Virus

Conditions	pmoles ^{3}H-TMP incorporation
No preincubation	2.50
Preincubated with no addition	2.20
Preincubated with 20 µg/ml. ribonuclease	0.69
Preincubated with 50 µg/ml. ribonuclease	0.31
Preincubated with 200 µg/ml. ribonuclease	0.08
Preincubated with no addition	3.69
Preincubated with 50 µg/ml. ribonuclease	0.52
Preincubated with 50 µg/ml. lysozyme	3.67
Preincubated with 50 µg/ml. cytochrome c	3.97

In experiment 1, for the preincubation, 15 µg of viral protein in 5 µl. of solution was added to 45 µl. of water at 4°C, containing the indicated amounts of enzyme. After incubation for 30 min at 22°C, the samples were chilled and 50 µl. of a 2-fold concentrated standard reaction mixture was added. The samples were incubated at 37°C for 45 min and acid-insoluble radio-activity was measured. In experiment 2, the same procedure was followed, except that the preincubation was for 20 min at 22°C and the 37°C incubation was for 60 min.

Ability of the Enzyme to Incorporate Ribonucleotides

The deoxyribonucleotide incorporation measured in these experiments could be the result of an RNA polymerase activity in the virion which can polymerize deoxyribonucleotides when they are provided in the reaction mixture. The VSV RNA polymerase and the R-MLV DNA polymerase were therefore compared. The VSV RNA polymerase incorporated only ribonucleotides. At its pH optimum of 7.3 (my unpublished observation), in the presence of the four common ribonucleoside triphosphates, the enzyme incorporated ^{3}H-GMP extensively[12]. At this pH, however, in the presence of the four deoxyribonucleoside triphosphates, no ^{3}H-TMP incorporation was demonstrable (Table 4). Furthermore, replacement of even a single ribonucleotide by its homologous deoxyribonucleotide led to no detectable synthesis (my unpublished observation). At pH 8.3, the optimum for the R-MLV DNA polymerase, the VSV polymerase catalysed much less ribonucleotide incorporation and no significant deoxyribonucleotide incorporation could be detected.

266

表 3. 核糖核酸酶对劳舍尔小鼠白血病病毒中 DNA 聚合酶活性的影响

条件	掺入到样品中的 ^{3}H–胸苷酸（^{3}H–TMP）的 pmol 数
未进行预孵育	2.50
预孵育时不加任何物质	2.20
预孵育时加 20 μg/ml 核糖核酸酶	0.69
预孵育时加 50 μg/ml 核糖核酸酶	0.31
预孵育时加 200 μg/ml 核糖核酸酶	0.08
预孵育时不加任何物质	3.69
预孵育时加 50 μg/ml 核糖核酸酶	0.52
预孵育时加 50 μg/ml 溶菌酶	3.67
预孵育时加 50 μg/ml 细胞色素 c	3.97

在实验 1 的预孵育过程中，将 5 μl 含 15 μg 病毒蛋白的样品溶液加入到 45 μl 含有如表中所示的一定量酶的 4℃ 水中。在 22℃ 下孵育 30 分钟后，将样品冷却并加入 50 μl 两倍浓缩的标准反应混合物。随后将此样品在 37℃ 下孵育 45 分钟，并测定酸不溶性物质的放射性。在实验 2 中，除了 22℃ 下的预孵育时间为 20 分钟和 37℃ 下的孵育时间为 60 分钟以外，其余步骤同实验 1。

酶掺入核糖核苷酸的能力

在上述实验中测到的脱氧核糖核苷酸被掺入的现象，可能是由病毒粒子中的一种 RNA 聚合酶的活性造成的，这种酶能够在反应混合物中存在脱氧核糖核苷酸时使脱氧核糖核苷酸发生聚合反应。因此，对 VSV 的 RNA 聚合酶与 R–MLV 的 DNA 聚合酶进行了比较。VSV 的 RNA 聚合酶只掺入核糖核苷酸。在溶液 pH 值达到该酶最适 pH 值 7.3（尚未发表的观察结果）且 4 种常见核苷三磷酸都存在的情况下，该酶能大量地掺入 ^{3}H– 鸟苷酸（^{3}H–GMP）[12]。但是，如果所用的是 4 种脱氧核苷三磷酸，那么在该 pH 值下是观察不到 ^{3}H–TMP 的掺入的（表 4）。此外，即使只将一种核苷三磷酸替换成与之对应的脱氧核苷三磷酸，也会导致检测不到合成作用（尚未发表的观察结果）。当 pH 值为 R–MLV 的 DNA 聚合酶的最适 pH 值——8.3 时，VSV 的聚合酶在催化核糖核苷酸掺入的能力上大为减弱，并且也检测不到脱氧核糖核酸被掺入的明显迹象。

Table 4. Comparison of Nucleotide Incorporation by Vesicular Stomatitis Virus and Rauscher Mouse Leukaemia Virus

Precursor	pH	Incorporation in 45 min (pmoles)	
		Vesicular stomatitis virus	Mouse leukaemia virus
³H-TTP	8.3	<0.01	2.3
³H-TTP (omit dATP)	8.3	N.D.	0.06
³H-TTP (omit dATP; plus ATP)	8.3	N.D.	0.08
³H-GTP	8.3	0.43	<0.03
³H-GTP	7.3	3.7	<0.03

When ³H-TTP was the precursor, standard reaction conditions were used (see Table 1). When ³H-GTP was the precursor, the reaction mixture contained, in 0.1 ml., 5 µmoles Tris-HCl (pH as indicated), 0.6 µmoles magnesium acetate, 0.3 µmoles mercaptoethanol, 9 µmoles NaCl, 0.08 µmole each of ATP, CTP, UTP; and 0.001 µmole ³H-GTP (1,040 c.p.m. per pmole). All VSV assays included 0.1 percent "Triton N-101" (ref. 12) and 2–5 µg of viral protein. The R-MLV assays contained 15 µg of viral protein.

The R-MLV polymerase incorporated only deoxyribonucleotides. At pH 8.3, ³H-TMP incorporation was readily demonstrable but replacement of dATP by ATP completely prevented synthesis (Table 4). Furthermore, no significant incorporation of ³H-GMP could be found in the presence of the four ribonucleotides. At pH 7.3, the R-MLV polymerase was also inactive with ribonucleotides. The polymerase in the R-MLV virions is therefore highly specific for deoxyribonucleoties.

DNA Polymerase in Rous Sarcoma Virus

A preparation of the Prague strain of Rous sarcoma virus was assayed for DNA polymerase activity (Table 5). Incorporation of radioactivity from ³H-TTP was demonstrable and the activity was severely reduced by omission of either Mg^{2+} or dATP from the reaction mixture. RNA-dependent DNA polymerase is therefore probably a constituent of all RNA tumour viruses.

Table 5. Properties of the Rous Sarcoma Virus DNA Polymerase

Reaction system	pmoles ³H-TMP incorporated in 120 min
Complete	2.06
Without magnesium acetate	0.12
Without dATP	0.19

A preparation of the Prague strain (sub-group C) of Rous sarcoma virus[16] having a titre of 5×10^7 focus forming units per ml. was provided by Dr. Peter Vogt. The virus was purified from tissue culture fluid by differential centrifugation. Before use the preparation was centrifuged and the pellet dissolved in 1/10 of the initial volume as described for the R-MLV preparation. For each assay 15 µl. of the concentrated Rous sarcoma virus preparation was assayed in standard reaction mixture by incubation for 2 h. An unincubated control sample had radioactivity corresponding to 0.14 pmole which was subtracted from the experimental values.

These experiments indicate that the virions of Rauscher mouse leukaemia virus and Rous

表 4. 水泡性口炎病毒和劳舍尔小鼠白血病病毒掺入核苷酸能力的对比

前体	pH 值	45 分钟的掺入量（pmol）	
		VSV	R–MLV
³H–TTP	8.3	<0.01	2.3
³H–TTP（未加 dATP）	8.3	未定义	0.06
³H–TTP（未加 dATP，加 ATP）	8.3	未定义	0.08
³H–GTP	8.3	0.43	<0.03
³H–GTP	7.3	3.7	<0.03

当所用前体为 ³H–TTP 时，用标准反应条件进行实验（见表 1）。当所用前体为 ³H–鸟苷三磷酸（³H–GTP）时，0.1 ml 反应混合物中含有：5 μmol Tris–HCl（pH 值如表中所示），0.6 μmol 醋酸镁，0.3 μmol 巯基乙醇，9 μmol NaCl，腺苷三磷酸（ATP）、胞苷三磷酸（CTP）和尿苷三磷酸（UTP）各 0.08 μmol 以及 0.001 μmol ³H–GTP（每 pmol 1,040 次放射性计数 / 分钟）。在所有的 VSV 检测中均加入 0.1% 的"曲拉通 N–101"（参考文献 12）及 2 μg ~ 5 μg 病毒蛋白。在检测 R–MLV 时加入 15 μg 病毒蛋白。

R–MLV 聚合酶只掺入脱氧核糖核苷酸。在 pH 值为 8.3 时很容易观察到 ³H–TMP 被掺入，但如果用 ATP 代替 dATP，合成过程就会完全被抑制（表 4）。而且，当存在 4 种核糖核苷酸时，几乎观察不到 ³H–GMP 被掺入的现象。在 pH 值为 7.3 时，R–MLV 聚合酶也没有掺入核糖核苷酸的活性。因此，R–MLV 病毒粒子中的聚合酶是对脱氧核糖核苷酸具有高度特异性的。

劳斯肉瘤病毒中的 DNA 聚合酶

用劳斯肉瘤病毒布拉格株制剂来检测 DNA 聚合酶的活性（表 5）。结果表明 ³H–TTP 的放射活性被掺入，而且当反应混合物中缺少 Mg²⁺ 或 dATP 时，酶活性都会大大降低。因此，RNA 依赖性 DNA 聚合酶很可能是所有致癌 RNA 病毒的一种组分。

表 5. 劳斯肉瘤病毒 DNA 聚合酶的性质

反应系统	反应 120 分钟后掺入到样品中的 ³H–TMP 的 pmol 数
完全的反应系统	2.06
无醋酸镁	0.12
无 dATP	0.19

由彼得 – 沃格特博士提供的劳斯肉瘤病毒布拉格株（C 亚株）制剂 [16] 的滴度为每 ml 5×10⁷ 个病灶形成单位。用差速离心法从组织培养液中纯化病毒。使用前先对样品进行离心，然后将沉淀物溶解为上述 R–MLV 实验中初始体积的 1/10。对于每次检测，取 15 μl 浓缩的劳斯肉瘤病毒样品，在标准反应混合物中孵育 2 小时后进行测定。未孵育的对照样品的放射性相当于 0.14 pmol，这个值要从各组实验数据中减去。

这些实验表明：在劳舍尔小鼠白血病病毒和劳斯肉瘤病毒的病毒粒子中含有一

sarcoma virus contain a DNA polymerase. The inhibition of its activity by ribonuclease suggests that the enzyme is an RNA-dependent DNA polymerase. It seems probable that all RNA tumour viruses have such an activity. The existence of this enzyme strongly supports the earlier suggestions[1-7] that genetically specific DNA synthesis is an early event in the replication cycle of the RNA tumour viruses and that DNA is the template for viral RNA synthesis. Whether the viral DNA ("provirus")[2] is integrated into the host genome or remains as free template for RNA synthesis will require further study. It will also be necessary to determine whether the host DNA-dependent RNA polymerase or a virus-specific enzyme catalyses the synthesis of viral RNA from the DNA.

I thank Drs. G. Todaro, F. Rauscher and R. Holdenreid for their assistance in providing the mouse leukaemia virus. This work was supported by grants from the US Public Health Service and the American Cancer Society and was carried out during the tenure of an American Society Faculty Research Award.

(**226**, 1209-1211; 1970)

David Baltimore: Department of Biology, Massachusetts Institute of Technology, Cambridge, Massachusetts 02139.

Received June 2, 1970.

References:

1. Green, M., *Ann. Rev. Biochem.*, **39** (1970, in the press).

2. Temin, H. M., *Virology*, **23**, 486 (1964).

3. Bader, J. P., *Virology*, **22**, 462 (1964).

4. Vigier, P., and Golde, A., *Virology*, **23**, 511 (1964).

5. Duesberg, P. H., and Vogt, P. K., *Proc. US Nat. Acad. Sci.*, **64**, 939 (1969).

6. Temin, H. M., in *Biology of Large RNA Viruses* (edit. by Barry, R., and Mahy, B.) (Academic Press, London, 1970).

7. Temin, H. M., *Virology*, **20**, 577 (1963).

8. Kates, J. R., and McAuslan, B. R., *Proc. US Nat. Acad. Sci.*, **58**, 134 (1967).

9. Munyon, W., Paoletti, E., and Grace, J. T. J., *Proc. US Nat. Acad. Sci.*, **58**, 2280 (1967).

10. Shatkin, A. J., and Sipe, J. D., *Proc. US Nat. Acad. Sci.*, **61**, 1462 (1968).

11. Borsa, J., and Graham, A. F., *Biochem. Biophys. Res. Commun.*, **33**, 895 (1968).

12. Baltimore, D., Huang, A. S., and Stampfer, M., *Proc. US Nat. Acad. Sci.*, **66** (1970, in the press).

13. Temin, H. M., and Mizutani, S., *Nature*, **226**, 1211 (1970) (following article).

14. O'Conner, T. E., Rauscher, F. J., and Zeigel, R. F., *Science*, **144**, 1144 (1964).

15. Crawford, L. V., and Crawford, E. M., *Virology*, **13**, 227 (1961).

16. Duesberg, P., and Robinson, W. S., *Proc. US Nat. Acad. Sci.*, **55**, 219 (1966).

17. Duff, R. G., and Vogt, P. K., *Virology*, **39**, 18 (1969).

种 DNA 聚合酶。该酶的活性能被核糖核酸酶抑制，这暗示它是一种 RNA 依赖性 DNA 聚合酶。这样看来，很可能所有的致癌 RNA 病毒都具有这种活性。这种酶的存在强有力地支持了以前的一个假设 [1-7]：在致癌 RNA 病毒的复制循环中，遗传特异性 DNA 的合成是一个早期事件，而且 DNA 是病毒 RNA 的合成模板。到底病毒 DNA（"前病毒"）[2] 是整合到了宿主基因组中还是仍然作为 RNA 合成的自由模板？这个问题有待于进一步的研究。还有一个问题也有必要解决：到底是宿主中的 DNA 依赖性 RNA 聚合酶还是一种病毒特有的酶催化了由 DNA 合成病毒 RNA 的过程？

我要感谢托达罗博士、劳舍尔博士和霍尔登里德博士协助提供了小鼠白血病病毒。本工作得到了美国公共卫生署和美国癌症协会的资助，是我在获得一个美国学会的教师研究奖期间进行的。

（荆玉祥 翻译；孙军 审稿）

RNA-dependent DNA Polymerase in Virions of Rous Sarcoma Virus

H. M. Temin and S. Mizutani

Editor's Note

When Howard Temin proposed his "DNA provirus hypothesis" in 1964, it challenged dogma and was met with scepticism. Based on the results of genetic experiments and the effects of metabolic inhibitors, he proposed that viral RNA is copied to DNA in infected cells. Then in 1970, Temin and Satoshi Mizutani, and American virologist David Baltimore, working independently, reported the discovery of a viral enzyme, now known as reverse transcriptase, that makes DNA from an RNA template. The results offered clear-cut support for the DNA provirus hypothesis, and helped earn Temin and Baltimore a Nobel Prize. As predicted, the discovery has also led to major advances in our understanding of gene transcription, cancer and human retroviruses.

INFECTION of sensitive cells by RNA sarcoma viruses requires the synthesis of new DNA different from that synthesized in the S-phase of the cell cycle (refs. 1, 2 and unpublished results of D. Boettiger and H. M. T.); production of RNA tumour viruses is sensitive to actinomycin D[3,4]; and cells transformed by RNA tumour viruses have new DNA which hybridizes with viral RNA[5,6]. These are the basic observations essential to the DNA provirus hypothesis—replication of RNA tumour viruses takes place through a DNA intermediate, not through an RNA intermediate as does the replication of other RNA viruses[7].

Formation of the provirus is normal in stationary chicken cells exposed to Rous sarcoma virus (RSV), even in the presence of 0.5 µg/ml. cycloheximide (our unpublished results). This finding, together with the discovery of polymerases in virions of vaccinia virus and of reovirus[8-11], suggested that an enzyme that would synthesize DNA from an RNA template might be present in virions of RSV. We now report data supporting the existence of such an enzyme, and we learn that David Baltimore has independently discovered a similar enzyme in virions of Rauscher leukaemia virus[12].

The sources of virus and methods of concentration have been described[13]. All preparations were carried out in sterile conditions. Concentrated virus was placed on a layer of 15 percent sucrose and centrifuged at 25,000 r.p.m. for 1 h in the "SW 25.1" rotor of the Spinco ultracentrifuge on to a cushion of 60 percent sucrose. The virus band was collected from the interphase and further purified by equilibrium sucrose density gradient centrifugation[14]. Virus further purified by sucrose velocity density gradient centrifugation gave the same results.

劳斯肉瘤病毒粒子中的RNA依赖性DNA聚合酶

特明，水谷哲

编者按

当霍华德·特明在 1964 年提出"DNA 前病毒假说"时，该假说因为与经典理论冲突而遭到了人们的质疑。特明根据遗传学实验的结果和代谢抑制剂的作用效果提出，在受感染的细胞中病毒的 RNA 复制为 DNA。随后在 1970 年，特明和水谷哲以及美国病毒学家戴维·巴尔的摩分别独立地研究并报道了一项发现，即有一种病毒酶能从 RNA 模板合成 DNA，这种酶现在被称为逆转录酶。上述结果显然支持了 DNA 前病毒假说，这项成果使特明和巴尔的摩赢得了诺贝尔奖。正如所预测的那样，这一发现对我们理解基因转录、癌症和人类逆转录病毒也产生了重大的影响。

敏感细胞被 RNA 肉瘤病毒感染需要合成新的 DNA，这种新合成的 DNA 不同于在细胞周期的 S 期合成的 DNA（参考文献 1、2 以及伯蒂格和特明尚未发表的研究结果）。致癌 RNA 病毒的产生对放线菌素 D 敏感 [3,4]。被致癌 RNA 病毒感染的细胞中含有与病毒 RNA 杂交的新 DNA[5,6]。这些基本的观测结果都支持 DNA 前病毒假说，即致癌 RNA 病毒的复制是通过一个 DNA 中间体进行的，而不是像其他 RNA 病毒那样是通过一个 RNA 中间体进行的 [7]。

即使在 0.5 μg/ml 放线菌酮存在时，在暴露于劳斯肉瘤病毒（RSV）的稳定期鸡细胞中也能正常形成前病毒（我们尚未发表的研究结果）。这一研究结果以及在牛痘病毒和呼肠孤病毒的病毒粒子中聚合酶的发现 [8-11] 都说明：在 RSV 的病毒粒子中或许存在着一种能以 RNA 为模板合成 DNA 的酶。我们在本文中要报告能支持这种酶存在的证据，另外我们也获悉戴维·巴尔的摩已经独立地在劳舍尔小鼠白血病病毒的病毒粒子中发现了一种类似的酶 [12]。

病毒来源和浓缩方法如前所述 [13]。所有操作均在无菌条件下进行。将浓缩的病毒置于 15% 的蔗糖层上面，底部是 60% 的蔗糖，用斯平科超速离心机的"SW 25.1"型转头在 25,000 转 / 分钟的速度下离心 1 小时。从界面处收集病毒带，然后用平衡的蔗糖密度梯度离心法进一步纯化 [14]。也可以用蔗糖速度密度梯度离心法进一步纯化病毒，得到的效果是一样的。

The polymerase assay consisted of 0.125 μmoles each of dATP, dCTP, and dGTP (Calbiochem) (in 0.02 M Tris-HCl buffer at pH 8.0, containing 0.33 M EDTA and 1.7 mM 2-mercaptoethanol); 1.25 μmoles of $MgCl_2$ and 2.5 μmoles of KCl; 2.5 μg phosphoenolpyruvate (Calbiochem); 10 μg pyruvate kinase (Calbiochem); 2.5 μCi of ^{3}H-TTP (Schwarz) (12 Ci/mmole); and 0.025 ml. of enzyme (10^8 focus forming units of disrupted Schmidt-Ruppin virus, $A_{280 nm}$ = 0.30) in a total volume of 0.125 ml. Incubation was at 40°C for 1 h. 0.025 ml. of the reaction mixture was withdrawn and assayed for acid-insoluble counts by the method of Furlong[15].

To observe full activity of the enzyme, it was necessary to treat the virions with a non-ionic detergent (Tables 1 and 4). If the treatment was at 40°C the presence of dithiothreitol (DTT) was necessary to recover activity. In most preparations of virions, however, there was some activity: 5–20 percent of the disrupted virions, in the absence of detergent treatment, which probably represents disrupted virions in the preparation. It is known that virions of RNA tumour viruses are easily disrupted[16,17], so that the activity is probably present in the nucleoid of the virion.

Table 1. Activation of Enzyme

System	^{3}H-TTP incorporated (d.p.m.)
No virions	0
Non-disrupted virions	255
Virions disrupted with "Nonidet"	
At 0° + DTT	6,730
At 0° – DTT	4,420
At 40° + DTT	5,000
At 40° – DTT	425

Purified virions untreated or incubated for 5 min at 0°C or 40°C with 0.25 percent "Nonidet P-40" (Shell Chemical Co.) with 0 or 1 percent dithiothreitol (DTT) (Sigma) were assayed in the standard polymerase assay.

The kinetics of incorporation with disrupted virions are shown in Fig. 1. Incorporation is rapid for 1 h. Other experiments show that incorporation continues at about the same rate for the second hour. Preheating disrupted virus at 80°C prevents any incorporation, and so does pretreatment of disrupted virus with crystalline trypsin.

聚合酶检测所用试剂的总体积为 0.125 ml，其中含有：脱氧腺苷三磷酸（dATP）、脱氧胞苷三磷酸（dCTP）和脱氧鸟苷三磷酸（dGTP）各 0.125 µmol（卡尔生物化学公司）（溶于 pH 值为 8.0 的 0.02 M Tris–HCl 缓冲液中，其中还含有 0.33 M EDTA 和 1.7 mM 2– 巯基乙醇）；1.25 µmol $MgCl_2$ 和 2.5 µmol KCl；2.5 µg 磷酸烯醇丙酮酸盐（卡尔生物化学公司）；10 µg 丙酮酸激酶（卡尔生物化学公司）；2.5 µCi ³H– 胸苷三磷酸（³H–TTP）（许瓦兹制药有限公司）（12 Ci/mmol）；0.025 ml 酶（通过破碎活性为 10^8 个病灶形成单位的施密特 – 鲁宾病毒得到，$A_{280 \, nm}$ = 0.30）。在 40℃ 下孵育 1 小时。取 0.025 ml 反应混合液，用弗朗法 [15] 对酸不溶性物质进行放射性计数检测。

为了观察这种酶的完整活性，必须用非离子型去垢剂来处理病毒粒子（表 1 和表 4）。如果处理过程是在 40℃ 下进行的，那么就需要用二硫苏糖醇（DTT）来恢复酶活性。不过，大多数没有用去垢剂处理的病毒粒子样品也有一定的活性——是破碎病毒粒子活性的 5% ～ 20%，这很可能说明在制样过程中有一些病毒粒子破碎了。众所周知，致癌 RNA 病毒粒子是很容易发生破碎的 [16,17]，所以活性很可能存在于病毒粒子的拟核中。

表 1. 酶的激活

系统	被掺入的 ³H–TTP（衰变次数 / 分钟）
无病毒粒子	0
未经破碎处理的病毒粒子	255
用"诺乃洗涤剂"破碎的病毒粒子	
在 0℃ 下，加入 DTT	6,730
在 0℃ 下，未加入 DTT	4,420
在 40℃ 下，加入 DTT	5,000
在 40℃ 下，未加入 DTT	425

用标准的聚合酶检测法测定：未经处理的纯化病毒粒子，或者用 0.25% 的"诺乃洗涤剂 P–40"（壳牌化学公司）处理并在不加或加入 1% DTT（西格马公司）的条件下于 0℃ 或 40℃ 孵育 5 分钟的纯化病毒粒子。

图 1 显示了破碎病毒粒子的掺入动力学曲线。掺入过程在 1 小时之内进行得很快。另有一些实验结果显示：掺入过程在第 2 个小时内仍能以大致相同的速率持续进行。在 80℃ 下预热破碎的病毒粒子会使掺入过程完全终止，而用结晶胰蛋白酶预处理破碎的病毒粒子也会有同样的现象出现。

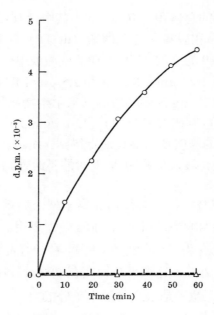

Fig. 1. Kinetics of incorporation. Virus treated with "Nonidet" and dithiothreitol at 0°C and incubated at 37°C (O—O) or 80°C (Δ- - -Δ) for 10 min was assayed in a standard polymerase assay. O, Unheated; Δ, heated.

Fig. 2 demonstrates that there is an absolute requirement for $MgCl_2$, 10 mM being the optimum concentration. The date in Table 2 show that $MnCl_2$ can substitute for $MgCl_2$ in the polymerase assay, but $CaCl_2$ cannot. Other experiments show that a monovalent cation is not required for activity, although 20 mM KCl causes a 15 percent stimulation. Higher concentrations of KCl are inhibitory: 60 percent inhibition was observed at 80 mM.

Table 2. Requirements for Enzyme Activity

System	^{3}H-TTP incorporated (d.p.m.)
Complete	5,675
Without $MgCl_2$	186
Without $MgCl_2$, with $MnCl_2$	5,570
Without $MgCl_2$, with $CaCl_2$	18
Without dATP	897
Without dCTP	1,780
Without dGTP	2,190

Virus treated with "Nonidet" and dithiothreitol at 0°C was incubated in the standard polymerase assay with the substitutions listed.

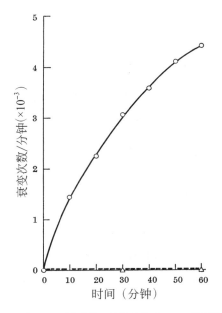

图 1. 掺入过程的动力学曲线。在 0℃ 下用"诺乃洗涤剂"和 DTT 处理病毒，并在 37℃（O—O）或 80℃（Δ - - - Δ）下孵育 10 分钟，然后用标准的聚合酶检测法进行测定。O 代表未加热的实验结果；Δ 代表加热的实验结果。

  图 2 表明 $MgCl_2$ 是掺入过程所必需的，其最适浓度为 10 mM。由表 2 中的数据可知：在聚合酶检测实验中，$MnCl_2$ 可以替代 $MgCl_2$，但 $CaCl_2$ 不行。虽然 20 mM KCl 能使活性增加 15%，但另一些实验结果显示一价阳离子并不是活性所必需的。高浓度的 KCl 会起抑制作用：当 KCl 浓度为 80 mM 时，观察到的抑制程度可达 60%。

表 2. 酶活性检测所需条件

系统	被掺入的 ^3H-TTP（衰变次数 / 分钟）
完全的反应系统	5,675
缺 $MgCl_2$	186
缺 $MgCl_2$，但有 $MnCl_2$	5,570
缺 $MgCl_2$，但有 $CaCl_2$	18
缺 dATP	897
缺 dCTP	1,780
缺 dGTP	2,190

在 0℃ 下用"诺乃洗涤剂"和 DTT 处理病毒样品，然后在标准的聚合酶检测实验条件下孵育，在每组实验中所用的替换物如表中所示。

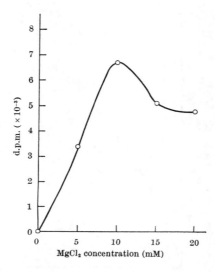

Fig. 2. MgCl₂ requirement. Virus treated with "Nonidet" and dithiothreitol at 0°C was incubated in the standard polymerase assay with different concentrations of MgCl₂.

When the amount of disrupted virions present in the polymerase assay was varied, the amount of incorporation varied with second-order kinetics. When incubation was carried out at different temperatures, at broad optimum between 40°C and 50°C was found. (The high temperature of this optimum may relate to the fact that the normal host of the virus is the chicken.) When incubation was carried out at different pHs, a broad optimum at pH 8–9.5 was found.

Table 2 demonstrates that all four deoxyribonucleotide triphosphates are required for full activity, but some activity was present when only three deoxyribonucleotide triphosphates were added and 10–20 percent of full activity was still present with only two deoxyribonucleotide triphosphates. The activity in the presence of three deoxyribonucleotide triphosphates is probably the result of the presence of deoxyribonucleotide triphosphates in the virion. Other host components are known to be incorporated in the virion of RNA tumour viruses[18,19].

The data in Table 3 demonstrate that incorporation of thymidine triphosphate was more than 99 percent abolished if the virions were pretreated at 0° with 1 mg ribonuclease per ml. Treatment with 50 μg/ml ribonuclease at 20°C did not prevent all incorporation of thymidine triphosphate, which suggests that the RNA of the virion may be masked by protein. (Lysozyme was added as a control for non-specific binding of ribonuclease to DNA.) Because the ribonuclease was heated for 10 min at 80°C or 100°C before use to destroy deoxyribonuclease it seems that intact RNA is necessary for incorporation of thymidine triphosphate.

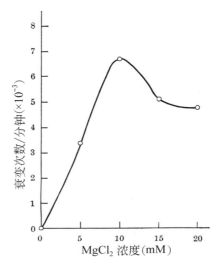

图 2. 对 MgCl$_2$ 的需求。在 0℃ 下用"诺乃洗涤剂"和 DTT 处理病毒样品，然后在 MgCl$_2$ 浓度不同的标准聚合酶检测体系中孵育病毒。

当聚合酶检测实验中所用的破碎病毒粒子的量发生变化时，掺入的量也随之变化，变化规律符合二级动力学。尝试了各种不同温度下的孵育之后，我们发现最适宜的温度范围很宽，在 40℃ ~ 50℃ 之间都可以。（最适温度范围处于较高的温度区可能与这种病毒的宿主通常是鸡有关。）尝试了在各种不同的 pH 值下进行孵育后，我们发现最适的 pH 值也有很宽的范围，在 8 ~ 9.5 之间。

表 2 说明 4 种脱氧核苷三磷酸对于完整活性来说都是必需的，但是，当仅仅加入 3 种脱氧核苷三磷酸时也会表现出一定的活性，甚至在只有 2 种脱氧核苷三磷酸时仍存在 10% ~ 20% 的活性。只加入 3 种脱氧核苷三磷酸时显示出的活性，很可能源自于病毒粒子中存在脱氧核苷三磷酸。现在已经知道宿主的其他一些组分可以被掺入到致癌 RNA 病毒粒子之中 [18,19]。

表 3 中的数据说明：如果在 0℃ 下用终浓度为 1 mg/ml 的核糖核酸酶预处理病毒粒子，那么胸苷三磷酸的掺入将被破坏 99% 以上。在 20℃ 下用 50 μg/ml 的核糖核酸酶处理并未完全阻止胸苷三磷酸的掺入，这说明病毒粒子的 RNA 有可能被蛋白质遮盖住了。（加入溶菌酶作为核糖核酸酶与 DNA 之间非特异性结合的对照。）因为使用前已将核糖核酸酶在 80℃ 或 100℃ 下加热了 10 分钟，这样就完全破坏了脱氧核糖核酸酶，所以完整的 RNA 对于胸苷三磷酸的掺入来说似乎是必需的。

Table 3. RNA Dependence of Polymerase Activity

Treatment	³H-TTP incorporated (d.p.m.)
Non-treated disrupted virions	9,110
Disrupted virions preincubated with ribonuclease A (50 μg/ml.) at 20°C for 1 h	2,650
Disrupted virions preincubated with ribonuclease A (1 mg/ml.) at 0°C for 1 h	137
Disrupted virions preincubated with lysozyme (50 μg/ml.) at 0°C for 1 h	9,650

Disrupted virions were incubated with ribonuclease A (Worthington) which was heated at 80°C for 10 min, or with lysozyme at the indicated concentration in the specified conditions, and a standard polymerase assay was performed.

To determine whether the enzyme is present in supernatants of normal cells or in RNA leukaemia viruses, the experiment of Table 4 was performed. Normal cell supernatant did not contain activity even after treatment with "Nonidet". Virions of avian myeloblastosis virus (AMV) contained activity that was increased ten-fold by treatment with "Nonidet".

Table 4. Source of Polymerase

Source	³H-TTP incorporated (d.p.m.)
Virions of SRV	1,410
Disrupted virions of SRV	5,675
Virions of AMV	1,875
Disrupted virions of AMV	12,850
Disrupted pellet from supernatant of uninfected cells	0

Virions of Schmidt-Ruppin virus (SRV) were prepared as before (experiment of Table 2). Virions of avian myeloblastosis virus (AMV) and a pellet from uninfected cells were prepared by differential centrifugation. All disrupted preparations were treated with "Nonidet" and dithiothreitol at 0°C and assayed in a standard polymerase assay. The material used per tube was originally from 45 ml. of culture fluid for SRV, 20 ml. for AMV, and 20 ml. for uninfected cells.

The nature of the product of the polymerase assay was investigated by treating portions with deoxyribonclease, ribonuclease or KOH. About 80 percent of the product was made acid soluble by treatment with deoxyribonuclease, and the product was resistant to ribonuclease and KOH (Table 5).

Table 5. Nature of Product

Treatment	Residual acid-insoluble ³H-TTP (d.p.m.)	
	Experiment A	Experiment B
Buffer	10,200	8,350
Deoxyribonuclease	697	1,520
Ribonuclease	10,900	7,200
KOH	—	8,250

A standard polymerase assay was performed with "Nonidet" treated virions. The product was incubated in buffer or 0.3 M KOH at 37°C for 20 h or with (A) 1 mg/ml. or (B) 50 μg/ml. of deoxyribonuclease I (Worthington), or with 1 mg/ml. of ribonuclease A (Worthington) for 1 h at 37°C, and portions were removed and tested for acid-insoluble counts.

表 3. 聚合酶活性的 RNA 依赖性

处理方法	被掺入的 ^{3}H–TTP（衰变次数 / 分钟）
未经处理的破碎病毒粒子	9,110
在 20℃ 下用核糖核酸酶 A（50 μg/ml）预孵育 1 小时的破碎病毒粒子	2,650
在 0℃ 下用核糖核酸酶 A（1 mg/ml）预孵育 1 小时的破碎病毒粒子	137
在 0℃ 下用溶菌酶（50 μg/ml）预孵育 1 小时的破碎病毒粒子	9,650

向破碎的病毒粒子中加入在 80℃ 下加热了 10 分钟的核糖核酸酶 A（沃辛顿），或者如表中所示浓度的溶菌酶，然后在特定的条件下孵育，之后对病毒粒子进行标准的聚合酶检测实验。

为了确定这种酶到底是存在于正常细胞的上清液中还是存在于 RNA 白血病病毒中，我们又进行了表 4 中的实验。即使在使用"诺乃洗涤剂"处理后，正常细胞的上清液也不具有活性。而禽类成髓细胞瘤病毒（AMV）的病毒粒子具有活性且在用"诺乃洗涤剂"处理后，其活性会提高 10 倍。

表 4. 聚合酶的来源

来源	被掺入的 ^{3}H–TTP（衰变次数 / 分钟）
SRV 病毒粒子	1,410
破碎的 SRV 病毒粒子	5,675
AMV 病毒粒子	1,875
破碎的 AMV 病毒粒子	12,850
未感染细胞上清液中的破碎沉淀物	0

用前文所述的方法（表 2 中的实验）制备施密特－鲁宾病毒（SRV）。由差速离心法得到禽类成髓细胞瘤病毒（AMV）的病毒粒子和未感染细胞的离心沉淀物。所有破碎的样品都在 0℃ 下用"诺乃洗涤剂"和 DTT 处理，并用标准的聚合酶检测实验进行分析。每个管中所用的样品分别来自 45 ml SRV 培养液、20 ml AMV 培养液和 20 ml 未感染细胞培养液。

为了研究聚合酶检测实验所得产物的性质，我们用脱氧核糖核酸酶、核糖核酸酶或 KOH 分别处理了部分样品。在用脱氧核糖核酸酶处理后有大约 80% 的产物能溶于酸，但产物能耐受核糖核酸酶处理或 KOH 处理（表 5）。

表 5. 产物的性质

处理方法	残留的酸不溶性 ^{3}H–TTP（衰变次数 / 分钟）	
	实验 A	实验 B
缓冲液	10,200	8,350
脱氧核糖核酸酶	697	1,520
核糖核酸酶	10,900	7,200
KOH	—	8,250

用标准的聚合酶检测实验分析"诺乃洗涤剂"处理后的病毒粒子。将产物在下列条件下进行孵育：37℃ 下在缓冲液或 0.3 M KOH 中孵育 20 小时；或者加入（A）1 mg/ml 或（B）50 μg/ml 脱氧核糖核酸酶 I（沃辛顿）或 1 mg/ml 核糖核酸酶 A（沃辛顿）在 37℃ 下孵育 1 小时。孵育后除去上清液，并对酸不溶性物质进行放射性计数检测。

To determine if the polymerase might also make RNA, disrupted virions were incubated with the four ribonucleotide triphosphates, including ^{3}H-UTP (Schwarz, 3.2 Ci/mmole). With either $MgCl_2$ or $MnCl_2$ in the incubation mixture, no incorporation was detected. In a parallel incubation with deoxyribonucleotide triphosphates, 12,200 d.p.m. of ^{3}H-TTP was incorporated.

These results demonstrate that there is a new polymerase inside the virions of RNA tumour viruses. It is not present in supernatants of normal cells but is present in virions of avian sarcoma and leukaemia RNA tumour viruses. The polymerase seems to catalyse the incorporation of deoxyribonucleotide triphosphates into DNA from an RNA template. Work is being performed to characterize further the reaction and the product. If the present results and Baltimore's results[12] with Rauscher leukaemia virus are upheld, they will constitute strong evidence that the DNA provirus hypothesis is correct and that RNA tumour viruses have a DNA genome when they are in cells and an RNA genome when they are in virions. This result would have strong implications for theories of viral carcinogenesis and, possibly, for theories of information transfer in other biological systems[20].

This work was supported by a US Public Health Service research grant from the National Cancer Institute. H. M. T. holds a research career development award from the National Cancer Institute.

(**226**, 1211-1213; 1970)

Howard M. Temin and Satoshi Mizutani: McArdle Laboratory for Cancer Research, University of Wisconsin, Madison, Wisconsin 53706.

Received June 15, 1970.

References:

1. Temin, H. M., *Cancer Res.*, **28**, 1835 (1968).

2. Murray, R. K., and Temin, H. M., *Intern. J. Cancer* (in the press).

3. Temin, H. M., *Virology*, **20**, 577 (1963).

4. Baluda, M. B., and Nayak, D. P., *J. Virol.*, **4**, 554 (1969).

5. Temin, H. M., *Proc. US Nat. Acad. Sci.*, **52**, 323 (1964).

6. Baluda, M. B., and Nayak, D. P., in *Biology of Large RNA Viruses* (edit. by Barry, R., and Mahy, B.) (Academic Press, London, 1970).

7. Temin, H. M., *Nat. Cancer Inst. Monog.*, **17**, 557 (1964).

8. Kates, J. R., and McAuslan, B. R., *Proc. US Nat. Acad. Sci.*, **57**, 314 (1967).

9. Munyon, W., Paoletti, E., and Grace, J. T., *Proc. US Nat. Acad. Sci.*, **58**, 2280 (1967).

10. Borsa, J., and Graham, A. F., *Biochem. Biophys. Res. Commun.*, **33**, 895 (1968).

11. Shatkin, A. J., and Sipe, J. D., *Proc. US Nat. Acad. Sci.*, **61**, 1462 (1968).

12. Baltimore, D., *Nature*, **226**, 1209 (1970) (preceding article).

13. Altaner, C., and Temin, H. M., *Virology*, **40**, 118 (1970).

14. Robinson, W. S., Pitkanen, A., and Rubin, H., *Proc. US Nat. Acad. Sci.*, **54**, 137 (1965).

为了测定这种聚合酶是否也能合成 RNA，我们将破碎的病毒粒子与包括 ^{3}H– 尿苷三磷酸（^{3}H–UTP）（许瓦兹制药有限公司，3.2 Ci/mmol）在内的 4 种核苷三磷酸一起孵育。在孵育混合液中，无论加入 $MgCl_2$ 还是 $MnCl_2$，都未能检测到任何掺入。在用脱氧核苷三磷酸进行孵育的一个平行实验中，我们发现被掺入的 ^{3}H–TTP 达到 12,200 衰变次数 / 分钟。

这些结果表明：在致癌 RNA 病毒的病毒粒子中存在着一种新的聚合酶。这种酶并不存在于正常细胞的上清液中，而是存在于禽类肉瘤病毒和白血病病毒等致癌 RNA 病毒的病毒粒子中。这种聚合酶似乎能够催化将脱氧核苷三磷酸掺入到以 RNA 为模板的 DNA 中的反应。目前我们正在进一步表征这种反应及其产物。如果我们的结果和巴尔的摩用劳舍尔小鼠白血病病毒取得的结果 [12] 能够得到确认的话，这两项结果将有力地支持如下观点，即 DNA 前病毒假说是正确的，并且致癌 RNA 病毒在细胞中时具有一个 DNA 基因组，而在病毒粒子中时则有一个 RNA 基因组。这一结果会对病毒致癌作用的机理，以及还可能会对其他生物系统中的遗传信息传递理论产生重大的影响 [20]。

本工作受到了国家癌症研究所获得的一项美国公共卫生署研究基金的资助。霍华德·特明拥有一项由国家癌症研究所提供的研究事业发展基金。

（荆玉祥 翻译；孙军 审稿）

15. Furlong, N. B., *Meth. Cancer Res.*, **3**, 27 (1967).

16. Vogt, P. K., *Adv. Virus. Res.*, **11**, 293 (1965).

17. Bauer, H., and Schafer, W., *Virology*, **29**, 494 (1966).

18. Bauer, H., *Z. Naturforsch.*, **21**b, 453 (1969).

19. Erikson, R. L., *Virology*, **37**, 124 (1969).

20. Temin, H. M., *Persp. Biol. Med.* (in the press).

A Bonding Model for Anomalous Water

L. C. Allen

Editor's Note

The structure of polywater, the putative new form of ultra-viscous water reported by Russian chemists, excited much speculation. Ordinary water contains molecules loosely bound into a vast network by hydrogen bonds. Was this network somehow made more robust in polywater? In the model of polywater proposed here by Leland Allen at Princeton University, a new form of hydrogen bonding links the water molecules, in which each hydrogen atom sits midway between two oxygens, rather than being asymmetrically located as in normal water and in ice. Curiously, this symmetrical hydrogen bond is now known to be possible, but only in ice subjected to extreme pressure. Polywater itself proved eventually to need no explanation, being a mere experimental artifact.

THERE is considerable current interest in the possible existence of a new form of water reported by Deryagin[1], not only because of the universal presence of water, but also because it would almost certainly require a new type of chemical bond. The oldest and simplest schematic representation of the electronic distribution in molecules is the dot diagrams of Lewis[2], and the usefulness of this description has been greatly enhanced by Linnett's[3] replacement of a single dot by the two symbols, "x" and "o". These correspond to the two different electron spin states and accommodate the independent effects of charge and spin correlation. The possibility of delocalizing a pair of electrons with opposite spins, not recognized by Lewis, makes a significant contribution to the hypothesized bonding scheme given here. Models such as this cannot predict whether or not the new material exists nor can they uniquely point to the most probable structure, but their inherent simplicity and suggestive pictorial description can be a very powerful aid in interpreting experiments.

It seems reasonable that the new form of water will have some general features in common with ice and the normal liquid, and so we may expect it to be an electrically neutral association of water molecules weakly bound together. Spectroscopic and theoretical results[4] show that hydrogen bonding in water shifts charge from hydrogen to oxygen and for symmetrically placed hydrogens (which are believed to exist because of missing OH vibrations in the observed spectra of anomalous water[5]) the charge separation between hydrogen and oxygen becomes large. Each hydrogen may lose as much as a quarter of an electronic charge to its two adjacent oxygen atoms. The analogy with ice and other oxygen containing solids suggests that the oxygen atoms will be four coordinate and thus the oxygens will carry a charge of approximately -1 and the hydrogens approximately $+\frac{1}{2}$. These values are consistent with the 300 cycle down field shift, relative to the normal liquid, observed recently by NMR[6,7]. Closed systems (rings) are generally favoured over

反常水的键合模型

艾伦

编者按

俄罗斯化学家们所报道的聚合水，是大家都公认的一种超黏水的新形式，这种水的结构激起了许多猜测。普通水所包含的分子通过氢键松散地结合成巨大的网络结构。难道在聚合水中这种网络结构会因某种原因而变得更加坚固吗？在本文中，普林斯顿大学的利兰·艾伦提出了一种聚合水的模型，在该模型中，连接着水分子的是一种新型的氢键，其中的每个氢原子都位于两个氧原子的中间，而不是像在正常水和冰中时那样非对称地排布。令人惊奇的是，目前已经知道这种对称的氢键是有可能存在的，只不过仅在高压下的冰中存在而已。最终证明聚合水本身并不需要任何解释，因为它仅仅是实验中的人为产物。

最近，大家对杰里亚金[1]发布的可能存在一种新形式水的报道非常关注，不仅因为水的广泛存在，还因为人们几乎可以肯定这种新形式水必然需要一种新型的化学键。刘易斯[2]的点图是反映电子在分子中分布的最古老和最简单的图示，后来林奈特[3]用两种符号——x和o代替了单一的点，因而大大提高了这一描述法的实用性。这两种符号对应于两种不同的电子自旋状态，从而适用于独立的电荷效应和自旋关联效应。刘易斯没有意识到具有相反自旋的一对电子有可能会发生离域，这种可能性对本文中假定的键合模型影响很大。这类模型不能预言新形式的水是不是存在，也无法唯一地确定其最可能的结构，但是它们所特有的简单性和以图表意的方法可以为解释实验现象提供非常有效的帮助。

似乎可以合理地认为，新形式水所具有的某些一般特性与冰和正常液体是一致的，因此我们可以猜测它是一种由水分子微弱地结合在一起的电中性缔合体。光谱和理论研究结果[4]表明：水中的氢键使电荷从氢原子转移到了氧原子上，而对于处在对称位置的氢原子（可以认为真实情况就是如此，因为在反常水的光谱中并未出现 OH 的振动[5]）来说，氢原子与氧原子之间的电荷分离是变大了。每个氢原子会失去一个电子电量的四分之一以转移到两个与之相邻的氧原子上。与冰和其他含氧固体的类比结果显示，氧原子应为四配位，因此每个氧所带的电荷数约为 –1，而氢大致为 $+\frac{1}{2}$。这些数值与最近通过核磁共振[6,7]得到的、与正常液体相比向低场位移了 300 周的现象是一致的。不论是在二维结构中还是在三维结构中，封闭体系（环）

open systems, both in two and three dimensions. In anomalous water, rings in three dimensions are favoured because they lower the energy of the relatively small, delocalized, covalent-like σ bonding and especially because of the large Madelung (ionic) energy which arises from the striking oxygen–hydrogen charge separation. A correspondingly short "O⋯O" separation may be realized (a reasonable value of 2.3–2.4 Å has been proposed[5]). The basic bonding unit displayed in Fig. 1a. Sheets of planar hexagons are favoured over puckered (cyclohexane-like) rings because, at any given "O⋯O" separation, distances across the ring are longer in the planar conformation and this reduces the large electrostatic repulsion between oxygens and between hydrogens. Four spin-up electrons at the corners of a tetrahedron and four spin-down electrons at the corners of an interpenetrating tetrahedron pointing the opposite way are arranged around each oxygen centre. As illustrated schematically in Fig. 1a, one spin-up electron on every oxygen is coupled to a spin-down electron on an adjacent oxygen to form a weak two electron covalent bond linking the O H O atoms. Planes of hexagons stack in the graphite-like pattern as shown in the top view (b) and edge on (c). Rings in the (c) projection are not as favourable as the sp[2] hybridized oxygens in the plane (a) and the O—H—O bond will be a little weaker and longer. The type of symmetric divalent hydrogen bonding under consideration here differs from the hydrogen bridges found in boron hydrides in that the end atoms are electron rich rather than electron deficient, and in this circumstance the bonding must compete with the well established conventional, asymmetric hydrogen bonding widely found for the electron rich, electro-negative atoms N, O and F. In regard to both the distributed charge, covalent-like component of the bonding and the oxygen-oxygen repulsion component, symmetrically placed hydrogens are decidedly less stable than the conventional asymmetric hydrogen bond and achievement of a stability approaching that of the asymmetric bond must be obtained through the properties of O^-. There are two sources of this added stabilization: first is the ionic lattice (Madelung) energy noted earlier. The second comes from the large instantaneous electron-electron correlation around the oxygen centre in anomalous water relative to that in the isolated water monomer or normal liquid. That is, the correlation energy for O^- is well known to be far greater than for O and the charge is shifted from O to a value much closer to O^- in anomalous water than is the case for the isolated monomer or for conventional hydrogen bonds. In addition to water, there have been report[1,5] of anomalous alcohols and acids. For these species a layer pattern is not possible but they may form single hexagonal "O H O" rings like (a) with other groups substituted for the external hydrogens.

通常都会优于开放体系。在反常水中，三维的环更具优势，因为它们会降低相对较小的类共价型离域 σ 键的能量，尤其是因为由显著的氢－氧电荷分离所导致的巨大的马德隆（离子）能。而相对较短的"O···O"间距（有人提出合理的值应为 2.3 Å ～ 2.4 Å[5]）是可以实现的。图 1a 中表示的是基本键单位。由多层平面六边形组成的结构要优于折叠的（环己烷型）环，因为对于任意给定的"O···O"间距，从环的一侧到另一侧的距离在平面构象中会更长，因而减少了氧原子与氧原子之间以及氢原子与氢原子之间巨大的静电斥力。排布在每个氧原子中心周围的是位于一个四面体各顶角处的四个上旋电子和位于另一个指向相反方向的与之相互贯穿的四面体顶角处的四个下旋电子。如图 1a 所示，每个氧原子上的一个上旋电子与一个相邻氧原子上的一个下旋电子耦合成了一个微弱的双电子共价键，连接着 O H O 原子。由六边形组成的平面按照类似石墨的模式堆叠，其顶视图如（b）所示，其侧视图如（c）所示。投影图（c）中的环相对于（a）中平面的 sp² 杂化氧原子来说不具有优势，其 O–H–O 键会稍弱一些和稍长一些。这里所考虑的对称二价氢键形式不同于在硼氢化合物中发现的氢桥，后者中的末端原子是富电子而非缺电子的，并且在这种情况下所成的键必须能比得上大家公认的、通常在富电子的电负性元素 N、O 和 F 中广泛存在的非对称氢键。无论对于键中电荷分散的共价型成分还是氧－氧互斥成分，处于对称位置的氢原子显然不如典型的非对称氢键稳定，因而必须利用 O⁻ 的性质以达到接近于非对称氢键的稳定性。稳定性的增加有两个来源：首先是前面提到的离子晶格（马德隆）能。其次，稳定性来源于反常水中的氧原子中心周围存在着大于孤立水单体或正常液体的瞬时电子－电子相关。也就是说，大家都知道 O⁻ 的相关能要远大于 O，而与孤立单体或典型氢键相比，反常水中电荷自 O 的转移结果要更接近于 O⁻ 得多。除了水之外，还有人报道过 [1,5] 反常的醇和酸。这些分子不可能具有层结构，但它们可以形成单一的六边形"O H O"环，就像（a）中所示的那样，不过外侧氢原子会被其他基团取代。

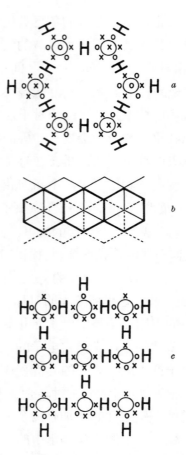

Fig. 1. *a*, Single hexagonal unit in one plane of anomalous water structure. Each oxygen surrounded by tetrahedral arrangement of four electrons with one spin direction (*x*) and an interpenetrating tetrahedron of four electrons with the opposite spin direction (*o*). *b*, Stacking pattern of planes in anomalous water. Pattern is identical to that in graphite and repeats every fourth plane. *c*, Edge-on view of planes. (One of the *x* and one of the *o* electrons which surround the oxygen atom are behind the page and not shown.)

Two other schematic electron distribution diagrams have been proposed for the bonding in anomalous water. In one of them[5], a pair of resonance structures is suggested—a hexagonal array of six neutral water molecules plus a set of three $(OH)^-$ units alternating with three $(H_3O)^+$ units. The neutral array does not suggest the nature of the bonding between the water molecules. The negative charge carried by the oxygen in $(H_3O)^+$ is too small and that in $(OH)^-$ too large, which makes this resonance form improbable. The other model[8] assumes symmetric hydrogen bonds and *x*s and *o*s distributed around oxygens much as in Fig. 1; but it does not emphasize the negative charge on oxygen. The oxygens are placed on a pseudo-wurtzite structure (like hexagonal ice I) or on a pseudo-zincblende structure (like cubic ice I). These structures are of higher energy than the one reported here because of unfavourable electrostatic repulsion terms. Lippincott *et al.*[5] also considered a structure of this sort but ruled it out partly on the grounds that it yields a density higher than observed for anomalous water (for an assumed "O···O" separation of

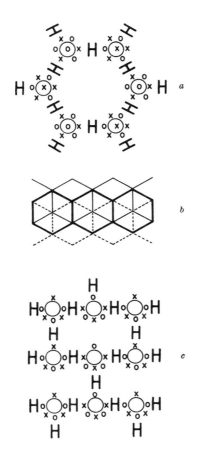

图 1. *a*，在反常水结构中的一个平面上的单个六边形单元。每个氧原子周围是排布在四面体顶角上的具
有同一自旋方向的四个电子 (*x*) 和排布在相贯穿四面体顶角上的具有相反自旋方向的四个电子 (*o*)。
b，反常水中层与层之间的堆叠模式。这种模式与石墨中的模式相同，每四层重复一次。*c*，层的侧
视图。(氧原子周围的一个 *x* 电子和一个 *o* 电子因位于页面的后方而无法显示出来。)

    对于反常水中的成键情况，也曾有人提出过另外两种示意性的电子分布图。其
中之一 [5] 是认为存在一对共振结构——由六个中性水分子排列成的六边形，再加上
由三个 (OH)⁻ 和三个 (H₃O)⁺ 交替排列组成的结构。中性的排列并不能反映水分子间
键的性质。因为 (H₃O)⁺ 中氧原子所带的负电荷太小，而 (OH)⁻ 中的则太大，所以这
种共振形式存在的可能性很小。另一个模型 [8] 假定氧原子周围的对称型氢键和 *x*、*o*
的分布都与图 1 中的情况非常相似；但是没有强调氧原子上的负电荷。氧原子排列
在准纤维锌矿结构 (就像六方晶系的冰 I) 或准闪锌矿结构 (就像立方晶系的冰 I) 中。
这些结构的能量都比本文报道的结构能量高，因为存在起反作用的静电互斥项。利
平科特等人 [5] 也构思出了属于这种类型的一个结构，但被推翻了，其中一部分原因
在于由他的模型推导出的密度要高于反常水的观测密度 (假定 "O···O" 的间距为

2.3 Å). In conclusion, it should be noted that quantum mechanical calculations have been carried out which indicate that the lattice geometry used here is the most probable one, and an attempt has been made to relate its computed properties to those observed experimentally[8].

I thank Mr. Peter A. Kollman for many stimulating conversations on this problem.

(227, 372-373; 1970)

Leland C. Allen: Department of Chemistry, Princeton University, Princeton, New Jersey 08540.

Received February 24, 1970.

References:

1. Deryagin, B. V., and Churayev, N. V., *Priroda*, 4, 16 (1968) (Translation in *Joint Pub. Res. Sev.*, No. 45, 989, 45989, US Department of Commerce, July 25, 1968).

2. Lewis, G. N., *J. Amer. Chem. Soc.*, **38**, 762 (1916).

3. Linnett, J. W., *J. Amer. Chem. Soc.*, **83**, 2643 (1961) and *Electronic Structure of Molecules* (Methuen, London, 1964).

4. Kollman, P. A., and Allen, L. C., *J. Chem. Phys.*, **51**, 3286 (1969).

5. Lippincott, E. R., Stromberg, R. R., Grant, W. H., and Cessac, G. L., *Science*, **164**, 1482 (1969).

6. Page, T. F., Jakobsen, R. J., and Lippincott, E. R., *Science*, **167**, 51 (1970).

7. Petsko, G. A., *Science*, **167**, 171 (1970).

8. Allen, L. C., and Kollman, P. A., *Science*, **167**, 1448 (1970).

2.3 Å）。总之，应该注意到，量子力学计算已经证明本文中所采用的晶格几何结构是最有可能的一种，并且我们已经在尝试将计算得到的性质与实验观测到的性质联系起来 [8]。

感谢彼得·科尔曼先生就这一问题曾与我进行过多次有启发的会谈。

（王耀杨 翻译；李芝芬 审稿）

Fertilization and Cleavage *in vitro* of Preovulator Human Oocytes

R. G. Edwards *et al.*

Editor's Note

Although *in vitro* fertilization (IVF) had yielded full term pregnancies in certain animals, in 1970 human IVF success remained elusive. Robert Edwards realised the importance of harvesting eggs just before ovulation, and set up a collaboration with gynaecological surgeon Patrick Steptoe, who used laparoscopy to recover eggs from infertile women at the appropriate point in their cycle. With further help from assistant Jean Purdy, the team trialled various culture media, and here they report the production of eight- or sixteen-celled human embryos by this method. Eight years later, the team were delighted to announce the birth of the first "test tube" baby, Louise Brown. IVF went on to become a major type of infertility treatment.

HUMAN oocytes removed from patients shortly before ovulation should assist the study of early human development[1]. Previously, oocytes in dictyotene had been prepared for fertilization by maturing them in culture after their recovery from excised ovaries. In animals, fertilization of oocytes *in vitro* and *in vivo* after their maturation in culture results in embryos incapable of sustained growth; foetal development to full term is achieved by recovering oocytes just before ovulation, for example in metaphase of the first meiotic division, and completing their maturation *in vitro* before fertilization. We now present data on the fertilization and cleavage *in vitro* of human ova recovered by laparoscopy just before ovulation; preliminary observations have been given elsewhere[2,3].

Development beyond the pronuclear stage has proved difficult in several species, for example in mice. We have few human embryos for study, and have based our work on observations of animal embryos. Whittingham[4] obtained viable young by fertilizing mouse ova *in vitro* with uterine spermatozoa, culturing the eggs to the 2-cell stage, and then transferring them into a recipient female. Whitten has shown[5] that mouse ova recovered in their pronuclear stage can now be grown to blastocysts with complete success. The media used by Whittingham and Whitten were developed from earlier work[6,7]. In addition to these media, we have also used Ham's F10 medium[8] which has been used with rabbit embryos[9], and Waymouth's medium MB752/1[10] and medium 199[11] which are both widely used in tissue culture.

Oocytes and Spermatozoa

Patients were given injections of human menopausal gonadotrophin and chorionic gonadotrophin to induce follicular growth and maturation. Laparoscopy was performed 30–32 h after the injection of HCG, and each follicle was aspirated separately[1]. The

排卵前的人类卵母细胞在体外的受精和卵裂

爱德华兹等

编者按

虽然已经能够利用体外受精（IVF）在某些动物中实现满期妊娠，但在 1970 年时，人们仍未确定是否能将 IVF 成功应用于人类。罗伯特·爱德华兹意识到在即将排卵前收集卵子的重要性，并与妇科医生帕特里克·斯特普托建立了合作关系，斯特普托曾通过腹腔镜手术提取过处于月经周期适当时间的不孕妇女的卵子。在助手琼·珀迪的进一步协助下，该研究小组尝试了各种不同的培养基，他们在本文中报道了以这种方法培养产生的 8 细胞期或 16 细胞期的人类胚胎。8 年以后，该研究小组兴奋地向世人宣布：第一个"试管"婴儿——路易丝·布朗诞生了。随后 IVF 逐渐成为治疗不孕症的主要方式。

从即将排卵的患者体内取出的人类卵母细胞应该有助于我们研究人类的早期发育 [1]。以前的做法是：从切除的卵巢中提取卵母细胞，然后将处于核网期的卵母细胞培养成熟以用于受精。在培养基中成熟的动物卵母细胞，无论是通过体外受精还是体内受精，所产生的胚胎都不能生长。只能通过提取出即将排出的卵母细胞，例如处于第一次减数分裂中期的卵母细胞，并于受精前在体外培养到成熟阶段，这样胎儿才能发育到足月。现在我们要给出一些关于在即将排卵时用腹腔镜手术提取出的人类卵子在体外受精和卵裂的结果；最初的观察结果已经发表在了其他出版物上 [2,3]。

已经证明有几个物种（例如小鼠）的胚胎在体外发育时很难超越原核期。由于我们仅有极少数人类胚胎可供研究，所以我们的研究成果基本上来自于对动物胚胎的观察。惠廷厄姆 [4] 曾用穿入子宫的精子使小鼠卵子在体外受精，将受精卵培养到 2 细胞期后再将其转移到受体母鼠中，通过这样的方法他得到了可存活的幼鼠。惠滕 [5] 曾指出：现在已经可以成功地把原核期提取的小鼠卵子培养到囊胚期。惠廷厄姆和惠滕所用的培养基是从前人的研究工作中 [6,7] 发展而来的。除这些培养基外，我们还使用了此前曾被用于兔胚胎培养 [9] 的哈姆氏 F10 培养基 [8]，以及被广泛用于组织培养的韦莫斯 MB752/1 培养基 [10] 和 M199 培养基 [11]。

卵母细胞和精子

为了诱导卵泡的生长和成熟，我们给患者注射了人绝经期促性腺激素和人绒毛膜促性腺激素。在给患者注射人绒毛膜促性腺激素 30 小时~32 小时后进行腹腔镜手

oocytes were suspended in droplets consisting of fluid from their own follicle (where available), and the medium being tested for fertilization. After incubation for 1–4 h at 37°C the oocytes were washed through two changes of the medium under test before being placed in the suspensions of spermatozoa. Preovulatory oocytes would be ready for fertilization, that is, in metaphase of the second meiotic division, by 3–4 h after collection. Many oocytes were obviously not preovulatory, and therefore unsuitable for fertilization, but all were placed in the fertilization droplets in order to simplify our procedure.

Ejaculated spermatozoa were supplied by the husband. The spermatozoa were washed twice by gentle centrifugation in the medium under test, and made up to a final concentration of between 8×10^5 and 2×10^6/ml. depending on the quality of the sample. The higher numbers were used with samples of poor quality containing many inactive spermatozoa, cellular inclusions, other debris, or viscous seminal fluid. The fertilization droplets were approximately 0.05 ml.

Oocytes classified as preovulatory were surrounded by layers of silvery-appearing corona and cumulus cells in a viscous matrix[1]. Oocytes classified as non-ovulatory were enclosed in a few layers of corona cells. Atretic oocytes had few or no cells. Initially, each oocyte was placed in its own fertilizing droplet, but later all the oocytes recovered from a patient were grouped together. The mass of cells surrounding preovulatory oocytes led inevitably to some dilution of the numbers of spermatozoa in the fertilization droplet.

Fertilization

Bavister's medium had been capable of sustaining fertilization in previous work[12-14], and was therefore used extensively. This medium was slightly modified during the work by reducing the sodium chloride to 0.75 g percent and increasing the KCl to 0.039 g percent, following the analysis of the amount of Na^+ and K^+ in human follicular fluid. Whittingham's medium was used unmodified, and both Waymouth's medium (Flow Laboratories) and Ham's F10 (Flow Laboratories) were modified by raising the pH to 7.5–7.6 with extra bicarbonate and supplementing with bovine serum albumin (0.36 g percent). Sodium pyruvate was also added to Waymouth's medium (1.1 mg percent). The gas phase was either 5 percent CO_2 in air, or 5 percent CO_2, 5 percent O_2 and 90 percent N_2.

The cumulus cells began to dissociate within 2–3 h of insemination, although corona cells remaining closely or loosely attached prevented the examination of some oocytes by low-power microscopy 15 h after insemination. The cells were left in place after attempts to remove them had led to damage of some oocytes. Criteria for judging fertilization were: (*i*) the observation by phase-contrast microscopy of two pronuclei, two polar bodies and, if possible, a sperm tail in the cytoplasm of the oocyte; (*ii*) identification of pronuclei in the ova in culture, using a stereoscopic low-power microscope (this method was inexact, and even impossible when cells persisted around the oocyte, but the eggs remained relatively

术，手术时分开单独吸取每个卵泡 [1]。将卵母细胞悬浮于由其自身卵泡液（如果能够得到的话）和用于受精试验的培养基组成的小液滴中。在 37℃ 下培养 1 小时 ~ 4 小时后，用待测培养基冲洗卵母细胞两次，然后将其置于精子的悬浮液中。排卵前的卵母细胞在被收集 3 小时 ~ 4 小时后就可以用于受精了，也就是说，这时正处于第二次减数分裂的中期。显然，其中有许多卵母细胞并不处在排卵前的状态，因此不适于进行受精，但是为了简化操作，我们还是把所有的卵母细胞都放到了受精小液滴中。

排出的精子由患者配偶提供。将精子在待测培养基中低速离心并冲洗两次，根据精子的质量进行调整使其终浓度介于 8×10^5/ 毫升 ~ 2×10^6/ 毫升之间。在质量较低的样品中含有许多无活力精子、细胞内含物、其他碎片或者黏稠的精液，对于这种样品就需要有更高数量的精子。受精小液滴的体积约为 0.05 毫升。

一般认为：排卵前的卵母细胞会被黏性基质中的数层银色冠细胞和卵丘细胞包裹 [1]；而尚未进入排卵状态的卵母细胞则被封闭在较少层的冠细胞之中。处于闭锁状态的卵母细胞只有极少的细胞包裹或者完全没有细胞包裹。一开始，每个卵母细胞都被置于其自身的受精小液滴中，但是随后所有从同一患者中提取的卵母细胞都被聚集到了一起。那些包围在排卵前卵母细胞周围的大量细胞必然会使受精小液滴中的精子数受到一定程度的稀释。

受 精 过 程

以前的研究工作曾证明巴维斯特培养基能够维持受精过程 [12-14]，因此该培养基被广泛应用。在分析了人类卵泡液中的 Na+ 含量和 K+ 含量之后，我们对此培养基进行了稍许调整：将 NaCl 的浓度降低到 0.75 克 /100 毫升，同时将 KCl 的浓度提高到 0.039 克 /100 毫升。对于惠廷厄姆培养基，我们在使用时未作任何调整；对于韦莫斯培养基（弗洛实验室）和哈姆氏 F10 培养基（弗洛实验室），我们都作了一些改良：加入额外的碳酸氢盐将 pH 值提高到 7.5 ~ 7.6，同时补充牛血清白蛋白（浓度为 0.36 克 /100 毫升）。在韦莫斯培养基中还加入了丙酮酸钠(浓度为 1.1 毫克 /100 毫升)。培养所用的气体环境为含 5% CO_2 的空气，或者为由 5% CO_2、5% O_2 和 90% N_2 组成的混合气体。

虽然在人工授精 15 小时后冠细胞仍然或紧或松地黏附着卵母细胞，这使得我们在低倍显微镜下无法仔细观察某些卵母细胞，但卵丘细胞在人工授精 2 小时 ~ 3 小时之内就开始脱离下来了。我们多次尝试将周围的这些细胞分离下来，结果导致一些卵母细胞被破坏，之后我们就保留了它们。判断是否受精的标准包括：（1）通过相差显微镜能在卵母细胞的细胞质中观察到两个原核、两个极体，并且还有可能看到一条精子尾巴；（2）用低倍体视显微镜能分辨出在培养的卵中有原核（这种方法并

undisturbed for further development); (*iii*) cleavage of the egg, preferably after the identification of pronuclei.

Data on the incidence of fertilization are given in Table 1. Only a few ova could be spared for examination by phase-contrast microscopy. Fertilization was observed in Bavister's medium, modified Waymouth's medium and in Whittingham's medium, but not in modified Ham's F10 on the sole occasion it was used. Low rates of fertilization sometimes seemed to be a consequence of the poor quality of the spermatozoa from some patients.

Table 1. Incidence of Fertilization *in vitro*

Medium	O_2 in gas phase	Total No. of oocytes	Non-ovulatory	Fertilization					
				Phase-contrast Microscopy			Low-power microscopy		
				Unfertilized	Fertilized	Others	1-celled	Pronucleate and cleaved	Pronuclei not seen, egg cleaved
Bavister's	20 percent	105	30	26	3+1*+1?	9	18	11†+2?‡	4
	5 percent	76	–	–	–	–	53§	6+2? ‡	15
	Combined	181	30	26	3+1*+1?	9	71§	17†+4?‡	19
Whittingham's	20 percent	19	3	5	–	3§	5§	2	1
Modified Waymouth's	20 percent	10	2	1	2	2	1	1	1?
Modified Ham's F10	5 percent	2	–	–	–	–	2	–	–

* Sperm in perivitelline space.

† Four of these eggs were transferred while pronucleate into the oviduct of a rabbit.

‡ Probably pronucleate.

§ One egg in each of these groups was found to possess two or more pronuclei between 48 and 72 h after insemination, and might have been undergoing rudimentary parthenogenetic development.

Cleavage

Between 12 and 15 h after insemination, the oocytes were gradually transferred from the medium used for fertilization into various other media for cleavage. At least five embryos were cultured in each medium, except for medium 199. All media were adjusted to a *p*H of approximately 7.3. A total of thirty-eight embryos cleaved in culture (Table 2). Two pronuclei had been observed in many of them. Almost all eggs cleaved twice, and a few completed their fourth cleavage.

不精确，当卵母细胞周围有许多细胞时，甚至无法进行观察，但卵的进一步发育没有受到太大的影响）；（3）卵的分裂，尤其是在观察到原核之后。

我们在表 1 中给出了受精发生率的数据。用相差显微镜只能观察到少数几个卵子。我们在巴维斯特培养基、经过改良的韦莫斯培养基和惠廷厄姆培养基中都观察到了受精的发生，但是在唯一一次使用改良的哈姆氏 F10 培养基时却没有观察到受精。造成受精率较低的原因有时似乎与某些患者的精子质量欠佳有关。

表 1. 体外受精的发生率

培养基	气相中的氧气含量	卵母细胞总数	尚未进入排卵状态的	受精					
				相差显微镜			低倍显微镜		
				未受精的	受精的	其他	单个细胞	有原核，有卵裂	未见原核，有卵裂
巴维斯特培养基	20%	105	30	26	3+1*+1?	9	18	11†+2?‡	4
	5%	76	—	—	—	—	53§	6+2?‡	15
	混合	181	30	26	3+1*+1?	9	71§	17†+4?‡	19
惠廷厄姆培养基	20%	19	3	5	—	3§	5§	2	1
改良的韦莫斯培养基	20%	10	2	1	2	2	1	1	1?
改良的哈姆氏 F10 培养基	5%	2	—	—	—	—	2	—	—

* 精子处在卵周隙中。

† 在形成原核时，将其中 4 个卵移植到兔子的输卵管中。

‡ 可能形成了原核。

§ 每组实验中都有一个卵在人工授精后 48 小时～72 小时之内被发现存在两个或多个原核，并且这些卵可能一直在进行初期的孤雌发育。

卵　　裂

在人工授精后 12 小时～15 小时之内，我们将卵母细胞从受精所用的培养基中逐渐地转移到用于卵裂的各种培养基中。除 M199 培养基外，在其他每种培养基中都至少培养了 5 个胚胎。所有培养基的 pH 值都被调至接近 7.3。在培养时共有 38 个胚胎发生了卵裂（表 2）。我们在其中的很多胚胎中发现了两个原核。几乎所有的卵都分裂了两次，有一些卵甚至完成了第 4 次分裂。

Table 2. Cleavage of the Embryos *in vitro*

Medium	Osmolality (mosm/kg)	O₂ in gas phase (percent)	Total No. embryos	Final No. of cells in the embryos							
				1	2	3	4	4–8	8	8–16	16 or more
Whittingham's	280–290	20	9	1*			1	2	4	1	
	280–290	5	2						2		
Whitten's	270	5	5	1*		1			1	2†	
	325	5	3						2†	1	
Waymouth's with 15 percent inactivated foetal calf serum	325	20	6	1‡				2	2	1	
199 with 20 percent inactivated foetal calf serum	292	20	1					1			
Ham's F10 with 20 percent inactivated foetal calf serum	287	5	2			2					
	300–305	5	10§					1¶	1**	4	3

* Reverted to 1-cell after initial cleavage.

† Both embryos had cells of dissimilar size, and cleaved erratically.

‡ Probably reverted to 1-cell after cleavage, but vision obscured by corona cells.

§ One embryo became infected at 2-cell stage.

¶ Cleavage erratic.

** Removed from culture and photographed in 8-cell stage.

Many ova cleaved regularly and evenly in Whittingham's medium, and most reached the 8-celled stage. One embryo behaved anomalously, for it divided into two cells and then reverted to one cell.

Whitten's medium is similar to Whittingham's except for having a lower osmotic pressure. Development became distorted when embryos were cultured in this medium. Cleavage became irregular, a 2-celled egg reverted to one cell, and cytoplasmic division seemed to occur without nuclear division in three embryos. For example, one embryo cleaved very rapidly from 3 cells to an apparently normal 8-celled embryo, but when flattened and stained[15] was found to have only three nuclei. When the osmotic pressure of this medium was increased by adding more Na^+ and K^+ ions, cleavage became more regular although slower than in other media.

Waymouth's medium supplemented with 15 percent v/v foetal calf serum failed to support development from the 8-celled stage, perhaps because of the high osmotic pressure: ova placed in it showed retractions of the cell surface. One embryo cultured in medium 199 became arrested in the 4-cell stage.

表 2. 胚胎在体外的卵裂

培养基	摩尔渗透压浓度（毫渗摩/千克）	气相中的氧气含量(%)	胚胎总数	胚胎中最终的细胞数							
				1	2	3	4	4~8	8	8~16	≥16
惠廷厄姆培养基	280~290	20	9	1*			1	2	4	1	
	280~290	5	2						2		
惠滕培养基	270	5	5	1*		1			1	2†	
	325	5	3						2†	1	
添加 15% 灭活胎牛血清的韦莫斯培养基	325	20	6	1‡			2	2	1		
添加 20% 灭活胎牛血清的 M199 培养基	292	20	1				1				
添加 20% 灭活胎牛血清的哈姆氏 F10 培养基	287	5	2			2					
	300~305	5	10§					1¶	1**	4	3

* 第一次卵裂后又回到了单细胞状态。

† 两个胚胎都具有大小不等的细胞，而且明显不稳定。

‡ 卵裂后很可能回到了单细胞状态，但因被冠细胞包围而看起来模糊不清。

§ 一个胚胎在 2 细胞期被感染。

¶ 卵裂不稳定。

** 在 8 细胞期从培养基中取出并拍照。

有很多在惠廷厄姆培养基中培养的卵发生了正常且均匀的卵裂，而且大多数达到了 8 细胞期。只有一个胚胎表现异常，因为它在分裂成两个细胞之后又退回到了单细胞状态。

惠滕培养基与惠廷厄姆培养基很相似，只是渗透压低一些。但是在将胚胎放在惠滕培养基中进行培养时，它们的发育就会变得不正常。卵裂变得毫无规则，有一个 2 细胞期的卵又重新回到了单细胞状态，有 3 个胚胎似乎在细胞核没有发生分裂的情况下出现了细胞质的分裂。例如，其中有一个胚胎很快地从 3 个细胞卵裂到了看似正常的 8 细胞期，但是在将其压片染色 [15] 后我们却发现这个胚胎中只有 3 个细胞核。如果通过添加更多的 Na+ 离子和 K+ 离子增加惠滕培养基的渗透压，则虽然卵裂速度要比用其他培养基培养时慢，但卵裂过程会变得更为正常。

用添加 15% 体积比胎牛血清的韦莫斯培养基进行培养不能使卵细胞发育到 8 细胞期以后的状态，这可能是由于渗透压太高造成的：在这一培养基中培养的卵细胞出现了表面萎缩。在 M199 培养基中培养的一个胚胎发育到 4 细胞期就中止了发育。

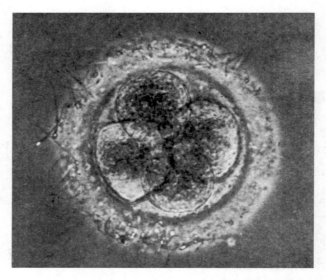

Fig. 1. A 4-celled egg grown in Waymouth's medium supplemented with calf serum. Development of this embryo had evidently been arrested.

Ham's F10 supplemented with 20 percent foetal calf serum was used at two osmotic pressures by adjusting the amount of water added; at 287 milliosmols/kg cleavage appeared abnormal in two embryos. At 300–305 milliosmols/kg seven embryos showed excellent cleavage to a stage approaching or beyond the 16-cell stage. Another embryo photographed in the 8-celled stage (Fig. 2) would probably have cleaved further.

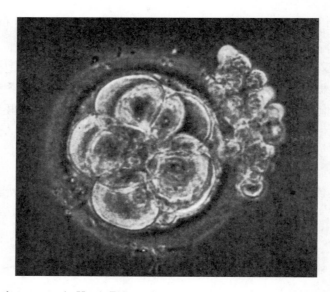

Fig. 2. An 8-celled egg grown in Ham's F10 supplemented with calf serum. It was removed from culture during cleavage, and could have been capable of further development.

The embryos were inspected at various times during culture. The first cleavage occurred

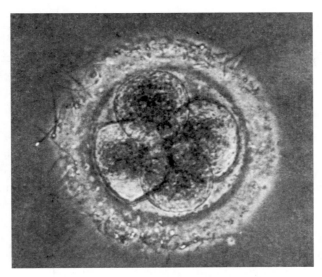

图 1. 一个在添加了牛血清的韦莫斯培养基中培养的 4 细胞期卵。这个胚胎显然已经停止了发育。

通过调节水的含量，我们制备了具有两种不同渗透压的含 20% 胎牛血清的哈姆氏 F10 培养基：在渗透压为 287 毫渗摩 / 千克的培养基中，有 2 个胚胎的卵裂看起来不太正常；在渗透压为 300 毫渗摩 / 千克～305 毫渗摩 / 千克的培养基中，有 7 个胚胎显示出完美的卵裂，接近或者超过了 16 细胞期。我们拍摄了另一个处于 8 细胞期的胚胎（图 2），这个胚胎很可能还会继续卵裂。

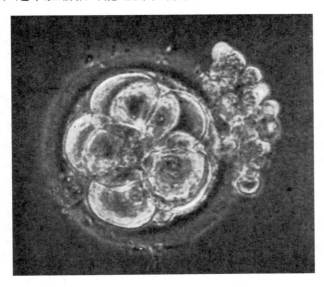

图 2. 一个在添加了牛血清的哈姆氏 F10 培养基中培养的 8 细胞期卵。这个胚胎是在卵裂期间被移出培养基的，要不然它也许还能继续发育。

我们在培养过程中的多个时间点对胚胎进行了检查。结果发现，第一次卵裂发

before 38 h post-insemination. The second cleavage occurred between 38 and $46\frac{1}{2}$h in seven embryos cultured in Whittingham's medium or Ham's F10, and the third cleavage between 51 and 62 h in four embryos. The fourth cleavage occurred before 85 h in embryos grown in Ham's F10. Timings of cleavage in other embryos did not differ from these estimates, but the intervals between recordings were too long for accurate estimates.

The embryos were left in culture until it was clear that development had ceased, that is, approximately 48 h after the previous recording of cell division. Many embryos were now displaying fragmentation of blastomores or other forms of degeneration. The blastomeres of many embryos that had cleaved normally possessed a single nucleus as judged by phase-contrast microscopy. Whole mounts or flattened preparations of two 16-celled, three 8-celled, and two 4–5-celled embryos revealed the same number of nuclei as cells in each embryo. One of the 16-celled embryos possessed mitoses. One embryo classified while living as 16-celled possessed twenty-one nuclei, although some were smaller than others.

Comment

The amount of free follicular fluid added to the fertilization droplets must have been small, except for that in the viscous cumulus masses surrounding the oocyte. Various factors in follicular fluid are believed to be necessary for stimulating the spermatozoa and inducing changes in the acrosome[16], and steroids present in follicular fluid or synthesized by the granulosa cells could also be involved. Recent studies have indicated that the acrosome is a modified lysosome[17], and capacitation could involve agents known to destabilize lysosomal membranes. Among the most potent of these agents are progesterone and other progestogens[18]. Progesterone has been identified in human follicular fluid aspirated with the oocytes (unpublished work of K. Fotherby and of ourselves), and granulosa cells cultured *in vitro* can also synthesize progesterone and other progestogens[19]. Ultrastructural examination has revealed the acrosomal changes following capacitation are seen as the spermatozoa penetrate between the cumulus cells[20]. We have measured the levels of oestradiol-17β and of LH in many of these fluids[21], and are currently measuring progesterone and 17α-hydroxyprogesterone (unpublished work of K. Fotherby and of ourselves). These fluids could then be tested for their efficacy in inducing the acrosome change in spermatozoa in relation to the known levels of the different steroids. It would seem to be a wise precaution to remove the cells surrounding the oocytes before testing agents inducing capacitation and fertilization *in vitro*.

Cleavage occurred in all ova seen to possess pronuclei, and in some others that could not be examined because of the enveloping cells. Human embryos may have metabolic needs similar to mouse embryos, as judged by their cleavage in simple defined media. Firm conclusions about the value of different media obviously cannot be drawn when so few ova were available. On occasions, four or five embryos were obtained from one

生在人工授精后 38 小时之内。有 7 个在惠廷厄姆培养基或哈姆氏 F10 培养基中培养的胚胎发生第二次卵裂的时间是在人工授精后 38 小时~46.5 小时之间，有 4 个胚胎的第三次卵裂发生在 51 小时~62 小时之间。使用哈姆氏 F10 培养基培养的胚胎发生第四次卵裂的时间均在人工授精后 85 小时之内。其他胚胎的卵裂时间与上述估计值相差无几，但是由于各次记录之间的时间间隔太长，因而无法得到精确的结果。

胚胎一直在培养基中培养，直到我们可以确认发育已经停止，更确切地说是在距离之前记录到细胞分裂的大约 48 小时之后。这时，在很多胚胎中出现了卵裂球的碎片化或者其他形式的退化现象。由在相差显微镜下的观察结果可以断定，许多发生正常卵裂的胚胎中的卵裂球具有单个的细胞核。通过检查 2 个处于 16 细胞期的胚胎、3 个处于 8 细胞期的胚胎以及 2 个处于 4 细胞期~5 细胞期的胚胎的整体包埋封片或压片标本，我们发现每个胚胎中的细胞核数都等于细胞数。有一个 16 细胞期的胚胎正在经历有丝分裂。另外一个被认为正处于 16 细胞期的胚胎则含有 21 个细胞核，不过其中有一些细胞核要比其他细胞核小。

评　论

加入到受精小液滴中的游离卵泡液必须很少，除非卵母细胞被大量有黏性的卵丘细胞包围。一般认为，卵泡液中的各种因子对于增强精子活力和诱导顶体反应是必需的 [16]，而且存在于卵泡液中或者由卵泡颗粒细胞合成的类固醇也有可能会参与这一过程。最近的研究表明，顶体就是一个被修饰过的溶酶体 [17]，一些已知能够降低溶酶体膜稳定性的物质可能参与了精子的获能过程。在这些物质中效力最强的是孕酮和其他一些孕激素 [18]。我们在与卵母细胞一同吸出的人卵泡液中曾发现过有孕酮存在（福瑟比和我们尚未发表的研究结果），而且体外培养的卵泡颗粒细胞也可以合成孕酮和其他孕激素 [19]。对超微结构的检查结果显示，精子获能后出现的顶体反应发生在当精子从卵丘细胞之间穿透时 [20]。此前我们已经在多种卵泡液中测定过 17β- 雌二醇和促黄体生成激素（LH）的含量 [21]，目前我们正在测定孕酮和 17α- 羟孕酮的含量（福瑟比和我们尚未发表的研究结果）。然后，我们就可以测定这些卵泡液在诱导精子顶体反应上的效能，这种效能与各种类固醇的已知含量有关。在检验可在体外条件下诱导精子获能和受精的化学物质时，预先清除掉卵母细胞周围的细胞似乎是一种明智的做法。

卵裂发生在所有能看到有原核的卵以及其他一些因被细胞包裹而无法观察到原核的卵中。根据人类胚胎和小鼠胚胎在一些配方明确的简单培养基中所发生的卵裂情况，就可以推断出人类胚胎的代谢需要可能和小鼠胚胎的类似。由于可利用的人卵细胞数目非常少，所以要准确判断不同培养基的效能显然是不可能的。在有些情

patient, and comparisons could be made between different media. Results with defined media were inferior to those obtained from Ham's F10 supplemented with foetal calf serum and with an osmotic pressure of around 300 osmols. Among various differences, F10 contains salts of heavy metals and more pyruvate than the other media. Development beyond the 8 or 16-cell stage might demand the presence of human oviductal or uterine secretions, and these could be collected with a small chamber placed in the uterus for a few hours[22]. The premature recovery of preovulatory oocytes might be another cause of the arrested development, and they might have to be aspirated even closer to the time of ovulation.

Analysis of the chromosome complement of the embryos can be undertaken now that some cleavages have been timed, although perhaps better delayed until later stages of development are available. Identification of a Y chromosome in some embryos is now critically needed to furnish formal proof to confirm the morphological evidence of fertilization used currently. The quinacrine dyes might detect the Y chromosome in interphase nuclei and mitoses, as they do in somatic cells[23,24], although caution will be necessary, for they fail to stain the Y in most spermatogonia[25], Chromosomal analysis of the embryos should also reveal anomalies in early development, for example, non-disjunction and especially triploidy arising through polyspermy or failure of polar body formation. When more preovulatory oocytes are available their parthenogenetic activation might be used to produce haploid strains of cells, as in mice[26].

One or more embryos have been produced from twenty-nine of the forty-nine patients under treatment in this work. The normality of embryonic development and the efficiency of embryo transfer cannot yet be assessed, although conditions for implantation in the treated patients should be favourable[1].

We thank Mr. B. D. Bavister, Dr. D. G. Whittingham and Professor C. R. Austin for their help, Mr. C. Richardson for his assistance with photographs, and the Ford Foundation, the Manchester Regional Hospital Board and the Oldham and District Hospital Management Committee for financial support. We also thank Searle Scientific Services for their steroid assay.

(**227**, 1307-1309; 1970)

R. G. Edwards, P. C. Steptoe and J. M. Purdy: Physiological Laboratory, University of Cambridge, and Oldham General Hospital, Lancashire.

Received August 25, 1970.

References:

1. Steptoe, P. C., and Edwards, R. G., *Lancet*, i, 683 (1970).

2. Edwards, R. G., in *Symposium on Actual Problems in Fertility, Stockholm* 1970 (Plenum, New York, in the press).

况下，我们可以从一名患者身上得到 4 个 ~ 5 个胚胎，这样就可以对不同的培养基进行比较。用配方明确培养基得到的效果比不上用渗透压约为 300 渗摩、添加了胎牛血清的哈姆氏 F10 培养基。F10 培养基含有重金属盐且丙酮酸盐的含量较其他培养基高，这是 F10 培养基与其他培养基的不同之处之一。8 细胞期或 16 细胞期以后的胚胎发育有可能需要人输卵管或子宫的分泌物，可以通过将一个小的容器放在子宫中几小时来收集这些分泌物 [22]。过早地取出排卵前卵母细胞可能是导致胚胎发育阻滞的另一个原因，也许吸出卵母细胞的时间应该更接近于排卵期。

既然我们已经确定了一些卵裂过程的时间，那么下一步就可以着手进行胚胎的染色体组分析了，不过也许推迟到能获得更靠后的胚胎发育阶段再进行这一分析会更好一些。为了提供正式的证据来证实目前所使用的受精的形态学证据，我们现在急需从一些胚胎中鉴定出 Y 染色体的存在。利用喹吖因类染料染色也许能检测出间期核中和有丝分裂期间的 Y 染色体，就像在体细胞中一样 [23,24]，不过必须小心谨慎，因为喹吖因类染料不能使大多数精原细胞中的 Y 染色体着色 [25]。对胚胎的染色体分析应该也能揭示出胚胎早期发育的异常，例如由多精受精或未能形成极体造成的不分离现象甚至出现三倍体。如果我们能得到更多的排卵前卵母细胞，也许就可以利用孤雌激活来产生单倍体细胞系，就像已经在小鼠中建立的细胞系那样 [26]。

在这项研究中接受治疗的共有 49 位患者，我们从其中 29 位患者处获得了一个或多个胚胎。目前我们还无法评估正常发育胚胎的比率以及胚胎移植的成功率，尽管受试患者自身的胚胎移植条件应该是很有利的 [1]。

感谢巴维斯特先生、惠廷厄姆博士和奥斯汀教授给予我们的帮助，感谢理查森先生帮助我们拍摄照片，感谢福特基金会、曼彻斯特地区医院董事会和奥尔德姆地区综合医院管理委员会在经费方面的资助。还要感谢瑟尔科学服务部帮我们作了类固醇的检测实验。

（吕静 翻译；王敏康 审稿）

3. Steptoe, P. C., in *Schering Symposium on Intrinsic and Extrinsic Factors in Early Mammalian Development* 1970 (edit. by Raspé, G.) (Advances in the Biosciences, 6) (Pergamon/Vieweg, in the press).

4. Whittingham, D. G., *Nature*, **220**, 592 (1968).

5. Whitten, W. K., in *Schering Symposium on Intrinsic and Extrinsic Factors in Early Mammalian Development* 1970 (edit. by Raspé, G.) (Advances in the Biosciences, 6) (Pergamon/Vieweg, in the press).

6. Brinster, R. L., *Exp. Cell Res.*, **32**, 205 (1963).

7. Whitten, W. K., and Biggers, R. L., *J. Reprod. Fert.*, **17**, 390 (1968).

8. Ham, R. G., *Exp. Cell Res.*, **29**, 515 (1963).

9. Daniel, J. C., and Olson, J. D., *J. Reprod. Fert.*, **15**, 453 (1968).

10. Waymouth, C., *J. Nat. Cancer Inst.*, **22**, 1003 (1959).

11. Morgan, J. F., Morton, H. J., and Parker, R. C., *Proc. Soc. Exp. Biol. Med.*, **73**, 1 (1950).

12. Bavister, B. D., *J. Reprod. Fert.*, **18**, 544 (1969).

13. Edwards, R. G., Bavister, B. D., and Steptoe, P. C., *Nature*, **221**, 632 (1969).

14. Bavister, B. D., Edwards, R. G., and Steptoe, P. C., *J. Reprod. Fert.*, **20**, 159 (1969).

15. Tarkowski, A. K., *Cytogenetics*, 5, 394 (1966).

16. Yanagimachi, R., *J. Exp. Zool.*, **170**, 269 (1969).

17. Allison, A. C., and Hartree, E. F., *J. Reprod. Fert.*, **22**, 501 (1970).

18. Weissman, G., in *Lysosomes in Biology and Pathology* (edit. by Dingle, J. T., and Fell, Honor B.) (North Holland, Amsterdam, 1969).

19. Channing, C. P., and Grieves, J. A., *J. Endocrinol.*, **43**, 391 (1969).

20. Bedford, J. M., *J. Reprod. Fert.*, Suppl. 2, 35 (1967).

21. Abraham, G. E., O'Dell, W. D., Edwards, R. G., and Purdy, J. M., *Acta Endocrinol.*, Suppl. No. 147, 332 (1970).

22. Edwards, R. G., Talbert, L., Isralestam, D., Nino, H. V., and Johnson, M. H., *Amer. J. Obst. Gynec.*, **102**, 388 (1968).

23. Pearson, P. L., Bobrow, M., and Vosa, C. G., *Nature*, **226**, 78 (1970).

24. George, K. P., *Nature*, **226**, 80 (1970).

25. Pearson, P. L., and Bobrow, M., *J. Reprod. Fert.*, **22**, 177 (1970).

26. Fraham, C. F., *Nature*, **226**, 165 (1970).

Evidence that Polywater Is a Colloidal Silicate Sol

W. D. Bascom *et al.*

Editor's Note

By the start of the 1970s, the evidence for polywater—an alleged new form of water with a waxy consistency—began to evaporate. A paper in *Science* reported an analysis of polywater "prepared by the standard methods" which revealed high concentrations of contaminants. The case for contamination was strengthened by this paper from researchers at the Naval Research Laboratory in Washington, D.C., which indicates that silicate ions from the glass walls of the capillaries in which polywater had been reported could accumulate and condense into a silicate gel. This accounted for the viscous substance without any need to invoke exotic new forms of water.

DERYAGIN and co-workers have presented evidence that a new form of water (anomalous water) is produced when normal water vapour condenses into minute, pristine glass or silica capillaries[1,2]. More recently, Lippincott *et al.*[3] produced water condensate in such capillaries and obtained its infrared and Raman spectra, from which they concluded that the condensate contained a high molecular weight polymeric form of water, or "polywater". A distinction should be made between the claims of Lippincott *et al.* for "polywater" and those of Deryagin *et al.* for anomalous water. The Russian workers do not claim that anomalous water is a high molecular weight polymeric water. Furthermore, they were extraordinarily careful in preventing electrolyte contamination of the condensate in many of their experiments. The work reported here indicates that salt contamination is an important consideration in the experiments described by Lippincott *et al.*

The Experiments

Capillaries with internal diameters of 50 μm to 5 μm were drawn from acid (HNO_3–H_2SO_4, 1:1) cleaned "Pyrex" and silica (GE 204) tubing. In some experiments the capillaries were loosely placed in "Pyrex" dishes over distilled water in a desiccator evacuated to about 40 mm Hg and held at $25°C \pm 1°C$. This is the procedure used by Lippincott *et al.*[3]. Other condensation experiments were conducted in an apparatus designed to allow the capillaries to be evacuated independently of the water to reduce the chance of spray reaching the capillaries during the pump-down. The apparatus had a chamber for the capillaries separated from the chamber for water by a grease-free vacuum valve. The water chamber was evacuated first, the valve closed and the capillaries introduced into the other chamber. This section was then evacuated, cut off from the pump and opened to the water.

The capillaries were inspected after 3–10 days' exposure to water vapour. To remove condensate for analysis, the liquid was expelled by air pressure using a gas tight syringe and hypodermic needle. The capillary was sealed into the needle with a drop of melted,

证明聚合水是胶状硅酸盐溶胶的证据

巴斯科姆等

编者按

在 20 世纪 70 年代初，证明聚合水这种和蜡一样柔软的所谓新形式水存在的证据开始销声匿迹。发表于《科学》杂志上的一篇论文报道了作者对"用标准方法制备"的聚合水的分析，结果发现其中含有高浓度的杂质。华盛顿海军研究实验室的研究人员在本文中又强调了污染问题，他们指出以前所报道的聚合水在玻璃毛细管壁上形成的硅酸盐离子能够聚集并凝成硅酸盐凝胶。这种现象用黏性物质就可以解释而不需要求助于异乎寻常的新形式水。

杰里亚金及其合作者曾提出证据证明：当正常的水蒸气在细小而洁净的玻璃或石英毛细管中凝结时，会生成一种新形式的水（即反常水）[1,2]。最近，利平科特等人 [3] 在这种毛细管中制备出了水的冷凝液并测试了它的红外光谱和拉曼光谱，据此他们断言该冷凝液中含有一种具有较高分子量的聚合态水，或称"聚合水"。应该对利平科特等人提出的"聚合水"与杰里亚金等人得到的"反常水"加以区分。俄罗斯的研究者们并没有声称反常水是一种高分子量的聚合水，而且他们在很多实验中都会格外小心地避免电解质对冷凝液的污染。本文中的研究结果说明：在利平科特等人所描述的实验中，盐类物质的污染是一个要考虑的重点问题。

实　验

内径为 5 μm ~ 50 μm 的毛细管是由酸（HNO_3–H_2SO_4，1:1）洗过的"派莱克斯"玻璃或石英（GE 204）拉制而成的。在一些实验中，多个毛细管被随意放在蒸馏水上方的"派莱克斯"盘内，置于抽真空至 40 mm 汞柱并保温在 25℃ ±1℃ 的干燥器内。这就是利平科特等人 [3] 所采用的方式。其他冷凝实验是在下面的装置中进行的：为了减少在抽真空时水雾喷溅到毛细管中去的机会，人们把装置设计成在不受水影响的情况下就能对毛细管抽真空。在该装置中，毛细管室与水室用一个无润滑脂的真空阀分隔。先将水室抽成真空，此时关闭阀门并将毛细管放入另一个样品室。然后再将毛细管室抽成真空，切断和泵的联系后开启与水的联系。

在毛细管暴露于水蒸气中 3 天 ~ 10 天之后对其进行检验。要取出供分析用的冷凝液，需用气密性的注射器和注射针凭借气压将液体排出。用一滴熔融的纯净石

purified paraffin. The condensate was expelled on to steel mirror surfaces and the residue examined by light microscopy. For electron probe analysis a pure, low-silicon copper was used instead of steel. The electron probe was an Applied Research Laboratory EMX 200. Infrared spectroscopic determinations were made with a Perkin–Elmer 457 spectrometer.

Silicon and Sodium in Condensate

Condensate was observed in both "Pyrex" and silica capillaries held over distilled water. For the capillaries in the desiccators the yield (number of capillaries with condensate) was about 50 percent. In the two-chamber apparatus the yield was 10–25 percent. Fig. 1A illustrates the appearance of condensate columns viewed with a reflected light microscope. When these capillaries were put in an evacuated chamber or left at 40–50 percent relative humidity for a few hours, most of the condensate evaporated except for a residue with a gel-like appearance. In Fig. 1B the gel had formed before the liquid phase had fully evaporated.

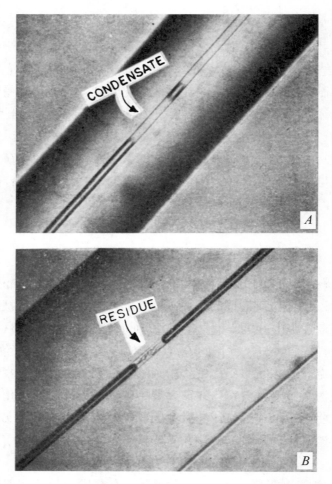

Fig. 1. Appearance of water condensate in a silica capillary immediately after removal from desiccator (A) and after most of condensate had evaporated (B). Capillary inner diameter is about 30 μm.

蜡将针头密封于毛细管中。在钢镜表面上排出冷凝液，并用光学显微镜观察残余物。对于电子探针分析，则要用一块纯净的低硅铜代替钢。所用的电子探针为应用研究实验室的 EMX 200。红外光谱测定是在珀金－埃尔默公司的 457 型光谱仪上进行的。

冷凝液中的硅和钠

我们对蒸馏水上方的石英毛细管和"派莱克斯"毛细管中的冷凝液都进行了观测。对于干燥器中的毛细管，产率（有冷凝液的毛细管的数量）约为 50%。在双样品室装置中，产率为 10% ~ 25%。图 1A 中显示的是用反射光显微镜观察到的冷凝液柱外观。将这些毛细管置于抽真空的样品室中或者在 40% ~ 50% 的相对湿度下放置数小时后，大部分冷凝液将挥发，只剩下一种凝胶状的残余物。从图 1B 中可以看出，凝胶是在液相完全挥发前形成的。

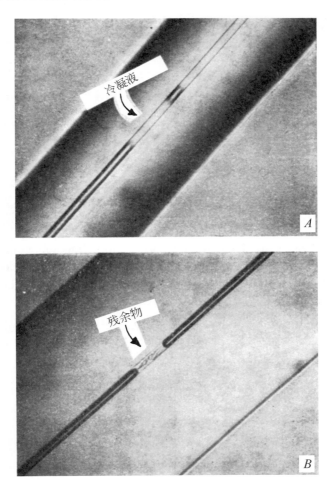

图 1. 石英毛细管中的冷凝水外观：(A) 刚刚从干燥器中取出和 (B) 大部分冷凝液挥发后。毛细管内径约为 30 μm。

Much of the condensate evaporated very rapidly when expelled on to steel mirror surfaces, leaving behind minute films of residue, some of which have a particulate appearance (Fig. 2). Close examination revealed that many had ridges near the edge, indicating a profile such as in Fig. 3.

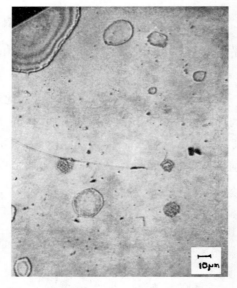

Fig. 2. Residues left by condensate formed in "Pyrex" and expelled on to a steel mirror.

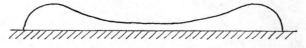

Fig. 3. Residue profile.

Residues from condensate in silica usually had a more homogeneous appearance (Fig. 4) than those from "Pyrex". The only particles that could be clearly associated with the silica derived residues are those clustered at the centre in Fig. 4. Other particles in the photograph are dust.

　　大部分冷凝液在被排出到钢镜表面上后挥发得很快，只留下少量的残余物薄层，其中一些具有微粒状的外观（图 2）。在仔细检查后发现：很多残余物的边缘附近有隆起，其侧面类似于图 3。

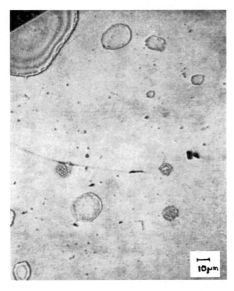

图 2. 在"派莱克斯"毛细管中形成的冷凝液被排出至钢镜表面上后留下的残余物。

图 3. 残余物的侧面。

　　在石英毛细管中形成的冷凝液残余物所具有的外观通常比在"派莱克斯"毛细管中形成的冷凝液残余物更均一（图 4）。唯一的一些可以确定为与源自石英毛细管的残余物明显相关的颗粒就是聚集在图 4 中心部位的那些。照片中的其他颗粒都是微尘。

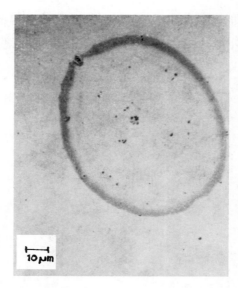

Fig. 4. Residue from condensate formed in silica and expelled on to a steel mirror.

Electron probe analysis of the residues from "Pyrex" revealed sodium and silicon in easily detectable amounts. Sodium was most strongly evident in the particulate matter within the residue and the silicon level was highest near the edge. These analyses were not pursued in detail because the corrosion of pristine glass surfaces is well known and the presence of sodium and silicon was not unexpected.

The residues from condensate in silica were thinner and therefore more difficult to analyse than the residues from "Pyrex". Nonetheless, the electron probe revealed significant levels of sodium and silicon in the thicker regions near the edges. Fig. 5A shows the secondary electron emission for such a region and B shows the silicon X-ray (SiK_α 7.1252) emission from this same region. The silicon level in this residue is about four times the background level. The relative intensities for silicon and sodium were approximately equal.

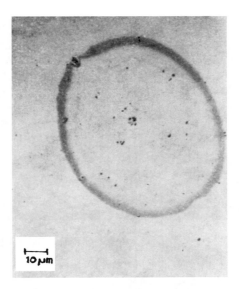

图 4. 在石英毛细管中形成的冷凝液被排出到钢镜表面上后留下的残余物。

　　对源自"派莱克斯"毛细管的残余物进行电子探针分析，结果发现很容易检测到钠和硅。钠在残余物内部的微粒状物质里非常常见，而硅在靠近边缘处含量最高。我们没有对上述分析结果进行仔细的追查，因为大家都知道洁净玻璃表面的腐蚀问题，而存在钠和硅并不令人感到意外。

　　在石英毛细管中形成的冷凝液的残余物会比较薄一些，因而比源自"派莱克斯"毛细管的残余物更难于分析。不过，电子探针在边缘附近的较厚区域中探测到了一定量的钠和硅。图 5A 显示出这一区域的次级电子发射，而图 5B 则是来自同一区域的硅 X 射线（SiK$_\alpha$ 7.1252）发射。这种残余物中的硅水平大约是背景水平的 4 倍。硅和钠的相对强度是大致相等的。

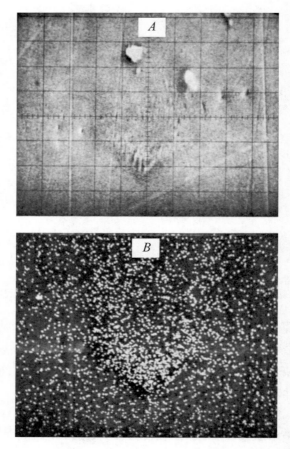

Fig. 5. Electron probe secondary electron emission (*A*) and silicon. X-ray emission (*B*) for a residue of condensate from silica. Cu substrate.

Residues of dilute sodium silicate solutions also showed the annular profile drawn in Fig. 3. Analysis of these residues with the electron probe revealed that it was often impossible to detect significant amounts of sodium or silicon in the thin central regions. For example, in Fig. 6 the silicon X-ray emission is displayed for a section of a sodium silicate residue left by a 0.1 µl. drop or a 0.1 percent solution. The arc of the rim clearly shows emission due to silicon but no significant emission is observed for the central region even though material was visible with the light microscope.

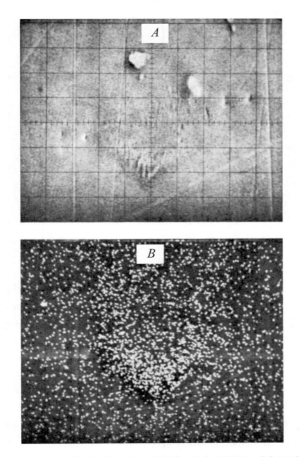

图 5. 在石英毛细管中形成的冷凝液的残余物 (A) 电子探针次级电子发射和 (B) 硅X射线发射。铜基质。

　　硅酸钠稀溶液的残余物也显示出如图 3 所描绘的环形轮廓。用电子探针对这些残余物进行分析后发现，在薄的中心区域通常很难探测到显著量的钠或者硅。例如，图 6 中显示的是由一滴 0.1 μl 或 0.1% 硅酸钠溶液挥发后残余物的一部分所产生的硅 X 射线发射。边缘的弧形显然表明发射源自于硅，但在中心区域却没有观测到任何显著的发射，尽管利用光学显微镜是可以看到中心区域有物质存在的。

Fig. 6. Electron probe silicon X-ray emission for a sector of a residue left by a drop of sodium silicate solution. Cu substrate.

We conclude from the electron probe results that silicon, sodium and possibly other cations are important if not principal constituents of these condensate residues. Failure to detect these elements in earlier work[3] may have occurred because the residues were too thin.

Infrared Spectra of "Polywater"

If silicates are part of the condensate, then it is possible to offer an alternative explanation for the infrared spectra of "polywater". Silicate solutions are quite alkaline and are thus capable of absorbing CO_2 from the atmosphere. The principal bands in the "polywater" spectrum are at 1,600 cm^{-1} and 1,400 cm^{-1} which are close to the frequencies for the antisymmetric and symmetric O–C–O stretching vibrations. To test this idea infrared spectra were obtained for residues left by drops of bicarbonate–silicate solutions on Irtran 2 plates. A typical result is given in Fig. 7 for the residue from a solution containing 1.5 g/l. of sodium silicate (mole ratio SiO_2 : Na_2O = 3.3) and 2.6 g/l. of $KHCO_3$. The bands at 1,650, 1,400 and 830 cm^{-1} are caused by bicarbonate and these same bands can be seen in the polywater spectra[3,4]. The broad band at 1,200–1,000 cm^{-1} is caused by silicate and the one between 3,700 cm^{-1} and 2,200 cm^{-1} is probably from residual water.

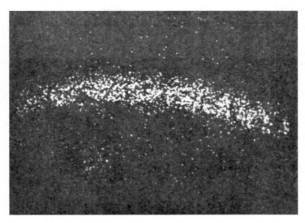

图 6. 由一滴硅酸钠溶液挥发后残余物的一部分所产生的电子探针硅X射线发射。铜基质。

我们根据电子探针的结果可以得出以下结论：硅、钠和其他可能的阳离子即使不是这些冷凝液残余物的主要成分，也会是有很大影响的成分。在早期的研究 [3] 中可能出现过检测不到这些元素的情况，因为残余物太薄了。

"聚合水"的红外光谱

如果硅酸盐是冷凝液的一部分，那么它就有可能为"聚合水"的红外光谱提供另外一种解释。硅酸盐溶液有较强的碱性，因而能够从大气中吸收 CO_2。"聚合水"光谱中的主要谱带位于 1,600 cm^{-1} 和 1,400 cm^{-1}，与反对称和对称 O–C–O 伸缩振动的频率接近。为了验证硅酸盐就是冷凝液的一部分，我们对数滴被置于艾尔特兰 II 样品板上的碳酸氢盐 – 硅酸盐溶液残余物进行了红外光谱测定。图 7 中显示出了一个典型的结果，即来自含 1.5 g/l 硅酸钠（摩尔比 SiO_2：Na_2O = 3.3）和 2.6 g/l KHCO$_3$ 溶液的残余物的红外光谱。位于 1,650 cm^{-1}、1,400 cm^{-1} 和 830 cm^{-1} 的谱带是由碳酸氢盐产生的，在聚合水的光谱中也能看到同样的谱带 [3,4]。位于 1,200 cm^{-1} ～ 1,000 cm^{-1} 的宽谱带是由硅酸盐产生的，而在 3,700 cm^{-1} 和 2,200 cm^{-1} 之间的宽谱带则可能来自残余的水分。

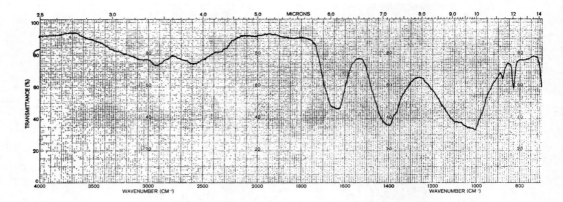

Fig. 7. Infrared spectrum of residue of a sodium bicarbonate–silicate mixture.

The spectrum given in Fig. 7 differs from the spectra reported for "polywater", just as the "polywater" spectra differ themselves[3,4]. After a study of the infrared spectra of a variety of bicarbonate–silicate mixtures, the reasons for these differences in the spectra became clear. It was found that the band intensities, positions and shapes were a function of (*a*) total solids concentration, (*b*) ratio of silicate to bicarbonate, (*c*) mole ratio of Na_2O and SiO_2, (*d*) age of the solution and the residue, (*e*) the rate and manner in which the solution dries, and (*f*) the presence of other anions or cations. It is believed that different combinations of these factors gave rise to the observed spectra. For example, the band at 1,650 cm^{-1} in Fig. 7 does not correspond exactly with the 1,600 cm^{-1} band for "polywater"[3,4]. When the bicarbonate–silicate residues were aged for a few days, however, there was a detectable shift of the band to 1,625 cm^{-1} and sometimes lower.

Origin of Silicate Anion

In these experiments the silicate anion could easily originate from a surface corrosion of the capillary walls. The surface hydrolysis of silicate glasses, especially pristine (freshly formed) surfaces, is well known[5]. The process involves the hydration of cationic sites to form an alkaline film capable of hydrolysing the silicate network. Frazer *et al.*[6] describe water adsorption on the inside of freshly blown glass bulbs and observed a visible condensate which they found to be strongly alkaline. They were also able to show that the alkaline film had left the surface rough and porous.

In the case of condensate from silica capillaries, the electron probe gave clear evidence of sodium as well as silicon which implies contamination because the silica itself does not contain significant amounts of sodium. The principal source of this contamination was probably the glassware holding the capillaries; the formation of a mist or spray from the water during pump-down is believed negligible, especially in the two chamber apparatus. Contamination from the glassware would occur if a water film sufficient to allow surface diffusion or creep of electrolyte on to and into the capillaries developed on the walls. In this connexion, it was noted that in all the condensation experiments there was clear evidence of moisture on the walls of the apparatus, formed, no doubt, during small

322

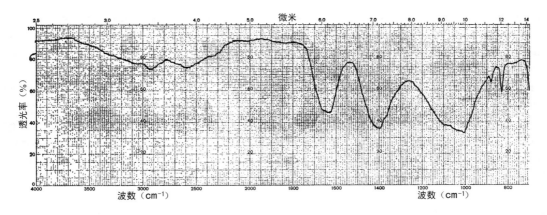

图 7. 碳酸氢钠–硅酸钠混合液残余物的红外光谱。

图 7 中给出的光谱与所报道的"聚合水"光谱不尽相同，就像"聚合水"之间的光谱也会有所不同一样 [3,4]。在对多种碳酸氢盐 – 硅酸盐混合物进行红外光谱研究之后，我们逐渐明确了产生光谱差异的原因。我们发现谱带强度、位置和形状与下列因素有关联：(a) 总的固体浓度，(b) 硅酸盐与碳酸氢盐的比例，(c) Na_2O 与 SiO_2 的摩尔比，(d) 溶液和残余物的存在时间，(e) 溶液变干的速率和方式，以及 (f) 是否存在其他阴离子或阳离子。我们认为，观测到的光谱就是在上述因素的不同组合下形成的。例如，图 7 中位于 1,650 cm⁻¹ 处的谱带并非精确地对应于"聚合水"的 1,600 cm⁻¹ 谱带 [3,4]。不过，在将碳酸氢盐 – 硅酸盐溶液残余物放置数天之后，会发现谱带位移到了 1,625 cm⁻¹ 处，有时甚至还会位移至更低。

硅酸根阴离子的来源

在聚合水实验中，由毛细管壁的表面腐蚀很容易生成硅酸根阴离子。众所周知，硅酸盐玻璃表面，尤其是洁净（新形成的）表面会发生水解 [5]。该过程涉及阳离子位点的水合作用从而形成一层能水解硅酸盐网络的碱性膜。弗雷泽等人 [6] 曾描述过新吹制玻璃泡内部的吸附水情况，他们观测到了一种具有强碱性的可见冷凝液。他们还指出，碱性膜会使表面变得粗糙多孔。

对源自石英毛细管的冷凝液来说，由电子探针结果可以很清楚地证明其中含有钠和硅，这表明有污染存在，因为石英本身不会包含显著量的钠。这种污染物的主要来源很可能是盛放毛细管的玻璃器具；在抽真空的过程中，由水形成的喷雾或者飞沫被认为是可以忽略的，尤其是在使用双样品室的装置时。如果器具壁上形成的水膜足以允许电解质通过表面扩散或滑移到达毛细管的表面和内部，那么来自玻璃器具的污染就会出现。就这一点来说，我们注意到，在所有冷凝实验中都可以找到明确的证据证明，装置壁上的水汽无疑是在室温的微小涨落过程中形成的。此外，

fluctuations in the room temperature. Moreover, if the "Pyrex" dish holding the capillaries was replaced with a polyethylene dish where the surface creep should be much reduced, the yield dropped from the usual 50 to about 15 percent.

Undoubtedly the contaminating salts can contribute to the corrosion of the pristine silica surface but, even with silica, such contamination may not be essential. Silica surfaces offer Si–OH groups for water adsorption and at monolayer coverage and higher ($P/P_0 > 0.4$) the film is mobile[7]. This film is also acidic, for conductivity studies indicate the charge carrier is H^+ or H_3O^+[7]. An acid-catalysed surface corrosion may therefore occur, especially on a pristine surface in which many Si–O–Si bonds are strained.

Initially, the corrosion product of silica or "Pyrex" would be silicic acid (or metal silicate) which would condense quickly into a colloidal silicate sol and ultimately to a colloidal gel if the solution is dried. Many of the properties attributed to "polywater", such as the gel-like appearance[3,8] and the birefringence[8,9] of the condensate residues, certainly suggest silicate. The high refractive indices reported for polywater[9] are also consistent with silicate solutions containing high proportions of metal cation[10].

The results reported here offer alternative explanations for the "polywater" phenomena. Samples of "anomalous water" prepared by the technique of Deryagin and co-workers have not yet been studied. They obtained condensate in very pure silica capillaries held in a platinum fixture with distilled water as the source of vapour[1]. This experiment would seem to remove any possibility of contamination by electrolyte. An acid-catalysed corrosion of pristine silica by adsorbed water alone, however, may lead to a silica sol, which could explain many of the anomalous properties they observed. We now hope to repeat these experiments and analyse the condensate.

(**228**, 1290-1293; 1970)

Willard D. Bascom, Edward J. Brooks and Bradford N. Worthington, III: Naval Research Laboratory, Washington, DC 20390.

Received June 10, 1970.

References:

1. Deryagin, B. V., Talaev, M. V., and Fedyakin, N. N., *Dokl. Phys. Chem.*, **165**, 807 (1965).

2. Deryagin, B. V., *Discussion Faraday Soc.*, **42**, 109 (1966).

3. Lippincott, E. R., Stromberg, R. R., Grant, W. H., and Cessac, G. L., *Science*, **164**, 1482 (1969).

4. Page, T. F., Jakobsen, R. J., and Lippincott, E. R., *Science*, **167**, 51 (1970).

5. Holland, L., *The Properties of Glass Surfaces*, chap. 3 (Wiley, New York, 1964).

6. Frazer, J. C. W., Patrick, W. A., and Smith, H. E., *J. Phys. Chem.*, **31**, 897 (1927).

7. Friplat, J. J., Jelli, A., Poncelet, G., and Andre, F., *J. Phys. Chem.*, **69**, 2185 (1965).

8. Willis, E., Rennie, G. K., Smart, C., and Pethica, B. A., *Nature*, **222**, 159 (1969).

9. Castellion, G. A., Grabar, D. G., Hession, J., and Burkhard, H., *Science*, **167**, 865 (1970).

10. Debye, P., and Nauman, R., *J. Phys. Chem.*, **65**, 8 (1961).

如果将盛放毛细管的"派莱克斯"盘替换成表面滑移可大幅减少的聚乙烯盘，产率就会从通常情况下的 50% 下降到约 15%。

毫无疑问，作为污染物的盐类会使洁净石英表面发生腐蚀，但就算石英毛细管表面存在盐类，这种污染恐怕也不是决定性的。石英表面具有适于吸附水的 Si–OH 基团，而且在单分子层或者更多分子层（$P/P_0 > 0.4$）覆盖的情况下，水膜是可以移动的 [7]。这种膜也是酸性的，因为电导性研究结果显示电荷载体为 H^+ 或者 H_3O^+ [7]。因此，一种酸催化的表面腐蚀可能会发生，尤其是在洁净表面上存在大量变形的 Si–O–Si 键时。

石英或者"派莱克斯"的初始腐蚀产物是硅酸（或者金属硅酸盐），它会快速凝结为胶状硅酸盐溶胶，并且最终在溶液变干时转变成胶状凝胶。"聚合水"的很多性质，如凝胶状外观 [3,8] 和冷凝后残余物的双折射性质 [8,9] 等都明确表明它是硅酸盐。所报道的聚合水高折射率 [9] 也与含高比例金属阳离子的硅酸盐溶液的性质相一致 [10]。

这里所报道的结果为"聚合水"现象提供了另外一些解释。我们还没有对利用杰里亚金及其同事们的技术制备出的"反常水"样品进行过研究。他们用蒸馏水作为蒸气源在由铂夹具固定的极纯石英毛细管中得到了冷凝液 [1]。这项实验似乎排除了任何由电解质带来污染的可能性。不过，仅仅因为吸收水分而导致洁净石英表面出现的酸催化腐蚀就有产生硅溶胶的可能性，从而可以解释他们观测到的很多反常性质。现在我们希望重复这些实验并对冷凝液进行分析。

（王耀杨 翻译；李芝芬 审稿）

Human Blastocysts Grown in Culture

P. C. Steptoe *et al.*

Editor's Note

Several months after they reported the successful production of eight- and sixteen-celled human embryos through *in vitro* fertilization (IVF), Patrick Steptoe, Robert Edwards and Jean Purdy report further advances. Improved tissue culture techniques meant the team were now able to keep their IVF embryos alive for longer. Two out of six IVF embryos developed into blastocysts— thin-walled hollow structures containing a cluster of cells called the inner cell mass from which the embryo can arise. Development to this key embryonic stage was seen as an important step along the pathway to producing the first human IVF birth, which took another seven years.

WE have already described the culture of cleaving human embryos to the sixteen celled stage[1], and we now wish to give details of a few embryos that have developed much further, including two that reached fully developed blastocysts. Methods were similar to those described before. Preovulatory oocytes recovered by laparoscopy[2] were fertilized in Bavister's medium[3], and transferred after 12–15 h into Ham's F 10 supplemented with human or foetal calf serum. Preliminary details of this work have been presented elsewhere[4].

Six embryos were cultured. The pH of the medium was 7.3, the osmotic pressure 300 mOsmol/kg, and the gas phase consisted of 5% oxygen, 5% carbon dioxide and 90% nitrogen. Two of the embryos developed to early morulae, one having more than twenty-three nuclei, and the other twenty-nine nuclei and one mitosis. After the sixteen cell stage, the blastomeres of these embryos became slightly mottled and the cell outlines were less distinct—an appearance similar to that found in many mouse morulae.

A blastocoelic cavity appeared in four embryos. In two of them, the cavity was small and eccentric and the inner cell mass and trophoblast failed to become fully differentiated. Staining revealed only sixteen and twenty nuclei in the two embryos. The small number of cells indicated that division had become out of step with the early development of the blastocoel. Two embryos which developed through typical morulae into fully expanded blastocysts will be described separately.

After 123 h culture in Ham's F 10 with 20% foetal calf serum, irregular light patches appeared throughout the tissue of one morula (blastocyst 1). Eleven hours later, a large blastocoelic cavity was seen, with thin cellular membranes traversing part of it. The cavity became increasingly clear as differentiation continued. After 147 h in culture, the blastocyst was greatly expanded, and apart from one small vesicle the blastocoelic cavity was completely clear. The zona pellucida was thin and stretched, and the trophoblast

在培养基中生长的人类囊胚

斯特普托等

编者按

就在帕特里克·斯特普托、罗伯特·爱德华兹和琼·珀迪报道怎样通过体外受精（IVF）成功获得 8 细胞和 16 细胞人类胚胎的几个月后，他们又报道了一些新的进展。对组织培养技术的改进意味着他们现在已经能够延长体外受精胚胎的存活期。在 6 个体外受精的胚胎中有 2 个发育成了囊胚——一种由被称为内细胞团的一组细胞组成的薄壁中空结构，由此可以产生胚胎。发育到这一关键胚胎发育阶段被认为是通往成功获得第一个人类试管婴儿的重要步骤，7 年之后世界上第一个试管婴儿诞生。

我们已经描述过怎样将卵裂中的人类胚胎培养到 16 细胞阶段 [1]，现在我们想详细描述一些生长到更靠后阶段的胚胎，其中有两个已经完全发育到了囊胚阶段。所用的方法和以前描述过的类似：将由腹腔镜手术获得的排卵前卵母细胞 [2] 放在巴维斯特培养基 [3] 中受精，在 12 小时~ 15 小时后转移到添加人血清或者胎牛血清的哈姆氏 F 10 培养基中。我们已经把这项研究的初步结果发表在了其他出版物上 [4]。

一共培养了 6 个胚胎。培养基的 pH 值为 7.3，渗透压为 300 毫渗摩 / 千克，而气相由 5% O_2、5% CO_2 和 90% N_2 组成。有两个胚胎生长到了早期桑葚胚，其中一个的细胞核超过了 23 个，而另一个含有 29 个细胞核和一个有丝分裂相。经过 16 细胞阶段之后，这些胚胎的卵裂球变得轻度杂色且细胞轮廓变得不那么清晰了——外观与在很多小鼠桑葚胚中看到的情形类似。

在 4 个胚胎中出现了囊胚腔。其中有两个囊胚腔很小并且是偏心的，其内细胞团和滋养层未能发生完全的分化。染色结果显示，在这两个胚胎中分别只有 16 和 20 个细胞核。这么少的细胞数量说明细胞分裂已经和囊胚腔的早期发育变得不一致了。下面我们将分别描述那两个经过典型的桑葚胚发育至完全膨胀的囊胚的胚胎。

用含有 20% 胎牛血清的哈姆氏 F10 培养基培养 123 小时后，我们发现在其中一个桑葚胚（囊胚 1）的组织内各部分均出现了不规则的光斑。11 小时之后，可以看到一个巨大的囊胚腔，其中的一部分被细胞形成的薄膜所穿过。随着分化的进行，囊胚腔变得越来越清晰。培养 147 小时后，囊胚充分膨胀，除了一个小的囊泡以外，囊胚腔已完全清晰。透明带很薄并处于被拉伸的状态，紧贴在透明带下方的滋养层

formed a clear layer of cells immediately beneath the zona. The blastocoel occupied three-quarters or more of the embryo, and the inner cell mass was distinct—far more so than is usual in mouse blastocysts. Giant cell transformation was not seen, but the embryo was not examined sufficiently closely to ensure that it had not occurred. The blastocyst was cultured for a further 2 h in its original medium plus 5 µg/ml. of "Colcemid". During this period the blastocyst contracted away from the zona, making it unsuitable for photography.

The blastocyst was placed in 1% sodium citrate for 2 min and fixed in fresh acetic methanol[5]. After staining with aceto-orcein, it was found to possess 112 nuclei and at least sixteen mitoses (Fig. 1). Several of the mitoses overlapped in the region of the inner cell mass and were unscoreable. Others were discrete but insufficiently spread so that we could only estimate that they were probably diploid.

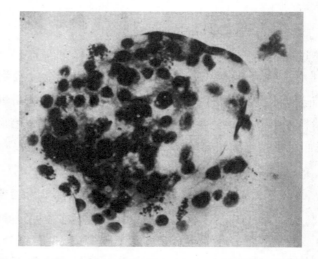

Fig. 1. Stained preparation of blastocyst 1. Many mitoses can be seen over the region of the inner cell mass (lower right) and a few elsewhere. The nuclei are even-sized.

The second blastocyst (blastocyst 2) developed approximately 24 h after the other. It was cultured in Ham's F 10 containing 25% human and 25% foetal calf serum. A blastocoelic cavity appeared after 159 h in culture. This cavity corresponded with that seen in the early stages of expansion in blastocyst 1, but the cell membranes traversing it were more pronounced and persisted for 12 h. Some of the trophoblastic cells had evidently failed to release their contents into the blastocoel. The thin zona pellucida and the shape of the inner cell mass were similar to those seen in blastocyst 1. Small extensions, somewhat resembling those seen in guinea-pig blastocysts[6], seemed to be passing through the zona pellucida (Fig. 2).

会形成一个清晰的细胞层。囊胚腔占据了胚胎体积的 3/4 甚至更多，而内细胞团很清晰——远远超过了通常在小鼠囊胚中所见到的清晰度。没有看到巨细胞转化，但因为我们对胚胎的观察不足够仔细，所以不能确定是否真的没有发生过。在原来的培养基中加入 5 微克 / 毫升"秋水仙酰胺"后再将囊胚继续培养 2 小时。在此期间，囊胚会因收缩而远离透明带，所以不适合拍照。

　　将囊胚在 1% 的柠檬酸钠中放置 2 分钟，并用新鲜的醋酸 – 甲醇固定[5]。经醋酸 – 地衣红染色后，我们发现它含有 112 个细胞核和至少 16 个有丝分裂相（图 1）。有几个分裂相在内细胞团区域重叠，因此无法对其作出判断。另一些虽然是相互分离的，但没有充分展开，因此我们只能猜测它们有可能是二倍体。

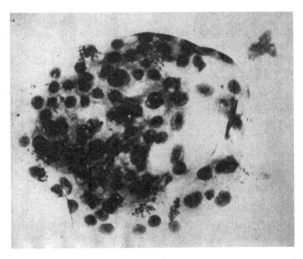

　　图 1. 染色的囊胚 1 标本。在内细胞团区域（右下方）以及其他一些区域可以看到许多有丝分裂相。细
　　　　胞核的大小是均一的。

　　第二个囊胚（囊胚 2）的发育时间比第一个囊胚晚大约 24 小时。它是在含 25%人血清和 25% 胎牛血清的哈姆氏 F 10 培养基中培养出来的。培养 159 小时后囊胚腔出现。这个囊胚腔与我们在囊胚 1 膨胀阶段早期所见到的囊胚腔相同，但是穿越它的细胞性膜更加明显并且持续了 12 小时之久。一些滋养层细胞显然未能将它们的内容物释放到囊胚腔内。薄薄的透明带和内细胞团的形态与在囊胚 1 中所见到的情况类似。一些小的且与在豚鼠囊胚中所见到的有些类似的延伸物[6]似乎穿过了透明带（图 2）。

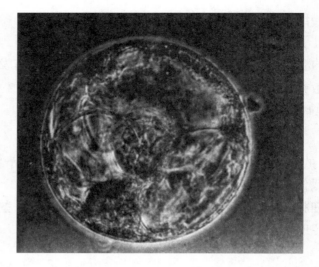

Fig. 2. Blastocyst 2 before it was fixed and stained. The thin zona pellucida and the underlying trophoblast can be seen; an extension is evidently emerging through the zona (at right). The inner cell mass (lower part of the embryo) is distinct. The cellular membranes persisting across the blastocoel can be seen.

The embryo was kept at room temperature for several hours before staining. It was found to have 110 nuclei. Bodies resembling sex chromatin were seen in a few nuclei.

We seem to have achieved this improved embryonic development through better handling of the cultures than previously. The preovulatory oocytes were kept at room temperature under reduced oxygen tension and 5% carbon dioxide until the spermatozoa were added. Small microdrops were used for culture, and enlarged when the embryos were eight celled. The embryos were left undisturbed for long periods after this stage.

We thank the Ford Foundation, the Oldham and District Hospitals Management Committee and the Manchester Regional Hospital Board for financial support, Mr. C. Richardson for photography and Professor C. R. Austin for encouragement.

(**229**, 132-133; 1971)

P. C. Steptoe, R. G. Edwards and J. M. Purdy: Oldham General Hospital, Lancashire, and Physiological Laboratory, University of Cambridge.

Received November 18, 1970.

References:

1. Edwards, R. G., Steptoe, P. C., and Purdy, J. M., *Nature*, **227**, 1307 (1970).

2. Steptoe, P. C., and Edwards, R. G., *Lancet*, i, 683 (1970).

3. Bavister, B. D., *J. Reprod. Fert.*, **18**, 544 (1969).

4. Edwards, R. G., *Harold C. Mack Symposium on the Biology of Fertilization and Implantation*, Detroit, October 1970 (in the press).

5. Tarkowski, A. K., *Cytogenetics*, **5**, 394 (1966).

6. Amoroso, E. C., *Memoirs of the Society for Endocrinology*, **6**, 50 (1959).

图 2. 在被固定和染色之前的囊胚 2。可以看到薄薄的透明带和位于其下的滋养层。显然有一条延伸物穿过了透明带（在右侧）。内细胞团（胚胎的下半部分）很清晰。可以看到一些由细胞形成的膜横穿过囊胚腔。

在染色前几小时，胚胎一直被保存在室温下。我们发现它含有 110 个细胞核。在若干个细胞核内可以见到类似于性染色质的小体。

看来，我们是通过较以往更好的处理方法达到了这一更靠后的胚胎发育阶段。在加入精子之前，排卵前的卵母细胞一直被保存在室温、较低氧分压及含 5% CO_2 的环境中。用小的微滴进行培养，并在胚胎达到 8 细胞期时扩大微滴的大小。在这一阶段之后很长时间内就不再干扰胚胎发育了。

感谢福特基金会、奥尔德姆地区综合医院管理委员会以及曼彻斯特地区医院理事会为我们提供了资金上的支持，还要感谢理查森先生对此进行拍照以及奥斯汀教授对我们的鼓励。

（毛晨晖 翻译；王敏康 审稿）

The DNA Replication Mystery

Editor's Note

Although by the early 1970s molecular biology was busily working out the functioning of important cellular components, the question of how DNA itself is replicated was unanswered. This News and Views article written by the staff of *Nature* is concerned with an enzyme called polymerase I, isolated from the bacterium *E. coli*, but, as the second paragraph of this article explains, the properties of the enzyme could not adequately account for the replication of DNA. Luckily, a second enzyme, polymerase II, was discovered by De Lucia and Cairns. Polymerase I was at the same time recognised to be an enzyme involved in the repair of mismatched sequences of DNA.

AS a group, molecular biologists have never fought shy of publicity and their propagandists have fed the popular image of the juggernaut subject advancing by enormous strides on all fronts. All fronts bar one, which is usually glossed over; for, although anybody reared on the current rash of molecular biology texts might be excused for thinking otherwise, the precise mechanism by which DNA is duplicated is almost as obscure today as ever.

To be sure, in the nineteen sixties Kornberg and his collaborators isolated from *Escherichia coli* an enzyme which can polymerize DNA and, for example, replicate infectious bacteriophage DNA *in vitro*. And until last year this enzyme, DNA polymerase I, was the only known enzyme with this capability. Small wonder therefore that many molecular biologists bent over backwards devising all sorts of ingenious schemes to explain how it might replicate DNA *in vivo*. But they laboured under one great disadvantage and probably in vain, for the properties of polymerase I (it makes DNA very slowly, it can only synthesize DNA in one, the 5' to 3' direction, and it is an effective exonuclease) are those expected of a DNA repair enzyme rather than a replicase. In other words, polymerase I has all the properties of an enzyme which edits DNA sequences, excising regions of mismatched base pairs and replacing them with the correct sequence, rather than replicates them.

The days of tortuous scheming are, however, over; the pressure is off polymerase I for two related reasons. First, at the end of 1969 De Lucia and Cairns isolated six mutant *E. coli* which lack or contain defective polymerase I but nonetheless survive and replicate their DNA normally. Second, several groups have detected and begun to isolate a second DNA polymerase, polymerase II, in these mutants. With at least two candidates at last in the lists, those molecular biologists concerned with defining the mechanism of DNA duplication are

DNA复制之谜

编者按

尽管在20世纪70年代初以前，分子生物学家们一直忙于研究重要细胞组分的功能，但人们对于DNA自身如何复制这一问题仍不清楚。这篇"新闻与观点"栏目中的文章是由《自然》杂志的编辑撰写的，文中提到一种从大肠杆菌中分离出来的被称为聚合酶I的酶。但是，正如本文第二段中所阐释的，该酶的性能不足以充分说明DNA的复制。幸运的是，德卢西亚和凯恩斯发现了第二种酶——聚合酶II。与此同时，人们认识到聚合酶I是一种参与DNA序列错配修复的酶。

作为一个群体，分子生物学家们从来不回避公众，他们的宣传员们在人们心目中塑造了分子生物学这个无往而不胜的主题正在各个前沿领域阔步前进的形象。但有一个前沿领域例外，而该领域常常被掩饰过去，因为任何一个受现有尚不成熟的分子生物学教科书所培养的人另有不同想法。虽然这是情有可原的，但人们对DNA复制精确机制的认识直至今天仍是一如既往地模糊不清。

诚然，在20世纪60年代，科恩伯格及其合作者们从大肠杆菌中分离出了一种酶，它能聚合DNA，譬如在体外复制出具有感染力的噬菌体DNA。而且直到去年，DNA聚合酶I还是已知的唯一一种具有这种能力的酶。因此，无怪乎许多分子生物学家回过头来想尽办法设计出各种别出心裁的方案以解释它怎样才可能在体内复制DNA。但是，他们的劳动处于一个相当大的不利因素之下，甚至很可能会徒劳无功：因为聚合酶I的特性（复制DNA的速度很慢，只能按一种方向——$5' \to 3'$方向合成DNA，并且是一种有效的核酸外切酶）表明：与其说它是一种DNA复制酶，倒不如说它是DNA修复酶。换言之，聚合酶I具有一个能编辑DNA序列的酶所具有的所有特征：可以剪切有错配碱基对的区域，并替换上正确的序列，而不是复制它们。

然而，这种费尽心机的设计时代已经结束，用以下两个相关联的原因就可以解释人们为什么得以从聚合酶I的窘境中解放出来。首先，1969年末，德卢西亚和凯恩斯分离出了6株缺少聚合酶I或含有缺陷型聚合酶I的大肠杆菌突变株，但菌体仍能存活，并能正常复制DNA。其次，有好几个研究小组已经在这些突变株中检测到并着手分离出了第二种DNA聚合酶——聚合酶II。在那些致力于阐明DNA复制机制的分子生物学家们现在的研究清单上终于有了至少两个候选对象，他们目前

currently far more intent on characterizing DNA polymerase II and searching for further species of DNA polymerase than on striving to accommodate polymerase I in hypothetical schemes of DNA replication. Few of them would now quarrel with the statement that the chief and probably sole function of polymerase I is DNA repair. If there are any waverers still sitting on the fence they should be finally decided by what Kelley and Whitfield have to say, on page 33 of this issue of *Nature*, about one of the six mutants isolated by De Lucia and Cairns.

De Lucia and Cairns, when they began their mutant hunt, argued that if polymerase I is a repair enzyme it should be possible to select mutant *E. coli* with a defective repair mechanism, because of a defective polymerase I, but still capable of normal DNA replication. They proved their point by isolating six such mutants, the first of which to be characterized proved to be an amber mutant. But although these strains lacked polymerase I activity and were unusually sensitive to ultraviolet light, there was no proof that the mutations were actually in the structural gene which specifies polymerase I. It might, for example, still be argued that the mutations were in a regulatory gene and result in a drastic reduction in the amount of polymerase I made. If that were the case, the handful of perfectly normal polymerase I molecules might all be sequestered immediately for DNA replication, which would proceed normally, leaving none available for DNA repair.

Because of such arguments it became a matter of considerable importance to find proof that any one of the six mutants De Lucia and Cairns isolated (all those mapped so far are in the same gene) contain a lesion in the structural gene directly specifying polymerase I. For, clearly, if the enzyme moleculd itself contains a mutation which reduces its capacity to polymerize DNA, and cells containing such mutant enzyme replicate their DNA but lack a repair mechanism, the straightforward conclusion is that the polymerase I is involved in repair but not replication. Of course, anybody absolutely determined to keep all options open could say that all the mutations by chance occur in that part of the polymerase I molecule, admittedly a large protein comprising about 1,000 amino-acids, which is involved in repair, leaving the part responsible for DNA replication intact. But that is surely less plausible.

Fortunately as Kelley and Whitfield have now convincingly shown, *pol 6*, one of the half dozen mutants, turns out to be a temperature sensitive mutation. They purified polymerase I from this mutant and wild type *E. coli* and compared the properties *in vitro* of the two enzyme. The wild type enzyme has the same activity at 37°C and 52°C and its optimum temperature is 55°C. By contrast the mutant enzyme had less activity at 52°C than 37°C and an optimum temperature of about 45°C. Further, the two enzymes differ in their response to various synthetic DNAs and, although immunologically similar, sensitive complement fixation tests at various temperatures indicate that they differ in precise conformation. In short, the *pol 6* mutation is in the structural gene specifying the enzyme. Polymerase I is therefore certainly involved in DNA repair, and although it is premature to state categorically that that is the enzyme's sole function, the odds are stacked very high against the idea that polymerase I has a role in DNA replication.

(**230**, 11-12; 1971)

更迫切要做的事情是：表征 DNA 聚合酶 II 的性质以及寻找其他种类的 DNA 聚合酶，而非极力设法让聚合酶 I 适应假想的 DNA 复制方案。现在，绝大多数分子生物学家都不会对以下陈述提出争议，即聚合酶 I 的主要功能是 DNA 修复，并且这很可能是它唯一的功能。如果还有摇摆不定者对此心存疑虑，相信等他们看了凯利和惠特菲尔德在本期《自然》杂志第 33 页上就德卢西亚和凯恩斯分离的 6 株突变体之一所发表的不得已的论述之后，就应该能作出最后的定论了。

当德卢西亚和凯恩斯开始寻找突变体的时候，他们主张：如果聚合酶 I 是一种修复酶，那么就应当可以筛选出一种由有缺陷的聚合酶 I 所导致的修复机制缺陷型大肠杆菌突变株，但这种突变体仍能进行正常的 DNA 复制。他们分离出了 6 株这样的突变体，从而证实了自己的观点，其中第一个被确认性质的突变体是一个琥珀突变体。然而，尽管这些突变株缺少聚合酶 I 的活性并对紫外线异常敏感，但仍无证据表明突变就发生在编码聚合酶 I 的结构基因中。譬如，仍有可能争论，突变是发生在调节基因上，从而导致制备的聚合酶 I 数量急剧降低。如果事实果真如此，那么少数几个完全正常的聚合酶 I 分子就有可能全部被马上分开以便于 DNA 复制，而在复制正常进行的情况下，也就再没有酶可供用于 DNA 修复了。

由于存在以上争论，所以找出证据证明德卢西亚和凯恩斯分离出的所有 6 株突变体（目前它们的突变体图谱都定位在同一个基因上）中的任意一株在直接编码聚合酶 I 的结构基因上存在缺陷就显得尤为重要了。因为显然，如果酶分子自身发生了一个能降低其聚合 DNA 能力的突变，并且含有这种突变酶的细胞能够复制 DNA 但却缺乏修复机制，那么就可以直截了当地得到结论：聚合酶 I 参与修复，而不参与复制。当然，那些决心非要穷尽一切可能性的人会说，所有的突变会恰巧发生在聚合酶 I 分子的某一部分，该部分是由 1,000 个氨基酸组成的大蛋白，这个大蛋白参与修复，而负责 DNA 复制的那部分蛋白则保持完整。但是，这种假设显然不太可能成立。

幸运的是，凯利和惠特菲尔德现在已经令人信服地证明了 6 株突变体中的 1 株——聚合酶 6 属于温度敏感型突变。他们对来自该突变型和野生型大肠杆菌中的聚合酶 I 进行了纯化，并比较了这两种酶的体外性质。野生型酶的活性在 37℃下和 52℃下是一致的，其最适温度为 55℃。相比之下，突变型酶在 52℃下的活性要低于在 37℃下的活性，并且其最适温度约为 45℃。此外，这两种酶对于各种人工合成的 DNA 的反应不同。尽管两者有相似的免疫特性，但在不同温度下的敏感补体结合实验表明，两者的精细构象并不相同。简言之，聚合酶 6 突变发生在编码这个酶的结构基因上。因此，聚合酶 I 肯定参与了 DNA 修复过程。尽管断言聚合酶 I 的唯一功能是参与 DNA 的修复为时尚早，但聚合酶 I 能在 DNA 复制中起到某种作用的观点几乎没有成立的可能性。

（吕静 翻译；顾孝诚 审稿）

Polywater and Polypollutants

P. Barnes *et al.*

Editor's Note

Here John Finney and his coworkers at Birkbeck seal the argument that "polywater" is water contaminated with impurities, rather than a new viscous form of pure water as claimed by its "discoverers", Boris Deryagin and coworkers in the Soviet Union. Finney was a student of J. Desmond Bernal, the eminent crystallographer who conducted pioneering work on the structure of water and ice and who helped introduce Deryagin's idea to the West. Finney himself went on to become an expert on water structure, and a hard-headed sceptic of claims that continued to arise about the exotic properties water might have. Despite this and other evidence that polywater was not real, Deryagin himself did not concede the matter until two years later.

THE concept of an entirely new species of water (known variously as polywater, water II, or anomalous water) owes its publicity principally to Deryagin[1] and his co-workers. Their conclusions have been based on their own experimental work on the physical properties of water condensates in fine glass capillaries, and also on the earlier indicative observations by independent workers (for example, ref. 2). Deryagin[1] in his latest article has reviewed his experimental work and confirmed that he still strongly believes in this new water species which, he claims, has abnormally high values for the molecular weight, viscosity (ten to twenty times greater), refractive index (1.48), boiling point (above 150°C) and anomalous density–temperature characteristics below room temperature. It has long been known that surface forces can greatly modify the properties of adjoining water layers. Deryagin himself could be said to be the principal pioneer of this work during the past 20 years or so, for which he has justifiably obtained universal recognition. It must be stressed, however, that his water II phenomenon is of a completely different order from this, for he claims that water II can exist independently of the surface from which it has been catalytically formed. He claims that it does not lose its anomalous properties unless vaporized above 700°C. In the early days of these investigations he discussed the problem with J. D. Bernal (early 1968) and of his difficulty in getting the work recognized. Bernal's continued ill-health prohibited him from doing any really active research himself on the topic, and he left it to us to carry out the investigations under his general guidance.

If Deryagin's chief contentions are correct, the problems facing the physical chemist are prodigious. He must interpret water II in terms of a completely new type of hydrogen bond which nevertheless can be easily formed during the condensation of slightly undersaturated vapours on to the appropriate surface. He must also explain why ordinary water—less stable than water II—is the predominant form in nature. Not surprisingly, Deryagin found it difficult to convince other scientists, and a man of lesser reputation

336

聚合水与聚合污染物

巴恩斯等

编者按

在本文中，约翰·芬尼和他在伯克贝克学院的同事们平息了有关"聚合水"的争论，他们认为聚合水是被杂质污染的水，并非如它的"发现者"——鲍里斯·杰里亚金及其在苏联的同事所描述的那样是纯净水的一种新的高黏度形式。芬尼是德斯蒙德·贝尔纳的学生，后者是对水和冰的结构进行过开创性研究的著名晶体学家，也是帮助把杰里亚金的想法引入西方的人。后来芬尼成为了一名水结构方面的专家，他对不断有人提出的水可能具有不寻常特性的看法一直持怀疑态度。虽然有这样那样的证据反对聚合水的存在，杰里亚金本人直到两年后才勉强承认自己的错误。

一种新类型水（有多种称呼，如聚合水、水 II 或者反常水）的概念能够如此普及主要归功于杰里亚金 [1] 和他的同事们。这一概念的得出是基于他们对水在细毛细玻璃管中冷凝液的物理性质的实验研究，以及早先由其他独立研究者所观察到的一些迹象（例如，参考文献 2）。杰里亚金 [1] 在最近发表的文章中回顾了他以往的实验结果，并坚定地说他仍然坚信这种新类型水的存在，他宣称：这种水的分子量、黏度（比正常水高 10 ~ 20 倍）、折射率（1.48）和沸点（高于 150℃）都超过了正常值，并且在低于室温时表现出反常的密度 – 温度特性。人们早就知道，表面张力可以显著改变相邻水层的性质。可以说，在过去的大约 20 年中，杰里亚金本人就是这项研究的主要先驱者之一，他也因此而获得了应有的名望。但是，必须强调的是，他的水 II 现象与上述情况完全不同，因为他声称水 II 能够独立于催化形成它的表面而存在。他宣称：只要水 II 不在超过 700℃时汽化，就不会失去自己的反常性质。在开展上述研究工作的早期，他曾与贝尔纳（1968 年初）探讨过这个问题，并谈及他在使研究结果获得认可时遇到的困难。当时贝尔纳的健康状况一直欠佳，这使他本人无法亲自进行关于这一主题的任何实质性研究，因此他委托我们在他的全面指导下完成调查工作。

如果杰里亚金的主要论点是正确的，那物理化学家将面临的问题就严重了。他们必须应用全新的氢键理论来解释水 II，这种氢键还得是当略微有点欠饱和的蒸气在适当表面上冷凝时能够顺利形成的。他们还必须解释，为什么稳定性不如水 II 的正常水会在自然界中占主导地位。所以我们对杰里亚金发现自己很难说服其他科学家一点也不感到奇怪，而一个名望不如他的人就更办不到了。不过，由于他不断地

337

would have surely failed to do so. However, his continued assertions led many groups in the western world (notably in Britain and the United States) to follow up his work. These groups produced results which seemed to both confirm and contradict his findings. Furthermore, several theoreticians (for example, refs. 3–9) actively pursued the problem of determining a suitable quantum mechanical picture for the new bonding required to explain the anomalous properties; needless to say, some of these models were highly speculative[10].

The evidence against the concept of water II has mostly accumulated very recently. Briefly, the contention is that the effects of even small amounts of certain impurities incorporated in the minute (say 10^{-10} to 10^{-5} g) samples have been underestimated. Deryagin's defence of water II may seem impressive, but we believe that his account gives, however unintentionally, an incomplete presentation of the facts, and in view of its possible wide influence we feel we must state clearly our findings. We therefore wish to explain how our work and of others have led us to reject water II as a real phenomenon, and to examine more critically some of the claims of Deryagin and his supporters.

The Phenomenon

Our investigations have been in progress for the past 2.5 years and we have used all known methods of production as well as introducing many modes of our own. Fuller details of this work are being prepared for publication later. (We have too much material to be included here, but some of our results have been mentioned by Hasted[11].) The degrees of anomality in our samples were determined chiefly from observations on (i) the phase separation effects[1], (ii) the gel-like residue obtained after evaporation, and (iii) the shape of the density–temperature curve obtained after certain corrections had been made for the effect of the narrow capillary bore. The method of production was continually refined so as to eliminate as many sources of contamination as possible. For example, before using a water pump (rather than a rotary pump) method, the residues obtained showed a higher carbon content as revealed by electron microprobe analysis and advanced mass spectrometric techniques. It was generally established that the degree of anomaly usually diminished as the apparatus and techniques were refined. We have now produced samples which are indistinguishable from ordinary pure water.

As a result of our studies and with some knowledge of the experiments of other workers, we have concluded that the most common sources of contamination in the general production of anomalous water are as follows (not in order). (1) Gross salt contamination, by surface migration and/or vapour transport, when salt solution (for example, K_2SO_4 or NaCl) methods of production are used. (2) Capillary residues (for example, nitrogenous or silicaceous) resulting from the capillary "cleaning" process. (3) Leaching out of the intrinsic glass components (silicon, sodium and so on) from the capillary walls. (4) Surface migration and vapour transport of contaminants inherent in the apparatus; for example, (i) greases from joints, "O"-rings, insufficiently cleaned glassware, and sample handling; (ii) residues arising from chemical cleaning of the apparatus (as in 2); (iii) back-streaming

重复自己的观点，使得西方世界中（尤其是在英国和美国）的很多研究小组继续跟进他的工作。这些研究小组所得到的结果既是对他论点的支持也是对他论点的反驳。此外，还有几位理论工作者（例如，参考文献3~9）积极致力于为解释反常性质所需的新键型找到一种适当的量子力学模型；无需赘言，其中的某些模型在很大程度上是基于猜测[10]。

大多数反对水 II 概念的证据是在近期积累起来的。简而言之，其观点就是，掺杂在微量样品（比如 10^{-10} g ~ 10^{-5} g）中的少量杂质所带来的影响一直被人们低估了。杰里亚金为水 II 所作的辩白看似给人留下了很深刻的印象，不过我们仍然认为：虽然他不是有意的，但他在报告中对事实的描述并不完整。考虑到由此可能造成的广泛影响，我们感到有必要将自己的发现陈说分明。因此，我们希望去解释如何由我们和其他人的研究结果得到无法接受水 II 是一种真实现象的结论，并且以更为严谨的方式来考查杰里亚金及其支持者们的某些论断。

现　象

在过去的两年半中，我们一直在从事这方面的研究，不但采用过所有已知的制备方法，还引入了我们自己发明的很多办法。关于这项研究的更为完整的细节将会在以后发表。（我们有很多材料，在此不能一一列举，不过哈斯特德[11]曾提到过我们的一些结果。）我们对样品反常程度大小的测定主要基于以下观测：（i）相分离效应[11]，（ii）挥发后得到的凝胶状残余物，以及（iii）在针对毛细管狭孔效应进行特定校正后得到的密度－温度曲线的形状。为了消除尽可能多的污染源，我们不断地对制备方法进行改进。例如，在使用水泵（而不是旋转泵）方式之前，曾用电子探针显微分析和先进的质谱技术探测到所得的残余物呈现出较高的含碳量。大家普遍认为，反常程度通常会随着装置和技术的改善而消失。我们现在制备出的样品与正常纯水没有什么区别。

根据我们的研究结果以及参考其他研究者的实验所得到的认识，我们断定在通常的反常水制备物中有以下几种最常见的污染源（不分主次）。（1）所有盐类污染：在使用各种盐溶液（例如 K_2SO_4 或 NaCl）制备法时，由表面迁移和 / 或蒸气传输所致。（2）毛细管残余物（例如含氮或含硅物质）：来源于"清洁"毛细管的过程。（3）从毛细管壁浸出的内部玻璃成分（硅和钠等）。（4）由装置中固有污染物的表面迁移和蒸气传输引起的污染；例如：（i）接合处的润滑油、"O"形环、未充分清洗的玻璃器件以及样品处理；（ii）对装置进行化学清洗后残余下来的物质（如同 2 中那样）；（iii）旋转泵油蒸气的回流，即使在使用冷阱的情况下仍会存在；（iv）装

of rotary pump oil vapours even with the use of cold traps; (iv) resident apparatus gases such as carbon dioxide; (v) gaseous or organic impurities located at apparatus occlusions, dust particles and so on.

Several groups have used the salt solution method, and their results must therefore be immediately discounted. Of those remaining, we wonder which apparatus could genuinely be claimed to be free of even the grease sources mentioned in (4i). The leaching products (source 3) are, of course, mostly unavoidable, and this, we believe, is why so much attention has been directed to identifying silicon as the principle impurity in anomalous water[12-15]. These contentions, however, of which most are based on little more than circumstantial evidence, are in complete contradiction with the facts. In the literature[16-20] and in our own work, impurity tests (most of which involve electron microprobe techniques) clearly show, with one exception[14], that silicon is either absent or present in amounts that are minute compared with other "offending elements". Yet publications persist in alluding to silicon. We stress this point because we believe it partly explains the long time taken to recognize water II as an impurity effect—people have been suspecting the wrong impurities. In the final analysis, the real offending impurities are those of source (4)—particularly the organic impurities emanating from apparatus occlusions and even the sample handling in some cases[20]. (It is worth noting that silicon vapours arising from the vacuum pump oil could also be present.) This is in keeping with the known facts on impurity tests (refs. 16–20 and our own work) in which organic substances (lipids and phospholipids) and the elements carbon, sodium, potassium, chlorine, sulphur (in rough order) notably appear in varying degrees of prominence. Even among the work supporting water II, Deryagin's samples are recognized to contain organic impurities (see later) and Lippincott *et al.*[4] admit to a small percentage of sodium and an unknown amount of carbon (see also other comments[19,22] on the work of Lippincott *et al.*)

For and against Polywater

It has been well established from the work of others and ourselves that the macroscopic and microscopic properties of water in fine capillaries can be greatly modified by the controlled addition of certain impurities. Indeed it has been demonstrated that (i) anomalous phase separation and density–temperature profiles can be obtained (refs. 12, 16, 18 and our own work) with solutions containing various salts, pump oils, silicon, hydrosols and other additives, such as Na and B, which leave their characteristic residues after evaporation of the ordinary water; (ii) the published infrared spectra of polywater have a strong resemblance to those of a number of chemical solutions[16-18,20-23] including carboxyl groups, bicarbonates, sulphates, sodium tetraborate, sodium and potassium nitrate, and particularly nitric acid and also human sweat. There can be little doubt that all the reported properties of anomalous water can be reproduced using an appropriate choice of additives. Clearly the exact impurity composition between different experiments and even between different samples must vary as do the reported properties of anomalous water. It is worth noting that different workers also use different concentrations; some use a very dilute mixture that exists before complete evaporation while others use only the residue.

置内所固有的气体，如二氧化碳；（v）滞留在装置中的气体杂质或有机杂质以及尘埃等。

　　有几个研究小组使用了盐溶液制备法，因此他们所得结果的可靠性必定会大打折扣。至于其余实验结果，我们想知道所用的装置是否确实没有受到包括（4i）中提到的油类污染源在内的影响。当然，浸出物（来源3）基本上是不可避免的，而且我们相信，这就是为什么有那么多研究人员致力于鉴别出反常水中主要杂质是硅 [12-15] 的原因。不过，这些论点中的大多数主要来自于偶然性的证据，它们与事实是完全矛盾的。在一些文献 [16-20] 和我们自己的研究中，由杂质检测结果（大多数情况下采用的是电子探针显微技术）可以很清楚地看到：除去一次例外 [14]，硅或者不存在，或者以与其他"令人不快的成分"相比微乎其微的量存在。但是各种出版物仍然坚持说成是硅。之所以强调这一点，是因为我们相信这就是为什么人们花了很长时间才认识到水 II 其实是一种杂质效应的原因——人们一直猜错了杂质。在最终的分析结果中，真正令人不快的杂质是来源（4）中的那些——尤其是从装置的滞留物中散发出来的有机杂质，在某些情况下甚至来源于样品处理过程 [20]。（值得注意的是，也有可能出现由真空泵油产生的硅蒸气。）这与由杂质检测得到的已知事实（参考文献 16~20 和我们自己的研究）一致。事实上，有机物（油脂和磷脂）以及碳、钠、钾、氯、硫等元素（大致顺序）都被发现以不同的量显著存在。即使是一些支持水 II 的研究也存在杂质问题：杰里亚金的样品中含有有机杂质（见下文），利平科特等人 [4] 也承认有很小比例的钠和未知量的碳存在（参见其他人对利平科特等人工作的评论 [19,22]）。

对聚合水的支持和反对

　　根据其他人的和我们自己的研究已经可以很充分地确定，细毛细管中的水的宏观和微观性质会由于某些杂质的控制性添加而发生显著的改变。事实上已经证明：（i）由含有各种盐类、泵油、硅、水溶胶以及诸如钠和硼之类的添加剂的溶液可以得到反常的相分离和密度–温度曲线，在正常水挥发后会留下它们特有的残余物（参考文献 12、16、18 和我们自己的研究）；（ii）已发表的聚合水的红外光谱与多种化学物质溶液的红外光谱 [16-18,20-23] 非常相似，其中包括含羧基化合物、碳酸氢盐、硫酸盐、四硼酸钠、硝酸钠和硝酸钾，尤其是还有硝酸和人类的汗水。几乎没有什么疑问的是，反常水的所有已知性质都会在选择适当添加剂的情况下再现。显然，不同实验、甚至不同样品中杂质的具体组成必定会随着所报道的反常水性质的不同而有所不同。值得注意的是，不同研究者使用的浓度也不尽相同；有些人用的是完全挥发之前的极稀的混合物，而另一些人则只使用了残余物。

On the question of organic impurities, Deryagin seems content to deduce from the analysis in collaboration with V. L. Talrose that "one *can state* that the amount of organic compounds one *can consider probable* in the columns of water is much smaller than the amount *necessary to explain* the marked differences from normal water" (our italics). Apart from the vague wording of this statement, two important issues are involved. First, implicit in Deryagin's thinking is that, if a certain concentration of impure water in bulk does not deviate from ordinary water, this will be true for the same concentration of impure water in fine capillaries (note that he uses this type of assumption with his "quartz powder experiment"). Knowing the considerable work (much of it by Deryagin himself) on the restructuring capabilities of both surfaces and impurities (see refs. 24 and 25), ought one to expect the microscopic properties of impure solutions in fine capillaries to be reflected in the bulk state? Here Deryagin seems to be in danger of falling into a pit of his own making. Second, the implication in the statement that the impurity concentration is small has certainly not been supported by analysis. According to Davis[20], the analysis of Talrose on Deryagin's samples revealed enormous concentrations of organic substances (not unlike human sweat). Deryagin, however, does not mention this.

Deryagin's experiments cover many years of work using several methods of production. He talks of purity tests in connexion with a later purer apparatus, yet as far as we know all his published data stem from work with the earlier impure apparatus. This point is vital and must be clarified.

On more specific points too there seem to be several implicit contradictions. The dexterity used in the surface tension measurements was apparently sufficient to detect a 3% rise for water II concentrations of 20% by weight! Yet elsewhere he dismisses another experiment (the effect of perturbation on viscosity) simply as having "assigned too much weight to the result". In addition, we wonder how the viscosity results might be affected by the "spontaneous motion" effect—an effect that Deryagin later describes as the sudden motion of an anomalous column when closer to one end of a capillary (that is, as it would be in a viscosity measurement). Also, how are these effects (and others like "daughter column production", distillation and so on) affected by the surface migration and vapour transport of both water and impurities? We know from the experiments of others[16,17] as well as ourselves that these factors cannot be neglected. One could raise many more objections specifically aimed at individual experiments. However, for brevity here, we must regard them as of minor importance compared with issues already mentioned.

Deryagin cites work in progress in the United States, Britain and Belgium to support his case. In fact his supporters are in a minority. Lippincott *et al.*, as we have shown, admit to the presence of impurities in addition to carbon, and their infrared spectra suspiciously resemble those of several solutions, particularly nitric acid. The work of Pethica *et al.*[26] which Deryagin regards as partially confirmatory is no longer regarded as such by at least one of the authors[15]. Our early (impure) work too could have been said to have confirmed Deryagin's results.

关于有机杂质的问题，杰里亚金似乎满足于根据他与塔尔罗斯合作进行的分析而得到的结论，"**可以这么说，可能存在于水柱中的有机化合物的量，要远远少于为解释**反常水与正常水之间显著差异**所必需的量**"（粗体是我们加的）。抛开这一陈述的含糊措辞不说，这里涉及了两个重要的问题。首先，杰里亚金的想法暗示着：如果大批量含一定浓度杂质的非纯水与正常水差不多，那么在细毛细管中同样浓度的非纯水也应与正常水保持一致（注意：他在他的"石英粉末实验"中应用了这类假定）。知道了大量关于调整表面性能及杂质性能（参见参考文献 24 和 25）的工作（其中很多是杰里亚金本人完成的），我们就能指望用细毛细管内不纯溶液的微观性质反映大批量状态下的情况吗？在这一点上，杰里亚金似乎有陷入自己挖的陷阱中去的危险。其次，这一陈述中所蕴含的杂质浓度很小的提法也肯定不会得到分析结果的支持。戴维斯曾提到过 [20]：塔尔罗斯对杰里亚金的样品进行了分析，结果发现其中有机物的浓度非常高（与人类的汗水差不多）。不过，杰里亚金并没有提及这一点。

杰里亚金的实验工作进行了很多年，他曾使用过若干种制备方法。他谈到了对后来的一台较纯净装置进行的纯度测试，但就我们所知，所有他已经发表的数据都出自于那台早期的不纯装置。这一点很重要，因而必须加以澄清。

对于一些具体的结论，似乎也隐含着几点矛盾之处。表面张力测量所具有的灵敏度显然已足以检测出重量百分比浓度为 20% 的水 II 的表面张力会增加 3%！但是在其他场合，他却拒绝接受另一个实验（关于黏度的干扰效应）的结果，只是因为"给结果分配了过多的分量"。另外，我们想知道"自发运动"效应如何影响黏度结果，杰里亚金后来将这种效应说成是反常水柱在接近毛细管一端时的突然运动（即，如同它在黏度测量中所表现的那样）。而且，这些效应（以及其他效应，如"子柱产物"、蒸馏等等）是如何受到水和杂质的表面迁移和蒸气传输影响的？我们从其他人的实验 [16,17] 和我们自己的实验中知道，这些因素是不可忽略的。还可以举出更多的反对意见，尤其是在针对具体某个实验时。但是，在这里为简洁起见，我们只能认为其他反对意见的重要性比不上已经谈到的那些问题。

杰里亚金引用美国、英国和比利时的研究进展以支持他的论点。实际上他的支持者只占少数。之前我们已经谈到，利平科特等人是承认除碳以外还有其他杂质存在的，而且他们得到的红外光谱疑似某几种杂质溶液的光谱，尤其是类似于硝酸。杰里亚金认为佩西卡等人的研究 [26] 部分证实了自己的观点，但现在他们中至少有一位作者 [15] 已不再抱有这种看法。我们的早期（含杂质的）研究也可以被看作是肯定了杰里亚金的结果。

Is it conceivable that Deryagin and his collaborators alone have found the formula for producing pure anomalous water, while all others at best make impure imitations? Were this so, then, by virtue of the apparent ease of its production in 100 μm capillaries (production time of only 1 h or so), the ease of its distillation from small capillaries into a larger tube, and its great stability, this would make anomalous water an ideal substance for collective preparation. If this were so, a simple calculation shows that in the years of Deryagin's experiments the production of a beaker full or even test-tube full of the substance should present no problem. Such a sample could then be made available for rigorous widespread examination.

Some of the work supporting the case for anomalous water may at first seem impressive. Closer examination, however, shows that much of the published work is careless, inconclusive and often misleading, if not wildly conjectural. Our final conclusions are: first, the observed properties of so-called anomalous water are simply the result of either gross impurities or impurity effects enhanced by surface proximity. Second, if sufficient precautions are taken to eliminate the appropriate contaminants, then the capillary products can become indistinguishable from ordinary water. Third, the different anomalous properties reported merely reflect the different types and levels of impurities characteristic of the methods of preparation. Fourth, although one can never dogmatically deny the existence of something not obtained, we think it highly unlikely that a pure anomalous water can exist.

We thank Dr. R. Clampitt for the advanced mass spectrometric work, and the Fulmer Research Institute for the electron microprobe analysis. We also thank Professors J. D. Bernal, C. H. Carlisle, J. B. Hasted, D. J. G. Ives, Dr. R. P. Bywater, Dr. R. Sill, Miss A. Rimel and Mr. J. Fullman for their help.

(**230**, 31-33; 1971)

P. Barnes, I. Cherry, J. L. Finney* and S. Petersen: Department of Crystallography, Birkbeck College, London WC1.

Received January 19, 1971.

References:
1. Deryagin, B. V., *Sci. Amer.*, **223**, 52 (1970).
2. Bangham, D. H., Mosallam, S., and Saweris, Z., *Nature*, **140**, 237 (1937).
3. Bellamy, L. J., Osborn, A. R., Lippincott, E. R., and Bandy, A. R., *Chem. Ind.*, 686 (1969).
4. Lippincott, E. R., Stromberg, R. R., Grant, W. H., and Cessac, G. L., *Science*, **164**, 1482 (1969).
5. Page, T. F., Jakobsen, R. J., and Lippincott, E. R., *Science*, **167**, 51 (1970).
6. Allen, L. C., and Kollman, P. A., *Science*, **167**, 1443 (1970).
7. Allen, L. C., *Nature*, **227**, 372 (1970).
8. Allen, L. C., and Kollman, P. A., *J. Amer. Chem. Soc.*, **92**, 4108 (1970).

---

* Present address: Department of Crystallography, University of Pittsburgh, Pennsylvania 15213.

是否可以认为，只有杰里亚金和他的合作者们找到了制备纯反常水的方法，而其他所有人充其量也只能得到不纯的仿制品？如果真是如此，那么利用在 100 μm 毛细管中容易制备的明显优势（制备时间只有大约 1 h）、从小毛细管蒸馏到较大的试管中的便利性以及它的高度稳定性就可以使反常水成为一种极为适合大批量制备的物质。如果真是如此，则通过简单的计算就可以得到：在杰里亚金进行实验的那些日子里，要制备满满一烧杯或者哪怕只是满满一试管的该物质应该毫无问题。那么，这样的样品就应该可以使严格而广泛的检验成为可能。

一些支持反常水存在的研究最初看来也许是令人印象深刻的。但是通过更细致的检验则发现，很多已发表的研究结果是不太谨慎和缺乏说服力的，而且如果在没有从多个角度进行大胆推测的前提下，通常会使人产生误解。我们得到的最终结论是：首先，能够观察到所谓反常水具有特殊性质的原因只不过是由于存在各种杂质，或者是由于临近表面而得到强化的杂质效应。其次，如果采用的预防措施足以消除相应的污染，那么毛细管中的产物就会变得与正常水毫无分别。第三，已见诸文献报道的不同反常性质仅仅反映出了各种制备方法所特有的不同类型和水平的杂质。第四，尽管谁也不能武断地否认一种尚未获得的物质的存在，但我们还是认为纯反常水能够存在的可能性极小。

感谢克兰皮特博士利用先进质谱技术协助我们进行了研究，并且要感谢富尔默研究院所作的电子探针显微分析。还要感谢贝尔纳、卡莱尔、哈斯特德、艾夫斯等几位教授和拜沃特博士、西尔博士以及赖姆尔小姐和富尔曼先生对我们的帮助。

（王耀杨 翻译；李芝芬 审稿）

9. Chua, K. S., *Nature*, **227**, 834 (1970).

10. Cherry, I., Barnes, P., and Fullman, J., *Nature*, **228**, 590 (1970).

11. Hasted, J. B., *Contemporary Phys.*, **12**, 133 (1971).

12. Everett, D. H., Haynes, J. M., and McElroy, P. J., *Nature*, **224**, 394 (1969).

13. Cherkin, A., *Nature*, **224**, 1293 (1969).

14. Bascom, W. D., Brooks, E. J., and Worthington, B. N., *Nature*, **228**, 1290 (1970).

15. Pethica, B. A., Thompson, W. K., and Pike, W. T., *Nature*, **229**, 21 (1971).

16. Rabideau, S. W., and Florin, A. E., *Science*, **169**, 48 (1970).

17. Rousseau, D. L., and Porto, S. P. S., *Science*, **167**, 1715 (1970).

18. Kurtin, S. L., Mead, C. A., Mueller, W. A., Kurtin, B. C., and Wolf, E. D., *Science*, **167**, 1720 (1970).

19. *Chem. Eng. News*, 35 (1970).

20. Davis, R. E., *Chem. Eng. News*, 73 (1970).

21. *Phys. Today*, **23**, 17 (1970).

22. Leiga, A. G., Vande, D. W., and Ward, A. T., *Science*, **168**, 114 (1970).

23. Falk, M., *Chem. Canada*, **22**, 30 (1970).

24. Speakman, J. C., *Chem. Commun.*, 32 (1967).

25. Currie, M., Curry, N. A., and Speakman, J. C., *J. Chem. Soc.*, A, 1867 (1967).

26. Willis, E., Rennie, G. K., Smart, C., and Pethica, B. A., *Nature*, **222**, 159 (1969).

Convection Plumes in the Lower Mantle

W. J. Morgan

Editor's Note

The idea that plumes of hot material well up within the Earth's mantle to create surface "hotspots" was postulated by John Tuzo Wilson in the 1960s to explain island chains such as Hawaii: they are blobs shed periodically from the plume head onto a moving tectonic plate. Here American geophysicist W. Jason Morgan develops this notion, suggesting that the plumes rise up from the lower mantle as manifestations of convection. His proposal that hotspot plumes are the main drivers of tectonic plate motion is a step too far, but Morgan's fertile idea touches on two important themes in geophysics: what are the fundamental modes of mantle convection, and can rising and sinking features pass unimpeded through the entire mantle?

THE concept of crustal plate motion over mantle hotspots has been advanced[1] to explain the origin of the Hawaiian and other island chains and the origin of the Walvis, Iceland–Farroe and other aseismic ridges. More recently the pattern of the aseismic ridges has been used in formulating continental reconstructions[2]. I have shown[3] that the Hawaiian–Emperor, Tuamotu–Line and Austral–Gilbert–Marshall island chains can be generated by the motion of a rigid Pacific plate rotating over three fixed hotspots. The motion deduced for the Pacific plate agrees with the palaeomagnetic studies of seamounts[4]. It has also been found that the relative plate motions deduced from fault strikes and spreading rates agree with the concept of rigid plates moving over fixed hotspots. Fig. 1 shows the absolute motion of the plates over the mantle, a synthesis which satisfies the relative motion data and quite accurately predicts the trends of the island chains and aseismic ridges away from hotspots.

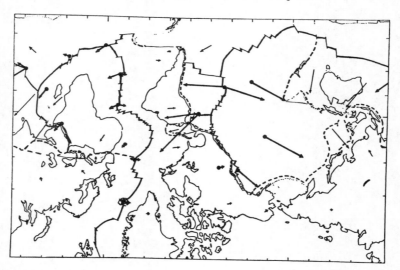

Fig. 1. The arrows show the direction and speed of the plates over the mantle; the heavier arrows show the plate motion at hotspots. This synthesis was based on relative plate motion data (fault strikes and spreading rates) and predicts the directions of the aseismic ridges/island chains emanating from the hotspots.

下地幔中的对流地幔柱

摩根

编者按

为了解释像夏威夷这样的岛链，约翰·图佐·威尔逊于20世纪60年代提出一个假说，即地幔内部的炙热物质流（译者注：这种地幔深部物质的柱状上涌体被摩根称为地幔柱）会不断上升并在表面形成"热点"：它们是一些周期性地从柱头处流入运动板块的块状物质。在本文中，美国地球物理学家贾森·摩根拓展了这一理论，他提出物质流从下地幔中升起说明存在对流作用。他认为热点流是板块运动的主要驱动力，这一观点未免有点离谱，但摩根富于创造性的想法触及了地球物理学的两个重要主题：什么是地幔对流的基本模式？上升和下降部分是否能无障碍地通过整个地幔？

为了解释夏威夷等岛链以及沃尔维斯、冰岛–法罗群岛等无震洋脊的成因，有人曾提出地壳板块在地幔热点之上运动的概念[1]。最近，无震洋脊模式又被用于阐释大陆的重建[2]。笔者曾证明[3]，夏威夷–帝王岛链、土阿莫土群岛和澳大利亚–吉尔伯特–马绍尔群岛链可能由刚性太平洋板块在三个固定热点上方的旋转运动而形成。对太平洋板块运动轨迹的推测与对海山古地磁场的研究结果相符[4]。研究还发现，根据断层走向与扩张速率推导出的板块相对运动与刚性板块在固定热点之上运动的观点是一致的。图1中标出了板块在地幔之上的绝对运动，这一结果是根据相对运动数据而合成的，并且非常准确地预测出了岛链及无震洋脊背离热点的运动趋势。

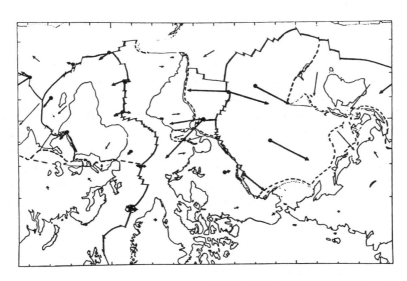

图 1. 箭头表示板块在地幔之上运动的方向和速度；粗箭头表示热点处的板块运动情况。该结果是根据板块相对运动数据（断层走向和扩张速率）合成的，从中可以预测出无震洋脊或岛链自热点向外扩散的方向。

I now propose that these hotspots are manifestations of convection in the lower mantle which provides the motive force for continental drift. In my model there are about twenty deep mantle plumes bringing heat and relatively primordial material up to the asthenosphere and horizontal currents in the asthenosphere flow radially away from each of these plumes. The points of upwelling will have unique petrological and kinematic properties but I assume that there are no corresponding unique points of downwelling, the return flow being uniformly distributed throughout the mantle. Elsasser has argued privately that highly unstable fluids would yield a thunderhead pattern of flow rather than the roll or convection cell pattern calculated from linear viscous equations. The currents in the asthenosphere spreading radially away from each upwelling will produce stresses on the bottoms of the lithospheric plates which, together with the stresses generated by the plate to plate interactions at rises, faults and trenches, will determine the direction in which each plate moves.

Evidently the interactions between plates are important in determining the net force on a plate, for the existing rises, faults and trenches have a self-perpetuating tendency. The plates are apparently quite tough and resistant to major changes, because rise crests do not commonly die out and jump to new locations and points of deep upwelling do not always coincide with ridge crests. (For example, the Galapagos and Réunion upwellings are near triple junctions in the Pacific and Indian Oceans. Asthenosphere motion radially away from these hotspots would help to drive the plates from the triple junctions, but there is considerable displacement between the "pipes to the deep mantle" and the lines of weakness in the lithosphere which enable the plates to move apart.) Also, a large isolated hotspot such as Hawaii can exist without splitting a plate in two. I believe it is possible to construct a simple dynamic model of plate motion by making assumptions about the magnitude of the flow away from each hotspot and assumptions about the stress/strain rate relations at rises, faults and trenches. Such a model has many possibilities to account for past plate motions; hotspots may come and go and plate migration may radically change the plate to plate interactions. But the hotspots would leave visible markers of their past activity on the seafloor and on continents.

This model is compatible with the observation that there is a difference between oceanic island and oceanic ridge basalts[5,6]. It suggests a definite chain of events to form the island type basalt found on Hawaii and parts of Iceland. Relatively primordial material from deep in the mantle rises adiabatically up to asthenosphere depths. This partially fractionates into a liquid and solid residual, the liquid rising through vents to form the tholeiitic part of the island. The latter alkaline "cap rocks" would be generated in the lithosphere vent after plate motion had displaced the vent from the "pipe to the deep mantle". In contrast, the ridge basalts would come entirely from the asthenosphere, passively rising to fill the void created as plates are pulled apart by the stresses acting on them. The differences in potassium and in rare earth pattern for island type and ridge type basalts may be explained by this model. Moreover, the 2 billion year "holding age" advocated by Gast[7] to explain lead isotope data of Gough, Tristan da Cunha, St Helena and Ascension Islands may reflect how long the material was stored in the lower mantle without change prior to the hotspot activity.

现在我认为，这些热点可以证明在下地幔中确实存在对流，对流为大陆漂移提供了驱动力。在我设计的模型中大约有 20 个深地幔柱在不断向上部的软流圈输送热量和较为原始的材料，而软流圈中的水平流则从各个地幔柱处沿半径向四周流动。每个上涌点将具有独特的岩石学特征与运动学特征，但我假定不存在与之对应的单一下降点，回流是均匀地分布于整个地幔之中的。埃尔萨瑟私下里曾声明：根据线性黏性方程，极不稳定的流体会形成雷暴云砧式流而非卷流或对流环模式。在软流圈中，从各上涌点沿半径向四周流出的流体将对岩石圈板块的底部产生压力，该压力与由洋脊、断层以及海沟处的板块间相互作用产生的压力一起决定了各个板块的运动方向。

显然，板块间的相互作用在决定板块上的净作用力方面非常重要，因为现今的洋脊、断层及海沟都有维持自身连续性的趋势。板块似乎非常坚硬并可以抵抗重大的变化，因为通常情况下隆起脊不会逐渐消失而是迁移到新的位置，而深处的上涌点也并不一定与脊峰线重合。（例如，加拉帕戈斯群岛和留尼汪岛上涌带就位于太平洋和印度洋的三联点附近。软流圈自这些热点处沿半径向四周的运动将有助于驱动板块远离三联点，但在"通往地幔深处的通道"与能使板块发生分离的岩石圈薄弱带之间还有相当大的位移。）另外，也可以存在类似于夏威夷这样的大型孤立热点，而并不将板块一分为二。我认为：通过设定从各热点处流出的流体量以及设定在洋脊、断层和海沟处应力与应变速率的关系，就可以构建出一个关于板块运动的简单动力学模型。利用这样一种模型可以对过去的板块运动作出多种可能的解释。或许热点在不断变化，或许板块迁移会使板块间的相互作用发生根本性的变化。但在海底和陆地上一定会留下热点曾经活动过的明显标志。

这个模型与洋岛玄武岩和洋脊玄武岩之间存在差异的观测结果相符 [5,6]。这说明在夏威夷地区以及冰岛部分地区发现的洋岛型玄武岩是由一系列确定的事件形成的。相对较为原始的物质从地幔深处绝热地上升至软流圈处。这些物质中的一部分可分离成液体和固态残留物，液体上升并从出口流出形成海岛上的拉斑玄武岩。后来的碱性"盖层"则可能是在板块运动迫使出口移出"通往地幔深处的通道"后在岩石圈出口处形成的。相反，洋脊玄武岩则完全来自于软流圈，它们从软流圈被动上升以充填板块在应力作用下分离而留下的空隙。利用该模型或许可以解释洋岛玄武岩与洋脊玄武岩在钾元素含量以及稀土配分模式方面存在的差异。另外，为了解释高夫岛、特里斯坦－达库尼亚岛、圣海伦娜岛以及阿森松岛上的铅同位素数据，加斯特 [7] 提出，需要有 20 亿年的"保持年龄"，而这可能反映了在热点活动之前这些物质储存于下地幔中一直未发生变化的时间长度。

My claim that the hotspots provide the driving force for plate motions is based on the following observations to be discussed below. (1) Almost all of the hotspots are near rise crests and there is a hotspot near each of the ridge triple junctions, agreeing with the notion that asthenosphere currents are pushing the plates away from the rises. (2) There is evidence that hotspots become active before continents split apart. (3) The gravity pattern and regionally high topography around each hotspot suggest that more than just surface volcanism is involved at each hotspot. (4) Neither rises nor trenches seem capable of driving the plates.

The symmetric magnetic pattern and the "mid-ocean" position of the rises indicate that the rises are passive. If two plates are pulled apart, they split along some line of weakness and in response asthenosphere rises to fill the void. With further pulling of the plates, the laws of heat conduction and the temperature dependence of strength dictate that future cracks appear down the centre of the previous "dike" injection. If the two plates are displaced equally in opposite directions or if only one plate is moved and the other held fixed, perfect symmetry of the magnetic pattern will be generated. The axis of the ridge must be free to migrate (as shown by the near closure of rises around Africa and Antarctica). If the "dikes" on the ridge axis are required to push the plates apart, it is not clear how the symmetric character of the rises could be maintained. The best argument against the sinking lithospheric plates providing the main motive force is that small trench-bounded plates such as the Cocos plate do not move faster than the large Pacific plate[8]. Also, the slow compressive systems would not appear to have the ability to pull other plates away from other units. The pull of the sinking plate is needed to explain the gravity minimum and topographic deep locally associated with the trench system[9], but I do not wish to invoke this pull as the principal tectonic stress. This leaves sub-lithospheric currents in the mantle and the question now is: are these currents great rolls (mirrors of the rise and trench systems), or are they localized upwellings (that is, hotspots)?

A recent world gravity map[10] computed for spherical harmonics up to order 16 shows isolated gravity highs over Iceland, Hawaii, and most of the other hotspots. Such gravity highs are symptomatic of rising currents in the mantle. Even if the gravity measurements are inaccurate (different authors have very different gravity maps), the fact remains that the hotspots are associated with abnormally shallow parts of the oceans. For example, note the depth of the million square kilometres surrounding the Iceland, Juan de Fua, Galapagos, and Prince Edward hotspots. The magnitude of the gravity and topographic effect should measure the size of the mantle flow at each hotspot.

There is evidence of continental expression of hotspot activity in the lands bordering the Atlantic: the Jurassic volcanics in Patagonia (formed by the present day Bouvet Island plume), the ring dike complex of South-west Africa and flood basalts in the Parana Basin (Tristan da Cunha plume), the White Mountain Magma series in New Hampshire (the same hotspot that made the New England Seamount Chain (Azores plume?)), the Skaegaard and the Scottish Tertiary Volcanic Province (Iceland plume) and perhaps others. I claim this line-up of hotspots produced currents in the asthenosphere which caused the continental break-up leading to the formation of the Atlantic. Likewise the Deccan Traps (Reunion plume) were symptomatic of the forthcoming Indian Ocean rifting. A search should be made for such continental activity,

　　我之所以认为热点为板块运动提供了驱动力是基于以下几个观察结果，下文中还将对这些结果进行深入讨论。（1）几乎所有的热点都位于隆起脊附近，并且在各洋脊的三联点附近都有一个热点存在，这与软流圈流体推动板块远离洋脊的观点一致。（2）有证据表明：在大陆分离之前，热点会变得很活跃。（3）每个热点周围的重力分布以及区域性的高地形说明：每个热点所影响到的并不仅仅是表层的火山活动。（4）无论是洋脊还是海沟似乎都不能驱动板块运动。

　　磁场呈对称分布及洋脊位于"大洋中"部说明洋脊是被动形成的。如果两个板块受到拉张，它们将沿某些薄弱带发生分离，随后软流圈会因此而上升以充填中间的空隙。根据热传导定律以及板块强度的温度依赖性，随着板块的进一步拉张，未来的裂缝将出现在以前侵入的"岩墙"下方中心处。倘若两个板块在相反方向上的位移相同，或者仅有一个板块运动而另一个固定不动，那么就会形成完全对称的磁场。脊轴必然能够自由迁移（如非洲与南极洲周围近于封闭的洋脊）。如果是脊轴上的"岩墙"推动了板块的分离，那么就不清楚洋脊的对称性是如何保持的了。推翻下沉岩石圈板块是主要驱动力的最有力的证据是：以海沟为边界的小板块，如科科斯板块，并不比较大的太平洋板块运动得更快 [8]。此外，缓慢压缩系统产生的牵引力似乎不足以使其他板块从别的系统单元中分离开来。下沉板块的牵引力被用于解释最小重力值和局部与海沟体系有关的深地形 [9]，不过我并不想把这种牵引力看作是主要的构造应力。因而可能的构造应力就只剩岩石圈下的地幔对流了，现在的问题是：它们是大型卷流（洋脊与海沟体系的典型特征），还是局部的上升流（即热点）？

　　从根据 16 阶球谐函数计算出的最新全球重力分布图 [10] 中可以看出，在冰岛、夏威夷和许多其他热点上方都存在着孤立的重力高。这种重力高是地幔上升流的特征。即使重力测量并不精确（不同人测得的重力分布图差异很大），还可以以热点与海洋中的异常浅水区有关作为证据。例如，可以关注一下冰岛、胡安·德富卡、加拉帕戈斯和爱德华王子热点周围几百万平方公里区域的深度。重力大小和地形效应应该可以反映出各热点处地幔上升流的大小。

　　在大西洋周边的陆地上存在着热点活动的陆相证据：巴塔哥尼亚地区的侏罗纪火山岩（由现今的布韦岛地幔柱形成）、非洲西南部的环形岩墙杂岩和巴拉那盆地中的溢流玄武岩（特里斯坦-达库尼亚地幔柱）、新罕布什尔州的白山岩浆系列（与形成新英格兰海山链的热点相同（亚速尔地幔柱？））、斯卡尔噶德和苏格兰第三纪火山区（冰岛地幔柱）等等。我认为，这一系列热点共同引起了流体在软流圈中的流动，进而导致大陆分离形成了大西洋。同样，德干玄武岩（留尼汪地幔柱）是印度洋裂谷即将形成的征兆。我们应该去寻找类似的陆地活动以解释在那里发现的裂

particularly in East Africa and the western United States (the Snake River basalts?) as an explanation for the rift features found there. There is a paucity of continental hotspots in Fig. 1; perhaps this is a bias due to continental complexity versus oceanic simplicity, but the model presented here predicts that most hotspots will be near a spreading rise.

I thank Kenneth Deffeyes and Fred Vine for their contributions to the ideas in this letter. This work was partially supported by the US National Science Foundation and the Office of Naval Research.

(**230**, 42-43; 1971)

W. J. Morgan: Department of Geological and Geophysical Sciences, Princeton University, Princeton, New Jersey.

Received December 21, 1970.

References:

1. Wilson, J. T., *Phil. Trans. Roy. Soc.*, A, **258**, 145 (1965).

2. Dietz, R. S., and Holden, J. C., *J. Geophys. Res.*, **75**, 4939 (1970).

3. Morgan, W. J., Hess Memorial Volume (edit. by Shagam, R.), *Mem. Geol. Soc. Amer.* (in the press).

4. Francheteau, J., Harrison, C. G. A., Sclater, J. G., and Richards, M. L., *J. Geophys. Res.*, **75**, 2035 (1970).

5. Engel, A. E. J., Engel, C. G., and Havens, R. G., *Geol. Soc. Amer. Bull.*, **76**, 719 (1965).

6. Gast, P. W., *Geochim. Cosmochim. Acta*, **32**, 1057 (1968).

7. Oversby, V. M., and Gast, P. W., *J. Geophys. Res.*, **75**, 2097 (1970).

8. McKenzie, D. P., *Geophys. J.*, **18**, 1 (1969).

9. Morgan, W. J., *J. Geophys. Res.*, **70**, 6189 (1965).

10. Kaula, W. M., *Science*, **169**, 982 (1970).

谷构造，尤其是在东非和美国西部地区（斯内克河玄武岩？）。从图 1 来看陆地上的热点很少，也许这是一种因陆地相对复杂和海洋相对简单而导致的偏见，不过利用本文给出的模型可以预测出，大多数热点将位于扩张脊附近。

感谢肯尼思·德费耶和弗雷德·瓦因为本文阐述的思想所作出的贡献。本研究在一定程度上得到了美国国家科学基金会和美国海军研究办公室的支持。

（齐红艳 翻译；张忠杰 审稿）

Implications of the "Wave Field" Theory of the Continuum from the Crab Nebula

M. J. Rees

Editor's Note

By 1971 it was well accepted that pulsars were rotating neutron stars. But the mechanism that actually generates the pulse was not known. British astrophysicist Martin Rees here explores the observational consequences of a particular model known at the time as the "wave field theory". The model required that radiation from some parts of the nebula had to be circularly polarized. But subsequent observations showed an insufficient amount of polarized light, meaning that the model was incorrect.

THE Crab Nebula almost certainly derives a continuing power input from a rotating neutron star associated with the pulsar NP 0532. Studies by Ostriker and Gunn[1] and others of the "oblique rotator" model suggest that the rotational braking of pulsars may be primarily due to emission of electromagnetic waves at the rotation frequency of ~30 Hz (or low harmonics thereof). Indeed, it had been suggested[2-4], even before pulsars were discovered, that neutron stars might emit by this mechanism. In the case of the Crab Nebula, this view naturally suggests the further speculation that the continuum emission from the "amorphous mass" may arise from relativistic electrons moving in a low frequency wave, rather than the usual synchrotron process. This "wave field" model is especially attractive when one recalls the difficulty of accounting for the presence of a large-scale ordered magnetic field in the nebula. In this article I shall show that the "wave field" theory of the Crab Nebula leads to some distinctive predictions, especially regarding the polarization of the continuum. It may therefore be possible to test its validity and thus, indirectly, to infer something about the energetic link between the nebula and the pulsar.

The rate of emission by an isotropic distribution of relativistic electrons moving in an electromagnetic field is determined by the electromagnetic energy density. It is therefore convenient to express the intensity of the 30 Hz wave in terms of the magnetic field for which $H^2/8\pi$ equals the wave energy density. We find

$$H_{eq} \simeq 1.8 \times 10^{-4} \left(\frac{L_{30 \text{ Hz}}}{5 \times 10^{38} \text{erg s}^{-1}} \right)^{\frac{1}{2}}$$
$$\left(\frac{r}{10^{18} \text{ cm}} \right)^{-1} (1 - \varepsilon)^{-\frac{1}{2}} \text{G} \qquad (1)$$

This approximate relation assumes that the wave propagates with speed c, but ignores the fact that strict dipole emission would be twice as intense along the rotation axis as in the equatorial plane. ε is the effective albedo at the boundary of the nebula, and the factor

蟹状星云连续谱"波场"理论的推论

瑞斯

编者按

到 1971 年时，脉冲星是旋转中子星这一观点已经得到了人们的普遍认可。但产生脉冲的真实机制尚不清楚。在本文中英国天体物理学家马丁·瑞斯探讨了那时被称为"波场理论"的一个特定模型在观测上的推论。这个模型要求来自星云中某些部分的辐射必须是圆偏振的。但是随后的观测结果显示圆偏振光的量不够，因此这个模型还是被推翻了。

几乎可以肯定：蟹状星云从一颗与脉冲星NP 0532 相关的旋转中子星中获得了持续的能量注入。奥斯特里克和冈恩[1]以及其他人对"倾斜转子"模型的研究表明，脉冲星的转动变慢可能主要是因为在 ~30 Hz 转动频率（或者它的低谐频）处的电磁波发射。确实，甚至在脉冲星被发现以前就已经有人提出[2-4]中子星有可能会以这种机制发射辐射。就蟹状星云而言，这一观点很自然地使人联想到：来自那些"不定形物质"（译者注：指星云中脉冲星周围的等离子体）的连续谱辐射可能来源于在一个低频波中运动的相对论性电子，而非通常的同步辐射过程。如果我们回想起在解释星云中存在大尺度有序磁场时所遇到的困难，就会对这个"波场"模型格外感兴趣。在这篇文章中，我将向大家说明由蟹状星云的"波场"理论可以作出哪些与众不同的预言，尤其是在关于连续谱的偏振方面。这样就为今后检验它的正确性提供了可能，并由此间接地得出星云与脉冲星之间存在能量上的联系的推论。

由在电磁场中运动的相对论性电子的各向同性分布而引起的辐射率取决于电磁能量密度。因此可以很方便地用波的能量密度等于 $H^2/8\pi$ 的磁场表达出 30 Hz 波的强度。我们发现：

$$H_{\text{eq}} \simeq 1.8 \times 10^{-4} \left(\frac{L_{30\ \text{Hz}}}{5 \times 10^{38}\,\text{erg s}^{-1}} \right)^{\frac{1}{2}}$$
$$\left(\frac{r}{10^{18}\,\text{cm}} \right)^{-1} (1 - \varepsilon)^{-\frac{1}{2}}\,\text{G} \tag{1}$$

这个近似关系式假设波以速度 c 传播，但它忽略了这样一个事实，即对严格的偶极辐射而言，其沿旋转轴的强度应该是赤道面中的两倍。ε 是星云边界处的有效

$(1-\varepsilon)^{-\frac{1}{2}}$ allows for possible reflexions. For the Crab all the terms in brackets will be ~1. Thus the wave energy density is comparable with that of the weakest magnetic field ($\sim 10^{-4}$ G) permitted by energetic and dynamical considerations. It is also useful to define an "equivalent electron gyrofrequency" $\Omega/2\pi \simeq 3\times 10^{6} H_{eq}$ Hz, because the parameter $f = \Omega/\omega$, where ω is the wave frequency, determines both the character of the orbits of electrons exposed to the wave and the radiation which these particles emit.

Throughout the Crab Nebula, we expect $f \gtrsim 10$ (taking $\omega/2\pi \simeq 30$ Hz). In this situation a relativistic particle of Lorentz factor γ emits at frequencies $\sim\gamma^2\Omega$, as in the case of synchrotron radiation, and not $\sim\gamma^2\omega$, as for standard inverse Compton emission[5-7]. Observable features of this "synchro-Compton" emission—and, in particular, its polarization—will be considered here. For the moment, however, it is sufficient to note that, in general terms, the usual results of synchrotron theory still hold, so that the standard inferences of the electron density and spectrum in the nebula remain applicable.

Some of the rotational energy lost by an "oblique rotator" would accelerate relativistic particles in the vicinity of the speed of light cylinder[1], but for our considerations to be relevant it is essential that a substantial fraction (~10% at the very least) should escape into the nebula as 30 Hz radiation. It is interesting to investigate the eventual fate of this wave energy. When the wave reaches the boundary of the nebula, only a fraction $\sim v_{exp}/c$ of its energy is used in pushing against the external medium, v_{exp} being the expansion velocity of the boundary. The bulk of the energy must be either reflected or absorbed. As we shall see, the high linear polarization of the continuum from the nebula implies that the 30 Hz radiation must be ordered rather than random, and this precludes more than ~50% reflexion (so that, in equation (1), $\varepsilon \lesssim 0.5$). This means that most of the wave energy must be deposited in a thin "skin" at the boundary and at the inner edges of the filaments. The densities are so low that there is no possibility of this energy being radiated thermally, so it seems inevitable that relativistic particles, probably chiefly electrons, will be generated. Thus the pulsar would be almost 100% efficient as an accelerator—whatever fraction of the energy escapes into the wave zone as 30 Hz emission will produce fast particles in the outer parts of the nebula.

Even though the wave field simulates a stationary magnetic field as regards the radiation emitted by relativistic electrons (except, as we shall see, in the important respect of circular polarization) the particle orbits are very different. An electron's general motion is a superposition of a uniform translation velocity and a periodic relativistic oscillation with Lorentz factor ~f. The form of this oscillation depends on the polarization properties of the low frequency wave: for linear polarization it is a "figure of eight" in a plane perpendicular to the H-vector, and for pure circular polarization it is a circle. All particles exposed to the wave must therefore be relativistic with $\gamma \gtrsim f$. Because the orbits of particles with $\gamma \gg f$ are basically straight lines, the wave field is ineffective for confining particles. But even a very weak magnetic field, which is negligible as regards the emission mechanism, could confine the particles adequately if it were sufficiently tangled. Alternatively the particles would be "mirrored" at the boundary by the external interstellar field and by the

反射率，而因子 $(1-\varepsilon)^{-\frac{1}{2}}$ 是允许有反射的。对蟹状星云来说，括号里的所有项都将为 ~1。因此波的能量密度就会与能量和动力学所允许的最弱磁场（~10^{-4} G）的能量密度相当。定义一个"等价电子回旋频率"$\Omega/2\pi \simeq 3 \times 10^6 H_{eq}$ Hz 也是很有用的，因为参数 $f = \Omega/\omega$（其中 ω 为波的频率）决定了波中电子轨道的性质以及这些粒子发出的辐射。

对于整个蟹状星云，我们预言 $f \gtrsim 10$（取 $\omega/2\pi \simeq 30$ Hz）。在这种情况下，洛伦兹因子为 γ 的相对论性粒子会在频率 ~$\gamma^2\Omega$ 下发射，而不会在频率 ~$\gamma^2\omega$ 下发射；前者与同步辐射时的情形相同，后者则相当于标准的逆康普顿辐射 [5-7]。本文将讨论这种"同步－康普顿"辐射的观测特征，尤其是它的偏振。不过，就现在的情况而言，注意到以下这一点就足够了：在一般情况下，同步辐射理论中的常见结论仍然有效，因此关于星云中电子密度和光谱的标准推论还可以沿用。

在一个"倾斜转子"所损失的转动能中，有一部分将加速光速圆柱附近的相对论性粒子 [1]，但为了使我们的考虑有意义，其中必须有很大一部分（最少 ~10%）以 30 Hz 的辐射逃逸到星云中去。研究波能量的最终去向是很有趣的。当波到达星云的边界时，在它的能量中仅有 ~v_{exp}/c 的部分被用于推动外面的介质，其中 v_{exp} 是边界的膨胀速度。大部分能量不是被反射就是被吸收。正如我们将要看到的，这个星云连续谱的高线偏振度意味着 30 Hz 辐射必定是有序的而不是随机的，这就排除了反射会高于 ~50% 的可能性（因而在式（1）中，$\varepsilon \lesssim 0.5$）。这意味着波的大部分能量会积聚在边界处和丝状结构内边缘处的一层薄"外皮"里。这里密度太低，以至于这些能量不可能转化为热辐射，如此看来，产生相对论性粒子（可能主要为电子）就成为一种不可避免的趋势了。于是脉冲星将会和加速器一样达到接近于 100% 的效率——不管以 30 Hz 辐射逃逸到充满波的区域的能量比例有多大，都将在星云的靠外部分产生快速粒子。

尽管这种波场能够模拟一个与相对论性电子所发射的辐射相关的静态磁场（除了我们将要看到的，在圆偏振这一重要方面），但各个粒子的轨道迥然不同。电子的一般运动是一个均匀的平动速度和一个洛伦兹因子为 ~f 的周期性相对论振动的叠加。这种振动的形式取决于低频波的偏振性质：对线偏振而言，它在垂直于 H 矢量的一个平面内呈"8 字形"；对于纯粹的圆偏振，它是一个圆。因此，波中的所有粒子都必须是满足 $\gamma \gtrsim f$ 的相对论性粒子。因为 $\gamma \gg f$ 的粒子的轨道基本上是直线，所以这种波场不能有效地限制粒子。然而，即使是一个在涉及辐射机制时可以忽略的非常弱的磁场也足以把粒子限制住，只要它能被充分缠结。或者，粒子可能会在边界处被外部星际场和丝状结构"镜面反射"，如果这些结构含有磁场的话。

filaments if these contain magnetic fields.

Self-consistency demands that the plasma density within the nebula should be low enough to allow the 30 Hz radiation to propagate. At first sight one might suspect that the formal plasma frequency $9 \times 10^3 n_e^{\frac{1}{2}}$ Hz would have to be below 30 Hz, which would lead to the exceedingly stringent condition that the electron density n_e throughout the nebula be $\lesssim 10^{-5}$ cm^{-3}. In the case of a "strong" wave $(f \gtrsim 1)$, however, this condition can be relaxed somewhat. For relativistic electrons with differential number spectrum $n(\gamma)$ the propagation condition is[8]

$$\int n(\gamma)\frac{\log \gamma}{\gamma}\mathrm{d}\gamma \lesssim 10^{-5} \text{ cm}^{-3} \qquad (2)$$

Because all the particles exposed to the wave have $\gamma \gtrsim f$ the propagation condition is $n_e \lesssim 10^{-5} f$ (ref. 1). Relation (2) is satisfied, with a factor $\gtrsim 10$ to spare, by the particles with $\gamma \gtrsim 100$ whose density can be directly inferred from observations of the continuum emission from the Crab at frequencies above a few MHz. As relation (2) is obviously not fulfilled by the general interstellar medium, the 30 Hz waves cannot propagate beyond the boundary of the nebula—indeed, the observable nebula would, in this picture, be delineated by the region which has been evacuated sufficiently for the wave to propagate. Also, the waves would be unable to penetrate the filaments in the nebula.

It would be agreeable if the "wave field" theory led to a clear-cut prediction of the surface brightness distribution over the Crab Nebula, but unfortunately this is not the case. The r^{-1} dependence of H_{eq} means that a particle radiates more efficiently near the centre, but there would not necessarily be an enhanced surface brightness around the pulsar because this effect is counteracted by the tendency of particles to be excluded, by the force of the wave, from regions where $f \gtrsim \gamma^{\frac{1}{2}}$.

A distinctive consequence of the "wave field" theory is that most of the continuum originates in the half of the nebula farthest from the observer. This is because the synchro-Compton emission is due to electrons coming towards the observer, and the radiation rate per electron is larger for particles moving at large angles to the wave propagation direction. One might, in principle, detect such an effect by determining the Faraday rotation due to those filaments whose radial velocities indicate that they lie on the back side of the nebula.

What polarization should the Crab Nebula possess if the continuum is synchro-Compton emission rather than straightforward* synchrotron radiation? It is easy to see that the

---

* If, as was suggested most recently by Hoyle[9], the field in the Crab Nebula were attached to a spinning neutron star and had been amplified by being tightly wound, the emission would again not be straightforward synchrotron radiation because the scale of the field reversals would be small compared with the relativistic electron gyroradii. In any case, the particle density in the nebula would not be high enough to carry the currents associated with the rapid field reversals, so a magnetohydrodynamic treatment may be inappropriate in this situation.

自洽性要求星云内的等离子体密度应该足够低以至于 30 Hz 辐射可以传播。乍一看人们也许会表示怀疑，如果要使等离子体的正常频率 $9 \times 10^3 n_e^{\frac{1}{2}}$ Hz 下降到 30 Hz 以下，就会产生非常严格的条件，即整个星云的电子密度 n_e 必须 $\leqslant 10^{-5}$ cm^{-3}。然而，在 "强" 波 ($f \gtrsim 1$) 的情况下，这个条件可以稍微放松一点。对于有差异性数量谱 $n(\gamma)$ 的相对论性电子，其传播条件为 [8]：

$$\int n(\gamma) \frac{\log \gamma}{\gamma} \mathrm{d}\gamma \leqslant 10^{-5} \text{ cm}^{-3} \tag{2}$$

因为波中的所有粒子都满足 $\gamma \gtrsim f$，所以传播条件是 $n_e \leqslant 10^{-5} f$（参考文献 1）。对于 $\gamma \gtrsim 100$ 的粒子，其密度可以直接从在高于几兆 Hz 频率观测蟹状星云连续谱辐射的结果中推测出来，这些粒子满足关系式（2），并富余一个 $\geqslant 10$ 的因子。因为一般的星际介质显然不满足关系式（2），所以 30 Hz 的波不能在星云边界之外传播——确实，在这个图景里，可观测的星云轮廓是由足够稀疏使得波可以传播的区域划定的。同时，波应该不能穿透星云中的丝状结构。

如果这个 "波场" 理论能够明确地预言整个蟹状星云的表面亮度分布，那当然再好不过；但不幸的是，情况并非如此。H_{eq} 对 r^{-1} 的依赖意味着粒子在靠近中心的地方辐射效率更高，但这并不一定能够说明脉冲星周围的表面亮度一定会增强，因为该效应被波的作用力将粒子从 $f \gtrsim \gamma^{\frac{1}{2}}$ 的区域驱逐出去的趋势抵消了。

"波场" 理论的一个与众不同的推论是：连续谱辐射中的大部分源自于星云离观测者最远的那一半。这是因为同步–康普顿辐射由朝向观察者运动的电子所产生，并且每个电子的辐射率对于相对波传播方向成大角度的粒子来说是比较大的。原则上，人们可以通过测量由丝状结构造成的法拉第旋转来探测这个效应，这些丝状结构的径向速度表明它们位于星云的背面。

如果连续谱是同步–康普顿辐射而不是直接的 * 同步辐射，那么蟹状星云的偏振应该是什么样的呢？很容易看到，在一个相干线偏振波中运动并满足 $\gamma \gg f$ 的电子

---

* 如果，正如霍伊尔 [9] 最近提出的，蟹状星云中的场附属于一颗自旋的中子星并且由于缠绕得很紧而被放大，那么其所发出的辐射同样不会是直接的同步辐射，因为场反转的尺度与相对论性电子的回旋半径相比是很小的。在任何情况下，星云中的粒子密度应该都不会高到足以承载与快速场反转有关的电流的程度，因此在这种情况下用磁流体动力学进行处理是不合适的。

synchro-Compton emission from an electron with $\gamma \gg f$ moving in a coherent linearly polarized wave will itself be highly linearly polarized in the direction of the projected E-vector of the low frequency wave. (Remember that the electron is deflected both by the E and the B-field of the wave.) When the low frequency wave is circularly polarized, the polarization of the synchro-Compton emission is best estimated by transforming to the "guiding centre" frame. In this frame an electron executes a circular orbit, with Lorentz factor f, in a plane which (except when the particle is traveling nearly in the propagation direction of the wave) is almost perpendicular to the direction of its mean velocity v. This motion would give rise to synchrotron-type radiation concentrated in a "fan" at angles $\pi/2 \pm O(f^{-1})$ to v. This radiation would be circularly polarized in opposite senses on the two sides of the orbital plane. In the transformation from the guiding centre frame to the source frame, however, the factor $(1-v/c \cos \theta)$ in the Doppler formula favours the emission from the forward hemisphere by a factor $\sim(1+f^{-1})/(1-f^{-1})$, which leads to a net polarization $\sim f^{-1}$. A more refined calculation using the methods of Roberts and Komesaroff[10] leads to the estimate $\sim 0.6 \, f^{-1}$. Therefore, synchro-Compton emission by electrons of all energies can possess circular polarization of order f^{-1}. The synchro-Compton continuum from any distribution of electrons moving in a circularly polarized low frequency wave should therefore be circularly polarized to this extent (the precise degree of polarization depending on the slope of the electron spectrum). This contrasts with the γ^{-1} dependence expected for synchrotron radiation[11], which leads to an undetectably small predicted degree of circular polarizartion in most astronomical objects even at radio frequencies.

The electromagnetic waves emitted by an ideal spinning magnetic dipole *in vacuo* would, in the equatorial plane, be completely linearly polarized, the electric vector lying perpendicular to the plane. At higher latitudes the waves would be elliptically polarized, and along the rotation axis the polarization would be purely circular. In order to compare the polarization predicted by the "oblique rotator" model with the observations of the Crab Nebula, we must assume an orientation for the dipole. In certain pulsar models the existence of an interpulse, as seen in NP 0532, indicates that the observer lies close to the equatorial plane. Guided by this, let us suppose that the rotation axis of NP 0532 lies in the plane of the sky. Then, provided that relation (2) is satisfied by a large enough margin for the effects of the medium to be negligible, the synchro-Compton radiation from the equatorial plane should be highly linearly polarized parallel to the rotation axis. The direction of linear polarization will be similar at other latitudes (and even along lines of sight intercepting the rotation axis there will be a linearly polarized contribution). Both the optical and the radio observations show fairly uniform linear polarization in a NW–SE direction over the inner part of the Crab Nebula. This would therefore imply that the pulsar's rotation axis also pointed in this direction.

The observed continuum from a point in the nebula at latitude θ relative to the pulsar should therefore display $\sim 60 \, f^{-1} \sin \theta$ percent circular polarization. If the pulsar's rotational axis lies in the plane of the sky, all points along a single line of sight through the nebula would contribute the same degree of circular polarization (the latitude-dependence being

所发出的同步 – 康普顿辐射本身就会是高度线偏振的，偏振的方向是低频波投影的 E 矢量方向。（记住：电子是在波的 E 场和 B 场的共同作用下偏转的。）当低频波为圆偏振时，最好通过变换至 "导向中心" 参考系来估算同步 – 康普顿辐射的偏振。在这个参考系中，电子是在一个几乎垂直于其平均速度 v 的平面内作圆轨道运动（除非当粒子近似沿着波的传播方向运动时）的，洛伦兹因子为 f。这种运动将产生集中在一个与 v 成 $\pi/2 \pm O(f^{-1})$ 角范围内的 "扇形区域" 中的同步辐射型辐射。这个辐射在轨道面的两边应该是方向相反的圆偏振。然而，在从导向中心参考系到源参考系的变换中，多普勒公式里的 $(1 - v/c \cos \theta)$ 因子使得来自前面半球的辐射多出一个 $\sim (1 + f^{-1})/(1 - f^{-1})$ 因子，这就导致了一个净的 $\sim f^{-1}$ 的偏振。采用罗伯茨和科梅萨罗夫[10] 的方法对上述过程进行更为精确的计算，得到的结果是 $\sim 0.6 \, f^{-1}$。因此，各种能量电子的同步 – 康普顿辐射可能会有量级为 f^{-1} 的圆偏振。由此可知，来自于在一个圆偏振低频波中运动的任意分布电子的同步 – 康普顿连续谱都应该有这么高的圆偏振（偏振度的具体数值取决于电子谱的斜率）。这与同步辐射对 γ^{-1} 的依赖[11] 相对，因而在大多数天体中即使是在射电频率下也只能预测出有探测不到的极小的圆偏振度。

由在真空中快速旋转的理想磁偶极子发出的电磁波在赤道面内应该是完全线偏振的，其电矢量垂直于赤道面。在纬度更高的地方，波应该是椭圆偏振的，而在沿旋转轴的方向，偏振应为纯粹的圆偏振。为了将由 "倾斜转子" 模型预言的偏振与对蟹状星云的观测结果进行比较，我们必须假设偶极子的取向。在某些脉冲星模型中，存在中间脉冲即说明观测者靠近赤道面，正如在 NP 0532 中所看到的情况。以此为依据，让我们假设 NP 0532 的旋转轴位于天球切面中。然后，只要一个介质效应可以忽略的足够大的边缘能够满足关系式（2），那么来自赤道面的同步 – 康普顿辐射应该在与旋转轴平行的方向上是高度线偏振的。在其他纬度处，线偏振的方向类似（甚至在沿着与旋转轴相交的视线方向上也会有线偏振的贡献）。光学和射电观测结果都显示出在蟹状星云的靠内部分沿西北—东南方向有相当均匀的线偏振。因此这可能表明脉冲星的旋转轴也指向这个方向。

因此，从星云中相对于脉冲星而言纬度为 θ 的一个点观测到的连续谱应该显示出百分比为 $\sim 60 \, f^{-1} \sin \theta$ 的圆偏振。如果脉冲星的旋转轴位于天球切面中，则在一条穿过星云的单一视线上的所有点都应对圆偏振度有相同的贡献（纬度依赖性被 f 对

cancelled by the r^{-1} dependence of f). The predicted degree of circular polarization would vary over the nebula, being proportional to the angular distance from the line of sight to the projected equatorial plane (assumed to be a line running NE–SW through the pulsar). The circular polarization should be greatest in the outermost parts of the nebula in the NW and SE directions, and should amount to a few percent. It would have opposite senses on the two sides, so the net circular polarization of the whole nebula could be very slight.

(Towards the outer parts of the nebula, one would expect a gradual increase in the density of low-γ electrons, which may cause the refractive index μ at 30 Hz (which is related to the integral in relation (2)) to drop significantly below unity. When $\mu<1$ the $<E^2>/<B^2>$ ratio of an electromagnetic wave exceeds its vacuum value, and the foregoing discussions of the polarization of synchro-Compton radiation are somewhat modified[5,6]. In particular, even when the low frequency wave is unpolarized, the synchro-Compton radiation will display linear polarization perpendicular to the projected propagation direction of the wave. Also, when μ differs from unity the low frequency wave will be refracted, and can no longer be assumed to propagate radially outward from the pulsar.)

In conclusion, the simple "wave field" model can account naturally for the high linear polarization in the Crab Nebula, and for the required highly efficient acceleration of relativistic electrons. The direction of the linear polarization determines the orientation of the rotation axis, so any independent evidence of the pulsar's alignment would provide a test of the theory. The simple model also indicates that the NW and SE parts of the nebula should display circular polarization—at radio, optical and X-ray wavelengths—amounting to a few percent. The estimated circular polarization would be somewhat reduced if the magnetic field of the pulsar were more complicated than a simple dipole, or if allowance were made for deflexion of the low frequency waves by irregularities within the nebula. Provided, however, that the low frequency waves are sufficiently well ordered to account for the observed linear polarization, it does not seem possible to reduce the predicted circular polarization by more than a factor ~2. Also, of course, circular polarization cannot, like linear polarization, be smeared out by differential Faraday rotation or similar effects. Therefore, if it were found that no parts of the Crab Nebula displayed even ~ 1% circular polarization, this would indicate that the 30 Hz waves certainly do not penetrate beyond the region of the wisps and would be strong evidence against the "wave field" model for the nebula. It would also suggest that the popular "oblique rotator" magnetic dipole model for NP 0532 would require some reappraisal.

I acknowledge valuable discussions with Drs. S. A. Bonometto, J. E. Gunn, F. C. Michel, J. P. Ostriker and V. L. Trimble.

(**230**, 55-57; 1971)

M. J. Rees: Institute of Theoretical Astronomy, Madingley Road, Cambridge.

Received December 15, 1970.

r^1 的依赖所抵消）。预测出的圆偏振度在星云内会有所不同，它与从视线到投影赤道面（假设为一条沿东北—西南方向穿过脉冲星的直线）的角距离成正比。圆偏振度应该在星云最外部的西北和东南方向上最高，并且应该能达到百分之几。它在两侧有相反的偏振方向，所以整个星云的净圆偏振可能会非常小。

（对于星云靠外的部分，我们可以预期低 γ 电子的密度会逐渐增加，这有可能导致 30 Hz 处的折射率 μ（与关系式（2）中的积分有关）降低到显著小于 1。当 μ<1 时，电磁波的 $<E^2>/<B^2>$ 值将超过其真空值，因而要对前面所讨论的同步－康普顿辐射的偏振情况进行一些修正 [5,6]。尤其是，即使在低频波无偏振时，同步－康普顿辐射也会显示出垂直于投影的波传播方向的线偏振。同样，当 μ 偏离 1 时，低频波将会被折射，因而不能再假设它是沿径向从脉冲星向外传播的。）

总之，利用简单的"波场"模型可以很自然地解释蟹状星云中的高线偏振度以及所要求的相对论性电子的高效加速。线偏振的方向决定了旋转轴的取向，所以任何关于脉冲星取向的独立证据都可以作为对这个理论的一种检验。这个简单的模型还表明，星云的西北和东南部分应该显示出百分之几的圆偏振，在射电、光学和 X 射线波段都是如此。如果脉冲星的磁场比一个简单的偶极子更复杂，或者如果考虑到低频波会因星云内的不规则结构而发生偏折，那么估算出的圆偏振度就会有所降低。然而，如果低频波的有序度非常高以至于可以用来解释观测到的线偏振，那么预测出的圆偏振就不太可能会降低至 50%以下。此外，圆偏振当然不会像线偏振那样被较差的法拉第旋转或与之类似的效应抹掉。因此，如果发现在蟹状星云中没有任何一个部分能显示出哪怕 ~1% 的圆偏振，这就可以说明，30 Hz 的波必然没有穿透波束区并且将可以作为反驳星云"波场"模型的有力证据。这还将表明，我们必须对得到广泛认可的 NP 0532 的"倾斜转子"磁偶极模型进行重新评估。

感谢博诺梅托博士、冈恩博士、米歇尔博士、奥斯特里克博士和特林布尔博士和我进行了很多次有价值的讨论。

（钱磊 翻译；蒋世仰 审稿）

References:

1. Ostriker, J. P., and Gunn, J. E., *Astrophys. J.*, **157**, 1395 (1969).

2. Hoyle, F., Narlikar, J. V., and Wheeler, J. A., *Nature*, **203**, 914 (1964).

3. Wheeler, J. A., *Ann. Rev. Astron. Astrophys.*, **4**, 393 (1966).

4. Pacini, F., *Nature*, **216**, 567 (1967).

5. Rees, M. J., *IAU Symposium No. 46*, "*The Crab Nebula*" (edit. by Davies, R. D., and Smith, F. G.) (Dordrecht, D. Reidel, in the press).

6. Rees, M. J., *Nature*, **229**, 312 (1971).

7. Gunn, J. E., and Ostriker, J. P., *Astrophys. J.* (in the press).

8. Zheleznakov, V. V., *Sov. Astron.*, **11**, 33 (1967).

9. Hoyle, F., *Nature*, **223**, 936 (1969).

10. Roberts, J. A., and Komesaroff, M. M., *Icarus*, **4**, 127 (1965).

11. Legg, M. P. C., and Westfold, K. C., *Astrophys. J.*, **154**, 499 (1968).

Configuration of Amino-Acids in Carbonaceous Chondrites and a Pre-Cambrian Chert

J. Oró et al.

Editor's Note

Chemist John Oró and his colleagues in Texas reported finding amino acids in carbon-rich meteorites (see next paper), raising questions about the role of meteorites as a source of raw ingredients for the origin of life. While the amino acids in living organisms consist only of the left-handed variant of their two mirror-image forms, those formed by non-living processes were expected to be equal mixtures of both forms. So detecting the relative amounts of left- and right-handed variants could identify biogenic contamination. Here Oró and his colleagues describe a new method for doing that, and apply it to samples of a meteorite and sedimentary rock. There is now debate, however, about whether a left-handed excess in meteorites might potentially be intrinsic.

IN connexion with studies on the origin and evolution of life on Earth[1], and its possible detection in space, we have developed a sensitive method for the analysis of protein amino-acids, which includes the simultaneous determination of their optical configuration[2]. The approach is based on the separation of enantiomeric N-trifluoroacetyl (N-TFA)–isopropyl esters by gas chromatography with an optically active stationary phase[3]. We wish to describe here the application of the method to meteorites and a Pre-Cambrian sediment.

The occurrence of traces of amino-acids in carbonaceous chondrites[4-8] has been ascribed to contamination and abiogenesis. But the determination of the configuration of these compounds seems to permit differentiation between these two possibilities. Amino-acids found in terrestrial living organisms are almost exclusively of the L configuration; in fossil material, however, the free or bound amino-acids slowly racemize. From data on the configuration of amino-acids from the interior of shells, Hare and Abelson[9] estimated a racemization period of about 10^5 yr. Recent results from our laboratory on tar covered bones from the Rancho La Brea, Los Angeles, show significant racemization after 12,000 yr. Thus, an L configuration of the amino-acids in meteorites would be evidence for contamination, whereas the presence of racemates would argue for chemical synthesis or for very old biogenic amino-acids.

We extracted samples (weighing 2 g) of Orgueil, Mokoia, and Murray meteorites, previously treated with organic solvents[10], with water and then hydrolysed at $100\,^\circ$C with 6 M HCl for 24 h. After filtration the hydrolysate was evaporated to dryness. We dissolved each residue in 2 ml. of distilled water, desalted on "Dowex 50" (20 ml.), and the amino-acids were eluted with 500 ml. of 2 M NH_4OH. After evaporation to dryness the residual amino-acids were transformed into N-TFA–isopropyl esters as described in ref. 2. Aliquots (in $CHCl_3$) were chromatographed

碳质球粒陨石与一块前寒武纪燧石中的氨基酸构型

奥罗等

编者按

化学家约翰·奥罗及其得克萨斯的同事报道称在富碳陨石中发现了氨基酸（参见下一篇文章），由此引发了陨石可以作为生命起源原始成分的一种来源的讨论。尽管生物体中所包含的氨基酸只有两种镜像形式中的一种——左手构型，但在无生命过程中形成的氨基酸则是两种构型的等量混合物。所以对左手构型和右手构型相对量的检测就可以分辨出生物源的污染。在本文中，奥罗及他的同事们描述了一种用于检测的新方法，还将这种方法应用于陨石和沉积岩样品。然而，直到现在人们还在争论陨石中左手构型的过剩是否会是其本身所固有的。

为了将对地球上生命起源和演化的研究结果[1]与在宇宙中可能观察到的相关结果联系起来，我们建立了一种灵敏的蛋白质氨基酸分析方法，这种方法还能同时测定它们的光学构型[2]。该方法的原理是应用具有光学活性固定相的气相色谱分离对映异构的N-三氟乙酰基（N-TFA）-异丙酯[3]。我们在此要描述的是如何把这种方法应用于陨石和一块前寒武纪沉积岩。

在碳质球粒陨石中存在痕量的氨基酸[4-8]已经被归结为污染和无生源过程。但是对于这些化合物的构型的确定可能会使人们得以区分出污染和无生源过程这两种可能性。在地球上的生物有机体中发现的氨基酸几乎毫无例外是L构型；而在化石中，自由氨基酸或结合氨基酸会缓慢地外消旋化。根据来自地壳内氨基酸的构型数据，黑尔和埃布尔森[9]估算出外消旋化的周期约为10^5年。最近我们实验室对来自洛杉矶兰乔拉布雷阿的被天然沥青覆盖的骨骼进行了研究，结果表明，在经过了12,000年之后有明显的外消旋化出现。因此，陨石中氨基酸的L构型将可以作为被污染的证据，而外消旋体的存在则支持化学合成过程或极为古老的生源氨基酸。

我们用水抽提了预先用有机溶剂处理过的奥盖尔、莫科亚和默里陨星的样品（重2克）[10]，接着于100℃下在6摩尔/升 HCl中水解24小时。将水解产物过滤后挥发至干。我们将每种残余物分别溶解在2毫升蒸馏水中，并用"道威克斯50"阳离子交换树脂（20毫升）脱盐，再用500毫升2摩尔/升NH_4OH提取出氨基酸。挥发至干后，用参考文献2中所描述的方法将残余的氨基酸转化为N-三氟乙酰基-

369

at 110° C on a 500 foot × 0.02 inch stainless steel capillary column, coated with N-TFA–L-valyl-L-valine cyclohexyl ester[2], using He as the carrier gas at 20 pounds/inch[2] and an FID. Two additional specimens of Murray (3.3 g and 4.6 g) which had not been treated with organic solvents were Soxhlet extracted with water for several hours and the water extracts hydrolysed and analysed in the same manner.

Chromatograms for Orgueil, Mokoia, and Murray meteorites are given in Figs. 1–3. We identified the peaks by comparison with standards and, for the Murray only, by GC-mass spectrometry[11]. Published data[4-6] on amino-acids in Orgueil are in agreement with the present results.

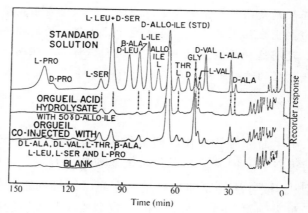

Fig. 1. Orgueil meteorite. Chromatogram of the N-TFA–isopropyl esters of the amino-acids from acid hydrolysis of the organic solvent and water extracted meteorite residue. D-Alloisoleucine was added to the meteorite as an internal standard. Taking the L-isoleucine peak in the second and third chromatogram as reference shows that the L-Val, L-Thr, β-Ala, L-Leu, and L-Ser peaks are increased on co-injection. The ratio of the alanine peaks is changed on co-injection of the DL standard, as expected. The small peak in the proline region does not coincide with the L-isomer (see co-injection), nor with the D-isomer (relative retention time).

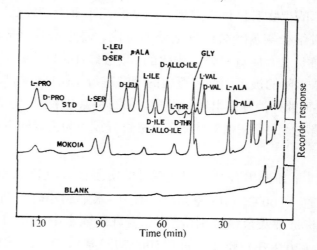

Fig. 2. Mokoia meteorite. Chromatogram of the N-TFA–isopropyl esters of the amino-acids from acid hydrolysis of the organic solvent and water extracted meteorite residue.

异丙酯。将试样（溶于CHCl₃中）在110℃下进行色谱分离，所用的色谱柱为一根500英尺×0.02英寸、涂有N–三氟乙酰基–L–缬氨酰–L–缬氨酸环己酯固定液的不锈钢毛细管柱[2]，载气为He，压力为20磅/平方英寸，检测器为火焰离子化检测器。将另外两份未经有机溶剂处理的默里陨星样品（3.3克和4.6克）用水进行索氏提取，几小时后，将水相提取物用同样的方法水解并分析。

图1~图3显示的分别是由奥盖尔、莫科亚和默里陨星样品得到的色谱图。我们通过与标准物进行比较来鉴别图中的各个峰。针对默里样品，我们还采用了气相色谱–质谱联用法[11]。一些已发表的有关奥盖尔样品中氨基酸的数据[4-6]与当前结果是一致的。

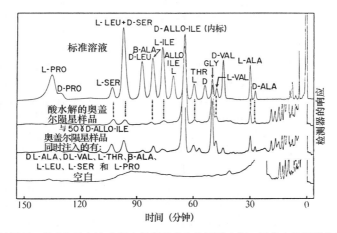

图 1. 奥盖尔陨星样品。将有机溶剂和水提取的陨星残余物用酸水解，再将由此得到的氨基酸的N–三氟乙酰基–异丙酯进行色谱分析。向陨星物质中加入D–别亮氨酸（D-ALLO-ILE）作为内标。以第二和第三个色谱图中L–异亮氨酸（L-ILE）的峰为参考，可以看出L–缬氨酸（L-Val）、L–苏氨酸（L-Thr）、β–丙氨酸（β-Ala）、L–亮氨酸（L-Leu）和L–丝氨酸（L-Ser）的峰因共同注入而得到了增强。正如预期的那样，丙氨酸峰的比例由于与DL标准物共同注入而发生了变化。脯氨酸区域中的小峰与L异构体（见共同注入时）和D异构体（相对保留时间）都不一致。

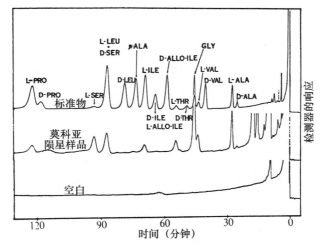

图 2. 莫科亚陨星样品。将有机溶剂和水提取的陨星残余物用酸水解，再将由此得到的氨基酸的N–三氟乙酰基–异丙酯进行色谱分析。

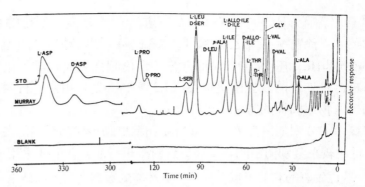

Fig. 3. Murray meteorite. Chromatogram of the *N*-TFA–isopropyl esters of the amino-acids from acid hydrolysis of the organic solvent and water extracted meteorite residue. L-Alloisoleucine was added as an internal standard.

These results suggest multiple sources for the amino-acids in carbonaceous chondrites. The data on Orgueil and Mokoia (Figs. 1 and 2; Table 1) show that the bound amino-acids in these meteorites are almost exclusively of the L configuration with the exception of D-alanine, which is present in amounts of 22.5% and 6.5%, respectively. Although it could be interpreted, on the basis of the exhaustive organic solvent and water washing of the meteorites, that the L-amino-acids are of extra-terrestrial origin, we believe that the bulk of the bound amino-acids are the result of terrestrial contamination by micro-organisms. The presence of some D-alanine is not against this conclusion, for this particular D isomer occurs in bacterial cell walls and other microbes. A minimum of 1,800 viable bacteria g[-1] of Mokoia has been observed[12], and non-viable micro-organisms have been estimated to be up to thirty times more abundant[13].

Table 1. Percentage of D-Enantiomers in the Amino-Acids from Hydrolysates of Carbonaceous Chrondrites and a Soil Sample

Amino-acid	$D/D+L \times 100$			
	Orgueil	Mokoia	Murray	Soil*
Alanine	22.5	6.5	13.0	8.6
Valine	0.0†	0.0†	2.4	0.5
Threonine	0.0†	0.0†	0.0†	0.0†
D-Alloisoleucine–L–isoleucine	‡	0.0†	3.8§	1.3
Leucine	0.0†	0.0†	¶	¶
Proline	0.0†	0.0†	12.3	4.2
Aspartic acid	0.0†	0.0†	24.6	8.0

* Taken 5–7 cm beneath surface in a grassy area of Memorial Park, Houston, Texas.

† Below limits of detection. A small amount of D-serine might be present in the L-leucine, since the peaks of the *N*-TFA–isopropyl esters of these two compounds overlap. For this same reason no data are given for the enantiomeric composition of serine.

‡ D-Alloisoleucine was added to this meteorite as an internal standard.

§ After correction for D-alloisoleucine, contained in added L-alloisoleucine (Fig. 3).

¶ On the assumption that the leucine peak contained a negligible amount of D-serine, the figures are 1.9% for Murray and 2.4% for the soil sample.

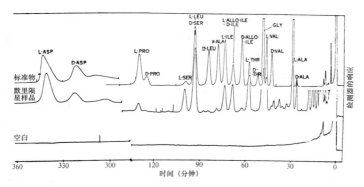

图 3. 默里陨星样品。将有机溶剂和水提取的陨星残余物用酸水解，再将由此得到的氨基酸的N–三氟乙
酰基–异丙酯进行色谱分析。加入L–别异亮氨酸作为内标。

上述结果表明碳质球粒陨石中的氨基酸可能有多重来源。奥盖尔和莫科亚样品
的数据显示（图1和图2；表1）：这些陨星样品中的结合氨基酸几乎全部是L构型，
只有D–丙氨酸例外，它在两个样品中的含量分别为22.5%和6.5%。尽管基于对陨星
样品用有机溶剂和水进行的彻底清洗有可能可以把这个现象解释为L–氨基酸具有地
外起源，但我们相信大部分结合氨基酸是源自地球上微生物造成的污染。一些D–丙
氨酸的存在与这一结论并不矛盾，因为这种特殊的D型异构体也存在于细菌的细胞
壁和其他微生物中。在每克莫科亚样品中至少观测到了1,800个活细菌[12]，而死去的
微生物估计还会比这高出30倍[13]。

表1. 碳质球粒陨石和一份土壤样品的水解产物中氨基酸D型对映异构体的百分比

氨基酸	D/(D+L) × 100			
	奥盖尔	莫科亚	默里	土壤*
丙氨酸	22.5	6.5	13.0	8.6
缬氨酸	0.0†	0.0†	2.4	0.5
苏氨酸	0.0†	0.0†	0.0†	0.0†
D–别异亮氨酰–L–异亮氨酸	‡	0.0†	3.8§	1.3
亮氨酸	0.0†	0.0†	¶	¶
脯氨酸	0.0†	0.0†	12.3	4.2
天冬氨酸	0.0†	0.0†	24.6	8.0

* 取自得克萨斯休斯敦纪念公园中一片草坪的地表以下5厘米～7厘米。

† 低于检测限。少量D–丝氨酸可能混在L–亮氨酸之中，因为这两种化合物的N–三氟乙酰基–异丙酯的峰
　是重合的。也是由于这个原因，没有给出丝氨酸的对映异构成分的数据。

‡ 向该陨星样品中加入D–别异亮氨酸作为内标。

§ 对D–别异亮氨酸的含量进行了校正，其中含有加入的L–别异亮氨酸（图3）。

¶ 假设亮氨酸峰中含有少到可以忽略的D–丝氨酸，则在默里样品中它的含量为1.9%，在土壤样品中为
　2.4%。

Murray, on the other hand, had not only 13% D-alanine, but also 2.4% D-valine, 3.8% D-alloisoleucine and as much as 12.3% D-proline and 24.6% D-aspartic acid in the water insoluble or bound amino-acid fraction (Fig. 3; Table 1). A microbiological count gave 6,000 viable bacteria g^{-1} for this meteorite[12], indicating considerable contamination. We therefore analysed a recent soil sample, which showed a similar pattern (Table 1) to that found for Murray. The figures for D-amino-acids in the soil are not as high as in the meteorite but they are significantly higher than the usual analytical racemization values[14].

Considering the relatively larger amounts of D-amino-acids in Murray, compared with the soil (the difference is about 7% on average) and the presence in the Murray chromatogram (Fig. 3) of many minor additional peaks, it seems that a small percentage of the amino-acids of this meteorite are racemic mixtures of possible abiotic origin. This interpretation gains support from an analysis of the water extracts of Murray, where peaks with the retention time of D and L-alanine were observed in approximately equal quantities (44% and 56% respectively), the total amount of this amino-acid in the hydrolysed water extracts being only 0.05 μg g^{-1} (unpublished observations). Final opinion should, however, be reserved until more information is available on the chemical synthesis of amino-acids from simple precursors during the entry of the meteorite through the atmosphere, or during the acid hydrolysis step, and on the configuration and inversion of amino-acids in soils. The presence of traces of β-alanine in Murray (Fig. 3) could also be an indication of abiogenesis, but it is known that this amino-acid can be formed by bacterial decarboxylation of aspartic acid[15].

A wide range of amino-acids has been detected in Pre-Cambrian sediments. It was suggested[16] that these compounds were formed biogenically 1–3×10^9 years ago. Abelson and Hare[17] have, however, demonstrated the L configuration of amino-acids from a Gunflint chert (1.9×10^9 yr old), using enzymatic and other tests. This conclusion has since been confirmed[18-20].

A hydrolysate of the Fig Tree chert prepared in Dr. Kvenvolden's laboratory[18] was analysed by gas chromatography with an asymmetric stationary phase in our laboratory. We found all the amino-acids reported earlier. With the exception of D-alanine, any peaks corresponding to D-isomers are negligible.

These results provide convincing evidence that the amino-acids in the Fig Tree chert are almost exclusively of the L configuration and argue for recent terrestrial contamination of the samples, as in the case of the Orgueil and the Mokoia meteorites. A similar argument can be made out for Murray, although in this case about 90% of the amino-acids probably result from biological contamination and the remainder (both D and L configurations) are of probable chemical origin. It remains to be seen whether the small amounts of racemic amino-acids were syngenetic with the meteorite parent body or were synthesized later during the extraterrestrial or terrestrial history of Murray. The presence of racemic mixtures of several amino-acids in the Murchison meteorite has been reported recently[21];

另一方面，在默里样品不溶于水的部分或含结合氨基酸的部分中，不仅含有13%的D-丙氨酸，还含有2.4%的D-缬氨酸、3.8%的D-别异亮氨酸，以及12.3%的D-脯氨酸和24.6%的D-天冬氨酸（图3；表1）。对该陨星样品进行微生物学计量得出每克含有6,000个活细菌[12]，这表明样品受到了相当程度的污染。因此我们分析了一份最近的土壤样品，它的情况与在默里样品中发现的情况类似（表1）。土壤中D-氨基酸的含量不如默里陨星中高，但是明显高于在通常情况下分析得到的外消旋数值[14]。

因为默里样品中D-氨基酸的含量相对较大，对照土壤样品（平均差值约为7%）和默里样品色谱图中出现的很多小附加峰，说明该陨星中的氨基酸有一小部分可能是与无生源过程相关的外消旋混合物。上述解释可以从对默里样品水相提取物的分析结果获得支持，从对应于D-丙氨酸和L-丙氨酸保留时间处的峰中可以看到两者的量大致相等（分别为44%和56%），这种氨基酸在水相提取物的水解产物中的总量仅为0.05微克/克（尚未发表的观测结果）。但最终的结论还应有所保留，除非我们能够获得关于由简单前体在陨星进入大气层期间或在酸水解步骤中能够化学合成氨基酸的更多信息以及关于土壤中氨基酸的构型和转化的更多信息。在默里陨星中存在痕量的β-丙氨酸（图3）也可以证明无生源说，但我们知道这种氨基酸可以通过细菌对天冬氨酸的脱羧作用形成[15]。

在前寒武纪沉积岩中检测到了很多种氨基酸。有人指出[16]，这些化合物是在10亿年～30亿年前由生物活动所形成的。不过，埃布尔森和黑尔[17]已用酶学和其他检测方法证实提取自冈弗林特燧石（年龄为19亿年）的氨基酸是L构型。这一结论后来得到了确认[18-20]。

我们实验室用具有不对称固定相的气相色谱对由克文沃尔登博士实验室[18]制备的无花果树燧石的水解产物进行了分析。我们发现了以前曾报道过的所有氨基酸；除D-丙氨酸以外，其他所有对应于D异构体的峰都是可忽略的。

这些结果为无花果树燧石中的氨基酸几乎毫无例外都是L构型提供了可靠的证据，并且支持样品在近期内曾受到过地球上物质污染这一说法，这与奥盖尔陨星和莫科亚陨星的情况是一样的。可以认为默里样品也同样受到了污染，虽然在默里陨星中，约有90%的氨基酸有可能来自于生物污染，而其余部分（不论是D构型还是L构型）则可能来自于化学上的成因。少量外消旋氨基酸到底是与陨星母体同时生成的，还是后来默里陨星在地球以外或在地球上度过的时期中合成的？这个问题仍有待于确定。最近有人报道在默奇森陨星中有若干种氨基酸的外消旋混合物存在[21]，

we have confirmed this observation.

We thank Dr. A. Cavaille, Dr. E. P. Henderson, Dr. C. B. Moore, Professor J. Orcel, and Dr. K. A. Kvenvolden for their help in obtaining samples. We also thank Mr. J. M. Gibert and Mr. J. C. Raia for assistance. This work was supported in part by grants from NASA.

(**230**, 107-108; 1971)

J. Oró, S. Nakaparksin, H. Lichtenstein and E. Gil-Av: Department of Biophysical Sciences, University of Houston, Houston, Texas 77004.

Received July 20, 1970; revised January 25, 1971.

References:
1. Oró, J., and Nooner, D. W., *Nature*, **213**, 1082 (1967).
2. Nakaparksin, S., Birrell, P., Gil-Av, E., and Oró, J., *J. Chromatog Sci.*, **8**, 177 (1970).
3. Gil-Av, E., Feibush, B., and Charles-Sigler, R., in *Gas Chromatography* (edit. by Littlewood, A. B.), 227 (Institute of Petroleum, London, 1967).
4. Anders, E., DuFresne, E. R., Hayatsu, R., Cavaille, A., DuFresne, A., and Fitch, F. W., *Science*, **146**, 1157 (1964).
5. Vallentyne, J. R., in *The Origin of Prebiological Systems and of their Molecular Matrices* (edit. by Fox, S. W.), 105 (Academic Press, New York and London, 1965).
6. Kaplan, I. R., Degens, E. T., and Reuter, J. H., *Geochim. Cosmochim. Acta*, **27**, 805 (1970).
7. Hayes, J., *Geochim. Cosmochim. Acta*, **31**, 1395 (1967).
8. Raia, J. C., thesis, Univ. Houston (1966).
9. Hare, O. E., and Abelson, P. J., *Carnegie Institution Yearbook*, **66**, 526 (1967).
10. Nooner, D. W., and Oró, J., *Geochim. Cosmochim. Acta*, **31**, 1359 (1967).
11. Gelpi, E., Koenig, W. A., Gibert, J., and Oró, J., *J. Gas Chromatog.*, **7**, 604 (1969).
12. Oró, J., and Tornabene, T., *Science*, **150**, 1046 (1965).
13. Claus, G., and Nagy, B., *Nature*, **192**, 594 (1961).
14. Nakaparksin, S., Gil-Av, E., and Oró, J., *Anal. Biochem.*, **33**, 374 (1970).
15. Oró, J., and Skewes, H. B., *Nature*, **207**, 1042 (1965).
16. Schopf, J. W., Kvenvolden, K. A., and Barghoorn, E. S., *Proc. US Nat. Acad. Sci.*, **59**, 639 (1968).
17. Abelson, P. J., and Hare, P. E., *Carnegie Institute Yearbook*, **67**, 208 (1967–68).
18. Kvenvolden, K. A., Peterson, E., and Pollock, G. E., *Nature*, **221**, 141 (1969).
19. Gil-Av, E., Charles-Sigler, R., Fischer, D., and Nurok, D., *J. Gas Chromatog.*, **4**, 51 (1966).
20. Pollock, G. E., and Oyama, V. I., *J. Gas Chromatog.*, **4**, 126 (1966).
21. Kvenvolden, K., Lawless, J., Pering, K., Peterson, E., Flores, J., Ponnamperuma, C., Kaplan, I. R., and Moore, C., *Nature*, **228**, 923 (1970).

这一观测结果已经得到了我们的确认。

感谢卡瓦耶博士、亨德森博士、穆尔博士、奥塞尔教授和克文沃尔登博士帮助我们获取样品。还要感谢吉贝特先生和拉亚先生的协助。本项研究得到了美国国家航空航天局的部分资助。

（王耀杨 翻译；周江 审稿）

Amino-Acids, Aliphatic and Aromatic Hydrocarbons in the Murchison Meteorite

J. Oró *et al.*

Editor's Note

From where did the earliest life on Earth get its raw ingredients? The discovery of complex carbon-based (organic) molecules in meteorites in the 1960s by John Oró at the University of Houston and others raised the possibility that life might have been seeded from compounds delivered from space. Here Oró and his coworkers explore the range of organic compounds that exist in carbon-rich meteorites, with an analysis of the composition of a fragment of the Murchison meteorite that fell over Australia in 1969. They describe a complex mixture of hydrocarbons—but the Murchison meteorite was already known to contain amino-acids too, the building blocks of proteins. It was later found even to carry the "bases" of nucleic acids.

TWO recently fallen carbonaceous chondrites have provided organic analytical results significantly different from those obtained with other carbonaceous chondrites[1-3]. The Allende meteorite, a type III carbonaceous chondrite which contains 0.27% carbon and 0.007% nitrogen[4], was shown to have only traces of extractable organic compounds[5]. Small amounts of aliphatic and aromatic hydrocarbons were released by heating while no significant amounts of nitrogen containing compounds were detected[6-8]. This is consistent with the extremely low nitrogen content of this carbonaceous chondrite. Another unique feature of this meteorite is the heterogenous distribution of certain carbon-containing inclusions[9]. The Murchison meteorite, a type III carbonaceous chondrite, contains substantial amounts of amino-acids, predominantly cyclic aliphatic hydrocarbons[10], which are consistent with the appreciable content of carbon and nitrogen of this meteorite (2 and 0.16% respectively). The amino-acids include non-protein components such as sarcosine and 2-methylalanine and, significantly, approximately racemic mixtures of D and L enantiomers of protein amino-acids such as alanine, valine and proline[10].

The presence of D and L enantiomers of protein amino-acids, and aspartic acid, has been observed before in the fraction containing the bound amino-acids of the Murray meteorite[11]. The predominance of the L configuration observed in this case, and a comparison with results obtained with soil hydrolysates, suggested that these amino-acids were derived essentially from terrestrial contamination[11], or that only a small percentage of them (less than 10% on average) were probably indigenous meteoritic amino-acids of a racemic composition[12]. A racemic composition was also indicated for the smaller amounts of supposedly free amino-acids (hydrolysed water extract) present in the Murray[12]. In a continuation of these studies we now have analysed the organic compounds of the Murchison meteorite by water extraction and combined gas chromatography and mass

默奇森陨星中的氨基酸、脂肪烃和芳香烃

奥罗等

编者按

地球上最早的生命是从哪里获得其原始成分的？20 世纪 60 年代，休斯敦大学的约翰·奥罗以及其他人在陨石中发现了以碳为主要原料的复杂（有机）分子，这大大增加了生命起源于来自太空的化合物的可能性（译者注：即无生源说或称自然发生说）。在本文中，奥罗及其合作者通过分析 1969 年坠落于澳大利亚的默奇森陨星的碎片成分，探测出了富碳陨石中的有机化合物范围。他们将其描述为一种复杂的烃类混合物，不过人们当时已经知道默奇森陨星中也含有构成蛋白质的基本物质——氨基酸。后来还发现其中甚至存在构成核酸的"碱基"。

最近坠落的两颗碳质球粒陨石的有机分析结果明显不同于由其他碳质球粒陨石得到的结果 [1-3]。阿连德陨石是一颗含碳量为 0.27%、含氮量为 0.007% [4] 的 III 类碳质球粒陨石，从中只能提取出极微量的有机化合物 [5]。在加热时有少量的脂肪烃和芳香烃释放出来，但没有检测到显著量的含氮化合物 [6-8]。这与该碳质球粒陨石的含氮量非常低是一致的。这颗陨石的另一个独有特征是其中某种含碳内含物的不均匀分布 [9]。默奇森陨石也属于 III 类碳质球粒陨石，它含有大量的氨基酸，占绝对优势的是环状脂肪烃 [10]，这与该陨石中含有大量的碳和氮是一致的（分别为 2% 和 0.16%）。默奇森陨星中的氨基酸不仅包括肌氨酸、2- 甲基丙氨酸等非蛋白质组成成分，更重要的是，它还包括诸如丙氨酸、缬氨酸和脯氨酸等蛋白质氨基酸的 D 型和 L 型对映异构体的近似外消旋混合物 [10]。

此前也曾在含结合氨基酸的默里陨星碎片中发现有蛋白质氨基酸的 D 型和 L 型对映异构体和天冬氨酸存在 [11]。在这个例子中可以看到 L 构型是占显著优势的，将其与从土壤水解产物中得到的结果相比较，说明这些氨基酸大多来源于地球上的污染 [11]，或者说其中只有比例很小（平均不足 10%）的部分有可能来源于具有外消旋组成的陨星固有氨基酸 [12]。外消旋组分的存在也说明默里陨星中所谓的自由氨基酸（水解后的水相提取物）的量会更少一些 [12]。作为上述研究的延续，如今我们利用水相萃取法以及气相色谱-质谱联用技术对默奇森陨星中的有机化合物进行了分析。

spectrometry.

A relatively large piece of the Murchison meteorite almost entirely covered with fusion crust was the primary source of material for this study. It had no visible fractures and a minimum of soil-staining and weathering, giving a very clean general appearance. Several inside pieces were taken after removing more than two centimetres of the fusion crust and outer surface from the specimen. One of the selected inside pieces was pulverized to less than 60 mesh size and processed for amino-acid analysis. About 20 g of this material was refluxed with 25 ml. of triply distilled water for 14 h. After decanting, filtering and washing, the meteorite residue was re-extracted for 1 h and all extracts were combined and evaporated to dryness in a current of pure nitrogen. The residue from the water extract was dissolved in 10 ml. of 6 M HCl and hydrolysed for 24 h *in vacuo* in a sealed tube at 100°C. After evaporation to dryness the hydrolysate was dissolved in water and desalted with "Dowex 50" (H⁺) ion exchange resin and eluted with water and 2 N NH₄OH (10×bed volume). The eluate was evaporated as described and the residual amino-acids were esterified with 3 M HCl–isopropanol at 100°C for 30 min and then converted into N-trifluoroacetyl–amino-acid–isopropyl esters[13,14]. Aliquots (in CHCl₃) of these derivatives were analysed by combined gas chromatography and mass spectrometry and by gas chromatography on optically active phases using methods described before[15,16].

Fig. 1*A* shows a representative gas chromatogram obtained by injection of 1 μl. of the N-TFA isopropyl esters into a 150 m × 0.5 mm interior diameter capillary gas chromatographic column coated with 3% SF-96 in an LKB 9000 gas chromatograph-mass spectrometer. This column, which has an efficiency of 180,000 plates, was also used for the analysis of the hydrocarbons. Preliminary mass spectrometric evidence was obtained for the presence of glycine, alanine, 2-methyl-alanine, amino-butyric acid, valine, glutamic acid, proline and some of the leucines. Glycine was the principal amino-acid observed (5.3 μg/g) and the others were found in amounts of the order of 0.1 μg/g or more (alanine 3.1 μg/g). An appreciable number of other amino-acids, and possibly amines, remain to be identified as shown by the relatively large number of components of the gas chromatogram. More than half of the major peaks have been identified, however, and most agree with the observations by Kvenvolden *et al.*[10]. Gas chromatographic analysis of the N-TFA–amino-acid-isopropyl esters on a 162 m long × 0.5 mm interior diameter capillary column coated with N-TFA–L-valyl-L-valine cyclohexyl ester gave evidence for the separation of D and L enantiomers of alanine and proline in approximately equimolar amounts. This provides evidence for the chemical formation of amino-acids in one or several of the following ways: (*a*) extraterrestrial abiotic synthesis, before, during or after the formation of the meteorite parent body; (*b*) extensive diagenesis, in the unlikely event that the primary amino-acids were of either L or D configuration; (*c*) formation by synthetic or decomposition reactions during the entry of the meteorite through the terrestrial atmosphere, and (*d*) chemical synthesis from amino-acid precursors during the hydrolysis of the water extracts. Although (*d*) cannot yet be ruled out, the first mode of synthesis seems the most likely[10-12].

　　一块几乎完全被熔凝壳所覆盖的较大的默奇森陨星碎片是这项研究的主要材料来源。它没有任何可见的裂缝，仅有最低限度的泥污和风化痕迹，这使得整体外观看上去非常干净。在从样品上移除超过 2 厘米厚的熔凝壳和外表面后，得到若干内部碎片。选定其中一块碎片将其研磨到小于 60 目尺寸后进行氨基酸分析。取约 20 克该物质与 25 毫升三次蒸馏水一起回流 14 小时。在倾析、过滤和洗涤之后，将陨星残余物重新萃取 1 小时，并将所有提取物合在一起，在纯净的氮气气流中挥发至干。将水相提取物的残渣溶解在 10 毫升的 6 摩尔/升 HCl 溶液中并令其在 100℃、真空下于密闭管内水解 24 小时。挥发至干后，将水解产物溶解于水中，用"道威克斯50"（H⁺）阳离子交换树脂除盐，再用水和 2 当量浓度 NH₄OH（10 倍柱床体积）洗提。将洗出液用上述方法挥发，残余的氨基酸用 3 摩尔/升 HCl– 异丙醇在 100℃ 下进行酯化，反应 30 分钟后即可转化为 N– 三氟乙酰基–氨基酸异丙酯 [13,14]。将上述衍生物试样（溶于 CHCl₃ 中）用气相色谱 – 质谱联用仪进行分析，并按照以前介绍过的方法 [15,16] 对其光学活性相采用气相色谱法进行分析。

　　图 1A 显示的是一张具有代表性的气相色谱图：将 1 微升 N– 三氟乙酰基 – 异丙酯注入 LKB 9000 气相色谱 – 质谱联用仪的内径为 150 米 × 0.5 毫米、涂有 3% SF–96 固定液的毛细管气相色谱柱中。这种有效塔板数为 180,000 的色谱柱也可用于对烃类物质的分析。前期通过质谱得到的结果证明了甘氨酸、丙氨酸、2- 甲基丙氨酸、氨基丁酸、缬氨酸、谷氨酸、脯氨酸以及一些亮氨酸的存在。甘氨酸是所观测到的主要氨基酸（5.3 微克 / 克），而其他氨基酸只有数量级为 0.1 微克 / 克的量或者略多些（丙氨酸为 3.1 微克 / 克）。气相色谱分析表明试样中存在着很多组分，因此仍有相当数量的其他氨基酸（可能还有胺类）需要鉴别。但有超过一半的主峰所代表的物质已经得到了确定，其中大部分与克文沃尔登等人 [10] 的观测结果相符。使用内部涂有 N– 三氟乙酰基 –L– 缬氨酰 –L– 缬氨酸环己酯固定液的长为 162 米、内径为 0.5毫米的毛细管色谱柱对 N– 三氟乙酰基 – 氨基酸异丙酯进行气相色谱分析，结果表明，丙氨酸和脯氨酸的 D 型和 L 型对映异构体能有效分离且摩尔量几乎相等。这为以下关于氨基酸的一种或几种化学形成途径提供了证据：（a）地球外非生物合成，在陨星母体形成之前、之间或之后；（b）大范围成岩作用，假如早期的氨基酸就具有 D 构型或 L 构型，当然这不太可能发生；（c）在陨星穿过地球大气层的过程中，通过合成或分解反应形成；（d）由氨基酸前体在水相提取物的水解过程中通过化学反应合成。尽管现在还不能完全排除（d），但第一种合成途径似乎是最有可能的 [10-12]。

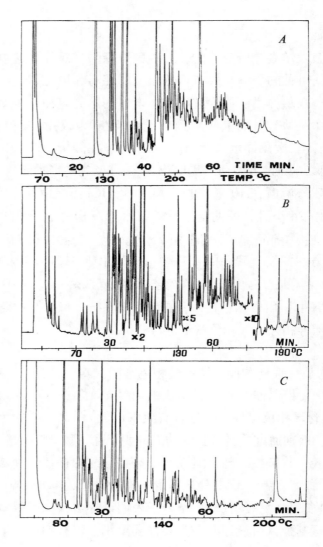

Fig. 1. Gas chromatograms obtained on an LKB 9000 gas chromatograph–mass spectrometer with a 150 m×0.5 mm stainless steel open tubular capillary column coated with SF-96 operated at 1.41 kg/cm² and the temperatures listed. A, N-TFA–isopropyl derivatives of the water extracted amino-acids. Column isothermal at 70°C for 10 min and programmed at 3% up to 200°C. The nine major peaks of this chromatogram are, from left to right: solvent front, unknown; alanine, unknown; glycine, unknown; valine, norleucine (internal standard), unknown; and glutamic acid. Almost all other peaks, including the above listed unknowns, have fragmentation patterns of amino-compounds. B, Alkanes from the pentane fraction of the benzene–methanol extract. They range from nine to sixteen carbon atoms. Saturated structures predominate in this range. The column was isothermal at 50°C for 10 min and programmed at 2°/min up to 200°C. C, Benzene fraction from benzene/methanol extract. The column was isothermal at 65°C for 15 min and programmed at 2°/min to 200°C.

Another of the inside pieces of our specimen, weighing 7.5 g, was used for the analysis of hydrocarbons. It was washed with 10 ml. of a mixture of benzene and methanol (3:1), dried, pulverized and Soxhlet extracted with 15 ml. of the same mixture in a modified all

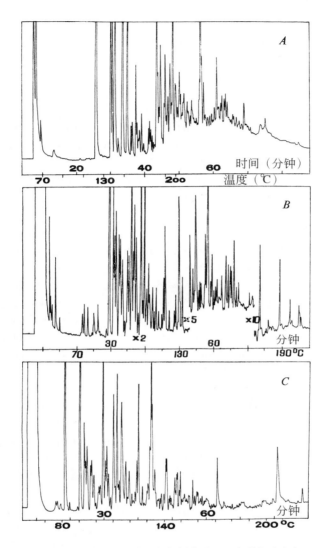

图 1. 用 LKB 9000 气相色谱–质谱联用仪获得的气相色谱图，色谱柱为涂有 SF-96 固定液的 150 米
×0.5 毫米不锈钢开管式毛细管柱，压力为 1.41 千克/平方厘米，温度标于图中。A，水相提取的
氨基酸的 N–三氟乙酰基–异丙基衍生物。将色谱柱于 70℃ 恒温 10 分钟，再以 3% 的速度程序升
温至 200℃。这张色谱图中的 9 个主要的峰从左到右分别是：溶剂前沿，未知；丙氨酸，未知；甘
氨酸，未知；缬氨酸，正亮氨酸（内标），未知；谷氨酸。几乎所有的其他峰，包括上面列出的未
知峰，都有氨基化合物的碎片模式。B，来自于苯–甲醇萃取物的戊烷馏分的烷烃。其范围从 9 个
碳原子到 16 个碳原子不等。饱和结构在此范围内占优势。将色谱柱在 50℃ 恒温 10 分钟，再以每
分钟 2℃ 的速度程序升温至 200℃。C，来自于苯/甲醇萃取物的苯馏分。将色谱柱在 65℃ 恒温 15
分钟，再以每分钟 2℃ 的速度程序升温至 200℃。

    我们从陨星样品中另取一块重 7.5 克的内部碎片进行烃类物质的分析。用 10 毫升
苯和甲醇（3:1）的混合物冲洗后，干燥，研磨成粉，并在改进的全玻璃装置中用

glass apparatus[17]. After refluxing for 3 h the extract was concentrated to a few microlitres and fractionated on a silica gel column with pentane, benzene and methanol[18]. About a 1/10 aliquot of the pentane fraction concentrated to a few microlitres was injected into the SF-96 capillary column.

Fig. 1B shows a representative gas chromatogram of the pentane fraction. The aliphatic hydrocarbons observed range from C_{10} to relatively high molecular weight components. The most abundant series corresponds to the branched saturated alkanes. They include predominantly monomethylated and dimethylated isomers. Intense ions that correspond to the loss of fragments with m/e 29, 43, 57 and higher values suggest the presence of branching at positions 2, 3, 4, and so on, respectively.

The C_nH_{2n-1}, C_nH_{2n-3} and C_nH_{2n-5} series were also observed but were substantially less abundant. Up to C_{15} the C_nH_{2n-1} ions seemed to belong to olefins rather than monocyclic alkanes, for the m/e doublets corresponding to the fragment ions C_nH_{2n-1} and C_nH_{2n-2}, for $n=5$, 6 or higher, characteristic of cyclics, were not present. The C_nH_{2n-3} series increased in intensity after the C_{14} region, and suggested bicyclic structures with aliphatic branching. Fig 1C shows a representative gas chromatogram of the hydrocarbon fraction eluted with benzene. Mass spectra with fragmentation patterns corresponding to naphthalene, phenanthrene or anthracene, and branched aliphatic chains were observed. These data, together with gas chromatographic retention times, indicate the presence of alkyl substituted dicyclic and tricyclic aromatic compounds[19]. There is an intriguing similarity in the composition and complexity of these hydrocarbon mixtures with those obtained by pyrolysis and other experiments of synthesis (see, for example, ref. 20). Preliminary analytical results by vaporization pyrolysis gas chromatography-mass spectrometry[8] have also shown the presence of large amounts of aliphatic and aromatic hydrocarbons and other organic compounds with heteroatoms (unpublished results).

Overall, the Murchison meteorite contains substantial amounts of extractable organic compounds, which give distribution patterns significantly different and much more complex than those observed previously, indicating abiotic synthesis, extensive diagenesis and related chemical processes, or both. This carbonaceous chondrite seems to be one of the first examined where the amount of terrestrial biological contamination is very small.

We thank R. S. Clarke, jun., and E. J. Olsen for specimens, and NASA for support.

(**230**, 105-106; 1971)

J. Oró, J. Gibert, H. Lichtenstein, S. Wikstrom and D. A. Flory: Departments of Biophysical Sciences and Chemistry, University of Houston, Houston, Texas 77004.

Received January 25, 1971.

15 毫升上述混合物进行索氏提取 [17]。回流 3 小时后，提取液被浓缩至几微升，然后在硅胶柱上用戊烷、苯和甲醇对提取物进行分离 [18]。将戊烷馏分中大约 1/10 的部分浓缩至几微升，然后注入 SF–96 毛细管柱。

图 1B 显示的是戊烷馏分的典型气相色谱图。从图中可以观察到脂肪烃的范围包括了从 C_{10} 到分子量相对较高的成分。含量较高的组分对应于有支链的饱和烷烃。其中主要是一甲基化和二甲基化的同分异构体。主要离子峰对应的碎片丢失为质荷比（m/e）29、43、57 以及更高数值，这表明支链分别在 2、3 和 4 位等位置存在。

还可以观察到 C_nH_{2n-1}、C_nH_{2n-3} 和 C_nH_{2n-5} 系列，但是含量要低很多。一直到 C_{15}，C_nH_{2n-1} 离子看起来都更像是属于烯烃而不是单环烷烃，因为对应于碎片离子 C_nH_{2n-1} 和 C_nH_{2n-2}（其中 n=5、6 或更大）的环状化合物的特征 m/e 双峰没有出现。C_nH_{2n-3} 系列在超过 C_{14} 后强度增加，说明是带有脂肪族支链的双环结构。图 1C 显示的是用苯洗脱的烃馏分的典型气相色谱图。质谱图的碎片峰分别对应于萘、菲或蒽，还检测到了脂肪族支链。以上这些数据和由气相色谱得到的保留时间都可以证明存在着烷基取代的双环和三环芳香结构 [19]。这些烃类混合物与那些通过热解和其他合成实验（例如，参见参考文献 20）得到的物质在组成和复杂性方面具有引人注目的相似性。由气相热裂解气相色谱 – 质谱法 [8] 得到的初步分析结果也表明了大量脂肪烃、芳香烃和其他含杂原子的有机物的存在（尚未发表的结果）。

总的来说，默奇森陨星中含有大量可提取的有机化合物，它们给出的分布图与以前得到的分布图差异很大，并且在复杂程度上也远远超过了以前的分布图。默奇森陨星中含有大量有机化合物说明：存在着非生物合成过程，或者大范围成岩作用及相关的化学过程，或者二者兼有。这颗碳质球粒陨石可能是人们最早检测的、地球生物污染量非常少的陨石之一。

感谢小克拉克和奥尔森为我们提供了样品，感谢美国国家航空航天局提供的支持。

（王耀杨 翻译；周江 审稿）

References:

1. Hayes, J. M., *Geochim. Cosmochim. Acta*, **31**, 1395 (1967).

2. Oró, J., and Nooner, D. W., *Nature*, **213**, 1085 (1967).

3. Gelpi, E., and Oró, J., *Geochim. Cosmochim. Acta*, **34**, 981 (1970).

4. King, jun., E. A., Schonfeld, E., Richardson, K. A., and Elridge, J. S., *Science*, **163**, 928 (1969).

5. Han, J., Simoneit, B. R., Burlingame, A. L., and Calvin, M., *Nature*, **222**, 364 (1969).

6. Oró, J., and Gelpi, E., *Meteoritics*, **4**, 287 (1969).

7. Simmonds, P. G., Bauman, A. J., Bollin, E. M., Gelpi, E., and Oró, J., *Proc. US Nat. Acad. Sci.*, **64**, 1027 (1969).

8. Levy, R. L., Wolf, C. J., Grayson, M. A., Gibert, J., Gelpi, E., Updegrove, W. S., Zlatkis, A., and Oró, J., *Nature*, **227**, 148 (1970).

9. Clarke, jun., R. S., Jarosewich, E., Mason, B., Nelen, J., Gomez, M., and Hyde, J. R., *Smithsonian Contributions to the Earth Sciences*, No. 5 (in the press).

10. Kvenvolden, K., Lawless, J., Pering, K., Petterson, E., Flores, J., Ponnamperuma, C., Kaplan, I. R., and Moore, C., *Nature*, **228**, 923 (1970).

11. Nakaparksin, S., dissertation, Univ. Houston (1969).

12. Oró, J., Nakaparksin, S., Lichtenstein, H., and Gil-Av, E., *Nature*, **230**, 107 (1971).

13. Nakaparksin, S., Gil-Av, E., and Oró, J., *Anal. Biochem.*, **33**, 374 (1970).

14. Roach, D., and Gehrke, C. W., *J. Chromatog.*, **44**, 269 (1969).

15. Gelpi, E., Koenig, W. A., Gibert, J., and Oró, J., *J. Chromatog. Sci.*, **7**, 604 (1969).

16. Nakaparksin, S., Birrell, P., Gil-Av, E., and Oró, J., *J. Chromatog. Sci.*, **8**, 177 (1970).

17. Oró, J., Updegrove, W. S., Gibert, J., McReynolds, J., Gil-Av, E., Ibanez, J., Zlatkis, A., Flory, D. A., Levy, R. L., and Wolf, C. J., *Geochim. Cosmochim. Acta*, **34**, Suppl., **1**, 1901 (1970).

18. Nooner, D. W., and Oró, J., *Geochim. Cosmochim. Acta*, **31**, 1359 (1967).

19. Olson, R. J., Oró, J., and Zlatkis, A., *Geochim. Cosmochim. Acta*, **31**, 1935 (1967).

20. Oró, J., Han, J., and Zlatkis, A., *Anal. Chem.*, **39**, 27 (1967).

Ball Lightning as an Optical Illusion

E. Argyle

Editor's Note

For centuries, eyewitness accounts have attested to an elusive atmospheric phenomenon known as ball lightning: the creation during thunder storms of spherical balls of luminous energy which float through the air, persist for several seconds before abruptly disappearing, and range in size from that of a small stone to several feet in diameter. The phenomenon has been controversial, because it is difficult to study scientifically. Several reported incidents in 1970 here led Edward Argyle to suggest that ball lightning is an optical illusion due to visual afterimages. Argyle's explanation remains one of many possibilities, and controversy over the causes or even the reality of ball lightning continues today.

DURING the past year there have been numerous publications on ball lightning[1-9], many attempting to account for the formation, properties and behaviour of lightning balls. None have questioned the reality of the phenomenon, in spite of the lack of progress toward an understanding of these baffling objects. Serious doubt about the existence of ball lightning was expressed by Humphreys[10] in 1936, and more recently by Schonland[11]. Both regarded the phenomenon as probably an optical illusion. Now that Altschuler *et al.*[8] have invoked nuclear reactions to account for the lightning ball it seems appropriate to re-examine the possibility of finding an explanation in the physiology of vision.

The phenomenon of visual afterimages in very complex, but is predominant effect—the negative afterimage—is well known. Of less frequent occurrence is the positive afterimage, which results from the observation of a light source which is very bright relative to the surround. In this communication I shall assume that a spherical region of ionized air and white hot particles is sometimes generated at the ground end of a lightning stroke by partial vaporization of Earth, vegetation or metal, and that the luminous intensity within the sphere is high enough to create a positive afterimage in the eye of an observer. In his comprehensive survey of reports on ball lightning Rayle[12] made the interesting discovery that "the number of persons reporting ball lightning observations is 44% of the number reporting observation of ordinary lightning impact points". This can be understood by assuming that about half of all strokes to ground generate a high luminosity ball at the impact point. Indeed, this sort of assumption is required whether ball lightning is real or illusory.

The behaviour and apparent properties of the positive afterimage are strikingly similar to those of ball lightning. Its shape will be the same as that of the exciting source, and it well commonly be described as a ball. The apparent size of the positive afterimage will be the same as that of the exciting source only if it is "projected" by the observer to the distance

球状闪电是一种视错觉

几个世纪以来的目击证据已证明有一种被称为球状闪电的神秘大气现象是存在的：在遭遇雷暴天气时会形成一些漂浮于空气中的具有光能的球状物，短暂停留几秒钟然后突然消失，它们的大小从一块小石头尺寸到几英尺直径不等。因为很难通过科学方式来研究这一现象，所以人们对此一直争论不休。1970 年报道的几桩事件使爱德华·阿盖尔联想到球状闪电可能是由视觉余像引起的错觉。阿盖尔的解释只是多种可能性中的一种，人们对球状闪电的成因甚至球状闪电的真实性的争论直到现在也没有停止。

去年发表的关于球状闪电的文章 [1-9] 数不胜数，其中有很多文章在试着解释闪电球的形成过程、属性特征和活动特点。尽管人们在理解这些莫名其妙的现象方面并未取得进展，但却从来没有人质疑过这一现象的真实性。1936 年，汉弗莱斯 [10] 对球状闪电的存在提出了强烈的质疑，最近舍恩兰德 [11] 也表达了同样的观点。他们都认为这一现象可能是一种视错觉。既然阿尔特舒勒等人 [8] 都已经引入了核反应来解释这个闪电球，那么人们似乎值得重新审视在视觉生理学中寻找一种解释的可能性。

虽然视觉余像现象非常复杂，但它最主要的效应——负余像是大家所熟知的。正余像的出现频率略低，它是在我们观察一个比周围环境亮得多的光源时产生的。在这篇文章中，我将要假设大地的水蒸气、植物或金属有时能够被闪电靠地面的一端击中，从而形成了由电离气体以及高温粒子组成的球状区域，并且从这个球内发出的光的强度足够高，以至于能在观察者的眼中形成一个正余像。雷勒 [12] 在他的报告中全面考查了有关球状闪电的情况，他发现了一个有趣的现象："报告观察到球状闪电的人数是报告看到一般闪电击中某个点的人数的 44%"。这一现象可以通过假设有大约半数的击中地面的闪电在击中点处产生了高光度的球来解释。事实上，无论球状闪电是真实的还是虚幻的，这类假设都是必不可少的。

正余像效应的行为和表观特性与球状闪电非常相似。正余像的形状总是和激发源的形状保持一致，人们通常会用一个球来描述正余像的形状。只有在正余像被观察者"投射"到与他和激发源之间的距离一样远时，所看到的正余像才会和激发源

of the source. If the source is outdoors, for example, but the observer focuses on the window through which it was seen, the apparent size will be reduced. Thus the relatively small size of indoor lightning balls is accounted for. Rayle[12] pointed out that linear size and distance were one of the few pairs of parameters that showed a significant correlation, but he did not go on to infer the implied limited range of angular diameters.

The colour of positive afterimages depends more on the brightness of the source than on its colour. There is no conflict with the yellows, oranges and occasional other colours reported for ball lightning. The degree to which the size, shape, brightness and colour of the lightning ball remains constant throughout its lifetime of a few seconds is the despair of both the theoretician[8,13-16] who seeks a plausible physical mechanism for it, and the experimenter[3] who tries to reproduce it. On the other hand, the approximate constancy of these features is characteristic of a positive afterimage.

Being a cone effect, the positive afterimage will usually be formed near the centre of the retina, and the observer, wishing to examine the supposed object, will attempt the impossible task of centring it exactly. The result is a linear drift of the projected positive afterimage across the observer's visual background, as the eye muscles try to correct the centring error. In natural circumstances this feedback motion will be combined with varying amounts of voluntary adjustment as the observer strives to make sense out of the motion.

Passage through physical surfaces such as a glass or metal screen is possible for positive afterimages and is reported for lightning balls[3,4]. In neither case is the surface burned or damaged, nor is the size, shape, colour or brightness of the ball altered by the penetration.

Positive afterimages last 2–10 s, depending on circumstances, and most lightning balls are reported to have a duration in the same range[12]. Positive afterimages disappear rather suddenly, as do lightning balls. Positive afterimages generate no sound but the typical observer finds it easy to imagine "suitable" accompanying sounds, if he has any relevant preconceptions. The ease with which most people "hear" appropriate sounds while observing natural phenomena has been documented by Beals[17], who found that most of the inhabitants of northern Canada claimed to have heard the aurora borealis. The spectrum of sounds reported was persuasively narrow and differed only moderately from observer to observer. Apparently it is no more maladaptive to hear the rustling of the northern lights than it is to hear the implosive pop of a disappearing lightning ball. Curiously, the disappearance of indoor lightning balls is reported often to be violent but seldom to be damaging.

The psychological principle for imagining odour is the same as for sound but fewer individuals have strong odour expectations and in only a few cases are odours reported. An appropriate odour would be one the observer associates with electrical apparatus, if he has some familiarity with it; or with deeper metaphysical concomitants of danger and mystery, such as fire and brimstone, if his associations tend to the supernatural. Such are

的大小相同。举例来说，如果激发源在户外，而观测者把注意力集中在窗户上，通过窗户看外面的激发源，那么他看到的尺寸会小于实际的大小。这样就可以解释在室内观察到的闪电球为什么相对较小了。雷勒 [12] 指出线性尺寸和距离是能表现出显著相关性的为数不多的参数中的一对，但是他没有继续提到这意味着角直径存在极限范围。

正余像的颜色主要取决于激发源的亮度，而非激发源的颜色。在关于球状闪电的报告中提到过黄色、橙色，偶尔还出现过其他颜色，这些颜色都是合理的。在几秒钟的生命期内，闪电球的尺寸、形状、亮度以及颜色能在一定程度上保持稳定的现象使想要寻找一个合理的机制来解释球状闪电的理论家 [8,13-16] 和想要再现球状闪电现象的实验家 [3] 感到无计可施。而另一方面，这些特征的近似稳定不变又恰好是正余像效应所特有的。

正余像属于视椎细胞效应中的一种，它通常会在视网膜中心附近成像，而想要看清这一假想目标的观察者，会试图使其更精确地聚焦在视网膜的中心，尽管这是不可能做到的。如果观察者的眼部肌肉试图校正这一偏离中心的误差，就会导致正余像投影在观察者的视觉背景中产生线性漂移。在自然环境中，当观察者努力弄清这种反馈运动的意义时，反馈运动将会与不同程度的自发调整动作结合在一起。

正余像穿过诸如玻璃屏或金属屏这样的物质表面是有可能的，这已在闪电球的报道中得到了证实 [3,4]。不论在哪种情况下，物质表面都不会被烧焦或破坏，而且余像的尺寸、形状、颜色或亮度也不会因为穿过过程而发生变化。

正余像可以持续 2 秒~10 秒，持续时间长短与周围环境有关，据报道大多数闪电球的持续时间具有同样的量级 [12]。与闪电球一样，正余像的消失会很突然。正余像在产生时是没有声音的，但是假如普通的观察者事先对该现象的产生有所预见，那么他会发现想象出"合适"的伴随音并不是一件很难的事情。比尔斯 [17] 已经证明：在观察自然现象时，多数人能轻而易举地"听到"适当的声音，他发现大多数居住在加拿大北部的居民曾声称听到过北极光的声音。报道的声音频谱有很高的吻合度，在不同观察者所描述的声音之间并没有太大的差别。显然，如果能够听到一个正在消失的闪电球发出的爆裂声，那么听到北极光的沙沙声也就是很自然的事了。奇怪的是，报道称人们在室内看到的闪电球在消失时通常是很猛烈的，但是几乎不会造成破坏。

根据心理学原理，在听觉和嗅觉上的幻觉是一样的，但是很少有人对气味有强烈的预期，因此关于球状闪电有气味的报道只有为数不多的几个例子。一种适当的气味可以让观察者联想到他所熟悉的某种电气设备；或者更玄妙地和危险、神秘联系起来。比如，如果他的联想朝超自然的方向延伸，他会联想到地狱里的磨难。以

the reported odours of ball lightning[18].

In bright daylight positive afterimages are a rare occurrence. But in subdued light, as during a thunderstorm, especially if the observer is indoors, a positive afterimage is readily formed by any source as intense as a frosted light bulb. Considering that lightning is primarily an outdoor phenomenon it is remarkable how many lightning balls are seen indoors. This strange fact can be understood if positive afterimages are involved.

That the unsuspecting observer of a chance natural phenomenon can be misled by a positive afterimage is more than speculation. Two of the eyewitnesses to the passage of the Revelstoke bolide[19] reported independently that the meteor had landed on low ground in the middle distance, and had bounced several times before going out. It is more likely that these observers each followed a positive afterimage down to zero elevation after the bolide passed behind distant mountains. At ground level a conflict between positive afterimage drift and physical anticipations led to an unstable situation in which the positive afterimage oscillated briefly before disappearing.

There are a few reports which indicate the release of large amounts of energy from the lightning ball. In the most famous of these cases, described by Goodlet[20], water in a rain barrel was heated by a lightning ball. If ball lightning is an optical illusion it will be necessary to categorize this and similar reports as unreliable. To do so would not be unreasonable in view of the many observations on record.

Final resolution of the question of the nature of ball lightning will no doubt depend more on the outcome of further experimentation than on the collection of more observer reports. Fortunately, the question of the reality of ball lightning is amenable to laboratory investigation. I have found it easy to simulate the lightning ball by using light bulbs, strobe-flash lamps and photographic flash bulbs as intense sources for the generation of drifting positive afterimages. This qualitative work requires verification, however. It is hoped that a laboratory equipped for psychovisual studies will take up the problem and report on the degree to which descriptions of "artificial" ball lightning resemble those of the natural phenomenon that are recorded in the scientific literature.

(230, 179-180; 1971)

Edward Argyle: Dominion Radio Astrophysical Observatory, Penticton, British Columbia.

Received December 7; revised December 20, 1970.

References:
1. Lowke, J. J., Uman, M. A., and Lieberman, R. W., *J. Geophys. Res.*, 74, 6887 (1969).
2. Jennison, R. C., *Nature*, 224, 895 (1969).

上谈到的是对球状闪电气味的报道 [18]。

在白天日光非常强烈的情况下，正余像是十分罕见的。但是，当光线暗淡的时候，比如恰好遇到雷暴天气，尤其是在观察者处于室内的情况下，任何一个亮度类似于磨砂灯泡的光源都很容易使正余像得以形成。因为闪电主要是发生在户外的现象，所以在室内看到那么多闪电球就会显得不同寻常。如果用正余像来解释，这一奇怪现象就不言自明了。

一个确信自己看到了自然界中偶尔发生的现象的观察者，很有可能是被正余像欺骗了，这一论点绝不仅仅是一个推测。两名看到了雷夫尔斯托克火流星下落的目击者 [19] 分别报告称流星落在了不远处的低地上，并且在地面上弹了几下才熄灭。很可能这两位观察者的视线在火流星落到远处的山峰后面之后，就跟随着正余像降到了海拔为零的地方。在地面上，正余像漂移与物理预期之间的偏差导致了一个不稳定的状态，处于这种状态下的正余像在消失之前会发生短暂的振动。

有几份报告指出，大量的能量会从闪电球中释放出来。最著名的例子要数古德利特 [20] 所描述的雨桶中的水被闪电球烧热的现象。如果球状闪电是一种视错觉，那么就应当将这个报告以及一些类似的报告归为不实的报告。这样做并非不讲道理，因为有很多观察记录可以证明这一点。

毫无疑问，要最终解决球状闪电的本质问题还需要更多的实验结果来验证，而非更大量地收集观察者的报告。幸运的是，通过实验研究就可以揭开球状闪电的真相之谜。我发现很容易用灯泡、频闪闪光灯和摄影闪光灯作为强光源模拟闪电球以产生漂移的正余像。不过，这种定性研究还需要得到进一步的证实。我们希望有一个配备心理视觉研究设备的实验室能够接受这一课题；并且希望在科学文献中对"人造"球状闪电的报道量接近于对自然现象中球状闪电的报道量。

（孟洁 翻译；肖伟科 审稿）

3. Powell, J. R., and Finklestein, D., *Amer. Sci.*, **58**, 262 (1970).

4. Covington, A. E., *Nature*, **226**, 252 (1970).

5. Bromley, K. A., *Nature*, **226**, 253 (1970).

6. Felsher, M., *Nature*, **227**, 982 (1970).

7. Hill, E. L., *Amer. Sci.*, **58**, 479 (1970).

8. Altschuler, M. D., House, L. L., and Hildner, E., *Nature*, **228**, 545 (1970).

9. Zimmerman, P. D., *Nature*, **228**, 853 (1970).

10. Humphreys, W. J., *Proc. Amer. Phil. Soc.*, **76**, 613 (1936).

11. Schonland, B., *The Flight of Thunderbolts* (Clarendon Press, Oxford, 1964).

12. Rayle, W. D., *NASA Technical Note TN D-3188* (Washington, DC, 1966).

13. Bruce, C. E. R., *Nature*, **202**, 996 (1964).

14. Singer, S., *Nature*, **198**, 745 (1963).

15. Hill, E. L., *J. Geophys. Res.*, **65**, 1947 (1960).

16. Wooding, E. R., *Nature*, **199**, 272 (1963).

17. Beals, C. S., *J. Roy. Astron. Soc. Canad.*, **27**, 184 (1933).

18. Barry, J. D., *J. Atmos. Terr. Phys.*, **29**, 1095 (1967).

19. Folinsbee, R. E., Douglas, J. A. V., and Maxwell, J. A., *Geochim. Cosmochim. Acta*, **31**, 1625 (1967).

20. Goodlet, B. L., *J. Inst. Elec. Eng.*, **81**, 1 (1937).

Polymorphism of Human Enzyme Proteins

W. H. P. Lewis

Editor's Note

The common notion that protein enzymes have, in any species, a well defined "primary structure"—their linear sequence of amino acids—has long been known to be a simplification. Here pathologist W. H. P. Lewis provides one of the early challenges to that notion, reporting a high degree of variability in the sequences of several human enzymes. Lewis uses the technique of electrophoresis, which separates molecules of different charge and shape, to identify several varieties or "polymorphisms" of common enzymes in different populations. These polymorphisms are heritable, and Lewis concludes that it is unlikely that any two individuals are identical in all their enzymes. We now know that even in individuals, specific enzymes can vary considerably in their activity too.

SINCE Landsteiner described the ABO blood group system[1], it has become increasingly obvious that human individuality is demonstrable at the molecular level. It seems probable that almost every protein, structural or enzymatic, can be made to reveal some degree of variability in human populations. The application of starch gel electrophoresis[2] during the past decade has been especially fruitful in revealing molecular variability of particular enzymes in man. Using this method it has been possible to show common variants in approximately one enzyme in three in one of the major population groups[3]. This finding is the more remarkable in view of the fact that starch gel electrophoresis can reveal differences only in charge or size. If, as seems to be the case, the type of structural variation revealed by this technique results from the substitution of a particular amino-acid for another of a different charge, then because a charge difference will result from only about one in three of all possible amino-acid substitutions, it seems likely that many more differences in primary enzyme structure occur.

Enzymes which have been studied so far have been chosen principally because the reactions which they catalyse can be coupled to a suitable chromogenic reaction, so that the site of enzyme activity can be revealed as a sharp zone after electrophoresis. There is no reason to suppose, therefore, that selection on this basis would lead to the study of enzymes which are more commonly variable than those which are not amenable to this type of study. Some of the enzymes which have been studied are listed in Table 1.

人类酶蛋白的多态性

卢亦思

编者按

通常认为，任何物种中的蛋白质酶都具有固定的"一级结构"（氨基酸的线性排列顺序），然而，大家早就知道这样的看法其实过于简单了。这篇文章是最早对这一看法提出异议的文章之一，在本文中病理学家卢亦思报道了几种人体酶的氨基酸系列的高度变异性。卢亦思利用能够根据电荷和大小差异而对分子进行分离的电泳技术鉴定出了存在于不同人群中的常见酶的几种不同形式，或者说"多态性"。这样的多态性是可以遗传的。卢亦思的结论是，任意两个个体其所有酶都相同这样的情形是不太可能的。现在我们已经知道：即使在一个个体中，特定酶的活性也可以发生着相当大的变化。

自兰德施泰纳描述了 ABO 血型分类系统以来 [1]，日益显而易见的是，人类的个体差异可以在分子水平上得到验证。似乎可能的是：几乎每一种蛋白质，无论是结构性蛋白还是酶蛋白，都能够用于揭示人群的一定程度的变异性。在过去的十年中，通过利用淀粉凝胶电泳法 [2]，人们相当有成效地揭示出了人体中特定酶分子的变异性。正是通过使用这种方法，人们才发现：在任意一个主要的人群中，大概每三种酶中就会有一种存在常见的变异体 [3]。考虑到淀粉凝胶电泳法只能揭示出酶蛋白所带电荷差异或大小差异这一事实，上述发现就更加值得我们思考。非常可能的情形是，利用这种技术检测出的结构差异是由一个特定的氨基酸被另一个带电不同的氨基酸所替代而引起的，而在所有可能的氨基酸替代中能导致电荷变化的只占约 1/3，所以发生在酶的一级结构水平的差异可能比检测到的还要多。

到目前为止，研究中选择酶的依据主要是看它们所催化的反应是否能和一个合适的显色反应偶联起来，因而在电泳后如果能产生显色条带就表明有酶的活性。没有理由认为根据这个原则选择酶会导致所研究的酶多为更容易变异的酶，而忽略了不适合用这种方法研究的酶。表 1 中列出了一些已被研究过的酶。

Table 1. Frequencies of the Commonest Allele in Different Population Groups of Some of the Enzymes which have been Studied by Starch Gel Electrophoresis

	Europeans	Negroes
Red cell acid[30] phosphatase	0.6–0.7	0.8
6-Phosphogluconate[31] dehydrogenase	0.96	0.72–0.87
Phosphoglucomutase		
PGM$_1$[16]	0.76	0.76–0.79
PGM$_2$[16]	1.0	0.95–0.99
PGM$_3$[22]	0.74*	0.66*
Peptidase A[5,19]	1.0	0.70–0.90
Peptidase D[18] (prolidase)	0.97	0.92
Adenosine deaminase[32]	0.90	0.90
Adenylate kinase[33]	0.95	0.99

*The commonest allele is not the same in the two populations studied for PGM$_3$.

The peptidases illustrate well the sort of information that can be obtained by the application of starch gel electrophoresis in association with a specific staining method. The occurrence of these enzymes in human tissues has been established for some time[4]; they catalyse the hydrolysis of the peptide bonds of small peptides consisting of two or three amino-acids. Their precise function is not known but they are probably involved in the terminal degradation of proteins both in intestinal absorption and protein catabolism. Like most other enzymes which have been studied, peptidases have been obtained from red blood cells because blood samples are readily obtained from families—an essential prerequisite for genetic studies.

After starch gel electrophoresis at pH 7.5, peptidase activity can be detected by the following reaction sequence[5],

$$\text{peptide} \xrightarrow{\text{peptidase}} \text{amino-acids}$$

$$\text{amino-acid} \xrightarrow{\text{amino-acid oxidase}} \text{keto-acid} + NH_4OH + H_2O_2$$

$$H_2O_2 + \text{dianisidine} \xrightarrow{\text{peroxidase}} \text{oxidized dianisidine} + H_2O$$

This results in a brown precipitate at the site of activity. Using this method and various dipeptides and tripeptides, it has been possible to characterize six distinct peptidases in human red blood cells[5,6] (Table 2). Their relative electrophoretic mobilities are shown in Fig. 1. Although some of these enzymes have overlapping substrate specificities there are wide differences in their patterns of substrate specificity. Moreover, three of these enzymes apparently contain at least one reactive sulphydryl group while the rest do not[5]. Further, gel filtration studies indicated that these enzymes also differ in molecular size[7].

表 1. 利用淀粉凝胶电泳法研究过的某些酶的最常见等位基因在不同人群中的出现频率

	欧洲人	黑人
红细胞酸性[30]磷酸酶	0.6~0.7	0.8
6-磷酸葡萄糖酸[31]脱氢酶	0.96	0.72~0.87
磷酸葡萄糖变位酶（PGM）		
PGM₁[16]	0.76	0.76~0.79
PGM₂[16]	1.0	0.95~0.99
PGM₃[22]	0.74*	0.66*
肽酶 A[5,19]	1.0	0.70~0.90
肽酶 D[18]（脯肽酶）	0.97	0.92
腺苷脱氨酶[32]	0.90	0.90
腺苷酸激酶[33]	0.95	0.99

* 在研究两个人群中的 PGM₃ 时发现其最常见的等位基因并不相同。

这些肽酶的例子很好地表明了将淀粉凝胶电泳法与一种特异染色方法结合在一起利用时所能获得的那类信息。人们确认人体组织中的确存在这些肽酶已经有一段时间了[4]；它们催化由两三个氨基酸组成的小肽的肽键的水解。虽然尚不知道它们的精确功能，但它们很有可能参与了蛋白质的最终降解，涉及在肠道中的吸收以及蛋白质的分解代谢。正如大多数其他被研究过的酶一样，肽酶也是从红细胞中获得的，因为从不同家庭成员获得血液样本是件比较容易做到的事，而这正是开展遗传学研究的必要前提。

在经过 pH 值为 7.5 条件下的淀粉凝胶电泳之后，可以通过如下反应顺序来检测肽酶的活性[5]：

$$肽 \xrightarrow{\text{肽酶}} 氨基酸$$

$$氨基酸 \xrightarrow{\text{氨基酸氧化酶}} 酮酸 + NH_4OH + H_2O_2$$

$$H_2O_2 + 联茴香胺 \xrightarrow{\text{过氧化物酶}} 氧化的联茴香胺 + H_2O$$

这些反应将导致在具有活性的位点处产生棕色沉淀。利用上述方法以及不同的二肽和三肽，人们才得以确定人类红细胞中存在的六种不同肽酶的特征[5,6]（表 2）。它们的相对电泳迁移率示于图 1。尽管其中一些酶的底物特异性有所重叠，但其底物特异性的模式却有很大的不同。此外，这些酶中有三种明显至少含有一个活性巯基，而其余的酶则不含有[5]。另外，凝胶过滤研究结果显示这些酶在分子大小上也有所不同[7]。

Table 2. Relative Activities of Human Red Blood Cell Peptidases against Various Amino-acid Peptides and Leucyl-β-naphthylamide (Leu-β-NA)

	A	B	C	D	E	F
Val-Leu	+++	–	–	–	–	–
Gly-Leu	+++	–	+	–	–	–
Leu-Gly	+++	–	+	–	–	–
Gly-Phe	++	–	+	–	–	–
Leu-Ala	++	–	++	–	–	–
Leu-Leu	++	–	++	–	+	–
Gly-Trp	++	–	++	–	–	–
Lys-Leu	+	+	+++	–	+	–
Lys-Tyr	+	+	+++	–	+	–
Pro-Phe	++	+	+++	–	–	–
Pro-Leu	++	+	+++	–	–	–
Phe-Leu	++	++	+++	–	+	–
Ala-Tyr	++	+++	+	–	±	–
Phe-Tyr	++	++	+++	–	+	–
Leu-Tyr	+++	++	+++	–	+	–
Leu-Gly-Gly	–	+++	–	–	±	–
Leu-Gly-Phe	–	+	–	–	±	–
Leu-Leu-Leu	–	++	–	–	+	+
Phe-Phe-Phe	–	++	–	–	++	±
Tyr-Tyr-Tyr	–	+	–	–	+	+
Phe-Gly-Phe-Gly	–	–	–	–	++	
Leu-β-NA	–	–	–	–	+	–
Leu-Pro	–	–	–	++	–	–
Phe-Pro	–	–	–	++	–	–

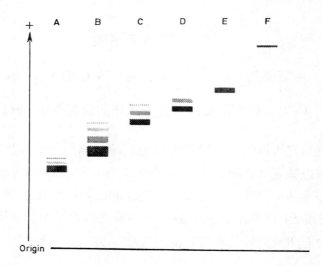

Fig. 1. Relative electrophoretic mobilities of human red cell peptidases at pH 7.5.

表 2. 人类红细胞肽酶对不同的氨基酸组成肽以及亮氨酰–β–萘酰胺（Leu–β–NA）的相对活性

	A	B	C	D	E	F
缬氨酰–亮氨酸	+++	–	–			
甘氨酰–亮氨酸	+++	–	+			
亮氨酰–甘氨酸	+++	–	+			
甘氨酰–苯丙氨酸	++	–	+			
亮氨酰–丙氨酸	++	–	++			–
亮氨酰–亮氨酸	++	–	++		+	
甘氨酰–色氨酸	++	–	++			
赖氨酰–亮氨酸	+	+	+++		+	
赖氨酰–酪氨酸	+	+	+++		+	
脯氨酰–苯丙氨酸	++	+	+++			
脯氨酰–亮氨酸	++	+	+++			
苯丙氨酰–亮氨酸	++	++	+++		+	
丙氨酰–酪氨酸	++	+++	+	–	±	–
苯丙氨酰–酪氨酸	++	++	+++		+	
亮氨酰–酪氨酸	+++	++	+++			
亮氨酰–甘氨酰–甘氨酸	–	+++	–	–	±	
亮氨酰–甘氨酰–苯丙氨酸	–	+	–	–	±	–
亮氨酰–亮氨酰–亮氨酸	–	++			+	+
苯丙氨酰–苯丙氨酰–苯丙氨酸		++			++	±
酪氨酰–酪氨酰–酪氨酸		+			+	
苯丙氨酰–甘氨酰–苯丙氨酰–甘氨酸		–			++	
亮氨酰–β–萘酰胺					+	
亮氨酰–脯氨酸	–	–	–	++	–	
苯丙氨酰–脯氨酸	–	–	–	++	–	–

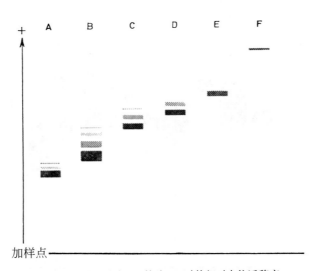

图 1. 人类红细胞肽酶在 pH 值为 7.5 时的相对电泳迁移率。

Biochemical evidence suggests that the six peptidases are distinct proteins, each with a characteristic primary structure and a characteristic specificity. It would be expected therefore that the primary structure of each peptidase would be coded for by a separate gene locus, so that a structural variant occurring in one peptidase would not be reflected in any of the others. This seems to be the case, and genetic studies have revealed further structural differences between these enzymes.

Peptidase A, a dipeptidase with a wide specificity (Table 2), has been studied in several different population groups. The variants shown in Fig. 2 are all rare except Pep A1, Pep A2–1 and Pep A2. Pep A1 is the commonest phenotype in all the population groups studied so far, while Pep A2–1 and Pep A2 occur in appreciable frequencies only in African populations, or in populations of African origin such as the West Indian group. Table 3 shows that the frequencies of these variants in different populations are quite similar, although Pep A2–1 and Pep A2 seem to occur most often in the Babinga pigmies[8], and are less common, as would be expected, in groups of mixed origin, such as the West Indians. A similar situation has been found with some other enzymes, for example glucose-6-phosphate dehydrogenase[9] and phosphoglucomutase, locus PGM_2[10].

Table 3. Frequencies of Peptidase A Variants in Various Population Groups

	Peptidase A								
	Total	1	2–1	2	3–1	4–1	5–1	6–1	7–1
Europeans	3,129	3,123	—	—	1	3	1	1	1
British resident Negroes	636	554	78	3	1	—	—	—	—
"Bantu" (South Africa)	100	87	11	2	—	—	—	—	—
Yoruba (Nigeria)	155	127	25	3	—	—	—	—	—
Cape Coloured (South Africa)	177	169	8	—	—	—	—	—	—
Cape Malay (South Africa)	104	96	8	—	—	—	—	—	—
Asiatic Indians	615	613	—	—	1	—	1	—	—

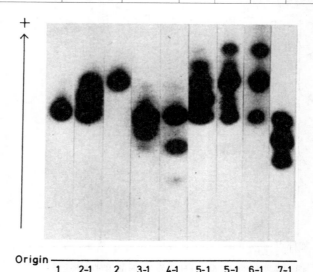

Fig. 2. Electrophoretic patterns of peptidase A variants.

生物化学证据表明：这六种肽酶是不同的蛋白质，每一种都有独一无二的一级级结构和底物特异性。可以假设性地认为每种肽酶的一级结构都是由一个独立基因位点编码的，因此，发生在一种肽酶中的结构变化就不会在任何其他肽酶中体现。事实似乎就是如此，而且遗传学研究揭示出了这些酶之间更多结构上的不同。

作为底物特异性很低的二肽酶（表2），肽酶A已经在几个不同的人群中被研究过。图2中所示肽酶A的变异体中，除肽酶A1、肽酶A2-1和肽酶A2以外，其他都非常罕见。在迄今为止研究过的所有人群中，肽酶A1是最常见的，而肽酶A2-1和肽酶A2仅在非洲人群或者源自非洲的人群如西印度人中以一定频率出现。表3中的数据说明这些变异体在不同人群中的出现频率是非常相近的，但肽酶A2-1和肽酶A2似乎只在巴宾加俾格米人中最为常见 [8]，而在混合起源的人群如西印度人中出现的频率较低，正如人们所预期的那样。对于其他一些酶，如6-磷酸葡萄糖脱氢酶 [9] 和磷酸葡萄糖变位酶（PGM$_2$编码基因）[10]，情形也类似。

表 3. 不同人群中肽酶 A 变异体的出现频率

	肽酶 A							
	总计	1	2-1	2	3-1	4-1	5-1	6-1	7-1
欧洲人	3,129	3,123	—	—	1	3	1	1	1
在英国居住的黑人	636	554	78	3	1	—	—	—	—
"班图人"（南非）	100	87	11	2	—	—	—	—	—
约鲁巴人（尼日利亚）	155	127	25	3	—	—	—	—	—
开普有色人种（南非）	177	169	8	—	—	—	—	—	—
开普马来人（南非）	104	96	8	—	—	—	—	—	—
移民美洲的印度人	615	613	—	—	1	—	1	—	—

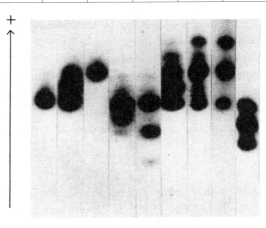

图 2. 肽酶 A 变异体的电泳图谱。

Family studies involving quite a large number of individuals indicate that the Pep A2–1 pattern occurs in people who are heterozygous for a pair of alleles which occur at an autosomal locus and which in homozygotes give rise to the Pep A1 and Pep A2 types. These alleles have been designated *Pep A*[1] and *Pep A*[2]. This type of inheritance is sometimes referred to as co-dominant because both alleles are expressed in the heterozygote in contrast to the dominant-recessive inheritance in which only the dominant allele is apparently expressed in the heterozygote.

This type of study also makes possible inferences about the molecular structure of an enzyme. The electrophoretic pattern of the presumed heterozygote Pep A2–1 consists of three main zones of activity, a zone with a mobility equivalent to each of the presumed homozygotes, Pep A1 and Pep A2, and a hand with almost exactly intermediate mobility, which is the most active. This type of electrophoretic pattern is thought to occur when the enzyme in homozygotes consists of at least two identical subunits[11]. If the subunit coded for by the *Pep A*[1] allele is represented by α^1 and that coded for by *Pep A*[2] is represented by α^2, then if in the heterozygous individual both alleles are active and their corresponding subunits combine at random, there are three possible structures, $\alpha^1\alpha^1$, $\alpha^1\alpha^2$ and $\alpha^2\alpha^2$. Moreover, if the two subunits are synthesized at an equal rate and are equally active and stable, then the three zones would be expected to have activity approximately in the ratio of 1:2:1, and this seems to be the case.

Another interesting feature of this particular enzyme is the occurrence of a series of rare phenotypes (Fig. 2). All these types are very rare, with frequencies of 1 in 1,000 or less in most population groups studied so far. Family studies suggest that these phenotypes occur in individuals who are heterozygous for one of a series of rare alleles, *Pep A*[3], *Pep A*[4], *Pep A*[5], *Pep A*[6] and *Pep A*[7], and the common allele *Pep A*[1]. In red blood cells two of these rare types, Pep A3–1 and Pep A4–1, have an electrophoretic pattern in which the characteristic electrophoretically slower components are weaker than the band corresponding to Pep A1. This might result if the subunits coded for by the rare alleles *Pep A*[3] and *Pep A*[4] were catalytically less active, were synthesized more slowly or were less stable. It seems likely that the last possibility is correct, for when these phenotypes are seen after electrophoresis of a tissue extract, for example placenta, the pattern is symmetrical and the three main bands have activity roughly in the ratio of 1:2:1. It seems likely that the stability difference is revealed in the red blood cell because of the relatively long half life of this type of cell, and presumably protein synthesis has ceased by the time that the nucleus is lost.

Another interesting variant in this group is Pep A5–1, which occurs in two forms; the pattern which is termed "reduced" in Fig. 2 is obtained when a fresh sample from an individual of this phenotype is electrophoresed, while the pattern termed "oxidized" is obtained if the sample is stored for a few days at 4°C before electrophoresis. If the stored sample is treated with mercaptoethanol, the resultant electrophoretic pattern is similar to that of the fresh sample. On the other hand, when a fresh sample is treated with oxidized glutathione it has an electrophoretic pattern indistinguishable from that of the stored

涉及大量个体的家族性研究结果显示，肽酶 A2-1 出现在常染色体位点上一对等位基因的杂合子人群中，而该等位基因的纯合子形式将产生肽酶 A1 和肽酶 A2。这些等位基因被命名为肽酶编码基因 A^1 和肽酶编码基因 A^2。这种类型的遗传方式有时被称作共显性，因为两个等位基因都在杂合子中表达了，它与显 – 隐性遗传方式不同的是，后者似乎只有显性基因才能在杂合子中被表达。

这样的研究使得我们去推测酶的分子结构成为可能。假想的肽酶 A2-1 杂合子在电泳图谱上应该包括三条主要的活性带，其中两条带的迁移率分别与假定的纯合子肽酶 A1 和肽酶 A2 相同，还有一条带的迁移率几乎精确地介于两者的中间位置，这条带活性最强。这样的电泳图谱之所以出现，被认为是因为纯合子的酶包含了至少两个相同的亚基[11]。如果用 α^1 代表由肽酶编码基因 A^1 编码的亚基，用 α^2 代表由肽酶编码基因 A^2 编码的亚基，那么如果在杂合子个体中这两个等位基因都被表达，并且它们对应的亚基随机组合，则有可能会出现以下三种结构：$\alpha^1\alpha^1$、$\alpha^1\alpha^2$ 和 $\alpha^2\alpha^2$。此外，如果这两个亚基的合成速率相同并且活性和稳定性也相同的话，那么就可以推出这三条电泳带的活性之比约为 1:2:1，而实验结果似乎正是如此。

与这种特定肽酶有关的另一个有意思的现象是一系列罕见表型的发生（图 2）。所有这些表型都非常罕见，它们在迄今为止研究过的大多数人群中的出现频率等于或低于 1/1,000。家族研究结果表明，这些表型的出现是因为杂合子个体中的等位基因中的一个是如下等位基因：肽酶编码基因 A^3、肽酶编码基因 A^4、肽酶编码基因 A^5、肽酶编码基因 A^6 和肽酶编码基因 A^7；而另一个是常见的肽酶编码基因 A^1。在红细胞中，两种罕见肽酶，肽酶 A3-1 和肽酶 A4-1，具有这样的电泳图谱：其中特征性的、电泳速度慢的组分的活性比对应于肽酶 A1 的那条带要更弱。这可能是由于罕见等位基因肽酶编码基因 A^3 和肽酶编码基因 A^4 编码的亚基催化活性更低、合成速度更慢或者更不稳定而造成的结果。似乎最后一种可能性最大，因为在组织（如胎盘）提取物经过电泳后，可以观察到这些表型，这时电泳带的模式呈对称状态，并且三条主要染色带的活性比例约为 1:2:1。似乎可能的情形是，这种稳定性的差别可以在红细胞中显现出来，因为红细胞的半衰期相对较长，而且很可能在其细胞核消失的时候，蛋白质的合成过程就已经停止了。

在这一组中另一种有趣的变异体是肽酶 A5-1，它以两种形式发生：图 2 中标有"还原形式"字样的结果是利用从该表型的个体中获得的新鲜样品进行电泳后得到的，而标为"氧化形式"的结果是将样本在 4℃ 下储存几天后再进行电泳得到的。如果储存样品先用巯基乙醇处理的话，那么所得到的电泳图谱就和新鲜样本的电泳图谱类似。另一方面，当用氧化型谷胱甘肽处理新鲜样品时，其电泳图谱就会变得与储

sample. It seems likely that the enzyme coded for by the variant allele, *Pep A⁵*, contains a reactive sulphydryl group, which is not present in other peptidase A subunits, and which undergoes an exchange reaction with oxidized glutathione so that a half molecule of oxidized glutathione forms a disulphide bond with the enzyme[12]. The addition of the acidic peptide glutathione to the enzyme molecule would explain the increase in electrophoretic mobility after storage of haemolysates. This variant reacts with various reagents known to react with sulphydryl groups and the electrophoretic changes produced by these reagents are consistent with the hypothesis I have outlined[13].

It seems probable that the genetic code is common to most species[14]. If so, it is possible to postulate the particular amino-acid substitution that has occurred in the subunit coded for by the *Pep A⁵* allele. The only amino-acid which has a reactive sulphydryl group which is found in proteins is cysteine. This amino-acid is neutral, and because there is an electrophoretic difference between the subunit coded for by *Pep A⁵* and that coded for by the common allele *Pep A¹*, in that they migrate further towards the anode so that there has been an increase in net negative charge, cysteine must have been substituted for an amino-acid which would be positively charged at pH 7.5. This could be either lysine or arginine. Examination of the genetic code shows that while the substitution of cysteine for arginine could result from a change in single base pair, the substitution of cysteine for lysine could not. It seems possible therefore that in this variant a particular arginine residue has been replaced by cysteine. A similar hypothesis was proposed for Pep A6–1, suggesting that in this case glutamic acid is substituted for a particular lysine residue[12].

A similar series of rare alleles has been described for several other enzymes, including peptidase B[5,15], phosphoglucomutase[16], and phosphohexose isomerase[17].

A polymorphism of peptidase D (prolidase) has also been described[18]. Variants occur in all the major population groups so far studied. Recently variants have also been described of peptidase C in African pigmies[19]. In each case a variant of a particular peptidase is not associated with any change in electrophoretic pattern of any of the other peptidases. This finding supports the biochemical evidence that these enzymes are distinct proteins, and suggests that they are coded for by separate gene loci. Moreover, studies of two families indicate that the loci controlling the structures of these pairs of enzymes are not closely linked, but are either well separated on the same chromosome or situated on different chromosomes.

Another interesting group of isozymes which illustrates this type of variation in human populations is phosphoglucomutase (PGM). These enzymes are very specific phosphotransferases which catalyse the reaction

$$\text{glucose-1-phosphate} \rightleftharpoons \text{glucose-6-phosphate}.$$

Using glucose-1-phosphate as the substrate it is possible to detect these isozymes after electrophoresis using glucose-6-phosphate dehydrogenase as a reagent, which oxidizes

存样品的电泳图谱难以相互区分。由变异体等位基因肽酶编码基因 A^5 编码的酶可能含有一个活性巯基，这样一个巯基在其他肽酶 A 亚基中并不存在，而且它能和氧化型谷胱甘肽发生交换反应，从而使半个分子的氧化型谷胱甘肽与该酶之间形成一个二硫键 [12]。用酸性谷胱甘肽被加合到酶分子上就可以解释为什么血液裂解液经过储存后电泳迁移率会增加。这个变异体能与已知能与巯基发生反应的多种试剂发生反应，而由这些试剂导致的电泳图谱变化与我所提出的假设是互相吻合的 [13]。

遗传密码似乎对大多数物种而言是相同的 [14]。如果真是这样的话，那么我们就能推断出由等位基因肽酶编码基因 A^5 编码的亚基中发生了特定氨基酸的替换。蛋白质中唯一一个含有活性巯基的氨基酸是半胱氨酸。这种氨基酸是中性的，既然由肽酶编码基因 A^5 编码的亚基与由常见等位基因肽酶编码基因 A^1 编码的亚基在电泳图谱上有所不同，前者更靠近阳极，所以出现了净负电荷的增加，由此可推断，半胱氨酸一定是替换了一个 pH 值 7.5 时带正电的氨基酸。这种氨基酸可能是赖氨酸或者精氨酸。对遗传密码的分析结果表明：尽管半胱氨酸替换精氨酸可以由一个碱基对的变化而引起，但半胱氨酸替换赖氨酸却不能。因此，可能的情况是，在这个变异体中有一个特定位置的精氨酸残基被替换成了半胱氨酸。对于肽酶 A6–1 也有类似的假设提出，即谷氨酸替换了一个特定位置的赖氨酸残基 [12]。

类似的罕见等位基因系列也在其他几种酶中被发现，包括肽酶 B[5,15]、磷酸葡萄糖变位酶 [16] 和磷酸己糖异构酶 [17]。

肽酶 D（脯肽酶）的多态性现象也被报道过 [18]。在迄今为止研究过的所有主要人群中都有肽酶 D 的变异体出现。肽酶 C 的变异体最近在非洲俾格米人中被报道过 [19]。在这些报道的例子中，每一种特定肽酶的变异体都与任意其他肽酶的电泳图谱的变化不相符。这一发现作为生物化学证据，也证明了这些肽酶确实是不同的蛋白质，并暗示它们是由独立的基因位点编码的。此外，人们对两个家族开展的研究所得结果表明，控制这些成对酶的结构的基因位点并不是紧密连锁的，它们或者在同一染色体上但完全独立，或者位于不同的染色体上。

能用于表征人群中出现这种变异性的另一组有趣的同工酶是磷酸葡萄糖变位酶（PGM）。这些酶都是特异性很强的磷酸转移酶，可以催化下述反应：

$$1\text{–磷酸葡萄糖} \rightleftharpoons 6\text{–磷酸葡萄糖}$$

用 1– 磷酸葡萄糖为底物可以在电泳后检测出这些同工酶，方法是：用 6– 磷酸葡萄糖脱氢酶为一种反应试剂，它能够氧化由磷酸葡萄糖变位酶催化产生的 6– 磷酸葡萄

the glucose-6-phosphate, formed by the action of the phosphoglucomutase, with the concomitant reduction of NADP to NADPH. The reduced coenzyme reacts with phenazine methosulphate and a tetrazolium salt resulting in a deposit of insoluble formazan blue at the site of enzyme activity. This method, used after electrophoresis at pH 7.4, has revealed a polymorphism of phosphoglucomutase in human populations[20]. The electrophoretic patterns of the three phenotypes, PGM1, PGM2–1 and PGM2, are shown in Fig. 3. This polymorphism occurs in most populations, although gene frequencies differ.

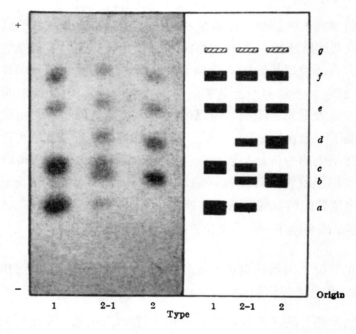

Fig. 3. Photograph and diagram of the electrophoretic patterns after electrophoresis of samples from individuals of the three common PGM types. (From ref. 20.)

Extensive family studies have shown that the different electrophoretic types result from the occurrence of a pair of autosomal alleles. Individuals who are PGM1 or PGM2 are apparently homozygous for one of these alleles. The electrophoretic pattern (Fig. 3) consists of two bands, which in PGM2 migrate further towards the anode than those given by PGM1. In PGM2–1 the electrophoretic pattern consists of four bands, corresponding in mobility to each of the isozymes seen in the homozygotes. The family studies indicate that individuals who are PGM2–1 are heterozygotes, and the products of each allele seem to be synthesized in this phenotype.

Electrophoresis of red cell lysates also reveals a second series of isozymes migrating further towards the anode which do not show any variation associated with that which occurs in the slower moving group (PGM_1). It was suggested that these faster moving isozymes (PGM_2) were controlled by a second gene locus, and later some variants were described which supported this hypothesis[10,16]. Moreover, the available evidence suggests that the

糖，并伴随着烟酰胺腺嘌呤二核苷酸磷酸酯（NADP）被还原成烟酰胺腺嘌呤二核苷酸磷酸（NADPH）。还原后的辅酶能与吩嗪 N– 甲硫酸盐和一种四唑盐反应，在具有酶活性的位置产生出不溶的蓝色甲臜沉积物。通过在 pH 值 7.4 条件下电泳后再使用这种方法染色，人们揭示出了人群中磷酸葡萄糖变位酶的多态性[20]。三种表型 PGM1、PGM2–1 和 PGM2 的电泳图谱示于图 3。这种多态性发生于大多数人群中，尽管基因频率有所不同。

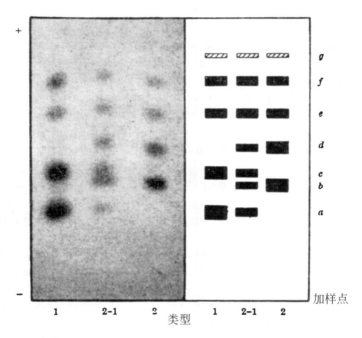

图 3. 对三种常见的 PGM 类型个体样品进行电泳检测后拍摄的电泳图谱照片和所作的图解。（来自参考文献 20）

　　大量家族研究的结果表明：这些不同的电泳类型是由一对常染色体等位基因的出现产生的。具有 PGM1 或者 PGM2 表型的个体从表观上看是其中一个等位基因的纯合子。其电泳图谱（图 3）显示为两条带（译者注：根据下文的描述，这里所说的两条带应该指的是靠近阴极的两条带），这两条带在 PGM2 中比在 PGM1 中更靠近阳极。PGM2–1 的电泳图谱包含四条带，分别对应于纯合子中每一种同工酶的迁移率。家族研究结果表明，PGM2–1 的个体是杂合子，在这种表型中似乎每个等位基因的产物都被合成了。

　　红细胞裂解物的电泳结果也表明：第二个系列的同工酶更加靠近阳极，而且它们没有显示出任何与移动更慢的 PGM_1 中所发生的变化相关的变化。有人提出这些移动速度较快的同工酶（PGM_2）是受另一个基因位点控制的，随后人们发现了一些能支持上述假说的变异体[10,16]。此外，目前已有证据显示，控制 PGM_1 和 PGM_2 一

loci controlling the primary structures of PGM$_1$ and PGM$_2$ are not closely linked, but are either well separated on the same chromosome or on different chromosomes[21].

Examination of placental extracts by electrophoresis revealed a third series of isozymes, PGM$_3$, which are relatively less active and which migrate further towards the anode than either PGM$_1$ or PGM$_2$. This group of isozymes of phosphoglucomutase also have common variation, which is genetically determined[22], as studies of twin placentae have shown. This group of isozymes is apparently present in most tissues, although it has not been possible to demonstrate significant activity in red blood cells. Fibroblast cultures, however, have been used for the study of the segregation of the variants of PGM$_3$ in families, and the results agree well with those obtained from the study of twin placentae[21].

The significance of the occurrence of these three different forms of phosphoglucomutase in man is not clear. It is interesting, however, that the electrophoretic patterns of the three groups of isozymes are quite similar, and that they seem to have similar if not identical molecular weights[23,24]. It is possible that they have related primary structures which have evolved by gene duplication from a single locus.

The implications of this type of variation in the primary structure of proteins in human populations are quite wide ranging, both for theoretical human biology and in the practical aspects of the study of the human organism. It is possible that common variants of a particular enzyme provide a pool of variability within the species, such that the constraints of the environment for the species as a whole are minimized, and the species is less vulnerable to environmental changes. Moreover, available techniques indicate that at least one in three enzymes has this type of variation. The chance of any two unrelated individuals being identical in terms of protein structure therefore seems to be extremely small. So far there is no experimental evidence to support the hypothesis that variation in the primary structure of enzyme proteins is the basis of much of the observed variation in the gross appearance of individuals. It seems reasonable to suppose, however, that many of the characters which are inherited in an obscure manner, and which are apparently controlled by many genes, are the result of structural variation at a molecular level of several different proteins.

The effect of a particular variant may well differ from one tissue to another. For example, a variant enzyme with a shorter half life than the usual form of the enzyme may not have any appreciable effect in a tissue with a fairly rapid cellular turnover, such as intestinal mucosa. On the other hand, in the erythrocyte, which has a relatively long half life and in which protein synthesis presumably ceases at about the time that the nucleus is lost, the activity of a particular structural form of an enzyme may be lost quite soon after the cell is released into the circulation. Such an unstable enzyme may result in a more rapid destruction of the erythrocyte, as for example occurs with some rare variants of enzymes in the anaerobic glycolytic pathway, such as pyruvate kinase[25], or there may be no obvious effect until the individual is exposed to a toxic compound such as a drug or a particular type of food, as is seen with two different variants of glucose-6-phosphate

级结构的基因位点并非紧密连锁，它们或者在同一染色体上但完全独立，或者位于不同的染色体上 [21]。

在用电泳检查胎盘提取物时发现了第三个系列的同工酶——PGM$_3$，它比 PGM$_1$ 或 PGM$_2$ 的活性弱一些，并且电泳后比 PGM$_1$ 或 PGM$_2$ 更靠近阳极。这一组磷酸葡萄糖变位酶的同工酶也具有共同的变异，而且是由遗传决定的 [22]，这一点已通过对双胞胎的胎盘研究得到了证实。尽管现在还不能证实这一组同工酶在红细胞中有明显的活性，但它们似乎存在于大多数组织中。然而，通过体外培养成纤维细胞对家族中 PGM$_3$ 变异体进行的分离工作所获得的结果与通过双胞胎胎盘的研究所获得的结果吻合得很好 [21]。

现在还不清楚这三种不同形式的磷酸葡萄糖变位酶在人体中产生的重要性。但有趣的是：这三组同工酶的电泳图谱非常相似，而且它们的分子量也非常接近，甚至可以说完全一样 [23,24]。它们的一级结构有可能是相关的，由一个单一的位点通过基因加倍而产生。

人群中蛋白质一级结构的这类变异涉及多方面含义，包括理论人类生物学以及人作为生物而被研究的实践方面。一种特定酶的多个常见变异体的出现可能为一个物种内部的多样性提供了一种储存，这样环境对某个物种的整体所产生的约束作用就降到了最低程度，因而降低了物种对环境变化的脆弱性。此外，利用已有技术得到的结果表明，至少有 1/3 的酶具有这种类型的变异。因此，任意两个不相干的个体从蛋白质结构而言完全相同的几率似乎是极其微小的。目前还没有实验证据能支持以下假说：酶蛋白一级结构的变异是个体之间在总体外观上存在差异的主要基础。但似乎可以合理地认为：通过一种并非清晰的方式遗传、表观上看受到多个基因控制的许多个体特征实际上是几种不同蛋白质在分子水平上发生结构变异的结果。

一种特定酶蛋白的变异体在不同组织中产生的效应可能是不同的。例如，一种半衰期比普通酶更短的变异体酶在像肠黏膜这样细胞代谢速度较快的组织中可能不会产生什么明显的效应。另一方面，在半衰期相对较长且蛋白质合成大约在细胞核消失时就会停止的红细胞中，一种具有特定结构形式的酶的活性会在细胞被释放进入到血液循环系统后以比较快的速度丢失。这样一种不稳定的酶可能会加速红细胞的破坏，在无氧糖酵解过程中发挥作用的一些罕见变异体酶（如丙酮酸激酶）就是其中的一个例子 [25]。或者，在个体接触到有毒化合物（如药物或特定类型的食物）之前变异体酶并不表现出明显的效应，比如 6- 磷酸葡萄糖脱氢酶的两种不同的变异

dehydrogenase[26,27]. In one case, treatment with the antimalarial drug, primaquine, induces a haemolytic crisis and, in the other, ingestion of the fava bean has a similar effect.

Another consequence of the occurrence of structural variants of enzymes would be that heterozygotes would have a least two structural forms of the enzyme, and if the enzyme were a dimer there would be three isozymes, four for a trimer and five for a tetramer. The proportions in which these isozymes were present in any tissue would clearly depend on several factors, including the stability of the subunits and of different combinations of subunits. The apparent activity would also depend on the relative catalytic efficiency of particular combinations of subunits. It also seems possible that these isozymes are present in different proportions throughout the life of the cell. Whether or not this phenomenon has any significance for the whole organism is not known.

Another possible effect of a difference in half life, and therefore of activity, of an enzyme may occur when the enzyme affected is part of a metabolic scheme which is made up of different pathways. If we consider a hypothetical three-enzyme system such as that illustrated, and if in the normal situation with normal concentrations of α, and β, 25 percent of A is converted to D, then if α is replaced by α' which is less stable or catalytically less active, the rate of conversion of A to B would be reduced and more of A could be metabolized to D.

$$A \underset{}{\overset{\alpha}{\rightleftharpoons}} B \underset{}{\overset{\beta}{\rightleftharpoons}} C$$
$$\big\Updownarrow \gamma$$
$$D$$

Such a situation in itself might not, in most conditions, have any demonstrable effect on the individual. But if the individual is faced with a metabolic challenge in which the concentrations of B or C are critical, then the effect may well be quite dramatic, as in the case of primaquine sensitivity[26,27].

On the other hand, the accumulation of a high concentration of D may in itself be toxic, and this situation is found with some inborn errors of metabolism, such as galactosaemia[28,29], although in these cases the level of activity of the affected enzyme is usually very low indeed, and perhaps beyond the limits of detection. There are of course many possible variations within even the simple scheme I have outlined. It seems probable that these "enzymopathies" are part of the same general phenomenon as the rare variants, but in this case the affected individual can apparently synthesize only an unstable enzyme, as an inactive enzyme is perhaps completely incapable of synthesizing the particular enzyme protein.

If the enzyme concerned in a particular metabolic error is common to most tissues, the study of the enzyme in erythrocytes makes it possible to study the enzyme without recourse to biopsy procedures. The occurrence of a polymorphism can provide good evidence that the enzymes under investigation in different tissues are the products of the

体[26,27]。在一个案例中，用抗疟药伯氨喹进行治疗时导致了溶血的危险后果；而在另一个案例中，食入蚕豆也产生了类似的效应。

酶结构变异体发生的另一种情形是，杂合子个体将至少产生酶的两种结构形式，如果这种酶以二聚体形式存在的话，就会形成三种同工酶，如果是三聚体酶就会形成四种，如果是四聚体就会形成五种。这些同工酶在任何组织中存在的比例显然取决于几个方面的因素，包括亚基的稳定性以及亚基之间各种组合的稳定性。其表观活性也取决于特定亚基组合形式的相对催化效率。另一种似乎可能的情形是，这些同工酶在细胞整个生命过程中的不同阶段以不同的比例存在。目前还不清楚这一现象对生物个体的整体而言是否具有重要意义。

由酶的半衰期以及活性的差别而导致的另一个可能的效应也许会发生于当所影响的酶参与一个代谢网络的时候，这个代谢网络一般由多条途径组合而成。如果我们考查一个如下图所示的假想的三酶系统，而且如果在正常情况下两种酶 α 和 β 的浓度正常，并有 25% 的 A 转变成了 D，那么，如果 α 被更不稳定或者催化活性更弱的 α' 所替代的话，则 A 向 B 的转化率就会降低，更多的 A 就会被代谢转变成 D。

$$A \;\underset{}{\overset{\alpha}{\rightleftharpoons}}\; B \;\underset{}{\overset{\beta}{\rightleftharpoons}}\; C$$
$$\Big\updownarrow\gamma$$
$$D$$

在大多数情况下，这样一种情形本身也许不会对个体产生任何可被测量的影响。但如果个体面对的是一种 B 或者 C 的浓度处于导致代谢危机的临界值的情形，那么效应就很可能是相当剧烈的，就像伯氨喹敏感性导致的结果那样[26,27]。

另一方面，高浓度 D 的积聚本身也许就是有毒性的，这种情况出现在某些先天性代谢障碍中，比如半乳糖血症[28,29]，不过在这些例子中所影响的酶的活性水平实际上总是很低，而且可能已经超出了检测的底限。即便是在我上面描述过的这个简单系统中，也势必会出现很多种可能的变体。似乎可能的是，这些"酶缺陷症"与罕见变异体一样，都是同一种常见现象中的一部分。但在这种情况下受到影响的个体表观上看只能合成一种不稳定的酶，因为一种无活性的酶有可能完全不能合成特定的酶蛋白。

如果一种与特定代谢障碍相关的酶普遍存在于大多数组织中，那么对红细胞中的酶进行研究就可以使不借助活组织检查来研究酶成为可能。多态性的发生可以为以下观点提供有力的证据，即不同组织中被研究的酶都是同一个基因位点的产物，

same gene locus and are therefore probably structurally identical.

(**230**, 215-218; 1971)

W. H. P. Lewis: Department of Pathology, St Helier Hospital, Carshalton, Surrey.

References:

1. Landsteiner, K., *Wein. Klin. Wschr.*, **14**, 132 (1901).

2. Smithies, O., *Biochem. J.*, **61**, 629 (1955).

3. Harris, H., *Proc. Roy. Soc.*, **B**, **174**, 1 (1969).

4. Adams, E., McFadden, M., and Smith, E. L., *J. Biol. Chem.*, **198**, 663 (1952).

5. Lewis, W. H. P., and Harris, H., *Nature*, **215**, 351 (1967).

6. Lewis, W. H. P., *Symp. Zool. Soc.*, **26**, 93 (1970).

7. Lewis, W. H. P., and Harris, H., *Ann. Human Genet.*, **33**, 89 (1969).

8. Santachiara-Benerecetti, S. A., *Atti. Assoc. Genet. Ital.*, **14**, 145 (1969).

9. Boyer, S. H., Porter, I. H., and Weilbacher, R. G., *Proc. US Nat. Acad. Sci.*, **48**, 1868 (1962).

10. Hopkinson, D. A., and Harris, H., *Nature*, **208**, 410 (1965).

11. Shaw, C. R., *Science*, **149**, 936 (1965).

12. Lewis, W. H. P., Corney, G., and Harris, H., *Ann. Human Genet.*, **32**, 35 (1968).

13. Hopkinson, D. A., and Sinha, K. P., *Ann. Human Genet.*, **33**, 139 (1969).

14. Crick, F. H. C., *Proc. Roy. Soc.*, B, **167**, 331 (1967).

15. Blake, N. M., Kirk, R. L., Lewis, W. H. P., and Harris, H., *Ann. Human Genet.*, **33**, 301 (1969).

16. Hopkinson, D. A., and Harris, H., *Ann. Human Genet.*, **30**, 167 (1966).

17. Detter, J. C., Ways, P. O., Giblett, E. R., Baughan, M. A., Hopkinson, D. A., Povey, S., and Harris, H., *Ann. Human Genet.*, **31**, 329 (1968).

18. Lewis, W. H. P., and Harris, H., *Ann. Human Genet.*, **32**, 317 (1969).

19. Sanachiara-Benerecetti, S. A., *Amer. J. Human Genet.*, **22**, 232 (1970).

20. Spencer, N., Hopkinson, D. A., and Harris, H., *Nature*, **204**, 742 (1964).

21. Parrington, J. M., Cruikshank, G., Hopkinson, D. A., Robson, E. B., and Harris, H., *Ann. Human Genet.*, **32**, 27 (1968).

22. Hopkinson, D. A., and Harris, H., *Ann. Human Genet.*, **31**, 395 (1968).

23. McAlpine, P. J., Hopkinson, D. A., and Harris, H., *Ann. Human Genet.*, **34**, 177 (1970).

24. Monn, E., *Intern. J. Protein Res.*, **1**, 73 (1969).

25. Valentine, W. N., Tanaka, K. R., and Miwa, S., *Trans. Assoc. Amer. Physicians*, **74**, 100 (1961).

26. Carson, P. E., Flanagan, C. L., Ickes, C. E., and Alving, A. S., *Science*, **124**, 484 (1956).

27. Szeinberg, A., Sheba, C., Hirshom, N., and Bodongi, E., *Blood*, **12**, 603 (1957).

28. Harris, H., *Human Biochemical Genetics* (Cambridge University Press, 1959).

29. Crome, L., and Stern, J., *The Pathology of Mental Defect* (Churchill, London, 1967).

30. Hopkinson, D. A., Spencer, N., and Harris, H., *Nature*, **199**, 969 (1963).

31. Giblett, E. R., *Genetic Markers in Human Blood*, 491 (Blackwell, Oxford, 1969).

32. Spencer, N., Hopkinson, D. A., and Harris, H., *Ann. Human Genet.*, **32**, 9 (1968).

33. Fildes, R. A., and Harris, H., *Nature*, **209**, 261 (1966).

因而它们很可能具有相同的结构。

（毛晨晖 翻译，昌增益 审稿）

Experimentally Created Incipient Species of *Drosophila*

T. Dobzhansky and O. Pavlovsky

Editor's Note

One of the earliest complaints about Darwin's theory of evolution was that there was no evidence that new species can be created in laboratory conditions. The paper by Theodosius Dobzhansky and his colleague Olga Pavlovsky describes their successful creation of an incipient species of the fruit fly. Dobzhansky was one of the outstanding geneticists of the 1930s and played an important part in the theoretical underpinning of modern genetics.

EXPERIMENTAL creation of new biological species by means of allopolyploidy—doubling the chromosome sets in interspecific hybrids—has been known for several decades. One of the classics in this field is the work of Karpechenko[1], who obtained a tetraploid *Raphanobrassica* (radocabbage) from hybrids between *Raphanus* (radish) and *Brassica* (cabbage). *Raphanobrassica* is almost fully fertile *inter se*, but forms highly sterile hybrids with the parental species. Some allopolyploid species existing in nature have been experimentally resynthesized; for example, the mint, *Galeopsis tetrahit*[2], bread wheats[3] and others. Though widespread and important in some plant families, species formation by allopolyploidy is uncommon in the living world at large. A different mode of origin of species is prevalent among sexually reproducing and out-breeding organisms. This is accumulation of genetic differences between geographically separated (allopatric) populations or races, followed by a gradual emergence of reproductive isolation between them[4,5]. Species formation through genetic divergence and its fixation by reproductive isolating mechanisms is a slow process, generally requiring many generations. For this reason, this kind of speciation has not been observed or reproduced in experiments. In a sense, we are in a situation today similar to that experienced by Darwin more than a century ago: differentiation of species is inferred from copious indirect evidence, but has not actually been observed. The experiments described here are therefore very unusual: what may be regarded as the crucial stage of the speciation process has taken place, and in part deliberately induced in laboratory experiments.

Superspecies *Drosophila paulistorum*

Drosophila paulistorum, a member of the *willistoni* species group of *Drosophila*, occurs in the American tropics, from Guatemala and Trinidad to southern Brazil. *D. paulistorum* is a compound of six semispecies or incipient species—genetically too different to be regarded as races of the same species, yet not different enough to be rated as six fully differentiated species[6,7]. It is difficult to cross the semispecies because of a pronounced ethological (sexual) isolation. No hybridization has been detected in nature. In the laboratory, when females

通过实验创建的果蝇端始种

多布赞斯基，帕夫洛夫斯基

编者按

人们对达尔文进化论最早的不满之一在于没有新物种可以在实验室条件下被创建出来的证据。特奥多修斯·多布赞斯基及其同事奥尔加·帕夫洛夫斯基的这篇论文描述了他们对自己成功创建出的一个果蝇端始种的研究。多布赞斯基是20世纪30年代的杰出遗传学家之一，他在奠立现代遗传学的理论基础方面作出过重要贡献。

利用异源多倍性——使物种间杂种的染色体组加倍——通过实验创建新生物学物种在几十年前就已经为人们所知。卡尔佩琴科的研究堪称该领域中的经典之作之一[1]；他从萝卜和甘蓝的杂交种获得了四倍体萝卜甘蓝。萝卜甘蓝的种内交配几乎是完全可育的，但与其亲本物种的杂交种是高度不育的。一些存在于自然界中的异源多倍体物种已经通过实验重新合成，例如薄荷、野芝麻[2]、普通小麦[3]等等。虽然通过异源多倍性形成物种在某些植物科属中广泛存在，并且还十分重要，但在整个生物界中并不算常见。物种起源的另一种不同模式在有性繁殖和远系繁殖的生物中是普遍存在的，即随着遗传差异在地理上隔离的（异域的）种群或地理宗之间积累，这些地理种群或地理宗间会逐渐出现生殖隔离[4,5]。遗传分化导致的物种形成以及生殖隔离机制对新物种的固定是一个缓慢的过程，通常需要经过很多世代。基于这个原因，这类物种形成从来没有在实验中被观察到过，或用实验重复出来过。从某种意义上讲，我们今天的处境与一个多世纪之前达尔文所面临的困难类似：物种分化是根据丰富的间接证据推断出来的，但是没有被真正观察到过。因此，本文中所描述的实验非同寻常：可以被认为是物种形成中最关键的阶段发生了，并且在一定程度上是在实验室条件下人为诱导出来的。

圣保罗果蝇超种

圣保罗果蝇是威氏果蝇中的一种，分布于美洲的热带地区，从危地马拉和特立尼达一直到巴西南部。圣保罗果蝇是6个半分化种或者说端始种的混合体，即它们在遗传学上非常不同以至于不能被看作是同一物种下的不同地理宗；但它们之间的差异也没有达到可以被看作是6个完全分化的物种的程度[6,7]。半分化种之间由于存在显著的行为（性）隔离而难于进行杂交；在自然界中也从未发现过它们杂交。在

and males of two semispecies are placed together, most of the matings occur within a semispecies. The exceptions, females of one semispecies inseminated by males of another, give progenies of apparently normal and vigorous hybrid daughters and sons. The hybrid females are fertile when backcrossed to males of either parental semispecies. The hybrid males are completely sterile.

The combination of these two isolating mechanisms permits sympatric coexistence of two, or even three, semispecies. Thus, the Central American semispecies occurs alone from Guatemala to Costa Rica and western Panama, but in central Panama it meets the Amazonian and Orinocan semispecies, The distribution of the Amazonian semispecies extends from Panama to Guiana, Rio Negro and the estuary of the Amazon (Belem). The Orinocan semispecies has been found in northern Colombia, Venezuela, Trinidad and Guiana. The Interior semispecies occurs on upper Orinoco, Rio Negro, upper Amazon and their tributaries. The Andean semispecies occurs alone in central and southern Brazil, Bolivia, Peru and Ecuador, but it meets the Amazonian and Interior semispecies in central and southern Colombia, Trinidad, Venezuela, Guiana and along the Amazon and Rio Negro. Finally, the Transitional semispecies occurs on the Pacific Coast of Colombia, in northern Colombia and northern Venezuela[7]. The semispecies are indistinguishable morphologically but they can be distinguished cytologically[8,9]; the easiest in practice and usually unambiguous method of recognition is outcrossing a strain to be diagnosed to six tester strains, one from each semispecies. Fertile hybrids are produced with only one of the six testers, that which represents the semispecies to which belongs the strain being tested.

Career of the Llanos Strain

A laboratory strain was established from a female captured on March 19, 1958, south of Villavicencio, in the Llanos of Colombia. The strain was classified as belonging to the Orinocan semispecies, because it crossed easily to, and gave fertile hybrids with, other Orinocan strains then available in the laboratory. The behaviour of the Llanos strain changed, however, between 1958 and 1963; in 1963 and thereafter, the male hybrids obtained from crosses of Llanos to Orinocan strains proved to be completely sterile. The possibility that the change in the behaviour of the Llanos strain might have resulted from accidental contamination was ruled out on two grounds. First, a cytological study of the Llanos strain in 1959 showed two polymorphic chromosomal inversions which were, at that time, found in no other strain. Llanos still carries these chromosomal polymorphisms. Second, in 1963, Llanos was systematically outcrossed to all other strains of *D. paulistorum* then available in the laboratory, and gave fertile male hybrids with none. The reality of the change is not in doubt[10,11].

实验室条件下，当两个半分化种的雌性个体和雄性个体被放置在一起时，绝大多数交配行为发生在同一个半分化种内。少数情况下，当一个半分化种的雄性个体给另一个半分化种的雌性个体受精后，雌性个体会产下看来既正常又有活力的雌性和雄性杂种。雌性杂种与任一半分化种的雄性亲本回交时都是可育的；雄性杂种则是完全不育的。

这两种隔离机制的组合使得 2 种甚至 3 种半分化种可以同域共存。因此，中美洲半分化种只出现在从危地马拉到哥斯达黎加及巴拿马西部，但是在巴拿马中部，它遇到了亚马孙半分化种和奥里诺科半分化种。亚马孙半分化种的分布范围是从巴拿马延伸至圭亚那、里奥内格罗河区以及亚马孙河的河口地区（贝伦）。奥里诺科半分化种分布于哥伦比亚北部、委内瑞拉、特立尼达以及圭亚那。内陆半分化种出现在奥里诺科河上游、里奥内格罗河区、亚马孙河上游以及它们的支流流域。安第斯半分化种只出现在巴西中部和南部、玻利维亚、秘鲁和厄瓜多尔，但它与亚马孙半分化种和内陆半分化种在哥伦比亚中部和南部、特立尼达、委内瑞拉、圭亚那地区以及亚马孙河和里奥内格罗河沿岸区相遇。最后，过渡半分化种出现在哥伦比亚的太平洋沿岸、哥伦比亚北部和委内瑞拉的北部[7]。这些半分化种从形态上无法分辨，但从细胞学上可以将它们区分开[8,9]。操作上最为简便并且通常都能得到明确结果的分辨方法是：将待测品系与 6 个半分化种的各一个品系进行异型杂交，可育的杂交后代只会从 6 个检验组合中的一个获得，这说明待测品系所属的半分化种与对应的试验品系相同。

亚诺斯品系的来龙去脉

1958 年 3 月 19 日在哥伦比亚亚诺斯大草原上的比亚维森西奥市南部捕获到一只雌性果蝇，并从它建立了一个实验室品系。这一品系被归为奥里诺科半分化种，因为它容易与当时实验室中拥有的其他奥里诺科果蝇杂交，并产下可育的杂交种。然而，在 1958 年到 1963 年间，亚诺斯品系的行为发生了改变；1963 年及那以后，由亚诺斯品系果蝇和奥里诺科品系果蝇杂交得到的雄性杂交种被证明是完全不育的。基于如下两个依据，由于意外污染而导致亚诺斯品系果蝇在行为上发生变化的可能性被排除了。首先，1959 年对亚诺斯品系的细胞学研究发现了当时其他品系所没有的两种多态性染色体倒位。亚诺斯品系现在仍携带有这些染色体多态性。其次，1963 年曾将亚诺斯品系与实验室中的所有其他品系的圣保罗果蝇进行了系统性的异型杂交，没有得到任何雄性可育的杂种。因此，上述行为改变的真实性是毋庸置疑的[10,11]。

In 1964, Professor H. L. Carson sent us a strain established from a female collected at Marco, on the upper Amazon, Brazil. This strain gave fertile hybrids only with Llanos. Later, many other strains of the Interior semispecies, to which Marco belongs, were found in equatorial South America[7,12]. Are we to conclude that the Llanos strain became transformed from a representative of the Orinocan semispecies to one of the Interior semispecies? Such a conclusion is not warranted, although we obviously do not know whether the Llanos strain would have given fertile male hybrids with the Interior semispecies in 1958 or 1959. What we do know is that although the Llanos strain has a pronounced sexual isolation from at least some Interior strains, it mates freely with the Orinocan strain. The isolation is fairly strong between Interior and Orinocan.

The lack of isolation between the Llanos and Orinocan strains was ascertained in 1964 with "male-choice" tests[10]; Virgin females of two strains, Llanos and an orange-eyed mutant found in an Orinocan strain from Georgetown, Guiana, were confined with males of one or the other of these strains. After about half the females had become inseminated, the females were dissected and the presence or absence of sperm in their seminal receptacles was determined under a microscope (see Table 1).

Table 1. Inseminated (+) and Uninseminated (–) Females of Two Strains of *Drosophila paulistorum*, Exposed to Males of One of These Strains

	Llanos ♀♀		Orincan ♀♀	
	+	–	+	–
Llanos ♂♂	56	34	36	54
Orinocan ♂♂	44	47	44	48

In tests of this kind, the "choice" is actually exercised by the females who accept some males in preference to others. Table 1 shows that Llanos males are accepted by females of their own kind more easily than by Orinocan females; Orinocan males are accepted equally by both kinds of females. In 1969, the experiments were repeated, using an observation chamber[13]. Virgin but mature females and males were introduced, in equal numbers, into a saucer-shaped chamber with a glass top, and the matings that occurred were recorded with the aid of a hand lens. To make the Llanos individuals distinguishable from the Orinocan, one or the other kind had one of their wings slightly clipped. Table 2 summarizes the observations made by Lee Ehrman[13] on matings between the Llanos strain and an Orinocan strain derived from Georgetown, Guiana.

Table 2. Matings Observed between Llanos and Orinocan Strains

Llanos ♀ × Llanos ♂	Llanos ♀ × Orinocan ♂	Orinocan ♀ × Llanos ♂	Orinocan ♀ × Orinocan ♂	Isolation coefficient
34	22	23	23	+0.11 ± 0.10

1964 年，卡森教授给我们寄来了一个由从巴西亚马孙河上游的马科地区采集到的一只雌蝇所建立的品系。这个品系只跟亚诺斯品系产生可育的杂交种。随后，更多内陆半分化种品系（前述马科果蝇品系即属于该半分化种）在南美洲赤道地区被发现[7,12]。我们是否可以由此得出结论——亚诺斯品系已经从典型的奥里诺科半分化种转变为内陆半分化种？这样一个结论是没有道理的，尽管我们显然并不知道在1958 年或 1959 年期间，亚诺斯品系的果蝇是否已经能跟内陆半分化种产生可育的雄性杂交种。我们所知道的是：虽然亚诺斯品系至少与一些内陆品系果蝇之间存在着明显的性隔离，但它却可以跟奥里诺科果蝇进行自由交配；而内陆品系和奥里诺科品系之间的性隔离是相当强的。

亚诺斯品系和奥里诺科品系果蝇之间不存在性隔离这一事实已经在 1964 年通过"雄性挑选"测验而得到证实[10]。来自两个品系的未交配过的雌蝇，包括亚诺斯品系和在圭亚那乔治敦发现的奥里诺科品系的橙眼突变体，被限制只能与其中一个品系的雄蝇进行交配。在半数左右的雌性个体受孕之后，通过对雌蝇进行解剖，在显微镜下确认她们的受精囊内是否存在精子（见表 1）。

表 1. 圣保罗果蝇两个品系的雌蝇在与其中一个品系的雄蝇共处后受精（＋）和不受精（－）的个体数量

	亚诺斯品系♀♀		奥里诺科品系♀♀	
	＋	－	＋	－
亚诺斯品系♂♂	56	34	36	54
奥里诺科品系♂♂	44	47	44	48

在这类测验中，"挑选"实际上是通过雌性个体更倾向于接受某些雄性个体而实现的。表 1 的数据表明：亚诺斯品系的雄蝇更容易被它们自己品系的雌蝇所接受；而奥里诺科品系的雄蝇则均等地被所有两个品系的雌蝇所接受。1969 年，使用一个观察室重复了这个实验[13]；将等量未交配过的成年雌蝇和雄蝇放入一个顶部带有玻璃盖的茶碟形观察室中，然后借助放大镜记录它们之间的交配情况。为了能区分亚诺斯品系个体和奥里诺科品系个体，其中一个品系的果蝇的翅膀被略微剪短。表 2 总结了李·埃尔曼对亚诺斯品系果蝇与来自圭亚那乔治敦的奥里诺科果蝇之间交配情况的观察结果[13]。

表 2. 亚诺斯品系和奥里诺科品系之间的交配情况

亚诺斯♀× 亚诺斯♂	亚诺斯♀× 奥里诺科♂	奥里诺科♀× 亚诺斯♂	奥里诺科♀× 奥里诺科♂	隔离系数
34	22	23	23	+0.11±0.10

The isolation coefficient is not significantly different from zero. This coefficient is +1 if the isolation is complete because only matings between likes take place, and −1 if matings only between unlikes are observed. Tests of the mating preferences of Llanos flies with other strains of the Orinocan and Interior semispecies, made by S. Perez-Salas[12], gave the isolation coefficients shown in Table 3.

Table 3. Isolation Coefficients of Crosses between Llanos and Other Strains

Llanos + Sarare, Orinocan	+0.33 ± 0.09
Llanos + Valparaiso, Interior	+0.18 ± 0.09
Llanos + Leticia, Interior	+0.12 ± 0.09
Llanos + Mitu, Interior	+0.24 ± 0.10
Llanos + Ocamo, Interior	+0.57 ± 0.08
Llanos + Ayacucho, Interior	+0.18 ± 0.12

Slight, but sometimes statistically significant, preferences for mating within a strain are often found in experiments with *D. paulistorum* in which two strains of the same semispecies are derived from ancestors collected in different localities. The Llanos strain crosses fairly easily with strains of both Orinocan and Interior semispecies, although the Interior semispecies are more strongly isolated ethologically from each other, and even more so from the other semispecies. We conclude that, having developed a sterility of male hybrids with the Orinocan semispecies, the Llanos strain did not acquire ethological isolation from the Orinocan. But can ethological isolation be superimposed on the hybrid sterility by means of artificial selection?

Selection for Isolation

Several workers[14-16] have induced or intensified ethological isolation between strains of the same or of different species. The techniques used in all these experiments are identical in principle. Two strains between which the isolation is to be developed are made homozygous for different recessive mutant genes. Females and males of the two strains are placed together and they are allowed to mate freely and to produce offspring. The part of that offspring coming from matings between the strains will be wild type in phenotype, whereas the progeny of matings of females and males of the same strain will show the recessive mutant traits. The wild type flies are discarded, and the mutants are allowed to become parents of the next generation. The progenies of the flies that mate within a strain are thus included, and those of the matings between the strains are excluded from parentage. This imposes a selective advantage on genetic constitutions which favour matings within and discriminate against matings between strains.

The variant of this technique that had to be used in experiments with *D. paulistorum* is rather laborious. The Llanos strain has produced a sex linked recessive mutant, rough eye.

隔离系数跟零没有显著差别。如果隔离是彻底的，那么这个系数就是 +1，因为交配只发生在同类个体之间；而如果只观察到异类个体之间发生交配，那么这个系数就是 –1。由佩雷斯–萨拉斯进行的亚诺斯品系果蝇与其他奥里诺科半分化种品系及内陆半分化种品系果蝇之间的交配偏好实验 [12] 得到了表 3 所示的隔离系数。

表 3. 由亚诺斯品系和其他品系杂交得到的隔离系数

亚诺斯 + 萨拉雷，奥里诺科	+0.33 ± 0.09
亚诺斯 + 瓦尔帕莱索，内陆	+0.18 ± 0.09
亚诺斯 + 莱蒂西亚，内陆	+0.12 ± 0.09
亚诺斯 + 米图，内陆	+0.24 ± 0.10
亚诺斯 + 奥卡莫，内陆	+0.57 ± 0.08
亚诺斯 + 阿亚库乔，内陆	+0.18 ± 0.12

在用从不同地点采集的祖先而衍生出的圣保罗果蝇同一半分化种的两个品系进行实验时，总能发现一些微小但有时统计上显著的交配偏好。亚诺斯品系果蝇与奥里诺科半分化种品系及内陆半分化种品系果蝇都可相当容易地进行杂交，不过内陆半分化种品系之间有更强的行为隔离，而且它们与其他半分化种间的隔离还会更严重一些。我们得到的结论是：虽然亚诺斯品系与奥里诺科半分化种品系间的雄性杂交种已经产生不育性，但亚诺斯品系并没有形成跟奥里诺科品系的行为隔离。然而，能否通过人工选择使其在杂种不育的基础上产生行为隔离呢？

隔离的选择

若干研究者 [14-16] 已经在同一物种的不同品系间或者不同物种间诱导出或强化了行为隔离。所有这些实验中所采用的技术在原理上都是一样的。要建立行为隔离的那两个品系分别是带有不同隐性突变基因的纯合体。把两个品系的雌性个体和雄性个体放在一起，并允许它们自由地交配和生育后代。由不同品系的个体交配而产生的那些后代在表现型上将是野生型，而由同一品系的雌雄个体交配产生的后代则会表现出隐性突变体性状。淘汰野生型果蝇，留下突变体作为下一代的亲本。因此，在家系中只保留由同一品系果蝇交配产生的后代，而那些由不同品系果蝇交配产生的后代就都被排除。这样就从家系的遗传构成上施加了祖护品系内交配、排斥品系间交配的选择压力。

在圣保罗果蝇实验中必须使用的这项技术经过改进后变得十分繁复。亚诺斯品系的果蝇已经产生了一个性连锁的隐性突变体——糙眼突变体。奥里诺科半分化种

An autosomal recessive mutant, orange eye, and sex-linked mutants, veinless wing and yellow body appeared in the Georgetown, Guiana, strain of the Orinocan semispecies. (Rough, orange and veinless were found by Mr. B. Spassky, and yellow by O. P.) In October 1966, pairs of experimental populations were started according to the following design. Between fifty and a hundred (usually seventy) virgin females of Llanos rough mutant are placed in a culture bottle with males of the same strain and of one of the Orinocan mutant strains. In another culture bottle, fifty to a hundred Orinocan mutant females are exposed to a mixture of the same Orinocan mutant males and of Llanos rough eyed males. Among the progeny, the hybrid females, coming from matings of unlike parents, are distinguishable by being wild type in phenotype. Non-hybrid females, coming from matings of like parents, show the traits of the respective mutants. The hybrid females are discarded, and the non-hybrid ones used as parents of the next generation. Because rough, yellow and veinless are sex linked, hybrid sons of the mutant mothers are not distinguishable from the non-hybrids. This is inconvenient but not fatal for the experiments, because the hybrid males are completely sterile. Because orange is autosomal it permits discrimination of hybrid and non-hybrid females as well as males. Six pairs of experimental populations were made:

1*A*: rough ♀♀ + rough ♂♂ + orange ♂♂

1*B*: orange ♀♀ + orange ♂♂ + rough ♂♂

2*A*: rough ♀♀ + rough ♂♂ + veinless ♂♂

2*B*: veinless ♀♀ + veinless ♂♂ + rough ♂♂

3*A*: rough ♀♀ + rough ♂♂ + yellow ♂♂

3*B*: yellow ♀♀ + yellow ♂♂ + rough ♂♂

Populations 1*A* and 1*B* are at present (December 1970) in the seventy-third generation of selection. Populations 2*A* and 2*B* were discontinued after sixty-five generations, and 3 *A* and 3 *B* after sixty generations of selection. The proportions of the like and the unlike males to which the females were exposed were adjusted to supply in different generations the strongest challenge to the discriminating abilities of the females. At the same time, enough mutant progeny must be produced to serve as parents of the next generation. In the early generations, the two kinds of males were usually equally numerous; later the like males were less numerous than the unlike. The total numbers of males were about equal to the numbers of females.

The selection for ethological isolation was successful in all six populations, although in none has anything like complete isolation been achieved. It can be stated that, as a rule, the proportions of hybrids among the progenies have decreased from early generations to the later ones. The progress of the selection seems, however, very uneven. For example, the percentages of hybrid females obtained in every tenth generation in population 1*A* were: F_1, 41.9; F_{10}, 17.3; F_{20}, 53.5; F_{30}, 31.8; F_{40}, 12.7; F_{50}, 13.9; F_{60}, 8.3; F_{70}, 31.8.

的圭亚那乔治敦品系中出现了一个常染色体的隐性突变体——橙眼，以及两种性连锁的突变体——无脉翅和黄体色（糙眼、橙眼和无脉翅是由斯帕斯基先生发现的；黄体色是由奥尔加·帕夫洛夫斯基发现的）。在 1966 年 10 月，按照以下方案开始了实验种群成对实验。在一个培养瓶中放置 50 只～100 只（通常是 70 只）未交配过的亚诺斯品系糙眼突变雌蝇，同时放入同一品系的雄蝇以及其中一种奥里诺科突变品系的雄蝇。在另一个培养瓶中，将 50 只～100 只奥里诺科突变雌蝇与同一突变品系的奥里诺科雄蝇及亚诺斯品系的糙眼突变雄蝇放在一起。在后代中，由不同品系亲本交配产生的杂种雌蝇可以通过表现型上的野生型性状而被区分出来。由相同品系亲本交配得到的非杂种雌蝇则表现出各自突变体的性状。淘汰杂种雌蝇，用非杂种雌蝇作为下一代的亲本。因为糙眼、黄体色和无脉翅是性连锁的，所以无法区分突变母本产生的雄性杂交子代和雄性非杂交子代。这虽然有所不便，但对本实验没有致命的影响，因为雄性杂交子代是完全不育的。由于橙眼是常染色体遗传的，因此它使我们既可以区分雄性杂交子代和非杂交子代也可以区分雌性杂交子代和非杂交子代。总共有如下 6 对实验种群：

$1A$：糙眼♀♀ + 糙眼♂♂ + 橙眼♂♂

$1B$：橙眼♀♀ + 橙眼♂♂ + 糙眼♂♂

$2A$：糙眼♀♀ + 糙眼♂♂ + 无脉翅♂♂

$2B$：无脉翅♀♀ + 无脉翅♂♂ + 糙眼♂♂

$3A$：糙眼♀♀ + 糙眼♂♂ + 黄体色♂♂

$3B$：黄体色♀♀ + 黄体色♂♂ + 糙眼♂♂

目前（1970 年 12 月）已经对种群 $1A$ 和 $1B$ 进行了 73 代的选择。种群 $2A$ 和 $2B$ 在选择了 65 代之后及种群 $3A$ 和 $3B$ 在选择了 60 代之后都没有再继续。雌蝇所面对的同品系和不同品系雄蝇的比例在不同的世代都被调整到足以对雌蝇的辨别能力构成最大的威胁。与此同时，必须保证能产生足够多的突变体后代以便用作下一代的亲本。在早期世代中，两类雄蝇的数目通常会一样多；后来，相同品系雄蝇的数目就会少于不同品系雄蝇的数目。雄蝇的总数大致与雌蝇的总数相当。

对行为隔离的选择在所有 6 个种群中都获得了成功，尽管没有哪一个达到了完全隔离。可以说，从早期世代到晚期世代，后代中杂交种的比例通常会有所下降。然而，选择的进展似乎很不均匀。例如：在种群 $1A$ 中，每隔 10 个世代所得到的杂种雌蝇的百分比是：F_1，41.9；F_{10}，17.3；F_{20}，53.5；F_{30}，31.8；F_{40}，12.7；F_{50}，13.9；F_{60}，8.3；F_{70}，31.8。

The unevenness is largely an artefact. It is caused in part by the inability mentioned earlier to distinguish the hybrid and the non-hybrid males with the sex-linked mutant rough; the proportions of fertile individuals among the rough-eyed male progenies in the different generations are therefore not exactly known. Another disturbing factor is that the rough, veinless, and yellow mutant markers considerably reduce the viability of their carriers. Only orange has a satisfactory viability. The hybrid females, being wild type, have an advantage in survival.

Ethological Isolation Observed

The proportions of hybrid offspring obtained in our experimental populations do not measure reliably the degree of the ethological isolation between the strains used. We accordingly used the observation chamber technique previously mentioned. Twelve females and twelve males of each of two strains (forty-eight flies in all) were introduced in a chamber without etherization. The chambers were observed for about 3 h, and the matings that took place were recorded. A female could mate only once during this time interval, whereas males were free to mate repeatedly. Our results are summarized in Table 4.

Table 4. Observed Matings between Selected and Unselected Strains of *Drosophila paulistorum*

	Strains		Matings				Isolation coefficient
Date	A	B	A♀×A♂	A♀×B♂	B♀×A♂	B♀×B♂	
March 1970	Llanos U	Orange S	41	13	11	40	0.55±0.08
March 1970	Rough S	Orinocan U	47	17	6	40	0.59±0.08
October 1969	Rough S	Orange S	52	4	4	41	0.67±0.07
June 1970	Rough S	Orange S	45	7	3	54	0.82±0.05
March 1970	Llanos U	Veinless S	60	2	12	42	0.76±0.06
October 1969	Rough S	Veinless S	43	8	10	41	0.64±0.08
June 1970	Rough S	Veinless S	44	8	11	45	0.64±0.07
March 1970	Llanos U	Yellow S	48	8	13	43	0.62±0.07
October 1969	Rough S	Yellow S	50	6	13	32	0.62±0.08
June 1970	Rough S	Yellow S	27	16	4	66	0.65±0.07

S, Selected; U, unselected.

The designation Llanos unselected refers to the wild type Llanos strain which had not been exposed to challenges of hybridization with Orinocan strains; rough selected is the rough-eyed mutant which had been so exposed for fifty generations by October 1969, and fifty-eight generations by March 1970; Orinocan unselected is the wild type Orinocan strain from Georgetown, Guiana; orange selected, veinless selected and yellow selected are the three mutants which arose in the Georgetown strain, and were selected for as many generations as their rough selected counterparts.

All the tests reported in Table 4 show statistically highly significant isolation coefficients, ranging from 0.55±0.08 to 0.82±0.05. It should be recalled that unselected Llanos with unselected Orinocan shows little, if any, preferential mating (isolation coefficient +0.11± 0.10, Table 2). Without doubt, the selection has developed an ethological isolation where perhaps only a trace of preference for mating within a strain existed before selection. It is furthermore remarkable that the tests in which one of the strains had been selected for

这种不均匀性在很大程度上是人为造成的。前文曾提到我们无法区分携带性连锁的糙眼突变的杂种雄蝇和非杂种雄蝇就是其中一部分原因；因此，我们不能准确地知道各世代糙眼雄性后代中可育个体的比例。另一个干扰因素是：糙眼、无脉翅和黄体色等突变标记显著地降低了携带者的生存力。只有橙眼个体的生存力还算令人满意。杂种雌蝇，因为是野生型，所以在存活率方面具有优势。

观察到的行为隔离

我们在实验种群中得到的杂交后代的比例不能可靠地衡量所选用品系之间的行为隔离程度。因此我们采用了前面提到过的观察室技术。从两个品系中各抽取 12 只雌蝇和 12 只雄蝇（总共 48 只果蝇）关在一个观察室中（不进行醚麻醉）。观察大约 3 小时，并记录所发生的交配事件。在这个时间间隔内雌蝇只能交配一次，而雄蝇可以自由地重复交配。表 4 给出我们的实验结果。

表 4. 施加选择的和未施加选择的圣保罗果蝇品系之间的交配情况

| 时间 | 品系 | | 交配情况 | | | | 隔离系数 |
	A	B	$A♀ \times A♂$	$A♀ \times B♂$	$B♀ \times A♂$	$B♀ \times B♂$	
1970 年 3 月	亚诺斯 U	橙眼 S	41	13	11	40	0.55±0.08
1970 年 3 月	糙眼 S	奥里诺科 U	47	17	6	40	0.59±0.08
1969 年 10 月	糙眼 S	橙眼 S	52	4	4	41	0.67±0.07
1970 年 6 月	糙眼 S	橙眼 S	45	7	3	54	0.82±0.05
1970 年 3 月	亚诺斯 U	无脉翅 S	60	2	12	42	0.76±0.06
1969 年 10 月	糙眼 S	无脉翅 S	43	8	10	41	0.64±0.08
1970 年 6 月	糙眼 S	无脉翅 S	44	8	11	45	0.64±0.07
1970 年 3 月	亚诺斯 U	黄体色 S	48	8	13	43	0.62±0.07
1969 年 10 月	糙眼 S	黄体色 S	50	6	13	32	0.62±0.08
1970 年 6 月	糙眼 S	黄体色 S	27	16	4	66	0.65±0.07

S：施加选择的； U：未施加选择的。
表中的"亚诺斯 U"指的是从未面对过与奥里诺科品系进行杂交这类挑战的野生亚诺斯品系；"糙眼 S"指的是到 1969 年 10 月和 1970 年 3 月为止分别已经面对过 50 代和 58 代这样的挑战的糙眼突变体；"奥里诺科 U"指的是来自圭亚那乔治敦的野生奥里诺科品系；"橙眼 S"、"无脉翅 S"和"黄体色 S"是乔治敦品系果蝇的三种突变体，它们被选择了跟对等的"糙眼 S"果蝇一样多的世代。

表 4 报告的所有测试都有统计上极显著的隔离系数，数值范围从 0.55 ± 0.08 到 0.82 ± 0.05。别忘了在未施加选择的亚诺斯品系和未施加选择的奥里诺科品系之间近乎没有什么交配偏好（隔离系数为 $+0.11 \pm 0.10$，表 2）。毫无疑问，连续选择已经建立起行为隔离，而在施加选择之前品系内可能仅存在极微弱的交配偏好。更值得关注的是：在测试中只曾对两个品系中的一个施加过隔离选择而对另一个不施加选择，

isolation and the other was unselected showed about as much isolation as did the tests where both strains had been selected (Table 4).

Status of the Llanos Strain

In 1958 and 1959, the Llanos strain was giving fertile hybrids with strains of the Orinocan semispecies. From 1963 on, it gave sterile hybrid males with the same strains. The reason for this change is uncertain. It may be that the change is related to the geographic origin of the Llanos strain. The region where it was collected lies between the known distribution areas of the Interior and Orinocan semispecies[7]. These semispecies seem more closely related to each other than to the remaining four semispecies. Nowhere do they coexist sympatrically although each of them does so with other semispecies. The genetic instability of the Llanos strain may have resulted from its being a form intermediate between, or even a hybrid of, Orinocan and Interior semispecies[12]. Another possibility is that the change was brought about by an alteration in the population of mycoplasma-like intracellular symbionts, which seem to be different in the different semispecies[17,18].

At any rate, no appreciable reproductive isolation arose between the changed Llanos and Orinocan strains. Without ethological isolation, hybrids between them can be produced freely. The hybrids seem to be vigorous. Hybrid females are fertile, and so are the males in the offspring of the backcrosses. There is no barrier to gene flow. The gradual building up of ethological isolation changes the situation. The isolation coefficients listed in Table 4 are mostly below the mean, but well within the range of isolation coefficients encountered in experiments with semispecies found in nature—0.28 ± 0.10 to 0.94 ± 0.03 (ref. 12). There are good reasons to think that ethological isolation is probably stronger in nature than under laboratory conditions. This makes some of the semispecies able to coexist in the same territory, sympatrically, without mixing. Orinocan and Interior semispecies are an exception—they are not sympatric. Isolation coefficients between strains of these semispecies obtained in laboratory experiments range from 0.28 ± 0.10 to 0.65 ± 0.08 (ref. 12), lower than we achieved (Table 4).

We conclude that the selected Llanos strain is comparable with the naturally existing semispecies. It could not, however, maintain itself if it were sympatric with the Orinocan semispecies. To render artificial selection possible, the Llanos strain was made homozygous for the mutant gene rough eye. This mutant reduces the viability of its carriers, whereas the hybrids with Orinocan, which have the rough eye suppressed by its dominant normal allele, are more vigorous. Natural selection for ethological isolation would occur if the hybrids were, on the contrary, at a disadvantage. The last step needed to make the Llanos semispecies capable of sympatric coexistence with the Orinocan semispecies is to free it from the rough-eye mutant, without disturbing the rest of its genotype responsible for the ethological isolation. This may not be easy to achieve, but it can be attempted.

所得到的隔离效果与在测试中曾同时对两个品系都施加过选择的隔离效果是相同的（表4）。

亚诺斯品系的现况

在1958年和1959年，亚诺斯品系与奥里诺科半分化种的品系杂交会产生可育的杂交后代。从1963年起，这两种品系的果蝇杂交却产生了雄性不育的杂交种。目前还不完全清楚为什么会发生这样的变化。也许这种变化与亚诺斯品系的地理起源有关。亚诺斯品系果蝇的采集区域位于内陆半分化种和奥里诺科半分化种的已知分布区之间[7]。这3个半分化种相互之间的进化关系似乎比它们与其他4个半分化种之间的关系更近。没有任何地方这3个半分化种是共同存在的，尽管它们各自都与其他半分化种有一定的重叠分布。亚诺斯品系的遗传不稳定性有可能是因为它是一种介于奥里诺科半分化种和内陆半分化种之间的中间形式，甚或是这两者的杂交种[12]。另一种可能性是这种变化源于种群中细胞内类菌原体共生体的改变，这些共生体在不同的半分化种中似乎是不一样的[17,18]。

不管怎样，在改变后的亚诺斯品系和奥里诺科品系之间没有出现明显的生殖隔离。因为不存在行为隔离，所以它们之间的杂交种可以自由形成。这些杂交种看上去很强健。杂种雌蝇是可育的，回交后代中的雄蝇也是如此。因此不存在基因流障碍。但是逐渐形成的行为隔离改变了这一状况。表4中列出的隔离系数大多低于平均值，不过都稳稳地落在实验得到的、自然界中半分化种的隔离系数的范围之内——从 0.28 ± 0.10 到 0.94 ± 0.03（参考文献12）。我们有合适的理由认为，自然界中的行为隔离很可能会强于在实验室条件下发生的行为隔离。这使得一些半分化种可以在同一个区域内共存，即分布区域重叠但并不发生混交。奥里诺科半分化种和内陆半分化种是个例外——它们并不同域。室内实验检测到这些半分化种的品系之间的隔离系数为 $0.28\pm0.10 \sim 0.65\pm0.08$（参考文献12），低于我们得到的数值（表4）。

我们的结论是：经过选择的亚诺斯品系与自然条件下存在的半分化种之间具有可比性。然而，当它与奥里诺科半分化种同域共存时，就无法维持自身的品系了。为了使人工选择得以实现，我们选用了亚诺斯品系糙眼突变的纯合体。这种突变会降低基因携带者的生存力，但它与奥里诺科半分化种的杂交种却具有更强的生存力，因为显性的正常等位基因抑制了糙眼表征的表达。与之相反，当杂种处于劣势时，对行为隔离的自然选择就会发生。使亚诺斯半分化种能够与奥里诺科半分化种同域共存所需的最后一个步骤是：在不影响负责行为隔离的其他基因型的前提下，弃除糙眼突变体。这也许不太容易做到，但可以去尝试。

This work was supported by grants from the US Atomic Energy Commission and the National Science Foundation (International Biological Program).

(**230**, 289-292; 1971)

Theodosius Dobzhansky and Olga Pavlovsky: The Rockefeller University, New York City, New York 10021.

Received January 14, 1971.

References:

1. Karpechenko, G. D., *Z. Indukt. Abstamm.-u. Vererbungsl.*, **48**, 1 (1928).

2. Müntzing, A., *Hereditas*, **16**, 105 (1932).

3. McFadden, E. S., and Sears, E. R., *J. Hered.*, **37**, 81, 107 (1946).

4. Mayr, E., *Animal Species and Evolution* (Belknap, Cambridge, 1963).

5. Dobzhansky, Th., *Genetics of the Evolutionary Process* (Columbia University Press, New York and London, 1970).

6. Dobzhansky, Th., and Spassky, B., *Proc. US Nat. Acad. Sci.*, **45**, 419 (1959).

7. Spassky, B., Richmond, R. C., Perez-Salas, S., Pavlovsky, O., Mourão, C. A., Hunter, A. S., Hoenigsberg, H., Dobzhansky, Th., and Ayala, F. J., *Evolution* (in the press).

8. Kastritsis, C. D., *Chromosoma*, **23**, 180 (1967).

9. Kastritsis, C. D., *Evolution*, **23**, 663 (1969).

10. Dobzhansky, Th., and Pavlovsky, O., *Proc. US Nat. Acad. Sci.*, **55**, 727 (1966).

11. Dobzhansky, Th., and Pavlovsky, O., *Genetics*, **55**, 141 (1967).

12. Perez-Salas, S., Richmond, R. C., Pavlovsky, O., Kastritsis, C. D., Ehrman, L., and Dobzhansky, Th., *Evolution*, **24**, 519 (1970).

13. Ehrman, L., *Evolution*, **19**, 459 (1965).

14. Koopman, K. F., *Evolution*, **4**, 135 (1950).

15. Knight, G. R., Robertson, A., and Waddington, C. H., *Evolution*, **10**, 14 (1956).

16. Kessler, S., *Evolution*, **20**, 634 (1966).

17. Williamson, D. L., and Ehrman, L., *Genetics*, **55**, 131 (1967).

18. Kernaghan, R. P., and Ehrman, L., *Chromosoma*, **29**, 291 (1970).

这项研究工作得到了来自美国原子能委员会和美国国家科学基金会（国际生物学计划）的经费支持。

（刘振明 翻译；张德兴 审稿）

Directed Genetic Change Model for X Chromosome Inactivation in Eutherian Mammals

D. W. Cooper

Editor's Note

The idea that one of the two X chromosomes inherited by female animals has to be inactivated was established by Mary Lyon in 1961. In humans the choice is random, but in female marsupials the X chromosome from the father is inactivated specifically. In this paper, Australian geneticist D. W. Cooper argues that this marsupial pattern is ancestral to that of placental animals (called eutherian, and including humans). It suggests that a controlling genetic element in the male-derived X in early female embryogenesis can hop at random to either X chromosome in a manner analogous to the chromosomal hopping of genetic factors in maize proposed by Barbara McClintock. The hypothesis has since been revised, but shows the wide impact of McClintock's Nobel-Prize-winning work.

IN 1961 Lyon put forward the single active X hypothesis to account for dose compensation of genes on the sex chromosomes of female eutherian mammals[1]. Under her hypothesis in the adult organism either the maternally or the paternally derived X is active in any one cell, but never both. The question of which X is to be inactivated is settled at a very early embryonic stage[2-4]. In female diploid individuals there is usually something near a 1:1 ratio of cells with active paternal to cells with active maternal X chromosomes[5]. The inactive X is detected cytologically as the heterochromatic Barr body or sex chromatin in interphase nuclei and because it synthesizes its DNA late, that is, it labels late[5]. Once established the inactivation is very stable. In abnormal individuals with more than two sex chromosomes all X chromosomes except one synthesize their DNA late and form Barr bodies[6]. Evidence from the phenotype of women with abnormal numbers of X chromosomes or X chromosomes with deletions suggests that the second X has some active genes[7]. With these exceptions, it can be said that cytological observations and studies on a number of sex linked genes have yielded considerable data supporting Lyon's hypothesis and none definitely against it[5,8,9].

Marsupial mammals are the closest extant group to eutherians[10]. Their system of sex determination is XX/XY[11,12] with the Y being male determining[12,13]. They have a late labelling X[11,14,15]. Sharman has obtained evidence that in kangaroos the late labelling X is always paternal in origin[14], this is, there is paternal rather than random X inactivation, a hypothesis which is supported by data on the inheritance of the enzymes glucose-6-phosphate dehydrogenase (G6PD)[16] and phosphoglycerate kinase (PGK)[17]. On the basis

真兽亚纲哺乳动物中X染色体失活的
定向遗传改变模型

编者按

1961年，玛丽·莱昂提出一种观点，认为雌性动物遗传继承的两条X染色体中的一条必然发生失活。在人类中，失活染色体的选择是随机的；但在雌性有袋动物中，却总是来自父本的那条X染色体发生特异性失活。澳大利亚遗传学家库珀在本文中提出理由证明，有袋动物的这种模式是有胎盘动物（即真兽亚纲动物，其中包括人类）的祖先模式。文中指出：在早期雌性动物的胚胎发育过程中，父源X染色体中的遗传控制元件会随机地跳到两条X染色体中的一条上，这种跳跃方式类似于芭芭拉·麦克林托克所发现的玉米中的遗传因子在染色体上的位置转移行为。虽然库珀的假说已经被后人修正，但从本文仍可以看出麦克林托克赖以获得诺贝尔奖的成果有多么大的影响力。

1961 年，莱昂提出了单一活性 X 染色体假说，用来解释雌性真兽亚纲哺乳动物的性染色体基因的剂量补偿效应 [1]。她在假说里提出：在成年生物体的每一个细胞中，不是来自母本就是来自父本的那条 X 染色体会具有活性，但永远不可能两者都具有活性。到底哪条 X 染色体会失活这一问题在胚胎的早期就已经决定了 [2-4]。在雌性二倍体个体中，母源 X 染色体有活性的细胞与父源 X 染色体有活性的细胞的比例通常接近于 1:1[5]。在间期细胞核中，细胞学检测显示失活的 X 染色体以异染色质巴氏小体或性染色质的形式存在，并且由于失活染色体上的 DNA 合成延迟，它被标记的时间也晚 [5]。失活一旦建立，就能达到很稳定的状态。在具有多于两条性染色体的异常个体中，除其中一条外，其余所有 X 染色体都较晚地合成 DNA 并且形成巴氏小体 [6]。从含有异常数目的 X 染色体或者 X 染色体存在缺失的妇女的表型中得出的证据显示，第二条 X 染色体（译者注：指失活的那条）上的某些基因仍是有活性的 [7]。将这些例外情况考虑在内，可以这样说：对许多性连锁基因的细胞学观察和研究已经给出了大量能证实莱昂假说的数据资料，并且没有资料明确反对这一观点 [5,8,9]。

有袋哺乳动物是现存的与真兽亚纲哺乳动物最接近的种群 [10]。它们的性别决定系统是 XX/XY[11,12]，其中 Y 染色体是雄性决定因素 [12,13]。它们有一条延迟标记的 X 染色体 [11,14,15]。沙曼发现袋鼠中延迟标记的 X 染色体总是源自父本 [14]，即父源 X 染色体失活而不是 X 染色体随机失活，葡萄糖 –6– 磷酸脱氢酶（G6PD）[16] 和磷酸甘油酸激酶（PGK）[17] 的遗传数据也支持这一假说。基于这一发现，我希望能够提出

433

of this finding I wish to propose a model of X inactivation in eutherians. The model postulates that random X inactivation in eutherians has evolved from an ancestral paternal X inactivation which has been retained in marsupials. It proposes that during male meiosis in both groups the X undergoes a directed genetic change. A controlling element, analogous to the kind described by McClintock in maize[18], is introduced into the X, probably by the Y. Then at a certain point in the very early development of eutherian females this controlling element is excised and later reinserted at random into one of the two chromosomes, thus setting up random X inactivation. Once reinserted, it remains fixed in that chromosome. The purpose of this article is to examine the adequacy with which the model accounts for data at present available and to propose new investigations which should test it more critically.

Maize Controlling Elements

Controlling elements may be exemplified by the activator–dissociator (Ac–Ds) system of maize[18]. This system is in many respects like an operon system in which both the "regulator" element (Ac) and the "operator" element (Ds) have the episome-like property of occasionally being able to move from one part of the genome to another (although there is no evidence that either is capable of autonomous existence in the cytoplasm). Controlling element is the term used to describe entities like Ac and Ds, in contradistinction to gene which is reserved for conventional Mendelian units. Apart from being capable of this occasional transposition, controlling elements segregate at meiosis in the normal way. When the Ds element is present at a particular locus, genes adjacent to it on the same chromosome have their activity suppressed to some degree. Their expression is said to be unstable. Action of Ds depends on the existence of one or more Ac elements in the genome, not necessarily on the same chromosome or its homologue. Ac also affects the activity of genes adjacent to it in the chromosome. The occasional transposition of Ac and Ds probably occurs during the replication cycle of the chromosome. The genes adjacent to the old location usually return to normal activity while those adjacent to the new locus become unstable in their expression. Removal, however, is often associated with the appearance of a new stable allele of the adjacent gene. The Ac–Ds system has a number of other peculiarities, only one of which need concern us here. Ds may undergo mutation-like events which McClintock terms "changes of state". This term serves to describe the fact that the initial response of Ds to Ac may differ from subsequent ones. For example, when first isolated Ds responded to Ac by promoting the formation of dicentric chromatid bridges (a property from which Ds derives its name). In further responses, these were chiefly absent and only activity of adjacent genes was affected.

Controlling Element of Mouse X

Several workers have studied a region of the mouse X called the inactivation centre, which governs the degree to, or the frequency with, which the translocated autosomal material is inactivated when the associated X material is inactivated as a consequence of random X inactivation[19-21]. The inactivation of X-linked genes is likewise under control of this region of the X[22,23]. Cattanach calls the inactivation centre a controlling element, because there is

一个真兽亚纲动物 X 染色体失活的模型。这个模型假定真兽亚纲动物的 X 染色体随机失活是从其祖先的一条父源 X 染色体的失活演变而来的，在有袋动物中至今仍保留着这种父源 X 染色体失活的现象。假说认为：这两个类群的雄性亲本在减数分裂时都发生了 X 染色体的定向遗传学改变。一种控制元件（与麦克林托克所描述的在玉米中发现的那种 [18] 类似）被导入到 X 染色体中，它可能是从 Y 染色体导入的。然后在雌性真兽亚纲动物发展早期的某个特定时间点上，这个控制元件被切除，随后随机地插入到这两条染色体中的一条，从而形成了 X 染色体随机失活。一旦插入，它就会被整合到那条染色体中。本文旨在检验这个模型是否足以解释目前已有的数据，并提出应该采用哪些新的研究手段对其进行更准确的测试。

玉米控制元件

也许可以用玉米的激活因子 – 解离因子（Ac–Ds）系统来诠释控制元件的概念 [18]。这个系统在诸多方面类似于一个操纵子系统，其中"调控"元件（Ac）和"操纵"元件（Ds）具有游离基因那样的特性，偶尔能够从基因组的一个部位移动到另一个部位（尽管没有证据证明它们能够在细胞质中自主存在）。控制元件是用来描述像 Ac 和 Ds 这类元件的术语，与孟德尔定义的传统基因不同。除了能够偶尔发生转座外，控制元件在减数分裂时的分离是正常的。当 Ds 元件出现在某个特殊位点时，与它邻近的处于同一条染色体上的基因的活性会受到一定程度的抑制。人们认为这些基因的表达不稳定。Ds 的活动依赖于基因组中一个或多个 Ac 元件的存在，这些 Ac 元件不必出现在同一条染色体上或者其同源染色体上。Ac 也会影响与其邻近的位于同一条染色体上的基因的活性。在染色体的复制周期中，可能 Ac 和 Ds 偶尔会发生转座。转座后，与旧位点相邻的基因常常恢复正常的活性，而邻近新位点的基因则在表达上变得不稳定。然而，控制元件的剪切一般与邻近基因中出现一个新的稳定等位基因有关。Ac–Ds 系统有许多特性，在本文中我们仅关注其中一种。Ds 可能会发生与麦克林托克称之为"状态改变"类似的突变。这种描述可以用以说明，Ds 对 Ac 的初始应答可能与后续应答不同。例如，当第一次分离时，Ds 对 Ac 的应答是促进双着丝粒染色单体桥的形成（Ds 的命名就是源自这一性质）。在进一步的应答中，这些作用基本消失了，只有邻近基因的活性会受到影响。

小鼠 X 染色体的控制元件

几位学者研究了小鼠 X 染色体中被称为失活中心的一个区域，当 X 染色体的随机失活引起相关的 X 染色体物质的失活时，易位的常染色体物质也失活，其发生程度和频率受失活中心的调控 [19-21]。X 染色体相关基因的失活也同样受到 X 染色体失活中心这一区域的控制 [22,23]。卡塔纳克将这段失活中心称作控制元件，因为他在研

an indication from his work on the flecked (X^T, T (1X), *Ct*) X autosome translocation that it behaves like a maize controlling element[19,24]. This translocation involves the insertion of autosomal material from linkage group 1 into the X, making it about 20% larger[19,25]. The inserted material bears genes from albino (*c*) to ruby eye (*ru-2*). The locus of insertion is near jimpy (*jp*) (Fig. 1), but whether on the side distal or proximal to Gyro (*Gy*) is not yet known. Cattanach's early data indicated change from one generation to the next in the amount of inactivation of the autosomal material in the X^T chromosome which could not all be satisfactorily explained by meiotic crossing over between X^T chromosomes governing different levels of inactivation[24]. He proposed instead that the controlling element was undergoing "changes of state". In a more recent investigation, the results obtained could all be explained by meiotic crossing over, but whether these later results render the change of state interpretation of the earlier results invalid is doubtful[19]. (There is some discussion as to how many controlling elements exist in the inactive X of the mouse[8,19]. Since only one region of the chromosome has so far been clearly implicated as being a controlling element, I will assume for the purposes of this paper that there is only one.)

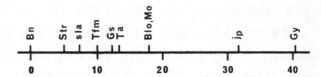

Fig. 1. Diagram of portion of the mouse X linkage group, showing position of sex linked genes discussed in the text. The diagram is from ref. 48. *Bn*, Bent tail; *Str*, striated; *sla*, sex linked anaemia; *Tfm*, testicular feminization; *Gs*, greasy; *Ta*, tabby; *Blo*, blotchy; *jp*, jimpy; *Gy*, gyro. The units are centimorgans.

Directed Change and Primary Paternal Inactivation

Cattanach and Perez have made an observation which suggests that the properties of the paternal X may differ from those of the maternal[26]. They have recently shown that female mice heterozygous for X^T chromosomes tend to have lower levels of variegation for albino when the rearranged X is inherited from the father rather than the mother. A maternal effect is not responsible for the differences between reciprocal crosses. This can be explained by postulating that a directed genetic change at male meiosis alters the properties of the X^T. As a consequence, the X^T inherited from the father associates less frequently with the controlling element.

If the primary step in establishing random X inactivation is paternal X inactivation, there should be mutant genes which convert the former to the latter. These genes may be defective controlling elements which cannot be transferred or genes governing enzymes mediating their transfer. There is some evidence which can be interpreted to mean that such genes do exist, the chief of which involves Searle's translocation. This, designated T16H, is a reciprocal X autosome translocation in the mouse[27-30]. With the exception of Cattanach's translocation, all mouse X autosome translocations render the male sterile. Hence all females heterozygous for Searle's translocation receive their rearranged

究 X 染色体 – 常染色体斑点易位（X^T, T(1X), Ct）时发现，失活中心的行为与玉米控制元件类似 [19,24]。发生这种易位时，连锁群 1 的常染色体组分插入到 X 染色体中，使 X 染色体增大了约20%[19,25]。插入部分包含从白化基因(c)到红眼基因(ru-2)的片段。插入位点靠近吉皮基因（jp）（图 1），但还不能确定插入位点是远离还是靠近陀螺基因 (Gy)。卡塔纳克早期的实验数据表明，X^T 染色体中失活的常染色体物质的量在每一代中都有所不同，仅仅用控制不同失活水平的 X^T 染色体在减数分裂中的交叉互换来解释这些变化并不能完全令人满意 [24]。对此，他提出这些控制元件发生了"状态改变"。在一项近期的研究中，用减数分裂交叉互换就可以解释所有获得的结果，但是这些最近的结果能否推翻基于状态改变对先前结果的解释还值得怀疑 [19]。（已经有一些关于小鼠失活的 X 染色体上到底存在多少控制元件的讨论 [8,19]。因为到目前为止，在染色体上只有一个区域被明确界定为控制元件，所以我认为要说明只存在一个控制元件应是这篇文章的目的。）

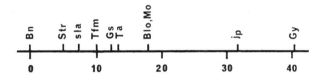

图 1. 小鼠 X 染色体连锁群的部分图解，图中标明了文中讨论过的性连锁基因的位置。本图来自参考文献 48。Bn，弯尾基因；Str，条纹基因；sla，伴性贫血症基因；Tfm，睾丸雌化基因；Gs，多脂基因；Ta，斑纹基因；Blo，斑点基因；jp，吉皮基因；Gy，陀螺基因。以厘摩为单位。

定向改变和最初的父源性失活

卡塔纳克和佩雷斯观察到父源 X 染色体的特性可能与母源 X 染色体不同 [26]。他们最近发现：当重组的 X 染色体来自父本而不是母本时，X^T 染色体杂合的雌性小鼠的白化病变异（译者注：指个体中白化与非白化表型区域随机杂合呈现）水平降低。而母本效应无法解释在正反交实验间出现的结果差异。如果假定父本在减数分裂时发生的定向遗传改变更改了 X^T 染色体的特性，那么上述现象就可以得到解释。因此，父本遗传的 X^T 染色体不太经常与控制元件相关。

如果建立 X 染色体随机失活的最初步骤是父源 X 染色体的失活，那么就应该有使父源 X 染色体失活转变为 X 染色体随机失活的突变基因存在。这些突变基因可能是不能够发生转移的有缺陷的控制元件，或者是介导控制元件发生转移的一些酶的调控基因。有证据表明这些基因的确存在，其中最主要的是瑟尔易位。这个被称作 T16H 的基因是小鼠中 X 染色体 – 常染色体相互易位形成的 [27-30]。除卡塔纳克易位外，所有小鼠 X 染色体与常染色体之间的易位都导致雄性不育。因此所有瑟尔易位的雌性杂合体的重组染色体都来自母本，它们的正常 X 染色体和常染色体来自父本。由

chromosomes from their mother and their normal X and autosomes from their father. Since the normal X is almost always inactive in these heterozygotes, Searle's translocation exhibits paternal X inactivation. In this respect it is unlike all other mouse X autosome reciprocal translocations, which by contrast show random inactivation of either the normal or rearranged chromosome.

It is particularly significant that the break in Searle's translocation maps is the same region of the X as the controlling element. The break in the X is given as 0.85 centimorgans from *Ta* on the side distal from *Blo* (ref. 30 and Fig. 1). But the precise relationship of the breakpoint to genes in this part of the linkage group remains obscure because the translocation evidently leads to some cross-over suppression[31]. Cattanach *et al*. have concluded that their controlling element lies very close to *Ta*[19]. The data of Grahn *et al*. suggest that the controlling element may be 8.2 centimorgans from *Gs* on the side distal from *Ta*[21]. Problems of classification have not been completely resolved in their material and so this mapping is tentative. At present there seems to be nothing against the suggestion of Cattanach *et al*. that the break in Searle's translocation may be in the controlling element, thus impairing its function[19]. In my model, its transfer to the maternal X is prevented.

An alternative explanation of non-random inactivation in Searle's translocation is that the translocated X segment can only be switched off for the segment containing the controlling element. Switching off of the re-arranged X would lead to the breakdown of dosage compensation for genes on the segment lacking the controlling element. Selection of cells with correct dose compensation would then account for the observed preponderance of cells with inactive normal chromosomes[5]. The finding that at least one and probably two other mouse X autosome translocations with break points near *Ta* show random X inactivation makes this explanation unlikely[20].

There are other examples of apparent or possible paternal X inactivation in eutherians. Studies on the G6PD of mules indicate that in most tissues there is preferential inactivation of the paternal donkey chromosomes[32,33]. This is interpreted here to mean that the lack of homology between the two distantly related X chromosomes hinders the incorporation of the controlling element into the maternal X. An X autosome translocation heterozygote with preferential late labelling of the normal X has been described in the domestic cow, without any information on the parental origin of the arrangement[34]. The explanation given for the behaviour of Searle's translocation is, of course, also applicable to this.

Unsolved Problems

The model advanced explains how random X inactivation evolved, how the choice of chromosome to be inactivated is made, its stability once made, and a number of hitherto unexplained aspects of X inactivation, particularly the behaviour of Searle's and Cattanach's translocations. It cannot, however, represent the whole truth, because several difficult questions remain unanswered.

于正常的 X 染色体在杂合状态时几乎是没有活性的，因此瑟尔易位表现为父源 X 染色体失活。在这方面，它与所有其他的小鼠 X 染色体 – 常染色体相互易位不同，相比之下，其他的小鼠 X 染色体 – 常染色体易位表现为正常或者重组的染色体随机失活。

瑟尔易位图谱的切点与 X 染色体上作为控制元件的区域相同，这一点特别重要。X 染色体的切点位于 *Blo* 的末端，距离 *Ta* 0.85 厘摩处（参考文献 30 和图 1）。但是断开点与连锁群这部分基因之间的确切关系仍旧是模棱两可的，因为易位明显导致了一些交叉抑制[31]。卡塔纳克等人认为控制元件的位置与 *Ta* 很接近[19]。格兰等人的数据显示：在 *Ta* 末端，距离 *Gs* 8.2 厘摩处可能是控制元件的位置[21]。由于分类问题尚未完全解决，因此这只是一个暂定的基因图谱。卡塔纳克等人认为瑟尔易位的切点可能位于控制元件上，因而削弱了控制元件的功能[19]。到目前为止，还没有事实可以反驳这个观点。在我的模型里，控制元件转移插到母源 X 染色体的情况是不会发生的。

对于瑟尔易位中非随机失活的另一种解释是：易位的 X 染色体片段只能被含有控制元件的片段所关闭。重组 X 染色体的关闭将导致缺少控制元件片段的基因剂量补偿中止。因此，对具有正确剂量补偿的细胞的选择可以用于解释为什么会观察到正常染色体失活的细胞在数量上占优势[5]。在小鼠中发现，至少有一个且可能还有另外两个易位切点在 *Ta* 附近的 X 染色体 – 常染色体易位现象体现为 X 染色体的随机失活。这一发现使上述解释变得不可能[20]。

在真兽亚纲动物中还有其他一些明显的或者可能的父源 X 染色体失活的例子。对骡子 G6PD 的研究发现：在大多数组织中，父源驴染色体优先失活[32,33]。本文所作的解释是：两个关系较远的 X 染色体之间缺少同源性，这阻碍了控制元件插入到母源 X 染色体中。在驯养的牛中发现，X 染色体 – 常染色体的易位杂合体中大多会出现标记延迟的正常 X 染色体，但没有任何关于这种排列的父本起源的信息[34]。当然，针对瑟尔易位的行为所给出的解释也可用于解释这一现象。

尚未解决的问题

这个模型解释了 X 染色体随机失活是如何形成的、染色体选择性失活是如何做到的、一旦形成后的稳定性和许多至今尚未解决的关于 X 染色体失活的问题，尤其是解释了瑟尔易位和卡塔纳克易位的现象。然而，它并不能解释所有的现象，因为还有几个难题仍未解决。

How can XO individuals in man and mouse be viable when their X is from the father, as it often can be[35-37]? Obviously the controlling element must somehow be jettisoned or inactivated very early in development if the model is correct. But why should this happen to the paternal X in XO individuals but not in normal females?

Only one X is active in women and men with multiple X chromosomes[6]. Where do the extra controlling elements come from in cases where the extra chromosomes are from the mother[37]? Perhaps the controlling element is retained during female meiosis and is included in a polar body, except when non-disjunction occurs leading to a multiple X gamete. This will explain the human data except for situations where four X chromosomes come from the mother, as in some XXXXY and XXXX individuals[37]. For these female germ line polysomy must be invoked.

Retention of the controlling element cannot occur in the mouse, however; Searle's translocation gives normal segregation ratios for genes near the controlling element locus[31], which it would not do if the chromosome with the controlling element was preferentially included in a polar body. The only report of multiple X individuals in the mouse concerns XXY types, which were the result of fertilization of a normal ovum by an XY sperm[38]. It is thus of some importance to my model to discover if more than one X can be inherited from the maternal parent in a viable mouse.

Other problems are posed by the fact that in women heterozygous for a normal X and either Xqi (isochromosomes for the long arm of the X), Xpi (isochromosomes for the short arm), Xq- (lack of a long arm), Xp- (lack of a short arm) or Xr (a ring X) invariably have the abnormal X late labelling, irrespective of whether the abnormal X is paternal or maternal in origin[37,39,40]. The only exception to this rule seems to be one report of an XXr individual with a late labelling normal X[41]. How does the controlling element select the abnormal X? And if Xqi, Xpi, Xq-, and Xp- can all be inactivated, where is the locus of the controlling element? Must it be at or near the centromere in man?

Some explanations is needed to account for situations where the second X is apparently active. In marsupials these are the ovaries and uterus of the early pouch young kangaroo[17] and possibly the ovaries of bandicoots[11]. In placental mammals, oocytes[5] and the early embryo[5,42-44] lack sex chromatin. Possibly the controlling element is not fixed in either X at these stages. Or alternatively the controlling element could act in adult somatic tissue in an operator-like manner as the site of action of a repressor protein, which is absent at these early stages. In this connexion, one may note that Steele[45] has recently shown that human female foetuses and newborn female infants have more G6PD activity than males of either class, while hypoxanthine guanine phosphoribosyl transferase was essentially the same in both sexes at these stages. The structural loci for both enzymes are sex linked. In this instance induction of greater activity of the one active X seems more likely than switching on of the second X.

对于人和小鼠中的 XO 个体，如果 X 染色体与通常情况下一样来自父本，那么这些个体是怎么存活的 [35-37]？如果这个模型正确，显然控制元件在发展的早期就必然会以一定方式被抛弃或者失活。但是为什么这种现象发生在 XO 个体的父源 X 染色体上，而不会发生在正常的雌性个体中？

具有多条 X 染色体的女性和男性中只有一条 X 染色体是有活性的 [6]。如果多余的染色体来自母亲 [37]，那么多出的控制元件来自于哪里？也许母本减数分裂时，控制元件被保留了下来，分布在一个极体里，但在染色体不分离导致多倍 X 染色体配体形成时除外。这可以解释人类的绝大多数现象，但不能解释在 XXXXY 和 XXXX 个体中 4 个 X 染色体都来自母本的情况 [37]。因为这种情况肯定会导致雌性生殖细胞系的多体性。

然而，在小鼠中控制元件不能被保留；在瑟尔易位中，靠近控制元件位点的基因的分离比例是正常的 [31]，如果含有控制元件的染色体优先分布到一个极体里，那么基因分离就不会发生。小鼠中报道的唯一一个 X 染色体多倍体的例子是 XXY 型，它是正常卵子与 XY 精子受精的结果 [38]。因此，在活体小鼠中发现不止一条 X 染色体来自母本这一点对我的模型来说很重要。

另一些难题是基于以下事实：女性杂合体总是由一条正常的 X 染色体和一条标记延迟的异常 X 染色体 Xqi（X 染色体长臂的等臂染色体）、Xpi（短臂的等臂染色体）、Xq-（缺少一个长臂）、Xp-（缺少一个短臂）或 Xr（环形 X 染色体）组成，不论异常的 X 染色体最初是来源于父本还是母本 [37,39,40]。这个规则的唯一例外似乎来自于一篇关于 XXr 个体的报道，这一个体含有延迟标记的正常 X 染色体 [41]。控制元件是如何选择异常的 X 染色体的？如果 Xqi、Xpi、Xq- 和 Xp- 都能被失活，那么控制元件的位点在哪里？它一定会在男性着丝粒上或其附近吗？

对于第二条 X 染色体明显有活性的现象，我们需要给出一定的解释。在有袋动物中，卵巢和子宫是抚育小袋鼠的早期袋状结构 [17]，在袋狸中可能是卵巢 [11]。在有胎盘的哺乳动物中，卵母细胞 [5] 和早期的胚胎 [5,42-44] 缺少性染色质。可能在这些阶段，控制元件还没有整合到任何一条 X 染色体中。又或者控制元件在成年体细胞组织中能以类似操纵基因的形式作为阻遏蛋白的活性位点，这种活性位点在早期阶段是不存在的。关于这一点，我们注意到斯蒂尔 [45] 最近发现：人类女性胎儿和新出生的女婴与对应阶段的男性相比有更多的 G6PD 活性，而在这些阶段中次黄嘌呤 – 鸟嘌呤磷酸核糖转移酶在两性中并没有本质上的差别。这两种酶的结构位点都是性连锁的。在这个例子中，诱导有活性的那条 X 染色体产生更大的活性要比能开启第二条 X 染色体的活性的可能性更大。

Possible Experimental Tests

Although it cannot explain all data on X inactivation, the model explains sufficient to make worthwhile investigations to test its chief assumptions, namely, directed genetic change of the X by the Y being the primary step in setting up random X inactivation followed by transfer of the inactivation to the maternal X. If these are correct, two kinds of mutation should exist. There should be mutations in the gene on the Y responsible for the directed genetic change. Males carrying them would give rise only to males. If the mutation is found in the mouse, matings with XO mice will give both male and female offspring, the latter being all XO. There should also be mutations which affect the transfer of the controlling element, and which will often result in paternal X inactivation. Such genes could be either X-linked or autosomal. Hopefully both sexes carrying them will be fertile, so that reciprocal crosses can be made to establish their nature rigorously, something which cannot be done with Searle's translocation. It is also possible that genes converting random X inactivation to paternal X inactivation are normally present in some eutherian species. Conversely, it is possible but rather less likely that there are marsupials which, unlike kangaroos, possess random X inactivation. There is need for a large survey of both marsupial and eutherian mammals to detect more sex-linked enzyme polymorphisms. So far no exceptions have been discovered to Ohno's thesis[5,46] of homology between the sex chromosomes of all eutherian and marsupial X chromosomes. Hence the best tactic in search for sex-linked isoenzymes is to use those enzymes known to be sex-linked in man, for example, G6PD[46] and PGK[47], a procedure which is now being followed in this laboratory.

I thank Professor R. A. Brink, Drs. B. M. Cattanach and D. L. Hayman and Professor G. B. Sharman for helpful comments. My experimental work on X inactivation in marsupials is supported by grants from the Australian Research Grants Committee.

(230, 292-294; 1971)

D. W. Cooper: Department of Genetics and Human Variation, La Trobe University, Bundoora, Victoria 3083.

Received December 10, 1970; revised February 23, 1971.

References:

1. Lyon, M. F., *Nature*, **190**, 372 (1961).

2. Axelson, M., *Hereditas*, **60**, 347 (1968).

3. Austin, C. R., *The Sex Chromatin* (edit. by Moore, K. L.), 241 (Saunders, Philadelphia, 1966).

4. Issa, M., Blank, C. E., and Atherton, G. W., *Cytogenetics*, **8**, 219 (1969).

5. Ohno, S., *Sex Chromosomes and Sex-Linked Genes* (Springer, Berlin, Heidelberg, New York, 1967).

6. Barr, M. L., *The Sex Chromatin*, 129 (edit. by Moore, K. L.) (Saunders, Philadelphia, 1966).

7. Hamerton, J. L., *Nature*, **219**, 910 (1968).

8. Lyon, M. F., *Ann. Rev. Genet.*, **2**, 31 (1968).

9. Lyon, M. F., *Phil. Trans. Roy. Soc.*, B, **259**, 41 (1970).

10. Simpson, G. G., *Evolution*, **13**, 405 (1959).

442

可能的实验检测

尽管这个模型不能解释所有 X 染色体失活的现象，但它却充分解释了一些有价值的研究结果，这些研究则验证了它的主要观点，即：X 染色体的定向遗传改变最先一步是通过 Y 染色体的失活，然后失活被转移到了母源 X 染色体中。如果上述观点正确，那么就应该存在两种突变。一种是 Y 染色体上负责定向遗传改变的基因发生的突变。父本只能将它们传给雄性后代。如果这种突变发生在小鼠中，那么与 XO 小鼠交配产生的雄性和雌性后代中的后者全都是 XO 型。另一种是影响控制元件易位的基因发生的突变，这种突变经常会导致父源 X 染色体失活。这样的基因既可以位于 X 染色体上，也可以位于常染色体上。带有这些突变基因的两性个体都是有望可育的，因此可以用正反交实验来严格解释它们的本质，这是瑟尔易位无法做到的。使 X 染色体失活转变为父源 X 染色体失活的基因也有可能会正常存在于某些真兽亚纲物种中。相反，可能性更小的情况是：有些有袋动物与袋鼠不同，它们发生 X 染色体随机失活。现在需要对有袋动物和真兽亚纲哺乳动物进行大量的调查以检测出更多的性连锁酶多态性。大野乾指出 [5,46]，所有真兽亚纲动物的性染色体和有袋动物的 X 染色体之间具有同源性。到目前为止还没有发现例外。因此，寻找性连锁的同工酶的最好策略是利用人类中已知的性连锁酶，比如 G6PD[46] 和 PGK[47]，这也是本实验室现阶段正在进行的工作。

感谢布林克教授、卡塔纳克博士、海曼博士和沙曼教授提出的宝贵意见。本人在有袋动物 X 染色体失活方面的实验研究承蒙澳大利亚科研拨款委员会的基金支持。

（郑建全 翻译；梁前进 审稿）

11. Hayman, D. L., and Martin, P. G., *Comparative Mammalian Cytogenetics*, 191 (edit. by Benirschke, K.) (Springer, New York, 1969).

12. Sharman, G. B., *Science*, **167**, 1221 (1970).

13. Sharman, G. B., Robinson, E. S., Walton, S. M., and Berger, P. J., *J. Reprod. Fertil.*, **21**, 57 (1970).

14. Sharman, G. B., *Nature*, **230**, 230 (1971).

15. Marshall-Graves, J. A., *Exp. Cell. Res.*, **46**, 37 (1967).

16. Richardson, B. J., Czuppon, A., and Sharman, G. B., *Nature New Biology*, **230**, 154 (1971).

17. Cooper, D. W., VandeBerg, J. L., Sharman, G. B., and Poole, W. E., *Nature New Biology*, **230**, 155 (1971).

18. McClintock, B., *Brookhaven Symp. Biol.*, No. 18, 162 (1965).

19. Cattanach, B. M., Perez, J. N., and Pollard, C. E., *Genet. Res.*, **15**, 183 (1970).

20. Russell, L. B., and Montgomery, C. S., *Genetics*, **64**, 281 (1970).

21. Grahn, D., Leu, R. A., and Hulesch, J., *Genetics*, **64**, 2 (2) s25 (abstr.) (1970).

22. Cattanach, B. M., *Genetics*, **60**, 168 (1968).

23. Cattanach, B. M., Pollard, C. E., and Perez, J. N., *Genet. Res.*, **14**, 223 (1969).

24. Cattanach, B. M., and Isaacson, J. H., *Genetics*, 57, 331 (1967).

25. Cattanach, B. M., *Genet. Res.*, **8**, 253 (1966).

26. Cattanach, B. M., and Perez, J. N., *Genet. Res.*, **15**, 43 (1970).

27. Searle, A. G., *Heredity*, **17**, 297 (1962).

28. Ford, C. E., and Evans, E. P., *Cytogenetics*, **3**, 295 (1964).

29. Ohno, S., and Lyon, M. F., *Chromosoma*, **16**, 90 (1965).

30. Lyon, M. F., *Genet. Res.*, **7**, 130 (1965).

31. Lyon, M. F., Searle, A. G., Ford, C. E., and Ohno, S., *Cytogenetics*, **3**, 306 (1964).

32. Giannelli, F., Hamerton, J. L., Dickson, J., and Short, R. V., *Heredity*, **24**, 175 (1969).

33. Hook, E. B., and Brustman, L. D., *Genetics*, **64**, 2 (2), s30 (abstr.) (1970).

34. Gustavsson, I., Fraccaro, M., Tiepolo, L., and Lindsten, J., *Nature*, **218**, 183 (1968).

35. Cattanach, B. M., *Genet. Res.*, **12**, 125 (1968).

36. Morris, T., *Genet. Res.*, **12**, 125 (1968).

37. Race, R. R., and Sanger, R., *Brit. Med. Bull.*, **25**, 99 (1969).

38. Cattanach, B. M., *Genet. Res.*, **2**, 156 (1961).

39. Klinger, H. P., Lindsten, J., Fraccaro, M., Barrai, I., and Dolinar, Z. J., *Cytogenetics*, **4**, 96 (1965).

40. Rowley, J., Muldal, S., Lindsten, J., and Gilbert, C. W., *Proc. US Nat. Acad. Sci.*, **51**, 779 (1964).

41. Pfeiffer, R. A., and Buchner, T., *Nature*, **204**, 804 (1964).

42. Austin, C. R., in *The Sex Chromatin*, 241 (edit by Moore, K. L.) (Saunders, Philadelphia, 1966).

43. Kinsey, J. D., *Genetics*, **55**, 337 (1967).

44. Hill, R. N., and Yunis, J. J., *Science*, **155**, 1120 (1961).

45. Steele, M. W., *Nature*, **227**, 496 (1970).

46. Ohno, S., *Ann. Rev. Genet.*, **3**, 495 (1969).

47. Valentine, W. N., Hsieh, H. S., Paglia, D. E., Anderson, H. M., Baughan, M. A., Jaffe, E. R., and Garson, O. M., *Trans. Assoc. Amer. Phys.*, **81**, 49 (1968).

48. Hawkes, S. G., *Mouse News Letter*, **43**, 16 (1970).

Pneumococci Insensitive to Penicillin

D. Hansman *et al.*

Editor's Note

Since the introduction of penicillin to treat human infections three decades earlier, capsular pneumococci bacteria were thought highly sensitive to the antibiotic. And although penicillin-insensitive mutants had been selected *in vitro*, resistant wild strains were not recognized until 1967, when penicillin-resistant pneumococci were isolated from a patient with lung damage. In this paper David Hansman and colleagues report two further pneumococci strains, isolated in Australia and New Guinea, that are relatively insensitive to both penicillin and cephalosporin antibiotics. The team note that penicillin is much used in New Guinea, and that transmission probably occurred between villages, much as cross-infection with tetracycline-resistant pneumococci has occurred within hospitals.

PNEUMOCOCCI of all capsular types have been regarded as highly sensitive to penicillin[1] since its introduction for the treatment of human infections in 1940. Although penicillin-insensitive mutants can be selected *in vitro* by repeated subculture in the presence of sub-inhibitory concentrations of penicillin[2-6], resistant wild strains were not recognized until 1967, when penicillin-insensitive pneumococci (type 23) were isolated from a patient with hypogammaglobulinaemia and bronchiectasis, who had received much antibiotic therapy, including penicillin[7]. We now report further strains of pneumococci, isolated in Australia and New Guinea, relatively insensitive to both penicillin and cephalosporin antibiotics.

These penicillin-insensitive pneumococci were isolated from an aboriginal child at Ernabella, South Australia, in 1967, and from fifteen New Guineans at Anguganak in the West Sepik district during a fourteen week period in 1969. Pneumococci were typed by the specific capsular reaction, using typing sera from the Statens Seruminstitut, Copenhagen, and the Danish system of naming types has been followed. The pneumococcus from the aborigine, which was isolated from the upper respiratory tract, was identified as a type 6 strains. Most of the Sepik isolates were also from carriers, but two were isolated from subjects receiving penicillin for respiratory infections: all were identified as type 4.

The penicillin-insensitive strains were Gram-positive cocci with the morphology of pneumococci; cultural characteristics and α-haemolysis on horse blood agar were also typical; bile solubility and sensitivity to ethyl hydrocupreine hydrochloride ("Optochin") were demonstrated. Diffuse turbidity was produced in horse serum broth and long chains, typical of rough pneumococci, were not formed. Capsules were readily demonstrated by the specific capsular reaction. When inoculated by the intraperitoneal route, both type 4

对青霉素不敏感的肺炎双球菌

汉斯曼等

编者按

自从 30 多年前青霉素被用于治疗人类的感染性疾病以来，人们一直认为具有荚膜的肺炎双球菌对青霉素很敏感。虽然已在体外筛选出对青霉素不敏感的突变株，但直到 1967 年从一位肺部损伤的病人体内分离出耐青霉素的肺炎双球菌时，抗性野生株才被人们所认识。在这篇文章中，戴维·汉斯曼及其同事们报道了另外两种来自于澳大利亚和新几内亚的肺炎双球菌菌株，它们对青霉素和头孢菌素类抗生素都相对不太敏感。该研究小组指出：在新几内亚，青霉素的使用量非常大，这种耐药性菌株很可能已经在村子与村子之间发生了传染，就像在医院内部发生的对四环素耐药的肺炎双球菌的交叉感染一样。

自从 1940 年青霉素被用于治疗人类的感染性疾病以来，人们一直认为所有具有荚膜的肺炎双球菌都对青霉素很敏感 [1]。尽管在体外通过青霉素亚抑菌浓度下的不断重复传代培养已经可以筛选出对青霉素不敏感的突变株 [2-6]，但直到 1967 年抗性野生株才被人们所认识，当时从一位患有低丙种球蛋白血症和支气管扩张的患者体内分离出了对青霉素不敏感的肺炎双球菌（23 型）。这位患者曾接受过多种抗生素的治疗，其中也包括青霉素 [7]。本文报道了另外两种来自于澳大利亚和新几内亚的肺炎双球菌菌株，它们对青霉素和头孢菌素类抗生素都相对不太敏感。

这些对青霉素不敏感的肺炎双球菌是 1967 年从居住在南澳大利亚厄纳贝拉的一个土著小孩和 1969 年在安古干纳克的西塞皮克区逗留 14 周期间从 15 个新几内亚人体内分离得到的。用来自哥本哈根丹麦国立血清研究所的分型血清进行特异荚膜反应将肺炎双球菌分型，并按照丹麦命名系统对其命名。从土著小孩的上呼吸道中分离得到的肺炎双球菌菌株被确认为 6 型。大多数来自塞皮克区的肺炎双球菌菌株是从带菌者体内分离出来的，但有两个是从因呼吸道感染而接受过青霉素治疗的患者体内分离得到的，它们都被确认为 4 型。

青霉素不敏感菌株是具有肺炎双球菌形态的革兰氏阳性球菌；其培养特征和在马血琼脂中的 α 溶血反应也很典型；实验证实它可溶于胆汁并对盐酸乙基氢化叩卟啉（"奥普托欣"）敏感。在马血清培养液中可产生弥漫性混浊，但没有形成粗糙型肺炎双球菌所特有的长链。通过特异性的荚膜反应很容易鉴别出有荚膜。当腹腔接种时，4 型和 6 型菌株都对小白鼠有毒性，接种量为 100 个或以下活力单位时即可

and type 6 strains were virulent for white mice, and inoculum of 100 viable units or less producing a fatal infection.

Disk diffusion sensitivity tests showed resistance to penicillin but sensitivity to ampicillin, tetracycline, chloramphenicol, erythromycin, lincomycin and also to sulphadiazine and trimethoprim. When tested by the radial streak method, using as inoculum a standard 2 mm loopful of a 4 h culture in serum broth, growth occurred to within 2 mm of a disk containing 1 U (0.6 µg) of penicillin G, whereas sensitive pneumococci tested as controls showed a zone of inhibition of 6 to 7 mm. Quantitative sensitivity tests were carried out by the plate titration method with horse blood agar, using antibiotic solutions which had been freshly prepared. Nine strains, including the Ernabella strain, were tested. The results (Table 1) indicated that the Ernabella and Anguganak isolates were uniformly insensitive to penicillin G, methicillin and cephalosporin antibiotics. Penicillin sensitive pneumococci of 16 different types (including types 1, 2, 3, 4 and 6) tested as controls were all inhibited by 0.02 µg of penicillin G/ml.

Table 1. Quantitative Antibiotic Sensitivity Tests with Insensitive and Control Pneumococci

	Minimal inhibitory concentration (µg/ml.)		Resistance ratio
	Test strains	Control strains	
Penicillin G	0.5	0.02	25
Methicillin	5 to 10	0.2	25 to 50
Ampicillin	0.1 to 0.2	0.05	2 to 4
Cephaloridine	0.5	0.05	10
Cephalothin	2.0	0.1	20

The minimal inhibitory concentrations of penicillin and methicillin were 25 to 50 times that required to inhibit the sensitive pneumococci used as controls. There was also a significant degree of resistance to cephaloridine and cephalothin. It may be noted that the penicillin-insensitive variants of pneumococci described by Gunnison et al.[6] were also insensitive to cephalothin. Quantitative tests by the plate titration method usually showed sharp end-points, indicating that populations of these isolates were largely homogeneous in their resistance to penicillins and cephalosporins.

Pneumococci resistant to sulphonamides were first encountered in 1940, 5 yr after the introduction of these drugs. Resistance appeared in many pneumococcal types and there was cross-resistance, so that pneumococci resistant to one sulphonamide were resistant to all. But resistance usually occurred only in strains isolated from subjects who had prolonged treatment with sulphonamides.

For many years it was assumed that pneumococci were invariably sensitive to those antibiotics which are effective in coccal infections. In 1963, however, strains resistant to tetracycline were recognized[8-11]. Such pneumococci are virulent for man, causing

产生致死性感染。

纸片扩散药敏试验的结果表明：它们对青霉素有抗性，而对氨苄西林、四环素、氯霉素、红霉素、林可霉素、磺胺嘧啶和甲氧苄氨嘧啶敏感。用径向条痕法进行试验时，接种物为一个在血清培养液中培养了 4 h 的 2 mm 标准菌环，供试菌种可在含有 1 U（0.6 μg）青霉素 G 的 2 mm 区域内生长，而作为对照的敏感型肺炎双球菌则出现了一个 6 mm ~ 7 mm 的受抑制区域。应用马血琼脂平板滴定法对包括厄纳贝拉菌株在内的 9 个菌株进行定量敏感性检测，所用抗生素溶液均为新鲜配制。实验结果（表 1）表明，来自厄纳贝拉和安古干纳克地区的分离菌株都表现出对青霉素 G、甲氧西林和头孢菌素类抗生素不敏感。在实验中用于对照的 16 种不同类型（其中包括 1、2、3、4 和 6 型）的青霉素敏感型肺炎双球菌都能被 0.02 μg/ml 的青霉素 G 所抑制。

表 1. 不敏感型肺炎双球菌和对照肺炎双球菌的定量抗生素敏感性检测

| | 最小抑菌浓度（μg/ml） | | 抗性比 |
	供试菌株	对照菌株	
青霉素 G	0.5	0.02	25
甲氧西林	5 ~ 10	0.2	25 ~ 50
氨苄西林	0.1 ~ 0.2	0.05	2 ~ 4
头孢噻啶	0.5	0.05	10
头孢噻吩	2.0	0.1	20

青霉素和甲氧西林的最小抑菌浓度是抑制敏感型肺炎双球菌对照菌株所需浓度的 25 到 50 倍。这些菌株对头孢噻啶和头孢噻吩也有明显的耐药性。应该注意的是，冈尼森等人 [6] 所描述的肺炎双球菌的青霉素抗性突变株对头孢噻吩也不敏感。用平板滴定法进行的定量敏感性检测通常会出现急剧变化的终点，说明这些被分离菌株的种群在对青霉素和头孢菌素的耐药性方面基本一致。

在磺胺类药物被应用了 5 年之后，1940 年人们首次发现肺炎双球菌对磺胺类药物有抗性。很多类型的肺炎双球菌已表现出耐药性，而且还存在交叉耐药性，以致对某一种磺胺类药物耐药的肺炎双球菌会对所有磺胺类药物都表现出耐药性。但这种耐药性通常只会出现在从长期接受磺胺治疗的患者体内分离得到的菌株中。

多年以来，人们一直认为肺炎双球菌对能够治疗球菌感染的抗生素总是很敏感。然而在 1963 年，科学家们发现了对四环素有耐药性的菌株 [8-11]。这类肺炎双球菌引

pneumonia and meningitis.

It may seem surprising that antibiotic-insensitive pneumococci should appear in a remote area such as the Sepik district, but much penicillin is used because respiratory and other infections are common in New Guinea. During the preceding 10 yr, the 507 inhabitants of the two villages at Anguganak had received 1,357 courses of procaine penicillin, which represents, on an individual basis, a course of penicillin every 3.7 yr. Moreover, during campaigns to control yaws, penicillin was administered to the entire population. Additional factors may be a high pneumococcal carrier rate, especially in children, and the heavy colonization of such carriers (ref. 12 and unpublished results). The isolation of the insensitive type 4 strain from fifteen individuals suggested that transmission had occurred, as these subjects lived in two nearby villages. This is analogous to cross-infection with tetracycline-resistant pneumococci which has occurred within hospitals[10,13].

In all other respects than antibiotic sensitivity, the penicillin-insensitive isolates have the characteristics of encapsulated pneumococci (results presented at the annual meeting of the Australian Society for Microbiology in 1970). Pneumococci of these types, 4 and 6, commonly cause infections in man, and epidemics of pneumonia due to type 4 pneumococci have been reported.

At present, the incidence of penicillin-insensitive pneumococci in Australia seems to be low: during 1965 to 1969 inclusive 1,242 smooth pneumococci were examined by a standard technique for sensitivity to penicillin G and other antibiotics (unpublished results of D. H.). Penicillin-insensitive strains from two subjects were detected during this period, and incidence of only 0.2%. The results of a preliminary examination of pneumococci from several districts in New Guinea suggest that the incidence of insensitive strains is greater than in Australia; studies of the distribution and frequency of such resistant strains are in progress.

We thank Dr. Phyllis Rountree of the Royal Prince Alfred Hospital, Sydney, for the pneumococcus isolated at Ernabella. These investigations were supported in part by a grant from the Wellcome Trust.

(**230**, 407; 1971)

David Hansman: Department of Bacteriology, The Adelaide Children's Hospital, North Adelaide 5006.

H. N. Glasgow, John Sturt, Lorraine Devitt and R. M. Douglas: Pneumonia Research Project, Anguganak and Port Moresby, New Guinea.

Received October 23, 1970.

起的肺炎和脑膜炎对人类来说是致命的。

虽然对抗生素不敏感的肺炎双球菌居然能出现在像塞皮克这样的偏远地区看似有点令人惊讶，但因为呼吸系统和其他感染在新几内亚很常见，所以青霉素在当地被大量使用。在过去的 10 年中，安古干纳克地区两个村子中的 507 位居民已经接受了 1,357 个疗程的普鲁卡因青霉素治疗。这意味着，对每个个体而言，平均每 3.7 年就要接受一个疗程的青霉素。除此之外，在开展防治雅司病（译者注：一种由雅司螺旋体引起的热带传染病）的活动时，全体居民都注射过青霉素。导致大量使用青霉素的其他一些因素可能还包括：肺炎双球菌的携带率很高，尤其是在儿童中；以及这些携带者的高度聚居（参考文献 12 及一些尚未发表的研究结果）。能从 15 个人体内分离出不敏感的 4 型菌株说明已经发生了传染，因为他们居住在两个邻近的村子里。这与在医院内部发生的对四环素耐药的肺炎双球菌的交叉感染类似 [10,13]。

除对抗生素敏感程度不同以外，青霉素不敏感菌株的所有其他特征都与具有荚膜的肺炎双球菌相同（研究结果公布于 1970 年澳大利亚微生物学会学术年会）。4型和 6 型肺炎双球菌通常会引起人类感染，而且已经有过由 4 型肺炎双球菌引起肺炎流行的报道。

目前，澳大利亚的青霉素不敏感肺炎双球菌感染发生率较低：从 1965 年到 1969 年，我们用标准方法检测了 1,242 个光滑型肺炎双球菌对青霉素 G 和其他抗生素的敏感性（戴维·汉斯曼尚未发表的研究结果）。在此期间检测到其中两位受试者体内出现了青霉素不敏感菌株，发生率仅为 0.2%。我们在新几内亚的一些地区对肺炎双球菌进行了初步的检测，结果表明，当地不敏感型菌株的发生率要高于澳大利亚；对此类抗药菌株的分布和发生率的研究还在进行中。

在此我们要感谢悉尼皇家阿尔弗雷德王子医院的菲莉丝·朗特里博士为厄纳贝拉地区肺炎双球菌的分离所做的工作。英国维康基金会为上述研究提供了一部分资金。

（董培智 翻译；王昕 审稿）

References:

1. Garrod, L. P., and O'Grady, F., *Antibiotic and Chemotherapy*, 57 (Livingstone, Edinburgh, 1968).

2. McKee, C. M., and Houck, C. L., *Proc. Soc. Exp. Biol. Med.*, **53**, 33 (1943).

3. Rake, G., McKee, C. M., Hamre, D. M., and Houck, C. L., *J. Immunol.*, **48**, 271 (1944).

4. Eriksen, K. R., *Acta Pathol. Microbiol. Scand.*, **22**, 398 (1945).

5. Eriksen, K. R., *Acta Pathol. Microbiol. Scand.*, **23**, 498 (1946).

6. Gunnison, J. B., Fraher, M. A., Pelcher, E. A., and Jawetz, E., *Appl. Microbiol.*, **16**, 311 (1968).

7. Hansman, D., and Bullen, M. M., *Lancet*, ii, 264 (1967).

8. Evans, W., and Hansman, D., *Lancet*, i, 451 (1963).

9. Richards, J. D. M., and Rycroft, J. A., *Lancet*, i, 553 (1963).

10. Turner, G. C., *Lancet*, ii, 1292 (1963).

11. Schaedler, R. W., Choppin, P. W., and Zabriskie, J. B., *New Engl. J. Med.*, **270**, 127 (1964).

12. Rountree, P. M., Beard, M., Arter, W., and Woolcock, A. J., *Med. J. Austral.*, **1**, 967 (1967).

13. Hansman, D., and Andrews, G., *Med. J. Austral.*, **1**, 498 (1967).

Synchrotron Radiation as a Source for X-Ray Diffraction

G. Rosenbaum *et al.*

Editor's Note

The new DESY synchrotron accelerator in Hamburg, Germany, had recently become operational. Here biologist Gerd Rosenbaum of the Max Planck Institute for Medical Research and his colleagues demonstrate the potential usefulness of this accelerator as an intense source of X-rays for imaging in biology. Relativistic electrons travelling around on DESY's circular path naturally emitted X-rays in beams roughly 100 times brighter than any produced by then standard X-ray sources. The researchers show that this source could be used to produce images of biological specimens that are far clearer than those using the best conventional sources. Synchrotron X-ray sources have now become indispensable for imaging in biology.

WHEN an electron is accelerated it emits radiation. At the very high energies used in DESY, the emitted radiation is confined to a narrow cone about the instantaneous direction of motion of the electron. Thus the synchrotron radiates tangentially. Synchrotron radiation is polychromatic, with a peak in the X-ray region for an electron energy of 7.5 GeV (see ref. 1 for the original theoretical description and refs. 2–4 for experimental details).

The DESY synchrotron uses bursts of 50 pulses/s and each 10 ms pulse contains 6×10^{10} electrons (10 mA average beam current). The injection energy is relatively low and the electrons are accelerated up to 7.5 GeV in the 10 ms.

Most of the X-radiation is emitted during the last 3 ms of each pulse: little radiation is produced at the lower electron energies, and so the time averaged intensity at 1.5 Å is about 20% of the peak value.

We have evaluated the spectral luminance (that is, the power in photons per second radiated per unit area, solid angle, and wavelength interval) of both the synchrotron and a fine-focus rotating anode X-ray tube (see Table 2). The values are 2×10^{22} (time averaged) and 3×10^{20} photons s^{-1} sterad^{-1} cm^{-2} Å^{-1} respectively at 1.54 Å, showing clearly that the synchrotron is, relative to present X-ray tubes, a very bright source. The actual advantage to be gained in a diffraction experiment depends critically on the optical system necessary to focus and monochromate the radiation. Three types of focusing monochromators used in normal X-ray diffraction can be used: bent glass mirrors, quartz monochromators and graphite monochromators.

454

作为X射线衍射光源的同步辐射

罗森鲍姆等

编者按

德国汉堡的新 DESY（Deutsches Elektronen Synchrotron: 德国电子同步加速器）最近开始运行。在本文中，马克斯·普朗克医学研究所的生物学家格尔德·罗森鲍姆及其同事们证明了这台加速器作为强 X 射线源在生物成像方面的潜在用途。在 DESY 环路中运动的相对论性电子自然发射的 X 射线束要比当时的标准 X 射线源所产生的射线束亮 100 倍左右。研究人员发现：使用这个源产生的生物样品的像比使用最好的传统 X 射线源要清晰得多。现在，同步加速器 X 射线源已经成为不可或缺的生物成像设备。

当一个电子被加速时，它会发出辐射。在 DESY 所用的非常高的能量下，发出的辐射被限于电子瞬时运动方向周围的窄锥体之内。因此同步辐射是沿切线方向发出的。同步辐射是多波长的辐射，对于能量为 7.5 GeV 的电子，其同步辐射的峰值落在 X 射线范围内（见参考文献 1 中对原始理论的描述及参考文献 2 ~ 4 中对实验细节的介绍）。

DESY 同步加速器采用每秒 50 个脉冲的爆丛，每 10 ms 脉冲含有 6×10^{10} 个电子（平均束流为 10 mA）。注入能量相对较低，电子在 10 ms 内被加速到 7.5 GeV。

大多数 X 辐射是在每个脉冲的最后 3 ms 内发射的：极少量的辐射来自较低的电子能量，所以在 1.5 Å 处的时间平均强度约为峰值的 20%。

我们已经估算出同步加速器和细焦旋转阳极 X 射线管的谱线亮度（即以单位面积、单位立体角和单位波长间隔内每秒发射的光子数表示的功率）（见表 2），在 1.54 Å 处分别为 2×10^{22}（时间平均）个和 3×10^{20} 个光子 s^{-1} sterad^{-1} cm^{-2} Å^{-1}。这清楚地表明：与目前的 X 射线管相比，同步加速器是一种亮度非常高的源。衍射实验能从中得到多大的实际好处在很大程度上取决于使辐射聚焦和单色化所必需的光学系统。在标准 X 射线衍射中可以应用三种类型的聚焦单色器：弯曲玻璃镜、石英单色器和石墨单色器。

A preliminary investigation of the properties of bent quartz monochromators[5] used with synchrotron radiation is reported here. We have chosen quartz because of its suitable elastic and optical properties which allow it to be used asymmetrically cut and bent to form an accurate focusing monochromator, with a comparatively large numerical aperture. It also behaves substantially as a perfect crystal with a reflectivity near unity in a narrow angular range. We predict that it should be possible to focus the synchrotron radiation down to a point (200×200 μm^2) with a Berreman[6] monochromator to give a total flux of 10^{10} photons s^{-1} at 1.5 Å, which is higher than the flux available from other known X-ray sources (Table 2); also the beam is well collimated. The flux density, the important parameter when using film, is comparatively even higher because of the small focus.

Because of its large mosaic spread (300 times greater than that of quartz) a graphite monochromator might seem advantageous for our application. When used with the white radiation from the synchrotron, however, the mosaic spread of graphite would produce a highly divergent reflected beam with considerable wavelength inhomogeneity, thus restricting us to small monochromator-film distances for reasonable spot diameters on the film. For these short distances it would not then be possible to collect radiation from a large area of graphite by focusing. Alternatively, for larger film distances the reflected beam would require collimation, which would again reduce the expected intensity. We do not, therefore, expect graphite to give more intensity than quartz. Furthermore, the optical and mechanical properties of graphite are much less convenient.

Experimental Details

All experiments took place in the F41 (synchrotron radiation) group bunker at DESY in Hamburg (Fig. 1 and 2). The experimental area can only be entered when the main beam shutter between the synchrotron and the bunker is closed so that all the experiments had to be done by remote control. The quartz crystal was mounted in the vacuum pipe leading to the synchrotron ring. The reflected beam came out through a beryllium window (0.5 mm thick) of diameter 1.5 cm. A rotating disk containing a slot was used as an attenuator. This and a lead shutter were mounted near the window. The rotating disk was arranged to run synchronously with the synchrotron. A film holder was mounted about 120 cm from the quartz crystal on a table movable by remote control. Intensities were recorded on Ilford Industrial G film. The monochromator (Steeg and Reuter) consisted of a slab of quartz ($45 \times 13 \times 0.3$ mm^3) with the face containing the long axis cut at about $8°$ to the 1011 planes. The slab was bent by two sets of pins. Before mounting the crystal in the beam, the curvature was pre-adjusted to the required radius with laser light. The final position of the focus was determined by through-focal photographs. The best focal line had a width of 180 μm and represented the image of the radiating electron beam in the synchrotron. (The total effective source size, including the betatron and synchrotron oscillations, was about 4 mm.) Photographs were also taken close to the monochromator, where the reflected beam was wide, to evaluate the total reflected flux. Experiments with aluminium filters were made to estimate the strength of the higher harmonics in the quartz reflected radiation.

456

本文报道了对用于同步辐射的弯曲石英单色器[5]性质进行的初步研究。我们选择石英是因为它具有合适的弹性和光学性质，因而可以对它进行非对称切割，并能使之弯曲形成一个具有相当大数值孔径的准确聚焦单色器。实质上它还是一个在窄角度范围内折射率接近于1的理想晶体。我们预言使用贝雷曼[6]单色器应该可以将同步辐射聚焦到一个点（$200 \times 200 \ \mu m^2$）上，在1.5 Å处给出的总通量为每秒10^{10}个光子，高于从其他已知X射线源得到的通量（表2）；束的准直也很好。因为焦距小，所以通量密度，这个在使用胶片进行测量时的一个重要参数，比起其他X射线源还会更高一些。

由于石墨有很大的嵌镶度（是石英的300倍），因而石墨单色器或许会有利于我们的应用。然而，当我们使用来自同步加速器的白辐射时，石墨的嵌镶度将导致产生波长相当不均匀的高度发散反射束，因此为了在胶片上形成一个大小合适的光斑，单色器－胶片的距离必须非常短。对于这么短的距离，通过聚焦来收集来自大面积石墨的辐射是不可能的。另一方面，在单色器－胶片距离较大的情况下，反射束需要准直，这也将降低强度的预期值。因此，我们不认为石墨能给出比石英更高的强度。此外，石墨的光学和力学性质在使用上也很不方便。

实验的详细过程

全部实验都是在汉堡DESY的F41(同步辐射)小组的掩体中进行的(图1和图2)。只有当同步加速器和掩体之间的主射束光闸关闭的时候，人才能进入实验区，所以整个实验必须通过遥控进行。石英晶体被放在通向同步加速器环的真空管内。反射束从一个直径为1.5 cm的铍窗（厚0.5 mm）中射出。用一个带有狭缝的旋转圆盘作为衰减器。这个衰减器和一个铅闸装在铍窗附近。使旋转圆盘与同步加速器同步运转。胶片的支架装在一张能通过遥控移动的实验台上，支架距石英晶体约120 cm。在伊尔福工业 G 胶片上记录强度。单色器（施特格和罗伊特）是由一个石英片（$45 \times 13 \times 0.3 \ mm^3$）构成的，其包含长轴的面的切割角度为相对1011面约成8°夹角。石英片的弯曲是通过两组销子实现的。在把晶体安装到光束中之前，先要用激光将曲率半径调整至所需的数值。用经过聚焦的照片确定焦点的最终位置。最佳聚焦线的宽度为180 μm，这代表了同步加速器内辐射电子束的像。（包括电子回旋加速器和同步加速器振荡在内的总有效尺寸约为4 mm。）照相也是在靠近单色器处进行的，在这里反射束很宽，便于估计总的反射通量。用铝滤波器所作的实验来估计在石英反射的辐射中高次谐波的强度。

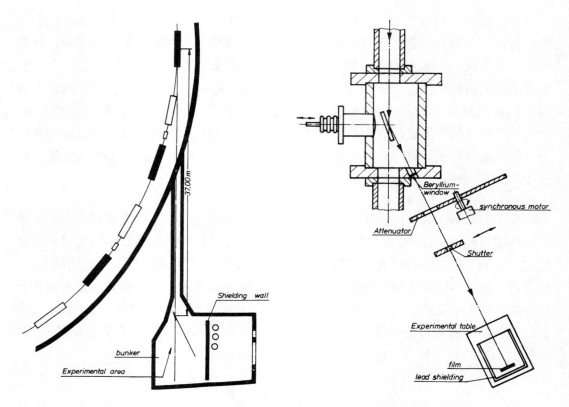

Fig. 1. The F41 bunker at DESY and its position with respect to the synchrotron.

Fig. 2. Monochromator housing and the experimental set-up.

With a source-to-monochromator distance of about 40 m the crystal, if set exactly for one wavelength (for example, in the Johann arrangement[5]), would give a focus at 10 m. The white radiation fortunately allowed us to relax this condition and obtain a more practical focal length (1.5 m) at the expense only of very little wavelength inhomogeneity (Table 1). Furthermore, the angular adjustment of the quartz monochromator was not critical. The central wavelength of the reflected beam was determined by measuring the angle between incident and reflected beam. The position and size of the Be-window limited our observations to Bragg angles of $13 \pm 1°$ (that is, 1.5 ± 0.15 Å).

Finally, a simple camera was constructed (specimen-film distance 40 cm), and a photograph (Fig. 3a) was taken of the equatorial reflexions from a 2 mm strip of the longitudinal flight muscle from the giant water bug *Lethocerus maximus*[7]. The entrance aperture of the camera was approximately 2 mm × 2 mm. A helium-filled tube minimized air absorption in the space between the radiation-pipe window and the camera. The exposure was 15 min with the synchrotron running at 5 GeV. On one side of the direct beam a large area of parasitic scattering is visible apparently resulting from the quartz and from the steel pins used to bend the quartz. Fortunately, the camera entrance-slits were not symmetrically positioned, so that a clear view of one side of the diffraction pattern

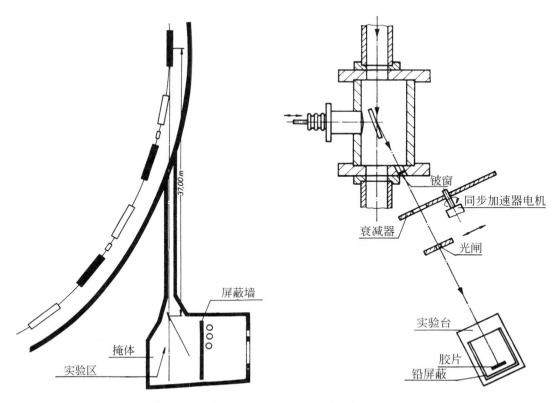

图 1. DESY中的F41掩体及其相对于同步加速器的位置。

图 2. 单色器的构造和实验装置。

如果源到单色器的距离约为 40 m，并且晶体对一个波长精确地设定（例如在约翰式聚焦系统中 [5]），那么给出的焦点将在 10 m 处。所幸的是，白辐射使我们可以放宽这个条件，从而在波长不均匀性损失很小的情况下得到一个更实际的焦距（1.5 m）（表 1）。此外，对石英单色器的角度调整并不是很重要。反射束的中心波长是通过测量入射束与反射束之间的夹角来确定的。铍窗的位置和尺寸把我们的观测范围限制在布拉格角为 13°±1° 之内（即 1.5 Å ± 0.15 Å）。

最后要构造的是一台简易的照相机（样品 – 胶片的距离为 40 cm），拍摄的照片（图 3a）为巨型水虫纵向飞行肌的一条 2 mm 带状区域 [7] 的赤道反射。照相机的进口孔径约为 2 mm×2 mm。用一只充有氦气的管使辐射 – 管窗与照相机之间的空间内空气吸收最小。在 5 GeV 运行的同步加速器的曝光时间为 15 min。在直射光束的一侧，明显可以看到由石英和用于使石英弯曲的钢质定位销造成的大面积寄生散射。所幸的是，照相机的进口狭缝并不是对称定位的，因此可获得一侧衍射条纹的清晰图像。与采用传统 X 射线源（图 3b，埃利奥特细焦旋转阳极管和弯曲石英单色器）

was obtained. The substantially greater width of the "20" line on the photograph made with synchrotron radiation, compared with that made using a conventional X-ray source (Fig. 3b, Elliott fine-focus rotating anode tube and bent quartz monochromator) has not been explained. The comparative intensity of the two photos shows that the synchrotron (at 5 GeV) is about ten times more effective than one of the most intense X-ray sources currently available.

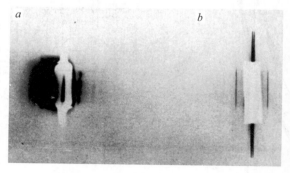

Fig. 3. Equatorial reflexions from dorsolongitudinal flight muscle of *Lethocerus maximus* recorded with: *a*, monochromated synchrotron radiation; electron energy 5 GeV, beam current 8 mA, exposure time 15 min, specimen film distance 40 cm; note the parasitic scattering on the left of the backstop arising from fluorescence from the monochromator holder; *b*, Elliott fine-focus rotating anode tube at 40 kV, 15 mA, exposure time 1 h, specimen film distance 36 cm. The strong line is the 20 reflexion (d=231 Å); the weak lines are the 21, 31 and 32 reflexions.

Calculated and Observed Intensities

Using the theory of Schwinger[1] and a programme written by Klucker, DESY group F41, we have calculated the intensities at 1.5 Å wavelength and at the harmonics of 1.5 Å: when the synchrotron runs at 7.5 GeV the second and third harmonics are twice as intense (photons/s) as the 1.5 Å radiation.

We have measured photographically the instantaneous intensity of the reflected beam passing the disk attenuator at the eighth ms of each synchrotron acceleration cycle. The contribution of higher orders has been estimated from measurements made through aluminium filters of various known thicknesses, and we have adopted values for the absorption coefficients[8]. The sensitivity of Ilford Industrial G film at 1.5 Å has been extrapolated from the calibrated value at 1.54 Å (ref. 9). The experimental conditions and data are summarized in Table 1.

Table 1. Data for Quartz Monochromator in Synchrotron Radiation Beam

Synchrotron	7.5 GeV, 10 mA beam current
Electron beam diameter	approximately 4 mm (=effective X-ray source diameter)
Distance	37 m from synchrotron to monochromator
Cross-fire of the incident beam	approximately 10^{-4} rad
Polarization	85% at 1.5 Å in the eighth ms of the cycle, polarized in the plane of the synchrotron
Be-window	0.5 mm (96 mg cm^{-2})

相比，用同步辐射制成的照片具有相对较大的"20"线宽度，这一现象目前尚未得到解释。从两张照片的相对强度可以看出，同步辐射（5 GeV）比现有的最强 X 射线源要有效约 10 倍。

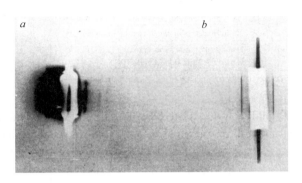

图 3. 拍摄巨型水虫背部纵向飞行肌的赤道反射，采用以下两种方式记录。*a*，单色的同步辐射；电子能量：5 GeV，束流：8 mA，曝光时间：15 min，样品与胶片的距离：40 cm；注意在托架左侧会出现由单色器支架的荧光引起的寄生散射。*b*，40 kV 和 15 mA 的埃利奥特细焦旋转阳极管，曝光时间：1 h，样品与胶片的距离：36 cm。强线是 20 反射（*d*=231 Å）；弱线是 21、31 和 32 反射。

计算强度和观测强度

根据施温格 [1] 的理论和由 DESY 的 F41 小组成员克卢克编写的程序，我们计算了 1.5 Å 波长处和 1.5 Å 谐波处的强度；当同步加速器在 7.5 GeV 运行时，二次和三次谐波的强度（每秒的光子数）是 1.5 Å 辐射的两倍。

我们用照相方法测量了在每个同步加速器加速周期第 8 个 ms 时通过圆盘衰减器的反射束的瞬时强度。从对不同已知厚度的铝滤波器所作的测量中估计出了高阶的贡献，我们还用到了一些吸收系数数据 [8]。伊尔福工业 G 胶片在 1.5 Å 处的灵敏度是由在 1.54 Å 处的校准值外推得到的（参考文献 9）。实验条件和数据汇总在表 1 中。

表 1. 同步辐射束中石英单色器的数据

同步加速器	7.5 GeV, 10 mA 束流
电子束直径	约 4 mm（= 有效X射线源直径）
距离	同步加速器距单色器 37 m
入射束的交叉发射	约 10^{-4} 弧度 (rad)
偏振	对于在同步加速器平面内的偏振：在周期的第8个 ms 内 1.5 Å 处为 85%
铍窗	0.5 mm（96 mg cm^{-2}）

461

Continued

Crystal	quartz cut at $\sigma = 8°30'$ to the 1011 planes, dimensions $45 \times 13 \times 0.3$ mm^3
Bender	pins: outer pair 40.5 mm inner pair 39.5 mm radius of curvature of crystal, 9 m
Wavelength	1.53 Å ($\theta = 13°15'$)
Wavelength spread	$\Delta\lambda = 3 \times 10^{-3}$ Å (due to deviation from Johann focusing and to finite source size)
Focus	1.5 m from crystal, line focus 180 μm wide
Angular aperture of reflected beam	horizontal: 2 mrad (convergence) vertical: 3–4 mrad (divergence)
Measured flux in line focus	1.8×10^9 photons s^{-1} mm^{-1} (of focal length) (at the eighth ms of the cycle)

The ratio of the intensity at 1.5 Å, evaluated as indicated above, to the calculated incident intensity per unit wavelength interval is an "integrated band pass" which was found to be

$$\int R(\lambda)d\lambda = 0.7 \times 10^{-4} \text{ Å}$$

Transforming the wavelength into an angle using Bragg's law we find an integrated reflectivity

$$\int R(\theta)d\theta = R_{int} = 1.0 \times 10^{-5} \text{ rad}$$

for a quartz crystal cut at $8°30'$ to the 1011 plane.

Quartz behaves essentially as a perfect dynamical diffractor[10]. Renninger[11] has calculated the reflectivity of a perfect quartz crystal (without corrections for absorption) to be

$$R_{int} = 4.4 \times 10^{-5} \text{ rad}$$

and Brogren[12] measured an integrated reflectivity of

$$R_{int} = 3.9 \times 10^{-5} \text{ rad}$$

for a polished quartz crystal cut parallel to the $10\overline{1}1$ planes. The case of an asymmetrically cut perfect crystal with absorption is treated in the Darwin–Prins theory. Using Zachariasen's formulae[13] we have calculated an integrated reflectivity of

$$R_{int} = 1.45 \times 10^{-5} \text{ rad}$$

for a quartz crystal cut at $8°30'$ to the $10\overline{1}1$ planes ($\lambda = 1.5$ Å) which agrees with our experimental value.

We emphasize that the aim of our experiments was not to make quantitative measurements of the reflectivity of quartz but to show that quartz is a suitable material

晶体	石英切割到相对1011面为 σ=8°30′ 的夹角，尺寸为 45 × 13 × 0.3 mm³
弯曲装置	定位销：外对 40.5 mm 内对 39.5 mm 晶体的曲率半径为 9 m
波长	1.53 Å (θ = 13°15′)
波长展开度	Δλ = 3 × 10⁻³ Å （源自约翰式聚焦的偏差以及有限源的尺寸）
焦点	距晶体 1.5 m，线聚焦的宽度为 180 μm
反射束的孔径张角	水平：2 mrad （会聚） 垂直：3 mrad～4 mrad （发散）
在线聚焦时测量的通量	（焦距处）1.8 × 10⁹ 个光子 s⁻¹ mm⁻¹ （在周期的第8个ms内）

由上述方法估计得到的在 1.5 Å 处的强度与单位波长间隔入射强度的计算值之比是一个"积分带通"，可由下式表示：

$$\int R(\lambda)\mathrm{d}\lambda = 0.7 \times 10^{-4}\ \text{Å}$$

用布拉格定律将波长转换为角度，我们得到了以相对 1011 面 8°30′ 夹角切割的石英晶体的积分反射率：

$$\int R(\theta)\mathrm{d}\theta = R_{\text{int}} = 1.0 \times 10^{-5}\ \text{rad}$$

石英在本质上是个理想的动态衍射器 [10]。伦宁格 [11] 已经计算出了一个理想石英晶体的反射率（未作吸收校正）：

$$R_{\text{int}} = 4.4 \times 10^{-5}\ \text{rad}$$

布罗格伦 [12] 通过测量得到了一个经平行于 10Ī1 面切割的抛光石英晶体的积分反射率：

$$R_{\text{int}} = 3.9 \times 10^{-5}\ \text{rad}$$

这类具有吸收的非对称切割理想晶体的情况按照达尔文－普林斯理论来处理。利用扎卡里亚森公式 [13]，我们计算了以相对 10Ī1 面 8°30′ 夹角切割的石英晶体的积分反射率（λ = 1.5 Å）：

$$R_{\text{int}} = 1.45 \times 10^{-5}\ \text{rad}$$

这与我们通过实验得到的数值是一致的。

需要强调的是：我们的实验目的并不是定量测量石英的反射率，而是要说明就

for the construction of a focusing monochromator for synchrotron radiation, and to check that there was no large disparity between the observed and calculated flux of monochromated synchrotron radiation. Our results show that the monochromator has properties which can be accurately predicted. We have emphasized neither the accurate determination of the attenuation ratio of the rotating disk nor the speed of the shutter. Moreover, the evaluation of the contribution from higher harmonics may be inaccurate. We estimate that the error in our result may amount to 50%. Furthermore, the state of the surface of the quartz crystal is difficult to control, although it has a considerable influence on the actual shape and height of the reflectivity curve[14,15].

Estimated Intensities for Various Configurations

We intend to set up a Berreman monochromator[6] to give a point-focused beam from a quartz crystal ground so as to give the required curvature in one plane and bent to the corresponding curvature in the second. There seem to be no theoretical reasons why this should not produce foci of similar dimensions to those that we have obtained with a simple bent crystal, especially as the geometry of the synchrotron beam relaxes some of the stringent conditions which the radii of curvature of the crystal must otherwise satisfy.

The estimated performance of such an arrangement for each of three typical configurations used in biological applications of X-ray diffraction is shown in Table 2, and the performance is compared with a "conventional" fine-focus rotating anode tube. The calculated intensities are based on the effective band pass give above, 0.7×10^{-4} Å.

Table 2. Biological Applications

Specimen	Elliott fine-focus X-ray tube*	DESY synchrotron with Berreman point-focusing monochromator‡
Single crystal	Standard collimator, 0.5 mm diameter	
	$A = 12.5$ cm	$D = 1$ m
$a=0.5$ mm	$d = 0.7$ mm	$d = 120$ μm
$b=0.5$ mm	$P = 10^9$ photons s^{-1}	$P = 4 \times 10^9$ photons s^{-1}
$L=7.5$ cm	$I = 2 \times 10^9$ photons s^{-1} mm^{-2}	$I = 2.5 \times 10^{11}$ photons s^{-1} mm^{-2}
Tobacco mosaic virus gel	Double-crystal focusing monochromator†	
		$D = 0.8$ m
$a = 0.6$ mm	$d = 80$ μm	$d = 100$ μm
$b = 1$ mm	$P = 10^7$ photons s^{-1}	$P = 3 \times 10^9$ photons s^{-1}
$L = 12$ cm	$I = 2 \times 10^9$ photons s^{-1} mm^{-2}	$I = 3 \times 10^{11}$ photons s^{-1} mm^{-2}
Insect muscle	Double-crystal focusing monochromator†	
		$D = 1.5\ (3)$ m
$a = 3$ mm	$d = 100$ μm	$d = 180\ (350)$ μm
$b = 0.3$ mm	$P = 5 \times 10^5$ photons s^{-1}	$P = 5 \times 10^8\ (2 \times 10^9)$ photons s^{-1}
$L = 40$ cm	$I = 5 \times 10^7$ photons s^{-1} mm^{-2}	$I = 1.5 \times 10^{10}$ photons s^{-1} mm^{-2}

a, Width of specimen; b, height of specimen; L, specimen film distance; A, anode specimen distance; D, focal length, that is, monochromator film distance; d, spot or focus diameter on film; P, X-ray power reaching the specimen; and I, flux density at the focus.

* Loaded with 40 kV, 50 mA into a 0.2×2 mm^2 electron focus at the anode in the first case, and 40 kV,

构成应用于同步辐射中的聚焦单色器而言，石英是一种很适合的材料，并证实了单色同步辐射的观测通量与计算通量之间并无很大的差异。我们得到的结果表明，单色器的性质是可以准确预言出来的。我们既没有强调对旋转圆盘衰减比的准确测定，也没有强调对光闸速率的准确测定。此外，对高次谐波贡献的估计也可能是不准确的。我们估计，在我们所得结果中的误差也许会达到 50%。此外，虽然石英晶体的表面状态对反射率曲线的实际形状和高度影响很大 [14,15]，但很难对它进行控制。

对三类样品的强度估计

为了从石英晶体底部给出一束点聚焦辐射，我们打算装配一台贝雷曼单色器 [6]，以便在一个平面上形成所需的曲率，并在第二个平面上也弯曲到相应的曲率。似乎无法用理论来说明为什么这样做得到的焦距不能与用简单弯曲晶体得到的焦距有类似的大小，尤其是在同步加速器束流的几何形状不那么严格时，晶体的曲率半径本应该满足的这时不满足了。

以这样一种方式用 X 射线衍射研究生物学中的三种典型样品，将估测的性能列于表 2，并把 DESY 的性能与"传统的"细焦旋转阳极管的性能进行了比较。强度的计算值是以前面给出的有效带通值 0.7×10^{-4} Å 为基础的。

表 2. 在生物学中的应用

样品	埃利奥特细焦X射线管*	配备贝雷曼点聚焦单色仪的DESY同步加速器‡
单晶	标准准直仪，直径为 0.5 mm	
	$A = 12.5$ cm	$D = 1$ m
$a = 0.5$ mm	$d = 0.7$ mm	$d = 120$ μm
$b = 0.5$ mm	$P = 10^9$ 个光子 s^{-1}	$P = 4 \times 10^9$ 个光子 s^{-1}
$L = 7.5$ cm	$I = 2 \times 10^9$ 个光子 s^{-1} mm^{-2}	$I = 2.5 \times 10^{11}$ 个光子 s^{-1} mm^{-2}
烟草花叶病毒凝胶体	双晶聚焦单色器†	
		$D = 0.8$ m
$a = 0.6$ mm	$d = 80$ μm	$d = 100$ μm
$b = 1$ mm	$P = 10^7$ 个光子 s^{-1}	$P = 3 \times 10^9$ 个光子 s^{-1}
$L = 12$ cm	$I = 2 \times 10^9$ 个光子 s^{-1} mm^{-2}	$I = 3 \times 10^{11}$ 个光子 s^{-1} mm^{-2}
昆虫的肌肉	双晶聚焦单色器†	
		$D = 1.5$ (3) m
$a = 3$ mm	$d = 100$ μm	$d = 180$ (350) μm
$b = 0.3$ mm	$P = 5 \times 10^5$ 个光子 s^{-1}	$P = 5 \times 10^8$ (2×10^9) 个光子 s^{-1}
$L = 40$ cm	$I = 5 \times 10^7$ 个光子 s^{-1} mm^{-2}	$I = 1.5 \times 10^{10}$ 个光子 s^{-1} mm^{-2}

a，样品宽度；b，样品高度；L，样品与胶片的距离；A，阳极与样品的距离；D，焦距，即单色器与胶片的距离；d，在胶片上的光斑或焦点直径；P，到达样品上的X射线功率；I，焦点处的通量密度。

* 对于第一个样品，将40 kV和50 mA加载到阳极处 0.2×2 mm² 电子焦点上；对于另外两个样品，

15 mA into a 0.14×0.7 mm² focus in the other two cases. This set is the most powerful fine-focus X-ray tube currently available.

† The setting of this Johann-type[5] monochromator is optimized for each type of specimen.

‡ Conditions of the synchrotron are as in Table 1, computed for 1.5 Å radiation.

The tube values were calculated from measurements made with Ilford Industrial G film and a rotating disk attenuator on an Elliot fine-focus rotating anode tube used with single and double focusing quartz monochromators.

Higher Intensities and Longer Wavelengths

Some possible methods of obtaining higher intensities and utilizing the continuous spectrum are as follows. (*a*) According to current plans, the DESY synchrotron current will be raised from 10 mA to 50 mA. Also the electrons will be kept at the maximum energy for 1 or 2 ms, giving overall a six-fold improvement. (*b*) Sakisaka[14] suggests that both the height and width of the rocking curve of quartz can be increased appreciably by gentle grinding. A gain of 2 or 3 should be possible without affecting the size of the focus. (*c*) For special applications, where only pulses of X-rays can be used, the synchrotron is a very advantageous source if the experiment can be synchronized with the periodic maximum emission from the synchrotron. The integrated reflectivity of quartz increases approximately linearly with wavelength up to 3–4 Å (ref. 12). The intensity of the synchrotron radiation decreases, however, in the wavelength range 1.5–4.5 Å, approximately as the inverse of wavelength. The reflected intensity is thus roughly independent of wavelength. Previously, long wavelength experiments were avoided because of the low conversion efficiency of the anode materials involved.

We thank the Direktorium of DESY for facilities; Dr. R. Haensel and group F41 for advice; Drs. U. W. Arndt and H. G. Mannherz (who prepared the muscle specimen) and Dr. J. Barrington Leigh for the use of his calculations for the Berreman monochromator. The equipment was constructed in the workshops of DESY and the Max-Planck-Institut, Heidelberg. G. R. and J. W. have EMBO short term fellow-ships.

(**230**, 434-437; 1971)

G. Rosenbaum and K. C. Holmes: Max-Planck-Institut für Medizinische Forschung, Heidelberg.
J. Witz: Laboratoire des Virus des Plantes, Institut de Botanique de la Faculté des Sciences de Strasbourg, Strasbourg.

Received March 3, 1971.

References:

1. Schwinger, J., *Phys. Rev.*, **12**, 1912 (1949).

2. Godwin, R. P., *Springer Tracts in Modern Phys.* (edit. by Höhler, G.), **51**, 1 (1969).

3. Haensel, R., and Kunz, C., *Z. Angew. Phys.*, **23**, 276 (1967).

将 40 kV和 15 mA 加载到 0.14×0.7 mm² 焦点上。这个装置是目前可用的最有效的细焦X射线管。

† 这种约翰式[5]单色器装置对每一种类型的样品都是最佳的。

‡ 同步加速器的条件如表1所列，以1.5 Å 的辐射进行计算。

X 射线管的数据是根据测量伊尔福工业 G 胶片和与单、双聚焦石英单色器协同使用的埃利奥特细焦旋转阳极管上的旋转圆盘衰减器所得到的结果计算出来的。

更高的强度和更长的波长

几个可能获得更高强度及连续光谱的方法是：(a) 按照目前的设计，可以将 DESY 同步加速器的电流从 10 mA 升至 50 mA。电子也将在 1 ms ～ 2 ms 内保持在最大能量，这样一来总强度可以提高至 6 倍。(b) 匈坂 [14] 提出，轻微的抛光可以使石英摇摆曲线的高度和宽度显著增加。在不影响聚焦尺寸的前提下，达到 2 倍或 3 倍的增益是有可能的。(c) 对于一些只能应用 X 射线脉冲的特殊情况，如果实验能与来自同步加速器的周期性最大辐射同步，那么同步加速器就是一个具有明显优势的源。石英的积分反射率基本上随波长呈线性递增，直到波长达到 3 Å ～ 4 Å 时（参考文献 12）。然而，在波长范围为 1.5 Å ～ 4.5 Å 时，同步辐射的强度却随波长的增加而下降，两者近似成反比。所以反射强度大致与波长无关。以前大家都会避免在长波下作实验，因为阳极材料在长波下的转换效率很低。

感谢 DESY 委员会为我们提供设备；感谢亨泽尔博士和 F41 小组所提的建议；感谢阿恩特博士和曼赫茨博士（肌肉样品是他们制备的），以及巴林顿·利博士对贝雷曼单色器的计算。这台设备安置在 DESY 车间以及德国海德堡的马克斯·普朗克研究所中。欧洲分子生物学组织为本文的两位作者——罗森鲍姆和维茨提供了短期奖金。

（沈乃澂 翻译；尚仁成 审稿）

4. Bathow, G., Freytag, E., and Haensel, R., *J. Appl. Phys.*, **37**, 3449 (1966).

5. Witz, J., *Acta Cryst.*, **A25**, 30 (1969).

6. Berreman, D. W., *Rev. Sci. Inst.*, **26**, 1048 (1955).

7. Pringle, J. W. S., *Prog. Biophys. Mol. Biol.*, 17, 3 (edit. by Huxley, H. E., and Butler, J. A. V.) (Pergamon, Oxford, 1967).

8. *International Tables of Crystallography*, 3.

9. Morimoto, H., and Uyeda, R., *Acta Cryst.*, **16**, 1107 (1963).

10. Bearden, J. A., Marzolf, J. G., and Thomsen, J. S., *Acta Cryst.*, **A24**, 295 (1968).

11. Renninger, M., *Z. Kristallograph.*, **107**, 464 (1956).

12. Brogren, G., *Arkiv. für Fysik*, **22**, 267 (1962).

13. Zachariasen, W. H., *Theory of X-ray Diffraction in Crystals* (Dover, New York, 1967).

14. Sakisaka, Y., *Proc. Math. Phys. Soc. Japan*, **12**, 189 (1930).

15. Evans, R. C., Hirsch, P. B., and Kellar, J. N., *Acta Cryst.*, **1**, 124 (1948); Gay, P., Hirsch, P. B., and Kellar, J. N., *Acta Cryst.*, **5**, 7 (1952).

Mitochondrion as a Multifunctional Organelle

R. B. Flavell

Editor's Note

Mitochondria—membrane-enclosed organelles found in most eukaryotic cells—are commonly described as the powerhouses of the cell, since their primary function is the manufacture of the molecular energy source ATP (which, as Richard B. Flavell says in this paper, involves electron transport and oxidation). Flavell, a molecular biologist at Cambridge, was concerned to correct this over-simplification, pointing out that the mitochondrion has many other essential tasks too, which do not depend on the presence of mitochondrial DNA. In particular, he says, it is involved in protein synthesis; we would today add calcium-ion signalling as a key role. Flavell argues that this means one should not interpret the invisibility of mitochondria in microscopy of anaerobes as evidence of their absence.

THAT the mitochondrion is the site of the electron transport chain and oxidative phosphorylation is well known and, indeed, the mechanism of oxidative phosphorylation is an active area of biochemical research. Within the outer mitochondrial membrane, however, many other kinds of metabolic reactions also occur. Thus, mitochondria contain enzymes involved in the Krebs cycle, the β oxidation of fatty acids, fatty acid biosynthesis[1], synthesis of some amino-acids[2], lipid catabolism, the urea cycle and glutamate and aspartate biosynthesis[3] as well as several oxidative enzymes not directly involved with oxidative phosphorylation, such as rotenone-insensitive NADH, cytochrome c reductase, monoamine oxidase and kynurenine hydroxylase[1]. This list is not exhaustive and will no doubt be extended in the years ahead.

Many of these enzymes or sequences of enzymes are biosynthetic or catabolic and consequently have end products not directly involved in energy metabolism, so that the mitochondrion has a biosynthetic and catabolic as well as an energetic role, which would suggest that unless all mitochondrial end products—biosynthetic, catabolic and energetic—can be provided by alternative metabolic systems, mitochondria are essential for cell survival in all conditions. This conclusion is rarely discussed in general articles on mitochondria and infrequently recognized in research reports on mitochondria. Thus a recently published article[4] began: "Mitochondria are DNA-containing, self-replicating organelles the functions of which are dispensable to yeast cells grown in the presence of a fermentable energy source". The issue is especially significant in the question whether or not anaerobic yeast cells possess mitochondria.

There are conflicting reports of the presence of mitochondria in anaerobically grown yeast cells. Electron microscopical studies suggest that anaerobic yeast cells lack mitochondria[5,6], but several workers have reported that if lipid precursors are included in

线粒体是一个多功能的细胞器

线粒体是在大多数真核细胞中存在的、膜包被的细胞器，它们通常被描述为细胞的动力工厂，因为其主要功能是制造生物分子的能量来源——三磷酸腺苷（正如理查德·弗拉维尔在本文中所述，三磷酸腺苷参与了电子传递和氧化过程）。剑桥大学的分子生物学家弗拉维尔认为应该对这种过于简单的概括进行修正，他指出线粒体还有很多不依赖于线粒体 DNA 存在的其他重要功能。他特别提到了线粒体在蛋白质合成中的作用；现在我们当然还要将钙离子信号转导添加到它的关键功能里。弗拉维尔认为：这说明人们不应该把运用显微镜术在厌氧生物中看不见线粒体的现象当作线粒体不存在的证据。

众所周知，线粒体是电子传递链和氧化磷酸化的场所，而且氧化磷酸化机制确实也是生化研究中的一个活跃领域。然而，在线粒体外膜内，还发生着许多其他类型的代谢反应。因此，线粒体包含的酶包括参与克雷布斯循环、脂肪酸 β–氧化作用、脂肪酸生物合成 [1]、某些氨基酸合成 [2]、脂分解代谢、尿素循环、谷氨酸盐和天冬氨酸盐生物合成 [3] 的酶以及几种不直接参与氧化磷酸化反应的氧化酶，诸如对鱼藤酮不敏感的还原型烟酰胺腺嘌呤二核苷酸（NADH）、细胞色素 c 还原酶、单胺氧化酶和犬尿氨酸羟化酶 [1]。这张单子并未穷尽所有，在今后的若干年中肯定还会有所扩展。

在这些酶或系列酶中，有许多是生物合成方面的或者分解代谢方面的，它们的最终产物并不直接参与能量代谢，因此线粒体不仅有能量方面的作用，还有生物合成和分解代谢方面的作用。这可能表明：除非线粒体的所有最终产物，包括生物合成的、分解代谢的和能量方面的，都可以由其他代谢系统来提供，否则在任何情况下线粒体对于细胞生存都是不可缺少的。这一结论在关于线粒体的一般文章中很少被论及，在与线粒体有关的研究报告中也难得被承认。无怪乎有一篇最近发表的文章 [4] 以这样的话作为开篇语："线粒体是含有 DNA 的、能够进行自我复制的细胞器，其功能对于生长在有可发酵能源环境中的酵母细胞来说是可有可无的"。这一观点在讨论厌氧酵母细胞是否拥有线粒体这一问题时尤其重要。

关于在无氧环境中生长的酵母细胞里到底有没有线粒体的问题，目前所报道的结果是相互矛盾的。电子显微镜的研究表明厌氧酵母细胞不具有线粒体 [5,6]；但也有几位

471

the defined growth medium, mitochondrial profiles can be seen in electron micrographs of anaerobically grown yeast cells, although some disagree[7].

Linnane *et al.* did not observe mitochondria in electron micrographs of anaerobic yeast cells[8], but they did recognize "reticular membranes" which appeared to differentiate into mitochondria in aerobic conditions (see also refs. 5, 7), and detailed biochemical studies[9,10] have confirmed their homology with mitochondria. Although the reticular membranes lack the enzymes and cytochromes for oxidative phosphorylation, they do possess mitochondrial DNA, mitochondrial ATPase and succinate dehydrogenase. These mitochondria have a similar—if not identical—"structural protein" fraction to those isolated from aerobic cells. These membrane structures in extracts from anaerobic cells possess similar percentages of extracted protein to those in extracts from aerobic cells[9], giving unequivocal biochemical evidence that mitochondria exist in anaerobic yeast cells, as would be expected from knowledge of their diverse functions.

In spite of this demonstration of the similarities between the membrane structures found in anaerobic yeast cells and the mitochondria in aerobic yeast cells, the membrane structures were called "promitochondria", not mitochondria, because they had neither the appearance of aerobic mitochondria in the electron microscope nor the ability to catalyse oxidative phosphorylation, but gained both these properties when the cells were exposed to oxygen[9,10]. I suggest that because the area of specialized cytoplasm enclosed by the outer mitochondrial membrane has diverse metabolic functions, the mitochondrion is incompletely defined by its appearance in the electron microscope and its oxidative phosphorylation activity. "Promitochondrion" is, therefore, inappropriate. It seems more appropriate to consider the units of specialized cytoplasm, organized within outer mitochondrial membranes around the mitochondrial DNA of anaerobic cells, as mitochondria lacking some of the components found in mitochondria of aerobic cells. Equally extreme variation in mitochondrial composition is found in some muscle cells, in which the synthesis of inner membrane and oxidative phosphorylation proteins is highly derepressed in response to large demands for ATP[11] and considerable variation in mitochondrial enzyme composition is expected from knowledge of the diversity of mitochondrial metabolism. Enzyme levels are frequently regulated by the concentration of their specific end product(s), so that in cells with different requirements for particular mitochondrial end products, mitochondria of differing enzyme composition are expected[12] and tissue specific differences in mitochondria from the same organism have been described[13].

Changes that occur in mitochondria after the transfer of yeast cells from an anaerobic to an aerobic environment, or from high glucose repression to low glucose repression, have been studied[14,15]. In these conditions a number of mitochondrial components, particularly those concerned with energy production, are preferentially synthesized in a process described as "mitochondrial biogenesis". This term has also been used in studies of the synthesis of mitochondrial components in animal cells[16-18]. It does not imply the synthesis of new mitochondria from pre-existing mitochondria as is almost certainly

472

研究者提出，如果在配方明确的培养基中含有脂质前体，那么从厌氧生长的酵母细胞的电子显微镜照片里就可以看到线粒体的轮廓，不过有些人并不同意这一观点 [7]。

虽然林纳内等人并没有在厌氧酵母细胞的电子显微镜照片中观察到线粒体 [8]，但是他们确实看到了"网状膜"，该网状膜在有氧条件下似乎可以分化成线粒体（参见参考文献 5 和 7），而且详细的生化研究 [9,10] 也证实了它们与线粒体的同源性。尽管这些网状膜不含有氧化磷酸化反应所需要的酶和细胞色素，但是它们确实含有线粒体 DNA、线粒体腺苷三磷酸酶和琥珀酸脱氢酶。这些线粒体的"结构蛋白"部分与从有氧细胞中分离出来的部分即使不完全相同，至少也比较相近。厌氧细胞提取物中的这些膜结构与有氧细胞提取物中的膜结构具有同样百分比的蛋白提取物 [9]，这一生物化学证据确凿无疑地证明，在厌氧酵母细胞中存在线粒体，此论点与我们根据对线粒体具有多种功能的认识所料想到的情况一致。

尽管上述证据已经表明，在厌氧酵母细胞中发现的膜结构与有氧酵母细胞中的线粒体具有相似性，但这种膜结构被人们称为"原线粒体"，而非线粒体，因为它们既无有氧线粒体在电子显微镜下的外观，也不能催化氧化磷酸化反应，然而一旦细胞被暴露于氧气之下，它们就会获得这两个特性 [9,10]。我认为：鉴于被线粒体外膜包被的特定细胞质区域具有多种不同的代谢功能，因而仅由其在电子显微镜下的外观及其氧化磷酸化活性来定义线粒体是片面的。因此，"原线粒体"这一名称并不恰当。似乎更恰当的说法是：把分布在厌氧细胞线粒体 DNA 周围、线粒体外膜内的特定细胞质单元看作是与有氧细胞中的线粒体相比缺少了某些成分的线粒体。人们在某些肌肉细胞中也发现了线粒体组分存在同等极端变异的情况，由于需要大量三磷酸腺苷，这些线粒体中的内膜合成及氧化磷酸化蛋白质的合成被高度去抑制 [11]，根据我们对线粒体代谢多样性的了解，可以料想到线粒体酶的组分也存在着相当大的变异。酶的水平通常受其特定终产物的浓度所调控，因此可以预料在对特定线粒体终产物有不同需求的细胞中会出现具有不同酶组分的线粒体 [12]，而且也有人曾描述过来自同一生物体的线粒体存在组织特异性上的差异 [13]。

有些人曾研究过将酵母细胞从无氧环境转移到有氧环境，或者从高葡萄糖阻遏作用环境转移到低葡萄糖阻遏作用环境之后线粒体内所发生的变化 [14,15]。在这些情况下，若干线粒体组分，尤其是那些与产生能量有关的组分，都在被称为"线粒体生物生成"的过程中优先合成。在研究动物细胞中的线粒体组分合成时，也用到了这一术语 [16-18]。这并不意味着从已经存在的线粒体合成新的线粒体，就像在

the case in all eukaryotes. Each mitochondrial component may be formed *de novo*, but formation of new organelles is by growth and division of pre-existing mitochondria. I suggest, therefore, that "mitochondrial differentiation" is more appropriate to describe the changes that occur when yeast cells are transferred from an anaerobic to an aerobic environment.

Descriptions[20,21] have been published of mitochondria isolated from "petite" strains of yeast which lack mitochondrial DNA, or the mitochondrial DNA of which has a severely restricted information content because it is composed almost entirely of adenine and thymine. Such mitochondria, which are of a similar size and buoyant density to those in the "grande" parent strain, lack the components of the electron transport chain but possess adenosine triphosphatase and other mitochondrial enzymes as well as an inner membrane[21]. Perlman and Mahler[21], therefore, raised the question of why mitochondria continue to be synthesized when their oxidative phosphorylation capacity is lost. Knowledge of the other essential functions of mitochondria provides the answer.

The presence of mitochondria in cells lacking mitochondrial DNA implies that in yeast the role of mitochondrial DNA in maintenance of mitochondria is limited, that is, the organelle is not genetically autonomous.

It has been suggested (refs. 22 and 23 and article in preparation by Flavell and Raven) that mitochondria have evolved from a prokaryote, able to catalyse oxidative phosphorylation, which sheltered in a primitive amoeboid-like cell and became stabilized there in a symbiotic relationship. At some time before the presumed symbiosis was established, the host cell must have been capable of living without the prokaryote, which would have been genetically autonomous. Since then considerable co-evolution of host cell and prokaryote has taken place.

The prokaryote has lost almost all its genetic information. Organization and compartmentalization have evolved in the eukaryotic cell such that the mitochondrion is now a fully integrated unit of the cytoplasm. Many biosynthetic and catabolic activities—as well as oxidative phosphorylation—must occur inside the outer mitochondrial membrane to be useful to the cell. This is well illustrated by auxotrophic strains of Neurospora which have metabolic deficiencies at the malate dehydrogenase step of the Krebs cycle, and other auxotrophic strains which have a metabolic block at the dehydroxy acid dehydratase step in isoleucine and valine biosynthesis. These strains, however, possess considerable malate dehydrogenase and dehydroxy acid dehydratase activity respectively, but possess metabolic blocks, because these enzymes are not localized in the mitochondria as in prototrophic strains, but remain outside the organelle in the cytophasm[24,25].

Although multienzyme complexes can be isolated intact with the mitochondria, this physical association of related enzymes is probably the result of evolution rather than

所有真核生物中几乎一定会发生的过程那样。每一种线粒体组分都可以从头生成，但新细胞器是通过已存在线粒体的生长和分裂而形成的。因此，我认为用"线粒体分化"来描述那些发生在把酵母细胞从无氧环境转移到有氧环境时的变化会更贴切一些。

有些人曾在发表的文章中 [20,21] 描述过从酵母"小"菌株中分离得到的线粒体。这些酵母菌株或者不具有线粒体 DNA，或者虽然具有线粒体 DNA，但因其几乎全部由腺嘌呤和胸腺嘧啶构成，所以仅含有非常有限的信息量。这些线粒体的大小和浮力密度与"大"亲本菌株中的线粒体相似，它们缺少电子传递链组分，但除了内膜之外还含有腺苷三磷酸酶和其他线粒体酶 [21]。因此珀尔曼和马勒 [21] 提出了这样的疑问：为什么在线粒体缺失氧化磷酸化能力时仍然可以继续被合成。对线粒体其他重要功能的认识给出了该问题的答案。

在缺少线粒体 DNA 的细胞中仍存在线粒体意味着，酵母中的线粒体 DNA 在维持线粒体方面的作用有限，也就是说，该细胞器不具有遗传自主性。

有人提出（参考文献 22 和 23 以及弗拉维尔和雷文正在准备之中的文章）：线粒体是从能够催化氧化磷酸化反应的原核生物演化而来的，它藏身于一种原始的变形虫样的细胞中，并以共生关系在那里稳定下来。在这种假设共生关系被确立之前的某一段时期，宿主细胞肯定曾一度不依赖于原核生物而存活，这时原核生物是遗传自主的。随后宿主细胞和原核生物发生了明显的协同演化。

原核生物几乎失去了自己的全部遗传信息。组织结构和区室化已在真核细胞中演化发生，因此现在的线粒体已经充分整合成了细胞质的一个单元。包括氧化磷酸化在内的许多生物合成和分解代谢活动都必须在线粒体外膜之内发生，这样才能对细胞有所用处。用脉孢菌的营养缺陷型菌株和其他营养缺陷型菌株可以很好地证明这一点，前者在克雷布斯循环的苹果酸脱氢酶一步存在代谢缺陷，后者则在异亮氨酸和缬氨酸合成过程中的脱羟基酸脱水酶一步存在代谢障碍。然而，虽然这些菌株分别具有相当高的苹果酸脱氢酶活性和脱羟基酸脱水酶活性，但还是存在代谢障碍，因为与原养型菌株一样，这些酶并没有定位在线粒体上，而是仍位于细胞器之外的细胞质中 [24,25]。

尽管多酶复合物可以完整地与线粒体一道分离出来，但线粒体和相关酶的这种物理联系很可能是演化的结果，而并非早先自主性的残留。不能把现在的线粒体看

remains of a former autonomy. The present-day mitochondrion cannot be viewed as a symbiotic prokaryote or in any sense as self-sufficient, but is similar to other cell compartments or organelles such as Golgi bodies, glyoxysomes, microbodies and so on, which, although not having a prokaryotic origin, have evolved, as has the mitochondrion, to facilitate cytophasmic organization, substrate and product channelling and metabolic pathway isolation.

Recently, great research emphasis has been placed on the electron transport system, oxidative phosphorylation, mitochondrial DNA and mitochondrial protein synthesis, which together with the endosymbiotic theory for the origin of mitochondria has, I think, propagated a view which fails to recognize the mitochondrion as a specialized area of cytoplasm of diverse functions and variable composition, the presence of which does not depend on mitochondrial DNA and is essential for eukaryotic life, even in anaerobic conditions. These features, however, cannot be ignored if we are to obtain a proper understanding of mitochondrial structure, function and replication.

(**230**, 504-506; 1971)

R. B. Flavell: Plant Breeding Institute, Trumpington, Cambridge CB2 2LQ.

Received February 24, 1971.

References:
1. Smoly, J. M., Kuylenstierna, B., and Ernster, L., *Proc. US Nat. Acad. Sci.*, **66**, 125 (1970).
2. Berquist, A., LaBrie, D. A., and Wagner, R. P., *Arch. Biochem. Biophys.*, **134**, 401 (1969).
3. Mahler, H. R., and Cordes, E. H., *Biological Chemistry*, 398 (Harper and Row, New York, 1966).
4. Goldring, E. S., Grossman, L. I., Krupruck, D., Cryer, D. R., and Marmur, J., *J. Mol. Biol.*, **52**, 323 (1970).
5. Wallace, P. G., and Linnane, A. W., *Nature*, **201**, 1191 (1964).
6. Morpurgo, G., Serlupi-Crescenzi, G., Tecce, G., Valente, F., and Venetacci, D., *Nature*, **201**, 897 (1964).
7. Polakis, E. S., Bartley, W., and Meek, G. A., *Biochem. J.*, **90**, 369 (1964).
8. Linnane, A. W., Vitols, E., and Nowland, P. G., *J. Cell. Biol.*, **13**, 345 (1962).
9. Criddle, R. S., and Schatz, G., *Biochemistry*, **8**, 322 (1969).
10. Plattner, H., Salpeter, M. M., Saltzgaber, J., and Schatz, G., *Proc. US Nat. Acad. Sci.*, **66**, 1252 (1970).
11. Lehninger, A., *The Mitochondrion*, 29 (Benjamin, New York, 1964).
12. Woodward, D. O., Edwards, D. L., and Flavell, R. B., *Symp. Soc. Exp. Biol.*, **24**, 55 (1970).
13. Kun, E., and Volfin, P., *Biochem. Biophys. Res. Commun.*, **23**, 696 (1966).
14. Clark-Walker, G. D., and Linnane, A. W., *J. Cell. Biol.*, **34**, 1 (1967).
15. Roodyn, D. B., and Wilkie, D., *The Biogenesis of Mitochondria* (Methuen, London, 1968).
16. Beattie, D. S., *J. Biol. Chem.*, **243**, 4027 (1968).
17. Kroon, A. M., and De Vries, H., *FEBS Lett.*, **3**, 208 (1969).
18. Haldar, D., Freeman, K., and Work, T. S., *Nature*, **211**, 9 (1966).
19. Luck, D. J. L., *J. Cell. Biol.*, **24**, 445 (1965).
20. Nagley, P., and Linnane, A. N., *Biochem. Biophys. Res. Commun.*, **5**, 989 (1970).
21. Perlman, P. S., and Mahler, H. R., *Bioenergetics*, **1**, 113 (1970).
22. Sagan, L., *J. Theoret. Biol.*, **14**, 225 (1967).
23. Nass, S., *Intern. Rev. Cytol.*, **25**, 55 (1969).
24. Munkres, K. D., Benveniste, K., Gorski, J., and Zuiches, C. A., *Proc. US Nat. Acad. Sci.*, 263 (1970).
25. Altmiller, D. H., and Wagner, R. P., *Biochem. Genet.*, **4**, 243 (1970).

作是一种共生的原核生物，或者从任何意义上来说认为它们可以像原核生物那样自给自足，而只能认为它们具有类似于其他细胞区室或细胞器（如高尔基体、乙醛酸循环体和微体等）的结构。尽管其他细胞区室或细胞器并不具有原核生物的起源，但它们和线粒体一样，都是朝着有利于细胞质组织架构、底物和产物疏导以及代谢路径分隔的方向而演化。

最近，人们把大部分的研究重点放在了电子传递系统、氧化磷酸化、线粒体 DNA 和线粒体蛋白质的合成上。我认为上述研究重点与线粒体起源的内共生理论都未能认识到：线粒体是具有多种功能和可变组分的细胞质中的一个特定区域，线粒体的存在并不依赖于线粒体 DNA，而且即便在无氧条件下，线粒体对真核生物的生存来说也是必需的。如果我们要获得对线粒体结构、功能和复制方面的正确认识，就不能忽视这些特征。

（刘皓芳 翻译；顾孝诚 审稿）

Transmission of Two Subacute Spongiform Encephalopathies of Man (Kuru and Creutzfeldt–Jakob Disease) to New World Monkeys

D. C. Gajdusek and C. J. Gibbs, jun.

Editor's Note

By the late 1960s it was known that Creutzfeldt–Jakob Disease and its South Pacific counterpart, kuru, could be transmitted experimentally from man to chimpanzee, but the ape's large size and expensive lifestyle made it an impractical choice for laboratory study. Here Daniel Carleton Gajdusek and Clarence J. Gibbs demonstrate transmissibility of the two human spongiform encephalopathies to four species of New World monkey, providing, they claim, a more pragmatic laboratory model of the brain-wasting diseases. Gajdusek, who later received a Nobel Prize for his work on kuru, had lived amongst the kuru-stricken South Fore people of Papua New Guinea, where, he concluded, the disease was transmitted by the ritualistic eating of dead relatives' brains.

NOW that kuru and Creutzfeldt–Jakob disease have been transmitted to four species of New World monkeys, spider monkeys (*Ateles geoffroyi*), capuchin monkeys (*Cebus* sp.), squirrel monkeys (*Saimiri sciurens*), and woolly monkeys (*Lagothrix lagothica*), these more readily available animals may replace the chimpanzee in the laboratory study of these two subacute degenerative diseases of the human brain.

Both diseases have been transmitted to the squirrel monkey and to the spider monkey using 10% suspensions of human brain, inoculated intracerebrally, with incubation periods of about 2 yr. Human kuru brain suspension has caused the same disease in the capuchin monkey 45 months after intracerebral inoculation (Fig. 1). Furthermore, experimental kuru in the spider monkey has similarly been transmitted to the squirrel monkey with an incubation period of 22 months, and experimental Creutzfeldt–Jakob disease of the chimpanzee to the squirrel monkey with incubation periods of 9 and 19 months, and to the woolly monkey after 21 months of incubation (Fig. 2). Thus, these diseases of man and the experimental diseases in the chimpanzee have now been transmitted to smaller, less expensive, more readily available and more easily cared for hosts than the chimpanzee.

两种人类亚急性海绵状脑病（库鲁病和克雅氏病）传染给了新大陆猴

盖杜谢克，小吉布斯

编者按

到 20 世纪 60 年代晚期的时候，人们就已经知道克雅氏病以及与之相关的流行于南太平洋岛上的库鲁病可以通过实验从人类传染给黑猩猩，但因为类人猿体型庞大、饲养成本昂贵，所以将它用作实验研究是很不实用的。丹尼尔·卡尔顿·盖杜谢克和克拉伦斯·吉布斯在本文中证实这两种人类海绵状脑病可以传染给四种新大陆猴，他们认为上述发现为实验室研究这两类脑损耗疾病提供了更实际的解决方案。后来盖杜谢克因为在库鲁病方面的研究而获得了诺贝尔奖。他曾与库鲁病泛滥的巴布亚新几内亚南弗部落一起生活，他得出的结论是：这种病的传播源于当地人在仪式上经常食用死亡亲属的脑。

既然现在已经可以把库鲁病和克雅氏病传染给四种新大陆猴——蜘蛛猴、卷尾猴、松鼠猴和绒毛猴，那么在实验室中研究这两种人脑亚急性退化性疾病时就可以用这些更容易得到的动物来取代黑猩猩。

用 10% 的人脑悬液进行脑内接种，在潜伏了大约两年后，松鼠猴和蜘蛛猴都被传染上了这两种疾病。人类库鲁病脑悬液使脑内接种 45 个月后的卷尾猴染上了同样的疾病（图 1）。此外，蜘蛛猴的实验性库鲁病同样能够在潜伏 22 个月后传染给松鼠猴；黑猩猩的实验性克雅氏病也能在潜伏 9 个月和 19 个月后传染给松鼠猴，还能在潜伏 21 个月后传染给绒毛猴（图 2）。由此可见，现在我们已经能够把这两种人类疾病和黑猩猩中的实验性疾病传染给比黑猩猩更小、更便宜、更容易获得并且更易于饲养的寄主。

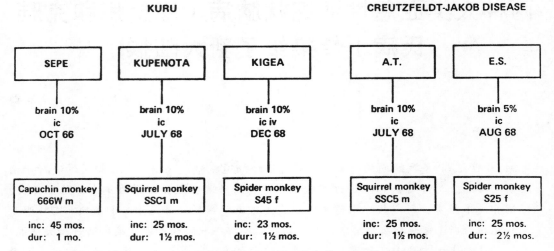

Fig. 1. Transmission of kuru and Creutzfeldt–Jakob disease to New World monkeys.

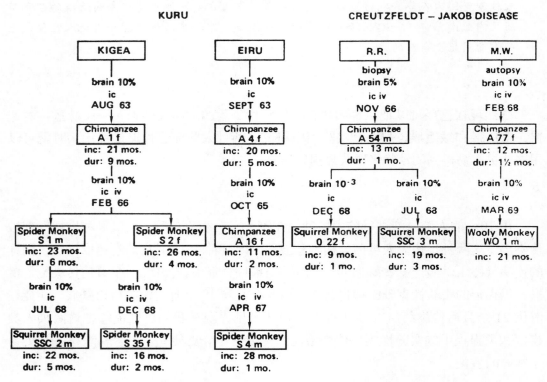

Fig. 2. Transmission of experimental kuru and Creutzfeldt–Jakob disease to New World monkeys.

Experimental kuru in the chimpanzee[1,2] was previously passed successfully to the spider monkey[3] with incubation periods of 23–28 months. It is now in third spider monkey to spider monkey passage and the incubation period on the second passage was 16 months (Fig. 2).

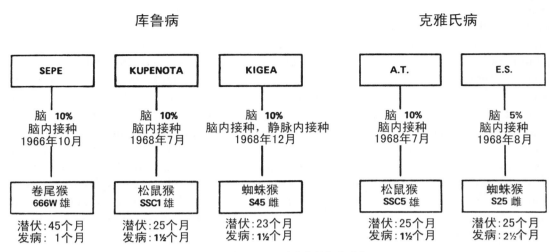

图 1. 库鲁病和克雅氏病传染给新大陆猴。

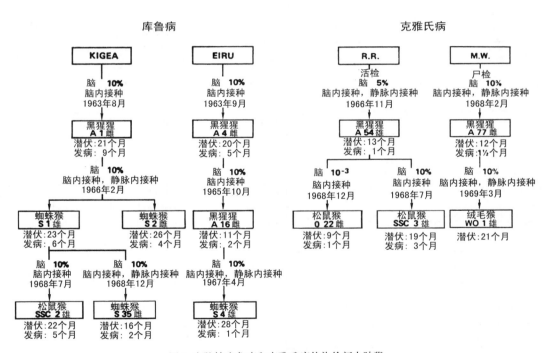

图 2. 实验性库鲁病和克雅氏病传染给新大陆猴。

之前我们曾把黑猩猩中的实验性库鲁病 [1,2] 成功地传染给了潜伏 23~28 个月后的蜘蛛猴 [3]。现在正处于第三个从蜘蛛猴到蜘蛛猴的传染过程之中，第二个传染过程的潜伏期为 16 个月（图 2）。

Kuru, known to be transmissible to the chimpanzee since 1965[1,2], has so far been transmitted from eleven different human patients to eighteen chimpanzees with incubation periods of 14–39 months after intracerebral inoculation (Fig. 3). We are now in the fifth chimpanzee to chimpanzee passage and the incubation period has dropped to 10 to 18 months. Infection is possible by either intracerebral or peripheral (combined intravenous, subcutaneous, intraperitoneal and intramuscular) inoculation, and by using bacterial-free filtrates through "Millipore" filters of 220 nm pore diameter. Both human and chimpanzee brains infected with kuru contain more than 10^6 chimpanzee infectious units per ml. Infectious virus is present in tissue pools of spleen, liver and kidney, as well as in the brains of chimpanzees affected with kuru, but so far intracerebral inoculation into chimpanzees of urine, blood, serum and cerebrospinal fluid from similarly affected humans and chimpanzees has not produced disease. Tissue suspensions of placenta and amnion from a patient who was delivered of an infant while late in her disease also failed to cause disease in the chimpanzee.

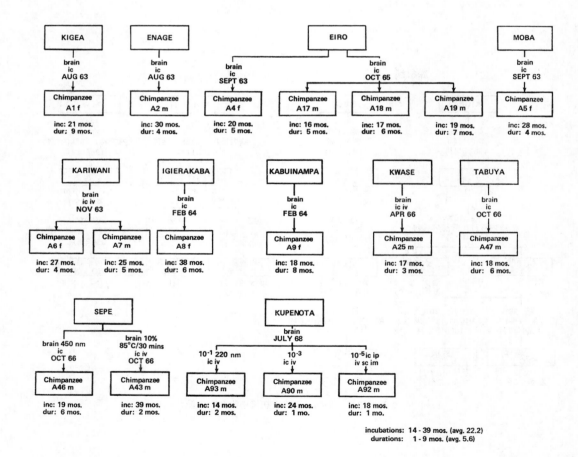

Fig. 3. Primary transmission of kuru from brain tissues of eleven human patients to eighteen chimpanzees.

自 1965 年起人们就已经知道库鲁病可以传染给黑猩猩[1,2]，到目前为止该病已经通过脑内接种的方式从 11 位人类患者传染到了 18 只黑猩猩中，潜伏期为 14~39 个月（图 3）。现在我们正处于第五个从黑猩猩到黑猩猩的传染过程之中，并且潜伏期已经降到了 10~18 个月。通过脑内或者外周（包括静脉内、皮下、腹腔内和肌肉内）接种经由孔径为 220 纳米的"密理博"滤膜过滤的无菌滤液就有可能导致感染。感染库鲁病的人脑和黑猩猩脑中的病毒含量都在 10^6 黑猩猩感染单位／毫升以上。传染性病毒除了存在于患库鲁病黑猩猩的脑内之外，还存在于脾、肝和肾的组织液中，但迄今为止通过给黑猩猩脑内接种同样感染库鲁病的人和黑猩猩的尿液、血液、血清和脑脊液均未使其染病。用一位在库鲁病晚期还分娩婴儿的女性患者的胎盘和羊膜组织悬液也不能使黑猩猩发病。

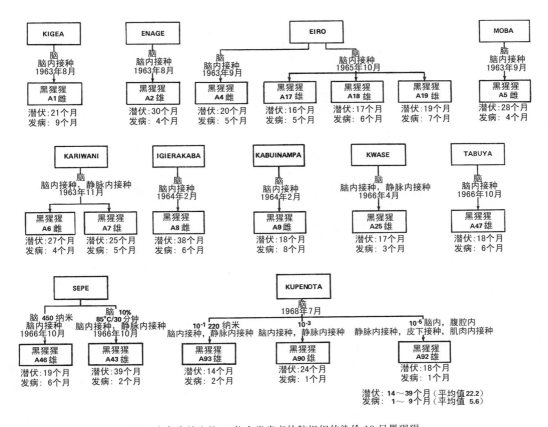

图 3. 库鲁病首次从 11 位人类患者的脑组织传染给 18 只黑猩猩。

Creutzfeldt–Jakob disease was first transmitted from man to the chimpanzee in 1968[4,5]; we have now transmitted the disease by cerebral inoculation brain tissue from ten human patients to eleven chimpanzees with incubation periods of 11–14 months. Furthermore, the brain tissue of one of these patients inoculated only peripherally (intravenously, intraperitoneally and intramuscularly) has caused the disease after 16 months of incubation. Serial passage of experimental Creutzfeldt–Jakob disease in the chimpanzee, with incubation periods of 10–14 months, has been possible using brain suspensions at dilutions of 10^{-1} and 10^{-3}.

A preliminary neuropathological survey by Dr. Kenneth Earle of the Armed Forces Institute of Pathology, and Dr. Peter Lampert of the University of California, San Diego School of Medicine, has revealed the presence of a gliosis, neuronal loss and status spongiosis in all the clinically positive New World monkeys, consistent with the diagnosis of experimental kuru or Creutzfeldt–Jakob disease (Fig. 4) and the detailed neuropathology of the individual animals is to be reported elsewhere (unpublished results of P. W. Lampert).

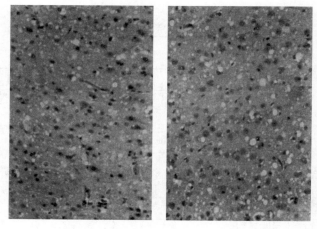

Fig. 4. Spongiform changes in the cerebral cortex of two squirrel monkeys: on the left (squirrel monkey SSC-1 in Fig. 1) inoculated with brain suspension from a kuru patient, and, on the right (squirrel monkey SCC-5 in Fig. 1), inoculated with brain suspension from a patient with Creutzfeldt–Jakob disease.

The squirrel monkey is, of course, the animal of choice for investigation of these diseases, should it be as sensitive an indicator of the viruses as the chimpanzee and if the incubation period were reduced on serial passage. In the spider monkey the incubation period of kuru was reduced from 23–28 months in first passage to 16 months in second passage. Consequently, passage of brain tissue from each affected squirrel monkey into other squirrel monkeys has been performed; and serial blind passage at 3–6 month intervals is in progress. Human brain suspension from twenty further cases of kuru and twenty of Creutzfeldt–Jakob disease has also been inoculated into New World monkeys. Titration of human and chimpanzee kuru brain suspensions known to be infectious at 10^{-5} dilution for the chimpanzee has been done in squirrel and capuchin monkeys.

克雅氏病首次从人传染给黑猩猩是在 1968 年 [4,5]，现在我们已经通过脑内接种 10 位人类患者的脑组织悬液将这种疾病传染到 11 只黑猩猩中，潜伏期为 11~14 个月。此外，其中一位患者的脑组织仅仅通过外周（静脉内、腹腔内和肌肉内）接种就已在 16 个月的潜伏期后使黑猩猩发病。使用稀释 10 倍和 10^3 倍的脑悬液已经可以在黑猩猩中以 10~14 个月的潜伏期连续传播实验性克雅氏病。

美国武装部队病理学研究所的肯尼思·厄尔博士和加州大学圣迭戈医学院的彼得·兰珀特博士经过初步的神经病理学研究发现：所有临床阳性的新大陆猴都出现了与实验性库鲁病或克雅氏病症状一致的神经胶质增生、神经元丢失和海绵状改变症状（图 4）。每个动物个体的详细神经病理学结果将在其他文章中报道（兰珀特尚未发表的结果）。

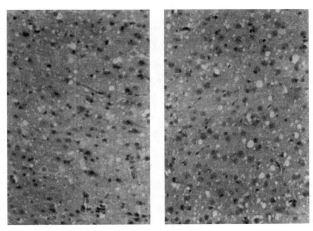

图 4. 两只松鼠猴大脑皮质中的海绵状改变：左图（图 1 中的松鼠猴 SSC-1），接种了一位库鲁病患者脑悬液之后的结果；右图（图 1 中的松鼠猴 SCC-5），接种了一位克雅氏病患者脑悬液之后的结果。

当然，松鼠猴是为研究这两种疾病而特殊挑选的动物，它作为病毒的指示物是否会与黑猩猩的敏感度一样高？在连续传播时潜伏期是否会减少？蜘蛛猴的库鲁病潜伏期在第一次传播时为 23~28 个月，到第二次传播时就减少至 16 个月。因此，我们用每只染病松鼠猴的脑组织感染其他松鼠猴；并且还在进行间隔期为 3~6 个月的盲目继代移植。另外 20 位库鲁病患者和 20 位克雅氏病患者的脑悬液也被接种到新大陆猴中。已知当稀释 10^5 倍时对黑猩猩有感染性的人和黑猩猩的库鲁病脑悬液已在松鼠猴和卷尾猴中进行滴定。

To achieve a degree of isolation which is unobtainable in any single primate holding facility we have used three widely separated facilities, in California, Louisiana, and Maryland. So far, dozens of additional chimpanzees and monkeys inoculated with brain and other organ suspensions from other subacute and chronic neurological disorders have lived in each colony in close contact with animals inoculated with material from kuru and Creutzfeldt–Jakob disease. Thus far, no neurological disease has appeared in any of these "control" animals, which further serves to indicate that experimental kuru and Creutzfeldt–Jakob disease are not communicable.

The squirrel, spider and capuchin monkeys and the chimpanzee are the only species out of twenty-three sub-human primates to develop kuru after inoculation with tissues from human kuru victims. Creutzfeldt–Jakob disease has been transmitted directly with human tissues to the squirrel and spider monkeys, as it was transmitted earlier to the chimpanzee. Furthermore, experimental Creutzfeldt–Jakob disease of the chimpanzee has been transmitted to the woolly monkey (Fig. 1). With the exception of the chimpanzee, none of the sixteen Old World species including the gibbon ape, and in addition the two other species of New World monkeys that were used*, has developed clinical disease after intracerebral inoculation with brain suspensions from patients suffering from kuru or Creutzfeldt–Jakob disease and from chimpanzees in which these diseases have been induced. The successful transmission of both the natural human and the experimental chimpanzee diseases into the squirrel monkey has therefore provided a new laboratory model, more convenient than the chimpanzee, for the study of these diseases.

We have no explanation for the susceptibility of the three species of New World monkeys to kuru, and the three species of these monkeys to Creutzfeldt–Jakob disease, whereas all the Old World monkeys studied have been resistant. There is still need for attempts to discover a broader host range for these slow virus infections in the hope that laboratory investigations may be further facilitated. In this regard it may be noted that our attempts to transmit both diseases to some thirty other mammalian and avian hosts by intracerebral inoculation of brain suspensions have been unsuccessful so far. But, in view of the finding of minimal kuru-like neuropathology in some inoculated animals dying without clinical neurological disease, we are involved in a further programme of blind passage in the species under suspicion.

Eckroade *et al*[6]. have successfully transmitted mink encephalopathy to the squirrel and stump-tailed monkey. This disease and scrapie are the two naturally occurring diseases

---

* Species used in transmission attempts were six New World monkeys: squirrel monkey (*Saimiri sciurens*), capuchin monkey (*Cebus* sp.), spider monkey (*Ateles geoffroyi*), woolly monkey (*Lagothrix lagothricha*), owl monkey (*Aotus trivirgatus*), and marmoset (*Callithrix* sp.); fifteen Old World monkeys: rhesus monkey (*Macaca mulata*), cynomolgous macaque (*M. irus*), stump-tailed macaque (*M.speciosa*), bonnet monkey (*M. radiata*), barbary ape (*M. sylvania*), pig-tailed macaque (*M. nemestrian*), African green monkey (*Cercopithecus aethiops* sp.), baboon (*Papio anubis*), langur (*Colobus* sp.), sooty mangabey (*Cercocebus atys*), patas (*Erythrocebus patas*), slow loris (*Nycticebus coucang*), talapoin (*Cercopithecus miopithecus*), tree shrew (*Ptilocercus lowii*), and bush baby (*Galago senegalensis*); two apes: chimpanzee (*Pan troglodytes troglodytes*) and gibbon ape (*Hylobatus lar*).

为了能达到在任何一个单独的灵长类动物圈养所中不可能达到的分离程度，我们使用了三个相隔很远的圈养所，分别位于加利福尼亚、路易斯安那和马里兰。迄今为止，另外几十只接种其他亚急性和慢性神经系统疾病患者脑悬液和其他器官悬液的黑猩猩和猴一直与每个聚居地内接种库鲁病和克雅氏病物质的动物在生活中密切接触。直到现在，在这些用于"对照"的动物中，没有一只染上神经系统疾病，这一结果进一步说明实验性库鲁病和克雅氏病是不会传染的。

松鼠猴、蜘蛛猴和卷尾猴以及黑猩猩是 23 种近似人类的灵长目动物中仅有的在接种人类库鲁病患者组织后能感染上库鲁病的物种。克雅氏病能直接由人类组织传染到松鼠猴和蜘蛛猴，就像它在较早时候能传染黑猩猩一样。此外，黑猩猩的实验性克雅氏病已能传染给绒毛猴（图 1）。除黑猩猩外，包括长臂猿在内的 16 种旧大陆猴以及另外 2 种新大陆猴 * 在脑内接种库鲁病或克雅氏病患者脑悬液和已感染这两种疾病的黑猩猩脑悬液后都没有产生临床疾病。因此，将人类的自然疾病和黑猩猩的实验性疾病成功地传染给松鼠猴就为研究这两种疾病提供了一类比黑猩猩更便利的新实验对象。

我们无法解释这 3 种新大陆猴对库鲁病的易感性，也不能解释新大陆猴中的 3 个物种对克雅氏病的易感性，而所有用于研究的旧大陆猴都具备抵抗力。我们仍需进一步尝试拓展这些缓慢病毒感染的寄主范围以期能使实验室研究更加便利。在这方面要说明的是：我们曾试图通过脑内接种脑悬液将这两种疾病传染给大约 30 只其他哺乳动物和鸟类寄主，但到目前为止尚未取得成功。然而，因为在一些无临床神经系统疾病死亡的接种动物中发现了极微小的库鲁病样神经病理学特征，所以我们还在继续进行可疑物种的盲目继代移植。

埃克罗德等人 [6] 已成功地将水貂脑病传染给了松鼠猴和短尾猴。这种病和羊瘙痒症是两类自然发生的疾病，我们将它们与库鲁病和克雅氏病归为一类并称之为亚

---

* 尝试用于传染的物种是 6 种新大陆猴：蜘蛛猴、卷尾猴、松鼠猴、绒毛猴、猫头鹰猴和绒猴；15 种旧大陆猴：恒河猴、食蟹猴、短尾猴、帽猴、地中海猕猴、豚尾猴、非洲绿猴、狒狒、叶猴、乌白眉猴、赤猴、懒猴、侏长尾猴、树鼩和灌丛婴猴；两种猿：黑猩猩和长臂猿。

which we have grouped with kuru and Creutzfeldt–Jakob disease and called subacute spongiform virus encephalopathies[7]. Scrapie virus has not yet produced clinical disease in a primate and, although sheep, goat and mouse strains of this virus have been inoculated into many species of monkeys and into the chimpanzee, all animals have remained well for periods of 3 to 5 yr. Reports of the transmission of scrapie to mink and of mink encephalopathy to goats and mice[8-10] reinforce the suspicion that the agents of these diseases are closely related. The crucial question of whether the viruses of kuru and Creutzfeldt–Jakob disease are related cannot be answered until serological identification of the viruses is possible and more is known of their properties. Whether one or both are related to the viruses of the two pathologically similar animal diseases remains to be determined.

(**230**, 588-591; 1971)

D. Carleton Gajdusek and Clarence J. Gibbs, jun.: National Institute of Neurological Diseases and Stroke, National Institutes of Health, Bethesda, Maryland.

Received December 10, 1970; revised February 9, 1971.

References:

1. Gajdusek, D. C., Gibbs, jun., C. J., and Alpers, M., *Nature*, **209**, 794 (1966).

2. Gajdusek, D. C., Gibbs, jun., C. J., and Alpers, M., *Science*, **155**, 212 (1967).

3. Gajdusek, D. C., Gibbs, jun., C. J., Asher, D. M., and David, E., *Science*, **162**, 693 (1968).

4. Gibbs, jun., C. J., Gajdusek, D. C., Asher, D. M., Alpers, M. P., Beck, E., Daniel, P. M., and Matthews, W. B., *Science*, **161**, 388 (1968).

5. Beck, E., Daniel, P. M., Matthews, W. B., Stevens, D. L., Alpers, M. P., Asher, D. M., Gajdusek, D. C., and Gibbs, jun., C. J., *Brain*, **92**, 699 (1969).

6. Eckroade, R. J., Zu Rhein, G. M., Marsh, R. F., and Hanson, R. P., *Science*, **169**, 1088 (1970).

7. Gibbs, jun., C. J., and Gajdusek, D. C., *Science*, **165**, 1023 (1969).

8. Marsh, R. F., thesis, Univ. Wisconsin (1968).

9. Zlotnik, I., and Barlow, R. M., *Vet. Rec.*, **81**, 55 (1967).

10. Barlow, R. M., and Rennie, J. C., *J. Comp. Pathol.*, **80**, 75 (1970).

急性海绵状脑病 [7]。迄今为止羊瘙痒症病毒还没有使灵长类动物产生临床疾病。尽管人们已经尝试过将这种病毒的绵羊、山羊和小鼠株接种到许多种猴子和黑猩猩中，但所有动物在 3 到 5 年内都很健康。关于羊瘙痒症传染给水貂以及水貂脑病传染给山羊和小鼠的报道 [8-10] 使我们更加怀疑在这些疾病的病原体之间是否存在着密切的关联。目前人们对库鲁病和克雅氏病的病毒是否相关这一重要问题还无法作答，除非可以通过血清学鉴定这些病毒并了解有关它们的更多特性。到底是其中一种还是两种都与这两种病理相似的动物疾病病毒相关，至今仍没有定论。

（李梅 翻译；袁峥 审稿）

Inhibition of Prostaglandin Synthesis as a Mechanism of Action for Aspirin-like Drugs

J. R. Vane

Editor's Note

Aspirin is one of the most widely used of synthetic drugs. It has been generally available since the beginning of the twentieth century, but for most of that time the basis for its effectiveness in treating pain, fever and other conditions has been unknown. In 1971, the physiologist John Vane published a mechanism for the action of aspirin and drugs like it which asserted that the drug functions by inhibiting the synthesis of the materials called prostaglandins—hormones produced in living cells which, in excess, can cause inflammation and of pain. Vane was awarded a Nobel Prize for his work in 1982 and was knighted in the same year.

THERE have been many attempts to link the anti-inflammatory actions of substances like aspirin with their ability to inhibit the activity of endogenous substances. Collier[1,2] calls aspirin an "anti-defensive" drug, and is largely responsible for studying its possible antagonism of the activity of endogenous substances such as kinins[3,4], slow reacting substance in anaphylaxis (SRS-A) (ref. 5), adenosine triphosphate[6], arachidonic acid[7,8] and prostaglandin $F_{2\alpha}$ (refs. 2 and 7).

A possible mechanism for some of the actions of anti-inflammatory acids was discovered by Piper and Vane[10] who found that lungs could release a previously undetected substance which, because of its action, they called "rabbit aorta contracting substance" or RCS. When isolated perfused lungs of sensitized guinea-pigs were challenged, RCS, along with histamine, SRS-A, prostaglandin E_2 (PGE_2) and prostaglandin $F_{2\alpha}$ ($PGF_{2\alpha}$) (ref. 11), were released. The release of RCS, which could also be provoked by bradykinin and SRS-A, was antagonized by aspirin-like drugs, as was the evoked bronchoconstriction. Because RCS has a short half-life (<5 min) it has not been isolated and its chemical nature is unknown. However, the finding that arachidonic acid, a prostaglandin precursor which induces bronchoconstriction, also releases RCS from perfused lungs[12] makes it possible that RCS is a prostaglandin or has a structure intermediate between arachidonic acid and PGE_2 or $PGF_{2\alpha}$. This release of RCS and the associated bronchoconstriction are also antagonized by aspirin-like drugs.

Prostaglandin release can often be equated with prostaglandin synthesis[13], for many tissues can be provoked to release more prostaglandin than they contain. The possibility arises, therefore, that anti-inflammatory substances such as aspirin inhibit the enzyme(s) which generate prostaglandins. The experiments described below were designed to test this possibility. Aspirin and indomethacin strongly inhibit prostaglandin synthesis; this may be the mechanism underlying some of their therapeutic actions.

490

抑制前列腺素合成是阿司匹林样药物的一种作用机制

文

编者按

阿司匹林是应用最广泛的合成药物之一。早在 20 世纪初，阿司匹林就已经得到了普遍的应用，但在那个时候的大部分时间里，人们并不了解阿司匹林治疗疼痛、发烧和其他一些病症的机理。1971 年，生理学家约翰·文提出了阿司匹林和阿司匹林样药物的一种作用机制，即认为这种药物的效用是通过抑制前列腺素的合成来实现的。前列腺素是活细胞产生的激素，过量时会引起炎症和疼痛。文因为这项工作在 1982 年获得了诺贝尔奖，并在同一年被授予英国爵士头衔。

为了把阿司匹林类物质的消炎作用与它们抑制内源性物质活性的能力联系起来，人们已经进行了很多次尝试。科利尔 [1,2] 称阿司匹林是一种"抗防御性"药物，他主要研究阿司匹林是否有可能拮抗激肽 [3,4]、过敏反应慢应物质（SRS-A）（参考文献 5）、三磷酸腺苷 [6]、花生四烯酸 [7,8] 和前列腺素 $F_{2\alpha}$（参考文献 2 和 7）等内源性物质的活性。

派珀和文 [10] 发现了消炎酸产生某些作用的一种可能机制。他们发现肺能释放出一种以前未检测到的物质。根据其生物活性，他们把这种物质称为"兔主动脉收缩物质"或简称为 RCS。当离体灌注的致敏豚鼠肺受到刺激时就会释放出 RCS，还有组胺、SRS-A、前列腺素 E_2（PGE_2）和前列腺素 $F_{2\alpha}$（$PGF_{2\alpha}$）（参考文献 11）。血管舒缓激肽和 SRS-A 也能激发 RCS 的释放，这种 RCS 的释放可以被阿司匹林样药物拮抗；阿司匹林样药物还可以拮抗激发产生的支气管收缩。因为 RCS 的半衰期很短（< 5 min），所以人们一直没有将它分离出来，也不知道它的化学性质。然而，人们发现有一种前列腺素的前体——花生四烯酸能诱导支气管收缩，并能激发灌注肺 [12] 释放 RCS，这说明 RCS 可能是一种前列腺素，或者具有介于花生四烯酸和 $PGE_2/PGF_{2\alpha}$ 之间的某种结构。由花生四烯酸诱导的 RCS 释放和与之相关联的支气管收缩都能被阿司匹林样药物所拮抗。

前列腺素的释放通常等同于前列腺素的合成 [13]，因为很多组织在受激时能够释放出的前列腺素多于本身所含有的量。因此，阿司匹林等消炎物质就有可能会抑制合成前列腺素的酶。下面的实验就是为验证这种可能性而设计的。阿司匹林和消炎痛强烈地抑制了前列腺素的合成，这或许就是它们发挥某些治疗作用的潜在机制。

Cell-free homogenates of guinea-pig lung synthesize prostaglandins E_2 and $F_{2\alpha}$ from arachidonic acid and the following is based on the procedure of Ånggård and Samuelsson[14]. Lungs from four adult guinea-pigs were excised rapidly and washed in ice-cold medium (a modified Bucher medium containing 20 mM KH_2PO_4, 72 mM K_2HPO_4, 27.6 mM nicotinamide, and 3.6 mM $MgCl_2$; pH 7.4). The lung tissue was homogenized in an MSE blade homogenizer at full speed for 1 min with a tissue: medium ratio of 1:4. The resultant suspension was transferred to a Potter–Elvehjem homogenizer and further homogenized by six up and down strokes of the "Teflon" pestle. The homogenate was then centrifuged at 900g for 15 min and the supernatant fluid was used. Fresh homogenates were made on the morning of each experiment.

Arachidonic acid was dissolved in ethanol (0.1 ml./mg) and diluted with a 0.2% (w/v) sodium carbonate solution (0.9 ml./mg), thus giving a solution of arachidonic acid of 1 mg/ml. This was further diluted to 200 μg/ml. with the modified Bucher medium.

Flasks containing 10 μg of arachidonic acid (0.05 ml.) and lung homogenate (1 ml.) were incubated aerobically at 37°C with gentle shaking for 30 min. A zero-time sample was taken. The reactions were stopped by heating the flasks in a boiling water bath until the protein in the sample coagulated (30–60 s) and then diluting five or ten-fold with 0.9% (w/v) saline. The samples were frozen if kept overnight, or kept on ice until assayed.

Prostaglandin-like activity was assayed[15] on isolated stomach strips[16] and colons[17] from the rat, superfused[18] in series with Krebs solution containing a mixture of antagonists[19] to make the assay more specific. Activity was assayed by bracketing the contractions induced by injections of diluted samples between smaller and larger contractions induced by the standards. In the dose range used (2–20 ng), PGE_2 contracted the stomach strips, but had no effect on the colons, whereas $PGF_{2\alpha}$ contracted the colons but had a much weaker effect than PGE_2 on the stomach strips. Activity was assayed on the rat colons in terms of $PGF_{2\alpha}$ and on the stomach strips in terms of PGE_2. But because $PGF_{2\alpha}$ had a small effect in the PGE_2 assay and the enzyme preparation also partially inactivated the PGE_2 generated[14], less emphasis has been placed on the PGE_2-like activity assayed in these experiments.

In some experiments, the reactions were terminated by acidifying to pH 3 with hydrochloric acid and extracting twice with ethyl acetate. The combined extracts were evaporated to dryness under reduced pressure. The residue was taken up in 0.2 ml. ethanol and chromatographed in the A I system[20] on thin-layer chromatography plates[21] with markers of 5 μg authentic prostaglandin E_2 and $F_{2\alpha}$. The strips on the developed chromatograms corresponding to the marker spots were separated, as was the area in between them. The rest of the chromatogram was divided into 1–3 cm strips. Each section was scraped into a test tube and shaken with 2 ml. Krebs solution. The supernatant was assayed on the rat colons and stomach strips.

豚鼠肺的无细胞匀浆能利用花生四烯酸合成前列腺素 E_2 和 $F_{2\alpha}$，以下是安加德和萨穆埃尔松 [14] 的实验步骤。先迅速剥离 4 只成年豚鼠的肺，然后用冰预冷的培养基（改良的布赫培养基，含 20 mM KH_2PO_4、72 mM K_2HPO_4、27.6 mM 烟酰胺、3.6 mM $MgCl_2$；pH 值 7.4）洗涤。将肺组织和布赫培养基按 1∶4 的比例在 MSE 叶片匀浆器中全速研磨 1 min 以匀浆肺组织。然后把得到的悬浮液转移到波特 – 埃尔维耶姆匀浆器中，再用"特氟隆"研棒上下研磨 6 次以进一步匀浆。将匀浆物在 900 g 下离心 15 min，取上清液备用。在每次实验当天的清晨制备新鲜匀浆。

将花生四烯酸溶解于乙醇（0.1 ml/mg）中，然后用 0.2%（重量体积比）的碳酸钠溶液（0.9 ml/mg）稀释，得到 1 mg/ml 的花生四烯酸溶液。然后再用改良的布赫培养基将上述溶液稀释到 200 µg/ml。

将含有 10 µg 花生四烯酸（0.05 ml）和肺组织匀浆物（1 ml）的瓶子在 37℃ 下的空气浴中温和振荡 30 min。保留一份零时间点时的样品。终止该反应的方法是：将瓶子在沸水浴中加热，直到样品中的蛋白质发生凝固（30 s ~ 60 s），然后用 0.9%（重量体积比）的生理盐水稀释 5 倍或 10 倍。样品在分析之前需要一直置于冰上，过夜的样品需要冷冻起来。

可以用从大鼠中分离的胃条 [16] 和结肠 [17] 来测定前列腺素样活性 [15]，并用含有混合拮抗物 [19] 的克雷布斯溶液连续灌流 [18] 以使检测结果更加准确。检测活性的方法是：将由注入稀释样品所诱导的收缩与一系列标准样品所诱导的较小或较大的收缩进行比较。在所用的剂量范围（2 ng ~ 20 ng）内，PGE_2 可使胃条收缩，但对结肠没有作用；而 $PGF_{2\alpha}$ 可使结肠收缩，但对胃条的收缩作用明显不如 PGE_2 对胃条的收缩作用强烈。因此 $PGF_{2\alpha}$ 的活性用大鼠结肠检测，PGE_2 的活性用胃条检测。但因为 $PGF_{2\alpha}$ 对 PGE_2 检测有少许影响，而且酶的制备过程也会使生成的 PGE_2 部分失活 [14]，所以在这类实验中，人们不太强调 PGE_2 样活性的检测。

在某些实验中，终止反应的方法是用盐酸酸化至 pH 值为 3，并用乙酸乙酯进行两次抽提。混合抽提物在减压条件下蒸发至干。残留物用 0.2 ml 乙醇溶解后，以 5 µg 明确的前列腺素 E_2 和 $F_{2\alpha}$ 为标准物在 A I 系统 [20] 的薄层色谱板上进行层析分离 [21]。在所得的层析图上，对应于标准物位置的条带以及它们之间的区域都被分离出去。将层析图的其余部分分成 1 cm ~ 3 cm 的小条带。将每一部分分别刮到一个试管中，然后加入 2 ml 克雷布斯溶液并摇匀。用上清液进行大鼠结肠和胃条的分析。

The zero-time samples contained (per ml.) 60–150 ng of $PGF_{2\alpha}$-like activity and 120–750 ng of PGE_2-like activity. This activity varied between samples of the same enzyme preparation by less than 5% and did not increase when the enzyme was incubated without arachidonic acid for 30 min. Incubation with arachidonic acid for 30 min increased $PGF_{2\alpha}$-like activity by 220–520 ng/ml. and PGE_2-like activity by 100–500 ng/ml., according to the enzyme preparation. Variation between different control samples of the same preparation was less than 7%.

Tests for Inhibition

Results were expressed as the generation of $PGF_{2\alpha}$ or PGE_2-like activity (30 min sample activity minus zero-time sample activity). To test for inhibition of prostaglandin synthesis, varying amounts of indomethacin, sodium acetylsalicylate, sodium salicylate or other substances were added to the incubation flasks in volumes of 0.1 ml. or less; inhibition of generation by a drug was expressed as the percentage inhibition of the control generation.

Indomethacin, sodium aspirin and sodium salicylate all inhibited the generation of $PGF_{2\alpha}$-like activity. The degree of inhibition varied from one enzyme preparation to another, but with any batch there was a linear relationship between percentage inhibition and log concentration of indomethacin or aspirin. The media used to dissolve the anti-inflammatory substances did not influence prostaglandin synthesis. The results from all experiments are shown in Fig. 1. The ID_{50} for indomethacin was 0.27 μg/ml. (0.75 μM), whereas that for aspirin was 6.3 μg/ml. (35 μM). Thus, on a weight basis, indomethacin was twenty-three times more potent than aspirin as an inhibitor of synthesis of $PGF_{2\alpha}$, and on a molar basis forty-seven times more potent. Sodium salicylate was less potent than aspirin as an inhibitor of synthesis of $PGF_{2\alpha}$-like activity and there was much more variation in the results (Fig. 1). Similar results were obtained when the activity of the samples was assayed on stomach strips in terms of PGE_2.

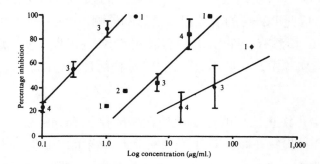

Fig. 1. Concentration (μg/ml.) of indomethacin (●), aspirin (■) and salicylate (◆) plotted on a log scale against the percentage inhibition of prostaglandin synthesis (assayed as $PGF_{2\alpha}$ on rat colons). The lines are those calculated for best fit. Numbers by the points indicate number of experiments. When three or more estimates were averaged, the standard error of the mean is shown.

零时间点的样品含有（每 ml）60 ng ~ 150 ng PGF$_{2\alpha}$ 样活性和 120 ng ~ 750 ng PGE$_2$ 样活性。同批次酶制剂不同样品之间的活性差异小于 5%；将酶在无花生四烯酸的条件下孵育 30 min 后，活性并没有增加。在有花生四烯酸的条件下孵育 30 min 后，根据酶制剂的不同情况 PGF$_{2\alpha}$ 样活性增加了 220 ng/ml ~ 520 ng/ml，PGE$_2$ 样活性增加了 100 ng/ml ~ 500 ng/ml。同批次酶制剂的不同对照样本之间的差异小于 7%。

抑制作用的检测

实验结果以产生的 PGF$_{2\alpha}$ 样活性或 PGE$_2$ 样活性（30 min 时间点的样品活性减去零时间点的样品活性）来表示。为了检测对前列腺素合成的抑制作用，我们将不同剂量的消炎痛、乙酰水杨酸钠、水杨酸钠或其他物质分别加入到孵育瓶中，体积不超过 0.1 ml。用相对于对照物的抑制百分率来表示药物的抑制作用。

消炎痛、阿司匹林钠和水杨酸钠都能抑制 PGF$_{2\alpha}$ 样活性的产生。不同批次酶制剂被抑制的程度不一样，但是在每一批实验中，抑制百分率与消炎痛或阿司匹林浓度的对数都呈线性关系。用于溶解消炎物质的溶剂不会影响前列腺素的合成。全部实验结果如图 1 所示。消炎痛的 ID$_{50}$（译者注：即抑制率达 50% 所需的药液浓度）为 0.27 μg/ml（0.75 μM），而阿司匹林的 ID$_{50}$ 为 6.3 μg/ml（35 μM）。因此，在重量相同的条件下，消炎痛抑制 PGF$_{2\alpha}$ 合成的效果是阿司匹林的 23 倍；而在摩尔数相同的条件下，消炎痛的抑制作用则为阿司匹林的 47 倍。水杨酸钠对 PGF$_{2\alpha}$ 样产物合成的抑制作用比阿司匹林弱，而且实验结果之间的差异也要大很多（图 1）。各个样品的 PGE$_2$ 胃条分析也给出了类似的结果。

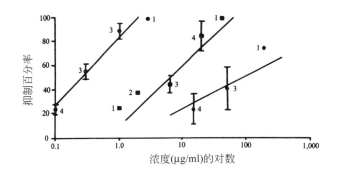

图 1. 消炎痛（●）、阿司匹林（■）和水杨酸盐（◆）的浓度（μg/ml）对数相对于前列腺素合成抑制百分率（基于用大鼠结肠对 PGF$_{2\alpha}$ 的活性分析）的曲线图。直线是通过计算得到的最佳拟合结果。标注的数字代表实验次数。当在三个或更多的估计值中取平均时，图中给出了平均标准误。

Hydrocortisone (50 µg/ml.) inhibited synthesis of $PGF_{2\alpha}$ and PGE_2-like activity by less than 20%; morphine (50 µg/ml.) or mepyramine (50 µg/ml.) had no effect. None of the drugs tested decreased the contractions of the assay tissues induced by PGE_2 or $PGF_{2\alpha}$; indeed there was sometimes a small potentiation of the responses.

Two samples (1.0 ml.) of enzyme were incubated without arachidonic acid: 1 µg $PGF_{2\alpha}$ was added to one and 1 µg PGE_2 to the other. After 30 min of incubation, the activity remaining was equivalent to 0.85 µg $PGF_{2\alpha}$ and 0.6 µg PGE_2.

In experiments with two different lung homogenates, samples containing arachidonic acid (10 µg/ml.) were incubated, extracted and the activity was separated by thin-layer chromatography in the A I system as described. In the first experiment, the zones corresponding to the prostaglandin markers showed substantial activity in the control 30 min incubation sample (160 ng $PGF_{2\alpha}$ and 50 ng PGE_2/ml. original sample), whereas the zero time sample showed much less (40 ng $PGF_{2\alpha}$ and 5 ng PGE_2/ml.). Similar samples incubated with indomethacin (5 µg/ml.) or aspirin (40 µg/ml.) showed little or no increase in $PGF_{2\alpha}$ or PGE_2-like activity over the zero-time sample.

In the second experiment, lower concentrations of indomethacin (1 µg/ml.) and aspirin (20 µg/ml.) were used. As Fig. 2 shows, indomethacin reduced the generation of activity in the $PGF_{2\alpha}$ zone to 25% of that in the control incubation but the activity in the PGE_2 zone was only reduced to 78%. With aspirin (20 µg/ml.) activity in the $PGF_{2\alpha}$ zone was reduced to about 56% and in the PGE_2 zone to 50%. Further identification of the PG-like activity in these experiments was considered unnecessary, for the enzyme system was the same as that used by Ånggård and Samuelsson[13], who identified PGE_2 and $PGF_{2\alpha}$ as the active products of the incubation.

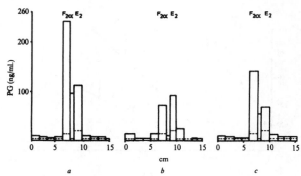

Fig. 2. Prostaglandin-like activity in samples of lung homogenate incubated for 30 min with arachidonic acid (10 µg/ml.), extracted with ethyl acetate and separated by thin-layer chromatography in the A I system. The chromatogram was divided into strips and the zone corresponding to the $PGF_{2\alpha}$ marker was assayed on rat colons in terms of $PGF_{2\alpha}$. The other zones were assayed on stomach strips in terms of PGE_2. The dotted lines represent the amount of PG-like activity in the sample at the start of the incubation. Indomethacin (1 µg/ml.) and aspirin (20 µg/ml.) reduced the generation of $PGF_{2\alpha}$ and PGE_2. a, Control; b, indomethacin; c, aspirin.

氢化可的松（50 µg/ml）对合成 $PGF_{2\alpha}$ 和 PGE_2 样产物的抑制仅能使其活性减少不到 20%；吗啡（50 µg/ml）或美吡拉敏（50 µg/ml）没有抑制作用。这些被检测的药物都不能降低由 PGE_2 和 $PGF_{2\alpha}$ 诱导的组织收缩，有时收缩反而会轻微增强。

两份酶样品（1.0 ml），一份加入 1 µg $PGF_{2\alpha}$，另一份加入 1 µg PGE_2，然后在无花生四烯酸的条件下孵育。孵育 30 min 后，$PGF_{2\alpha}$ 和 PGE_2 的剩余活性分别相当于 0.85 µg 的 $PGF_{2\alpha}$ 和 0.6 µg 的 PGE_2。

在两个不同的肺组织匀浆实验中，样品在有花生四烯酸（10 µg/ml）的条件下孵育，然后萃取，并用前面提到过的 A I 系统薄层层析法分离活性物质。在第一个实验中，孵育了 30 min 的对照样品在与前列腺素标准物相对应的区域中（原始样品：160 ng $PGF_{2\alpha}$/ml，50 ng PGE_2/ml）显示出很强的活性，而零时间点样品的活性则要小很多（40 ng $PGF_{2\alpha}$/ml，5 ng PGE_2/ml）。同样的样品与消炎痛（5 µg/ml）或阿司匹林（40 µg/ml）共孵育后，$PGF_{2\alpha}$ 和 PGE_2 样活性与零时间点样品的活性相比增加很少或者没有增加。

在第二个实验中，我们采用了更低浓度的消炎痛（1 µg/ml）和阿司匹林（20 µg/ml）。如图 2 所示，跟对照的孵育过程相比，消炎痛使 $PGF_{2\alpha}$ 区域的活性减少到 25%，但 PGE_2 区的活性却只下降至 78%。阿司匹林（20 µg/ml）使 $PGF_{2\alpha}$ 区的活性降低到约 56%，使 PGE_2 区的活性降低至 50%。没有必要对这些实验中的 PG 样活性进行进一步的鉴定，因为所用的酶系统与安加德和萨穆埃尔松[13]的酶系统没有区别，而安加德和萨穆埃尔松已经确认这种酶系统的孵育活性产物就是 PGE_2 和 $PGF_{2\alpha}$。

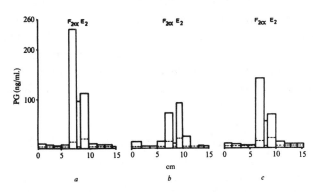

图 2. 经花生四烯酸（10 µg/ml）孵育 30 min、乙酸乙酯萃取和 A I 系统薄层层析分离的肺匀浆样品中的前列腺素样活性。层析图被划分为不同的条带，用大鼠结肠检测与 $PGF_{2\alpha}$ 标准物相对应的区域的 $PGF_{2\alpha}$ 活性。用胃条检测其他区域的 PGE_2 活性。虚线表示样品在孵育开始时的 PG 样活性。消炎痛（1 µg/ml）和阿司匹林（20 µg/ml）抑制了 $PGF_{2\alpha}$ 和 PGE_2 的合成。a, 对照；b, 消炎痛；c, 阿司匹林。

The results show that the three anti-inflammatory acids tested inhibit the synthesis of prostaglandins. It is not yet known how the inhibition is brought about. If it is by competition with arachidonic acid for the active site of the enzyme, this might explain why all of these anti-inflammatory substances contain an acidic group. It would also explain why hydrocortisone, an anti-inflammatory substance of a different type, has little or no inhibitory action against the prostaglandin synthesizing enzyme(s).

Correlation with Therapeutic Actions

Anti-inflammatory acids have three principal actions; antipyretic, anti-inflammatory and analgesic. They also antagonize bronchoconstriction and some other smooth muscle contractions induced by substances such as bradykinin[1] and have a tendency to induce gastro-intestinal irritation. Can any of these actions be explained by a direct inhibition of prostaglandin synthesis?

First, we consider antipyretic action. When injected into the third ventricle of cats, PGE_1 induces fever[22,23]. It is the most potent substance yet found with this action, being much more active than 5-hydroxytryptamine, PGE_2 or $PGF_{2\alpha}$; $PGF_{2\alpha}$ has little pyretic activity. The antipyretic substance 4-acetamidophenol does not antagonize fever induced by PGE_1. These facts are compatible with the idea that the rise in temperature in a fever is induced by synthesis and release of RCS or of a known prostaglandin such as PGE_1, either in the temperature-regulating area of the hypothalamus or at a place from which it can reach this area. Anti-inflammatory substances might reduce temperature in a fever by preventing such prostaglandin synthesis. A necessary corollary of such a mechanism of action is that a prostaglandin whose synthesis is inhibited by these drugs does not regulate normal body temperature, which is unaffected by antipyretic drugs.

Anti-inflammatory action can also be explained. An E-type prostaglandin is found in exudate[24] during the secondary phase of inflammation induced by carageenin in the rat. Prostaglandins, identified as a mixture of PGE_1, PGE_2, $PGF_{1\alpha}$ and $PGF_{2\alpha}$, have also been isolated from fluid perfusing the skin of patients with allergic eczema[25]. In rat or man, PGE_1 or PGE_2 injected intradermally induces an inflammatory response[26]. Thus abolition of prostaglandin synthesis by this group of acidic substances may be a basis for their anti-inflammatory action.

Analgesic action is less easily explained. Although PGE_1 and PGE_2 and larger doses of $PGF_{1\alpha}$ and $PGF_{2\alpha}$ induce a weal and flare response similar to that caused by histamine release when injected intradermally in man[26], the only subjective effect reported was a sensation of warmth and a slight itching. It is unlikely, therefore, that any of these prostaglandins mediate skin pain. Thus, unless another untested prostaglandin or RCS is involved, there seems no link between a peripheral analgesic action of the anti-inflammatory acids and inhibition of prostaglandin synthesis.

Prostaglandin infusions, however, induce headache[27], so the relief by aspirin-like drugs

结果表明：这三种消炎酸都能抑制前列腺素的合成。但目前尚不清楚这种抑制作用是如何产生的。如果作用机制是通过与花生四烯酸竞争酶的活性位点，那么就有可能解释为什么这些消炎物质都含有一个酸性基团，并且还可以解释为什么另一类消炎物质——氢化可的松就几乎或者完全不具有竞争前列腺素合成酶的能力。

与治疗作用的关系

消炎酸有三种基本功能：退热、消炎和止痛。它们也可以抑制支气管收缩以及其他一些由血管舒缓激肽 [1] 等物质诱导的平滑肌收缩，并有可能刺激胃肠。这些效应是否都能用直接抑制前列腺素的合成来解释呢？

首先，我们来看退热作用。当 PGE_1 被注射到猫的第三脑室时，会引起发热 [22,23]。在人们已知的所有物质中，PGE_1 是具有这种功效的最有效的物质，它比 5- 羟色胺、PGE_2 和 $PGF_{2\alpha}$ 的活性高出很多；$PGF_{2\alpha}$ 基本上没有引起发热的功效。而可以退热的物质 4- 乙酰氨基酚不能缓解由 PGE_1 所引起的发热。这些事实与以下观点一致，即认为在下丘脑的温度调节区域或者在其他可以通向该区的地方存在着 RCS 或某种已知前列腺素，如 PGE_1 等，的合成和释放过程，发烧时的体温升高就是由这种合成和释放过程引起的。消炎类物质通过抑制前列腺素的合成或许可以起到退烧的作用。由这种作用机制必然可以推出：其合成可被这些药物抑制的前列腺素不参与调节身体的正常体温，因为正常体温不受退热药物的影响。

消炎作用也能得到解释。在用角叉菜胶诱导大鼠发炎的第二阶段，我们在分泌物 [24] 中发现了一种 E 型前列腺素。分离过敏性湿疹患者皮肤中的化脓液体，我们得到了含有 PGE_1、PGE_2、$PGF_{1\alpha}$ 和 $PGF_{2\alpha}$ 的前列腺素混合物 [25]。皮内注射 PGE_1 或 PGE_2 通常会引起大鼠或人类的炎症反应 [26]。因此，这组酸性物质对前列腺素合成的抑制可能就是它们能起到抗炎作用的基础。

止痛作用不太容易得到解释。虽然由 PGE_1 和 PGE_2 以及较大剂量的 $PGF_{1\alpha}$ 和 $PGF_{2\alpha}$ 可以诱导类似于给人皮内注射组胺释放剂时由组胺释放引发的风团和潮红反应 [26]，但被报道的唯一主观反应仅仅是感到温暖和轻微的瘙痒。由此可见，这些前列腺素能传递皮肤疼痛的可能性都不太大。所以除非还有另外一种未检测出来的前列腺素或 RCS，否则很难在消炎酸的外周止痛作用与前列腺素的合成被抑制之间建立联系。

注射前列腺素会诱发头痛 [27]，因此阿司匹林样药物对此类疼痛（或因发炎引起

of such pain (or of pain induced by inflammation) may be explained by an inhibition of prostaglandin synthesis. Collier[28] develops further the possible link between prostaglandin production and pain.

The anti-bronchoconstrictor action may also be due to inhibition of the synthetic pathway for prostaglandins. We have already shown that challenge of sensitized guinea-pig lungs or injection of bradykinin or partially purified SRS-A into unsensitized lungs induces the release of RCS, PGE_2 and $PGF_{2\alpha}$ (refs. 10 and 11). Because the release of RCS was abolished by anti-inflammatory acids, as was the bronchoconstriction induced by bradykinin and SRS-A (ref. 1), we postulated that RCS may be the mediator of the bronchoconstrictor response. Vargaftig and Dao[12] have shown that arachidonic acid also releases RCS and that the release is inhibited by aspirin-like drugs and we have confirmed this (unpublished work). At the time of our first publication on RCS (ref. 10), we were unsure of the contribution that this substance made to the contractions of the tissues used to assay simultaneously the release of prostaglandins. We have assessed this contribution recently; whereas RCS contracts rat stomach strip, it has much less effect on chick rectum or rat colon (Piper and Vane, unpublished work). Re-examination of the tracings from these experiments shows that aspirin-like drugs not only prevented RCS release but also reduced activity on chick rectum and rat colon, indicative of a reduced output of PGE_2 and $PGF_{2\alpha}$ (see, for instance, Fig. 7 in Piper and Vane[10]).

Prostaglandin $F_{2\alpha}$ is bronchoconstrictor[5,29], so the antagonism of bronchoconstriction induced by bradykinin, SRS-A, arachidonic acid and so on may be due to antagonism of release (which probably means synthesis) of RCS or of synthesis and release of $PGF_{2\alpha}$ or both. The ratio of activities against bradykinin-induced bronchoconstriction (indomethacin 2; aspirin 1, salicylic acid 0.03; ref. 1) certainly fits with the relative lack of activity of sodium salicylate against the formation of $PGF_{2\alpha}$. Until RCS can be stabilized or generated in a pure form, however, its contribution to the process of anaphylaxis and to bronchoconstriction induced by anaphylactic mediators cannot be assessed.

Side Effects

The aspirin-like drugs all induce gastro-intestinal symptoms which may include peptic ulceration[30]. Prostaglandin synthesis and release can be provoked by many different forms of mechanical stimulation, including gentle massage[13]. Contractions of the gastro-intestinal tract churn the contents. It is possible, therefore, that the associated mechanical stimulation of the mucosa leads to synthesis intramurally of a prostaglandin which in some way protects the mucosa from damage. Inhibition of prostaglandin synthesis by aspirin-like drugs would remove this protective mechanism.

Whether inhibition of prostaglandin synthesis accounts for all the activities of the anti-inflammatory acids remains to be elucidated. Clearly, the blood concentrations[31] of indomethacin in man after an oral dose of 200 mg (7.5 µg/ml. at peak; 3.2 µg/ml. after 4 h), even when 90% binding[31] to plasma proteins is allowed for, are higher than concentrations needed to inhibit prostaglandin synthesis in these experiments.

的疼痛）的缓解也许可以用抑制前列腺素的合成来解释。科利尔[28] 对前列腺素合成与疼痛之间的可能联系进行了进一步的阐述。

抗支气管收缩作用可能也是由前列腺素的合成通路被阻抑引起的。我们已经证明，刺激致敏豚鼠肺或者给脱敏的豚鼠肺注射血管舒缓激肽或部分纯化的 SRS-A 会诱发 RCS、PGE_2 和 $PGF_{2\alpha}$ 的释放(参考文献 10 和 11)。由于消炎酸能阻止 RCS 的释放，也能阻止由血管舒缓激肽和 SRS-A 诱导的支气管收缩（参考文献 1），因此我们推测 RCS 有可能就是支气管收缩反应的传递者。瓦尔加夫季格和达奥[12] 曾指出：花生四烯酸也能释放出 RCS，而阿司匹林样药物会阻止 RCS 的释放。并且我们的实验也证实了这一点(尚未发表的研究结果)。在第一次发表有关 RCS 的论文(参考文献 10)时，我们还不能确定这种物质对能用于同步检测前列腺素释放量的组织的收缩有什么贡献。最近我们对这方面的贡献进行了分析，发现 RCS 虽然能使大鼠胃条收缩，但是对小鸡直肠或大鼠结肠的收缩作用非常有限（派珀和文，尚未发表的研究结果）。再次检查这些实验中的细节，我们发现阿司匹林样药物不仅阻止了 RCS 的释放，而且降低了小鸡直肠和大鼠结肠的活性，这说明 PGE_2 和 $PGF_{2\alpha}$ 的排出量下降了（比如，见派珀和文 [10] 文章中的图 7）。

前列腺素 $F_{2\alpha}$ 是支气管收缩剂 [5,29]，因此阿司匹林样药物对由血管舒缓激肽、SRS-A 和花生四烯酸等诱导产生的支气管收缩的抑制可能是因为其抑制了 RCS 的释放（很可能就是合成），或者抑制了 $PGF_{2\alpha}$ 的合成和释放，或者兼而有之。几种药物对由血管舒缓激肽诱导产生的支气管收缩的抑制活性之比（消炎痛为 2；阿司匹林为 1；水杨酸为 0.03；参考文献 1）显然与水杨酸钠相对缺乏抑制 $PGF_{2\alpha}$ 合成的活性相吻合。除非 RCS 可以稳定存在或以纯净形式产生，否则很难评估它在由过敏性物质引起的过敏和支气管收缩过程中的作用。

副 作 用

所有阿司匹林样药物都会引起包括消化性溃疡在内的胃肠道症状[30]。有很多种不同形式的机械刺激，如轻轻地按摩[13]，可以激发前列腺素的合成和释放。胃肠道的收缩使其内容物受到搅动。因此，与黏膜相关联的机械刺激可能会导致壁内前列腺素的合成，从而在某种程度上保护了黏膜使其免受伤害。而阿司匹林样药物对前列腺素合成的抑制会使这种保护机制失效。

用抑制前列腺素的合成能否解释消炎酸的所有功效还有待于进一步阐明。显然，在成人口服 200 mg 消炎痛之后，即使将消炎痛与血浆蛋白的结合率[31] 放宽至 90%，人体血液中的消炎痛浓度[31]（峰值为 7.5 μg/ml；4 h 后为 3.2 μg/ml）依然高于实验中抑制前列腺素合成所需的浓度。

One fact that needs explanation is the apparent lack of activity of sodium salicylate as an inhibitor of prostaglandin synthesis, for this substance has about the same potency as aspirin in antipyretic and anti-inflammatory tests[1]. One possibility is that salicylate is more potent as an inhibitor of synthesis of PGE_1 from dihomo-γ-linolenic acid than it is of the synthesis of PGE_2 from arachidonic acid. Certainly, with the probability of a series of iso-enzymes synthesizing from different substrates various prostaglandins (perhaps including RCS) with widely different pharmacological properties, the number of degrees of freedom is more than sufficient to allow explanation of the variations in potencies and properties within the whole group of aspirin-like substances.

There are several other implications of these results, some of which are listed below. First, inhibition of prostaglandin synthesis, perhaps using a more active enzyme preparation[32] than the one used here, together with different substrates, may provide a simple and rapid primary screen for anti-inflammatory drugs of the indomethacin type. Second, one of the few simple *in vitro* antagonisms shown by aspirin-like drugs is against arachidonic acid-induced contractions of some isolated smooth muscle preparations such as the guinea-pig ileum[7]. This suggests that some of the contractile actions of arachidonic acid may be brought about by an intramural synthesis of a prostaglandin. This problem deserves attention, as does the possibility that bioassay of prostaglandins may be improved by addition of a synthesis inhibitor, such as indomethacin, to the fluid bathing the assay tissues.

There is also the possibility that use of anti-inflammatory acids could be extended to ameliorate conditions thought to be brought about by prostaglandin release. For example, some evidence[33] suggests that release of $PGF_{2\alpha}$ occurs during labour. It may therefore be worthwhile testing an anti-inflammatory acid as an inhibitor of unwanted abortion or miscarriage. It would also be interesting to know whether these drugs reduce the efficacy of the intra-uterine device which may work as a contraceptive through prostaglandin release[34].

These results show that biologists now have a simple means of preventing prostaglandin synthesis and release and thereby assessing the functions of prostaglandins in individual cells or tissues, or in the body as a whole. The conclusions described here are supported by the results discussed in the next two articles[35,36].

I thank Mr. N. Pitman for technical help and the Wellcome Trust and Medical Research Council for grants.

(*Nature New Biology,* **231**, 232-235; 1971)

J. R. Vane: Department of Pharmacology, Institute of Basic Medical Sciences, Royal College of Surgeons of England, Lincoln's Inn Fields, London WC2A 3PN.

Received May 6, 1971.

需要解释的一个事实是：虽然水杨酸钠所具有的退热和消炎功效[1]与阿司匹林相差无几，但它对前列腺素合成的抑制作用非常有限。一种可能性是，水杨酸盐对合成二高 $-\gamma-$ 亚麻酸来源的 PGE_1 的抑制作用要比对合成花生四烯酸来源的 PGE_2 的抑制作用更强烈。当然，由于一系列同工酶在不同底物上有可能会合成药理学性质迥然不同的前列腺素（可能包括 RCS），因此人们在解释所有阿司匹林样物质的不同药效和性能时有充分的自由度。

这些结果还隐含着其他几种可能，以下列出了其中一部分。首先，或许可以将对前列腺素合成的抑制作为一种初步筛选消炎痛类消炎药的简单而快捷的方法，这也许需要采用一种比现在所用的酶制剂活性更高的酶制剂[32]并配合不同的底物。第二，阿司匹林样药物在体外表现出的其中一种拮抗作用就是拮抗由花生四烯酸诱导的某些离体平滑肌样品的收缩，比如豚鼠回肠等[7]。这表明一些花生四烯酸诱导的收缩反应可能源自内壁中某种前列腺素的合成过程。这一问题值得重视。另外，也许可以通过在待测组织的液体浴中加入一种合成抑制剂（例如消炎痛）来提高前列腺素的生物鉴定水平，这种可能性也值得引起注意。

另一种可能是：消炎酸还可以用来缓解由前列腺素释放引起的症状。例如，一些证据[33]表明在分娩过程中会释放出 $PGF_{2\alpha}$。因此，检测消炎酸对意外流产或早产的抑制作用或许是一件有意义的事情。而且了解这类药物是否会降低依靠前列腺素的释放[34]而起避孕作用的宫内节育器的有效性也很有意义。

这些研究结果表明：生物学家们现在已经掌握了一种能抑制前列腺素合成和释放的简单方法，因而能够分析前列腺素在单个细胞、组织或者整个机体中的功能。后面两篇文章[35,36]所讨论的结果支持了本文中的这些结论。

感谢皮特曼先生在技术上给予我的支持，以及维康基金会和医学研究理事会在研究经费上给予的资助。

（彭丽霞 翻译；孙军 莫韫 审稿）

References:

1. Collier, H. O. J., *Adv. Pharmacol. Chemother.*, 7, 333 (1969).

2. Collier, H. O. J., *Nature*, 223, 35 (1969).

3. Collier, H. O. J., and Shorley, P. G., *Brit. J. Pharmacol. Chemother.*, 15, 601 (1960).

4. Collier, H. O. J., and Shorley, P. G., *Brit. J. Pharmacol. Chemother.*, 20, 345 (1963).

5. Berry, P. A., and Collier, H. O. J., *Brit. J. Pharmacol. Chemother.*, 23, 201 (1964).

6. Collier, H. O. J., James, G. W. L., and Schneider, C., *Nature*, 212, 411 (1966).

7. Jacques, R., *Helv. Physiol. Pharmacol. Acta*, 23, 156 (1965).

8. Berry, P. A., thesis, Council for National Academic Awards, London, 91 (1966).

9. Collier, H. O. J., and Sweatman, J. F., *Nature*, 219, 864 (1968).

10. Piper, P. J., and Vane, J. R., *Nature*, 223, 29 (1969).

11. Piper, P. J., and Vane, J. R., in *Prostaglandins, Peptides and Amines* (edit. by Mantegazza, P., and Horton, E. W.), 15 (Academic Press, London, 1969).

12. Vargaftig, B. B., and Dao, N., *Pharmacology* (in the press).

13. Piper, P. J., and Vane, J. R., in *Prostaglandins* (edit. by Ramwell, P., and Shaw, J.) (NY Acad. Sci., in the press, 1971).

14. Ånggård, E., and Samuelsson, B., *J. Biol. Chem.*, 240, 3518 (1965).

15. Ferreira, S. H., and Vane, J. R., *Nature*, 216, 868 (1967).

16. Vane, J. R., *Brit. J. Pharmacol. Chemother.*, 12, 344 (1957).

17. Regoli, D., and Vane, J. R., *Brit. J. Pharmacol. Chemother.*, 23, 351 (1964).

18. Gaddum, J. H., *Brit. J. Pharmacol. Chemother.*, 8, 321 (1953).

19. Gilmore, N., Vane, J. R., and Wyllie, J. H., *Nature*, 218, 1135 (1968).

20. Gréen, K., and Samuelsson, B., *J. Lipid Res.*, 5, 117 (1964).

21. Willis, A. L., *Brit. J. Pharmacol.*, 40, 583P (1970).

22. Milton, A. S., and Wendlandt, S. J., *J. Physiol.*, 207, 76P (1970).

23. Feldberg, W., and Saxena, P. N., *J. Physiol.* (in the press, 1971).

24. Willis, A. L., in *Prostaglandins, Peptides and Amines* (edit. by Mantegazza, P., and Horton, E. W.), 31 (Academic Press, London, 1969).

25. Greaves, M. W., Søndergaard, J., and McDonald-Gibson, W., *Brit. Med. J.*, 2, 258 (1971).

26. Crunkhorn, P., and Willis, A. L., *Brit. J. Pharmacol.*, 41, 49 (1971).

27. Bergström, S., Carlson, L. A., and Weeks, J. R., *Pharmacol. Rev.*, 20, 1 (1968).

28. Collier, H. O. J., *Nature* (in the press).

29. James, G. W. L., *J. Pharm. Pharmacol.*, 21, 379 (1969).

30. Goodman, L. S., and Gilman, A., *The Pharmacological Basis of Therapeutics*, fourth ed. (Collier-Macmillan, London, 1970).

31. Hucker, H. B., Zacchei, A. G., Cox, S. V., Brodie, D. A., and Cantwell, N. H. R., *J. Pharmac. Exp. Therap.*, 153, 237 (1966).

32. Nugteren, D. H., Beerhuis, R. K., and Van Dorp, D. A., *Recl. Trav. Chim. Pays-Bas Belg.*, 85, 405 (1966).

33. Karim, S. M. M., *Brit. Med. J.*, 4, 618 (1968).

34. Chaudhuri, G., *Lancet*, i, 480 (1971).

35. Smith, J. B., and Willis, A. L., *Nature New Biology*, 231, 235 (1971).

36. Ferreira, S. H., Moncada, S., and Vane, J. R., *Nature New Biology*, 231, 237 (1971).

Aspirin Selectively Inhibits Prostaglandin Production in Human Platelets

J. B. Smith and A. L. Willis

Editor's Note

In this, one of a trio of papers published back-to-back, pharmacologists J. B. Smith and A. L. Willis suggest a mechanism of action for aspirin. They show that platelets in the blood of volunteers who have taken aspirin can no longer produce prostaglandins, complex chemicals thought to regulate inflammation. Similar effects are shown for two other anti-inflammatory drugs, sodium salicylate and indomethacin, leading them to suggest that the anti-inflammatory effects of all three drugs occur by inhibition of prostaglandin production.

ASPIRIN reduces the adhesiveness to glass of platelets in citrated plasma[1], reduces platelet aggregation by washed connective tissue fragments[2], and inhibits the second wave of aggregation induced by ADP, adrenaline and thrombin[3-5]. Aspirin also inhibits the release from washed pig or human platelets of permeability factors which differ from 5-hydroxytrypt amine and histamine and cause contraction of the guinea-pig ileum[6]. One of these factors could be prostaglandin E_2 (PGE_2). This compound increases vascular permeability[7,8] and contracts guinea-pig ileum[9]. When washed human platelets are incubated with thrombin it is formed and appears extracellularly, together with prostaglandin $F_{2\alpha}$ ($PGF_{2\alpha}$)[10].

The following experiments, which were initiated independently of those described in the accompanying two articles[11,12], were designed to test whether aspirin and other anti-inflammatory drugs inhibit the production of prostaglandins, which may be important mediators of inflammation.

The effects of aspirin and other drugs were investigated on the production of prostaglandins and "the release reaction" induced by thrombin, that is, release of 5-hydroxytryptamine, adenine nucleotide and lysosomal enzymes[13]. We looked for the release of a lysosomal phospholipase A (ref. 14) because the production of PGE_2 and $PGF_{2\alpha}$ in tissues is thought to be brought about by cyclization of arachidonic acid liberated by the action of phospholipase A (ref. 15) and the incorporation of molecular oxygen[16,17].

Platelet-rich plasma was obtained from healthy donors, who had not taken aspirin for some days previously, by centrifuging blood containing 5.8 mM EDTA at $900g$ for 15 min at $18°C–20°C$. For *in vitro* experiments the plasma was incubated with 0.5 µM 3^1-^{14}C-5-hydroxytryptamine creatinine sulphate (58 Ci/mol) for 1 h at $18°C–20°C$, thereby incorporating radioactivity into the platelets[18]. The platelets were washed[19] once and

阿司匹林选择性抑制人血小板中前列腺素的合成

史密斯，威利斯

编者按

这篇文章是三篇连续发表的相关论文中的一篇，作者是药理学家史密斯和威利斯，他们在本文中提出了阿司匹林的一种作用机制。他们指出，在服用阿司匹林的志愿者的血小板中不再能合成前列腺素，前列腺素被认为是可调节炎症反应的复杂化学物质。其他两种消炎药——水杨酸钠和消炎痛也能产生类似的效应。这使他们提出上述三种药物的消炎作用都源于对前列腺素合成的抑制。

阿司匹林能降低柠檬酸钠血浆中血小板对玻璃的黏附性[1]，减少由清洗过的结缔组织碎片造成的血小板聚集[2]，并能抑制由二磷酸腺苷、肾上腺素和凝血酶诱导的血小板再次聚集[3-5]。阿司匹林也能抑制一些与5-羟色胺和组胺不同但能引起豚鼠回肠收缩的渗透性因子从清洗过的猪血小板或人血小板中释放出来[6]。前列腺素 E_2（PGE_2）可能是其中的一个因子。这种化合物能增加血管的渗透性[7,8]，并能使豚鼠的回肠收缩[9]。当清洗过的人血小板与凝血酶共同孵育时，形成的前列腺素 E_2 和前列腺素 $F_{2\alpha}$（$PGF_{2\alpha}$）出现在了细胞外[10]。

前列腺素有可能是炎症的重要介质，为了验证阿司匹林和其他消炎药能否抑制前列腺素的合成，我们设计了如下几个实验，这些实验与前一篇和后一篇文章中[11,12]描述的实验是独立展开的。

我们研究了阿司匹林及其他药物对前列腺素合成和由凝血酶诱导的"释放反应"（即5-羟色胺、腺嘌呤核苷酸和溶酶体酶的释放[13]）的作用效果。一般认为，组织中的 PGE_2 和 $PGF_{2\alpha}$ 是在磷脂酶 A 作用下（参考文献 15）释放的花生四烯酸发生环化并结合分子氧而形成的[16,17]，因此我们检测了溶酶体磷脂酶 A 的释放情况（参考文献 14）。

取数天内未服用过阿司匹林的健康供者的血液，在 18℃～20℃、相对离心力为 $900g$ 下将含 5.8 mM 乙二胺四乙酸的这些血液离心 15 min，即得到富含血小板的血浆。在体外实验中，将血浆和 0.5 μM 3^1-^{14}C-5-羟色胺肌酐硫酸盐（58 Ci/mol）于 18℃～20℃下孵育 1 h 从而使放射性掺入到血小板中[18]。对血小板进行一次清洗[19]，然后使其重新悬浮于缓冲盐溶液（134 mM NaCl；5 mM D-葡萄糖；15 mM 三羟甲

resuspended in a buffered saline solution (134 mM NaCl; 5 mM D-glucose; 15 mM Tris-HCl, pH 7.4). Portions (6 ml.) of this suspension, containing 5–20×10^8 platelets/ml., were shaken at 37°C for 5 min with 0.06 ml. thrombin (bovine thrombin, Leo Laboratories, Hayes, Middlesex; 500 NIH units/ml. buffered saline), 2 min after the addition of solutions of various drugs (0.001–0.120 ml.). These samples were then cooled to 0°C and centrifuged at $2,400\,g$ for 10 min. A portion (4.5 ml.) of the supernatant was adjusted to pH 2.5–3.0, extracted for prostaglandins with ethyl acetate and, after drying under reduced pressure, the prostaglandins were bioassayed as described before[20]. The rest of the supernatant was assayed for its content of ^{14}C-5-hydroxytrypt-amine[18], β-N-acetyl glucosamidase[21] and phospholipase A$_1$ (ref. 22) (pH optimum 4.0).

Aspirin considerably reduced the production of prostaglandins by platelets although it had no effect on the release of 5-hydroxytryptamine, β-N-acetyl glucosamidase or phospholipase A$_1$ (Table 1). The dose of aspirin causing a 50% inhibition of the production of prostaglandins was 0.3 μg/ml. (1.7 μM). In two experiments indomethacin was about ten times more potent than aspirin, whereas sodium salicylate was about ten times less potent. Hydrocortisone (100 μg/ml.) had no effect. Aspirin (10 and 100 μg/ml.) did not interfere with the extraction and assay of prostaglandins nor did it increase the small amounts of prostaglandin which remained in the platelet pellet[10].

Table 1. Effects of Aspirin Added to Resuspended Platelets on the Thrombin-induced Formation of Prostaglandins and on "the Release Reaction"

Aspirin addition and concentration (μg/ml.)	Second addition and concentration	^{14}C-5-HT release %	Activity/ml. supernate		
			β-N-Acetyl glucosamidase (mU)	Phospholipase A$_1$ (mU)	PG* (ng)
—	—	4.7	0.44	0.13	ND
—	PGE$_2$ 20 ng/ml.	4.9	0.37	0.06	15
—	Thrombin 5 U/ml.	77.7	2.53	1.12	53
0.01	Thrombin 5 U/ml.	74.1	2.55	0.91	48
0.10	Thrombin 5 U/ml.	75.5	2.55	0.98	35
1.00	Thrombin 5 U/ml.	73.2	2.32	0.91	18
10.00	Thrombin 5 U/ml.	74.7	2.77	1.01	7

*Assayed as PGE$_2$ on the rat fundus strip.
ND, Not detectable (less than 0.1 ng PGE$_2$/ml.).
There were 4.78×10^8 platelets/ml. of suspension and the platelets contained 3.2 mU β-N-acetyl glucosaminidase per 10^8 cells. Phospholipase A$_1$ was not assayed in platelets because endogenous substrate may effect the results (Silver, Smith and Webster, unpublished observations).

The effects of aspirin given to three volunteers were then examined. Blood was taken before and 1 h after taking two tablets (600 mg) of aspirin. Platelets were washed and re-suspended as soon as the second sample of platelet-rich plasma had been obtained. The two suspensions from each donor were incubated simultaneously with 5 U/ml. thrombin

基氨基甲烷盐酸盐，pH 值 7.4）中。将这个每 ml 含 5×10^8 个 ~ 20×10^8 个血小板的悬液分成若干份（每份 6 ml），与 0.06 ml 凝血酶（牛凝血酶，由米德尔塞克斯郡海斯的利奥实验室提供；每 ml 缓冲盐水中含 500 NIH 单位凝血酶（译者注：1 NIH 单位相当于 7.5 国际单位 U，1 U 指在特定条件下每 min 催化 1 mmol 底物转化为产物的酶量））在 37℃ 下振荡 5 min，随后加入各种药液（0.001 ml ~ 0.120 ml）再振荡 2 min。然后将这些样品冷却到 0℃ 并在相对离心力 2,400 g 下离心 10 min。将一部分上清液(4.5 ml)的 pH 值调至 2.5 ~ 3.0，随即用乙酸乙酯抽提出前列腺素，在减压干燥后用以前报道过的方法 [20] 对前列腺素进行生物鉴定。用余下的上清液检测 ^{14}C–5– 羟色胺 [18]、β–N– 乙酰氨基葡萄糖苷酶 [21] 和磷脂酶 A_1 的含量（参考文献 22）（最适 pH 值为 4.0）。

虽然阿司匹林对 5– 羟色胺、β–N– 乙酰氨基葡萄糖苷酶和磷脂酶 A_1 的释放没有影响（表 1），但它可以使血小板合成的前列腺素明显减少。抑制 50% 前列腺素合成所需的阿司匹林的剂量为 0.3 μg/ml（1.7 μM）。在两次实验中，消炎痛的抑制作用都大约是阿司匹林的 10 倍，而阿司匹林的抑制作用又是水杨酸钠的 10 倍左右。氢化可的松（100 μg/ml）没有抑制作用。阿司匹林（10 μg/ml 和 100 μg/ml）对提取和检测前列腺素并无影响，也不会增加残留在血小板团中的少量前列腺素的量 [10]。

表 1. 加入到血小板悬液中的阿司匹林对由凝血酶诱导的前列腺素合成的影响和对"释放反应"的影响

是否添加阿司匹林及其添加浓度（μg/ml）	二次添加物及其添加浓度	^{14}C–5– 羟色胺肌酐硫酸盐的释放率 %	每 ml 上清液的活性		
			β–N– 乙酰氨基葡萄糖苷酶 (mU)	磷脂酶 A_1 (mU)	前列腺素 * (ng)
—	—	4.7	0.44	0.13	ND
—	PGE$_2$ 20 ng/ml	4.9	0.37	0.06	15
—	凝血酶 5 U/ml	77.7	2.53	1.12	53
0.01	凝血酶 5 U/ml	74.1	2.55	0.91	48
0.10	凝血酶 5 U/ml	75.5	2.55	0.98	35
1.00	凝血酶 5 U/ml	73.2	2.32	0.91	18
10.00	凝血酶 5 U/ml	74.7	2.77	1.01	7

* 检测的是用大鼠胃底条测出的 PGE$_2$。
ND 代表未检出（少于 0.1 ng PGE$_2$/ml）。
悬液中血小板的浓度为每 ml 4.78×10^8 个，血小板每 10^8 个细胞包含 3.2 mU β–N– 乙酰氨基葡萄糖苷酶。
我们没有检测血小板中磷脂酶 A_1 的含量，因为内源物质可能会影响结果（西尔弗、史密斯和韦伯斯特，尚未发表的观察结果）。

随后我们又检测了阿司匹林对三个志愿者所起的作用。分别在志愿者服用 2 片阿司匹林（600 mg）之前和之后 1 h 采血。在采集到第二个富含血小板的血浆样品后，立即清洗并重悬血小板样品。将每位供血者的两份血小板悬液在 37℃ 下与

for 5 min at 37°C; supernatants were prepared as described and portions were taken for the assay of prostaglandins, β-N-acetyl glucosamidase, β-glucuronidase, phospholipase A₁ and nucleotide[23].

Aspirin administration inhibited the production of prostaglandins in the platelet in a system in which "the release reaction" was unimpaired (Table 2). Indomethacin (50 mg) taken by two volunteers, and indomethacin (100 mg) taken by one volunteer, inhibited the production of prostaglandins by 51, 64 and 83% respectively without affecting the release of lysosomal enzymes. No change in the production of prostaglandins was found in platelets of one individual who took codeine (60 mg) or two individuals who took nothing.

Table 2. Comparison of the Supernatants of Thrombin Treated Platelet Suspensions from Three People before and after taking 600 mg Aspirin

Donor	R. S. (female)		B. S. (male)		J. W. (male)	
Aspirin	Before	After	Before	After	Before	After
Platelet count (×10⁸/ml. platelet suspension)	13.8	15.3	11.5	11.4	9.64	9.94
Activity/ml. supernatant after thrombin treatment						
Nucleotide (n mol)	106	110	134	111	83	90
β-N-Acetyl glucosamidase (mU)	13.0	15.8	17.2	13.1	11.2	13.0
β-Glucuronidase (mU)	1.10	1.58	2.48	1.91	0.81	1.04
Phospholipase A₁ (mU)	0.99	1.22	3.57	2.97	0.99	1.49
Prostaglandin (ng)*	160	16	168	5	103	20

*Assayed as PGE_2 on the rat fundus strip and uncorrected for loss (estimated to be 20 to 30%) during extraction.

Aspirin inhibits "the release reaction" when induced by collagen or low concentrations of thrombin[24]. In our experiments relatively high concentrations of thrombin (5 U/ml.) were used and as a result aspirin did not inhibit the release of the platelet constituents. The production of prostaglandins is thus dissociated from "the release reaction". The finding that the production of prostaglandins is inhibited by aspirin, while the release of phospholipase A is unaffected, strongly suggests that one action of aspirin on platelets is inhibition of the conversion of arachidonic acid into prostaglandins. Other work from this laboratory (see preceding article[11]) has shown that aspirin inhibits the synthesis of prostaglandins from arachidonic acid in guinea-pig lung homogenates.

In these experiments, prostaglandin production in human platelets was inhibited by sodium salicylate, aspirin and indomethacin and this effect occurred after oral administration of the latter two drugs. Prostaglandins have been identified in exudate during the second phase of inflammation induced by carageenin in the rat[20] and in inflamed skin of patients with allergic contact eczema[25]. Low concentrations of PGE_1 or PGE_2 cause pronounced erythema when injected intradermally in man[5,26]. If the prostaglandins are indeed important mediators of inflammation[27], the clinical effectiveness of aspirin and indomethacin as anti-inflammatory agents could be explained by the inhibition of the production of prostaglandins.

5 U/ml 凝血酶共孵育 5 min。根据前述方法制备上清液，然后分成若干份，分别用于检测前列腺素、β–N– 乙酰氨基葡萄糖苷酶、β– 葡萄糖苷酸酶、磷脂酶 A_1 和核苷酸 [23]。

服用阿司匹林会抑制一个系统内血小板中前列腺素的合成，但并不影响血小板的"释放反应"（表 2）。对于两位服用 50 mg 消炎痛的志愿者和一位服用 100 mg 消炎痛的志愿者，其前列腺素合成的抑制率分别为 51%、64% 和 83%，但都没有影响到溶酶体酶的释放。在一位服用过可待因（60 mg）的志愿者和两位没有服用过任何药物的志愿者的血小板中，未发现前列腺素的合成有什么变化。

表 2. 三个志愿者服用 600 mg 阿司匹林之前和之后，其血小板经凝血酶处理后悬液的上清液的结果对比

供血者	R.S.（女性）		B.S.（男性）		J.W.（男性）	
阿司匹林	服用前	服用后	服用前	服用后	服用前	服用后
血小板计数（×10⁸/ml 血小板悬液）	13.8	15.3	11.5	11.4	9.64	9.94
每 ml 经凝血酶处理后的上清液的活性						
核苷酸（n mol）	106	110	134	111	83	90
β–N– 乙酰氨基葡萄糖苷酶（mU）	13.0	15.8	17.2	13.1	11.2	13.0
β– 葡萄糖苷酸酶（mU）	1.10	1.58	2.48	1.91	0.81	1.04
磷脂酶 A_1（mU）	0.99	1.22	3.57	2.97	0.99	1.49
前列腺素（ng）*	160	16	168	5	103	20

* 检测的是用大鼠胃底条测出的 PGE_2，未对抽提过程中的损失（大约 20% ~ 30%）进行修正。

阿司匹林能抑制胶原蛋白或者低浓度凝血酶诱导的"释放反应"[24]。我们在实验中使用了浓度较高的凝血酶（5 U/ml），所以阿司匹林没有抑制血小板中各种成分的释放。由此可见，前列腺素的合成与"释放反应"并无关联。研究结果显示，阿司匹林能抑制前列腺素的合成但不影响凝脂酶 A 的释放，这充分说明阿司匹林在血小板中所起的一个作用是抑制花生四烯酸向前列腺素的转化。我们实验室中的其他研究工作（见前一篇文章 [11]）也表明：阿司匹林能抑制豚鼠肺匀浆物中的花生四烯酸合成前列腺素。

在这些实验中，水杨酸钠、阿司匹林和消炎痛都可以抑制人血小板中的前列腺素合成，并且这种抑制作用会发生在口服后两种药物之后。在由角叉菜胶诱导的大鼠炎症的第二阶段渗出物中 [20] 以及在过敏性接触性湿疹患者的发炎皮肤中 [25] 均发现了前列腺素。给人皮下注射低浓度 PGE_1 或 PGE_2 会使人出现非常明显的红斑 [5,26]。如果前列腺素确实是炎症的重要介质 [27]，那么作为消炎药的阿司匹林和消炎痛的治疗作用就可以用抑制前列腺素的合成来解释。

We thank Professor G. R. Webster for advice on the assay of phospholipase A and the Medical Research Council for financial support.

(*Nature New Biology*, **231**, 235-237; 1971)

J. B. Smith and A. L. Willis[*]: Department of Pharmacology, Institute of Basic Medical Sciences, Royal College of Surgeons of England, Lincoln's Inn Fields, London WC2A 3PN.

Received May 6, 1971.

References:

1. Morris, C. D. W., *Lancet*, i, 279 (1967).

2. Weiss, W. J., and Aledort, L. M., *Lancet*, ii, 495 (1967).

3. Zucker, M. B., and Peterson, J., *Proc. Soc. Exp. Biol. Med.*, **127**, 547 (1968).

4. O'Brien, J. R., *Lancet*, i, 779 (1968).

5. Macmillan, D. C., *Lancet*, i, 1151 (1968).

6. Packham, M. A., Nishizawa, E. E., and Mustard, J. F., *Biochem. Pharmacol.*, Suppl., 171 (1968).

7. Crunkhorn, P., and Willis, A. L., *Brit. J. Pharmacol.*, **36**, 216P (1969).

8. Crunkhorn, P., and Willis, A. L., *Brit. J. Pharmacol.*, **41**, 49 (1971).

9. Piper, Priscilla J., and Vane, J. R., *Nature*, **223**, 29 (1969).

10. Smith, J. B., and Willis, A. L., *Brit. J. Pharmacol.*, **40**, 545P (1970).

11. Vane, J. R., *Nature New Biology*, **231**, 232 (1971).

12. Ferreira, G. H., Moncada, S., and Vane, J. R., *Nature New Biology*, **231**, 237 (1971).

13. Holmsen, H., Day, H. J., and Stormorken, H., *Scand. J. Haematol.*, Suppl., 8 (1969).

14. Smith, A. D., and Winkler, M., *Biochem. J.*, **108**, 867 (1968).

15. Bartels, J., Kunze, H., Vogt, W., and Wille, G., *Naunyn-Schmiedeberg's Arch. Pharmak. Exp. Pathol.*, **266**, 199 (1970).

16. Bergström, S., Danielsson, H., and Samuelsson, B., *Biochim. Biophys. Acta*, **90**, 207 (1964).

17. Samuelsson, B., *Progr. Biochem. Pharmacol.*, **3**, 59 (1967).

18. Mills, D. C. B., Robb, I. A., and Roberts, G. C. K., *J. Physiol.*, **195**, 715 (1968).

19. Haslam, R. J., *Nature*, **202**, 765 (1964).

20. Willis, A. L., *J. Pharm. Pharmacol.*, **21**, 126 (1969).

21. Holmsen, H., and Day, H. J., *J. Lab. Clin. Med.*, **75**, 840 (1970).

22. Cooper, M. F., and Webster, G. R., *J. Neurochem.*, **17**, 1543 (1970).

23. Davey, M. G., and Lüscher, E. F., *Biochim. Biophys. Acta*, **165**, 490 (1968).

24. Evans, G., Packham, M. A., Nishizawa, E. E., Mustard, J. F., and Murphy, E. A., *J. Exp. Med.*, **128**, 877 (1968).

25. Greaves, M. W., Sondergaard, J., and McDonald-Gibson, W., *Brit. Med. J.*, **2**, 258 (1971).

26. Juhlin, L., and Michaëlsson, G., *Acta Dermatol. Vener.*, **49**, 251 (1969).

27. Willis, A. L., in *Prostaglandins, Peptides and Amines* (edit. by Mantegazza, P., and Horton, E. W.), 31 (Academic Press, London, 1969).

[*] Present address: Department of Physiology, Stanford University, Stanford, California 94305.

感谢韦伯斯特教授在磷脂酶 A 的检测方面为我们提出了宝贵的建议，还要感谢医学研究理事会为我们提供了经费上的支持。

（彭丽霞 翻译；莫韫 孙军 审稿）

Indomethacin and Aspirin Abolish Prostaglandin Release from the Spleen

S. H. Ferreira *et al.*

Editor's Note

Prostaglandins are lipid molecules produced by cells for a wide variety of reasons, and are particularly associated with pain signals and tissue inflammation. Suppression of prostaglandins can therefore reduce pain and inflammation, and in this and an accompanying paper in the same issue of *Nature New Biology* British pharmacologist John Vane and his coworkers propose that this is essentially the mechanism by which aspirin (and the related drug indomethacin) exerts its analgesic effects. They show here that the two substances suppress prostaglandin synthesis in dog spleens. This discovery of the mode of action of one of the most important drugs in widespread use won Vane the 1982 Nobel Prize in medicine or physiology.

PROSTAGLANDIN release can be evoked from many tissues by physiological, pathological or mechanical stimulation[1]. In one of the accompanying articles Vane[2] has demonstrated that prostaglandin synthesis by lung homogenate is blocked by anti-inflammatory acids. In the other, Smith and Willis[3] have shown that prostaglandin production induced by the action of thrombin on platelets is also inhibited by these agents.

The dog spleen releases large amounts of prostaglandins, identified as a mixture of PGE_2 and $PGF_{2\alpha}$, when stimulated either by sympathetic nerve excitation, by adrenaline or by noradrenaline[4-6]. The release of prostaglandin can be reproduced consistently by repetition of the same stimulus and in much greater amounts than can be extracted from the tissues[4,6]. Therefore the release represents fresh synthesis of prostaglandins rather than mobilization from an intracellular reservoir. Thus the spleen affords an experimental model in which anti-inflammatory drugs can be tested as inhibitors of prostaglandin synthesis when the organ and cell integrity are preserved and prostaglandin synthesis is promoted by a naturally occurring mediator.

Spleens were perfused with Krebs-dextran solution by the method described earlier[6,7]. Eleven dogs of either sex (6–18 kg) were anaesthetized with pentobarbitone sodium (30 mg/kg given intravenously). The abdomen was opened and the splenic pedicle was carefully dissected to separate the splenic artery, vein and nerves. The dog was given heparin (1,000 IU/kg intravenously) and the splenic artery and vein were cannulated with polyethylene tubing. The spleen was then removed and perfused through the artery with Krebs solution containing 2–3% dextran (molecular weight 110,000; Fisons) warmed to 37°C and delivered from a constant output pump at a rate of 15–30 ml./min. A second roller pump took part of the splenic outflow at 10 ml./min to superfuse a series of isolated

消炎痛和阿司匹林阻断脾脏前列腺素的释放

费雷拉等

编者按

前列腺素是由细胞产生的脂质分子，产生的原因有很多，并且与疼痛信号和组织炎症有着特殊的联系。因此，对前列腺素的抑制能够缓解疼痛和炎症。在这篇以及前面一篇发表于同一期《自然·新兴生物学》杂志上的相关文章中，英国药理学家约翰·文及其同事们指出这就是阿司匹林（以及相关药物消炎痛）能够发挥镇痛作用的基本机制。他们在本文中证明上述两种药物可以抑制狗脾脏中前列腺素的合成。文因为发现了一种被人们广泛使用的最重要的药物——阿司匹林的作用机理而获得了 1982 年的诺贝尔生理学暨医学奖。

在生理学、病理学或机械刺激下，许多组织会释放出前列腺素 [1]。在一系列相关文章的其中一篇中，文 [2] 已经提出消炎酸可以抑制肺匀浆中前列腺素的合成。在另一篇文章中，史密斯和威利斯 [3] 指出这些药物也能抑制由血小板中凝血酶诱导的前列腺素合成。

在受到交感神经兴奋、肾上腺素或去甲肾上腺素的刺激时，狗的脾脏会释放出大量前列腺素——被认为是 PGE_2 和 $PGF_{2\alpha}$ 的混合物 [4-6]。反复进行相同的刺激，前列腺素的释放过程会持续不断地出现，其数量远远超过从这些组织中可以萃取出来的前列腺素的量 [4,6]。由此可见，释放意味着前列腺素的新鲜合成，而不是细胞内储存的前列腺素的排出。因此，如果能保证器官和细胞的完整性，并且前列腺素的合成能够被一种天然的介导物所诱导，那么脾就可以成为一个鉴定消炎药物是否会抑制前列腺素合成的实验模型。

按照以前报道过的方法 [6,7] 用克雷布斯 – 葡聚糖溶液灌注脾脏。将 11 只雌狗或雄狗（6 kg ~ 18 kg）用戊巴比妥钠麻醉（按 30 mg/kg 的剂量静脉注射）。然后打开腹腔，小心切开脾蒂，分离脾动脉、脾静脉和脾神经。给狗注射肝素（静脉注射 1,000 IU/kg）后，用聚乙烯管插入脾动脉和脾静脉。随后取出脾脏并用加热至 37℃、含 2% ~ 3% 葡聚糖的克雷布斯溶液（分子量为 110,000；费森斯公司）从动脉灌注脾脏，用一台恒功率泵以 15 ml/min ~ 30 ml/min 的速度输送溶液。用另一台滚柱泵以 10 ml/min 的速度抽取部分脾脏流出液以灌注一系列分离的受试组织。在 6 cm ~

assay tissues; excess effluent was allowed to run to waste against a hydrostatic pressure of 6–12 cm. Four assay tissues were used, usually including a rat stomach strip[8], a rat colon[9] and a chick rectum[10], and sometimes including a gerbil colon[11]. This combination of tissues allows differentiation between prostaglandin E_2 and $F_{2\alpha}$ (refs. 5 and 6). The assay tissues were rendered insensitive to catecholamines, acetylcholine, histamine and 5-hydroxytryptamine by infusing a mixture of antagonists[6] into the Krebs solution superfusing them. In some experiments a smaller amount (1 ml./min or 5 ml./min) of the splenic effluent was used to superfuse the assay tissues; the superfusion rate was made up to 10 ml./min with fresh Krebs solution from another channel in the roller pump.

The spleen was supported on a plastic tray hanging from a strain gauge, the output from which was displayed on one channel of a pen recorder. Thus, contractions of the spleen were recorded as decreases in weight. The splenic perfusion pressure and the reactions of the assay tissues were displayed on other channels of the pen recorder. The spleen was kept warm by a lamp, the output of which was electronically controlled to maintain a thermistor placed on the surface of the spleen at 37°C.

Substances used were adrenaline bitartrate, indomethacin, sodium acetyl salicylate, sodium salicylate and hydrocortisone dihydrogen succinate. To make sure that the antagonist did not change the sensitivity of the assay tissues, it was infused from the beginning of the experiment into the splenic outflow. To test the effect of the antagonist on the spleen the infusion was changed from the splenic outflow to the splenic inflow.

There was usually a basal output of prostaglandins from the spleen, as shown by contraction of the assay tissues when the splenic outflow was first used to superfuse them. This basal output was estimated in three experiments by intermittently applying the splenic outflow to the assay tissues for periods of 3 min. Assayed as PGE_2 there was an output of 10–20 ng/ml. of splenic effluent. The relative contractions of the assay tissues showed that this output was a mixture of E and F prostaglandins.

When adrenaline (200 ng/min or 6–10 ng/ml. during 3 min) was infused intra-arterially splenic perfusion pressure increased. The spleen contracted, as shown by a loss in weight and by the increase in splenic effluent running to waste. There was an increase in prostaglandin output which, from the reactions of the assay tissues, was chiefly PGE_2. Estimated as PGE_2 there was an increase in prostaglandin output of 10–80 ng/ml. After the adrenaline infusion was stopped the spleen gradually returned to its initial weight. During this period the output was assessed by infusions of prostaglandins directly to the assay tissues. Repetition of the adrenaline infusion at 20–40 min intervals had similar effects on perfusion pressure, splenic weight, and prostaglandin output, even though there was a gradual increase in perfusion pressure throughout the experiment. After 3–5 h of perfusion the splenic weight also tended to increase and when this occurred there was a smaller reduction in weight induced by adrenaline infusions.

When indomethacin (0.37–4 μg/ml.) was infused into the spleen the assay tissues gradually

12 cm 的静压下放掉多余的流出液。受试组织有 4 种，通常是大鼠胃条 [8]、大鼠结肠 [9] 和小鸡直肠 [10]，有时也包括沙鼠结肠 [11]。联合采用这些组织可以使我们区分出前列腺素 E_2 和 $F_{2\alpha}$（参考文献 5 和 6）。我们在用于灌注的克雷布斯溶液中加入了一种由多种拮抗剂组成的混合物 [6]，目的是使这些受试组织失去对儿茶酚胺、乙酰胆碱、组胺和 5– 羟色胺的敏感性。在有些实验中，用于灌注受试组织的脾脏流出液会更少一些（1 ml/min 或 5 ml/min）；通过滚柱泵的另外一个通道灌注新鲜克雷布斯溶液的速度被控制在 10 ml/min。

将脾脏置于一个悬挂在应变计上的塑料托盘中，应变计的输出信号在描笔式记录器的一个频道上显示出来。由此可以得到脾脏收缩与脾脏重量减少之间的关系。脾脏灌注压和受试组织的反应在描笔式记录器的其他频道上显示。用一盏灯使脾脏保温，并用电子器件控制灯的输出功率以便使放在脾脏表面的热敏电阻的温度保持在 37℃。

实验中所用的药物有：酒石酸肾上腺素、消炎痛、乙酰水杨酸钠、水杨酸钠和氢化可的松二氢琥珀酸酯。为了确保拮抗剂不会对受试组织的敏感性造成影响，在实验一开始，我们就将拮抗剂注入脾脏流出液。为了检测拮抗剂对脾脏的影响，药液先加入脾脏流出液，再加入脾脏流入液。

当开始用脾脏流出液浇盖受试组织时，由受试组织的收缩可以看出：脾脏通常会有一个基础的前列腺素输出。通过三次用脾脏流出液不连续地灌注受试组织长达 3 min 的实验估算出了这个基础输出量，如果以 PGE_2 衡量，则脾脏流出液中的输出量可以达到 10 ng/ml ～ 20 ng/ml。由受试组织的相对收缩情况可知：上述输出物是前列腺素 E 和 F 的混合物。

当在动脉内注入肾上腺素（200 ng/min 或 6 ng/ml ～ 10 ng/ml 持续 3 min）时，脾灌注压就会升高。脾脏重量减轻和脾脏流出液的增加表明脾脏发生了收缩。从受试组织的反应可以看出，前列腺素输出的增加部分主要是 PGE_2。以 PGE_2 估算，前列腺素输出的增加量为 10 ng/ml ～ 80 ng/ml。一旦停止注入肾上腺素，脾脏就会慢慢恢复到它原来的重量。在此期间，输出量用直接注入受试组织的前列腺素的量来评估。如果每隔 20 min ～ 40 min 就重复进行一次肾上腺素的注入，那么灌注压、脾脏重量和前列腺素输出不会有太大的改变，虽然灌注压在整个实验中是在缓慢增加的。灌注 3 h ～ 5 h 后，脾脏的重量还会趋于增加，并且当脾脏重量增加时，由注入肾上腺素所诱导的重量减轻会更少一些。

当消炎痛（0.37 μg/ml ～ 4 μg/ml）被注入脾脏时，受试组织会逐渐松弛。同时，

relaxed. At the same time their sensitivity to prostaglandin infusions increased, suggesting that the basal output of prostaglandin from the spleen was being inhibited and that the assay tissues had previously been desensitized to additional prostaglandin infusions by the presence of this basal output. This was confirmed by intermittent application of the splenic outflow to the assay tissues. The sensitivity of the tissues to prostaglandin infusions was diminished during superfusion with splenic outflow but returned when normal Krebs solution was used. In later experiments the interference with the prostaglandin assay by the basal output was minimized by using only a small proportion of the splenic outflow to superfuse the tissues.

Indomethacin infusions into the spleen did not affect the splenic weight or the splenic perfusion pressure. The increase in prostaglandin output induced by adrenaline infusion, however, was abolished. In the first experiment indomethacin (4 µg/ml. for 15 min) completely abolished prostaglandin output, as did a concentration of 750 ng/ml. for 15 min (four experiments). In two other experiments indomethacin at 370 ng/ml. (1 µM) was used. In one there was a partial inhibition (60%) of prostaglandin output after 15 min of indomethacin infusion. In the other experiment the infusion was made for a further 15 min and there was then complete abolition of prostaglandin output. In all these experiments, after the indomethacin infusion was stopped, there was a gradual return of prostaglandin output induced by adrenaline infusion, which reached at least 60% of the initial output within 1–3 h and sometimes 100%.

Fig. 1 illustrates one of these experiments. The first panel shows the reaction of the assay tissues to prostaglandin E_2 (20 ng/ml.). When adrenaline was infused into the spleen there was a rise in perfusion pressure and a fall in spleen weight. The prostaglandin output, assayed as PGE_2, was about 20 ng/ml. After the adrenaline stimulation, the prostaglandin output, perfusion pressure and spleen weight gradually returned to initial levels. The indomethacin infusion (0.37 µg/ml.) which had so far been made into the splenic output was then made into the spleen. During the next 25 min the assay tissues, especially the rat stomach strip, gradually relaxed. They were then much more sensitive to PGE_2, 10 ng/ml. giving greater contractions than those produced by 20 ng/ml. previously. Adrenaline infusion into the spleen now induced a larger increase in perfusion pressure, a larger decrease in spleen weight but no prostaglandin release. The indomethacin was then given once more into the splenic outflow. The next adrenaline infusion shown was made 70 min after stopping the indomethacin treatment of the spleen. Although the effects on perfusion pressure were still greater than in the control period, the change in spleen weight had decreased to control values. There was also an output of prostaglandins which, assayed as PGE_2, was more than 10 ng/ml. In three of these experiments the solvent for the indomethacin (4% ethanol plus Krebs solution) was infused into the spleen. This did not change the prostaglandin output, the rise in perfusion pressure or fall in spleen weight induced by adrenaline infusion. In four of the six experiments with indomethacin the splenic contraction induced by adrenaline stimulation was clearly potentiated during the period in which prostaglandin release was abolished. In two experiments there was also a potentiation of the pressor response to adrenaline during the abolition of prostaglandin

它们对前列腺素注入的敏感性也会增加，这说明脾脏的基础前列腺素输出受到了抑制。之前由于这种基础输出的存在，受试组织对前列腺素的再注入失去了敏感性。这一点已经从用脾脏流出液不连续浇盖受试组织的实验中得到了证实。在用脾脏流出液灌注时，组织对前列腺素注入的敏感性下降，但当改用标准克雷布斯溶液时，组织的敏感性得到恢复。在后来的实验中，我们用很少量的脾脏流出液来灌注这些组织以便将基础输出对前列腺素分析的干扰降至最低。

将消炎痛注入脾脏后，脾重量和脾灌注压并未受到任何影响，但前列腺素的输出量也就不再会因为受到肾上腺素浸液的诱导而增加了。在第一个实验中，消炎痛（4 μg/ml，15 min）使前列腺素的输出完全被抑制，这与浓度为 750 ng/ml 消炎痛作用 15 min 的效果相同（四次实验）。在另外两个实验中，我们使用了 370 ng/ml（1 μM）的消炎痛。其中一个实验的结果是：在注入消炎痛 15 min 后，前列腺素的输出受到了部分抑制（60%）。在另一个实验中，我们又将注入时间延长了 15 min，这样前列腺素的输出就被完全抑制住了。在所有这些实验中，当消炎痛的注入停止时，由肾上腺素浸液所诱导的前列腺素输出会逐渐恢复，在 1 h ～ 3 h 内，输出量至少可以恢复到初始值的 60%，有时甚至能达到 100%。

图 1 显示了其中一次实验的结果。第一列数据表示受试组织对前列腺素 E_2（20 ng/ml）的反应。当用肾上腺素注入脾脏时，灌注压升高，脾脏重量下降。前列腺素的输出，以 PGE_2 计算，约为 20 ng/ml。肾上腺素的刺激完成后，前列腺素输出、灌注压和脾脏重量都会逐渐恢复到原来的水平。之前一直被加入到脾脏流出液中的消炎痛浸液（0.37 μg/ml）此时也被加入到脾脏中。在接下来的 25 min 之内，受试组织，尤其是大鼠胃条，会逐渐松弛。在这之后，受试组织变得对 PGE_2 更加敏感，10 ng/ml 浓度引起的收缩要大于之前由 20 ng/ml PGE_2 所引起的收缩。这时在脾脏中注入肾上腺素会使灌注压有更为显著的增加，脾脏重量的下降也更为明显，但并没有释放出前列腺素。随后消炎痛被再次加入到脾脏流出液中。图中显示的肾上腺素浸液的下一次刺激是在停止用消炎痛处理脾脏 70 min 以后进行的。虽然此时对灌注压的影响仍然高于对照期，但脾脏重量的变化已经减少到了对照值。另外，前列腺素还有一个输出量，以 PGE_2 计算，其值高于 10 ng/ml。在三次这样的实验中，消炎痛的溶剂（含 4% 乙醇的克雷布斯溶液）也被我们注入了脾脏，它们对由肾上腺素浸液诱导的前列腺素合成、灌注压升高和脾脏重量下降均没有任何影响。在六次使用消炎痛的实验中，有四次当前列腺素释放被阻断时，由肾上腺素刺激诱导的脾脏收缩在效力上明显增强。在两次实验中，当前列腺素释放受到抑制时，肾上腺素仍能导致压强的升高；但是其中只有一次在停止用消炎痛浸渍脾脏时，灌注压的升高能恢

release but in only one of these did the rise in perfusion pressure return to the previous levels when the indomethacin infusion to the spleen was stopped.

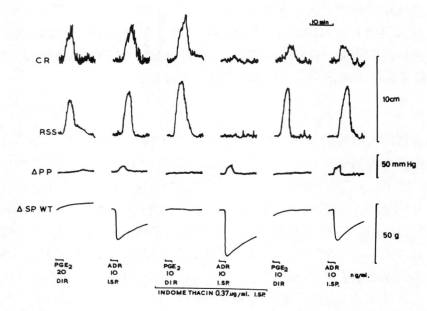

Fig. 1. A spleen from an 8.5 kg dog was perfused with Krebs-dextran solution at a rate of 20 ml./min. A continuous sample (10 ml./min) of the splenic outflow, with combined antagonists added, was used to superfuse the assay tissues. The figure shows the effects of prostaglandins on a chick rectum (CR; top) and a rat stomach strip (RSS). The next two tracings (bottom) show changes in perfusion pressure (ΔPP) and spleen weight (ΔSP. wt.). Except when infused into the spleen indomethacin was added to the splenic outflow to give a concentration of 0.37 μg/ml. The first panel shows contractions of CR and RSS induced by prostaglandin E_2 (20 ng/ml. DIR). Next an adrenaline infusion into the spleen (ADR 10 ng/ml. I. SP) induced a rise in perfusion pressure, a fall in spleen weight and an output of prostaglandins equivalent to PGF_2 at about 20 ng/ml. Indomethacin (0.37 μg/ml.) was then infused into the spleen. During the next 25 min the assay tissues relaxed (not shown) and were then more sensitive to PGE_2 (10 ng/ml. DIR). Adrenaline (40 min after start of indomethacin) now caused a greater increase in perfusion pressure, a greater decrease in spleen weight, but no output of prostaglandin. After stopping the indomethacin infusion into the spleen, the reactivity of the assay tissues gradually decreased and the output of prostaglandin induced by adrenaline infusion into the spleen gradually returned. The adrenaline stimulation shown was made 70 min after stopping the indomethacin. The rise in perfusion pressure was still larger, but the fall in spleen weight had returned to the original size.

Aspirin was much less effective as an inhibitor of prostaglandin release. At 15 μg/ml. (one experiment) there was 60% inhibition and at 40 μg/ml. (two experiments) there was 75% and 100% inhibition. Sodium salicylate (20 and 40 μg/ml.; two experiments) did not change the prostaglandin output induced by adrenaline infusion into the spleen. Hydrocortisone (2 μg/ml., one experiment; 25 μg/ml., two experiments) was also ineffective. In these experiments, after salicylic acid or hydrocortisone had been shown to be ineffective, prostaglandin output was reduced by indomethacin or aspirin.

复到原来的水平。

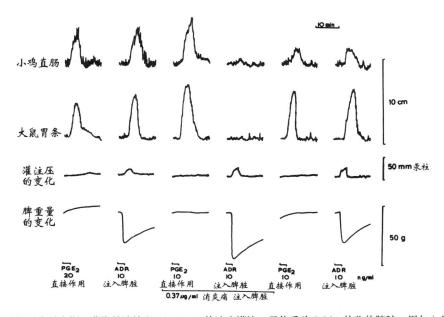

图 1. 我们用克雷布斯 – 葡聚糖溶液以 20 ml/min 的速度灌注一只体重为 8.5 kg 的狗的脾脏。用加入几种拮抗剂后脾脏的流出液样品（10 ml/min）持续灌注受试组织。这张图表明了前列腺素对小鸡直肠（CR，顶部）和大鼠胃条（RSS）的影响。最下面的两条曲线（底部）表示的是灌注压的变化（ΔPP）和脾重量的变化（ΔSP. wt.）。除了灌注脾脏时之外，消炎痛以 0.37 μg/ml 的浓度被加入到脾脏流出液中。第一列数据表示由前列腺素 E_2（20 ng/ml 直接作用）诱导的 CR 收缩和 RSS 收缩。第二列是由在脾脏中注入肾上腺素（ADR 10 ng/ml 注入脾脏）所诱导的灌注压上升、脾重量下降和前列腺素输出（以 PGE_2 计算，约为 20 ng/ml）。随后将消炎痛（0.37 μg/ml）注入脾脏。在接下来的 25 min 时间里，受试组织变得松弛（未显示），并且对 PGE_2（10 ng/ml 直接作用）的敏感性更高。这时，肾上腺素（加入消炎痛 40 min 后）会使灌注压的升高更加明显，而脾重量会降得更低，但是没有前列腺素输出。当我们停止在脾脏中注入消炎痛后，受试组织的敏感性逐渐降低，由在脾脏中注入肾上腺素而诱导的前列腺素输出将逐渐恢复。图中显示的肾上腺素刺激是在停止注入消炎痛 70 min 后进行的。灌注压的升高依然很明显，但脾重量的下降已经恢复到了原来的水平。

　　阿司匹林对前列腺素释放的抑制作用明显不及消炎痛。15 μg/ml 阿司匹林（一次实验）所产生的抑制率为 60%；40 μg/ml 阿司匹林（两次实验）所产生的抑制率为 75% 和 100%。水杨酸钠（20 μg/ml 和 40 μg/ml；两次实验）并不影响将肾上腺素注入脾脏所诱导的前列腺素合成。氢化可的松（2 μg/ml，一次实验；25 μg/ml，两次实验）也没有抑制效果。在这些实验中，首先发现的是水杨酸或氢化可的松对抑制前列腺素无效，随后才发现消炎痛或阿司匹林可使前列腺素的输出减少。

Both in human platelets[12] and dog spleen[4,6] prostaglandin output represents fresh prostaglandin synthesis. Thus we have now shown in cell-free homogenates[2], in isolated cells[3] and in a whole organ perfused *in vitro* (in this article), in experiments covering three species, that indomethacin is a potent inhibitor of prostaglandin synthesis. The concentrations used in the perfused spleen experiments were less than those reported in human plasma after an oral dose of 200 mg[13]. It is possible therefore that this activity of indomethacin may be the basis of some of its therapeutic actions. Neither hydrocortisone nor salicylate was effective in reducing prostaglandin output from the spleen. Hydrocortisone is an anti-inflammatory substance of a different nature but salicylate is from the same group as aspirin and indomethacin and contains the carboxy group. The lack of action of salicylate in these experiments does not necessarily mean that prostaglandin synthesis is unimportant in inflammation and pyrexia, for salicylate may be more effective against the synthesis of a prostaglandin such as PGE_1 from dihomo-γ-linolenic acid than it is against the synthesis of PGE_2 from arachidonic acid. PGE_1 is more effective than PGE_2 as a pyretic agent[14] and may also be important in inflammation[15]. In both these cases salicylate is about as potent as aspirin[16].

Hedqvist[17] has shown that prostaglandin E_2 release in the spleen may be a feedback mechanism, controlling the output of noradrenaline from sympathetic nerves. He measured the effects of PGE_2 on the increase in perfusion pressure induced by injections of noradrenaline; they ranged from potentiation to inhibition, depending on the concentration of prostaglandin used. These results may explain the variability in the effects of indomethacin on the rise in perfusion pressure induced by adrenaline in our experiments. Certainly the use of indomethacin in the perfused spleen preparation will allow further assessment of the hypothesis proposed by Hedqvist. The use of indomethacin as a prostaglandin synthesis inhibitor will also allow definition of the functions of prostaglandins in cells, tissues or in whole animals.

We thank Mr. P. Holgate for technical assistance and the Wellcome Trust for grants.

(*Nature New Biology*, **231**, 237-239; 1971)

S. H. Ferreira, S. Moncada and J. R. Vane: Department of Pharmacology, Institute of Basic Medical Sciences, Royal College of Surgeons of England, Lincoln's Inn Fields, London WC2A 3PN.

Received May 7, 1971.

References:

1. Piper, Priscilla J., and Vane, J. R., in *Prostaglandins* (edit. by Ramwell, P., and Shaw, J.), *Ann. NY Acad. Sci.*, **180**, 363 (1971).

2. Vane, J. R., *Nature New Biology*, **231**, 232 (1971).

3. Smith, J. B., and Willis, A. L., *Nature New Biology*, **231**, 235 (1971).

4. Davies, B. N., Horton, E. W., and Withrington, P. G., *J. Physiol.*, **188**, 38P (1967).

5. Ferreira, S. H., and Vane, J. R., *Nature*, **216**, 868 (1967).

在人血小板 [12] 和狗脾脏 [4,6] 中，前列腺素的输出意味着前列腺素的新鲜合成。因此我们分别用三个不同物种的无细胞匀浆物 [2]、分离出的细胞 [3] 以及体外灌注的整个器官（本文中）所进行的实验都验证了消炎痛是一种能强烈抑制前列腺素合成的物质。在灌注脾脏实验中所用的消炎痛浓度要低于人口服 200 mg 消炎痛后血浆中的报告浓度 [13]。因此，消炎痛的这种活性可能就是它具有某些治疗作用的基础。氢化可的松和水杨酸盐都不能减少脾脏中前列腺素的输出。氢化可的松是一种在化学结构上有所不同的消炎物质，而水杨酸盐与阿司匹林和消炎痛都属于同一类别，它们都含有羧基。水杨酸盐在上述实验中缺乏活性并不一定意味着前列腺素合成在发炎和发烧时是无关紧要的，因为水杨酸盐对合成 PGE_1 等二高 -γ- 亚麻酸来源的前列腺素的抑制可能会强于对合成 PGE_2 等花生四烯酸来源的前列腺素的抑制。PGE_1 比 PGE_2 更易引起发烧 [14]，在导致发炎上可能也很重要 [15]。在发烧和炎症的治疗上，水杨酸盐和阿司匹林的效果大致相同 [16]。

赫德奎斯特 [17] 曾指出脾脏释放前列腺素 E_2 的过程可能是一个反馈机制，调控着交感神经内去甲肾上腺素的输出。他检测了 PGE_2 对由注射去甲肾上腺素诱导的灌注压升高的影响。随着所用前列腺素浓度的不同，PGE_2 对灌注压升高的影响可在增强和抑制之间转化。这些结果或许可以解释为什么在我们的实验中消炎痛会对由肾上腺素诱导的灌注压升高有不同的影响。很显然，用消炎痛灌注脾脏可以使我们更深入地评估赫德奎斯特提出的假设。此外，采用消炎痛作为前列腺素合成的抑制剂还能使我们明确前列腺素在细胞、组织甚或整个动物体中的功能。

我们衷心感谢霍尔盖特先生在技术上的帮助以及维康基金会在经费上的资助。

（彭丽霞 翻译；莫韫 审稿）

6. Gilmore, N., Vane, J. R., and Wyllie, J. H., *Nature*, **218**, 1135 (1968).

7. Gilmore, N., Vane, J. R., and Wyllie, J. H., in *Prostaglandins, Peptides and Amines* (edit. by Mantegazza, P., and Horton, E. W.), 21 (Academic Press, London, 1969).

8. Vane, J. R., *Brit. J. Pharmacol. Chemother.*, **23**, 360 (1964).

9. Regoli, D., and Vane, J. R., *J. Physiol.*, **183**, 513 (1966).

10. Mann, M., and West, G. B., *Brit. J. Pharmacol. Chemother.*, **5**, 173 (1950).

11. Ambache, N., Kavanagh, L., and Whiting, J., *J. Physiol.*, **176**, 378 (1965).

12. Smith, J. B., and Willis, A. L., *Brit. J. Pharmacol.*, **40**, 545P (1970).

13. Hucker, H. B., Zacchei, A. G., Cox, S. V., Brodie, D. A., and Cantwell, N. H. R., *J. Pharmacol. Exp. Ther.*, **153**, 237 (1960).

14. Milton, A. S., and Wendlandt, S. J., *J. Physiol.*, **207**, 76P (1970).

15. Willis, A. L., in *Prostaglandins, Peptides and Amines* (edit. by Mantegazza, P., and Horton, E. W.), 31 (Academic Press, London, 1969).

16. Collier, H. O. J., *Adv. Pharmacol. Chemother.*, **7**, 333 (1969).

17. Hedqvist, P., *Life Sci.*, **9**, 269 (1970).

Possible Clonal Origin of Common Warts
(*Verruca vulgaris*)

R. F. Murray, jun. *et al.*

Editor's Note

In the days before modern molecular approaches for proving clonality, researchers had to resort to more esoteric methods. Here Robert Murray and colleagues use a trick involving the cytosolic enzyme glucose-6-phosphate dehydrogenase to infer a possible clonal origin of common warts. The team realised that women heterozygous for the X-chromosome-linked gene have two populations of cells, each expressing a single phenotype corresponding to one or other of the two alleles. They found that verrucal tissue from such donors contained just one phenotype, a result consistent with a clonal origin. Although human papilloma virus had yet to be identified as the causative agent of warts, researchers were aware of the links between certain viruses and cancers, making this research all the more significant.

FEMALES heterozygous for the X-linked glucose-6-phosphate dehydrogenase (G6PD) locus have two populations of cells, each expressing a single phenotype corresponding to one or the other of the two alleles[1-3]. Where subjects are heterozygous for the A and B electrophoretic variants of G6PD[4], one cell population will show only the A electrophoretic variant and the other only the B. The study of these variants has been used to throw light on the origin of certain tumours. Thus, uterine leiomyomas from Negro females heterozygous for G6PD variants A and B are of only one phenotype, although the adjacent uninvolved tissue shows both phenotypes[5], which is consistent with a clonal or unicellular origin for this tumour. Similarly, chronic granulocytic leukaemia[6] is probably of clonal origin, like the metastatic lesions from one patient with chronic lymphocytic leukaemia[7]. On the other hand, studies of metastatic lesions from a colonic malignancy[7] and epidermoid carcinomas of the cervix have revealed[8] the presence of both G6PD phenotypes, which implies a multiclonal origin.

We have used this technique for the study of *verruca vulgaris* or common warts—thickenings or projections of the epidermis, classified as benign tumours of the skin, caused by a spherical virus 50 μm in diameter[9] which is structurally similar to the polyoma virus[10].

Verrucal tissue was obtained in a dermatology clinic from Negro females. Lesions were diagnosed as typical verruca vulgaris by J. H. The study included only lesions with typical appearance[11], and measuring 2–8 mm in diameter. They were excised surgically without removing adjacent normal tissue. The root of the wart was destroyed by cryotherapy and the specimen placed in a sterile tube containing about 2 cc of TC 199 tissue culture medium. Venous blood was taken from the patient (5–10 cm³) and placed in heparinized,

寻常疣为克隆性起源的可能性

小默里等

编者按

在还不能运用现代分子生物学方法来证明克隆性之前，研究人员不得不采取一些更为深奥难懂的方法。在本文中，罗伯特·默里及其同事们采用了一种与胞浆酶葡萄糖 –6– 磷酸脱氢酶有关的方法来推断寻常疣是否有可能为克隆性起源。该研究小组认为：X 染色体连锁基因的女性杂合子有两种类型的细胞，每一种都代表了一种单一的表型，对应于两个等位基因中的一个或者另一个。他们发现来自这类患者的疣组织只有一种表型，这一结果与克隆性起源是一致的。虽然那时候人们还没有确定人类乳头状瘤病毒就是疣的病原体，但研究人员意识到某些病毒与癌症之间是有关联的，这使本文中的研究工作显得尤为重要。

X 连锁葡萄糖 –6– 磷酸脱氢酶（G6PD）位点的女性杂合子有两种类型的细胞，每一种都代表了一种单一的表型，对应于两个等位基因中的一个或者另一个 [1-3]。当被测对象是 G6PD 的 A 和 B 电泳变异体的杂合子时 [4]，它的一群细胞将仅仅表现为 A 电泳变异体，而另一群则只表现出 B 电泳变异体的特点。人们已经开始用对这些变异体的研究成果来解释某些肿瘤的起源。因此，来自黑人女性身上的 G6PD A 和 B 变异体杂合子的子宫平滑肌瘤只有一种表型，尽管邻近肿瘤的未受累组织可以表现出两种表型 [5]，这与该肿瘤为克隆性起源或单细胞起源是一致的。同样，慢性粒细胞性白血病 [6] 可能也是克隆性起源，与一个慢性淋巴细胞性白血病患者的转移性病变是一样的 [7]。而另一方面，人们对结肠恶性肿瘤的转移性病变 [7] 和宫颈表皮样癌的研究结果表明 [8] 两种 G6PD 表型均存在，这间接说明了一种多克隆起源。

我们将这项技术应用于对寻常疣的研究——寻常疣指的是表皮的增厚或突起，它被归为皮肤的良性肿瘤，是由一种直径为 50 μm[9] 的球形病毒引起的，这种病毒在结构上类似于多瘤病毒 [10]。

疣组织是从一个皮肤病诊所的多位黑人女性患者身上获得的。詹姆斯·霍布斯将这种病诊断为典型的寻常疣。本研究所涉及的仅仅是具有典型表现 [11] 且直径为 2 mm ～ 8 mm 的病变区。把它们用手术切除的时候没有触及邻近的正常组织。用冷冻法破坏掉疣的根部，然后将样本置于一个含有约 2 ml TC 199 组织培养基的无菌试管里。从患者身上采集静脉血（5 ml ～ 10 ml），并放入经肝素化处理的无菌容器

sterile containers and stored at 4°C until analysed (usually within 48 h). There was no significant loss of G6PD activity from the wart tissue in this time. Some samples were stored at −20°C until analysed. The G6PD phenotype of the red cells and corresponding wart specimens was determined on the same run. At the conclusion of each run the gel was sliced and stained[12] for zones of G6PD activity.

Only one specimen of verrucal tissue was obtainable from each individual, although if lesions were of sufficient size, they were cut into pieces and two or more runs made.

Adjacent normal skin tissue was not used to determine the patient's phenotype to minimize possible scarring after removal of the verrucae. Other evidence[13,14], however, indicates that the erythrocyte G6PD phenotype in heterozygotes is usually an adequate qualitative refiexion of the phenotype of skin or other tissues. In exceptional cases, the red cell phenotype is falsely homozygous although false homozygosity in skin in the presence of a heterozygous red cell phenotype has not been described. Thus, any resulting misclassification will probably result in a loss of information, but not misleading information.

Tissue and blood from twelve Afro-American females were tested. On starch gel electrophoresis wart tissue showed a single principal zone of G6PD activity and a slower minor zone. The former zone has the same mobility as that visible in mammalian liver and epidermal tissue and was found to have substrate specificity for galactose-6-phosphate dehydrogenase activity[15,16]. The mobility of this zone did not vary with the phenotype of the wart tissue.

Six of twelve patients studied were heterozygous for G6PD electrophoretic variants as determined from their red blood cell phenotypes (Table 1). In two of the six heterozygotes, the phenotype of the wart tissue was A only and in four cases B only. The blood of the remaining six patients showed only a single phenotype (one A and five B). The G6PD phenotype in the wart and blood was the same in each case. Three large warts, one from a heterozygote and two from homozygotes, were each cut into four approximately equal pieces, but the phenotype was the same in each piece.

Table 1. G6PD Phenotype of Blood and Wart Tissue of Twelve Afro-American Females Determined by Starch Gel Electrophoresis

No.	G6PD phenotype, blood	No.	G6PD phenotype, wart
5	B+	5	B+
1	A+	1	A+
6	A+ B+	4	B+
		2	A+

Verrucal tissue from individuals heterozygous for the common A and B electrophoretic variants of G6PD showed only one phenotype in each case tested, which is consistent with

内，然后在 4℃ 下保存直至用于分析（通常不超过 48 h）。在这段时间里，疣组织内的 G6PD 活性不会有明显的丧失。有些样本在使用前被保存于 –20℃ 下。在每一轮实验中，我们都会同时检测红细胞和对应疣样本的 G6PD 表型。每一轮实验结束后，对电泳胶进行切片并染色 [12] 以便观察具有 G6PD 活性的条带。

我们从每个人身上只取一个疣组织样本，但如果病变区足够大的话，可以把它们切成小块，用于 2 次或 2 次以上的实验。

我们不用邻近的正常皮肤组织来确定患者的表型，以减少疣摘除后可能出现的疤痕。但有其他证据 [13,14] 表明：杂合子中红细胞的 G6PD 表型常常足以定性反映皮肤或其他组织的表型。在一些特殊的病例中，红细胞的表型是假纯合子，不过现在还没有人描述过红细胞表型为杂合子时的皮肤假纯合子表型。这样一来，在分类上出现的任何错误都有可能会导致信息的丢失，但不会误导信息。

我们共检测了 12 名美国黑人女性的组织和血液。从淀粉凝胶电泳的结果来看，疣组织显示出一条主要的 G6PD 活性区带，还有一条较慢的次级区带。前一区带的移动能力与在哺乳动物肝脏和表皮组织中所看到的情况相同，而且其底物特异性与半乳糖 –6– 磷酸脱氢酶相同 [15,16]。无论疣组织的表型发生什么变化，这个区带的移动性都不会随之改变。

在我们所研究的 12 名患者中，有 6 名患者经红细胞表型分析之后被确定为 G6PD 电泳变异体的杂合子（表 1）。在 6 名杂合子个体中，有 2 名的疣组织表型只表现为 A，而另外 4 名只表现为 B。剩余 6 名患者的血液只表现出单一的表型（1 名为 A 和 5 名为 B）。疣组织和血液的 G6PD 表型在每个病例中均相同。我们将三个较大的疣（一个来自杂合子，另两个来自纯合子）分别切成四个大致相等的块，但每个块的表型都是相同的。

表 1. 由淀粉凝胶电泳测得的 12 名美国黑人女性血液和疣组织的 G6PD 表型

患者数	血液的G6PD表型	患者数	疣的G6PD表型
5	B+	5	B+
1	A+	1	A+
6	A+B+	4	B+
		2	A+

在每一个被检测的病例中，普通 G6PD 电泳变异体 A 和 B 杂合子个体的疣组织都只有一种表型，这支持了寻常疣是克隆性起源的假说。可以由此认为疣病毒感染

the hypothesis that verruca vulgaris is of clonal origin. This suggests that the verrucal virus infects a patch of cells all of the same G6PD phenotype, or that it infects only a single epidermal cell. The available data (six heterozygotes) are too limited to differentiate clearly between origin from a single cell or from a patch, especially as a normal patch size may be of the order of a thousand cells or more[5]. It is also possible that cells with both G6PD phenotypes are infected, but that one type is lost during cell proliferation.

Viral infection would be expected to involve a rather large target with spread to thousands of adjacent cells assuming a reasonable titre of the virus. If the proliferative process involves the spread of the virus, this should result in a lesion of multicellular origin, showing both G6PD phenotypes. On the other hand, if the process involves a change in a single cell or a small group of cells, what we have found would be expected, namely, evidence for single cell or clonal origin. The acidophilic inclusion bodies that are characteristic of pathologic sections of verruca vulgaris might still represent virus particles that have replicated with the proliferating cells rather that spread from an initial point of infection.

With the recent implication of viruses in the aetiology of some animal malignancies like the Rous sarcoma, and the murine leukaemias, and evidence that a tumour, like Burkitt's African lymphoma, is of possible clonal origin[17] and may be caused by reovirus 3 (ref. 18), the behaviour of viruses in causing tumour-like lesions takes on considerable significance. The somatic mutation that has been hypothesized by many to lead to neoplastic change might, in some cases, be preceded by the viral invasion of a susceptible cell or clone of cells, or all cells may harbour in a symbiotic fashion this virus and a somatic mutation may induce its oncogenic properties.

We thank Dr. S. M. Gartler for advice and suggestions. This work was supported by a grant from the US Children's Bureau and by a general research support grant from the US Public Health Service.

(**232**, 51-52; 1971)

Robert F. Murray, jun., James Hobbs and Brownell Payne: Medical Genetics Unit, Department of Paediatrics, Howard University College of Medicine, Washington DC 20001.

Received January 14, 1971.

References:

1. Davidson, R. G., Nitowsky, H. N., and Childs, B., *Proc. US Nat. Acad. Sci.*, **50**, 481 (1963).

2. Beutler, E., and Baluda, M. C., *Lancet*, i, 189 (1964).

3. DeMars, R., and Nance, W. E., *Wistar Inst. Symp. Monog.*, No. 1, 35 (Wistar Institute Press, Philadelphia, 1964).

4. Boyer, S. H., Porter, I. H., and Weilbacher, R. G., *Proc. US Nat. Acad. Sci.*, **48**, 1868 (1962).

5. Linder, D., and Gartler, S. M., *Science*, **150**, 67 (1965).

了一片具有相同 G6PD 表型的细胞，或者仅仅感染了一个表皮细胞。现有的数据（6个杂合子）太少，以至于难以明确地区分到底是来源于一个细胞还是一片细胞，尤其是当正常细胞的数量可能达到了 1,000 个或者更多的时候 [5]。也有可能两种 G6PD表型的细胞都被感染，但其中一种表型在细胞增殖的过程中丢失了。

如果病毒的滴度合适的话，它将传播到数千个邻近的细胞，造成相当大面积的感染。如果细胞增殖过程涉及病毒的传播，那么就会导致一种表现出两种 G6PD 表型的多细胞起源的病变。另一方面，如果该过程涉及单个细胞或者一小组细胞的改变，那么我们所发现的结果就可以作为支持单细胞或者克隆性起源的证据，这与预期的结果一致。寻常疣的病理学特征性嗜酸性包涵体或许仍然代表了随着细胞的增殖已经发生了复制的病毒颗粒，而不是从感染的初始部位传播过来的病毒颗粒。

近年来的迹象表明病毒是一些诸如劳斯肉瘤和鼠类白血病等动物恶性肿瘤的病因，以及得到了类似非洲伯基特淋巴瘤这样的肿瘤可能为克隆性起源 [17] 并有可能是由呼肠孤病毒 3 引起（参考文献 18）的证据，因而病毒引起肿瘤样病变的行为就具有了非常重要的意义。有不少人认为体细胞突变是引起肿瘤变化的原因。在某些情况下，体细胞突变有可能发生在病毒侵染易感细胞或细胞克隆之后，或者这种病毒是以共生的方式藏匿于所有细胞之中，而体细胞突变也许能诱发病毒的致癌作用。

感谢加特勒博士为我们提出了一些意见和建议。本工作得到了美国儿童局的一项基金以及美国公共卫生署的一项一般研究经费补助金的资助。

（毛晨晖 翻译；袁峥 审稿）

6. Fialkow, P. J., Gartler, S. M., and Yoshida, A., *Proc. US Nat. Acad. Sci.*, **58**, 1468 (1967).

7. Beutler, E., Collins, Z., and Irwin, L. E., *New Engl. J. Med.*, **276**, 389 (1967).

8. Park, I., and Jones, H. W., *Amer J. Obstet. Gynec.*, **102**, 106 (1968).

9. Allen, A. C., *The Skin, a Clinicopathological Treatise*, 775 (Grune and Stratton, New York, 1967).

10. Williams, M. G., Howatson, A. F., and Almeida, J. D., *Nature*, **189**, 895 (1961).

11. Lewis, G. M., and Wheeler, C. E., *Practical Dermatology*, 520 (Saunders, Philadelphia, London, 1967).

12. Fildes, R. A., and Parr, C. W., *Nature*, **200**, 890 (1963).

13. Nance, W. E., *Cold Spring Harbor Symp. Quant. Biol.*, **29**, 415 (1964).

14. Gandini, E., Gartler, S. M., Angiuni, N., Argiolas, N., and Dell'Acqua, G., *Proc. US Nat. Acad. Sci.*, **61**, 945 (1968).

15. Ohkawara, A., Halperin, J., Barber, P., and Halperin, K. M., *Arch. Dermatol.*, **95**, 412 (1967).

16. Ohno, S., Payne, H. W., Morrison, M., and Beutler, E., *Science*, **153**, 1015 (1966).

17. Fialkow, P. J., Klein, G., Gartler, S. M., and Clifford, P., *Lancet*, i, 348 (1970).

18. Stanley, N. F., *Lancet*, i, 961 (1966).

Carbon Compounds in Apollo 12 Lunar Samples

B. Nagy *et al.*

Editor's Note

Samples of lunar "soil" (mineral powder, or regolith) were brought back by Apollo 11, the first manned mission to the Moon's surface. The Apollo 12 mission was more systematic in collecting rocks and regolith. Here geochemist Bartholomew Nagy and his coworkers, including the Nobel laureate chemist Harold Urey who pioneered research on the chemical origin of life, report that the Apollo 12 samples contain traces of organic (carbon-based) compounds, including small traces of amino acids (potentially contaminants from handling). While some carbon on the lunar surface originates in the stream of charged particles coming from the Sun (the solar wind), carbon deeper in the rock samples was puzzling. There was no suggestion, however, of an origin involving life.

SMALL quantities of carbon compounds have been found in three samples of surface fines (12001, 34, 12033, 8 and 12042, 13), in one sample from the bottom of a 15 cm deep trench dug by the astronauts (12023, 8), in two core samples from 9 and 39 cm below the lunar surface (12025, 60 and 12028, 207, respectively) and in the interior of a lunar rock (12022, 81). The locations where these samples were collected, the site of the lunar descent module, and the basic topography of the collection area are shown in Fig. 1. We identified hydrocarbons (in the parts per billion range, except CH_4) using a pyrolysis instrument containing a helium atmosphere at $700°C$, connected to a tandem gas chromatograph-mass spectrometer. The gaseous components were analysed by vacuum pyrolysis at $681°C$ and $1,084°C$. Some gaseous components were separated with high resolution mass spectrometry. A search for amino-acids was carried out using Soxhlet extraction with hot water and ion exchange chromatography. In addition, an extensive examination with transmitted light and scanning electron microscopy was made in an attempt to establish the locales of the organic molecules and to shed some light on their possible origin(s) and history. It is difficult to interpret the results unequivocally, which is not surprising in view of the difficulties encountered with the explanations of the Apollo 11 and 12 findings. This is illustrated by the apparent disparity in age of lunar fines and rocks[1,2].

阿波罗12号月球样品中的含碳化合物

纳吉等

编者按

人类搭乘阿波罗11号首次登上了月球，并带回了一些月球表面的"土壤"（矿物粉末或表土）。在阿波罗12号登月任务中，采集岩石和表土样品的工作就更加系统化了。地球化学家巴塞洛缪·纳吉及其同事（包括诺贝尔化学奖获得者哈罗德·尤里）率先发起了对生命化学起源的研究，他们在本文中报告称：在阿波罗12号采集的样品中含有痕量的有机物（碳基化合物），包括超痕量的氨基酸（可能源自处理样品时的污染）。虽然可以认为月球表面上的碳是由来自太阳的带电粒子流（太阳风）产生的，但岩石深处的碳实在令人费解。然而，这一研究并没有带给我们关于生命起源的更多提示。

目前已经在以下这些样品中发现了少量的含碳化合物：三份表面微粒土样品（12001，34；12033，8和12042，13），一份宇航员从15 cm深的沟槽底部挖出的样品（12023，8），两份在月球表面以下9 cm和39 cm处采得的土芯样品（分别为12025，60和12028，207）以及一份取自月球岩石内部的样品（12022，81）。上述样品的采集地点、登月舱的降落位置以及采集区域的基本地貌见图1。我们是利用工作在700℃氦气氛下并与气相色谱–质谱联用仪相连的热解装置鉴定出碳氢化合物（除CH_4外都在十亿分之一或称p.p.b.量级）的。对气体组分的分析采用681℃和1,084℃真空热解。有些气体组分是用高分辨质谱进行分离的。在寻找氨基酸的过程中我们使用了以热水为溶剂的索氏提取法和离子交换色谱法。此外，我们还用透射光显微镜和扫描电子显微镜进行了大范围的检查，目的在于确定有机分子所处的位置并尝试说明它们的来源和历史。很难毫不含糊地对研究结果加以解释，从解释阿波罗11号和阿波罗12号发现物时所遇到的种种困难来考虑，这并不令人惊奇。可以用月球上的微粒土和岩石在年代上的明显不同[1,2]来说明两者之间的差异。

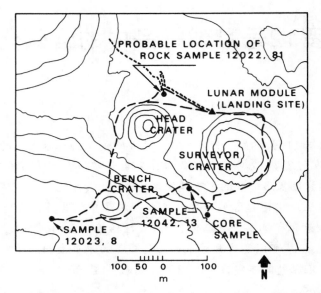

Fig. 1. Location of samples referred to in Figs. 2 and 3. Sample 12033, 8 was collected north of Head Crater on the second Extra Vehicular Traverse. The location of sample 12001, 34 was not accurately noted by NASA, although it was indicated that it was collected near the landing module (modified from ref. 10). - - -, First Eva traverse; – – –, second Eva traverse; ——, elevation contour lines at 5 feet intervals.

Vacuum Pyrolysis

Lunar samples were pyrolysed *in vacuo* in a quartz tube designed to fit the gas inlet system of the mass spectrometer. This system was modified so that all evolved gases could be directed into the ion source of the mass spectrometer on reaching the desired pyrolysis temperatures. Before pyrolysis, the quartz tube containing the sample was degassed for 20 min by the mass spectrometer pumping system. A portable furnace was then placed around the quartz tube. The pyrolysis temperatures were kept constant during the mass spectral analyses.

Total carbon based on p.p.m. of carbon from CH_4, CO, and CO_2 was determined for Apollo 12 fines, core material and one rock chip. Before mass spectrometric determinations were made, calibration curves were calculated from various quantities of these gases. To prevent ambiguity with respect to the amount of CO in the lunar samples, we made high resolution determinations at $m/e = 28$, to distinguish the relative intensities of CO, N_2, and C_2H_4.

All lunar samples were vacuum pyrolysed at 681°C. After pumping out the gases from the mass spectrometer, the samples were subsequently pyrolysed at 1,084°C and analysed as before. The contribution of carbon to the gases is shown in Table 1. The core samples and the fines showed CO_2 in almost equal quantities from the 681°C and 1,084°C pyrolysis. In addition, the total carbon from CO_2 was approximately the same in surface fines and

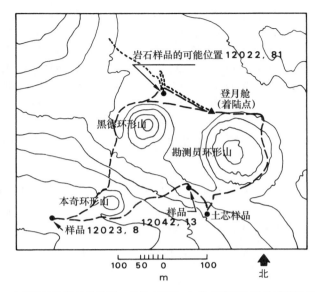

图 1. 在图 2 和图 3 中所涉及的样品的位置。样品 12033，8 是在第二次舱外活动路线上的黑德环形山北部采集的。美国国家航空航天局没有准确地注明样品 12001，34 的位置，仅指出是在着陆舱附近采集到的(根据参考文献 10 进行了修改)。- - -，第一次舱外活动路线；－ － －，第二次舱外活动路线；——，5 英尺间隔的等高线。

真 空 热 解

将月球样品置于为适应质谱的气体进样系统而设计的石英管内并在真空中热解。调节系统以保证生成的所有气体在到达所需的热解温度时都能被导入到质谱仪的离子源中。在热解前，用质谱仪的真空系统对盛放样品的石英管进行 20 min 的除气处理。接着在这个石英管的周围安插一个可移动的加热炉。在质谱分析过程中热解温度保持恒定。

阿波罗 12 号采集的微粒土、土芯物质和岩屑样品中的总碳量来自于 CH_4、CO 和 CO_2，以 p.p.m.（译者注：百万分之一）表示。在进行质谱检测前，我们根据对不同量上述气体的计算作出相应的校准曲线。为了避免在判断月球样品中的 CO 含量时出现不确定性，我们在 $m/e = 28$ 处进行了高分辨测定，以便区分出 CO、N_2 和 C_2H_4 的相对强度。

所有的月球样品都在 681℃ 下进行真空热解。当质谱仪抽空所有气体后，样品接着在 1,084℃ 下热解，并按前述方法进行分析。表 1 中列出了碳在气体中的含量。根据 681℃ 和 1,084℃ 的热解结果，土芯样品和微粒土中的 CO_2 量几乎相同。此外，在表面微粒土样品和两份土芯样品中，来自 CO_2 的总碳量是大致相同的。不过，岩

in the two core samples. The rock chip, however, yielded 80% of the total CO_2 present when pyrolysed at 681°C and contained almost three times more CO_2 than any other sample. The CO content was roughly half of the amount found in all other samples. In all other samples pyrolysis at 1,084°C released 90% of the CO. CH_4 was produced in approximately equal amounts at both pyrolysis temperatures in all samples. The rock chip produced the most CH_4. Some of the CH_4 could be attributed to contamination, because the Ottawa quartz sand control from the LRL cabinet where the lunar samples were processed yielded about one-third the amount of CH_4 found in the lunar samples when pyrolysed under identical conditions.

Table 1. Vacuum Pyrolysis, Combined Results for 681°C and 1,084°C

Sample	p.p.m. C from CO, CO_2 and CH_4
12028, 207 (core 39 cm below lunar surface)	96.2
12025, 60 (core 9 cm below lunar surface)	111.2
12042, 13	140.8
12001, 34	115.2
12023, 8	109.2
12033, 8	108.6
12022, 81 (rock chip from interior of lunar rock)	89.6

All of the Apollo 12 lunar samples (except the rock chip) received in this laboratory were stored under nitrogen at the LRL. Pyrolysis at 681°C with high resolution determinations at $m/e = 28$ showed a large amount of nitrogen for all samples. The nitrogen content was approximately 40% greater than the CO content at 681°C, even though the samples were placed under high vacuum for 20 min before heating. The subsequent pyrolysis at 1,084°C showed a considerable decrease in the nitrogen content to less than one-third that of CO.

Helium Pyrolysis

The lunar samples were pyrolysed in a stream of He at 700°C for 7.5 min in a modified Hamilton pyrolysis unit[3-5]. The He stream (3–5 ml./min) from the fused quartz pyrolysis tube was connected to a Perkin–Elmer model 226 gas chromatograph. It also served as the carrier gas for this unit. In turn the gas chromatograph was connected by means of a Watson–Biemann molecular separator to a Hitachi RMU-6E mass spectrometer. A small trap, cooled with liquid nitrogen, was placed between the pyrolyser unit and the gas chromatograph so that, following pyrolysis, the trapped pyrolysis products could be introduced as a single sample into the gas chromatograph by means of a small portable oven which quickly heated the trap to 250°–300°C. The gas chromatograph contained a 50 feet × 0.02 inch internal diameter polyphenyl ether capillary column and a hydrogen flame detector.

Because it has been reported that similar aromatic hydrocarbons can be synthesized when methane is heated to 1,000°C over silica gel[6], we passed methane over pre-pyrolysed lunar fines (12001, 34) at 700°C for 7.5 min. No evidence of any synthesis was observed (Fig. 3E). It could be argued that the initial pyrolysis, which removed the carbon compounds,

屑样品在 681℃ 的热解中产生了总 CO_2 量的 80%，并且所含的 CO_2 量近乎是任何其他样品的 3 倍。CO 的含量大致为所有其他样品中含量的一半。所有其他样品在 1,084℃ 热解时都释放出 90% 的 CO。全部样品在两个热解温度下都产生了近乎等量的 CH_4。岩屑样品产生的 CH_4 最多。可以把一部分 CH_4 归因于污染，因为来自专门处理月球样品的月球物质回收实验所处理间的渥太华石英砂对照样品在同样条件下被热解时，也产生了约为在月球样品中发现量的 1/3 的 CH_4。

表 1. 真空热解，综合 681℃ 和 1,084℃ 下的结果

样品	来自于 CO、CO_2 和 CH_4 的 p.p.m. 碳量
12028, 207（月球表面以下 39 cm 处的土芯）	96.2
12025, 60（月球表面以下 9 cm 处的土芯）	111.2
12042, 13	140.8
12001, 34	115.2
12023, 8	109.2
12033, 8	108.6
12022, 81（月球岩石内部的岩屑）	89.6

本实验室接收的所有由阿波罗 12 号采集的月球样品（除岩屑外）都曾被月球物质回收实验所保存于氮气中。在 m/e=28 处对 681℃ 下热解产物进行高分辨测定所得的结果表明：所有样品都含有大量的氮气。在 681℃ 时氮气的量比 CO 的量多出约 40%，尽管在加热前我们已将样品置于高真空中长达 20 min。随后在 1,084℃ 下的热解结果显示，氮气含量大幅下降至不足 CO 量的 1/3。

氦 热 解

将月球样品置于改进的哈密顿热解装置中，在 700℃ 下于氦气流中热解 7.5 min[3-5]。来自熔凝石英热解管的氦气流（3 ml/min ～ 5 ml/min）被接入到一台珀金 - 埃尔默 226 型气相色谱仪上。氦气也是这个装置中的载气。接着将气相色谱仪经由一台沃森 - 比曼分子分离器连接到日立 RMU-6E 质谱仪上。热解器和气相色谱仪之间有一个用液氮来冷却的小型冷阱，这样，在热解之后收集到的热解产物就可以各自作为单独的样品通过一台能迅速将冷阱加热至 250℃ ～ 300℃ 的小型可移动加热器而引入到气相色谱仪中。该气相色谱仪中装有一根内径为 50 英尺 ×0.02 英寸的聚苯醚毛细管柱和一台氢焰检测器。

由于已经有人报道过将甲烷置于硅胶上加热到 1,000℃ 就可以生成类似芳香族化合物的烃类物质 [6]，我们将甲烷在 700℃ 时通过预热解过的月球微粒土（12001, 34）长达 7.5 min。没有观测到有任何合成现象出现（图 3E）。有人可能会说：初始热解

destroyed any "catalytic" effect the fines might have had before heating. This argument is, however, tenuous because of the lack of experimental evidence. Another He pyrolysis control was run using a $CO-H_2$ (1/2.5, v/v) gas mixture over pre-pyrolysed lunar fines (12023, 8) at 700°C for 7.5 min, and did not show any of the hydrocarbons found in the lunar samples.

He pyrolysis of lunar fines, the two core samples, and a rock chip (Figs. 2 and 3) showed the presence of primarily CO, CO_2, CH_4 and H_2. Many organic compounds were present in the p.p.b. range, together with lesser amounts of Ne and possibly COS. (See captions for Figs. 2 and 3.) It may be possible, however, that some of the higher molecular weight hydrocarbons were artefacts resulting from the He pyrolysis technique. In a control experiment benzene was pyrolysed in He at 600°C and yielded traces of, predominantly, biphenyl with lesser amounts of naphthalene. Pre-Cambrian rock samples which had given He pyrolysis products similar to those found in the lunar samples were subjected to vacuum pyrolysis at 500°C and 600°C using a liquid nitrogen cold trap and showed only ions of m/e=76, 78, 91, 92, 154, 177 which indicate the presence of benzene, toluene, alkyl benzenes, biphenyl, and so on, plus smaller molecular weight hydrocarbons below m/e=78. It was also determined in a separate experiment with this cold trap vacuum pyrolysis technique that biphenyl can be destroyed by pyrolysis at temperatures of 700°C and above. The results showed degradation and intramolecular rearrangement to products such as naphthalene.

过程去除了含碳化合物，因而破坏了微粒土在加热前可能会具有的"催化"效应。不过因为缺乏实验证据，所以这种说法是空洞无力的。我们还进行了另一组氦热解的对照实验，即将 $CO-H_2$（体积比为 1/2.5）气体混合物在 700℃时通过预热解过的月球微粒土样品（12023,8）长达 7.5 min，结果在月球样品中并未发现有任何烃类物质。

月球表面微粒土、两份土芯样品和一片岩屑的氦热解结果（图 2 和图 3）显示主要产物为 CO、CO_2、CH_4 和 H_2。很多有机物的存在量在 p.p.b. 级的范围之内，还有更微量的 Ne 和可能存在的 COS。（参见图 2 和图 3 的说明文字。）不过，某些分子量较高的烃类物质有可能是由氦热解技术导致的人工产物。在对照实验中，将苯在 600℃氦气氛下热解，产生的痕量物质主要为联苯，并含有少量萘。前寒武纪岩石样品的氦热解产物与在月球样品中所发现的类似；将前寒武纪岩石样品在 500℃和 600℃下进行真空热解并由液氮冷阱引入质谱，结果只发现了 m/e = 76、78、91、92、154 和 177 的离子，表明存在苯、甲苯、烷基苯和联苯等物质以及低于 m/e = 78 的较小分子量的烃。在另一次单独的实验中，我们还用这种冷阱真空热解技术证明：在 700℃或更高温度下的热解中，联苯是会被破坏的。这些结果表明联苯通过降解和分子内重排生成了诸如萘等产物。

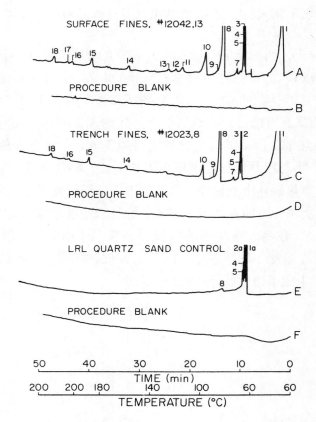

Fig. 2. Gas chromatograms of the pyrolysis products of *A*, surface lunar fines (sample 12042, 13), *C*, lunar trench fines (sample 12023, 8), and *E*, LRL Ottawa quartz sand control. Peak identities, all traces: 1, H_2, CH_4, CO; 2, C_2H_4, C_2H_6; 3, CO_2, C_3H_6; 4, C_4H_8; 5, C_4H_6; 6, C_5H_8 (small peak preceding peak 7 in trace *A* only); 7, C_5H_6; 8, benzene; 9, thiophene; 10, toluene; 11, C_2 alkyl benzene; 12, o-xylene; 13, styrene; 14, indene; 15, naphthalene; 16 and 17, methyl naphthalenes; 18, biphenyl. For trace *E* only: 1a, CH_4, C_3H_8; 2a, CO_2, C_2H_4. Additionally, on trace *A*: 1, also contains Ne; 2, C_2F_4; and on trace *C*: 2, CO_2. Compounds 9, 11 and 13–18 may well be artefacts synthesized in the pyrolyser as Nagy and Preti *et al.* pointed out[12,13].

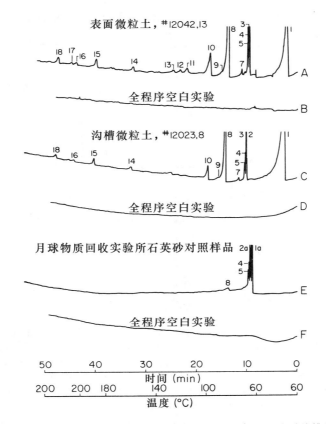

图 2. 热解产物的气相色谱图。*A*，月球表面微粒土（样品12042,13）；*C*，月球沟槽中的微粒土（样品12023,8）；*E*，月球物质回收实验所的渥太华石英砂对照样品。谱峰代号如下，对所有迹线：1，H_2、CH_4、CO；2，C_2H_4、C_2H_6；3，CO_2、C_3H_6；4，C_4H_8；5，C_4H_6；6，C_5H_8（7号峰前面的小峰，仅出现在迹线*A*中）；7，C_5H_6；8，苯；9，噻吩；10，甲苯；11，取代基为二碳的烷基苯；12，邻二甲苯；13，苯乙烯；14，茚；15，萘；16和17，甲基萘；18，联苯。迹线*E*特有的峰：1a，CH_4、C_3H_8；2a，CO_2、C_2H_4。此外，对于迹线*A*：1，还含有Ne；2，C_2F_4。对于迹线*C*：2，CO_2。正如纳吉和普雷蒂等人所指出的那样，化合物 9、11以及13～18很可能是在热解器中生成的人工产物[12,13]。

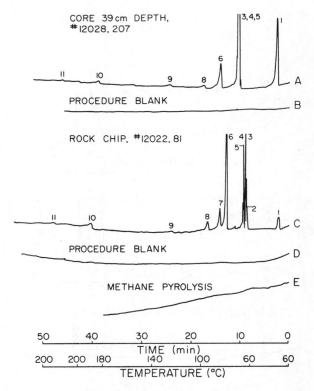

Fig. 3. Gas chromatograms of the pyrolysis products of (*A*) lunar core, 39 cm depth (sample 12028, 207); (*C*) lunar rock chip (sample 12022, 81), and (*E*) CH_4 pyrolysis over pre-pyrolysed lunar fines (sample 12001, 34). Peak identities, all traces: 1, H_2, CH_4, CO; 2, CH_4; 3, C_2H_4; 4, C_3H_6; 5, C_4H_8; 6, benzene; 7, thiophene; 8, toluene; 9, styrene; 10, naphthalene; 11, biphenyl. Additionally, on trace *A*: 3 also contains C_2F_4, $C_2H_2F_2$; 4, $C_4F_4H_2$; 5, C_3F_6; 6, C_4H_6; and on trace *C*: 1, CO absent; 3, CH_4, CO, CO_2; 4, CO_2, Ne, possibly COS; 5, CO_2, C_3H_6. Compounds 7 and 9–11 can be artefacts.

Trace amounts of fluorocarbon compounds were also observed in some of the pyrolysed samples, but these were probably "Teflon" contaminations. A "Teflon" control pyrolysis, using "Teflon" supplied and used by the NASA Manned Spacecraft Center, showed these same fluorocarbon compounds. An Ottawa quartz sand control, which was exposed in the same cabinet at the LRL where the lunar samples were processed, was also He pyrolysed; Fig. 2*E* shows its gas chromatogram. Note that it shows no compounds beyond the small benzene peak. It has been reported (R. B. Erb, personal communication) that the container in which this sample was shipped was cleaned with benzene.

Amino-Acid Analyses

Three samples of lunar fines, 12001, 34 (4.1703 g), 12023, 8 (9.0000 g) and 12033, 8 (9.0015 g), were analysed for their amino-acid content by hot water Soxhlet extraction and by ion exchange column chromatographic techniques[7]. Complete parallel procedure blanks were run at the same time. The water used for the extraction was triple distilled and all glassware was cleaned with acid. Before the ion exchange chromatography the extracts

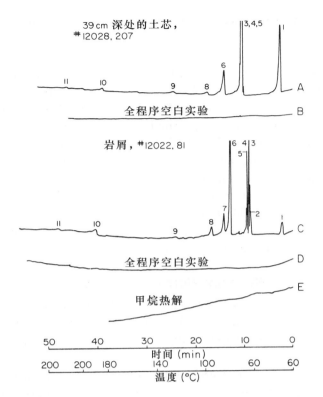

图 3. 热解产物的气相色谱图。(A）月球土芯样品，来自地面以下 39 cm 深处（样品 12028, 207）；(C）月球上的岩屑（样品 12022, 81）；(E）在经预热解的月球微粒土（样品 12001, 34）上进行的 CH_4 热解。谱峰代号如下，对所有迹线：1，H_2、CH_4、CO；2，CH_4；3，C_2H_4；4，C_3H_6；5，C_4H_8；6，苯；7，噻吩；8，甲苯；9，苯乙烯；10，萘；11，联苯。此外，对于迹线 A：3 中还含有 C_2F_4 和 $C_2H_2F_2$；4，$C_4F_4H_2$；5，C_3F_6；6，C_4H_6。对于迹线 C：1，没有 CO；3，CH_4、CO、CO_2；4，CO_2、Ne，可能有 COS；5，CO_2、C_3H_6。化合物 7 和 9 ～ 11 可能是人工产物。

在一些热解后的样品中还发现了痕量的碳氟化合物，不过它们很可能是来自"特氟隆"（译者注：聚四氟乙烯塑料）的污染。我们用美国国家航空航天局载人航天器中心提供和使用的"特氟隆"进行对照热解实验，结果发现了相同的碳氟化合物。我们对与月球样品同在一个月球物质回收实验所处理间的一份渥太华石英砂对照样品也进行了氦热解实验；其气相色谱结果见图 2E。请注意在小的苯峰之后该图中并没有出现其他化合物。据说（厄尔布，个人交流）在运输过程中盛放该样品的容器曾用苯清洗过。

氨基酸分析

我们用热水索氏提取法和离子交换柱层析技术对三份在月球上采集的微粒土样品——12001, 34（4.1703 g）、12023, 8（9.0000 g）和 12033, 8（9.0015 g）进行了氨基酸含量的分析 [7]。同时还进行了全程序空白实验。提取所用的水是经过三次蒸馏的，且每一件玻璃器皿都用酸清洗过。在用离子交换色谱法进行分析之前，我们

and the corresponding blanks were checked for bacterial contamination. The cultures showed no growth.

The analyses of the three lunar samples indicated the presence of only traces of amino-acids in the low p.p.b. range. After subtracting the amino-acids in the blanks from the lunar sample chromatograms, samples 12001, 34 and 12023, 8 showed traces of urea, aspartic acid, threonine, serine, glycine, alanine and ornithine. The highest concentration of amino-acids occurred in sample 12001, 34. NASA reported that this sample was likely to be contaminated. The amino-acid distribution found is similar to that expected from hand contamination[8]. In sample 12023, 8 the total amount of amino-acids is approximately 1/20 of that in sample 12001, 34 and the distribution again suggests hand contamination. In sample 12033, 8 the amino-acid content appeared to be zero. Urea, however, was present even in this sample. It seems, therefore, that these samples did not contain the amino-acids found in Apollo 11 fines[3].

Electron Microscopic Studies

All samples of lunar fines were studied before and after pyrolysis at 700°C in He and at 1,084°C in vacuum, using a Leitz Ortholux microscope with a transmitted light and oil immersion objective having a magnification of 950.

In the fines, silicate spheres, "tear drop", and dumbbell shaped particles (with and without large inclusions) were commonly found among the irregularly shaped mineral matter. The spheres and dumbbells resembled the spheres and dumbbells found in the Apollo 11 fines but there were some subtle differences. In all of the untreated fines which we examined, many of the spheres and dumbbells appeared to be more irregular than the almost perfect spheres found in the Apollo 11 fines. Some particles had relatively large inclusions, while other spheres had no inclusions at all; others had an appearance similar to the heat treated (1,200°C) Apollo 11 spheres. Only the untreated sample 12042, 13 contained very few large inclusions, although numerous smaller inclusions were also observed in this sample. In the same sample, an elongated dumbbell (Fig. 4A) and a bead enclosed in an irregularly shaped glass fragment were found. In the untreated sample 12033, 8, reported to be an ash layer[9], there was an elongated and twisted dumbbell, which gave the appearance of having started to elongate and melt on heating. There was also a small hole at one end of this particle.

检查了提取物和相应空白样品的细菌污染情况。没有发现培养菌表现出生长的迹象。

这三份月球样品的分析结果表明：只有p.p.b.级的氨基酸存在。在从月球样品色谱图里扣除空白样中的氨基酸后，发现样品12001，34和12023，8中含有痕量的尿素、天冬氨酸、苏氨酸、丝氨酸、甘氨酸、丙氨酸和鸟氨酸。氨基酸浓度最高的样品是12001，34。美国国家航空航天局报道称这份样品很可能遭到了污染。已发现的氨基酸分布与根据手触污染预测到的情况类似[8]。样品12023，8中的氨基酸总量大概是样品12001，34的1/20，而其分布也暗示着存在手触污染。样品12033，8的氨基酸含量似乎为0。不过，即使在样品12033，8中也有尿素存在。因此，事实似乎表明这些样品并不含有在阿波罗11号微粒土样品中所发现的氨基酸[3]。

电子显微镜研究

我们用一台带有放大倍数为950的油浸物镜的莱茨－奥托卢克斯透射光显微镜对所有月球微粒土样品在700℃氢热解和在1,084℃真空热解之前以及之后都进行了研究。

在微粒土样品中，我们经常能从形状不规则的矿物质里找到硅酸盐球、"滴斑"和哑铃形微粒（有或者没有大的内含物）。这些球状物和哑铃状物类似于在阿波罗11号微粒土样品中所发现的球状物和哑铃状物，但有一些细微的差别。在我们检测过的所有未经处理的微粒土中，很多球状物和哑铃状物似乎比在阿波罗11号微粒土中所发现的近乎完美的球体显得更不规则些。有些微粒中含有较大的内含物，而另一些球状物完全不含内含物；其余则具有与在经过热处理（1,200℃）的阿波罗11号微粒土中发现的球体相类似的外观。只有未经处理的12042，13样品含有极少的大内含物，但在该样品中仍然可以观察到大量的较小内含物。在同一个样品中我们看到了一个拉长的哑铃（图4A）和一粒被封闭于一个形状不规则的玻璃碎片中的熔珠。据报道样品12033，8属于火山灰层[9]，在未经处理的该样品中，有一个长而扭曲的哑铃状物，看上去像是在加热时要开始伸长和熔化的样子。在该微粒的一端还有一个小洞。

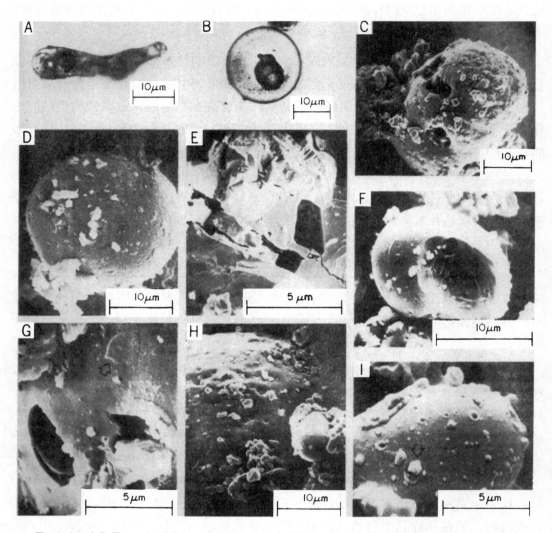

Fig. 4. *A* and *B*, Transmitted light photomicrographs of "twisted" glass dumbbell and glass sphere with opening, respectively; *C* and *D*, scanning electron micrographs of beads after pyrolysis at 1,084°C; *E*, freshly broken surface of interior rock chip (note absence of vesicles); *F*, partially broken glass bead showing cavity near the surface; *G*, a portion of a thin walled glass bead with broken openings (note arrow pointing to a flat object, probably produced by collision with a molten particle); *H*, part of a glass bead showing what appear to be several blow holes; *I*, one end of a glass dumbbell showing holes produced by hypervelocity impacts. Note arrow pointing to larger and slower velocity particle which caused imprint but did not penetrate the surface.

Morphologically, the core samples were no different from the surface fines, with the possible exception that many of the glass beads were covered with attached, fine, particulate matter. The glass beads from the core samples also showed numerous well defined cavities and inclusions. The lunar rock showed no vesicles or holes. The morphological effects of pyrolysis on all the samples at 700°C and 1,084°C are summarized in Table 2.

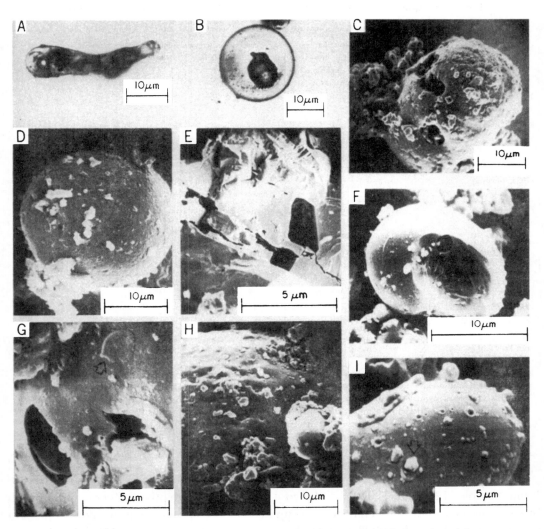

图 4. A 和 B 分别是用透射光显微镜拍摄的"扭曲"玻璃哑铃和有孔玻璃球的照片；C 和 D 为在 1,084℃ 热解后对熔珠拍摄的扫描电子显微镜照片；E，岩石内部的岩屑新切开的断面（请注意没有气泡）；F，部分破裂的玻璃熔珠在表面附近出现空穴；G，有破口的薄壁玻璃熔珠的一部分（请注意箭头所指的片状物，很可能产生自与一个熔融微粒的碰撞）；H，玻璃熔珠的一部分，看上去好像有若干个气孔；I，玻璃哑铃的一端，上面有由超速撞击导致的小孔。请注意图中箭头所指的是一个只留下印痕但未穿透表面的大且速度慢的微粒。

从形态学角度来看，可能除了很多玻璃熔珠表面会有附着于其上的细小颗粒状物质以外，土芯样品和表面微粒土样品并没有什么不同。来自于土芯样品的玻璃熔珠还呈现出大量轮廓分明的空穴和内含物。在月球岩石样品中没有发现气泡或小孔。表 2 总结了 700℃ 和 1,084℃ 热解对所有样品形态的影响。

Table 2. Morphological Features and Differences Observed under Transmitted Light

Sample No.	Untreated lunar material	Pyrolysed at 700°C in He	Pyrolysed at 1,084°C in vacuum
12001, 34 fines (a)	Numerous distorted spheres and dumbbells with large central and/or small inclusions. Some spheres without inclusions have the appearance of recrystallized structures	Inclusions unchanged; some well defined blow holes	No inclusions; openings but no well defined blow holes
12023, 8 fines (b)	As above	Same as above	No inclusions; well defined blow holes; one thick irregular glass fragment containing a bead 21 μm in diameter, with inclusion
12033, 8 fines (c)	As above	No inclusions; no well defined blow holes	No blow holes; beads almost unrecognizable
12042, 13 fines (d)	As above, with the exception of few large central inclusions, numerous small inclusions	Inclusions unchanged, many small blow holes	No inclusions; beads deformed; irregular and well defined holes are visible
12025, 60 fines. Core, 9 cm below surface (e)	Spheres covered with fine particulate matter; broken and deformed beads; inclusions and well defined blow holes	Small blow holes, inclusions	No inclusions; no blow holes; beads deformed
12028, 207 fines. Core, 39 cm below surface (f)	As above; one well formed 77 μm elongated dumbbell with inclusion	Same as above	Same as above
Rock 12022, 81 (g)	No inclusions; no blow holes	No inclusions; no blow holes	Not examined

(a) Documented fines collected near Lunar Module. (b) Documented fines from Lunar Environment Sample Container; collected from the bottom of 15 cm trench inside north rim of Sharp Crater. (c) This sample is regarded to be an ash layer; documented and dug near north rim of Head Crater. (d) Documented collection in an area of "wrinkled texture" near rim of Surveyor Crater. (e) Top of double core tube No. 2010, collected on rim of 10 m diameter crater south of Halo Crater. (f) Bottom of double core tube No. 2012 (same collection site). (g) Inside chip from documented olivine dolerite. This rock was partially buried and was located approximately 120 m north-west of the Lunar Module.
Sample locations (a)—(g) are taken from ref. 10.

Lunar samples 12023, 8, 12042, 13, the core sample from a depth of 39 cm, and a freshly broken surface of the rock chip, were examined by a scanning electron microscope. The core sample and sample 12023, 8 were also examined after pyrolysis at 1,084°C. The fines were mounted on the electron microscope pedestal with a drop of absolute methanol. The rock chip was mounted with double adhesive tape. All sample preparations for electron microscopy were performed in the clean room of the Naval Weapons Center at China Lake, California. The pyrolysed fines showed much less tendency to adhere to the bare pedestal surface than did the untreated samples. The samples were coated with an ~500 Å thick layer of gold-palladium alloy by vacuum deposition[3] and then inserted in the scanning electron microscope.

The pyrolysis at 1,084°C seems to have led to the development of rough surfaces on the beads (Fig. 4C and D). Smooth beads were difficult to find and larger holes were more noticeable in the beads with rough surfaces than in the unpyrolysed beads. These effects might indicate softening of the glass accompanied by degassing at the pyrolysis temperature.

表 2. 在透射光下观测到的形态特征与差异

样品编号	未经热处理的月球物质	700℃氢热解	1,084℃真空热解
12001，34 微粒土（a）	大量扭曲的球状物或哑铃状物，中心有大的和 / 或小的内含物。某些没有内含物的球状物具有重结晶结构的外观	内含物未发生变化；出现了一些轮廓分明的气孔	无内含物；有开口但没有轮廓分明的气孔
12023，8 微粒土（b）	如上	同上	无内含物；有轮廓分明的气孔；一块有内含物并包含 21 μm 直径熔珠的不规则厚玻璃体
12033，8 微粒土（c）	如上	无内含物；无轮廓分明的气孔	无气孔；有几乎不可辨认的熔珠
12042，13 微粒土（d）	如上，不同之处是中心几乎没有大的内含物，有大量小的内含物	内含物未发生变化，出现了很多小气孔	无内含物；熔珠变形；可以看到不规则且轮廓分明的小孔
12025，60 微粒土。表面以下 9 cm 处的土芯样品（e）	表面覆盖着细小颗粒物的球；破碎和变形的熔珠；内含物和轮廓分明的气孔	小气孔，内含物	无内含物；无气孔；熔珠变形
12028，207 微粒土。表面以下 39 cm 处的土芯样品（f）	如上；一个形状完好、有内含物的 77 μm 拉长哑铃状物	同上	同上
岩石 12022，81（g）	无内含物；无气孔	无内含物；无气孔	未检测

（a）在登月舱附近采集到的有记录的微粒土。（b）来自月球环境标本容器的有记录的微粒土；从夏普环形山内北部边缘处深 15 cm 的沟底采集。（c）该样品被认为属于火山灰层；从黑德环形山北部边缘附近被挖掘出来并有记录。（d）在勘测员环形山附近的"褶皱构造"区域采集到的有记录的样品。（e）第 2010 号双层岩心管的顶部，采集地点是在黑洛环形山南方一直径为 10 m 的环形山的边缘。（f）第 2012 号双层岩心管的底部（同一采集地点）。（g）从有记录的橄榄石粗玄岩内部取得的岩屑。这块被部分掩埋的岩石位于登月舱西北约 120 m 处。

样品采集地点（a）~（g）引自参考文献 10。

我们用扫描电子显微镜检测了月球样品 12023，8、12042，13、来自深 39 cm 处的土芯样品以及岩屑新切开的断面。还检测了 1,084℃热解后的土芯样品和 12023，8 样品。用一滴无水甲醇将微粒固定在电子显微镜的样品台上。岩屑用双面胶带固定。所有用电子显微镜检测的样品都是在加州中国湖美国海军武器中心的无尘室中制备的。经热解处理的微粒远比未经热解处理的微粒更不容易黏在空样品台的表面。利用真空沉积法[3] 在样品表面镀上一层厚约 500 Å 的金钯合金，然后将其置入扫描电子显微镜中。

1,084℃热解似乎会导致熔珠粗糙表面的扩展（图 4C 和 D）。在热解之后的样品中很难发现表面光滑的熔珠，而且粗糙表面熔珠中较大的孔也比在未经热处理的熔珠中见到的更醒目。这些结果或许可以说明在热解温度下的脱气过程同时伴随着玻璃的软化。

The freshly broken surface of the lunar rock showed no vesicles, only massive crystalline structure with fissures which were possibly arranged along cleavage planes (Fig. 4E); conchoidal fractures were also present. Other untreated samples showed a number of interesting features. From the particle illustrated in Fig. 4F, a chip was removed, probably by impact, resulting in a conchoidal surface and revealing an internal cavity very near to the original surface of this glass bead. Fig. 4G shows part of a thin walled glass bead with irregular shaped broken holes and a plaque (note arrow), probably resulting from a completely molten, impacting object. Fig. 4H is particularly noteworthy because it contains numerous small openings which resemble blow holes. The end of a dumbbell shown in Fig. 4I is covered with what appear to be impact craters with lips, which might have been caused by impacts from hypervelocity particles of about $0.1–0.2$ μm in size. Lower velocity and larger impacting particles, ~ 1.0 μm in diameter, show impact prints but remained attached to this dumbbell without penetrating its surface (note arrow).

There seem to be subtle differences between the morphologies of the Apollo 11 and 12 lunar fines. The abundance of what appear to be degassing blow holes, distorted particles and so on may suggest a different thermal history at the Apollo 12 landing site. It appears that the carbon compounds are present in some of the enclosures of the fines, and there seem to be carbon compounds dissolved in the lunar rock (interior) that we examined. This lunar rock contained no vesicles. One can account for the carbon in the Apollo 12 fines partially from solar wind emplacement[11]. It is, however, difficult to account for the carbon in the interior of the rock by this mechanism. Degassing of the Moon could be one mechanism which might account for the carbon in the interior of igneous lunar rocks.

We thank Drs. T. Timothy Myoda, Marjorie Lou and Barbara Rowley and Mrs. Johanne C. Dickinson, Roberta deFiore, Urmi Patel and Janet Greenquist for help with the experiments. This work was sponsored by a NASA contract.

(**232**, 94-98; 1971)

Bartholomew Nagy, Judith E. Modzeleski, Vincent E. Modzeleski, M. A. Jabbar Mohammad, Lois Anne Nagy and Ward M. Scott: Department of Geosciences, University of Arizona, Tucson, Arizona 85721.
Charles M. Drew, Joseph E. Thomas and Reba Ward: Naval Weapons Center, China Lake, California 93555.
Paul B. Hamilton: Alfred I. duPont Institute, Wilmington, Delaware 19899.
Harold C. Urey: Department of Chemistry, University of California at San Diego, La Jolla, California 92037.

Received May 25, 1971.

References:
1. Silver, L. T., *Geol. Soc. Amer. Abstract*, **2**, 684 (1970).
2. Wasserburg, G. J., and Papanastassiou, D. A., *Geol. Soc. Amer. Abstract*, **2**, 715 (1970).
3. Nagy, B., Drew, C. M., Hamilton, P. B., Modzeleski, V. E., Murphy, Sr. M. E., Scott, W. M., Urey, H. C., and Young, M., *Science*, **167**, 770 (1970).
4. Nagy, B., Scott, W. M., Modzeleski, V. E., Nagy, L. A., Drew, C. M., McEwan, W. S., Thomas, J. E., Hamilton, P. B., and Urey, H. C., *Nature*, **225**, 1028 (1970).
5. Scott, W. M., Modzeleski, V. E., and Nagy, B., *Nature*, **225**, 1129 (1970).

　　在月球岩石的新断面上没有发现气泡，只有大量带有裂纹的晶体结构，这些裂纹有可能是沿解理面排布的（图4E）；此外还有贝壳状断口。其他未经处理的样品呈现出很多值得关注的特征。如图4F所示的微粒，很可能是由于撞击使一块碎片脱离，从而生成了贝壳状表面并在非常接近于这一玻璃熔珠原始表面的部位出现了一个内部空穴。图4G是一块薄壁玻璃熔珠的一部分，上面有形状不规则的破洞和一个斑痕（注意箭头所指），可能是由一个完全熔融的冲击物造成的。图4H格外引人注意，因为它含有大量类似于气孔的小开口。图4I显示的是一个哑铃状物的末端，它的表面上有一些带凸边的冲击坑，可能是由约0.1 μm ～ 0.2 μm大小的高速粒子冲撞而产生的。由速度较低并且体积较大（直径约1.0 μm）的粒子所造成的撞击印痕只附着于该哑铃状物之上而未能穿透其表面（注意箭头所指）。

　　看来，在阿波罗11号和12号月球微粒土样品的形态之间存在着细微的差别。排气孔和变形微粒等的大量存在也许可以说明在阿波罗12号着陆点处的物质有不同的受热过程。看来含碳化合物在某些微粒土样品的外壳中是存在的，而且在我们检测过的月球岩石（内部）中似乎也存在着融于其中的含碳化合物。这块来自月球的岩石没有气泡。一种解释是阿波罗12号微粒土样品中的碳有一部分来自于太阳风的入侵[11]。但是用这种机制很难解释岩石内部的碳。月球的排气过程也许可以作为解释月球火成岩内部含碳的一种机制。

　　感谢蒂莫西·迈奥达博士、玛乔丽·洛乌博士和芭芭拉·罗利博士以及约翰妮·迪金森、罗伯塔·德菲奥里、乌尔米·帕特尔和珍妮特·格林奎斯特在实验中为我们提供的帮助。本项研究得到了美国国家航空航天局的资助。

（王耀杨 翻译；周江 审稿）

6. Oró, J., and Han, J., *J. Gas Chromatog.*, **5**, 480 (1967).

7. Hamilton, P. B., *Anal. Chem.*, **35**, 2055 (1963).

8. Hamilton, P. B., *Nature*, **205**, 284 (1965).

9. *NASA Lunar Sample Information Catalog Apollo 12*, 121 (1970).

10. *NASA Apollo 12 Preliminary Science Report*, sample description on pp. 137-144, map on p. 33 (1970).

11. Moore, C. B., Larimer, J. W., Lewis, C. F., Delles, F. M., and Gooley, R. C., *Geol. Soc. Amer. Abstract*, **2**, 628 (1970).

12. Nagy, B., *Geotimes*, **15**, 18 (1970).

13. Preti, G., Murphy, R. C., and Biemann, K., *Apollo 12 Lunar Science Conference*, Houston, Texas (1970).

Nonbiotic Origin of Optical Activity

L. Mörtberg

Editor's Note

All the molecules in living things are asymmetrical in the sense that they contain at least one atom that is attached to other parts of the molecule in such a way that they cannot be superimposed on the another by rotation, although the reflexion of the molecule in an imagined plane can make them superimpose on each other accurately. This asymmetry is described as optical asymmetry. The standard explanation of the phenomenon is that, in the evolution of early life forms, one optical arrangement must have been energetically favoured, but as yet there is no agreement on what stage in early life was critical to this distinction between alternative arrangements. This paper advocated another explanation—that in the early planetary system before living things had made their appearance, interaction between the Sun and the Earth would have led to the formation of predominantly optically asymmetric molecules. The origin of optical asymmetry in biochemistry is still an open question.

T HE origin of optically active compounds has been a question of debate since the days of Pasteur and among the various explanations that have been postulated are (a) autocatalytic propagation of asymmetry by an individual molecule that happened to be first in a D-L-pair, (b) photochemical reactions with chiral or circularly polarized light[1] produced by reflexion or magnetic fields, (c) interaction with asymmetric minerals like quartz and (d) inherent energetic difference between antipodal molecules perhaps connected with nuclear asymmetry as manifested in radioactive β-decay[2].

All these hypotheses except the last rest on the assumption of local and/or occasional excess of one of the antipodal forms of an asymmetric agent. In the absence of any explanation as to how such excesses could arise over sufficiently wide areas and periods of time, they therefore reduce to hypotheses about chance occurrences[3]. In the following a possible relationship between asymmetry in a planetary system and molecular asymmetry is discussed.

It is well known that magnetic fields can rotate the plane of polarization of plane polarized light traveling through a medium (Faraday effect)[4]. The rotation R, which is positive for clockwise rotation viewed in the direction of light travel, is given by: $R = VIH \cos \varphi$ where V is the so called Verdet constant characteristic of the medium at a given temperature and wavelength, H is the strength of the magnetic field, I is the distance of light travel and φ is the angle between the lines of force of the field and the direction of light propagation. φ changes from zero for the parallel to $180°$ for the anti-parallel case.

旋光性的非生物起源

默特贝里

编者按

生物体中的所有分子都是不对称的，这意味着其中至少有一个原子，它与分子其他部分相连接的方式使分子无法通过旋转与另一个分子重叠，尽管该分子的对映体与该分子可以通过一个假想平面精确地相互重合。这种不对称性被称为光学不对称性。对此现象的标准解释是这样的：在早期生命形式的进化中，有一种光学构型必定在能量上是优先的，但到底是早期生命中的哪一个阶段对在两种光学构型之间产生差异起决定作用，这一问题目前尚没有定论。本文倡导的是另一种解释，即：在生命出现以前的早期行星系统中，太阳与地球间的相互作用是形成占主要地位的光学不对称分子的原因。光学不对称性的生物化学起源至今仍是一个悬而未决的问题。

旋光性化合物的起源自巴斯德时代以来一直是一个争论不休的问题，目前已经提出的几种解释包括（a）通过恰好首先出现在一个 D–L 对中的单个分子所进行的不对称自催化增殖，（b）借助由反射或磁场产生的手性光或圆偏振光[1]而进行的光化学反应，（c）与石英等不对称矿物质的相互作用，以及（d）对映体分子之间固有的能量差异，可能与核的不对称性有关，就像在放射性 β 衰变中所表现的那样[2]。

除了最后一个以外，其他三个假说都依赖于这样的假定：局部地和 / 或偶然地使原本处于均衡的多种非对称模式中的一种变得过量。由于无法说明这种过量如何能够在足够宽广的区域和某些时间阶段内出现，所以它们全都被归为与偶发事件相关的假说[3]。下面将要讨论的是行星系统中的不对称性与分子的不对称性之间可能存在的关系。

众所周知，磁场可以使穿过介质的平面偏振光的偏振面发生旋转（法拉第效应）[4]。若以从沿着光行进方向看去的顺时针旋转方向为正向，则旋光度 R 可以表示为：$R = VIH \cos\varphi$。其中 V 被称为费尔德常数，是介质在给定温度和波长时所特有的；H 是磁场强度，I 是光穿越介质的距离，而 φ 则是场力线与光传播方向之间的夹角。φ 的变化是从平行时的 0°到反平行时的 180°。

The equation shows that R will be zero when $\varphi=90°$ and will change sign when the direction of propagation of light is reversed. The rotation is equivalent to a speed or refractive index difference between the equally strong right and left circularly polarized beams into which the plane polarized one can be split. This is given by: $R =\pi l/\lambda(n_l - n_r)$ where n_l and n_r are the refractive indices of the left and right handed beams respectively and λ the wavelength. The right handed beam is as much accelerated as the left handed beam is retarded.

Light passing no-perpendicularly through a boundary from one region to another (Fig. 2) with a different refractive index will be refracted. A magnetic field non-perpendicular to the direction that the light would take in the second region will cause a refractive separation of right and left circularly polarized light, because the refractive indices for the two circularly polarized beams will differ as a result of the field.

All this can be applied to a spherical planet orbiting a large light-emitting central body, the "sun". The dimensions of the two bodies are taken to be small relative to the distance between them. The planet has an atmosphere with an increasing density and refractive index on going towards its centre. Furthermore, it has an axial rotation and a magnetic dipole field, the axis of which coincides with the rotational one. The dipole midpoint is in the planetary centre. The following is a discussion of the effect on one of the plane polarized components of which an unpolarized beam is composed.

(1) Let the equatorial plane be parallel to the orbital one (Fig. 1). On the upper part of the "northern" hemisphere the magnetic field then has a component parallel to the light rays from the "sun". Here the rays travel almost parallel to the atmospheric "boundary". A refractive separation of right and left circularly polarized light will therefore arise. For a positive Verdet constant the latter beam will be retarded and refracted down more steeply into the atmosphere. More of the right handed light will therefore disappear out into space and the planetary atmosphere will here be enriched in the oppositely polarized light. The refractive index gradient should multiply the separation effect (Fig. 2). (Apart from changes in direction and strength of the magnetic field that the travelling light rays will encounter because of the dipolar nature of the field this picture should remain qualitatively true.) In the lower part of the "southern" hemisphere the situation will clearly be the reverse.

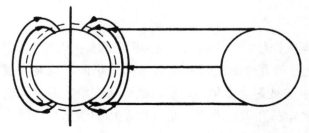

Fig. 1. A planet orbiting a "sun" as described in point (1) in the text. The planet is represented by the solid circle to the left and the "sun" is to the right. The light rays are symbolized by straight arrows. The dashed circle represents the "boundary" between atmosphere and space. The curved arrows represent the lines of force of the magnetic field going from "south" to "north".

这个等式表明：当 $\varphi = 90°$ 时，R 就是 0；而当光传播方向反转时，R 会改变符号。旋转等价于可由一束平面偏振光分裂而成的相同强度右旋与左旋圆偏振光线之间的速度或折射率差异。这可以表示为：$R = \pi l/\lambda(n_l - n_r)$，其中 n_l 和 n_r 分别是左旋和右旋光线的折射率，λ 是波长。右旋光线的加速与左旋光线的减速等量。

在沿着非垂直方向从一个区域穿过边界进入具有不同折射率的另一个区域时（图 2），光线会发生折射。如果存在一个与光线进入第二个区域时的行进方向不垂直的磁场，就会使右旋与左旋圆偏振光发生折射分离，因为两条圆偏振光线的折射率会在磁场的影响下出现不同。

所有这一切都可以应用于一颗围绕大型发光中心体——"太阳"运行的球状行星。假设两个天体的尺度与它们之间的距离相比是很小的。行星大气的密度和折射率越靠近其核心越大。此外，行星还沿轴向旋转并有一个磁偶极场，磁偶极场的轴与旋转轴恰好重合。偶极中点就是行星的中心。下面要讨论组成一条非偏振光线的其中一个平面偏振成分所受到的影响。

（1）令赤道面与轨道面平行（图 1）。于是在"北"半球的上半部分，该磁场就包含了一个与"太阳"光平行的成分。在这里，光线的行进方向几乎平行于大气的"边界"。因而会产生右旋和左旋圆偏振光的折射分离。如果费尔德常数为正，则左旋圆偏振光将会被减速并且以更为陡峭的方式折射向下进入大气。因此会有更多的右旋光消失于太空之中，而这时行星大气中的反向偏振光则会得到加强。折射率梯度将助长分离效应（图 2）。（如果光线在行进中没有遇到由场的偶极性质所造成的磁场方向和强度的变化，那么这一描述应该能保持定性上的正确性。）很明显，在"南"半球的下半部分，情况将是相反的。

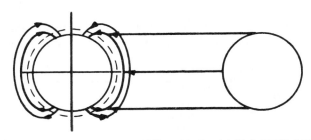

图 1. 正文第（1）点中所描述的围绕"太阳"运转的一颗行星。左侧的实线圆代表行星，而"太阳"则位于右侧。光线用直箭头表示。虚线圆代表大气与太空之间的"边界"。弯箭头代表从"南"到"北"的磁力线。

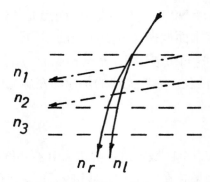

Fig. 2. The enhancement by a refractive index gradient of the separation in a magnetic field of two oppositely circularly polarized light beams. The beams are represented by solid arrows. n_r being the refractive index of the right circularly polarized beam and n_l that of the oppositely polarized beam. The broken line arrows represent the lines of force of the magnetic field. n_1, n_2 and n_3 represent the downwards increasing refractive indices for the light in the absence of the field in three different layers of matter.

In the region where the light comes in almost at right angles to the atmosphere, little refraction will occur. Symmetry reasoning shows that no net excess of one circularly polarized light form and hence of photochemically produced asymmetric material should be found over the planet taken as a whole.

The system is symmetric, for it is superimposable on its mirror image. (The mirror image of a magnet parallel to a mirror has the poles inverted.)

(2) Let the planet have its equatorial plane tilted at an angle α with respect to its orbit (Fig. 3). The magnetic field in the "southern" hemisphere and also somewhat "north" of the equator now has a component antiparallel to the light. On the upper part of the "northern" hemisphere the situation is more complicated. In certain latitudes between "pole" and "polar-circle" the field has a component parallel to the light during the "day". "Twelve hours" later the opposite is true. Thus here the effects during "day" and "night" will oppose each other. A small area immediately surrounding the "north" pole, where the field-lines are almost parallel to the planetary axis, constitutes an exception to this, however. In this area a component of the field will be parallel to the rays all the time. It is difficult to say precisely which effect should predominate on the northern hemisphere as a whole, for the effect will depend on the magnetic "inclination" angle and hence on the magnetic dipole length in relation to the "dimensions" of the atmosphere.

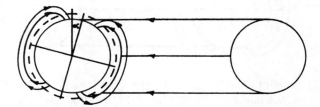

Fig. 3. A planet with its equator tilted at an angle α relative to its orbit as described under point (2) in the text. Everything else is as in Fig. 1.

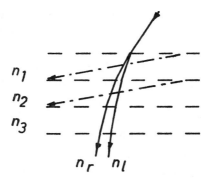

图 2. 两条反向圆偏振光线在磁场中的分离随折射率梯度而增加。光线用实箭头表示，n_r 是右旋圆偏振光线的折射率，n_l 是反向偏振光线的折射率。虚线箭头代表磁力线。n_1、n_2 和 n_3 表示在没有外场存在的情况下光线在三个不同的物质层中向下依次增加的折射率。

在光线以接近于直角进入大气的区域中，几乎没有折射发生。对称性推理表明：若将行星视为整体来看，应该不会出现一种圆偏振光形式的净过剩，因而也就不会有以光化学方式产生的不对称物质。

这个行星系统是对称的，因为它可以与自己的镜像重叠。（平行于镜面的磁体的镜像具有反转的磁极。）

（2）假设行星的赤道面相对于它的轨道倾斜一个角度 α（图3）。于是"南"半球以及赤道"以北"的一些地方的磁场就具有了反平行于光线的成分。在"北"半球的上半部分情况更为复杂。在位于"极"与"极圈"之间的某些纬度，场有一个在"白天"中平行于光线的成分。"12 小时"以后，情况正好相反。于是在这里，"白天"和"夜晚"时的效应将是截然相反的。但是，紧挨着"北"极四周的一小片区域是个例外，这里的场线几乎平行于行星轴。在这片区域中，场的一个成分将始终与光线平行。很难确切地说出对整个北半球而言哪种效应会是主要的，因为这种效应取决于磁场的"倾斜"角，从而也取决于与大气"尺度"相关的磁偶极长度。

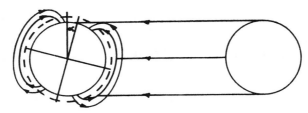

图 3. 一颗赤道面相对于其轨道的倾斜角度为 α 的行星，如正文第（2）点中所述。其他条件均与图 1 相同。

When α is close to 90, the light in the polar region facing the "sun" will enter the atmosphere almost perpendicularly and refraction should be unimportant. In the equatorial zone with the rays coming in practically tangential to the atmosphere and antiparallel to the field the separation will be at a maximum, with enrichment in the right handed component. Thus in this situation enrichment of light circularly polarized in the same sense will occur at the equator and a bit north of it. Furthermore, for an α value of 90, even the "southern" hemisphere will be reached by some light that has been refracted by the atmosphere. This amount of light reaching the "southern" hemisphere during "summer" in the "northern" hemisphere will of course be smaller than the amount reaching the "south" during "summer" there. At the "equinoxes", that is, when "day" and "night" are equally long, the situation will be as under point (1). For a circular orbit therefore one hemisphere will have a "yearly" net excess of one circularly polarized light form while the other will have an equal excess of the opposite form. No net effect should thus result counted over the whole planet and the whole year.

In any given position in the orbit, the system in non-superimposable on its mirror image and is asymmetric. "Half a year" later the mirror image turns up, however. There is thus symmetry when the whole "year" is considered.

(3) Let the orbit be elliptical (Fig. 4). When the "sun" is large in comparison with the planet, the former is located in one focal point of the orbit. Kepler's second law states that radius vector r from the "sun" to the planet always sweeps out the same area in a given time interval. The area swept out when the planet moves through the angle $d\theta$ is $r\,d\theta$. The time required is thus proportional to $r\,d\theta$. The intensity of a light source is proportional to $1/r^2$. The total light energy falling on the planet then obviously is proportional to the product of intensity and time, that is $d\theta/r$. With polar coordinates as in Fig. 4 the equation of the ellipse is

$$r = \frac{b^2}{a + c\cos\theta}$$

where $2a$ is the length of major, $2b$ that of the minor axis and $2c$ is the distance between the focal points. Integration gives

$$\int_{\theta_1}^{\theta_2} \frac{d\theta}{r} = \frac{a}{b^2}(\theta_2 - \theta_1) + \frac{c}{b^2}(\sin\theta_2 - \sin\theta_1)$$

If $\theta_2 - \theta_1 = \pi$ it follows that the amount of light received by the planet is

$$\frac{a}{b^2}\pi - \frac{2c}{b^2}\sin\theta_1$$

when it moves between θ_1 and $\theta_1 + \pi$, and $0 < \theta_1 < \pi$, but is

$$\frac{a}{b^2}\pi + \frac{2c}{b^2}\sin\theta_1$$

when it continues from $\theta_1 + \pi$ to θ_1.

562

当 α 接近于 90°时，极区中面朝"太阳"的光将会以几乎垂直的方向进入大气，因而折射应该是不重要的。在赤道地区，光线以基本上与大气相切并反平行于磁场的方向进入，分离将会达到最大，从而加强了右旋光的成分。于是在这种情况下，圆偏振光的加强因同样原因将出现在赤道以及赤道稍微偏北一些的地方。此外，当 α 角为 90°时，即使在"南"半球，也会有某些被大气折射的光到达那里。在"北"半球的"夏季"，光线到达"南"半球的量当然要少于在"南"半球的"夏季"时到达"南"半球的量。在"二分点"，也就是当"白天"与"黑夜"长度相等的时候，就会出现第（1）点中提到的情况。因此，对于圆形轨道来说，一个半球每"年"将有某一种圆偏振光形式的净过量，而另一个半球则会有同样多相反圆偏振光形式的过量。因此从整个行星全年的情况来看，净效应为零。

在轨道中任意给定的位置上，行星系统与它的镜像不可重叠，因而是不对称的。然而"半年"以后镜像会发生反转。因此在考虑全"年"的情况时是存在对称性的。

（3）令轨道为椭圆形（图 4）。当"太阳"比行星大时，前者位于椭圆形轨道的一个焦点处。开普勒第二定律告诉我们：在给定的时间间隔内，从"太阳"指向行星的径向量 r 总是扫过相同的面积。当行星走过 $d\theta$ 角时扫过的面积为 $rd\theta$。因而所需的时间正比于 $rd\theta$。光源的强度正比于 $1/r^2$。所以到达行星上的总光能显然应正比于强度与时间的乘积，即正比于 $d\theta/r$。如图 4 所示，用极坐标表示椭圆的方程为：

$$r = \frac{b^2}{a + c\cos\theta}$$

其中 $2a$ 是长轴的长度，$2b$ 是短轴的长度，$2c$ 为两焦点之间的距离。积分得到：

$$\int_{\theta_1}^{\theta_2} \frac{d\theta}{r} = \frac{a}{b^2}(\theta_2 - \theta_1) + \frac{c}{b^2}(\sin\theta_2 - \sin\theta_1)$$

若 $\theta_2 - \theta_1 = \pi$，则可以推出：当行星从 θ_1 运动到 $\theta_1 + \pi$ 且 $0 < \theta_1 < \pi$ 时，它所接受的光的量为：

$$\frac{a}{b^2}\pi - \frac{2c}{b^2}\sin\theta_1$$

而当它继续从 $\theta_1 + \pi$ 运动到 θ_1 时，则为：

$$\frac{a}{b^2}\pi + \frac{2c}{b^2}\sin\theta_1$$

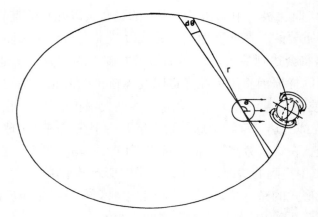

Fig. 4. A planet with tilted equator and elliptical orbit as described under point (3) in the text. The ellipse represents the orbit. θ is the angle between radius vector (as defined in the text) for any given position and the position closest to the "sun". The equator is seen in perspective. Everything else is as in Fig. 1.

We now consider the amounts of light that the two hemispheres get during their respective "summers". The "seasons" will change between "summer" and "winter" at the "equinoxes". The latter holds, where a line through the "sun", parallel to the intersection between the equatorial and orbital planes, cuts the orbit. Clearly, the "equinoxes" are π radians apart and the hemisphere that has "summer" when the planet is close to the "sun" will get most light in accordance with the integration above. (A pronounced example is Mars.)

As discussed in point (2), for a large α, one form chiral light predominates in the equatorial region when one hemisphere has "summer" and vice versa. Given these "seasonal" excesses of the respective circularly polarized light forms, the light form that is in excess, when the hemisphere that receives most light, has "summer" should predominate on the planet as a whole over a "year". Thus the photochemically produced materials of the enantiomeric forms predominating when this hemisphere has "summer", will likewise predominate. When the intersection between orbit and equator is parallel to the major axis (that is $\theta_1 = 0$) "seasons" will be equally long on the two hemispheres and they will also have equal amounts of light energy.

The system is asymmetric in each point in the orbit and also over a whole "year" when $\alpha \neq 0$. This can be deduced as in the previous cases. The magnitudes of such effects are difficult to estimate and would undoubtedly be small on the present Earth. The small values, for gases, of the Verdet constants (generally higher, however, at shorter wavelengths where light is photochemically more effective), the thinness of the atmosphere and ensuing shallowness of the refractive index gradient, the weakness of the magnetic field, the small angle between the equator and the elliptic, and most of all the absence of a large eccentricity of the present orbit should all cause only small effects. Going back many billions of years the situation could, however, have been quite different in all these respects. Furthermore, there is at present no general way of telling theoretically how much

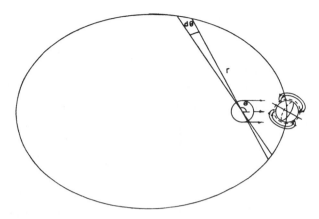

图 4. 一颗具有倾斜的赤道并以椭圆轨道运行的行星，如正文第（3）点中所述。椭圆代表轨道。θ 是任意给定位置的径向量（同正文中的定义）与最接近于"太阳"的位置之间的夹角。从透视图中可以看到赤道。其他条件均与图 1 相同。

现在我们来考虑两个半球在它们各自的"夏季"中所接收到的光的量。在"二分点"处，"季节"会在"夏季"和"冬季"之间变化。"二分点"在一条穿过"太阳"的直线上，与赤道面和轨道面的交线保持平行，并切割轨道。很明显，两个"二分点"相隔 π 弧度，从上面的积分结果可以看出：当行星接近"太阳"时，处于"夏季"的那个半球将会接收到大部分阳光。（火星就是一个典型的例子。）

如第（2）点中所述，对于一个比较大的 α 角，当一个半球处于"夏季"时，手性光的其中一种形式会在赤道地区占主要地位，而且反之亦然。分别对两种圆偏振光形式给出"季节性"的过剩量，当接收大部分光的那个半球处于"夏季"时，过剩的那种光形式应该在整个行星的全"年"中都占主要地位。所以当这个半球处于"夏季"时，以光化学方式产生的优势光学异构形式的物质也会占主要地位。当轨道与赤道交线平行于长轴（即 $θ_1 = 0$）时，两个半球上的"季节"就会一样长，并且它们也将得到等量的光能。

在轨道中的每一点上，行星系统都是不对称的，而且当 α ≠ 0 时对全"年"来说也是如此。这一点可以从前面几种情况中推导出来。这些效应的数量级是很难估计出来的，而对于现在的地球来说，它们的数值无疑是很小的。对气体而言，它们的费尔德常数很小（不过在波长较短处一般会大一些，此时光有更显著的光化学效应），这时大气的稀薄以及由此引发的折射率梯度的浅薄、磁场的微弱、赤道与椭圆之间的角度很小，以及所有因素中最为重要的一个——现有轨道的离心率不够大等都只能导致很小的效应。但在数十亿年以前，所有这些方面的情况都可能会大为不同。此外，目前还没有一种通用的方法能够从理论上说明某个由圆偏振光导致的光化学

chemical asymmetry a given photochemical reaction with circularly polarized light will produce[5].

With roughly the same reasoning as above, one could visualize similar effects that could cause net asymmetry on an entire planet. Take, for example, a rotating "sun" that possesses a magnetic field coinciding with its axis and has its equator tilted relative to the orbit of a planet. If the planet has an elliptical orbit, unequal amounts of light from the two hemispheres of the "sun", will fall on it. Faraday effects in the "solar" atmosphere should work in the same way as described above for planets. The net result should be excess of one chiral form of light on the planet even without planetary atmosphere, magnetic field, and tilting of the planetary axis, all in analogy with previous reasoning. The Zeeman effect, which is closely related to the Faraday effect, could work in the same overall way.

Some factors which could increase the differences in amounts of enantiomeric molecular species when the antipodes of the starting material are already present in unequal amounts would be many consecutive reactions, where the asymmetric force, that is the asymmetric light, intervened at most individual steps (compare Harada where the case for presumed inherent antipodal energy differences is treated). If a sufficiently large number of steps are involved, this might give rise to large differences in amounts of enantiomeric end-products, even when the initial difference is small. A further case would be one in which many asymmetric molecules react with each other in many consecutive reactions. Diastereomeric discrimination at each step might here add up to large differences in the end. An attempt at making a quantitative estimate of the effects for various hypothetical "primitive earth" conditions by numerical treatment with a computer is being undertaken.

I thank Professor P. Å. Albertsson and Dr. V. P. Shanbhag for valuable discussions on this subject.

(**232**, 105-107; 1971)

Lars Mörtberg: Department of Biochemistry, University of Umeå, 901 87 Umeå.

Received November 30, 1970; revised March 19, 1971.

References:

1. Kuhn, W., and Braun, E., *Naturwissenschaften*, **17**, 227 (1929).

2. Ulbricht, T. L. V., *Quart. Rev.*, **13**, 48 (1959).

3. Harada, K., *Naturwissenschaften*, **57**, 114 (1970).

4. Waring, C. E., and Custer, R. L., in *Techniques of Organic Chemistry* (edit. by Weissberger, A.), **1**, Part 3, 2497 (Interscience, New York, 1960).

5. Hallas, G., *Organic Stereochemistry*, 56 (McGraw-Hill, London, 1965).

反应能产生出多大程度的化学不对称性[5]。

利用与上述内容大致相同的推理，我们可以设想一下能在整个行星上导致净不对称的类似效应。例如：假设有一个旋转的"太阳"，它有一个与自身的轴相重合的磁场，而且它的赤道相对于行星轨道而言是倾斜的。如果这颗行星的轨道是椭圆形的，那么来自"太阳"两半球的光就会以不等的量落在它上面。"太阳"大气中的法拉第效应将会以如上所述的相同方式影响行星。净结果应该是行星上出现光的一种手性形式的过剩，即使在没有行星大气、磁场及行星轴倾斜的情况下也会如此，一切都与前述推理类似。在这个过程中，与法拉第效应密切关联的塞曼效应也在以同样的方式发挥作用。

当起始物质的对映体已经呈现出数量上的不相等时，能增大光学异构分子物种在数量上的差异的因素可能会是大量的连续反应，其中不对称性的推动力，即不对称的光，最多只能干扰个别步骤（对比哈拉达的工作，他处理了假定对映体的固有能量存在差异的情况）。如果涉及了足够多的步骤，就有可能会导致光学异构终产物在数量上的巨大差异，即使在初始差异很小的情况下也是如此。下一步会发生的情况是许多不对称分子在多个连续反应中相互起作用。这里，非对映体在每一步中的差别也许到最后会累积成巨大的差异。目前正在尝试通过计算机的数据处理对由各种假想"原始地球"条件所产生的效应进行定量估算。

感谢阿尔贝特松教授和尚贝格博士就这一主题与我进行了有价值的讨论。

（王耀杨 翻译；肖伟科 审稿）

Establishment of Symbiosis between *Rhizobium* and Plant Cells *in vitro*

R. D. Holsten *et al.*

Editor's Note

Leguminous plants such as those of the major food crops are able to survive only because their roots have structures that turn nitrogen in the air into nitrogenous chemicals essential for the wellbeing of the plants. This experiment, from a commercial laboratory in the United States, demonstrated that the process is indeed accomplished by the invasion of structures formed in the roots of plants by bacteria of the genus *Rhizobium*. The demonstration that the symbiosis between the bacteria and the plants can be established in the laboratory was a confirmation of what biologists believed but of which they nevertheless needed proof.

SYMBIOTIC fixation of atmospheric nitrogen by leguminous plants is perhaps the most quantitatively important agency by which this element is incorporated into the biosphere, and is the principal process for maintaining nitrogen fertility in agriculture. The interaction of plants of the family Leguminoseae and specific bacteria of the genus *Rhizobium* in this symbiotic relationship is not yet well understood, probably because of the absence of a suitable defined experimental system. Other workers have used isolated plant roots in combination with the appropriate bacteria[1-4], and, more recently, plant cell and tissue culture[5]. Although stimulation of plant cell differentiation and lignification apparently resulted, no evidence for intercellular bacterial symbiosis could be found.

We have attempted to establish a symbiotic N_2-fixing relationship with plant cells and microorganisms *in vitro*, using the techniques of aseptic plant cell culture in conjunction with the sensitive acetylene–ethylene assay for nitrogenase activity. We consider that such a system can be used further to elucidate the factors which control nodulation processes and N_2-fixing activity *in vivo*.

Soybean Root Cell Cultures

Seeds of soybean (*Glycine max* var. Acme) were surface sterilized by immersion in a commercial hypochlorite solution ("Zonite", Chemway Corp., Wayne, New Jersey) for 15 min, and rinsed with sterile distilled water. Seed was placed on the surface of an agar (1% w/v) solidified medium composed of the mineral salts (MS medium)[6] supplemented with sucrose, 30 g/l., for germination in the dark at $26°\pm1°C$. All media were sterilized by autoclaving at $121°C$ for 15 min.

When the primary root was approximately 4 cm long, it was excised aseptically, and a 5 mm explant was removed 2.5 cm behind the growing tip. This explant of root origin was

在体外建立根瘤菌和植物细胞间的共生关系

霍尔斯滕等

编者按

豆科植物（如主要粮食作物中的那些豆科植物）能够生存下来的原因仅仅在于它们的根部具有许多可以把空气中的氮转化为植物良好生长所必需的含氮化合物的结构。本文描述的实验来自美国的一个商业实验室，该实验表明，这一过程确实是由根瘤菌属的细菌入侵植物根内所形成的结构来实现的。细菌和植物之间的共生关系可以在实验室条件下建成的事实证实了生物学家们虽然一直非常确信但仍需要拿出证据的观点。

豆科植物对大气氮的共生固定在数量上也许可以算是将氮元素整合进入生物圈的一种最为重要的方式，并且也是农业上维护氮素肥力的主要过程。也许是因为缺乏一种合适且确定的实验体系，所以人们至今仍不能完全理解在这种共生关系中豆科植物与根瘤菌属的一些特殊细菌之间的相互作用。其他一些研究者利用离体的植物根与适当的细菌相结合 [1-4]；最近还有人使用了植物细胞培养与组织培养的方法 [5]。尽管显然产生了刺激植物细胞分化和木质化的效果，但没有发现可以说明细胞间细菌共生关系的证据。

我们尝试结合利用无菌植物细胞培养技术与可以灵敏测定固氮酶活性的乙炔 – 乙烯还原法，在体外建立植物细胞与微生物之间的一种共生固氮关系。我们认为，这样一个体系可以用来进一步阐释那些控制体内结瘤过程与固氮活性的因素。

大豆根细胞的培养

通过将大豆（阿克姆）种子在商用次氯酸盐溶液（商品名为"花碧玉"，沁威公司，韦恩市，新泽西州）中浸泡 15 分钟使种子表面消毒，然后用无菌蒸馏水清洗。将种子置于琼脂固化的培养基（重量体积比为 1%）表面，这种培养基由矿物盐（MS 培养基）[6]组成，每升添加 30 克蔗糖。种子在 26℃±1℃ 的黑暗中发芽。实验中的所有培养基均在 121℃ 下高压蒸汽灭菌 15 分钟。

当初生根长到大约 4 厘米长时，将它在无菌条件下切开，并在其生长锥后 2.5 厘米处切出一块 5 毫米的外植体。将这个来自根部的外植体置于 50 毫升琼脂固化的

placed on the surface of 50 ml. of agar-solidified MS medium supplemented with 15% whole coconut milk (CM, Grand Island Biological Co.) and 2 mg/l. 2,4-dichlorophenoxya -cetic acid (2,4-D) contained in a cotton stoppered 250 ml. Erlenmeyer flask. The medium was adjusted to pH 6.0 before autoclaving. The explanted root section was incubated at $26°±1°C$ in the dark.

An actively growing mass of undifferentiated cells (callus) was produced on the root explant in 10–14 days. The callus was then aseptically removed and portions subcultured to fresh MS medium supplemented with 15% CM and 2 mg/l. 2,4-D. In these and subsequent subcultures, we used a liquid medium similar to that described, with 225 ml. of medium in a modified 1,000 ml. flask (Blaessig Glass Co., Rochester, New York)[7], as well as 50 ml. agar-solidified medium in 250 ml. Erlenmeyer flasks. The liquid cultures were incubated on a klinostat rotating at 1 r.p.m.[8] in the dark at $26°±1°C$. An actively growing cell and callus population with a cell doubling time of the order of 18 h was established in the liquid environment over a 14–21 day period. Subculture of the liquid system was carried out at 20–30 day intervals to maintain an actively dividing cell population. Cotyledonary tissue was similarly treated to establish cell cultures from this source.

Bacterial Growth

Rhizobium japonicum strains 61A76 (supplied by Dr. Joe C. Burton of the Nitragin Co., Milwaukee, Wisconsin) and ATCC 10324 were grown in a liquid culture medium composed of (in g/l.): K_2HPO_4, 1.0; KH_2PO_4, 1.0; $FeCl_3 \cdot 6H_2O$, 0.005; $MgSO_4 \cdot 7H_2O$, 0.36; $CaSO_4 \cdot 2H_2O$, 0.17; KNO_3, 0.70; yeast extract, 1.0; mannitol, 3.0. The medium was adjusted to pH 6.4 before autoclaving at 121°C for 15 min. A bacterial inoculum was added to 40 ml. portions of the above medium contained in 125 ml. Erlenmeyer flasks and incubated at $30°±1°C$ with constant shaking. Subcultures of the bacterial cultures were carried out at 7 day intervals to maintain vigorous stocks. At regular intervals aliquots of the *R. japonicum* cultures were examined microscopically and checked for nodulating activity by application to seedlings of Acme or Kent variety soybeans maintained in a Sherer–Gilette CEL 255–6 growth chamber under a 16 h photoperiod.

Establishment of a Symbiotic Relationship

A large culture flask from the klinostat containing 225 ml. of MS medium with 15% CM, 2 mg/l. 2,4-D and containing an actively growing root cell and callus population of approximately 15 g fresh weight was inoculated with 0.1 ml. ($260×10^6$ cells/ml.) of a liquid suspension culture of actively dividing *R. japonicum* and returned to the klinostat for incubation. After 3–7 days of incubation, the flask contents were poured through sterile cheesecloth. Plant cells and callus pieces retained on the cheesecloth (designated stage 1) were washed with 250 ml. of sterile MS medium, transferred to fresh growth media of varying composition, and incubated in the conditions described. Concomitantly, portions of the cell population inoculated with bacteria, as well as control tissue without bacteria,

MS 培养基表面。之前在培养基中补充了 15% 的全脂椰奶（简称 CM，格兰德艾兰生物公司）和 2 毫克 / 升的 2,4- 二氯苯氧基乙酸（简称 2,4–D），并将其装入塞有棉花塞的 250 毫升锥形瓶中。在高压蒸汽灭菌之前将此培养基的 pH 值调至 6.0。将这个根部外植体在温度为 26℃±1℃的黑暗中进行培育。

经过 10 ~ 14 天，在根部外植体上长出了一块生长旺盛的未分化细胞（愈伤组织）。在无菌条件下将此愈伤组织取下，并分成数份置于含有 15% CM 和 2 毫克 / 升 2,4–D 的新鲜 MS 培养基上进行传代培养。在这些以及随后的传代培养实验中，我们采用了一种与前面描述过的培养基类似的液体培养基，使用了放在 1,000 毫升改良烧瓶（布莱西希玻璃公司，纽约州罗切斯特市）中的 225 毫升培养基[7]，以及放在 250 毫升锥形瓶中的 50 毫升琼脂固化培养基。将液态培养体系置于缓转器上以 1 转 / 分的转速[8]在温度为 26℃±1℃的黑暗中进行培育。14 ~ 21 天后，在液体环境中形成了一个生长旺盛的细胞和愈伤组织群体，其细胞倍增时间可达 18 小时左右。为了保持住一个积极分裂的细胞群体，以 20 ~ 30 天为间隔对这个液态体系进行传代培养。采用类似方法处理大豆子叶组织，以建立同一来源的细胞培养体系。

细菌的生长

将大豆根瘤菌菌株 61A76（由威斯康星州密尔沃基市根瘤菌剂公司的乔·伯顿博士提供）和 ATCC 10324 放置于包含以下成分的液态培养基中进行培育（单位为克 / 升）：K_2HPO_4，1.0；KH_2PO_4，1.0；$FeCl_3 \cdot 6H_2O$，0.005；$MgSO_4 \cdot 7H_2O$，0.36；$CaSO_4 \cdot 2H_2O$，0.17；KNO_3，0.70；酵母提取物，1.0 和甘露醇，3.0。调节此培养基的 pH 值到 6.4，然后在 121℃下高压蒸汽灭菌 15 分钟。将细菌接种物加入到含有 40 毫升上述液态培养基的 125 毫升锥形瓶中，并在 30℃±1℃下持续摇动培育。为了保持种子菌株的旺盛活力，每隔 7 天进行一次细菌培养物的传代培养。每隔一定时间，用显微镜检查分份的大豆根瘤菌培养物，并检测其结瘤活性，方法是用它来感染在谢勒 – 希列特 CEL 255–6 型生长室中以 16 小时为光照期培养出的阿克姆大豆或者肯特大豆幼苗。

共生关系的建立

在缓转器的大培养瓶中放入 225 毫升含 15% CM 和 2 毫克 / 升 2,4–D 的 MS 培养基以及鲜重约为 15 克的生长旺盛的根细胞和愈伤组织群体，再接种 0.1 毫升（260×10^6 个细胞 / 毫升）积极分裂的根瘤菌液态混悬培养液，然后将培养瓶重新放在缓转器上进行培育。培育 3 ~ 7 天后，用无菌纱布过滤培养瓶中的液态混悬物。再用 250 毫升的无菌 MS 培养液清洗留在纱布上的植物细胞和愈伤组织（指定为阶段 1），然后将残留物转移至含有不同组分的新鲜培养基中，并按前述条件进行培育。与此同时，用乙炔 – 乙烯还原法对细菌接种过的细胞群体和没有细菌接种的对照组

were assayed for nitrogenase activity using the acetylene–ethylene assay procedure[9]. Dry weight determinations were performed after drying the tissue for 48 h at 60°C.

Cytological Examination of Tissue

Random samples of the soybean root cell cultures from bacteria-inoculated and control flasks were prepared for paraffin sectioning by fixing in formalin : acetic acid : ethanol (5 : 5 : 90 v/v) or in Fleming's osmic acid fixative for 24 h at room temperature. The tissues were then dehydrated through the ethanol series before being embedded in "Paraplast" (MP 56°–57°C) for sectioning. Sections were cut at 8–10 μm, stained with safranin-fast green or Van Gieson's Nile blue and examined with a Zeiss microscope fitted with phase contrast optics.

At the same time similar cell samples were overlaid with 5% glutaraldehyde in Millonig's phosphate buffer (*p*H 7.2–7.4) and fixed for 60 min at room temperature. The fixed samples were rinsed for 20 min, post fixed for 60 min at room temperature with 1% OsO_4, washed with phosphate buffer for 20 min, and dehydrated through an ethanol series up to 100% propylene oxide. The samples were then embedded in "Epon 812", polymerized at 60°C for 24 h, and sectioned at 500 Å using a diamond knife. The resulting sections were stained with uranyl acetate followed by Karnowsky's lead and examined in an RCA EMU-3G electron microscope.

Invasion of Cultured Root Cells

Examination of paraffin sections prepared at the time the bacteria-inoculated liquid plant cell cultures were transferred to fresh growth media (stage 1, day 3–7) revealed the presence of structures resembling the infection threads found in *in vivo* nodulating soybean root systems. These "pseudo-infection threads" of the *in vitro* system were observed to penetrate the undifferentiated cell mass for a considerable distance before entering the cell cytoplasm (Fig. 1). *Rhizobia* were observed within the thread-like structures as they traversed the intercellular spaces within the cell mass. Whenever *Rhizobia* entered a plant cell from the terminus of a "pseudo-infection thread", they multiplied to displace the plant cell contents completely with bacteria (Fig. 2). No other morphologically differentiated cells (for example conducting elements) were found in any of the bacterially populated plant cell masses at this developmental stage.

织进行固氮酶活性分析 [9]。将组织在 60℃下干燥 48 小时，然后测量干重。

组织的细胞学检查

取接种过细菌的大豆根细胞培养物随机样本和对照培养瓶中的随机样本，用福尔马林、乙酸和乙醇的混合液（体积比为 5∶5∶90）或者用弗莱明铱酸固定剂在室温下固定 24 小时，以备制作石蜡切片。然后先将组织通过梯度乙醇脱水，再将其包埋于塑化石蜡（熔点为 56℃ ~ 57℃）中，以便进行切片。随后以 8 微米 ~ 10 微米的厚度切片，并用蕃红－固绿或者范吉森尼罗蓝染色，再在配有相差光学装置的蔡司显微镜下观察切片。

同时，将类似的细胞样品表面涂覆含 5% 戊二醛的米隆尼氏磷酸盐缓冲液（pH 值为 7.2 ~ 7.4），并在室温下固定 60 分钟。将固定后的样品用清水冲洗 20 分钟，并用 1% 的 OsO_4（四氧化铱）在室温下再次固定 60 分钟，接着用磷酸盐缓冲液清洗 20 分钟，然后经过梯度乙醇脱水，再用 100% 的环氧丙烷处理。接着将样品包埋于"环氧树脂 812"中，并在 60℃下聚合 24 小时，然后用金刚石刀切成厚度为 500 Å 的切片。将得到的切片先用醋酸铀酰再用卡诺斯基铅进行着色，然后在 RCA EMU-3G 型电子显微镜下进行观察。

侵入培养的根细胞

对将接种细菌的液态植物细胞培养物转移至新鲜生长培养基（第 1 阶段，3 ~ 7 天）时制备的石蜡切片进行观察，发现存在一些结构，这些结构与体内结瘤的大豆根系中的侵染丝相类似。我们观察到，这些体外系统中的"伪侵染丝"在进入细胞的细胞质之前，就已经穿入未分化细胞群中很长一段距离了（图 1）。当这些丝状结构穿越细胞群中的细胞间隙时，我们观察到丝状结构中有根瘤菌。一旦根瘤菌从"伪侵染丝"的末端进入植物细胞，它们就会进行繁殖，将植物细胞中的物质完全替换成细菌（图 2）。在处于这一发展阶段的任何被细菌填充的植物细胞群中，还没有发现过其他形态的分化细胞（例如疏导细胞）。

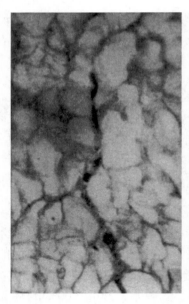

Fig. 1. Paraffin section of a callus culture showing *Rhizobium japonicum* penetration through an infection thread-like structure (×600).

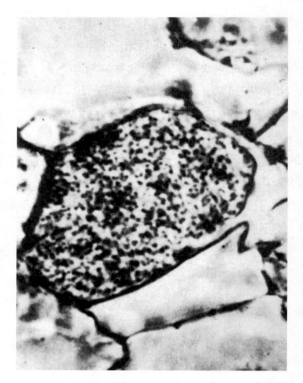

Fig. 2. Callus cell filled with *R. japonicum* after initial penetration.

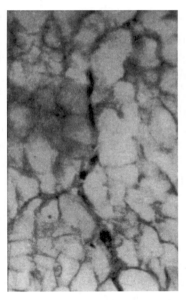

图 1. 愈伤组织培养物的石蜡切片。图中显示出大豆根瘤菌通过一个类似侵染丝的结构进行侵入（放大600倍）。

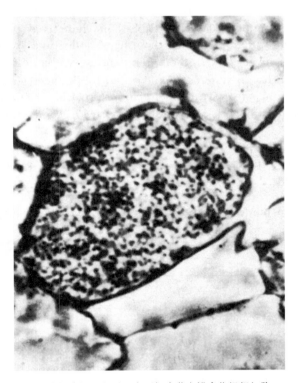

图 2. 在初步侵入之后，大豆根瘤菌充满愈伤组织细胞。

Continued Development of the Symbiotic System

Following the initial penetration of the plant cells by *Rhizobia* (3–7 days after bacterial inoculation of the cell culture flask), the cell cultures were transferred to fresh media, both liquid and agar-solidified, for development of stage 2. The following media were utilized: (1) MS, (2) MS plus 10–15% whole CM and (3) MS plus 10–15% whole CM and 2 mg/l. 2,4-D. Control cultures of soybean root cells (without bacteria) were transferred to similar media and incubated in the same conditions. All cultures were incubated for 7–20 days after transfer before being examined for bacterial penetration and for nitrogenase activity. Light-grown cultures received approximately 500 foot-candles of light from Duro-Test Optima lamps (Duro-Test Corp., North Bergen, New Jersey).

Fig. 3 shows that the degree of rhizobial invasion after transfer of the cultured soybean root cells is related to the growth factor additions to the MS medium. Most extensive invasion is found after transfer of bacterially populated plant cells to MS medium containing no exogenous growth supplements (Fig. 3a). With the addition of whole CM (Fig. 3b) and the combination of CM and 2,4-D (Fig. 3c) the number of cells inhabited by the *Rhizobia* is markedly reduced. Assays for nitrogenase activity under each of the tested culture conditions (Tables 1 and 2) show this activity to vary directly with the degree of bacterial invasion (Table 1). The tissue without rhizobial involvement shows little acetylene–ethylene reducing activity (Table 1) in these assays[11,12]. Table 2 shows that although there is wide variation in the response of individual Acme soybean root cell cultures to *R. japonicum* strain 61A76, there is a definite symbiotic relationship capable of fixing N_2 established in liquid systems, as measured by the acetylene–ethylene technique. Attempts to establish an active symbiotic relationship using Kent variety soybean root cells in liquid culture have been less successful. Even with Acme variety soybeans, the use of a different strain of *R. japonicum* (ATCC 10324) resulted in a lower over-all nitrogenase activity although electron microscopy showed bacterial penetration of the cultured cells. Cotyledonary tissue has shown no propensity to establish a symbiotic association in the conditions of this study.

Table 1. Acetylene to Ethylene Reduction by Soybean Root Cell Cultures inoculated with *Rhizobium japonicum* Strain 61A76

	nmol C_2H_4/g fresh weight $\times24$ h	
	Light	Dark
MS	72.8	318.6
MS+10% CM	36.6	129.0
MS+10% CM+2 p.p.m. 2,4-D	7.7	37.9
Uninoculated control MS+10% CM+2 p.p.m. 2,4-D	0.4	2.1

The assay was carried out 21 days after initial bacterial inoculation and after transfer to semi-solid agar medium for 14 days. Incubation was under continuous light or dark conditions following initial establishment of symbiosis.

共生体系的持续发展

在植物细胞开始被根瘤菌侵入之后（细胞培养瓶接种细菌后的 3 ~ 7 天），将细胞培养物转移至新鲜的培养基中，包括液体培养基和琼脂固化培养基，用来进行第 2 阶段的培育。使用的培养基如下：（1）MS；（2）MS 添加 10% ~ 15% 全脂 CM；（3）MS 添加 10% ~ 15% 全脂 CM 和 2 毫克 / 升 2,4–D。将大豆根细胞的对照培养物（不含细菌）转移至同样的培养基中，并在同样的条件下进行培育。在转移后将所有培养物培育 7 ~ 20 天，然后检测细菌侵入情况和固氮酶活性。光照下生长的培养物所接收的照度约为 500 英尺烛光，光源是杜罗试验最佳配置灯（杜罗试验公司，北伯根，新泽西州）。

由图 3 可以看出：在培养的大豆根细胞被转移后，根瘤菌的入侵程度与 MS 培养基中添加的生长因子之间存在着关联。将被细菌填满的植物细胞转移到不含任何外源生长添加剂的 MS 培养基中后，细菌的入侵范围最广（图 3a）。当添加全脂 CM（图 3b）和 CM 与 2,4–D 的混合物（图 3c）时，被根瘤菌占据的细胞数量明显减少。对上述每一种试验条件下的培养进行固氮酶活性检测的结果（表 1 和表 2）显示，酶活性与细菌入侵程度直接相关（表 1）。在这些分析测试中，没有根瘤菌介入的组织几乎不具有将乙炔还原为乙烯的活性（表 1）[11,12]。表 2 显示：尽管两个阿克姆大豆根细胞培养物对根瘤菌菌株 61A76 的反应有很大的差别，但乙炔 – 乙烯还原法的测定结果表明，在这些液态系统中形成了一种确定的能够固氮的共生关系。尝试用肯特大豆根细胞在液态培养体系中建立有效共生关系的成功率较低。即使是阿克姆大豆，在使用另一种大豆根瘤菌菌株（ATCC 10324）时得到的总固氮酶活性也会偏低一些，尽管通过电子显微镜术已经看到细菌侵入了培养细胞。在上述研究条件下，未曾发现子叶组织有建立共生关系的倾向。

表 1. 接种大豆根瘤菌菌株 61A76 的大豆根细胞培养物将乙炔还原为乙烯的活性

	纳摩尔 C_2H_4 每克鲜重 × 24 小时	
	光照	黑暗
MS	72.8	318.6
MS +10% CM	36.6	129.0
MS +10% CM + 2 p.p.m. 2,4–D	7.7	37.9
未经接种的对照物 MS +10% CM + 2 p.p.m. 2,4–D	0.4	2.1

这项分析测试是在初次接种细菌后 21 天和在转移至半固体琼脂培养基后 14 天进行的。在共生体系初步建立后开始培育，培育条件为连续光照或者避光。

Table 2. Acetylene to Ethylene Reduction by Two Separate Soybean Root Cell Cultures containing *R. japonicum* Strain 61A76 in Symbiotic Relationship

	nmol C_2H_4/g dry weight × 24 h	
	1	2
Tissue + 61A76 bacteria	638	88.0
Uninoculated control	307	25.7

Assays were made 3–5 days after addition of the microorganisms to liquid culture.

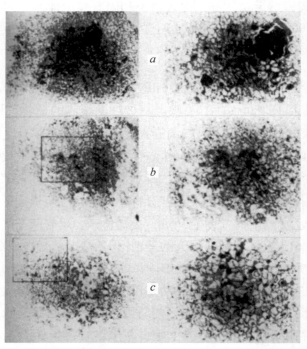

Fig. 3. Sections of callus tissue infected with *R. japonicum* showing the effects of growth supplements on development of the symbiotic association. See text for details of treatments. Left, ×350; right, ×700.

Electron Microscopic Examination of Symbiotic Cultures

Examination of *Rhizobium*-plant cell cultures with the electron microscope confirmed that *Rhizobia* have entered the cultured plant cells and displaced the normal cytoplasmic components (Fig. 4). In some cases the *Rhizobia* were enclosed within a vesicle which is morphologically analogous to the vesicles found in nodules obtained from whole soybean root systems (Fig. 5). It was further observed that the *Rhizobia* within the cultured root cells contained an inclusion which was similar in appearance to an inclusion of whole soybean nodule bacterioids designated as a polymer of β-hydroxybutyrate. This inclusion became more prominent with increasing time of incubation of the synthetic symbiotic system (up to 15–20 days after transfer). Microscopic examinations of uninoculated tissue showed that there were no microorganismal contaminants present. The media used for maintenance of the plant cell cultures were also found to be devoid of microorganisms and N_2-fixing activity; the bacterial inoculum contained only *Rhizobia* and exhibited no N_2-fixing activity. Thus it is clear that free-living N_2-fixing bacteria are not responsible for our observations.

表 2. 含有存在共生关系的大豆根瘤菌菌株 61A76 的两个独立大豆根部细胞培养物将乙炔还原为乙烯的活性

	纳摩尔 C_2H_4 每克干重 × 24 小时	
	1	2
组织 + 61A76 细菌	638	88.0
未经接种的对照物	307	25.7

分析测试是在将微生物加入到液体培养基中后 3 ~ 5 天进行的。

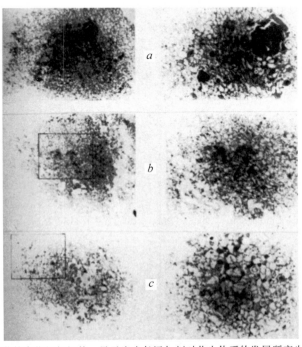

图 3. 感染大豆根瘤菌的愈伤组织切片，显示出生长添加剂对共生体系的发展所产生的影响。实验处理细节参见正文中的叙述。左图：放大350倍；右图：放大700倍。

用电子显微镜观察共生培养物

对根瘤菌－植物细胞培养物的电子显微镜观察结果证实：根瘤菌进入了培养的植物细胞内部，并替换了正常的细胞质成分（图 4）。在有些样本中，根瘤菌被封入了一个囊泡，这个囊泡在形态上类似于来自完整大豆根系统的根瘤中的囊泡（图 5）。进一步的观察发现：培养的根细胞中的根瘤菌含有一种内含物，这种内含物在表观上类似于完整大豆根瘤类菌体中的内含物，它的成分被认定为 β- 羟基丁酸的聚合物。这种内含物会随着在人造共生体系中培育时间的增加（一直到转移后15 ~ 20 天）而变得更加显著。用显微镜对未接种的组织进行观察，结果显示不存在微生物的污染。用于维持植物细胞培养物的培养基也被证明不具有微生物和固氮活性；细菌接种体只含有根瘤菌而没有表现出任何固氮活性。因此很明显，自生固氮菌与我们观察到的结果无关。

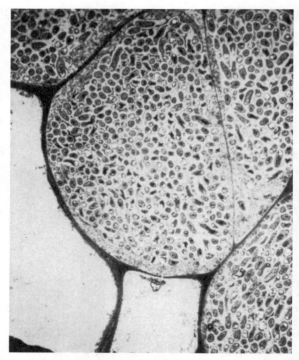

Fig. 4. Electron micrograph of cultured soybean callus infected with *R. japonicum* (×4,160).

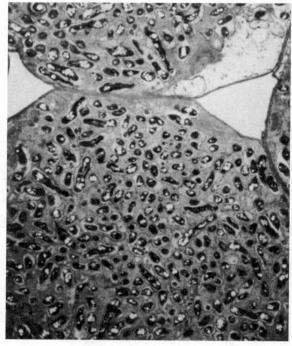

Fig. 5. Electron micrograph of a soybean root nodule infected with *R. japonicum* showing accumulation of β-hydroxybutyrate (×4,160).

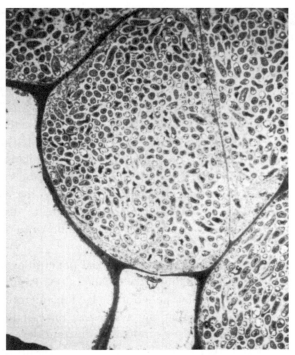

图 4. 培养的大豆愈伤组织被大豆根瘤菌感染后的电子显微镜照片（放大4,160倍）。

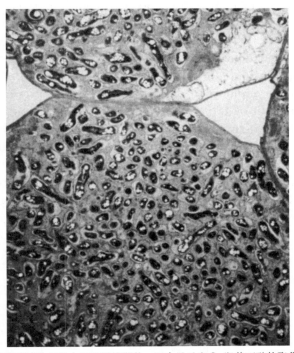

图 5. 大豆根瘤被根瘤菌感染后的电子显微镜照片。图中显示出 β– 羟基丁酸的聚集（放大 4,160 倍）。

581

Functionality of the Symbiotic Relationship

The functional system we have described provides a new tool for the elucidation of the mechanisms controlling nodulation and subsequent N_2-fixation in symbiotic associations.

The morphology of symbiosis *in vitro* is analogous to that of intact soybean root nodules[13,14]. *Rhizobia* within the cytoplasm of the cultured cells, as in root nodules, are at times enclosed within a vesicle. The intracellular bacteria (bacterioids?) are shown to contain an inclusion which has been tentatively identified as poly-β-hydroxybutyrate[15]. A structure similar in appearance to the infection thread of nodulating systems *in vivo* has been observed in the early stages of bacterial penetration of the cultured plant cells in the liquid milieu. This apparent mode of rhizobial entry into the cultured cells and the subsequent multiplication of the intracellular microorganisms to displace completely the cell cytoplasm are again analogous to processes which are known to occur *in vivo*.

It has further been found that following initial bacterial penetration of the cultured cells, depletion of exogenous supplies of plant growth factors (cytokinins and auxins) in the environment leads to increased cellular penetration by the microorganisms and greater nitrogenase induction. This suggests that the symbiosis, once initiated, is self-sufficient and that any exogenous additions tend to suppress its normal development and function. This agrees with the proposed roles of plant growth regulators in the establishment and maintenance of nodulated symbiotic systems *in vivo*[16,17]. Thus it may be possible to control the process of effective nodulation with factors which alter the levels of endogenous plant growth regulators such as auxins during the critical phases of invasion.

The reduction of acetylene to ethylene as a measure of nitrogenase activity shows that the N_2-fixing potential of the symbiosis increases with the proportion of cellular invasion by microorganisms, and the addition of plant growth factors depresses nitrogenase activity as well as the development of the symbiotic morphology. It should therefore be possible to increase the overall N_2-fixing activity of the system by regulating the degree of cell penetration and subsequent nitrogenase induction through chemical means.

Light does not seem to stimulate the symbiosis *in vitro* once it has been established; but cells grown in the light resisted rhizobial challenge, and no working symbiosis could be established in these cultures. It is possible that cells grown in the light develop a natural defence mechanism against invasion by microorganisms *in vitro*, perhaps through the phytochrome system[18].

The acetylene to ethylene reducing activities (and nitrogenase activity by analogy) achieved so far in the *in vitro* symbiotic system are of the order of 1% of those found in soybean nodules. Microscopic examinations of the symbiotic cell masses in culture showed that only 1–10% of the total cell population was infected with intracellular microorganisms. The activity per cell may therefore be comparable with that found in whole root nodules where more than 90% of the cells appear to contain bacteria. It is also pertinent (Fig.

共生关系的功能性

我们所描述的功能体系为阐释共生体系中控制结瘤的机制以及随后发生的固氮作用的机制提供了一个新的工具。

体外共生在形态上类似于完整的大豆根瘤[13,14]。存在于培养细胞的细胞质中的根瘤菌，与在根瘤中的根瘤菌一样，有时会被封闭在一个囊泡中。胞内细菌(类菌体？)被证明含有一种内含物，其成分暂时被认定为 β– 羟基丁酸[15]。当细菌刚开始侵入液态环境中培养的植物细胞时，我们观察到了一种在外观上与体内结瘤系统的侵染丝相类似的结构。根瘤菌侵入培养细胞的表观模式，以及胞内微生物随后能繁殖到完全取代细胞的细胞质的模式，也与已知在体内发生的过程类似。

进一步又发现：在细菌开始侵入培养细胞之后，培养环境中植物生长因子（细胞分裂素和植物生长素）的外源供应被耗尽将导致微生物侵入细胞加强，并诱导产生更强的固氮酶活性。这表明共生体系一旦启动，便可以自给自足；而且任何外源添加物都会抑制其正常的发展和功能。关于植物生长调节剂在体内建立和维持成瘤共生体系中所起的作用，早已有人提出看法[16,17]，以上实验结果恰好与这种看法一致。因此，也许可以利用一些能改变内源植物生长调节剂水平的因素（如入侵过程关键时期的植物生长素水平）来控制有效成瘤的过程。

利用乙炔还原成乙烯的量来表征的固氮酶活性数值表明，共生体系的固氮潜能随着被微生物入侵的细胞比例的增加而增强，而添加植物生长因子不但会抑制共生体系的形态发展，也会抑制固氮酶的活性。因此，通过化学手段来调节细菌侵入细胞的程度以及随后诱导的固氮酶活性，以增强这个共生体系的总体固氮活性，应当是有可能实现的。

体外共生体系一旦建立，光似乎就不能再对它产生刺激作用了；但在光照下生长的细胞能抵制根瘤菌的入侵，因此无法在这些培养物中建成有效的共生体系。在光照下生长的细胞有可能会形成一种对抗体外微生物入侵的天然防卫机制，这也许是通过光敏色素系统实现的[18]。

到目前为止，从体外共生体系中获得的使乙炔转变成乙烯的还原活性（以及由此推出的固氮酶活性）是在大豆根瘤中发现的 1% 左右。用显微镜对培养物中共生细胞群体的观察结果显示：在整个细胞种群中，只有 1%～10% 的细胞被细胞内的微生物感染。但在根瘤中看似有超过 90% 的细胞含有细菌，因此每个细胞的活性有可能与完整根瘤中的细胞活性相当，这也与细菌感染只发生在愈伤组织表面下的细

3) that infection occurs only in the subsurface cells of the callus where physiological conditions might be expected to simulate more closely the cortex of intact roots. The initial infection of the tissue culture occurs through a modification of a peripheral cell of the callus mass and not through a root hair cell as in intact roots. This suggests that symbiosis *in vivo* might also be expected to occur through penetration of epidermal cells other than root hairs in suitable conditions.

We thank Mrs. Mary Ann Mattson and Mr. M. L. Van Kavelaar for technical assistance.

(**232**, 173-176; 1971)

R. D. Holsten, R. C. Burns, R. W. F. Hardy and R. R. Hebert: Central Research Department, E. I. du Pont de Nemours and Company, Wilmington, Delaware 19898.

Received January 25, 1971.

References:

1. Lewis, K. N., and McCoy, E., *Bot. Gaz.*, **95**, 316 (1933).

2. McGonagle, M. P., *Nature*, **153**, 528 (1944).

3. Raggio, N., Raggio, M., and Burris, R. H., *Biochim. Biophys. Acta*, **32**, 274 (1959).

4. Raggio, M., Raggio, N., and Torrey, J. G., *Amer. J. Bot.*, **44**, 325 (1957).

5. Veliky, I., and LaRue, T. A., *Naturwissenschaften*, **54**, 96 (1967).

6. Murashige, T., and Skoog, F., *Physiol. Plant.*, **15**, 473 (1962).

7. Steward, F. C., and Shantz, E. M., *Chemistry and Mode of Action of Growth Substances* (edit. by Wain, R. L., and Wightman, F.), 312 (Academic Press, New York, 1956).

8. Caplin, S. M., and Steward, F. C., *Nature*, **163**, 920 (1949).

9. Hardy, R. W. F., Holsten, R. D., Jackson, E. K., and Burns, R. C., *Plant Physiol.*, **43**, 1185 (1968).

10. Millonig, G., *J. Appl. Phys.*, **32**, 1637 (1961).

11. Gamborg, O. L., and LaRue, T. A. G., *Nature*, **200**, 604 (1968).

12. Stewart, E. P., and Freebairn, H. T., *Plant Physiol.*, **42**, Suppl., S-30 (1967).

13. Goodchild, D. J., and Bergersen, F. J., *J. Bact.*, **92**, 204 (1966).

14. Holsten, R. D., Hebert, R. R., Jackson, E. K., Burns, R. C., and Hardy, R. W. F., *Bact. Proc.*, 149 (1969).

15. Klucas, R. V., and Evans, H. J., *Plant Physiol.*, **43**, 1458 (1968).

16. Kefford, N. P., Brockwell, J., and Zwar J. A., *Austral. J. Biol. Sci.*, **13**, 456 (1960).

17. Thimann, K., *Proc. US Nat. Acad. Sci.*, **22**, 511 (1936).

18. Lie, T. A., *Plant and Soil*, **30**, 391 (1969).

胞相一致（图3），可以设想此处的生理条件更近似于完整根部的皮层。在组织培养中，初期感染是通过改变愈伤组织的外周细胞而发生的，并不像在完整根部中那样，是通过根毛细胞发生的。这表明体内共生或许也可以被设想为是在适当条件下通过侵入表皮细胞发生的，而不是通过侵入根毛发生的。

感谢玛丽·安·马特森夫人和范卡维拉先生为我们提供了技术上的支持。

（刘振明 翻译；顾孝诚 审稿）

Re-evaluation of the Palaeogeographic Argument for an Expanding Earth

A. Hallam

Editor's Note

The idea that the Earth is very slowly expanding has a long history. Most such proposals were far-fetched, although one stemmed from a serious suggestion that gravity weakened over very long times. Hungarian geophysicist László Egyed invoked that idea to explain his observation that the percentage of the Earth covered by land seemed to have increased since the early Palaeozoic era, implying that the oceans occupy less surface area. Here geologist Anthony Hallam at Oxford challenges this interpretation of Egyed's data, saying that it might instead result from a thickening of the continental crust, due to well understood tectonic processes. The expanding-Earth hypothesis is generally rejected now, but still has adherents.

EGYED[1] has inferred that the Earth was expanding at a mean rate of 0.5 mm yr^{-1} during Phanerozoic time. The evidence on which he based this conclusion was taken from two series of palaeogeographic maps showing the distribution of land and sea since the early Cambrian, by Strakhov and H. and G. Termier respectively. With the aid of a planimeter Egyed estimated the percentage of continental areas covered by the sea for successive geological periods and was able to demonstrate clearly a secular decline since the early Palaeozoic with the more or less regular downward trend having superimposed on it a series of shorter phase oscillations.

As the volume of ocean water is hardly likely to have decline during Phanerozoic time, and might indeed have been augmented by a small percentage, Egyed argued that the facts could only be explained by a gradual increase in the Earth's volume, so that ocean water drained more or less progressively from the continents into the growing oceans.

The essential palaeogeographic facts are not in dispute. As plotted in Fig. 1, the two groups of data, though differing appreciably, are in accord as regards the decline through time of areas of the continents inundated by seawater, the only notable (but temporary) reversal of this general trend being in the late Cretaceous. Of the two sets of data, that of the Termiers, based as it is on more numerous time intervals, gives a more accurate idea of the oscillatory nature of the change. The modification of the Cambro-Ordovician data proposed by Holmes[2] is accepted here. Apart from the areas of metamorphic rocks in Africa and elsewhere that were probably marine sediments originally, missed by the Termiers, it should be borne in mind that the older the rocks the greater is the likelihood of their having been removed by subsequent erosion or deeply buried beneath younger sediments beyond the limits of intensive drilling. For these reasons the amount of the

586

再议有关地球膨胀的古地理学证据

哈勒姆

编者按

地球在以非常缓慢的速度膨胀的观点由来已久。但是大多数这类想法都很牵强，其中只有一个是基于严肃的推理，即考虑到在漫长的时间内地球引力在不断削弱。匈牙利地球物理学家拉斯洛·埃杰德引用地球膨胀说解释了他观察到的现象：地球表面陆地面积所占的比例似乎自早古生代以来在不断上升，这意味着海洋将占据更少的地表面积。在本文中，牛津大学的地质学家安东尼·哈勒姆对用地球膨胀说来解释埃杰德的观察结果提出了质疑。他指出这一现象可能是由于大家所熟知的板块构造过程所引起的陆壳加厚现象。如今，地球膨胀说已经被大多数人所抛弃，但仍不乏一些支持者。

埃杰德[1] 曾推断，地球在整个显生宙时期的平均膨胀速率为 0.5 毫米 / 年。他得到这一结论是基于两套古地理系列图，它们分别由斯特拉霍夫和泰尔米埃夫妇绘制，图中给出了早寒武纪以来地球上的陆海分布情况。利用求积仪作为辅助工具，埃杰德估算出了连续几个地质时期内被海洋覆盖的陆地面积的百分比，由此可以明确地说明：自早古生代以来，该比例长期保持着一种下降的趋势，这种趋势或多或少地表现出一定的规律性，并有一系列的短期振荡叠加其上。

由于在显生宙时期海水的体积几乎不可能减少，甚至还有可能会略微增大，因此埃杰德认为这一事实只能用地球体积在逐渐增大来解释，这样海水才会不断地从陆地退向逐步扩张的海洋。

人们对于古地理学的这些基本事实并无争议。如图 1 所示，虽然两组数据存在显著的差异，但两者都表明，随着时间的推移，被海水淹没的陆地面积呈逐渐下降的趋势，唯一一次与这种一般趋势明显（但只是暂时的）相逆的情况出现在白垩纪晚期。在这两组数据中，泰尔米埃夫妇的数据所基于的时间间隔更为密集，因而能够更准确地体现出这种变化的振荡性。霍姆斯[2] 对寒武纪–奥陶纪的数据所作的修正是可接受的。应该时刻牢记，除了非洲的变质岩地区以及其他有可能由海洋沉积物形成的岩石地区以外，越古老的岩石就越有可能被后续的侵蚀作用所破坏，或者被深埋于新的沉积物之下而超出钻探能力之外，而泰尔米埃夫妇恰恰忽视了这一点。这就是为什么在大多数古地理图中，被海水淹没的陆地面积的持续减少量很可能会

secular decline is more likely than not to be underestimated in most palaeogeographic maps.

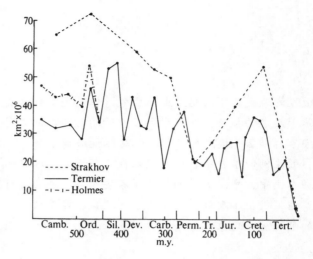

Fig. 1. Areas of continents covered by sea in Phanerozoic time.

Both Egyed and those who have accepted his argument[2-4] have failed to consider an alternative explanation of the facts, that the average thickness of the continents has increased slightly through the course of the Phanerozoic. The isostatic uplift consequent on such increase would inevitably have the effect of reducing the area of marine inundation. There are grounds for believing that changes of this sort might, in fact, have taken place.

In the first place, many ancient shields have persisted for millions of years as positive areas and sediment sources. Maintenance of relief following removal of sediment would naturally result from isostatic adjustment, but obviously this could not persist indefinitely because the shields would achieve isostatic stability with low relief and relatively thin crust. In fact such shields often have crustal thicknesses greater than the average[5], even though metamorphic rocks of granulite facies may be exposed at the surface. Extensive tracts of the Archaean shields consist of the so called Greenstone Belts, which are believed to signify appreciably thinner crusts in early Pre-Cambrian times, perhaps only 12–15 km. This is based on various data, including the chemistry of the metabasalts and comparisons with present day island arcs[6]. The implication is that the shields have undergone a progressive "sialic underplating" since the early Pre-Cambrian as a result of slow differentiation in the underlying mantle.

In the second place, geochemical and other data suggest that the andesites of island arc complexes and the associated granitic batholiths in regions such as western North America originate primarily by differentiation of basaltic magmas arising from descending slabs of ocean floor along subduction zones, with only limited contamination by continental

被人们低估的原因。

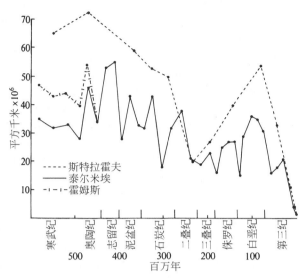

图 1. 在显生宙时期被海水覆盖的陆地面积。

埃杰德以及认可其观点的学者 [2-4] 都没有考虑到关于上述事实的另一种解释，那就是，在整个显生宙时期陆地的平均厚度是略有增加的。而由陆地厚度增长所导致的均衡隆升必然会造成海水覆盖面积的减少。我们有理由相信这种变化可能真的发生过。

首先，许多古老的地盾作为正地形和沉积物物源已经存在了数百万年。沉积物被搬运走以后，均衡调整自然会使其维持原有地貌。不过，这种情况显然不能无限持续，因为地盾在地势起伏较小、地壳相对较薄时会达到均衡稳定状态。实际上这些地盾的地壳厚度通常会高于平均值 [5]，即使在麻粒岩相的变质岩有可能暴露于地表的情况下也是如此。太古代地盾的广大区域由所谓的绿岩带组成，绿岩带被认为是说明地壳在前寒武纪早期时明显较薄的一个标志，厚度可能仅为 12 千米 ~ 15 千米。这是根据几组不同数据得来的，其中包括变质玄武岩的化学组成以及与现今岛弧的比较结果 [6]。这就意味着：自前寒武纪早期以来，由于下伏地幔中的缓慢分异作用，这些地盾曾经历过渐进的"硅铝质底侵作用"。

其次，来自地球化学和其他方面的数据表明：诸如在北美洲西部这样的地区，岛弧联合体中的安山岩以及相关的花岗岩岩基主要是由从沿俯冲带的洋底俯冲板片中喷出的玄武质岩浆的分异作用形成的，仅存在少量的陆壳物质的混染 [7,8]。根据自

crustal materials[7,8]. At the rate of thickening implied by volcanicity since the Miocene, the whole of the Japanese crust could have been generated in about 3×10^9 yr[7]. This process provides a ready mechanism for creating continents which is consistent with the tenets of plate tectonics. Many former geosynclinal regions emerged from the sea following major orogenies and became incorporated into cratons bordering the ancient shields and so something more than lateral accretion is involved. Sutton[9] has incorporated such facts into his notion of chelogenic cycles, whereby tectonically mobile belts characterized by flysch-type marine sedimentation and vulcanicity are transformed into stable shield areas or cratons, on which only continental or shallow marine sediments were laid down, the latter often only at the margins. The conversion of the Caledonian geosyncline of the North Atlantic region into the "Old Red Sandstone Continent" in Devonian times is a good example, because it persisted as a positive area until well into the Mesozoic, when it was disrupted by the drifting apart of North America and Europe.

An approximate estimate of the amount and rate of thickening of the continental crust can be obtained by considering estimates of the changes in relative position of sea level in the past 600 million yr or so. Egyed[1] estimated that sea level in Cambrian times was about 500 m higher than today, if Strakhov's data were to be relied upon, or 275 m higher in the middle Ordovician, using the Termiers' data. Kuenen[10] was able to show from the world hypsographic curve that under present conditions a eustatic rise of 100 m would flood about 1/4 to 1/5 of the continents and a rise of 200 m nearly 1/3. He considered that the present continents have abnormally high relief and so thought that at most periods in the past a 100 m rise would flood more than 1/3 of the continental area. The palaeogeographic maps available to Kuenen seldom showed more than 1/3 of the continents submerged, and he concluded that the biggest transgressions did not involve eustatic rises of more than 200 m.

These figures suggest that the Termiers' data might be more accurate than those of Strakhov. An independent check on the maximum area covered by the Jurassic seas[11] also gives a figure (24%) much closer to that of the Termiers (27%) than Strakhov (39.5%).

If we take 300 m as a figure of the right order of magnitude for the amount of secular lowering of sea level since the early Palaeozoic, this would be accounted for by an average thickening of the continental crust of perhaps twice this amount. Such a figure implies an increase of only about 1 mm in 10^3 yr, with no more than about 2% of the present average thickness of the continental crust being added in the last demi-eon. Modest, almost negligible, change of this kind could be accounted for readily by the processes previously discussed. With such a plausible alternative interpretation being available the simple palaeogeographic argument for an expanding Earth cannot reasonably be sustained.

The shorter phased eustatic oscillations superimposed on the gradual lowering of sea level, given crude and oversimplified expression in Fig. 1, are to be accounted for in other ways. Whereas glacially controlled eustatic changes dominated Pleistocene palaeogeography

中新世以来的火山活动而得出的板块加厚速率，整个日本地壳的形成经历了约 30 亿年 [7]。该过程提供了一个现成的陆地形成机制，而这个机制与板块构造原理是相符的。在大规模造山运动之后，许多之前为地槽的地区露出了海面，围绕着古老地盾边界并成为克拉通的一部分，因而其中所涉及的就不仅仅是侧向加积作用了。萨顿 [9] 将上述事实纳入到了他的地盾形成旋回理念中。该理念认为：以复理石型海洋沉积作用和火山活动为特征的构造活动带均转变成了稳定的地盾或克拉通，只有陆源沉积物或浅海沉积物可以沉积在地盾或克拉通之上，而浅海沉积物通常仅存于其边缘。泥盆纪时期，北大西洋地区的加里东地槽转化成"老红砂岩陆地"就是一个很好的实例，因为它从前一直是一个正地形，直到进入中生代以后才因北美和欧洲大陆的分离而遭到破坏。

根据对过去大约 6 亿年间海平面相对位置变化的粗略判断，可以大致估算出陆壳加厚的量及加厚速率。埃杰德 [1] 利用斯特拉霍夫的数据推断出，寒武纪时海平面比现在高出约 500 米；利用泰尔米埃夫妇的数据得出，在中奥陶纪时海平面比现在高出约 275 米。屈嫩 [10] 根据全球等高线图得出了以下结论：在当前条件下，海平面上升 100 米就会有大约 1/4 ～ 1/5 的陆地面积被淹没，若上升 200 米则会淹没接近 1/3 的陆地。考虑到当今陆地具有异常高的地形，他认为，在过去的大多数时期里，海平面上升 100 米就有可能造成 1/3 以上的陆地面积被海水淹没。屈嫩在他能够找到的所有古地理图中，几乎没有发现超过 1/3 的陆地被淹没的情况，所以他认为：史上规模最大的海进过程也未能使海平面上升超过 200 米。

上述估算表明，泰尔米埃夫妇的数据可能比斯特拉霍夫的数据更准确。泰尔米埃夫妇的数据（27%）也比斯特拉霍夫的数据（37.5%）更接近于用另外一种方法测算出的侏罗纪时期的海水最大覆盖率（24%）[11]。

假如我们把 300 米看作是海平面自早古生代以来持续下降总量的一个合适的数量级，那么利用陆壳的平均增厚量是该值的大致两倍就可以对此作出解释。这个数值意味着：每 1,000 年中，陆壳厚度仅仅增加了大约 1 毫米；在过去的 5 亿年中，陆壳增加的总厚度还不到现今陆壳平均厚度的 2%。对于海平面的变化，只有少到几乎可以忽略的部分可以直接用之前所讨论的过程来解释。既然现在可以采用这样一种较为合理的解释，那么用简单的古地理学证据来说明地球的膨胀就不再是一种明智的选择了。

可以用其他方式来解释以下这个在图 1 中表现得过于粗略和简单化的现象，即较短周期的海平面升降振荡叠加于海平面逐渐降低的总趋势之上。虽然更新世古地

it is doubtful whether the melting and freezing of polar ice played more than a minor role further back in time. Thus even the well documented late Palaeozoic Ice Age of the southern continents had no clearly perceptible large scale effect. On the contrary, the apparent disappearance of the ice sheets at the close of the Palaeozoic coincided with a pronounced marine regression rather than a transgression. The dominant control was much more likely to have been variations in the cubic capacity of the ocean basins due to the uplift and subsidence of mid-oceanic ridges and trench systems[12]. Evidence is now accumulating to suggest that uplift and subsidence of mid-oceanic ridges correlate respectively with increases and decreases of seafloor spreading rates[13]. The more fundamental control is presumably temporal variations in heat flow from the mantle.

The two most notable departures from a more or less gradual lowering of relative sea level in the Phanerozoic are the pronounced regression of the late Permian and early Triassic, and the equally striking transgression of the late Cretaceous. This is brought out more clearly in the less accurate Strakhov curve of Fig. 1. In fact both curves probably over-estimate by a considerable margin the area of continent covered by the sea at the close of the Palaeozoic, which was closer to the minimal values of the Pleistocene than anything before or since. Both phenomena probably relate to significant plate movements. Valentine and Moores[14] have argued that the suturing of Palaeozoic continents to form "Pangaea II" would be a sufficient cause of regression in the late Permian. With regard to the late Cretaceous, a major transgression could have been produced by one, or both, of the following factors: an acceleration of spreading rate or an increase in the length of the oceanic ridge system as significant dispersal of both northern and southern sectors of Pangaea got under way. The probable timing of continental breakup[15] suggests the latter cause to be sufficient.

I thank Dr. E. R. Oxburgh and Dr. S. W. Richardson for their helpful comments.

(**232**, 180-182; 1971)

A. Hallam: Department of Geology and Mineralogy, University of Oxford.

Received June 3, 1971.

References:

1. Egyed, L., *Geofis. Bura Apl.*, **33**, 42 (1956).

2. Holmes, A., *Principles of Physical Geology*, second ed. (Nelson, London, 1965).

3. Carey, S. W., in *Continental Drift: a Symposium* (University of Tasmania, 1958).

4. Creer, K. M., *Nature*, **205**, 539 (1965).

5. Oxburgh, E. R., *Geol. Soc. Lond. Spec. Publ.*, No. 3, 251 (1969).

6. Anhaeusser, C. R., Mason, R., Viljoen, M. J., and Viljoen, R. P., *Bull. Geol. Soc. Amer.*, **80**, 2175 (1969).

7. Oxburgh, E. R., and Turcotte, D. L., *Bull. Geol. Soc. Amer.*, **81**, 1665 (1970).

8. Dickinson, W. R., *Rev. Geophys. Space Phys.*, **8**, 813 (1970).

9. Sutton, J., *Proc. Geol. Assoc. Lond.*, **78**, 493 (1967).

理学界普遍认为冰川变化是影响海平面升降的主要因素，但在更早的时期极地冰川的消融与冻结是否也起到了不小的作用尚无法确定。例如，即使是曾在南方大陆上确实出现过的晚古生代大冰期，也未能对海平面的升降造成明显可见的巨大影响。相反，在古生代末期，与冰盖的显著消亡相伴随的不是海进而是一次明显的海退。因此，最主要的影响因素很可能是由洋中脊以及海沟体系的隆升和下沉所造成的大洋盆地在容积上的变化 [12]。从当前积累的证据可以看出，洋中脊的隆升和下沉分别对应于海底扩张速率的增加和减小 [13]。由此看来，更为基本的控制因素可能是地幔热流的暂时性变化。

显生宙期间，在相对海平面逐渐降低的大致趋势下，出现了两次非常显著的偏离，分别是从二叠纪晚期到三叠纪早期的大规模海退和白垩纪晚期的同等规模的海进。从图 1 中精度较差的斯特拉霍夫曲线中可以更清晰地看到这两次偏离。图 1 中的两条曲线很可能都在很大程度上高估了海水在古生代末期所覆盖的陆地面积，实际上，与之前或之后的任何时期的值相比，该值更接近于更新世时期的最小值。这两次偏离的出现很可能都与板块的大规模运动有关。瓦伦丁和穆尔斯 [14] 曾指出：古生代时各大陆发生联合并形成了"泛古陆 II"，这一现象足以解释在二叠纪晚期发生的海退。而白垩纪晚期的大规模海进则可能是由以下因素中的一个或两个共同造成的：一个是海底的加速扩张；另一个是由泛古陆南北两部分开始分散而导致的洋脊体系总长度的增加。从大陆可能发生分解的时间 [15] 来看，用后一种因素来解释应该就足够了。

感谢奥克斯伯格博士和理查森博士提出的宝贵意见。

（齐红艳 翻译；李三忠 审稿）

10. Kuenen, Ph. H., *Marine Geol.* (Wiley, New York, 1950).

11. Hallam, A., *Earth Sci. Rev.*, **5**, 45 (1969).

12. Hallam, A., *Amer. J. Sci.*, **261**, 397 (1963).

13. Van Andel, T., and Heath, G. R., *Mar. Geophys. Res.*, **1**, 5 (1970).

14. Valentine, J. W., and Moores, E. M., *Nature*, **228**, 657 (1970).

15. Smith, A. G., and Hallam, A., *Nature*, **225**, 139 (1970).

"Self-recognition" in Colonial Marine Forms and Flowering Plants in Relation to the Evolution of Immunity

F. M. Burnet

Editor's Note

The Australian F. MacFarlane Burnet was one of the pioneers of the modern understanding of the immune response of animals (including people) to infectious pathogens. For his pioneering work he was awarded a Nobel Prize for medicine in 1960. In this article, he raises questions about the similarities between immune reactions in plants as well as animals and speculates about the relationship between immunity and the genetic code.

THERE is a growing tendency to regard the evolutionary origin of adaptive immunity, as manifested in ourselves and in the standard experimental mammals of the laboratory, as being related to something other than defence against pathogenic microorganisms. In 1959 Thomas[1] suggested that there were two mammalian phenomena which might be relevant to the understanding of immunity and its evolution—pregnancy and malignant disease. Both suggestions have subsequently been discussed extensively and the relationship of the foetus as a mass of antigenically foreign cells embedded in the maternal tissues to the mother's immune system has provoked much interest and experimentation[2,3]. Similarly, the antigenic quality of a large proportion of autochthonous tumours became one of the central themes of recent oncological research[4-7]. I have written extensively[8] on the concept of immunological surveillance, which postulates that antigenic patterns abnormal to the genotype which arise by somatic mutation may provoke an antigenic response and play a part in preventing or delaying the appearance of malignant disease.

All metazoan forms must have a capacity to inhibit the multiplication of bacteria and other potential pathogens in their tissues and in that sense they are possessors of an immune system. For obvious anatomical and functional reasons, if we are to consider the evolution of the mammalian immune system, we must confine ourselves to the vertebrates and their immediate ancestral forms. Recently there have been intensive studies of sea lamprey[9,10] and hagfish[11-13] as representative modern cyclostomes, the most primitive extant vertebrates. It is probably a fair summary of the results to say that homograft rejection is well shown; there are other T-type (cell-mediated) responses and restricted and weak antibody responses. The immunoglobulins have typical vertebrate characteristics but they are in very low concentration[10].

群体海洋生物和开花植物中的"自我识别"与免疫进化的关系

伯内特

编者按

澳大利亚的麦克法兰·伯内特作为先驱之一,建立了动物(包括人)对传染性病原体的免疫反应的现代解释。由于所作的开创性工作,他在 1960 年被授予诺贝尔医学奖。在这篇文章中,他就动植物间免疫反应的相似性提出了一些问题,并思考了免疫和遗传密码间的关系。

根据在我们自己体内以及在实验室标准实验哺乳动物体内所发现的情况,人们越来越倾向于将适应性免疫的进化起源与除抵御病原微生物外的某些因素关联起来。1959 年,托马斯[1] 提出,哺乳动物中有两种现象可以用免疫和免疫的进化来解释——怀孕和恶性疾病。这些建议后来被广泛讨论。胎儿可以被看作是一团嵌入到母体组织中的抗原性外源细胞,其与母体免疫系统的关系激起了科学家们的极大兴趣,他们对此进行了大量实验[2,3]。类似地,大部分原发肿瘤的抗原特性已经成为近来肿瘤学研究的中心议题之一[4-7]。我在一本专著中[8] 广泛讨论了免疫监视的概念,认为由体细胞突变引起的基因型异常的抗原模式可能会诱发抗原反应,并在阻止或延缓恶性疾病的发生中起着一定的作用。

所有后生动物(译者注:此处指多细胞动物)都一定具有抑制细菌和其他潜在病原体在自身组织内繁殖的能力。从这个意义上讲,它们要拥有一套免疫系统。基于显而易见的解剖学和功能方面的原因,如果我们要考虑哺乳动物免疫系统的进化,就必须将我们的注意力集中在脊椎动物和它们最直接的祖先上。最近已经对海生七鳃鳗[9,10] 和盲鳗进行过深入研究[11-13],它们是现代圆口纲脊椎动物的代表,也是现存最原始的脊椎动物。对这些结果的合理总结很可能可以说明同种移植排斥反应已得到很好的体现;还有其他 T 细胞型的(细胞介导)反应和一些受限且微弱的抗体反应。其免疫球蛋白虽然具有典型的脊椎动物特征,但浓度很低[10]。

Studies of Colonial Tunicates

No immunological studies have yet been made to my knowledge of the protochordates and the work of Oka[14] on the genetics of compatibility in colonial ascidians has not been considered previously for its immunological implications. Here I shall explore the possibility that Oka's studies of colonial tunicates (*Botryllus*) and the less extensive studies of Theoder[15] of the anthozoan (*Eunicella*), also a colonial form, may throw light on primitive types of "self and not-self" recognition from which adaptive immunity may have evolved.

The colonial ascidian *Botryllus* produces star shaped colonies, each ray being an individual with its own inlet and outlet pores for seawater circulation and feeding, but with a common vascular system ending in a series of peripheral ampullae. The colony is initiated by a larva that develops from a fertilized ovum, but once the larva has settled down it buds off new individuals to form the colony. Each colony is therefore essentially a clone of genetically identical units. As might be expected, therefore, if colony I is divided into two and the parts allowed to grow separately and then brought into contact, the two daughter colonies fuse together and reconstitute a single colony. If, however, an unrelated colony II of the same species is brought into contact with colony I there is a positive rejection and a barrier of necrotic material develops between the two colonies. Finally, if another compound ascidian of the same general type, *Botrylloides*, comes into contact with *Botryllus* I or II, nothing happens. One will grow over the other as if it were just an inert attachment surface. Clearly, therefore, there is recognition of foreignness within the species and recognition must always be the basic phenomenon of immunity.

Sexual reproduction of *Botryllus* is dominated by mechanisms to avoid self-fertilization since the organisms are hermaphrodite, liberating both sperm and ova into the environment. To summarize Oka's work, it is convenient to accept his assumption, which is validated by much preliminary work, that fusion or rejection between colonies depends on a single locus with many alleles which can be referred to as recognition genes. All natural colonies are heterozygous and can be represented as AB, CD and so on. At the margin of each colony or regenerated sub-colony there is a row of ampullae (with a single cell wall) the contents of which are part of the common blood circulation of the colony. It is the reaction of contact between these ampullae which determines the gross character of the interaction between two colonies. When two parts of the same AB colony are brought together again, the walls of adjacent ampullae fuse and a lumen is developed to extend the common circulation. When an F1 generation is produced, the progeny from an AB× CD cross will be of four different types: AC, AD, BC and BD. Any two sets of these which have a gene in common—AC/BC, AC/AD etc.—will show the same type of fusion and integration of the circulation. Where there is no common gene—AC/BD, AD/BC—the ampullae in contact undergo necrosis, producing a barrier between the two colonies.

The other feature of interest concerns cross-fertilization. These organisms are hermaphrodite and there are special arrangements to prevent self-fertilization. The gametes which are, of course, haploid are A or B from AB and C or D from DC. Self-

对群体被囊动物的研究

据我所知，目前还没有针对原索动物的免疫学研究，此前人们并没有把奥卡[14]关于群体海鞘相容性的遗传学研究看作是免疫学方面的工作。这里我将探究以下可能性：利用奥卡对群体被囊动物（菊海鞘）的研究以及西奥多[15]对另一种群体动物——珊瑚虫（网柳珊瑚）的小范围研究，或许可以揭示出"自我和非我"识别的原始类型，适应性免疫可能就是由此演化而来的。

一种群体海鞘——菊海鞘形成星形群落，每一射线都是一个个体，各自用自己的进水孔和出水孔进行海水的循环和进食。但是它们共用一套末端位于一系列外周壶腹的脉管系统。群落始于由一个受精卵发育而来的幼体，但是一旦这个幼体定居下来，就会出芽产生新的个体，最终形成群落。因此，每个群落本质上是一个由相同遗传单元组成的克隆体。正如我们所料，如果群落 I 一分为二，并且两个部分都能独立生长，然后使它们相互接触，那么这两个子群落就会融合在一起，重组为一个单一的群落。然而，如果将一个属于同一物种但不相关的群落 II 与群落 I 放在一起互相接触，就会发生主动排斥，并且两个群落间会形成一道由坏死物质组成的屏障。最后，如果用另一种大致相同类型的混合海鞘——拟菊海鞘，与菊海鞘 I 或 II 放在一起互相接触，将什么都不发生。一种会覆盖在另一种上生长，就好像下面只是一种非生物的附着表面。因此，很明显，菊海鞘能够识别同一物种内的外来物质，而识别通常是免疫的基本现象。

由于菊海鞘是雌雄同体，且同时向环境中释放精子和卵子，因而这种生物体的有性繁殖由一些能够避免自体受精的机制所支配。要总结奥卡的工作，方便的方法是接受他的假设，这些假设已经被很多初步工作证实，那就是群落间的融合或排斥取决于具有很多等位基因的某一单基因座，可以认为这些等位基因就是识别基因。所有自然的群落都是杂合的，可以用 AB、CD 等来表示。在每一群落或者再生亚群落的边缘存在一排壶腹（具有单一的细胞壁），壶腹的内容物是群落共同血液循环的一部分。两个群落间相互作用的总体特征由这些壶腹间的接触反应决定。当同属于 AB 群落的两部分再次放在一起时，邻近壶腹的壁相互融合，发育成一个共同的内腔，将二者独立的循环扩展为一个共同的循环。当 F1 代产生时，AB 与 CD 杂交的后代会有四种不同的类型：AC、AD、BC 和 BD。其中具有一个共同基因的任何两个组合，如 AC/BC、AC/AD 等，会表现出同种类型的融合和循环整合。如果不存在共同基因，如 AC/BD、AD/BC，则接触的壶腹会发生坏死，从而在两个群落间形成一道屏障。

值得关注的另一个特征是异体受精。这些生物体都是雌雄同体，具有阻止自体受精的特殊办法。它们的配子必然是单倍体，其中 A 或 B 来自 AB，C 或 D 来自于

fertilization does not occur presumably because of the layer of follicular cells which surrounds the ovum. The nature of this structure is not elaborated in Oka's review[14] but the cells surrounding an A ovum from an AB individual are presumably diploid and AB, and prevent the entry of either an A or a B spermatozoon. Any other type of spermatozoon, such as C or D, encounters no obstruction.

Other Colonial Forms

Both phenomena seem "designed" to ensure the greatest degree of heterozygosity in all viable colonies. It is virtually impossible for a homozygous colony to be formed and, at the same time, the situation cannot be muddied by the fusion of unrelated colonies. Both seem to produce colonies which are at a disadvantage for survival, although it is not easy to see just what the disadvantage is. Oka points out that the situation is directly analogous to the self-incompatibility of angiosperms such as plums, but it is even more analogous to the findings of Theodor[15] on some colonial coelenterates (Anthozoa). It may well be of importance for survival that colonial marine forms should be able to distinguish their own colony from another. In the sea-fan *Eunicella* the colony has a branching form supported by a firm sclero-protein axis on which there is a continuous sheath of living cells from which the polyps derive a dense efflorescence. Taking 25–30 mm segments of the branches, Theodor denuded a central 2 or 3 mm portion to expose the rigid non-living axis. Two such preparations were combined so that the two denuded areas formed the meeting point of a right-angled cross. When such preparations were maintained in suitable aquaria, regrowth eventually covered the denuded regions. If both segments were from the same colony all four growing surfaces fused without any sign of discontinuity. When one segment was from colony A and the other from B, A and B tissues failed to fuse and a clear line of demarcation was visible. When two different genera, *Eunicella* and *Lophogorgia*, were placed in contact there was a damaging interaction in the form of the development of "blistery" tissue along the surface of contact.

Self-recognition in *Botryllus*

As far as the evolution of adaptive immunity is concerned, it can be assumed that the phenomena Oka described for colonial ascidians, and probably also those of Theodor in the Anthozoa, facilitate the achievement and maintenance of heterozygosis. In the better studied system of Oka, the aspect of immediate interest to the immunologist is the destructive interaction between cells lacking appropriate common alleles of the recognition genes. This, however, has no more than a superficial resemblance to the cytotoxic action of sensitized lymphocytes on a larger cell. There must be three distinct sets of recognition phenomena. First, a somatic cell in contact with another recognizes that they possess at least one common recognition allele and as a result the necrotic response[2] is inhibited. Second, a somatic cell in contact with another which has no common specific allele but is otherwise genetically similar (of the same species) can recognize this conspecificity in the sense that it induces mutual necrosis. This is not seen when wholly unrelated forms make contact. Third, a sperm (haploid) recognizes the presence of the same allele by a gene product present in the periovular cells and cannot fertilize such an egg.

DC。没有发生自体受精的原因可能是有一层卵泡细胞包围着卵子。奥卡的综述 [14] 并没有详尽阐述这种结构的性质，只提到围绕在来自 AB 个体的 A 卵子周围的细胞有可能是二倍体并且是 AB，这样就阻止了 A 精子或 B 精子的进入。而其他类型的精子，例如 C 或 D，将可以毫无阻碍地进入。

其他群体生物

以上两种现象看上去是为了确保在所有可繁殖后代群落中的杂合程度最大化而"设计"的。现实中不太可能形成纯合子群落；与此同时，情况也不会因不相关群落的融合而被搅乱。这两种情况看上去都产生了不利于生存的群落，虽然不容易发现不利之处到底是什么。奥卡指出这种情况恰好与李子等被子植物的自交不亲和性类似，但是它更类似于西奥多 [15] 在一些群体腔肠动物（珊瑚虫）中的发现。群体海洋生物应该能区别自身群落与其他群落，这对于生存来说很可能具有重要意义。海扇形网柳珊瑚的群落具有分支结构，其中的支撑体是坚固的硬蛋白轴，轴上有一层由活细胞组成的连续鞘状结构，珊瑚虫致密的骨骼就是由这些活细胞分泌的。西奥多取分支上 25 mm~30 mm 的断片，剥开中间的一段 2 mm 或 3 mm 的部分，以暴露坚硬的非生物轴。准备这样的两段，将它们结合在一起，使两个剥离的区域形成直角交叉的接触点。将这样的制备物长期置于合适的鱼缸中，再生结构会最终覆盖剥离区域。如果两个断片来自于同一群落，那么所有四个生长表面就会完全连续地融合在一起。如果一段源自群落 A，另一段源自群落 B，A 和 B 的组织就不能融合，可以看到两者之间有一条清晰的分界线。如果两个不同的属（网柳珊瑚和柔枝柳珊瑚）被放在一起互相接触，就会发生破坏性相互作用，表现为沿接触表面形成"起泡"组织。

菊海鞘的自我识别

就适应性免疫的进化而言，可以假定：是奥卡所描述的群体海鞘现象，也可能是西奥多所描述的珊瑚虫现象，促进了杂合性的实现和维持。在奥卡的更为完善的研究系统中，最令免疫学家感兴趣的方面是：细胞间因为缺乏合适的作为识别基因的共同等位基因，从而产生破坏性相互作用。然而，这与致敏淋巴细胞对较大细胞的细胞毒作用只具有表面上的相似性。这里必然存在三种不同情况下的识别现象。第一，一个体细胞与另一个体细胞接触，认出它们至少拥有一个共同的识别用等位基因，因而坏死反应 [2] 被抑制。第二，一个体细胞与另一个虽不具有共同的特定等位基因但在其他方面有类似遗传学特征（属于同一物种）的体细胞接触，会识别出这种同种性，从而引起相互坏死。如果是完全不相关的生物互相接触，则不会出现这一现象。第三，精子（单倍体）通过卵周细胞内的基因产物识别出相同等位基因的存在，从而不能使这样的卵子受精。

The concept of recognition is so important that these three examples justify discussion in some detail. The essence of the matter is that organism tissue or cell A comes into contact or other definable relationship with two or more generally similar entities, X^1, X^2, X^3 and so on, and in one instance (say, with X^1) a demonstrable and reproducible reaction occurs which is not seen with X^2, X^3 etc. A is then said to be capable of positive recognition of X^1. Sometimes, as in the case of *Botryllus*, the individual reaction by which recognition of one character as against "any others" is shown takes the form of an inhibition of necrosis or some otherwise inevitable response. The crux of the matter is that recognition is only meaningful when it is a recognition of one out of many alternative candidates. An antibody reacts visibly with only one of a thousand antigens. In the *Botryllus* examples we must postulate that there is a positive recognition of the presence of a common allele in the somatic cell genome, a positive recognition of conspecificity by the mutually damaging reaction and a positive recognition by the sperm that the follicular cells of the ovum have the same R allele, since it can fertilize "all other" combinations which lack that allele.

Nature of Recognition

All those positive recognitions are conventionally and almost certainly correctly interpreted as representing specific union, reversible or irreversible, between chemical groupings on the surfaces of the interacting cells. There are possible ways by which like chemical groupings can recognize each other as exemplified in the growth of any crystal, but where proteins are concerned this seems to be a cumbersome approach inappropriate for the extremely heterogeneous micro-environment where all recognition reactions occur. All immunologists, every biochemist concerned with enzyme-substrate relationships and every pharmacologist interested in drug-receptors implicitly accept the axiom that all such specific ("recognizing") reactions are based on sterically complementary $(+/-)$ chemical patterns. We are bound to do the same here, but to do so brings us immediately up against a genetic difficulty whose solution may be of first rate importance for immunological theory. Two of the examples of recognition seem to be recognition by cell X that cell Y has an allele identical to its own. If we exclude, as we must, any suggestion that recognition involves interaction between nucleic acids, this seems that any mutation to a new allele must in some way produce corresponding but complementary changes in both $+$ and $-$ patterns of the mutual recognition sites. It is extremely difficult to conceive any way by which information in a DNA sequence (A) can provoke the formation of another DNA sequence which will code for a complementary three-dimensional structure that will react specifically with the product of A. It seems more promising to consider the situation where the $+$ and $-$ complementary receptors are controlled by distinct genes. There is much to be said for an *ad hoc* assumption that both $+$ and $-$ types of recognition gene are derived by duplication from a common progenitor gene, but they would require to be capable of independent mutation. We have to assume that a mutation in, say, the $+$ gene cannot be expressed until a corresponding mutation arises in the $-$ gene. If such a process were to function there would have to be a high mutation rate in genes, a situation which has obvious relevance to the genetics of immune pattern and to Jerne's ideas[16] of a special relationship between the potential antibody patterns transmissible by the germ line and histocompatibility antigens.

　　识别的概念太重要了，以至于值得详细讨论以上三个例子。识别问题的关键是生物组织或细胞 A 与两个或更多大致类似的实体 X^1、X^2、X^3 等发生接触或发生其他可定义的关系。如果在一个例子中（比如与 X^1）发生了可论证和可重复的反应，但与 X^2 和 X^3 等则未见此类现象，那么就可以说 A 能够主动识别 X^1。有时，例如就菊海鞘来说，赖以识别一种特征有别于"所有其他"特征的个体反应表现为抑制坏死或其他一些不可避免的反应。此问题的关键是，识别只有在能从很多可供选择的候选项中识别出一个时才是有意义的。一个抗体显然只会与上千抗原中的一个发生反应。在菊海鞘的例子中，我们必须假定存在三种主动识别：一是通过体细胞基因组中的一个共同等位基因的主动识别，二是通过发生相互破坏反应的同物种间的主动识别，三是通过精子的主动识别——精子可以识别出卵子的卵泡细胞是否含有相同的 R 等位基因，因为它可以使"所有其他"缺乏该等位基因的组合受精。

识别的本质

　　所有主动识别通常都被几乎确定无疑地解释为代表了相互作用细胞表面上化学基团之间的可逆或不可逆的特异性结合。比如化学基团可以通过一些可能的方式相互识别，这已被任一晶体的生长过程所证实；但是对蛋白质而言，这看上去是一种很繁复的方式，不太容易与发生每种识别反应的极端异质的微环境相适应。所有免疫学家、每一位关注酶–底物关系的生化学家和每一位对药物–受体感兴趣的药理学家都绝对接受如下公理，即所有这些特异（"识别"）反应都基于空间互补（+/−）的化学模式。我们注定要采用空间互补的处理方法，但是这样做会使我们立刻面临遗传学上的难题，其解决方案对于免疫学理论来说可能具有第一位的重要性。两个识别的例子看上去是：细胞 X 发现细胞 Y 具有同一等位基因，从而实现识别。如果正如我们必须要做的那样，我们排除了识别涉及核酸间相互作用的任何建议，那么似乎任何产生某种新等位基因的突变必然会以某种方式在相互识别位点的 + 和 − 模式中产生相应但互补的变化。很难想象，DNA 序列（A）中的信息可以通过任何一种方式引起另一 DNA 序列的形成，后者将编码某一互补的三维结构，这一结构将与 A 的产物发生特异性反应。看上去考虑以下情况更有前景，即 + 和 − 这对互补受体由不同的基因控制。识别基因的 + 型和 − 型均源自某共同祖先基因的复制，但要求它们能够独立突变，对于这一特殊假说还有很多需要交代。举例来说，我们不得不假设：在 + 基因中的一个突变将不被表达，直到 − 基因中发生相应的突变。如果这一过程具有功能，那基因中的高突变率也就是必然的了，这种情况显然与免疫模式的遗传学以及杰尼的想法 [16] 相关联，杰尼认为在可通过生殖细胞遗传的潜在抗体模式和组织相容性抗原之间存在着一种特殊的关系。

All that I have been discussing in regard to the colonial ascidians is solely concerned with germ line genetics. Each cell is regarded as expressing appropriately the instructions of the germ line genome. Somatic genetic changes come later in the story.

The situation in *Botryllus* is represented schematically in Fig. 1. Here it is assumed that at each surface of contact with an adjacent cell there are + and − receptors for the two relevant alleles of each heterozygous diploid colony. A positive receptor is shown as a knob, a negative one as a depression. By hypothesis, +/− union stabilizes the two adjacent cell surfaces, and in the absence of any +/− unions mutual disorganization with liberation of damaging products takes place. It is inexpedient to attempt any biological explanation of this phenomenon except to point out that in all larval–adult metamorphoses there is extensive cell destruction in which some such processes must be involved and also that similar cell damage is seen in all severe T-D immune reactions in mammals.

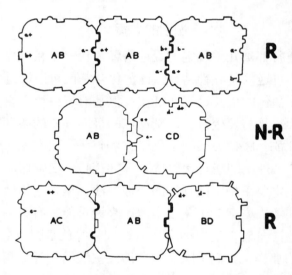

Fig. 1. A diagram to suggest the type of +/− relationship between recognition units that is postulated for
Botryllus. A positive receptor is shown as a projection, the corresponding complementary negative
receptor by a depression of the same shape. Where there is a reciprocal relationship (R) allowing
receptor union (heavy line), the relation is stabilized. In its absence (N-R), fusion is impossible.

Relation to Immune Response

At most this can only be a foreshadowing of the adaptive immune system of vertebrates. There is, for example, no hint as to how the capacity to recognize foreign qualities of conspecific cells evolved and there are manifest differences of the tunicate system from that subserving tissue integrity (the T-immune system) in vertebrates. Like every biological invention the utilization of steric complementarity involves both the informational store in the genome and the protein molecules needed for its phenotypic expression. There arises immediately the outstanding problem of how mutation and other informationally random genetic processes can produce complementary structure in the products of two

604

我一直在讨论的关于群体海鞘的所有内容都只与生殖细胞遗传学有关。每个细胞都被认为是适当地表达了生殖细胞基因组的指令。体细胞的遗传学改变将在本文稍后部分进行描述。

菊海鞘中的情况如图 1 所示。这里假设：相邻细胞的每一接触表面都存在 + 受体和 − 受体，分别代表每一杂合二倍体群落的两个相关等位基因。如图所示，球形凸起表示正受体，凹陷表示负受体。根据假设，+/− 结合使两个相邻细胞的表面稳定，在 +/− 结合完全缺失的情况下，会发生相互解体，并释放出破坏性产物。对于这一现象，任何用生物学解释的尝试都是不明智的，除非可以说明以下两点：一是在所有幼体 − 成体的变态过程中存在着大面积的细胞破坏，在细胞破坏时还必须涉及一些识别过程；二是哺乳动物中所有严重的 T–D 免疫反应也都可见类似的细胞破坏。

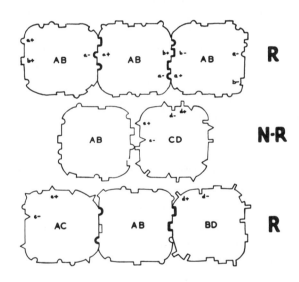

图 1. 以菊海鞘为例表示识别单元间 +/− 关系类型的示意图。凸起代表正受体，与凸起形状匹配的凹陷代表相对应的互补负受体。一旦出现允许受体结合（粗线）的相互关系（R），这种关系就会是稳定的。在不满足这种关系（N-R）的情况下，融合是不可能的。

与免疫反应的关系

这充其量只能算是脊椎动物适应性免疫系统的铺垫。例如：没有迹象表明识别外源同种细胞的能力是如何进化的，而且在被囊系统与脊椎动物中促进组织整体性的系统（T− 免疫系统）之间存在着明显差异。与每一生物学创造一样，对空间互补性的利用牵涉到基因组中的信息贮存和表型表达所需要的蛋白质分子。这样就立刻引发了一个难解决的问题：在两种不同的基因产物中，突变和其他能使信息发生随机遗传的过程如何能产生互补结构。然而，一旦发现了这种进化过程，它就能够提

distinct genes. Yet once that evolutionary discovery had been made it could provide the raw material from which in colonial organisms means could have evolved to ensure the genetic integrity of the colony and to avoid the long term dangers of self-fertilization and inbreeding. A continuation of biological invention along the same general path could in principle lead to the construction of a vertebrate immune system. For this to happen, there are three requirements: first, mutual recognition systems would have to be elaborated and certain cells differentiated to specialize in recognition and in the local damaging response; second, recognition functions of such cells would have to become progressively specialized until there existed a wide diversity of immune patterns, each limited to a single clone, and third, such "immunocytes", in certain conditions of specific stimulation, would have to be able to take on the blast form and proliferate.

It is probably unwise to attempt to imagine the various steps by which such changes could be made. One can foresee a period of great research activity in these fields of tissue fusion and rejection in invertebrates and protochordates during the next decade. Undoubtedly a variety of intriguing phenomena will be uncovered, differing from group to group. Some may be further along the road toward adaptive immunity than the colonial ascidians. Much more extensive comparative studies are called for and in due course analysis of the results should allow a clear evolutionary history to emerge. Whatever form that history eventually takes we can be certain that gene duplication (gene expansion) plays a major part, and that progressive specialization of cell function and phenotypic restriction will be as conspicuous as it is in all other organs and functions.

Viviparity and Parasitism

Evolution is much more than an expansion and specialization of rudimentary functions present in the form we choose as a starting point. It is a process of modification for more effective survival of populations. Major evolutionary changes probably always mean that a major danger to survival has appeared and must be overcome or that a new ecological niche has arisen to be occupied by species which can first make the necessary adaptations. Often, of course, the two reasons overlap.

A year or two ago I suggested that when free swimming marine protovertebrates ancestral to cyclostomes first appeared it is conceivable that one of the early results was the emergence of a new ecological niche, survival by parasitism on one's own kind. The stimulus to develop this point of view was the immense ecological effect of the entry of the sea lamprey into the great lakes of North America around 1930[17]. Lampreys are cyclostomes that live by blood sucking—one lamprey can kill 14 kg of fish per annum—and there were countless streams running into the lakes which were suitable for larval development. Lamprey proliferation reduced the economically significant fish species to such a level that the lakes' fishing industry was destroyed. The subsequent ecological history of the Great Lakes is of great interest but not relevant to my theme, which is that with the entry of an effective predator-parasite in the form of a cyclostome a major ecosystem was wholly changed. If free swimming protovertebrates in Cambrian seas represented the current evolutionary success, a wide "radiation" into new ecological

供一些原始材料以使群体生物体的进化能保证群落的遗传整体性以及避免自体受精与同系繁殖的长期危险性。大致沿同一方向进化的连续生物学创造原则上会导致脊椎动物免疫系统的形成。要实现这一点，需要三个前提条件：第一，相互识别的系统必须十分精细，并且分化出了一些专门用于识别和用于局部破坏反应的细胞；第二，这些细胞的识别功能必须逐渐特化，直到能够产生多种多样的免疫模式，每一免疫模式限制在单克隆内；第三，在某些特定的刺激条件下，这样的"免疫细胞"必须能以爆发形式大量增殖。

试图想象出实现这些变化所需的多步过程很可能是不明智的。可以预见未来十年将是大量研究活动集中在无脊椎动物和原索动物的组织融合与排斥领域的时期。毫无疑问，很多有趣现象将会被一批一批地揭示出来。一些研究可能会进一步沿适应性免疫方向进行，而不是沿群体海鞘方向发展。当务之急是进行更加广泛的比较研究，从对结果的正确分析中应该能够得到一段清晰的进化史。无论进化史最终将以何种形式呈现，我们都可以断定基因复制（基因扩展）在其中起着主要的作用，并且细胞功能的不断特化和表型的限制都与在所有其他器官和功能中一样明显。

胎生和寄生

进化的意义远远超过基本功能的扩展和特化，我们选择基本功能的存在形式作为起点。进化是为使种群更有效生存而进行的修正过程。主要的进化变化通常意味着生存遇到了一个巨大的危机，必须战胜这种危机；或者意味着出现新生态位，并被第一个能作出必要适应性改变的物种占领。当然，这两种原因经常是交织在一起的。

一两年前我曾提出：当在海洋中自由游泳的原始脊椎动物——圆口类的祖先开始现身时，可以想象早期结果之一是出现了一个新生态位，即通过在同类身上寄生来实现生存。产生这种观点的诱因源自 1930 年前后海洋七鳃鳗进入北美五大湖所造成的巨大生态效应 [17]。七鳃鳗是靠吸食其他鱼类血液生存的圆口纲脊椎动物——一条七鳃鳗每年能杀死 14 千克鱼——适于七鳃鳗幼体发育的湖泊有数不清的河流汇入。七鳃鳗数目的激增使重要经济鱼种的减少达到这些湖泊的渔业蒙受损失的地步。五大湖随后的生态史非常引人注目，但与我的主题无关，我的主题是：随着圆口纲脊椎动物这类强大捕食性寄生动物的引入，主要生态系统发生了彻底的变化。如果在寒武纪海洋中自由游泳的原始脊椎动物与当前的进化产物一样具有很强的繁殖力，那么进入新生态位的广泛"辐射"必然会随之很快开始。现有证据表明，类似七鳃

niches must have begun immediately. There is evidence that lamprey-like forms were present in the Silurian[18], presumably living like modern lampreys but necessarily on other cyclostomes until fishes had evolved.

Against this background I asked[19] whether parasitism of a cyclostome by its own young or by related species might not provide an urgent demand for the development of a more refined capacity to recognize the difference between self and not-self. This could be the evolutionary stimulus needed to set the construction of an adaptive immune system on its way. In the light of what has been published since, I should now be inclined to state the possibilities slightly differently. What I failed to comment on was the significance of viviparity which appears in many lower organisms including tunicates and fish as well as in mammals. When a living embryo is nourished in the tissues of the parent the situation is barely distinguishable from parasitism, and oscillation between a controlled situation and uncontrolled parasitism must have occurred not infrequently. There may well have been a special predilection for viviparous larvae kept under control in their own parental environment to make an early switch to parasitism on a similar type of organism.

Comparison with Homograft Reactions

At this stage it is necessary to attempt a formal comparison at the genetic level of what is observed in the colonial ascidians and what holds for homograft reactions in mammals. If in both the simplifying assumption is made that histocompatibility is determined by alleles of a single gene, we can consider the results of matings between heterozygous animals whose genotypes are AB and CD, AB being used for the female in each case. For both types of animal the F1 generation will contain the genotypes AC, AD, BC and BD. In *Botryllus* all possible offspring will fuse (be compatible) with the parent. In a mammal, skin grafts from any of the offspring will be rejected. The evolutionary problem is how to pass from the first condition to the second.

First, it is necessary to establish a process by which recognition can have a second type of sequel. Instead of serving only as a means of stabilizing cell interaction at contact surfaces, recognition must under other circumstances be followed by a damaging liberation of cell products. Second, complementary patterns must be provided which can recognize not only gene products which can be produced by the individual itself but also those characteristic of all the patterns (histocompatibility antigens) which it is within the capacity of the species to produce.

The requirements can be discussed in relation to Fig. 2, which is a simple diagram of an offspring in a situation in which it is potentially parasitic on the mother's tissues. On a simple extension of the *Botryllus* situation, the cells should tolerate each other and the parasitic relationship should develop easily. In the situation of incipient parasitism that we have pictured, the biological requirement, if the parasite is to be expelled, is that the parent AB should produce a specialized cell with what in *Botryllus* would be a − type C receptor analogous to an immune receptor (cell-fixed antibody) in a vertebrate. Such a cell must be able to reach the region of contact between AB and AC and, following

鳗的生物出现于志留纪[18]，据推测，它们的生活方式类似于现在的七鳃鳗，但是必须寄生在其他圆口纲脊椎动物身上，直到进化出鱼类。

以此为背景，我提出以下问题[19]：一种被同类幼体或相关物种寄生的圆口纲动物，会不会并不急迫需要发育出更佳识别自我和非我之间差异的能力。对这种能力的需求可以成为进化的刺激因素，适应性免疫系统的构建在确立时需要这种刺激。基于迄今为止已经发表的结果，我现在倾向于以稍有不同的方式阐述一些可能性。对于胎生在包括被囊动物和鱼类在内的众多低等生物体以及哺乳动物中的意义，我还无法作出评价。一个活的胚胎在母体组织中被滋养时的情况与寄生几乎没有什么差别，在可控的胎生和不可控的寄生之间的摇摆必然会经常发生。母体很可能对生活在其环境中的受控胎生幼体具有一种特殊的偏好，正是这种偏好实现了寄生在类似类型生物体中的早期转化。

与同种移植反应的比较

在此阶段，有必要尝试对群体海鞘中所观察到的现象和造成哺乳动物同种移植反应的原因进行基因水平上的正式比较。在两种情况中，如果都简单假设组织相容性由单个基因的等位基因决定，那么我们可以考虑基因型分别为 AB 和 CD 的杂合动物之间进行交配的结果，每次都选择 AB 作为母本。两种类型动物的 F1 代将包含以下基因型：AC、AD、BC 和 BD。在菊海鞘中，所有可能的子代都会与亲代融合（是相容的）。而在哺乳动物中，移植自任何子代的皮肤都会被亲代排斥。如何从第一种情况发展到第二种情况是进化学上的一个难题。

首先，需要建立一个过程，识别能够通过这一过程产生第二种类型的结果。识别的后果不仅仅是使细胞在接触表面的相互作用稳定化，在另一些情况下，紧随识别之后的必然是细胞产物的破坏性释放。第二，必须提供互补模式，这种互补模式不仅能够识别个体自身产生的基因产物，而且能识别所有该物种可接受的模式所特有的基因产物（组织相容性抗原）。

根据图 2 可以讨论一些必要的条件，图 2 是关于子代在某种情况下具有寄生在母体组织上的潜能的一个简单示意图。基于对菊海鞘这种情况的简单拓展，细胞间应该能够相互容忍，并且应该很容易发展寄生关系。在我们已经描绘出的初期寄生的情况下，如果要阻止寄生，那么生物学前提是：亲本 AB 应产生一种特化的细胞，并且在菊海鞘体内的这种细胞应具有一种与脊椎动物中的免疫受体（细胞结合抗体）类似的–型受体 C。这种细胞必须能够到达 AB 和 AC 间的接触区域，随着对 C 的识别，

recognition of C, provoke a destructive local reaction. The parasitic embryonic form and the adjacent host cells will be killed, thrown off and the region repaired. The result will be wholly equivalent to the repair of a traumatic wound or of a patch of localized bacterial or other type of parasitic intrusion on a surface. Every aspect of such a reaction except what was due to the specialized anti-C cell is within the capacity of any invertebrate. Survival of any metazoan requires that it can deal with incipient infection by bacteria and repair minor injuries. Highly complex activities may be required but they do not require an adaptive immune system. To complete the sequence shown in Fig. 2 we need only to add an immunological barrier between the two sets of tissue, something with the same function as is usually ascribed to the trophoblast in placental mammals.

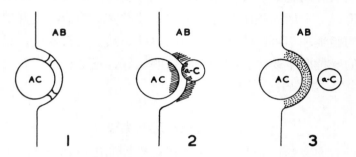

Fig. 2. A schematic diagram to indicate possible relationships of viviparous offspring (AC) to maternal tissues (AB) (see text).

So far I have been considering the danger that a viviparously produced embryo in the wrong place might become a damaging parasite. Essentially the same considerations apply if we take the broader possibility of a primitive cyclostome becoming a parasite of any other available species of cyclostomes that were not able to develop a means of protection. On this view the first evolutionary task of the free-swimming progenitors of the vertebrates was to devise a way of recognizing whether a group of living cells within its body was self or not-self. If "not-self", then in some way it must be eliminated. In retrospect one must assume that there must have developed "markers"—what we now call histocompatibility antigens by which cells genetically proper to the individual can be distinguished from foreign ones even if these are essentially similar in other respects.

Evolution of the Vertebrate Pattern

The requirement for segregation of the communities of colonial forms has sufficient similarity to suggest that the basic recognition mechanism was adapted to this new "immunological" requirement. But in the tunicates the recognition factors conduced to stable relationships between cells. As long as our potential parasite has one such "marker" in common it could, on the basis of pre-vertebrate analogies, expect to be tolerated. There are plenty of analogies, both in the history of evolution and of human war, where an initial advantage to one contestant can eventually provide the means by which it is defeated. Again thinking retrospectively, the essential change that must have been made was to produce specialized wandering cells or immunocyte prototypes in

引起该处的破坏性反应。寄生性胚胎和邻近的寄主细胞将被杀死，然后被抛出，该区域得以修复。这种结果完全等同于外伤修复以及局部细菌斑块或表面上其他类型的寄生性侵入的修复。除了由特化的抗 C 细胞引起的部分之外，这种反应的每一方面都在任何无脊椎动物的能力范围之内。所有后生动物为了生存都必须能够处理由细菌引起的初期感染和修复细小伤口。这可能是一种很复杂的行为，但并不需要具备适应性免疫系统。为了达到图 2 显示的结果，我们仅需要在两个系列的组织间加上一道免疫屏障，它的功能通常被认为与有胎盘类哺乳动物胚胎滋养层的功能相同。

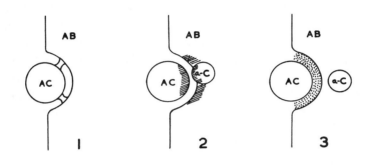

图 2. 表明胎生子代（AC）与母体组织（AB）的可能关系的示意图（见正文）。

到目前为止，我一直在考虑以下这种危险，那就是胎生动物在错误位置产生的胚胎可能会变成一种破坏性的寄生物。当我们把可能性拓展至原始圆口类脊椎动物成为不能发展保护手段的任意一种现存圆口类物种的寄生物时，也可以采用本质上相同的处理。按照这种观点，自由游泳的脊椎动物祖先的第一进化要务是，设计出一种方式以识别自身体内的一组活细胞是自我还是非我。如果是"非我"，那就必须以某种方式消除它。现在想起来应该假设之前已经发展出"标记"——我们现在称之为组织相容性抗原，通过这种抗原可以将对于个体来说基因正常的细胞与外源细胞区别开来，即使两者在其他方面基本一致。

脊椎动物模式的进化

各种群体生物的隔离都要求非常类似的条件，这说明基本识别机制可以适应这一新的"免疫学"的需要。但是在被囊动物中，识别因子导致了细胞间的稳定关系。只要我们说的潜在寄生物有这样一个共同的"标记"，那么根据与原脊椎动物的类比，就可以认为潜在寄生物会被容忍。在进化史和人类的战争史中有大量这样的例子，某一竞争者最初的优势可能最终转变为导致其失败的因素。再回想一下，必然发生的本质变化是产生专门的游走细胞或者免疫细胞原型。在后者中 +/- 接触不会使邻近细胞表面稳定，而是发生潜在的坏死相互作用。这样可能会导致出现自动强

which +/− contact led not to stabilization of adjacent cell surfaces but to a potentially necrotic interaction. This would have the automatic capacity to enforce "suicide" of any immunocytes whose immune receptors (−) corresponded to (+) groupings on accessible cell surfaces and therefore ensure that only not-self (−) groupings were represented on the surviving immunocytes. It requires only a minor extension of the intra-genomic mechanism discussed in regard to *Botryllus* to ensure that (−) receptors corresponding to all the (+) receptors likely to be produced as a result of somatic (or germinal) mutation within the species should be those most commonly produced. In other words, the dominant (−) (that is, immune pattern) receptors in the primitive immunocyte population correspond to the other (+) receptors (histocompatibility antigens) that are characteristic of the species. Once again this brings us very close to the Jerne concept. At this speculative level of discussion it is immaterial whether the new patterns arise by somatic mutation or by germ-line mutation. Since there would be advantages to be gained if on the basis of what was transmitted in the germ line it was easy to ensure that all the "not-self" histocompatibility patterns of the species should be represented in the complementary patterns (−) of the immunocytes, there would be a drive to establish the necessary information in the germ line. Perhaps it is not altogether naive to suggest that when the genetic mechanism which generates diversity of immune pattern is properly understood it will be relatively easy to rewrite this concept of the evolutionary origin of immune specificity in the relevant terms. For the present, nothing would be gained by going beyond the present very general statement.

If this general approach is to serve as a stimulus to further comparative study of the evolution of immune responses, it is important to make one final point. In the lamprey and in primitive fishes there are active immune responses to homografts and delayed necrotic response to Freund's complete adjuvant, but antibody production is poor. In current immunological terminology T-responses are much better developed than B, and in line with many other indications this points to the T system—concerned with homograft immunity, delayed hypersensitivity and so on—being the more primitive. In any investigation of invertebrates or pre-vertebrate chordates for evolutionary precursors of an adaptive immune system, conventional tests for antibody production are likely to prove futile. The best approaches are probably (1) to test for differences between the responses to auto and homografts of skin or other tissue, and (2) to compare the histological response where a region has been damaged by physical means with what results from injection of material likely to induce a response with an immunological component, such as that seen in the lamprey given Freund's complete adjuvant.

More Research Needed

The capacity to recognize the difference between self and not-self appears early in animal evolution and is well marked in at least two colonial marine forms: *Eunicella*, an anthozoan (Coelenterata), and *Botryllus*, a colonial ascidian (Tunicata). In the ascidian, Oka's work has allowed analysis of the genetics of recognition in terms not wholly remote from the histocompatibility antigens of mammalian immunology. If the current opinion is correct that vertebrates arose from the chordate larvae of some primitive intermediate between echinoderm and tunicate, it is legitimate to look at what is necessary to derive primitive

612

制免疫细胞"自杀"的能力，这些被强制"自杀"的免疫细胞的免疫受体（−）对应于可接触细胞表面上的（＋）型，因而确保在存活的免疫细胞上只有非我（−）型存在。就菊海鞘而论，它只需要基因内机制的微小延伸就可以确保大量生成与所有可能由体细胞（或生殖细胞）突变产生的（＋）受体相对应的（−）受体。换句话说，在原始免疫细胞群中的显性（−）（也就是免疫模式）受体对应的是其他一些能代表物种特征的（＋）受体（组织相容性抗原）。这又一次使我们非常接近于杰尼的概念。就这种推测水平上的讨论而言，是通过体细胞突变还是通过生殖细胞突变引发新模式这一问题并不重要。如果以生殖细胞系中所传递的物质为基础，就很容易确保物种的所有"非我"组织相容性模式都能被免疫细胞的互补模式（−）所代表，这样会有助于在生殖细胞中产生一种建立必需信息的推进力。或许不能完全把以下看法当成异想天开：当能正确理解产生免疫模式多样性的遗传学机制时，用相关术语重写免疫特异性的进化起源这一概念就变得相对容易。就目前的水平而言，想超出现有的通用化陈述是不可能取得成功的。

如果这种通用的方法能促进对免疫反应进化的深层对比研究，那么制定一个终点是十分重要的。七鳃鳗和原始鱼类会对同种移植物产生积极的免疫反应，对弗氏完全佐剂会产生延迟坏死反应，但是生成的抗体很少。在现在的免疫学术语中，T反应发展得远强于B反应，并且与许多其他现象一致，这表明T系统——涉及同种移植免疫、迟发型超敏反应等——是更原始的系统。在研究各种无脊椎动物或原脊椎脊索动物的适应性免疫系统的进化前体时，常规的抗体产物检测方法很可能会失效。最佳方法可能是：（1）检验皮肤或其他组织在自体移植和同种移植后所产生的反应间的差异，（2）比较遭受物理破坏区域的组织学反应与注入可能会和一种免疫成分产生反应的物质后所导致的结果，例如给七鳃鳗注射弗氏完全佐剂后所观察到的结果。

深入研究的必要性

识别自我与非我间差异的能力出现于动物进化的早期，且在至少两种群体海洋生物中有很好的体现：网柳珊瑚，一种珊瑚虫（腔肠动物）；以及菊海鞘，一种群体海鞘（被囊动物）。在对海鞘的研究中，奥卡已经能够运用与哺乳动物免疫学中的组织相容性抗原有一点儿关系的术语来分析识别遗传学了。如果目前的看法是正确的，即认为脊椎动物是由棘皮动物和被囊动物之间的某种作为原始中间体的脊索动物幼

vertebrate immune responses as seen in the extant cyclostomes from the recognition processes in *Botryllus*. A far-reaching reorganization is clearly necessary and the "invention" of the immunocyte as a mobile cell specialized to carry receptors for recognition of foreign pattern must have been the important step. The borderline between viviparity and parasitism may have been important as well as the very early differentiation of some cyclostomes to a semi-parasitic way of life. Without much more factual information it is impossible even to sketch the early stages. Intuitively, however, one can feel that much more extensive study of invertebrates and protochordates, particularly at the genetic level, may be specially enlightening in regard to the nature of the processes by which diversity of immune pattern arises and the evident importance of histocompatibility genes in determining the nature of that diversity, as Benacerraf, Jerne, McDevitt and others have emphasized.

"Self-recognition" in Flowering Plants

As Oka has pointed out, there are important similarities in the self-sterility of *Botryllus* colonies and self-incompatibility in flowering plants. Under the guidance of Professor J. S. Turner and Miss Mary Ellis, I have consulted enough of the recent literature on self-incompatibility in plants to feel that it might be helpful for an immunologist to offer some comments on self-incompatibility in plants in the light of the foregoing discussion of the evolution of self-recognition in animals.

Self-incompatibility is very common in flowering plants and has been well known since Darwin's time. There is much to suggest that by enforcing heterozygosity it has been of great importance in the "explosive success" of angiosperm evolution. There are a number of different mechanisms, but the commonest and most widely studied example is that shown by failure of the haploid pollen tube to grow through the diploid stylar substance and to effect fertilization[20]. Many but not all such examples are controlled by a single locus with a very large number of possible alleles. In order to keep the topic as simple as possible I shall confine myself wholly to this class. It has been studied in *Petunia, Lilium, Oenothera, Trifolium* and *Nicotiana* among others.

In general the phenomenon of self-incompatibility takes the following form. Pollen from an individual plant is incapable of setting seed in flowers of that plant or in other plants of the same incompatibility group, that is, with a common, S^1 say, self-incompatibility allele. S^1 pollen, however, is fully active in fertilizing any other plant of the species. Similar findings hold for other types of pollen. The number of distinct S alleles in a species can be very high: seventy-eight are mentioned in red clover and more than twenty-four in cherries. The condition is usually symmetrical, but in some species the incompatibility is one-sided in the sense that pollen from plants of strain A will fail to fertilize strain B, but B pollen can fertilize strain A.

To take a classical example. Crane and Lawrence[21] tabulated fifty-two varieties of cherry to show that they fell into twenty-four compatibility groups, the three largest containing nine, eight and four varieties respectively. All the incompatibilities shown in the table

614

体进化而来，那么就会合理地看待从菊海鞘的识别作用衍生出原始脊椎动物免疫反应所需要的条件，原始脊椎动物的免疫反应可从现存圆口类动物中看到。影响深远的重组明显是必需的；而"创造"出可以流动的免疫细胞，使其专门用于携带能识别外源模式的受体，也一定会是很重要的一步。胎生和寄生之间的界限可能非常重要，其重要性与一些圆口类动物在很早以前分化为半寄生生活方式等同。在没有更多确凿证据的情况下，即使想对早期阶段的大概情况进行描述也是不可能的。但还是能够直观地感觉到通过拓展对无脊椎动物和原索动物的研究，特别是在基因水平上的研究，有可能在以下两方面受到特别的启示：一是关于免疫模式多样性的产生进程的本质，二是关于组织相容性基因在决定免疫模式多样性的本质中的显著重要性，正如贝纳塞拉夫、杰尼、麦克德维特和其他人所强调的那样。

开花植物中的"自我识别"

像奥卡已经指出的那样，菊海鞘群落的自交不育性和开花植物的自交不亲和性之间存在着重要的相似性。在特纳教授和玛丽·埃利斯小姐的指导下，我已经查阅了足够多的关于植物自交不亲和性的最新文献。我的感觉是：对于一名免疫学家来说，用动物中自我识别进化的前述讨论来评论植物中的自交不亲和性可能会有助于自己的研究。

自交不亲和性在开花植物中是很普遍的，自达尔文时代起就广为人知了。有很多结果表明，强制杂合性在被子植物进化的"爆发式成功"中具有非常重要的意义。自交不亲和性有多种不同的作用机理，但是最普通的也是研究最广泛的例子是，单倍体花粉管不能生长穿过二倍体花柱内物质和实现受精[20]。尽管数量众多，但并非所有这样的例子都是由单个基因座上的大量可能的等位基因控制的。为了使话题尽可能简化，我会把讨论内容完全限制在这类例子中。其中已经研究过的有矮牵牛花、百合、月见草、三叶草和烟草等。

自交不亲和性现象的表现通常是：某一株植物的花粉不能使自身或属于同一自交不亲和性组中的其他植株的花结籽，即这些植株都具有某一共同的自交不亲和性等位基因，比如说是 S^1。虽然如此，S^1 花粉具有完全活性，能够使此物种内任意其他植株受精。类似的发现也适用于其他种类的花粉。在某一物种内，不同的 S 等位基因的数量可以非常高：在红三叶草中据称有 78 个 S 基因，比樱桃中的 24 个要多。不亲和性通常是对称的，但是在有些物种中，不亲和性是一边倒的，也就是说，品种 A 植株的花粉不能使品种 B 受精，但是品种 B 的花粉能使品种 A 受精。

举一个经典的例子。克兰和劳伦斯[21]将 52 个樱桃品种列成表格以说明可以将它们分为 24 个相容性组，3 个最大的相容性组分别包括 9、8 和 4 个品种。表中显

are symmetrical. This is, however, by no means universal among cultivated fruits; there are some strikingly one-sided examples among plums, and apple varieties in general show quantitative differences in the capacity to set seed instead of the relatively clear cut results + or − of cherries. Confining ourselves to the latter, the failure of the pollen tube to develop in styles of self type must be looked on as a positive recognition mediated by components in pollen tube surface and stylar tissue, both of which are coded for by a common allele. The ability for the pollen tube to grow and reach the ovule in any other strain is at this level a negative finding.

In a recent discussion of the general problem, Lundqvist[22] has described three essential genetic features. First, the S allele has two sites (pollen tube and stylar tissue) for phenotypic expression. Second, these two gene products are exactly coordinated to bring about incompatibility by their interaction. Third, a changed allele may lose its characteristic phenotypic expression at one site while fully active at the other.

If only the usual symmetrical form of self-incompatibility is considered, plants seem formally similar to *Botryllus*, as Oka had pointed out. If instead of using S^1, S^2 and so on for the alleles we use the A, B, C and D nomenclature, as for the colonial ascidians, the rules governing the behaviour of heterozygote forms are as follows for two plants AB and CD. Both are self-incompatible, that is, when either A or B pollen grains lodge on the stigma of an AB flower, growth of the pollen tube is inhibited. When A or B pollen lodges on CD, however, the combinations are all fertile and AC, AD, BC and BD offspring can be obtained. When these are mated, the types of offspring are:

♀AD×AC♂	AC, CD	♀AC×AD♂	AD, CD
BC×AC	AB, AC	AC×BC	AB, BC
BD×AC	AB, AD, BC, CD		

These are essentially the same rules as obtain in *Botryllus*. The symmetry of the reaction is not always complete and it is well known that irradiation of pollen will often allow fertilization of the normally self-incompatible strain from which it was obtained. This has made it possible to produce homozygous plants which still cannot be fertilized by normal pollen of the original strain. There are also a number of natural examples of one-sided incompatibility as well as various degrees of partial compatibility. One gains the impression that as in so many other genetic phenomena an intensely complex set of genetic factors is concerned and that specially suitable material must be chosen to provide a system expressible in simple terms. The change from self-incompatibility to compatibility is operationally extremely easy to detect and measure and it has therefore attracted many workers. Perhaps one of the most striking of their results is that irradiation is more likely to delete an S allele than to produce any other type of mutant.

At the physiological and biochemical level there is much on record about specific situations, but few generalizations have been established from the several examples of

示的所有不亲和性都是对称的。虽然如此，在栽植的水果品种中，这绝不是普遍现象；在李子中存在一些显著一边倒的例子；苹果品种通常会表现出在结籽能力方面的数量差异，而不是樱桃中 + 或 − 的相对清楚的界线。就后者而言，花粉管在自身类型的花柱上不能发育，这必然被看作是一种由花粉管表面和花柱组织中的成分介导的主动识别，这两种成分均由同一个等位基因编码。在任意其他品种中，花粉管能够生长并到达胚珠即说明不存在自交不亲和性。

在最近一次对这一普遍问题的讨论中，伦德奎斯特[22]描述了三个基本的遗传学特征。第一，S 等位基因有两个表型表达位点（花粉管和花柱组织）。第二，这两个基因产物能通过相互作用协调一致地导致不亲和性。第三，一个已发生变化的等位基因可能在一个位点失去它的表型表达特征，而在其他位点却具有全部活性。

像奥卡所指出的那样，如果只考虑自交不亲和性中常见的对称形式，那么植物就会与菊海鞘具有形式上的相似性。如果对于这些等位基因，我们不使用 S^1、S^2 等名称，而是和研究群体海鞘时一样采用 A、B、C、D 等来命名，那么对于两株植物 AB 和 CD，其杂合子的形式应遵循如下规则。两者都是自交不亲和，也就是说，当 A 或 B 的花粉颗粒落到一朵 AB 花的柱头上时，花粉管的生长会受到抑制。虽然如此，当 A 或 B 的花粉落到 CD 的柱头上时，所有组合方式都能结果，由此得到的子代是 AC、AD、BC 和 BD。当这些子代杂交时，产生的下一代的类型是：

♀AD×AC♂	AC, CD		♀AC×AD♂	AD, CD
BC×AC	AB, AC		AC×BC	AB, BC
BD×AC	AB, AD, BC, CD			

以上这些与从菊海鞘中总结出的规则基本相同。反应的对称性并不一定总能实现，大家都知道，正常自交不亲和品种的花粉经辐射后通常能使自体受精。这使产生纯合植物成为可能，这种纯合植物仍然不能被原始品种的正常花粉受精。自然界中还存在许多一边倒的不亲和性的例子，以及程度不同的部分亲和性的例子。由此得到的印象是：正如研究许多其他遗传现象时一样，这项研究也要涉及极其复杂的一系列遗传因子，必须选择特别合适的材料以提供一个可用简单方式体现的系统。从操作上来讲，发现和检测从自交不亲和性到亲和性的变化是很容易做到的，因此吸引了众多研究者。在他们的研究成果中，最为显著的一个也许是：相较于产生任意其他类型的突变体，辐射处理更可能的后果是去除 S 等位基因。

在生理学和生物化学水平上有许多关于具体情形的记载，但是根据不同物种中自交不亲和性的几个例子，几乎没能概括出普适的结论。很多作者，特别是林斯肯

self-incompatibility in different species. A number of writers, notably Linskens[23], have spoken of antigen–antibody reactions and applied serological methods. Lewis[24] identified individual antigens in pollen extracts of *Oenothera* by Ouchterlony methods and correlated each with a specific incompatibility allelotype. He obtained similar findings in the stylar tissue of *Petunia*, while Linskens, using radioisotopic labelling, was able to show that a complex of pollen protein and style protein was formed in the course of incompatible pollination. Knox *et al.*[25], using immunofluorescence techniques, showed that most of the antigens capable of provoking antibody in rabbits immunized with simple saline extracts of ragweed pollen were located in the inner (intine) part of the cell wall of the pollen grain. Studies by immuno-electrophoresis showed that their pollen extracts contained as least seven antigens, some of which were likely to be enzymes known to be present in the intine. They noted, however, the possibility that some of the wall-associated antigenic material could be concerned with incompatibility reactions. One might add that it would be even more interesting to look for a possible relationship in some appropriate species between the incompatibility protein coded by the S allele and the protein responsible for allergic reactions to the pollen in human subjects.

The nature of the process by which the pollen tube fails to grow effectively is of no obvious importance in the present context. It is said that there are various morphological changes—the generative nucleus fails to divide and the vegetative nucleus disappears—and, as would be expected, there are a variety of enzymatic changes. From our point of view, the nature of the specific interaction between a pollen substance and a style substance is the important matter. What happens after that has no bearing on vertebrate immunology.

There are many reasons for avoiding the use of the terms antigen and antibody, but we can legitimately use the concept of mutual recognition between cell surfaces. The facts of self-incompatibility in plants demand that there is a positive recognition by which a pollen tube carrying allele A has a surface protein which on "recognizing" another protein in the style also carrying allele A interacts with it, so triggering the progressive degeneration of the pollen tube. Strictly speaking, some substance other than protein might be concerned, but from every point of view the concept that the substance is a protein directly coded for by the allele seems to be the only one worth consideration. All the current hypotheses make this assumption.

Probably only two basic hypotheses are possible. Both agree that one allele codes for proteins in two different sites. Both have been formulated by Lewis, the second being the one he currently favours. In the first, the allele codes for two distinct proteins, one for the pollen tube, one for the style. The proteins S^P and S^{st} have a complementary configuration analogous to antigen–antibody or enzyme–substrate. In the second, the allele is a complex which codes for (*a*) specific protein pattern common to both sites; (*b*) activator for protein production in pollen tube, and (*c*) activator for protein production in style. For reasons associated with the fact that grasses have two loci, S and Z, concerned with self-incompatibility, Lewis postulates that the primary gene product takes the form

斯[23] 曾谈到过一些抗原抗体反应以及适用的血清学方法。刘易斯[24] 使用乌赫特朗尼法鉴别了月见草花粉提取物中的抗原，并使每一个抗原都与特定的不亲和性等位基因型联系在一起。他在矮牵牛花的花柱组织中也有类似的发现；而林斯肯斯用放射性同位素标记法显示，花粉蛋白和花柱蛋白的复合体是在不相容的授粉过程中形成的。诺克斯等人[25] 利用免疫荧光技术证实：用豚草花粉的简单生理盐水提取物使兔子免疫后，大多数能激活兔子体内抗体的抗原位于花粉颗粒的细胞壁内部（内壁）。免疫电泳的研究结果表明：在花粉提取物中至少含有 7 种抗原，其中的一些很可能是已知存在于内壁中的酶。然而他们特别提到，一些与细胞壁关联的抗原物质有可能参与了不亲和反应。也许还应补充一点，更有趣的研究方向是：在一些合适的物种中，寻找 S 等位基因编码的不亲和蛋白与使人类被试者产生花粉过敏反应的蛋白之间的可能关系。

从本文的研究角度考虑，花粉管不能有效生长这一过程的本质并不具有明显的重要性。据说其中存在各种各样的形态学变化——生殖核不能分裂并且营养核消失，以及像预期的那样，多种酶发生变化。依我们之见，花粉物质和花柱物质间特异性相互作用的本质才是关键问题。之后发生的事与脊椎动物免疫学没有关系。

尽管有很多理由阻止我们使用抗原和抗体这两个术语，但我们可以正当地使用细胞表面间的相互识别概念。在植物中发现的众多自交不亲和性现象表明存在一种主动识别：携带 A 等位基因的花粉管中具有一种表面蛋白，一旦这种蛋白"识别"出同样携带等位基因 A 的花柱中的另一蛋白，就会与之发生相互作用，从而引发花粉管的逐步退化。严格地说，除了蛋白，可能还会有其他一些物质与识别有关，但是从各个角度看，似乎只有以下概念才是唯一值得考虑的事情，即这种物质是一种由等位基因直接编码的蛋白。目前所有的假说都支持这一假定。

或许只有两种基本假说是可行的。两者都认为一个等位基因编码两个不同位点的蛋白。刘易斯已经系统地阐述过这两种假说，目前他更推崇的是第二种。在第一种假说中，等位基因编码两种不同的蛋白，一种在花粉管，一种在花柱。S^p 和 S^{st} 蛋白具有互补的结构，类似于抗原－抗体或酶－底物。在第二种假说中，等位基因是一个复合体，编码：(a) 两个位点共有的特异蛋白模式；(b) 在花粉管中产生蛋白所需的激活因子；(c) 在花柱中产生蛋白所需的激活因子。草类具有两个基因座，分别是 S 和 Z，都与自交不亲和性相关。为了给出与此相关的原因，刘易斯假设，最初

of a dimer. When this makes contact with an identical dimer on the interacting surface, union, presumably involving an allosteric molecule, occurs and the tetramer functions as a growth inhibitor. The idea is admittedly based on the structure of haemoglobin or immunoglobulin G, and, as Lewis[26] himself points out, cannot even be tested experimentally until the dimer and tetramer molecules are available for physical and chemical evaluation.

No one seems to have claimed that a decision can yet be made between the two possibilities: interaction of two identical proteins (or polypeptide determinants) or of sterically complementary patterns.

Simply because I am primarily concerned only in looking for analogies with immunological processes that involve the recognition of self from not-self, I should like to elaborate Lewis's first hypothesis of sterically complementary proteins along the lines we have adopted for *Botryllus*. The concept then becomes for S alleles A and B that as the pollen grain germinates and the tube begins to grow, a specific interaction between chemical groupings A+ on pollen tube, A– in the cells of the style and/or A– on pollen tube, A+ in the cells of the style results in cessation of growth. In view of the symmetry of the relationship, we assume that both + and – patterns are present on both sides and that the cells of style, being diploid, will carry + and – patterns of each gene A + B.

Because there are many plants which are self-fertilizing and more which show minor degrees of self-incompatibility, it is probable that + – contact is merely an initiating signal which, depending on other evolved cellular mechanisms, may be neutral, stimulatory or inhibitory as in self-incompatible species and varieties. Without having any detailed knowledge of the process of morphogenesis in plants, one can postulate that, as in animals, there must be some interchange of information between adjacent cells, part at least of which will take the form of + – union between specific patterns. The point to be made is simply that the possibility and the need for intercellular information exchange has provided an opportunity for the evolution of means of recognizing the difference between self and not-self when this was required for evolutionary purposes, whether to prevent self-fertilization or to produce an adaptive immune system.

The still totally unresolved problem of how a single allele can produce two mutually reactive proteins in the two relevant sites again draws attention to the currently teasing question in animal immunology as to how the capacity to produce a certain type of antibody is firmly linked to a specific histocompatibility antigen. Obviously the answer must come from the isolation of the reactive S proteins in pollen tube and stylar tissue, and assuming that they are polypeptides to determine the difference in amino-acid sequence corresponding to allelic change.

Reverting once more to Jerne's[16] concept that the organism "knows" what are the structures of the histocompatibility antigens which the species can produce, we can hardly avoid pondering—heretically, no doubt—whether there is any genetic way by which

的基因产物表现为二聚体形式。当这一二聚体在相互作用表面上与同样的二聚体相接触时，两者发生相互结合，可以假定能形成一种变构分子，这种四聚体的功能是抑制生长。诚然，上述假设是基于血红蛋白或免疫球蛋白 G 的结构而建立的，而且正如刘易斯[26]自己所指出的那样：在获得可用物理法和化学法鉴定的二聚体和四聚体分子之前，根本无法用实验来验证上述想法。

目前还未曾有人在以下这两种可能性的取舍上表明过自己的态度：是由于两个同样蛋白（或多肽决定因子）的相互作用，还是由于空间互补模式的相互作用。

仅仅因为我主要关心的只是寻找对识别自我与非我的免疫过程的模拟，所以我倾向于按照我们研究菊海鞘的方式详尽说明刘易斯阐述过的第一种假说——关于空间互补蛋白的假说。于是 S 等位基因概念就化为 A 和 B，当花粉颗粒萌发、花粉管开始生长时，花粉管上的化学基团 A + 与花柱细胞中的化学基团 A– 之间的特异性相互作用，和 / 或花粉管上的化学基团 A– 与花柱细胞中的化学基团 A + 之间的特异性相互作用，会导致花粉管生长中止。考虑到这种关系的对称性，我们假定两者都存在 + 模式和 – 模式，花柱细胞是二倍体，因而会携带每一 A+B 基因的 + 和 – 模式。

因为有很多植物是自体受精，而更多植物只表现出很小程度的自交不亲和性，所以 + – 接触可能仅仅是一种启动信号，依赖于进化而来的其他细胞机制。这些信号可以是中性的、刺激的或抑制的，后者正如自交不亲和性物种和变种中所表现的那样。在不详细了解植物中形态发生过程的情况下，我们可以假定：像动物中那样，植物的邻近细胞间一定也存在某种信息交换，至少有一部分会采用特殊模式间的 + – 结合形式。我只不过想说明：当为了进化的目的需要识别自我和非我间的差异时，细胞间信息交换的可能性和需要早已为识别方式的产生准备好了一个机会，不管进化的目的是为了防止自体受精还是为了产生适应性免疫系统。

仍然完全未解决的问题是，单个等位基因如何能在两个相关位点中产生两个互相反应的蛋白，这再一次把人们的注意力吸引到目前极具挑战性的问题上，即：在动物免疫学中，产生某种类型抗体的能力是如何与特殊的组织相容性抗原紧密地联系在一起的。很明显，答案必然来自花粉管和花柱组织中参与反应的 S 蛋白的分离，如果它们就是能根据等位基因变化决定氨基酸序列差异的多肽。

再一次重提杰尼[16]的概念，即生物体"知道"本物种所能产生的组织相容性抗原的结构，我们不得不考虑——毫无疑问，这与常规思路背道而驰——是否存在一

a nucleotide sequence coding for an amino-acid group A–B–C–D can automatically produce another sequence P–Q–R–S (say) which can "recognize" it. One has an intuitive feeling that the "choice" of the twenty biological amino-acids and the form of the genetic code might in the last analysis depend on some such requirement for mutual recognition.

(**232**, 230-235; 1971)

F. M. Burnet: School of Microbiology, University of Melbourne, Parkville, Victoria 3052.

Received June 22, 1971.

References:

1. Thomas, L., in *Cellular and Humoral Aspects of the Hypersensitive States* (edit. by Lawrence, H. S.), 529 (Hoeber-Harper, New York, 1959).

2. Billingham, R. E., *New Engl. J. Med.*, **270**, 667 and 720 (1964).

3. Currie, G. A., van Doorninck, W., and Bagshawe, K. D., *Nature*, **219**, 191 (1968).

4. Burnet, F. M., *Brit. Med. Bull.*, **20**, 154 (1964).

5. Hellström, K. E., and Möller, G., *Prog. Allergy* (*Karger*), **9**, 158 (1965).

6. Klein, G., *Ann. Rev. Microbiol.*, **20**, 223 (1966).

7. Prehn, R. T., *Ann. NY Acad. Sci.*, **164**, 449 (1969).

8. Burnet, F. M., *Immunological Surveillance* (Pergamon, Oxford, London, New York, Toronto, Sydney, 1970).

9. Finstad, J., and Good, R. A., *J. Exp. Med.*, **120**, 1151 (1964).

10. Marchalonis, J. J., and Edelman, G. M., *J. Exp. Med.*, **127**, 891 (1968).

11. Papermaster, B. W., Condie, R. M., and Good, R. A., *Nature*, **196**, 355 (1962).

12. Acton, R. T., Weinheimer, P. F., Hildemann, W. H., and Evans, E. E., *J. Bact.*, **99**, 626 (1969).

13. Hildemann, W. H., and Thoenes, G. H., *Transplantation*, 7, 506 (1969).

14. Oka, H., in *Profiles of Japanese Science and Scientists* (edit. by Yukawa, H.), 198 (Kodansha, Tokyo, 1970).

15. Theodor, J. L., *Nature*, **227**, 690 (1970).

16. Jerne, N. K., in *Immune Surveillance* (edit. by Smith, R. T., and Landy, M.), 343 (Academic Press, New York and London, 1970).

17. Howell, J. H., in *Phylogeny of Immunity* (edit. by Smith, R. T., Miescher, P. A., and Good, R. A.), 263 (University of Florida, Gainesville, 1966).

18. Ritchie, A., *Palaeontology*, **11**, 21 (1968).

19. Burnet, F. M., *Acta Pathol. Microbiol. Scand.*, **76**, 1 (1969).

20. East, E. M., and Mangelsdorf, A. J., *Proc. US Nat. Acad. Sci.*, **11**, 166 (1925).

21. Crane, M. B., and Lawrence, W. J. C., *The Genetics of Garden Plants*, third ed., 185 (London).

22. Lundqvist, A., *Genetics Today* (edit. by Geerts, S. J.), **3**, 637 (Pergamon, Oxford, 1965).

23. Linskens, H. F., *Genetics Today* (edit. by Geerts, S. J.), **3**, 629 (Pergamon, Oxford, 1965).

24. Lewis, D., *Proc. Roy. Soc.*, B, **140**, 127 (1952).

25. Knox, R. B., Heslop-Harrison, J., and Reed, C., *Nature*, **225**, 1066 (1970).

26. Lewis, D., *Genetics Today* (edit. by Geerts, S. J.), **3**, 657 (Pergamon, Oxford, 1965).

种遗传学方式，通过它，编码一个氨基酸组 A–B–C–D 的核苷酸序列能自动产生另一氨基酸序列，（比如说是）P–Q–R–S，使 P–Q–R–S 能"识别"A–B–C–D。给人的一种直观感觉是，可能在最后的分析中要根据某种相互识别需求来确定对生物体内 20 种氨基酸的"选择"以及遗传密码的形式。

（吕静 翻译；刘京国 审稿）

Detection of Radio Emission from Cygnus X–1

L. L. E. Braes and G. K. Miley

Editor's Note

Cygnus X–1 was one of the first X-ray emitting objects found when a rocket with an X-ray detector was launched in 1964. But X-ray detectors in those days had very crude spatial resolution. Luc Braes and George Miley here report variable radio emission coming from that region of the sky, and show that it stems from the radio counterpart to Cyg X–1. This enabled identification of Cyg X–1's orbit, and we now know that Cyg X–1 is a black hole of about 9 solar masses co-orbiting with a blue supergiant star. They are separated by only about 20 percent of the distance between the Earth and Sun, and the wind from the star feeds a disk of material around the black hole, which the black hole is accreting.

THE X-ray source Cyg X–1 is known to be highly variable and recently has been found to pulsate with a period of 73 ms (ref. 1). Here we report the detection of its radio counterpart at a frequency of 1,415 MHz.

Two sets of observations at 1,415 MHz were made with the Westerbork synthesis radio telescope of a 1°×1° field centred near the position of Cyg X–1. The bandwidth was 4 MHz. Baselines ranging in length from 36 to 1,471 m were used, resulting in a synthesized beam of half-power diameter 23″ in right ascension and 40″ in declination. The first observations on February 28, 1971, from 10 h 29 min to 15 h 02 min UT showed no source stronger than 0.005 flux units near the X-ray position. The field was observed again during April 28–29 from 23 h 04 min to 11 h 06 min UT, and in the map resulting from these observations there is an unresolved source within the X-ray error box.

The flux density of the radio source is 0.021±0.004 f.u. and its position, determined by a least-squares fit to the antenna pattern, is in 1950 coordinates: α=19 h 56 min 28.9 s±0.2 s, δ=35° 03′56″± 3″. This can be compared with the X-ray position determined by the Uhuru satellite which is α=19 h 56 min 25 s ± 15 s, δ=35° 03′25″± 1′ (unpublished work of Tananbaum et al.). Because of the close agreement in position and because this radio source is so strongly variable, it is almost certainly associated with Cyg X–1. A search at the radio position may therefore enable the X-ray source to be identified optically. A likely candidate is the ninth magnitude star AGK2 +35° 1,910 only 1″ from our position, but photometric and spectroscopic observations are needed to confirm the identification. Further study of the radio emission is also of great importance. Simultaneous measurements over a range of frequencies should reveal whether its radio spectrum is non-thermal as in the case of Sco X–1 (refs. 2 and 3), and observations with high time resolution are essential to determine whether the radio source is a pulsar.

探测到天鹅座X-1的射电辐射

布拉埃斯，米利

编者按

天鹅座 X–1 是 1964 年一枚载有 X 射线探测器的火箭升空后所发现的第一批 X 射线源之一。但是在当时，X 射线探测器的空间分辨率很差。卢克·布拉埃斯和乔治·米利在本文中报道了来自该天区的随时间变化的射电辐射，并证明其来源于天鹅座 X–1 的射电对应体。这使得人们可以确定天鹅座 X–1 的轨道。现在我们知道，天鹅座 X–1 是一个大约 9 倍太阳质量的黑洞，它与一颗蓝超巨星互相绕转。两者之间的距离只有日地距离的 20% 左右，蓝超巨星的星风被吸积并在黑洞周围形成吸积盘。

大家都知道，天鹅座 X–1 是一个变化剧烈的 X 射线源，最近发现它的脉动周期为 73 ms（参考文献 1）。本文报道我们在频率 1,415 MHz 处探测到了它的射电对应体。

我们用韦斯特博克综合孔径射电望远镜在 1,415 MHz 处进行了两组观测，观测区域是大致以天鹅座 X–1 为中心的 1°×1° 天区。观测带宽为 4 MHz。基线长度从 36 m 到 1,471 m，因而综合波束的半功率宽为赤经方向 23″，赤纬方向 40″。我们在 1971 年 2 月 28 日进行了第一次观测，时间是世界时 10 h 29 min 至 15 h 02 min，结果并没有发现在 X 射线源位置附近有强于 0.005 流量单位的源。我们在世界时 4 月 28 日 ~ 29 日 23 h 04 min 至 11 h 06 min 又对该区域进行了一次观测。观测成图后发现在 X 射线源位置的误差框范围内有一个不可分辨的源。

该射电源的流量密度为 0.021±0.004 流量单位。用最小二乘法拟合天线方向图得到它的位置在 1950 历元：$\alpha = 19\ h\ 56\ min\ 28.9\ s\pm0.2\ s$, $\delta = 35°03′56″\pm3″$。这一结果与由乌呼鲁卫星得到的 X 射线位置 $\alpha = 19\ h\ 56\ min\ 25\ s\pm15\ s$, $\delta = 35°03′25″\pm1′$（塔南鲍姆等人尚未发表的研究结果）大致相当。由于两者的位置吻合并且该射电源的流量变化剧烈，几乎可以肯定它就是天鹅座 X–1 的对应体。因此在射电位置处进行搜索或许可以从光学上识别出该 X 射线源。九等星 AGK2 +35° 1,910 就是一个可能的候选者，它仅与我们现在的位置相差 1″，但还需要通过测光和光谱观测进行确认。对射电辐射的进一步研究也是非常重要的。在一定频率范围内进行同时观测应能确定它的射电谱是否就是类似于天蝎座 X–1 的非热谱（参考文献 2 和 3）。高时间分辨率的观测对于确定这个射电源是不是脉冲星是至关重要的。

625

During the preparation of this article we learned from Drs. R. M. Hjellming and C. M. Wade that the Cyg X–1 radio source has been detected independently at a frequency of 2,695 MHz with the NRAO interferometer at Green Bank. Their position is in good agreement with that given here.

The Westerbork Radio Observatory is operated by the Netherlands Foundation for Radio Astronomy with the financial support of the Netherlands Organization for the Advancement of Pure Research (Z.W.O.).

(**232**, 246; 1971)

L. L. E. Braes and G. K. Miley: Leiden Observatory, Leiden 2401.

Received June 28; revised July 9, 1971.

References:

1. Oda, M., Gorenstein, P., Gursky, H., Kellogg, E., Schreier, E., Tananbaum, H., and Giacconi, R., *Astrophys. J. Lett.*, **166**, L1 (1971).

2. Hjellming, R. M., and Wade, C. M., *Astrophys. J. Lett.*, **164**, L1 (1971).

3. Braes, L. L. E., and Miley, G. K., *Astron. Astrophys.* (in the press).

在准备这篇文章的过程中，我们从耶尔明博士和韦德博士那里得知，其他人也独立地探测到了天鹅座 X–1 射电源，他们使用了位于格林班克的美国国家射电天文台的干涉仪，观测频率为 2,695 MHz。他们测得的位置与本文中给出的位置非常吻合。

韦斯特博克射电天文台由荷兰射电天文学基金会负责管理，经费上的支持来自荷兰纯理论研究提升组织。

（岳友岭 孟洁 翻译；肖伟科 审稿）

Magnetospheric Electric Fields and the Super-rotation of the Earth's Upper Atmosphere

H. Volland

Editor's Note

In 1964, scientists documented a "super rotation" of the Earth's upper atmosphere — a rotation faster than the Earth's solid mass itself. Here atmospheric scientist Hans Volland suggests that a novel interaction between the high atmosphere and the ionospheric plasma might be the cause. As he notes, the Earth's magnetosphere induces an electric field in the ionosphere, which causes a prevailing eastward drift of ions. In the equatorial plane, the resulting velocities would be roughly 60 m/s. Collisions between ions and neutral air at such heights, he suggests, would drag the neutral atmosphere along, producing the right direction of atmospheric rotation, also with roughly the right magnitude. Scientists continue to explore the true cause of super-rotation today.

SEVERAL mechanisms have been proposed to explain the super-rotation of the Earth's upper atmosphere discovered by King-Hele[1]. These mechanisms can be divided into two general groups. The first considers the absorption of solar radiation within the upper atmosphere as the original driving force for the super-rotation, whereas the second assumes the primary source to lie outside the upper atmosphere. The first group can be subdivided into three parts which give differing hypotheses to explain the transformation of solar radiation energy into kinetic energy of the super-rotation.

First, King-Hele[1] considered the geostrophic component of the zonally averaged longitudinal wind as the prevailing wind which he observed. Such wind can be set up by pressure gradients directed towards the poles as the result of the net surplus of solar heat input into the lower latitudes as compared with the heat input into the polar regions. Hines[2] has pointed out, however, that this wind component must be rather small due to the large ageostrophic wind component which results from ion-neutral collisions. Quantitatively[3], confirmation of this results in a prevailing west wind of the order of 5 m s^{-1} at F2 layer heights which is at least one order of magnitude smaller than the winds suggested by King-Hele derived from satellite drag data[4]. Moreover, that wind component is zero at the equator which is inconsistent with the findings of King-Hele.

Second, super-rotation (or prevailing west winds) may be set up by non-linear coupling between the diurnally varying pressure and density fields originating from the solar heat input[5-7]. Here, prevailing west winds blow only within the lower latitudes ($|\phi| < 30°$) while at middle and high latitudes the prevailing wind component changes into an east wind.

Third, nonlinear coupling may occur due to a diurnally varying impulse exchange

磁层电场与地球高层大气的特快自转

福兰德

编者按

1964 年，科学家们证实了在地球的高层大气中存在着"特快自转"现象——其自转速度大于地球的固体实体本身。大气学家汉斯·福兰德在本文中指出，高层大气和电离层等离子体之间的异常相互作用可能就是特快自转现象出现的原因。如他所述，地球磁层在电离层诱发了一个电场，从而产生了离子向东漂移的趋势。在赤道面上，这个漂移速度约为 60 m/s。他认为：在这样的高度上，离子与中性气体的碰撞将会在中性大气中产生拉力，由此产生的大气自转的方向和速度的数量级都很合适。现在，科学家们仍在不断探索大气特快自转的真正原因。

人们提出了若干种机制来解释金 – 海莱 [1] 发现的地球高层大气的特快自转现象。这些机制可分为两大类。第一大类认为，高层大气内部对太阳辐射的吸收是特快自转的原动力；而第二大类则认为，主要驱动力来自于高层大气以外。第一大类又被细分成三个小类，每个小类分别用不同的假说对太阳辐射能转化为特快自转的动能进行了解释。

首先，金 – 海莱 [1] 认为区域性的平均纵向风的地转分量就是他所观测到的盛行风。这种风是由指向两极的压力梯度形成的，而压力梯度又是因输入低纬地区的太阳热量相对于两极地区的净过剩所致。不过，海因斯 [2] 曾指出：这种风的地转分量肯定会非常小，因为离子与中性粒子的碰撞会导致非地球自转风的分量较大。从数量上来说 [3]，要满足上述观点就必须承认在 F2 层高度处盛行西风的风速大约为 5 m/s，这一数值至少要比金 – 海莱根据卫星阻力数据得到的风速 [4] 小一个数量级。另外，该风在赤道上的分量为零，这也与金 – 海莱的结果不一致。

其次，特快自转（或盛行西风）可能是由太阳热量输入引起的日变化的压力场与密度场之间发生非线性耦合而产生的 [5-7]。在这里，盛行西风仅存在于低纬度地区（$|\phi| < 30°$）；在中高纬度地区，盛行风转变成了东风。

第三,非线性耦合可能是由中性粒子与离子之间冲量交换的日变化引起的,其中,

between neutrals and ions where the electric polarization field of the Sq region acts as a linking mechanism[5]. This effect, however, seems to be insignificant for the generation of a prevailing wind component[7]. Rishbeth[8] proposed a new coupling mechanism between neutrals and ions at F layer heights which should result in a prevailing west wind. Here, the linking chain is an electric polarization field of (what he calls) the F layer dynamo. This mechanism seems to work only if the dynamo region of the E layer is dynamically decoupled from the F layer. It can be shown, however, that the predominant wind system at E layer heights which drives the Sq current belongs to the same tidal mode as the wind of the F layer derived by Kohl and King[9] and by Geisler[10]. That mode propagates through the E and the F regions continuously increasing in magnitude and only slightly changing its phase and latitudinal structure[3].

Following an idea of Cole[11], we want to discuss a hypothesis which belongs to the second class of driving mechanisms. It is a zonally averaged electric field of magnetospheric origin observed by Mozer and Manka[12] at balloon altitudes. This electrostatic field can be derived from a potential (my unpublished results)

$$\Phi = \frac{r_0 A \sqrt{\rho}}{\sin\theta} \left(\rho \geqslant 1; \theta \neq \begin{Bmatrix} 0 \\ \pi \end{Bmatrix} \right) \tag{1}$$

with $\rho = r/r_0$, r=distance from the Earth's center, $r_0 \sim 6{,}570$ km (upper boundary of the dynamo region), θ = polar distance and $A = 3.5$ mV m^{-1}.

The electric field strength components at F layer heights and above and outside the polar regions are

$$E_\theta = \frac{A \cos\theta}{\sqrt{\rho} \sin^2\theta}$$

$$E_r = -\frac{A}{2\sqrt{\rho} \sin\theta} \tag{2}$$

The plasma of the F layer drifts within the combined electric and geomagnetic fields like

$$v_i = \frac{\mathbf{E} \times \mathbf{B}}{B^2} \tag{3}$$

where B is the geomagnetic induction. In the case of an ideal co-axial geomagnetic dipole field, equations (2) and (3) result in a prevailing eastward drift of the ions of

$$(v_i)_\lambda = \frac{A}{2B_0 \sqrt{\rho} \sin^2\theta} \left(\rho \geqslant 1; \theta \neq \begin{Bmatrix} 0 \\ \pi \end{Bmatrix} \right) \tag{4}$$

where B_0 is the geomagnetic induction at the equator. At F2 layer heights ($\rho \sim 1$) and within the equatorial plane ($\theta = \pi/2$) this velocity is $(v_i)_\lambda \sim 60$ m s^{-1} increasing with latitude.

The neutral air at F layer heights in the absence of external forces is dragged by the

630

Sq 区的电极化场（译者注：来自由太阳引潮力和热潮力引起的大气潮汐运动产生的电流体系）是以一种联动机制的形式起作用的 [5]。然而，这种效应对于盛行风分量的产生似乎没有什么影响 [7]。里斯贝斯 [8] 提出了在 F 层高度处中性粒子与离子之间的一种新的耦合机制，这种机制下能够形成盛行西风。在这里，耦合链是（他称之为）F 层发电机的一个电极化场。该机制似乎只有在 E 层的发电机区域被 F 层动态解耦时才能起作用。然而，可以看出：在 E 层高度处驱动 Sq 电流的主导风系与科尔和金 [9] 以及盖斯勒 [10] 获得的 F 层风系属于同一种潮汐模式。该模式通过 E 层区和 F 层区传播，在数量级上不断增大，而相位和纬向结构却变化很小 [3]。

顺着科尔的思路 [11]，我们来讨论一下一个归属于第二类驱动机制的假说。莫泽尔和曼卡 [12] 在探空气球高度处所观测到的是磁层成因的区域性平均电场。该静电场可以由一个电势得到（本人尚未发表的研究结果）：

$$\Phi = \frac{r_0 A \sqrt{\rho}}{\sin\theta} \left(\rho \geqslant 1; \theta \neq \left\{ \begin{matrix} 0 \\ \pi \end{matrix} \right\} \right) \tag{1}$$

其中：$\rho = r/r_0$，r 为距地心的距离，r_0 约为 6,570 km（发电机区域的上部边界）；θ 为极距；$A = 3.5$ mV/m。

F 层高度处及以上的电场强度分量和极区以外的电场强度分量分别为：

$$E_\theta = \frac{A \cos\theta}{\sqrt{\rho} \sin^2\theta}$$
$$E_r = -\frac{A}{2\sqrt{\rho} \sin\theta} \tag{2}$$

F 层的等离子体在电场与地磁场的混合场中的漂移为：

$$v_i = \frac{\mathbf{E} \times \mathbf{B}}{B^2} \tag{3}$$

其中 B 为地磁感应强度。在一个理想的同轴地球偶极子磁场中，由式（2）和式（3）可以得出离子向东漂移的速度为：

$$(v_i)_\lambda = \frac{A}{2B_0 \sqrt{\rho} \sin^2\theta} \left(\rho \geqslant 1; \theta \neq \left\{ \begin{matrix} 0 \\ \pi \end{matrix} \right\} \right) \tag{4}$$

其中 B_0 为赤道处的地磁感应强度。在 F2 层的高度上（$\rho \sim 1$）并处于赤道面内（$\theta = \pi/2$）时，该速度 $(v_i)_\lambda$ 约为 60 m/s，且随纬度的升高而增加。

根据下面的公式，在没有外力的条件下，F 层高度上的中性气体会受到来自电

ionospheric plasma according to

$$v_\lambda \sim \frac{v_c}{v_v + v_c}(v_i)_\lambda \tag{5}$$

where v_c is the non-neutral collision number and v_v is a measure for the molecular viscosity force acting on the neutral gas[3]. Since v_c decreases like the electron density with altitude above the maximum of the F2 layer, and since $v_v < v_c$ at F layer heights, we expect from equations (4) and (5) a prevailing west wind of the neutral component of the air which has its maximum at F layer heights. It has the right direction and the right order of magnitude to be consistent with the observations of King-Hele.

(**232**, 248-249; 1971)

H. Volland: Astronomical Institutes, University of Bonn.

Received June 9, 1971.

References:
1. King-Hele, D. G., *Planet. Space Sci.*, **12**, 835 (1964).
2. Hines, C.O., *Planet. Space Sci.*, **13**, 169 (1965).
3. Volland, H., and Mayr, H. G., NASA-Document X-621-71 (GSFC, Greenbelt, Maryland, 1971).
4. King-Hele, D. G., Scott, D. W., and Walker, D. M. C., *Planet. Space Sci.*, **18**, 1433 (1970).
5. Challinor, R. A., *Planet. Space Sci.*, **16**, 557 (1968).
6. Challinor, R. A., *Planet. Space Sci.*, **17**, 1097 (1969).
7. Challinor, R. A., *Planet. Space Sci.*, **18**, 1485 (1970).
8. Rishbeth, H., *Nature*, **229**, 333 (1971).
9. Kohl, H., and King, J. W., *J. Atmos. Terr. Phys.*, **29**, 1045 (1967).
10. Geisler, J. E., *J. Atmos. Terr. Phys.*, **29**, 1469 (1967).
11. Cole, K. D., *Planet. Space Sci.*, **19**, 59 (1971).
12. Mozer, F. S., and Manka, R. H., *J. Geophys. Res.*, **76**, 1697 (1971).

离层的等离子体的拉力：

$$v_\lambda \sim \frac{v_c}{v_v + v_c}(v_i)_\lambda \tag{5}$$

其中，v_c 为非中性碰撞数，v_v 为作用于中性气体上的分子黏滞力的一个量度 [3]。因为在 F2 层最大值以上，同电子密度一样，v_c 会随高度的增加而减小，并且在 F 层高度处 $v_v < v_c$，所以我们可利用式（4）和式（5）得到一股由空气中的中性成分形成的盛行西风，并且其速度在 F 层达到最大。这一结果无论在方向上还是在数量级上都与金－海莱的观测结果一致。

（齐红艳 翻译；于涌 审稿）

Estimation of Nuclear Explosion Energies from Microbarograph Records

J. W. Posey and A. D. Pierce

Editor's Note

Physicists in the 1970s sought accurate means for estimating the yield of nuclear explosions, especially in tests then being conducted by the United States and the Soviet Union. Here Joe Posey and Allen Pierce report on the accuracy of a new formula they had derived to make such estimates from the detection of very weak air waves from the initial blast. Their formula relates the explosion energy to the peak-to-trough magnitude of the pressure variation in the wave, and also to the 3/2 power of its period. As they show using data collected for a number of weapons tests conducted in 1961 and 1962, their expression fitted all the data very well, especially for explosions weaker than about 11 megatons.

FOLLOWING the US and USSR atmospheric test series in 1954–1962, numerous microbarograph records[1-8] of air waves generated by nuclear bomb tests were published. Previous theoretical interpretations[7,9] of such waveforms have required some explicit knowledge of the average atmospheric temperature and wind profiles above the path connecting source to microbarograph. Such profiles are never sufficiently well known and vary from point to point, and as seemingly small changes in the profiles cause relatively large changes in the waveforms, it would seem to be difficult to estimate the explosion energy yield to even order of magnitude accuracy from such records. Recently, however, in a further account of this work to be published elsewhere, we have succeeded in deriving an approximate theoretical relationship between certain waveform features and energy yield which is insensitive to changes in atmospheric structure. This relationship is given by

$$E = 13 \, p_{\text{FPT}} \left[r_e \sin\left(r/r_e\right) \right]^{\frac{1}{2}} H_s \left(c T_{1,2} \right)^{3/2} \tag{1}$$

where E is energy release, p_{FPT} is the first peak to trough pressure amplitude (see Fig. 1), r_e is radius of the Earth, r is the great circle distance from burst point to observation point, H_s is a lower atmosphere scale height, c is a representative sound speed, and $T_{1,2}$ is the time interval between first and second peaks. The purpose of the present communication is to describe the extent to which the above relation agrees with the existing available data.

根据微压计记录估计出的核爆炸能量

波西，皮尔斯

编者按

20 世纪 70 年代，物理学家们曾试图找到一种能精确估计核爆炸输出能量的方法，特别是因为可以在美国和苏联即将实施的核爆炸试验中进行估算。乔·波西和艾伦·皮尔斯在本文中阐述了他们为估计核爆炸能量而推导出来的一个新公式的精确性，这个公式是根据对最初爆炸产生的极弱空气波的测量得到的。他们在公式中将核爆炸输出能量与次声波上的波峰–波谷间压力变化幅度及其周期的 3/2 次方联系起来。他们利用在 1961 年和 1962 年核武器试验之后所采集到的大量数据来说明上述公式与所有数据都符合得很好，尤其是对于输出能量小于 11 兆吨左右的核爆炸。

继美国和苏联在 1954 年至 1962 年间对大气所作的一系列测试之后，有不少人发表了由核弹试验产生的空气波的微压计记录数据 [1-8]。如果要用以前的理论 [7,9] 来解释这些波形，就需要较为确切地知道连接爆炸源和微压计之间路径上方的平均气温和风廓线。这样的风廓线是不可能精确得到的，并且在每一个点上的值都是有所不同的，而且因为风廓线中看似微小的变化就能使波形发生相当大的改变，所以即使只是想要根据这些微压计记录值估计出核爆炸产生能量输出的数量级恐怕也并非易事。然而，我们最近将在别处发表的一篇文章中对此项工作进行进一步的报道——我们成功地推导出了特定波形特征和能量输出之间存在的近似理论关系，这种方法对大气结构变化不是很敏感。其关系式如下：

$$E = 13\, p_{\text{FPT}} \left[r_e \sin (r/r_e) \right]^{\frac{1}{2}} H_s \left(c\, T_{1,2} \right)^{3/2} \tag{1}$$

式中：E 代表释放出的能量，p_{FPT} 是从第一个波峰到波谷的压力变化幅度（见图 1），r_e 表示地球半径，r 表示从爆炸点到观测点的大圆距离，H_s 表示低层大气标高，c 表示声速，而 $T_{1,2}$ 是第一个波峰与第二个波峰之间的时间间隔。本篇论文的目的在于阐述上述关系式与实际测量数据之间的符合程度。

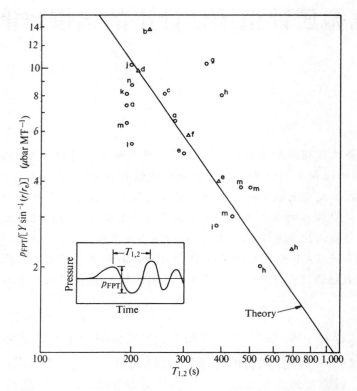

Fig. 1. Comparison of data with the theoretical relationship between amplitude and period of infrasonic waveforms generated by nuclear explosions. The data points are lettered a to n corresponding to particular events defined in the text. $\bigcirc$, Donn and Shaw; $\triangle$, Harkrider.

The various points shown in Fig. 1 correspond to individual microbarograms recorded at Pasadena, California; Berkeley, California; Terceira, Azores; Fletcher's Ice Island; Whippany, New Jersey; Ewa Beach, Hawaii, and Palisades, New York, after the Soviet explosions of (a) September 10 (10 MT), (b) September 11 (9 MT), (c) September 14 (7 MT), (d) October 4 (8 MT), (e) October 6 (11 MT), (f) October 20 (5 MT), (g) October 23 (25 MT), (h) October 30 (58 MT), and (i) October 31, 1961 (8 MT) and the US explosions of (j) May 4 (3 MT), (k) June 10 (9 MT), (l) June 12 (6 MT), (m) June 27 (24 MT), and (n) July 11, 1962 (12 MT). Here the estimate of the yield (in equivalent megatons of TNT where one MT equals 4.2×10^{22} ergs) is taken from Båth[10]. All the records used are taken from the articles of Harkrider[7] and of Donn and Shaw[8]. Pressure amplitudes for Harkrider's records were computed using his microbarograph response data. Pressure amplitudes for the Donn and Shaw records were determined according to the premises (W. Donn, private communication) that (a) all records recorded by Lamont type A microbarographs are to the same scale and (b) the clip to clip amplitude of off scale oscillations was 350 μbars. The ordinate in Fig. 1 gives $p_{FPT}/[Y\sin^{-\frac{1}{2}}(r/r_e)]$ in μbar MT^{-1} where Y is the explosion yield in MT. The abscissa gives the period $T_{1,2}$ in s. Note that the plot is full logarithmic. The

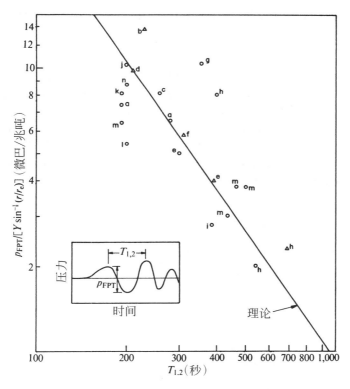

图 1. 核爆炸所产生的次声波的振幅和周期数据与理论关系式的对比。其中标有字母 a 到 n 的数据点分别对应于文章中所定义的特殊事件。〇 表示唐和肖的记录数据；△ 表示哈克赖德的记录数据。

　　图 1 中所示的各个点分别对应于：在苏联核爆炸之后于加州帕萨迪纳、加州伯克利、亚速尔群岛特塞拉岛、弗莱彻浮冰岛、新泽西州惠帕尼、夏威夷州埃瓦海滩和纽约州帕利塞兹测量的微压计记录结果，测量时间分别为 1961 年 (a) 9 月 10 日 (10 兆吨)，(b) 9 月 11 日 (9 兆吨)，(c) 9 月 14 日 (7 兆吨)，(d) 10 月 4 日 (8 兆吨)，(e) 10 月 6 日 (11 兆吨)，(f) 10 月 20 日 (5 兆吨)，(g) 10 月 23 日 (25 兆吨)，(h) 10 月 30 日 (58 兆吨) 和 (i) 10 月 31 日 (8 兆吨)；在美国核爆炸之后于上述地点测量的微压计记录结果，时间为 1962 年 (j) 5 月 4 日 (3 兆吨)，(k) 6 月 10 日 (9 兆吨)，(l) 6 月 12 日 (6 兆吨)，(m) 6 月 27 日 (24 兆吨) 和 (n) 7 月 11 日 (12 兆吨)。本文中对核爆炸能量输出值的估计（相当于多少兆吨三硝基甲苯爆炸所释放的能量，其中 1 兆吨 $= 4.2 \times 10^{22}$ 尔格）利用了贝斯的结果 [10]。所有测量记录均来自哈克赖德 [7] 以及唐和肖 [8] 的文章。哈克赖德记录值中的压力变化幅度是由他的微压计响应数据计算得到的。唐和肖记录值中的压力变化幅度是根据以下假设得到的（唐，私人交流）：(a) 所有用拉蒙特 A 型微压计所作的记录都采用了同样的标度 (b) 标度以外振动的削波幅度为 350 微巴。图 1 中纵坐标 $p_{\mathrm{FPT}}/[Y\sin^{-\frac{1}{2}}(r/r_{\mathrm{e}})]$ 的单位为微巴 / 兆吨，其中爆炸能量输出 Y 的单位是兆吨。横坐标周期 $T_{1,2}$ 的单位为秒。请注

solid line represents the theoretical relation, equation (1) with c and H_s taken as 310 ms^{-1} and 8 km, respectively.

The scatter about the theoretical curve could be due to various causes; one which seems especially likely is the undulation in amplitude due to the horizontal refraction and subsequent focusing or defocusing caused by departures of the atmosphere from perfect stratification. We may note also that much of the scatter would not be present if we had omitted data corresponding to explosions of greater than 11 MT. The general trend of longer period signals being of lower amplitudes than signals recorded elsewhere but which were generated by the same event seems to be amply substantiated by the data.

(**232**, 253; 1971)

Joe W. Posey and Allan D. Pierce: Department of Mechanical Engineering, Massachusetts Institute of Technology.

Received June 17, 1971.

References:

1. Yamamoto, R., *Bull. Amer. Meteorol. Soc.*, **37**, 406 (1956).

2. Araskog, R., Ericsson, U., and Wagner, H., *Nature*, **193**, 970 (1962).

3. Carpenter, E. G., Harwood, G., and Whiteside, T., *Nature*, **192**, 857 (1961).

4. Farkas, E., *Nature*, **193**, 765 (1962).

5. Jones, R., *Nature*, **193**, 229 (1962).

6. Wexler, H., and Hass, W. A., *J. Geophys. Res.*, **67**, 3875 (1962).

7. Harkrider, D. G., *J. Geophys. Res.*, **69**, 5295 (1964).

8. Donn, W., and Shaw, D., *Rev. Geophys.*, **5**, 53 (1967).

9. MacKinnon, R., *Quart. J. Roy. Meteorol. Soc.*, **93**, 436 (1967).

10. Båth, M., Rept. A 4270-4271 (Seismological Institute, Univ. Uppsala, 1962).

意图 1 中的横纵坐标均采用对数形式。实线代表由式（1）给出的理论关系，其中 c 和 H_s 的取值分别为 310 米 / 秒和 8 千米。

　　理论曲线的发散可能是由多种原因造成的，其中有一个可能性非常大，即由地平大气折射以及随之而来的因大气层偏离理想层而产生的聚焦或散焦所导致的振幅波动。我们也注意到：如果忽略大于 11 兆吨的爆炸所对应的数据，那么大部分发散将不复存在。由上述数据似乎足以证明这样的趋势：对于由同样事件产生的信号，周期较长信号的幅度要低于在别处记录的信号的幅度。

（韩少卿 翻译；尚仁成 审稿）

Sex Pheromone Mimics of the American Cockroach

W. S. Bowers and W. G. Bodenstein

Editor's Note

The specificity of insect sex pheromones is questioned here with the discovery of a number of plant extracts shown to drive male American cockroaches "wild with desire". Male cockroaches (*Periplaneta americana*) respond to a female-produced airborne pheromone by fluttering their wings, extending their abdomen and attempting to copulate. But identical behaviour is seen when males are exposed to certain conifer-derived essential oils and flowing plant extracts, William Bowers and William Bodenstein report. The plant products differ chemically from the natural pheromone, which the researchers extracted from the midguts of virgin females. This is the first documented report of a sex pheromone-like substance found in plants.

DURING an investigation of several essential oil preparations for juvenile hormone activity[1], we discovered that a volatile component(s) in several coniferyl needle distillates stimulated apparent sexual excitement in male American cockroaches, *Periplaneta americana* (L.). The response, consisting of movement, wing flutter, extended abdomen and attempted copulation, was behaviourally identical to that elicited by the natural sex pheromone of this insect[2] and in marked contrast to the behaviour (hyperactivity) induced by exposure to highly irritating chemicals such as amyl acetate.

Needle and cone oil distillates of spruce, *Picea rubra* Link, and fir, *Abies siberica* Ledeb., *Abies alba* Mill., were fractionated by column chromatography over "Florisil", and the active fractions were examined by gas–liquid chromatography. (A column 4 mm × 2 m was used, packed with 0.75% methyl silicone on 200 mesh gas chrom P.) The effluent of the column was directed into a 2 1. jar containing ten male cockroaches which had been isolated from female cockroaches for 6 weeks. Sexual display by the cockroaches was associated with only one peak in these fractions. Final purification of the pheromonal substance was carried out by preparative gas chromatography. (An F and M Model 775 Prepmaster equipped with gold plated injector block and stainless steel columns 0.75 inches ×16 feet was used. It contained 4% methyl silicone on 150 mesh "Chromosorb W".)

By its pleasing and characteristic odour the active compound was tentatively characterized as bornyl acetate, a known constituent of the source trees. Comparison with standards by gas–liquid chromatography and by infrared, nuclear magnetic resonance and mass spectroscopy confirmed its identity.

美洲蜚蠊的性外激素类似物

鲍尔斯，博登施泰因

编者按

因为作者发现完全可以从植物中提取出一些能使雄性美洲蜚蠊"神魂颠倒"的物质，所以昆虫性外激素具有特异性的提法在本文中受到了质疑。雄性蜚蠊（美洲大蠊）对一种由雌性蜚蠊产生并能在空气中传播的激素所作出的反应是：扇动翅膀、扩张腹部和试图交配。然而，当雄性蜚蠊暴露于某些松类植物精油和开花植物的提取物中时也会表现出同样的行为，威廉·鲍尔斯和威廉·博登施泰因在本文中讨论了这一现象。这些植物源物质的化学成分与研究人员从蜚蠊处女虫中肠中分离出来的天然性外激素并不相同。这篇文章是第一篇报道来源于植物的性外激素类似物的文献。

在研究激活保幼激素所必需的几种精油制品时 [1]，我们发现在多种松柏针叶的馏分中有一种易挥发的成分能够刺激雄性美洲蜚蠊（拉丁学名为美洲大蠊）产生明显的性兴奋。性冲动反应包括飞来飞去、扇动翅膀、扩张腹部以及试图交配，与在这种昆虫天然性外激素作用下所产生的行为 [2] 完全一样，但与由暴露于醋酸戊酯等强刺激性化学物质中所诱发的行为（极度活跃）相去甚远。

用以硅酸镁为载体的柱层析法分离由云杉（红果云杉）和冷杉（西伯利亚冷杉和欧洲冷杉）的针叶和球果蒸馏出来的油分，并用气-液色谱法鉴定其中的活性成分（所用色谱柱的尺寸为 4 mm × 2 m，在 200 目的硅藻土型色谱载体 P 上涂渍 0.75% 的甲基硅酮）。将色谱柱的流出物直接导入一只装有 10 只雄性蜚蠊的容积为 2 升的育虫瓶里，这些雄性蜚蠊已经和雌性蜚蠊隔离了 6 周。在洗脱组分中只有一个峰与蜚蠊性兴奋的产生相对应。用制备气相色谱法对性外激素组分进行最后的分离纯化（使用的是配备有镀金注射模块和 0.75 英寸 × 16 英尺不锈钢柱的 F 和 M 型 775 制备母机。在 150 目的"硅烷化白色硅藻土"担体上含有 4% 的甲基硅酮）。

根据这种活性化合物所散发出来的令人愉悦的特征性气味，我们把它初步鉴定为乙酸冰片酯，它也是这些原料树中的一种已知成分。通过与气-液色谱、红外光谱、核磁共振谱以及质谱的标准物进行比较，可以确认该活性化合物的成分就是乙酸冰片酯。

Bioassays were performed according to Bodenstein[3]. Thus, the compound in hexane solution, was absorbed on a piece of Whatman No. 1 filter paper (1 cm^2) and held within the 2 1. rearing jar with forceps. The sensitivity of male cockroaches to the natural sex pheromone and to the pheromone mimics is greatly magnified by maintaining the males in isolation from females for at least 4–6 weeks before attempting bioassays. The response of newly segregated males is erratic or indifferent except to extremely high concentrations of natural pheromone, whereas isolation for several weeks makes them highly sensitive and uniform in response.

Related compounds such as camphor and borneol were inactive, although the propionate ester prepared from borneol was very active. Other plant-derived essential oils were examined for activity and, of these, α- and β-santalol were found to be equivalent to bornyl acetate in activity with *Periplaneta* (Table 1). Although the L and D bornyl acetate standards were of the highest optical purity obtainable it is possible that the slight activity of the L isomer was due to minute contamination with the D isomer. Alternatively, partial racemization may take place during the period of exposure or at the receptor site of the insect.

Table 1. Compounds that Elicit Sexual Display in Isolated Male *Periplaneta americana*

Compound	Active concentration* (mg/cm^2)
L-Bornyl acetate	7.0
D-Bornyl acetate	0.07
α-Santalol	0.07
β-Santalol	0.07
$C_{15}H_{24}$ plant hydrocarbon	0.14

* Threshold concentration of compound on 1 cm^2 of Whatman No.1 filter paper which induces sexual display in at least eight of ten groups of male cockroaches containing ten males per group.

After these studies we examined several flowering plant species for sex pheromone-like activity with *Periplaneta* by briefly soaking various parts of the plants in hexane or methanol and offering the extract on filter paper to the isolated groups of male cockroaches by the usual bioassay. Of one hundred common plants, eighteen were found to produce behaviour characteristic of exposure to the natural sex pheromone (Table 2). The freshly cut stems of several species, notably *Aralia spinosa* L. and several Compositae produced strong responses from the male cockroaches without solvent extraction. The active material seemed to be present mostly in the fruits and in the stems just beneath the outer cuticle, and varied with the season or stage of growth of the plants. In addition to these plants a very active hydrocarbon fraction has been obtained from the fruits and buds of *Liquidambar styraciflua* L. and *Liriodendron tulipifera* L. The pheromonal principle was readily obtained by rinsing the plants (or steeping for a few minutes) in hexane. Column chromatography over Florisil gave a highly active hydrocarbon fraction. Final purification was achieved by column chromatography on silver nitrate coated silica gel. The active hydrocarbon constituent from several of these plants was found to be identical in a comparison by gas–liquid chromatography, infrared spectroscopy, nuclear magnetic resonance and mass

按照博登施泰因所用的方法进行生物测定 [3]。首先用一片沃特曼 1 号滤纸（1 cm²）吸收己烷溶液中的该化合物，然后用镊子将其放入容积为 2 升的育虫瓶中。在进行生物测定前将雄性蜚蠊与雌性蜚蠊隔开至少 4~6 周，雄性蜚蠊对天然性外激素和上述性外激素类似物的敏感性会因此而得以放大。隔离时间不长的雄性蜚蠊对天然性外激素的反应不是很稳定或者十分微弱，除非使用浓度极高的天然性外激素，然而长达数周的隔离则可以使蜚蠊的敏感性和反应均一性大大提高。

相关化合物，比如樟脑和冰片，是无活性的，但是由冰片制备的丙酸酯却具有很高的活性。我们还检测了其他植物精油的活性，结果发现 α- 和 β- 檀香醇对于大蠊的活性与乙酸冰片酯相当（表 1）。尽管 L- 和 D- 乙酸冰片酯标准物的光学纯度已经达到了目前能够达到的最高水平，但 L 异构体中仍存在弱活性，这可能源自微量 D 异构体的污染。也有可能是 L - 乙酸冰片酯在暴露过程中或者在昆虫的受体部位发生了部分外消旋化。

表 1. 能使经过隔离的雄性美洲大蠊产生性兴奋的化合物

化合物	活性浓度 * （mg/cm²）
L- 乙酸冰片酯	7.0
D- 乙酸冰片酯	0.07
α- 檀香醇	0.07
β- 檀香醇	0.07
$C_{15}H_{24}$ 植物烃	0.14

* 每 cm² 沃特曼 1 号滤纸上的该化合物能够诱导共 10 组每组 10 只雄性蜚蠊中至少 8 组产生性兴奋的
   阈值浓度。

在这些研究结束之后，我们又检测了几种开花植物作为大蠊的性外激素类似物的活性，方法是：将植物的不同部分短时间地浸泡在己烷或者甲醇中，然后用滤纸吸取并按照常规的生物测定方法将其作用于几组经过隔离的雄性蜚蠊。在 100 种常见植物中，我们发现有 18 种能使动物表现出类似于接触天然性外激素的行为（表 2）。有几种植物（尤其是多刺楤木和数种菊科植物）新切下来的茎能够在不用溶剂提取的情况下使雄性蜚蠊产生强烈的反应。有活性的成分似乎主要存在于果实和茎中紧挨着表皮的部分，并会随着季节或植物生长阶段的不同而变化。除了这 18 种植物以外，我们还从美国枫香和北美鹅掌楸的果实和芽中提取到一种活性很强的烃类组分。通过用己烷漂洗（或者浸泡数分钟）的方法很容易获得其中的性外激素成分。我们用以硅酸镁为载体的柱层析法分离出了一种活性很强的烃类组分。最后的分离纯化采用的是以硝酸银包覆的硅胶为载体的柱层析法。在比较了气－液色谱、红外光谱、核磁共振谱和质谱的分析结果之后，我们发现从几种植物中分离得到的活性烃类组

spectroscopy. In the mass spectrum, the parent ion gave a molecular weight of 204, consistent with the empirical formula $C_{15}H_{24}$. This assignment was fully supported by the fragmentation pattern. Approximately 0.1 µg of this material was capable of exciting eight out of ten groups of isolated male cockroaches. A study of its structure has been undertaken.

Table 2. Flowering Plants[3] containing Hydrocarbons causing Sex Pheromone-like Behaviour in *Periplaneta americana* Male Cockroaches

Simaroubaceae
Ailanthus altissima (Mill.) Swingle
Araliaceae
Aralia hispida Vent., *nudicaulis* L., *racemosa* L., *spinosa* L.
Labiatae
Perilla frutescens (L.) Britton
Compositae
Achillea millefolium L.
Ambrosia artemisiifolia L., *trifida* L.
Chrysanthemum cinerariaefolium (Trev.) Vis., *leucanthemum* L., *morifolium* (Ramat.), Hemsl.
Erigeron annuus (L.) Pers., *canadensis* L.
Eupatorium hyssopifolium L., *purpureum* L.
Rudbeckia hirta L.
Solidago juncea Ait.

The discovery of a diversity of structures which elicit this characteristic sexual display in *Periplaneta* is very disconcerting in view of the oft reported specificity of sex pheromones. Although a relationship between these plant products and the natural cockroach sex pheromone may eventually be established, we are certain that none are identical with the natural attractant. To investigate this possibility we extracted virgin female midguts as described by Bodenstein[3], obtained a highly active lipid extract. The active principle withstood refluxing in 5% methanolic potassium hydroxide but was destroyed by treatment with 10% methanolic base. Pheromonal activity was destroyed by brief treatment with sodium borohydride in methanol and then quantitatively regenerated by oxidation with chromic acid in acetone. Treatment of the crude extract in hexane solution with a drop of bromine eliminated activity, but debromination with zinc dust in 5% acetic acid in ether restored about one-half the original activity. This brief study leads us to speculate that the natural attractant is an unsaturated ketone with a hindered ester moiety or containing other base labile groups. By trapping the effluent from gas chromatographic columns we have obtained unweighable samples (<50 µg) of the natural pheromone which can be diluted 1 billion times and still elicit the characteristic mating display from male cockroaches. Thus, none of the plant derived pheromonal mimics are as active as the natural pheromone.

We hope that the information derived from structural characterization of the active plant hydrocarbons taken together with the known active compounds such as bornyl acetate and santalol will provide leads in the elucidation of the structure of the natural sex pheromone.

分均属于同一类物质。由质谱分析得出母离子的分子量是 204，这与实验式 $C_{15}H_{24}$ 相吻合。其裂解后的质量分布也完全支持这一分子式。大约 0.1 μg 该物质就能使 10 组经过隔离的雄性蜚蠊中的 8 组产生性兴奋。对其结构的研究已经开始进行。

表 2. 含有能使雄性美洲大蠊产生类似性冲动反应的烃类物质的开花植物 [3]

苦木科
臭椿
五加科
硬毛楤木、裸茎楤木、甘松、多刺楤木
唇形科
紫苏
菊科
千叶蓍
美洲豚草、三裂叶豚草
除虫菊、滨菊、白菊花
一年篷、加拿大飞篷
泽兰、紫苞泽兰
黑心菊
一枝黄花

　　性外激素的特异性常常见诸报道，而现在却发现有好几种结构都能使大蠊产生性兴奋，这使人感到十分尴尬。虽然我们最终也许能在这些植物源物质与蜚蠊天然性外激素之间建立起某种关系，但我们可以肯定，没有一种植物源物质在结构上与天然引诱剂完全相同。为了研究这种可能性，我们按照博登施泰因所述的方法 [3] 分离出了蜚蠊处女虫的中肠，得到了一种活性很高的脂质提取物。这种活性成分在 5% 氢氧化钾甲醇溶液中回流后仍能保持活性，但用 10% 氢氧化钾甲醇溶液处理则会被破坏。用硼氢化钠甲醇溶液短暂处理性外激素可使其失去活性，然后通过铬酸的丙酮溶液将其氧化从而使活性得以定量恢复。在粗提物的己烷溶液中加入一滴溴能使其灭活，但用锌粉在 5% 乙酸的醚溶液中进行脱溴反应即可恢复大约一半的原初活性。我们根据这些简单的研究过程推测，天然引诱剂是带有一个阻碍酯基或者含有其他不稳定碱性基团的不饱和酮。通过收集从气相色谱柱中流出的物质，我们可以得到一些不可称量的天然性外激素样品（<50 μg），它们在被稀释 10 亿倍之后仍能诱导雄性蜚蠊出现特征性的交配表现。因此，任何一种来源于植物的性外激素类似物都不可能具有和天然性外激素同样强的活性。

　　我们希望由这些有活性的植物源烃类物质以及由乙酸冰片酯和檀香醇等已知活性化合物的结构特征得到的信息能够为我们提供一些解释天然性外激素结构的线索。

Although it has been shown that a plant substance is necessary for sex pheromone release in an insect[4], this is the first report of a sex pheromone-like substance taken directly from plants.

We thank Dr. William L. Ackerman, Dr. Theodore R. Dudley, Dr. E. E. Terrell, Dr. Elbert L. Little and Dr. Melvin L. Brown for assistance in the identification of the plant materials. Coniferyl oil distillates were given by Ungerer and Co. and Fritsche Bros. and santalol by Givaudan Inc.

(**232**, 259-261; 1971)

William S. Bowers and William G. Bodenstein: Entomology Research Division, Agricultural Research Service, US Department of Agriculture, Beltsville, Maryland 20705.

References:
1. Bowers, W. S., Fales, H. M., Thompson, M. J., and Uebel, E. C., *Science*, **154**, 1020 (1966).

2. Roth, L. M., and Willis, E. R., *Amer. Midland Naturalist*, **47**, 61 (1952).

3. Bodenstein, W. G., *Ann. Entomol. Soc. Amer.*, **63**, 336 (1970).

4. Riddiford, L. M., *Science*, **158**, 139 (1967).

尽管已经有人报道过昆虫释放性外激素需要一种植物成分[4]，但是本文首次报道了直接从植物中提取的性外激素类似物。

感谢威廉·阿克曼博士、西奥多·达德利博士、特雷尔博士、埃尔伯特·利特尔博士和梅尔文·布朗博士帮助我们鉴别各种植物材料。松柏油馏分由恩格乐公司和弗里切兄弟公司提供；檀香醇由奇华顿公司提供。

（毛晨晖 翻译；沈杰 审稿）

Monosodium Glutamate Induces Convulsive Disorders in Rats

H. N. Bhagavan *et al.*

Editor's Note

Fanning the flames of the debate over whether monosodium glutamate (MSG) causes "Chinese-restaurant syndrome", H. N. Bhagavan and colleagues here report tremors and seizures in rats injected with the food additive. Three years earlier, reports of adverse reactions to Chinese food had been described, with MSG mooted as the culprit. But subsequent research produced conflicting data. In 1995, a report prepared for the US Food and Drug Administration concluded that MSG and related substances are "safe food ingredients for most people when eaten at customary levels," but cautions that some people may be intolerant to large quantities of this flavour enhancer.

THE physiological and pharmacological effects of L-glutamate have received much attention since its implication in the aetiology of the "Chinese restaurant syndrome"[1-3]. Although an excess of L-glutamic acid (GA) as the monosodium salt (MSG) was known to cause retinopathy in experimental animals[4-7], brain lesions have been noticed only recently[8-10]. There seems to be no agreement about its pharmacological and neurophysiological effects in humans[11] and experimental animals[12].

While investigating glucose metabolism[13-15], we used L-glutamate (as MSG) as a gluconeogenic precursor *in vivo* (unpublished), and observed that rats became somnolent after intraperitoneal administration of carrier doses. In a study of the effect of L-glutamate on the *in vivo* incorporation of amino-acids into cerebral proteins (unpublished), several animals experienced severe tonic-clonic convulsions, usually between 30 and 120 min after intraperitoneal injection of a large dose of MSG (2 mmol/100 g body weight). Some convulsions terminated in death. We have now made a detailed study of the incidence of seizures following treatment with MSG. As well as taking an electroencephalogram (EEG) during the convulsions, we studied the influence of pyridoxine on the incidence of these convulsive disorders, for pyridoxine is directly involved in the metabolism of GA and gamma-amino-butyric acid (GABA).

We used weanling Sprague–Dawley male rats maintained on either laboratory chow (Teklad), or pyridoxine-control or deficient diets of the following composition: vitamin-free casein, 22%; sucrose, 69%; corn oil, 4%; salt mixture (Northern Regional Research Laboratories), No. 446, 4%; vitamin-fortification mixture (pyridoxine-free), 1%. This basal diet supplemented with 30 mg of pyridoxine HC1/kg served as the pyridoxine-control diet. Controls weighed 380–550 g (10–20 weeks old) and the deficient animals 80–120 g

谷氨酸一钠诱发大鼠痉挛性障碍

巴加万等

编者按

巴加万及其同事的这篇文章挑起了大家对谷氨酸一钠（MSG）是否会引起"中国餐馆综合征"的争论（译者注：MSG 是味精的主要成分），他们报告称大鼠在被注射食品添加剂后会出现颤抖和痉挛症状。三年前，有人列举了食用中国菜后出现不良反应的诸多报道，指出罪魁祸首是 MSG。但后来的研究得到了相反的结论。1995 年，一份为美国食品和药品监督管理局提供的报告所显示的结论是：MSG 及其相关物质"在食用常规水平时，对绝大多数人来说是安全的食品添加剂"，但也要警惕在大量食用这种调味剂后某些人可能会无法耐受。

由于牵涉到"中国餐馆综合征"的病因 [1-3]，L– 谷氨酸盐的生理和药理作用受到了广泛关注。尽管人们知道过量 L– 谷氨酸（GA）的单钠盐（MSG）会导致实验动物视网膜病变 [4-7]，但其对大脑的损害直到最近才被注意到 [8-10]。看似人们在 MSG 对人类 [11] 以及实验动物 [12] 的药理学和神经生理学作用上还没有达成一致的意见。

在研究糖代谢时 [13-15]，我们使用 L– 谷氨酸盐（和 MSG 一样）作为体内糖异生的前体（尚未发表），结果观察到大鼠在腹腔内注射负荷量 L– 谷氨酸盐之后变得嗜睡。在体内研究 L– 谷氨酸盐对氨基酸合成大脑蛋白质的影响时（尚未发表），数只动物出现了严重的强直阵挛性抽搐，这种症状通常在腹腔内注射大剂量 MSG（2 mmol/100 g 体重）后 30 min ~ 120 min 内发生。一些痉挛最终导致死亡。现在我们已经对注射 MSG 后出现的痉挛进行了详细研究。除了在痉挛过程中采集脑电图之外，我们还研究了维生素 B_6 对这些痉挛性障碍的影响，因为维生素 B_6 直接参与 GA 和 γ– 氨基丁酸（GABA）的代谢。

我们使用刚断乳的 SD 雄性大鼠作为实验动物，给予实验室动物饲料（特克拉德实验室）或维生素 B_6 对照饲料或如下成分的缺陷型饲料：不含维生素的酪蛋白，22%；蔗糖，69%；玉米油，4%；盐混合物（北部地区研究实验室），第 446 号，4%；维生素加强的混合物（不含维生素 B_6），1%。这个基础饲料再加上每 kg 体重 30 mg 的盐酸维生素 B_6 作为维生素 B_6 对照饲料。对照组动物的体重为 380 g

(9–12 weeks old). MSG (2.5 mmol/ml.) was injected intraperitoneally (2.0 mmol/100 g body weight). Pyridoxine HC1 (5.0 mg per 100 g body weight) was administered intraperitoneally to some animals 30 min before MSG treatment. For EEG recording, animals were prepared under pentobarbital and chlorprothixene anaesthesia with chronically implanted stainless steel electrodes and then allowed to recover for 1 week before recordings were taken.

Table 1 summarizes the incidence of the various symptoms observed during 2 h after injection of MSG. Marked somnolence was observed in 99% of the animals within 5–20 min. After this (1 h after injection), 52% of the animals salivated copiously, and 31% then displayed what we have described as spastic tremors, varying in intensity from mild to severe myoclonic jerking sometimes followed by vigorous running about the cage and stereotyped biting. This behaviour occurred significantly more often (χ^2=5.25; d.f.=1; P<0.05) in rats on the pyridoxine-control diet pretreated with pyridoxine than in animals on the same diet pretreated with 0.9% NaCl. Seizures, which occurred 30–120 min after MSG injection, were invariably preceded by spastic tremors, and terminated in death in some cases, although the animals usually recovered within 2–3 min and resumed the spastic tremors until the next seizure. The largest proportion of seizures was observed in the animals fed pyridoxine-control diet and pretreated with pyridoxine; the lowest proportion was found in the pyridoxine-deficient and laboratory chow animals, both pretreated with pyridoxine.

Table 1. Incidence of Somnolence, Hypersalivation, Spastic Tremors, Seizures and Death in MSG*-treated Rats

Diet	Pretreatment	Somnolence		Hypersalivation		Spastic tremors		Seizures		Death†	
		N	%	N	%	N	%	N	%	N	%
Laboratory chow (21)	Pyridoxine HCl‡	20	95	6	29	5	24	1	5	2	10
Laboratory chow (22)	0.9% NaCl	22	100	16	73	7	32	5	23	6	27
Pyridoxine-control (25)	Pyridoxine HCl	25	100	15	60	15	60	7	28	9	36
Pyridoxine-control (25)	0.9% NaCl	25	100	17	68	6	24	5	20	8	32
Pyridoxine-deficient (15)	Pyridoxine HCl	15	100	4	27	2	13	1	7	1	7
Pyridoxine-deficient (11)	0.9% NaCl	11	100	4	36	2	18	1	9	3	27
Total (119)		118	99	62	52	37	31	20	17	29	24

Figures in parentheses indicate the number of animals.
* 2 mmol/100 g body weight, intraperitoneal.
† During 24 h after injection.
‡ 5 mg/100 g body weight.

To ascertain whether the effects of MSG could be attributed to the administration of excess sodium *per se* and/or to the tonicity of the solution injected, two groups (eight and four rats respectively) were injected with either NaCl or sodium DL-lactate (2.5 mmol/ml., 2 mmol/100 g body weight). None of the animals developed any symptoms characteristic of MSG treatment.

Of the eleven MSG-treated animals from which EEG recordings were taken, five displayed tonic-clonic convulsions during the 2 h recording session. The seizures were characterized

～ 550 g（10~20 周龄），缺陷饲料组动物的体重为 80 g～ 120 g（9~12 周龄）。MSG（2.5 mmol/ml）经腹腔注射给予（2.0 mmol/100 g 体重）。盐酸维生素 B_6（5.0 mg/100 g 体重）则在一些动物注射 MSG 前 30 min 经腹腔注射给予。为了记录脑电图，动物在戊巴比妥和氯普噻吨麻醉下长期埋植不锈钢电极，经过一周的恢复后开始记录数据。

表 1 总结了在注射 MSG 之后 2 h 内观察到的各种症状的发生率。在 5 min～ 20 min 内 99% 的动物出现了明显的嗜睡。之后（注射后 1 h），52% 的动物大量地流涎，随后 31% 的动物出现了我们曾描述过的那种痉挛性颤抖，严重程度轻重不一，最严重的出现肌阵挛性抽动，有时随后出现在笼子里狂乱地跑动和刻板地咀嚼。维生素 B_6 对照饲料组用维生素 B_6 预处理的大鼠，表现出的这种行为明显多于相同饲料组用 0.9% NaCl 预处理的大鼠（χ^2=5.25；自由度 =1；P<0.05）。注射 MSG 后 30 min～ 120 min 内出现的痉挛毫无例外都发生在痉挛性颤抖之后，有时以死亡终结，不过动物通常会在 2 min～ 3 min 内恢复并重新进入痉挛性颤抖直至下一次发作。观察到动物痉挛发生比例最高的是维生素 B_6 对照饲料组并用维生素 B_6 预处理的动物；而发生比例最低的则是用维生素 B_6 缺乏饲料和实验室动物饲料喂养的动物，两者都用维生素 B_6 预处理。

表 1. MSG* 处理大鼠的嗜睡、唾液分泌增多、痉挛性颤抖、痉挛和死亡的发生率

饲料	预处理	嗜睡		唾液分泌增多		痉挛性颤抖		痉挛		死亡†	
		N	%	N	%	N	%	N	%	N	%
实验室动物饲料（21）	盐酸维生素 B_6‡	20	95	6	29	5	24	1	5	2	10
实验室动物饲料（22）	0.9% NaCl	22	100	16	73	7	32	5	23	6	27
维生素 B_6 对照饲料（25）	盐酸维生素 B_6	25	100	15	60	15	60	7	28	9	36
维生素 B_6 对照饲料（25）	0.9% NaCl	25	100	17	68	6	24	5	20	8	32
维生素 B_6 缺乏饲料（15）	盐酸维生素 B_6	15	100	4	27	2	13	1	7	1	7
维生素 B_6 缺乏饲料（11）	0.9% NaCl	11	100	4	36	2	18	1	9	3	27
总计（119）		118	99	62	52	37	31	20	17	29	24

圆括号内数字代表实验动物的数量。

* 2 mmol/100 g 体重，腹腔内注射。

† 注射后 24 h 内。

‡ 5 mg/100 g 体重。

为了确定 MSG 的作用是否可以归因于给予过量的钠和 / 或注射液的张力，我们给两组动物（8 只大鼠和 4 只大鼠）分别注射了 NaCl 或者 DL– 乳酸钠（2.5 mmol/ml，2 mmol/100 g 体重）。没有一只动物发生注射 MSG 后出现的症状特征。

MSG 处理的动物中有 11 只动物记录了脑电图，有 5 只动物在 2 h 的记录时间内出现了强直阵挛性抽搐。这种形式的痉挛发作具有高幅尖波的典型特征。

by high amplitude spikes typical of this form of convulsion.

Thus MSG in a dose smaller than that used by Olney[8] in adult mice, and by Adamo and Ratner[12] in infant rats, can induce tonic-clonic seizures in adult rats. Administration of pyridoxine to animals which already had an excess of this vitamin (30 mg/kg diet) significantly increased the occurrence of spastic tremors. It should be noted that we used intra-peritoneal administration rather than the subcutaneous method of the previous authors.

The types of seizure seen in the rat are remarkably similar to those noted by Wiechert et al.[16-18] in dogs and rats after intracisternal injection of L-glutamate (but not other amino-acids), and pyridoxal-5′-phosphate (PLP). Wiechert et al.[16-18] and Elliot and van Gelder[19] have suggested that the balance between GA and GABA but not the absolute amount of GABA per se[20] is a decisive factor in the control of cerebral neuronal activity. Unphysiological shifts in this balance have been implicated in the onset of seizures. Our findings suggest that intraperitoneally administered L-glutamate in the dose used may cross the blood-brain barrier, which would affect the steady state levels of GA and GABA, thus inducing seizures. The effect of pyridoxine, on the other hand, may be a consequence of differential stimulation of the two enzyme systems—GA decarboxylase and GABA aminotransferase—the latter having a higher affinity for PLP[21]. The resulting change in the relative concentrations of GA and GABA may determine the seizure activity. Other possibilities such as a disturbance in the electrolyte balance do exist and a detailed neurochemical study of L-glutamate-induced convulsions is necessary.

We thank George Strutt, Robert Brackbill and John Koogler, jun., for technical assistance. This investigation was supported in part by the National Institute of Neurological Diseases and Stroke and general research support, US Public Health Service.

(**232**, 275-276; 1971)

H. N. Bhagavan and D. B. Coursin: Research Institute, St Joseph Hospital, Lancaster, Pennsylvania 17604.
C. N. Stewart: Department of Psychology, Franklin and Marshall College, Lancaster, Pennsylvania 17604.

Received October 27, 1970; revised January 18, 1971.

References:

1. Schaumburg, H. H., and Byck, R., *New Engl. J. Med.*, **279**, 105 (1968).

2. Ambos, M., Leavitt, N. R., Marmorek, L., and Wolschina, S. B., *New Engl. J. Med.*, **279**, 105 (1968).

3. Schaumburg, H. H., Byck, R., Gerstl, R., and Mashman, J. H., *Science*, **163**, 826 (1969).

4. Lucas, D. R., and Newhouse, J. P., *Amer. Med. Assoc. Arch. Ophthalmol.*, **58**, 193 (1957).

5. Potts, A. M., Modrell, R. W., and Kingsbury, C., *Amer. J. Ophthalmol.*, **50**, 900 (1960).

6. Freedman, J. K., and Potts, A. M., *Invest. Ophthalmol.*, **1**, 118 (1962).

7. Olney, J. W., *J. Neuropathol. Exp. Neurol.*, **28**, 455 (1969).

8. Olney, J. W., *Science*, **164**, 719 (1969).

9. Olney, J. W., and Sharpe, L. G., *Science*, **166**, 386 (1969).

10. Olney, J. W., and Ho, O., *Nature*, **227**, 609 (1970).

这样，MSG 的剂量比奥尔尼 [8] 在成年小鼠中以及阿达莫和拉特纳 [12] 在幼年大鼠中所用的剂量更小就能够导致成年大鼠的强直阵挛性发作。将维生素 B_6 用于已经是维生素 B_6 过量（30 mg/kg 饲料）的动物，能显著增加痉挛性颤抖的发生率。应当注意，我们使用的是腹腔内注射的方式而不是上述文献作者所用的皮下注射方式。

在大鼠中看到的发作类型与维歇特等人 [16-18] 在狗和大鼠脑池内注射 L– 谷氨酸盐（而不是其他氨基酸）和 5′– 磷酸吡哆醛（PLP）后发现的发作类型非常相似。维歇特等人 [16-18] 以及埃利奥特和范格尔德 [19] 曾提示，控制大脑神经元活性的决定性因素是 GA 和 GABA 之间的平衡而非 GABA 本身的绝对含量 [20]。这种平衡的非生理性偏移被认为与痉挛发作有关。我们的研究结果提示：腹腔内注射的所使用剂量的 L– 谷氨酸盐有可能穿过了血脑屏障，这会影响到 GA 和 GABA 水平的稳定状态进而诱发痉挛。另一方面，维生素 B_6 的作用可能源自于其对两个酶系统（GA 脱羧酶和 GABA 氨基转移酶）的不同刺激所导致的结果，后者对 PLP 有更高的亲和力 [21]。GA 和 GABA 相对浓度的变化可能决定了痉挛发作。其他可能性（如电解质平衡的紊乱）确实存在，因此有必要对 L– 谷氨酸盐诱发的抽搐进行细致的神经化学研究。

感谢乔治·斯特拉特、罗伯特·布拉克比尔和小约翰·库格勒为我们提供了技术支持。本研究的部分经费来自于美国国立神经疾病与中风研究所，此外美国公共卫生署还为本项目提供了一般性研究支持。

（毛晨晖 翻译；李素霞 审稿）

11. Morselli, P. L., and Garattini, S., *Nature*, **227**, 611 (1970).

12. Adamo, N. J., and Ratner, A., *Science*, **169**, 673 (1970).

13. Bhagavan, H. N., Coursin, D. B., and Dakshinamurti, K., *Arch. Biochem. Biophys.*, **110**, 422 (1965).

14. Bhagavan, H. N., Maruyama, H., and Coursin, D. B., *Abstr. Seventh Intern. Cong. Biochem., Tokyo*, 802 (1967).

15. Bhagavan, H. N., Coursin, D. B., and Stewart, C. N., *Life Sci.*, **8**, 299 (1969).

16. Wiechert, P., and Herbst, A., *J. Neurochem.*, **13**, 59 (1966).

17. Wiechert, P., and Göllnitz, G., *J. Neurochem.*, **15**, 1265 (1968).

18. Wiechert, P., and Göllnitz, G., *J. Neurochem.*, **17**, 137 (1970).

19. Elliot, K. A. C., and van Gelder, N. M., *J. Neurochem.*, **3**, 28 (1958).

20. Kamrin, R. P., and Kamrin, A. A., *J. Neurochem.*, **6**, 219 (1961).

21. Roberts, E., Rothstein, M., and Baxter, C. F., *Proc. Soc. Exp. Biol. Med.*, **97**, 796 (1958).

New Hominid Skull from Bed I, Olduvai Gorge, Tanzania

M. D. Leakey *et al.*

Editor's Note

The problems of Louis Leakey's perhaps over-bold definition of the genus *Homo*, consequent on the description of *Homo habilis* in 1964, came back to haunt him. This paper is a description of a crushed skull from the lower levels at Olduvai that resembled *Homo* from the more recent Bed II — but which differed in various ways. Leakey saw no reason to modify his bold claims in his 1964 paper, but neither that it was necessary to suppose that the new skull represented a female *Homo habilis*. The first author of this paper is Louis' archaeologist wife Mary, who continued to live and work at Olduvai until her death in 1996.

THE cranium described by L. S. B. L. later in this article (Olduvai Hominid 24) was found by P. Nzube in October 1968 (ref. 1) at a site in Olduvai Gorge that lies in the eastern part of the gullies known as DK, approximately 300 m east of the living site in lower Bed I that was excavated during 1962 and 1963.

The Site

The cranium was embedded in a mass of calcareous matrix measuring approximately 20×12×8 cm. All the bones were covered by matrix with the exception of a small portion of the right supra-orbital region and the posterior part of the palate. Indeed, so few identifiable parts were visible that it is remarkable it was recognized as hominid. The deposit on which it was found consists of a tuffaceous clay that can be traced over a wide area in Bed I, extending from the eastern part of the Gorge as far west as the FLK sites. This horizon overlies the basalt and is in turn overlain by the marker tuff IB for which an apparently reliable average date of 1.8 m.y. has been obtained by K/Ar dating[2]. At the hominid site (DK East), the tuffaceous clay is 3 m thick but the thickness varies considerably at different localities, depending on the surface configuration of the underlying lava. The clay at several other sites has yielded artefacts and fossil bones, including the molar tooth of Olduvai H. 4, found at MK during 1959, that has been attributed to *Homo habilis*[3] as well as the only remains of a chalicothere known from Olduvai.

After the discovery of the cranium the surface deposit was sieved extensively and an area of approximately 400 m[2] was eventually worked over. Three complete and some broken teeth were recovered as well as substantial portions of the maxillae, part of the occipital,

在坦桑尼亚奥杜威峡谷第I层中新发现的原始人类头骨

利基等

编者按

路易斯·利基的麻烦可能在于对人属的定义过于大胆，人属的定义来自于他在1964年对能人的描述，这个定义后来又反过来困扰着他。这篇论文描述了一件在奥杜威遗址靠下层位发现的已被压碎的头骨，它类似于在更晚的第II层中发现的人属头骨，但又在很多方面有所不同。利基认为没有必要修正他在1964年的论文中所作的大胆定义，但又不能完全肯定新发现的头骨代表的是女性能人。这篇文章的第一作者是利基的太太考古学家玛丽，她一直在奥杜威峡谷生活和工作，直到1996年去世。

路易斯·利基在下文中所描述的头骨（第24号奥杜威原始人类）是由尼祖毕于1968年10月（参考文献1）在奥杜威峡谷的一处遗址发现的，该遗址坐落于通常所说的DK冲沟的东部，位于第I层下部的生活遗址以东约300 m处，这个生活遗址是在1962年至1963年间被发掘出来的。

关于该遗址

该头骨被包裹在大块的石灰质围岩中，经测量该石灰质围岩的大小约为20 cm×12 cm×8 cm。除小部分右眶上区和上腭后部外，其余所有骨头都被围岩所覆盖。的确，可鉴别的部分实在太少，以至于人们对能将它判定为原始人类的头骨而感到惊诧。我们发现该头骨之下的沉积物是由凝灰质黏土组成的，这种黏土分布在第I层中从峡谷的东部向西一直延伸到FLK遗址的广大区域中。该层位覆盖在玄武岩之上，其自身又被标志层凝灰岩IB所覆盖，由K/Ar年代测定法[2]得到这种标志层凝灰岩的平均年代为180万年，这个数据看来还是比较可靠的。在该原始人类遗址处（DK东部），凝灰质黏土有3 m厚，但在不同地点，凝灰质黏土的厚度差别很大，这取决于地下熔岩的地表形态。在其他几处遗址的黏土中发现了人工制品和骨头化石，包括第4号奥杜威原始人类的臼齿，这是1959年间在MK发现的，该臼齿被归入能人[3]名下，还有从奥杜威发掘出来的唯一一个爪兽类动物的遗骸。

在该头骨被发现之后，通过对地表堆积物的广泛筛查，最终确定了约400 m²的搜索区域。从中又找到了三枚完整的牙齿以及一些破碎的牙齿，还发现了绝大部分上颌骨、部分枕骨、几块顶骨破片和额骨的左眶上区。有些破片是在侵蚀斜坡下

several fragments of the parietals and the left supra-orbital region of the frontal bone. Some fragments were found low down the erosion slope and at a depth of just under 1 m from the present ground level: others lay on the surface, close to the block of matrix containing the cranium. It is evident that the specimen had been exposed for many years and that, as fragments broke off, some rolled down the slope and were buried under hill wash, while others became detached more recently and remained on the surface near the parent block. No trace of the canine and incisor teeth was found and it is likely that they broke off first and were transported downhill by erosion, possibly as far as the present river course.

The matrix in which the cranium was embedded is indistinguishable from the limestone concretions that frequently occur within the tuffaceous clay that overlies the basalt at DK and elsewhere (the mandibular fragment containing the molar of Olduvai H. 4 was similarly embedded). These concretions often form round fossil bones that can be seen as central cores when the blocks are broken open.

Crocodile remains predominate among the faunal material from this site and more than 2,000 teeth were found. Tortoise plates, shells of Urocyclid slugs, fish vertebrae and scales, bird bones and pieces of ostrich eggshell were also relatively common. Mammalian bones and teeth included those of primates, rodents, carnivores, equids, suids, giraffids and bovids. There were also more that 37,000 unidentifiable bone fragments. The state of preservation of these remains is very similar to that of the cranium and many were also found embedded in limestone concretions.

Associated Stone Industry

Apart from a few quartzite flakes and chips, no artefacts were found, but the living floor previously excavated at DK—which included the circle of lava blocks considered to represent an artificial structure—has yielded a large series of artefacts that represent the contemporary stone industry[4]. This site consists of a living floor within the same tuffaceous clay that occurs at DK East and is similarly overlain by Tuff IB. In some places the accumulation of occupation debris rests on the surface of the lava, so that the living floor is at a slightly lower level than the layer of limestone concretions from which the cranium is believed to have eroded. Artefacts recovered from the living floor and from the clay above amount to 1,198 specimens, consisting of 154 tools, 187 utilized pieces and 857 debitage. The industry is typical of the Oldowan as it occurs throughout Bed I. It includes choppers of various forms, generally made on water-worn lava cobbles, polyhedrons, discoids, sub-spheroids, heavy and light duty scrapers and burins. Although the tools are of the usual Oldowan types, a proportion of the choppers, polyhedrons and discoids are smaller than those from higher levels of Bed I.

The associated faunal material includes all the species noted at DK East with the addition of *Elephas* and *Deinotherium*. Crocodile remains are similarly the most numerous.

的低处找到的，深度仅为现在的地面水平以下 1 m：其余样本位于地表，就在包含头骨的围岩块附近。很明显，该标本已暴露多年，并且因为骨头破片都折断了，有些破片就沿着斜坡滚下而被埋在了坡滑之下，另外一些破片则是后来分解开的，因而仍留在离母体块很近的地表上。没有发现犬齿和门齿的半点痕迹，很可能它们是最先发生断裂的，然后由于侵蚀作用沿着坡向下滑，可能一直滑进了目前的河道中。

很难将包裹该头骨的围岩与石灰岩结核体区分开来，后者通常存在于覆盖在 DK 和其他地方的玄武岩之上的凝灰质黏土之内（包含第 4 号奥杜威原始人类的臼齿的下颌骨断片也被相似的围岩包裹）。这些结核体常常会在骨头化石周围形成，当块状物被打开时，就可以看到中心的核是骨头化石。

在该遗址发现的动物群材料中，鳄鱼的遗骸占主导地位，有 2,000 多枚鳄鱼牙齿被发现。龟甲、蛄蝓壳、鱼脊椎和鱼鳞、鸟骨和鸵鸟蛋壳碎片也是相对常见的遗骸。找到的哺乳动物骨骼和牙齿包括灵长类的、啮齿类的、食肉类的、马科的、猪科的、长颈鹿科的和牛科的。还有 37,000 多块无法鉴定的骨骼碎片。这些遗骸的保存状况与头骨的保存状况很相似，其中有很多碎片也被发现包裹于石灰岩结核体中。

共生的石器业

除了一些石英岩片和碎屑之外，没有发现任何人工制品，但早先在 DK 挖掘出的居住地面——所包含的熔岩块围成的圈被认为是一种人造结构——曾出土过一系列代表当时石器工业的人工制品 [4]。该遗址由一个居住地面构成，和 DK 东部的遗址一样都处于同样的凝灰质黏土中，而且也同样被凝灰岩 IB 所覆盖。在有些地方，人类活动留下的生活垃圾积聚在熔岩的表面，所以居住地面所在的层位略微低于人们认为头骨曾在此被侵蚀出来的石灰岩结核层。从居住地面以及覆盖于其上的黏土中发现的人工制品总计达到了 1,198 件，包括 154 件工具、187 件使用器具和 857 件废片。这种工业是奥杜威文化的典型特征，它广泛分布于第 I 层之中。包括通常由用水磨蚀的熔岩卵石制造而成的各式砍砸器、多面体、盘状器、亚球状器、重型和轻型刮削器以及雕刻器等。尽管这些工具都属于奥杜威文化常见的类型，但一部分砍砸器、多面体和盘状器要比从第 I 层较高层位出土的同类物体小。

共生的动物群材料包括了在 DK 东部发现的所有物种，此外还有亚洲象属和恐象属。鳄鱼遗骸在这两处都是数量最多的。

Restoration of Olduvai H. 24

The tools used by R. J. C. in the removal of matrix from Olduvai H. 24 were a chisel-ended dental pick and a small hammer, a diamond drill and an S. S. White Industrial Air-Abrasive machine. Acetic acid could not be used because although the exposed pieces of bone had become hardened by weathering, those not exposed were softer than the matrix.

Parts of the matrix contained impressions of bone fragments that had fallen out during weathering. Some of these were found during excavation and it was possible to fit them back into position and thus build up the cranium into the form it had been before they became detached. It was apparent that the specimen was reasonably complete but had been badly crushed and distorted, the chief pressure having been downward and backward from the brow region, with the result that the nasal bones, although complete and perfectly preserved, were lodged down behind the infra-orbital region. The glabella, still attached to the nasals, was crushed, and the brow ridges were squeezed close together on top of the glabella.

Fig. 1. Cast of Olduvai H. 24 after partial cleaning and before reconstruction.

The vault fragments were first separated and then completely cleaned of matrix under a binocular microscope. The facial fragments were more difficult to separate because they were interlocked and rammed against each other, but once they were free of matrix there were perfect joins between the nasals and the rest of the face and between the right brow ridge and the right orbital margin, just above the fronto-zygomatic suture.

The base of the cranium had been depressed into the brain cavity and was rammed against the right petrous, and the basi-occipital had been pushed under the vomer.

After thorough cleaning, consideration of sutures, bone thickness and curvature it was found that all the vault fragments but one joined together and that there was contact from the foramen magnum almost to the glabella. The sides of the vault, however, were not

660

第 24 号奥杜威原始人类的复原

克拉克用来剔除第 24 号奥杜威原始人类上的围岩的工具包括：一件牙科医生用的末端类似凿子的工具、一把小榔头、一个金刚石钻头和一台怀特工业公司生产的气压喷砂磨光器。不能使用醋酸的原因是：尽管被暴露的骨头破片已经由于风化作用而变硬，但是未暴露的那些部位要比围岩软。

部分围岩中含有风化期间脱落的骨头断片的印痕。只要在挖掘时找到一部分骨头断片，就有可能把它们拼接到原来的位置，由此将头骨复原成断片分离之前的样子。显而易见的是：这个标本相当完整，只是在严重的挤压下发生了变形，主要压力来自于眉区的下面和后面，这使得虽然得以完整保存下来的鼻骨被卡到了眶下区之后。眉间区仍与鼻部相连，但已被压碎，眉脊在眉间区顶部被挤压在了一起。

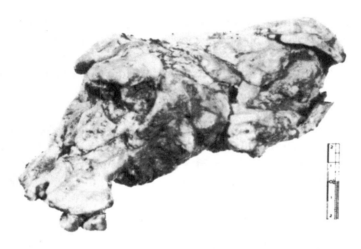

图 1. 部分清理后、进行复原前的第 24 号奥杜威原始人类的模型。

先分离出颅顶破片，然后在双目显微镜下将围岩完全去除。由于面部破片相互纠结、彼此挤压，因而比较难于分离，但是一旦将它们与围岩分离开来，就会看到鼻部与面部其他部分之间以及右眉脊和额颧缝之上的右眶缘之间的完美连接。

头骨底部被压进脑腔，与右侧颞骨岩部挤在一起，而枕骨底部被推至犁骨之下。

彻底进行清洗之后，从骨缝、骨骼厚度和曲率的情况来看，除一块骨头之外，其余所有颅顶破片都被挤压在了一起，并且从枕骨大孔差不多到靠近眉间处。然而，并没有发现颅顶的侧面。后部已经严重变形，为了将该区域正确地连接到一起，有

present. The posterior part was considerably crushed and in order for the joins in this region to lock properly it was necessary to straighten out the buckled lambdoid region by breaking through the bone along one crushed bend and by partially cutting and breaking the bone just above the suture.

The crowns of the left P^4, M^1 and right M^1 that were found during sieving fitted back directly on to the palate, but the left P^3 and the fragment of right M^2 had to be placed in position with plaster supports. A small but perfect contact between the mesiolingual fragment of the right M^3 and the major portion of this tooth could be seen under the microscope. The two pieces were fitted together and were placed in position on the palate by means of an impression that had been left in the matrix.

The cranium is still warped slightly and it is doubtful whether it can be completely straightened out, particularly as the sides of the vault are missing. The right petrous and tympanic plate are still in their crushed position and it would be a major operation to attempt to restore these bones to their proper relationship. The base of the cranium is also still depressed into the brain cavity and its thinness in places and the fact that it is covered with a network of fine cracks inhibit the possibility of restoration. The crushing of the whole cranium has also to be taken into account when considering the cranial capacity, which must inevitably have been greater than the absolute capacity as measured now.

Description of Olduvai H. 24

This specimen now consists of the following parts: almost the entire supra-orbital region of the frontal, the greater part of the vault, a considerable part of the occipital bone, nearly all the sphenoid, nearly all the right temporal bone and a considerable part of the face and palate, including the nasal bones. (Measurements are given in Tables 1 and 2.)

Table 1. Measurements of Olduvai H. 24 Cranium (in mm)

Glabella to inion cord	147.0
Glabella to bregma cord	88.5
Bregma to inion cord	78.5
Bimastoid crest breadth	122.0
External orbital angle width	107.0
Minimum frontal width	75.0
Foramen magnum length	28.5
Foramen magnum width	25.0
Length nasal bones	19.5
Nasion to prosthion	60.0
Nasion to orale	61.0
Nasion to left side of pyriform aperture	38.5
Nasion to naso-spinale	36.0
Naso-spinale to prosthion	25.0
Maximum breadth of pyriform aperture	25.0
Palatal width at alveolae of M^1	37.0

必要沿着一个破碎的弯曲部分将骨头拆开并局部切割和打断位于骨缝正上方的骨头来弄直已变形的人字形区域。

筛查时发现：左 P^4、M^1 和右 M^1 的齿冠可以直接安回到上腭上去，但左 P^3 和右 M^2 的破片就只能借助石膏来回复原位了。在显微镜下可以看到：右 M^3 近中舌侧的破片与这颗牙齿的主体部分之间存在着一个虽小但很完美的衔接。将这两部分拼在一起，并参照留在围岩上的印痕把它们安装到上腭上的适当位置处。

这件头骨还是稍微有点弯曲，尚不确定是否可以将其完全弄直，特别是在颅顶侧面缺失的情况下。右侧颞骨岩部和鼓板仍然处于它们被压碎时的位置，尝试将这些骨头按原有的关系复位将是一项很重要的工作。头骨基底部仍处于被挤压进脑腔的位置，它在某些地方厚度很薄以及被细裂纹的网络所覆盖的现状使复原工作难以完成。当衡量颅容量时，也应该把整个头骨的破碎程度纳入考虑当中，实际容量必定大于现在测量出来的绝对容量。

对第 24 号奥杜威原始人类的描述

当前，该标本由以下几部分组成：额部的几乎整个眶上区、绝大部分颅顶、大部分枕骨、几乎整个蝶骨、几乎全部右颞骨以及大部分面部和上腭，包括鼻骨。（具体测量结果见表 1 和表 2。）

表 1. 对第 24 号奥杜威原始人类头骨的测量结果（单位：mm）

眉间 – 枕骨隆突索	147.0
眉间 – 前囟索	88.5
前囟 – 枕骨隆突索	78.5
两乳突脊间的宽度	122.0
眶外角宽度	107.0
前额最小宽度	75.0
枕骨大孔长度	28.5
枕骨大孔宽度	25.0
鼻骨长度	19.5
鼻根到齿槽中点	60.0
鼻根到切牙颌内缝终点	61.0
鼻根到梨状孔左侧	38.5
鼻根到鼻棘点	36.0
鼻棘点到牙槽中点	25.0
梨状孔的最大宽度	25.0
M^1 齿槽处的上腭宽度	37.0

Table 2. Measurements of Teeth of Olduvai H. 24 (in mm)

Left side	Bucco-lingual breadth	Mesio-distal length
P³	(12.0)	9.0
P⁴	(12.5)	9.1
M¹	(13.0)	12.6
M³	(14.5)	12.0

(1) The frontal bone. The supra-orbital region on the right side is almost intact as well as most of the glabella region. A large part of the left supra-orbital region is also preserved but it does not extend quite as far as the external orbital angle. There is also a small piece missing between the left supra-orbital fragment and the glabella region. On the right side the external orbital angle is intact and in normal articulation with the orbital process of the zygomatic. The supra-orbital region as a whole, while forward projecting, is not very massive. The glabella contact with the nasal bones at nasion is preserved and nasion lies well behind the overhanging glabella. Behind the supra-orbital region there is a depressed valley that is more pronounced above the glabella than on either side. In such parts as are preserved the frontal bone rises from this valley in a low curve towards bregma. There is sufficient of the frontal bone to be reasonably certain of the glabella–bregma length, which is approximately 90 mm.

On the right side of the cranium the region immediately behind the external orbital angle and the supra-orbital torus is well preserved. Part of this area is also present on the left side so that the minimum frontal width can be closely estimated. The figure is 75 mm.

(2) The parietals. Although neither of the two parietal bones is intact, the whole of the sagittal suture is preserved so that the bregma–lambda cord and arc can be measured with reasonable accuracy: these are 76.5 mm and 81.0 mm respectively. On either side of the sagittal suture the parietal bones extend laterally with only a slight downward curve for about 50 mm. Although the lateral parts of both parietals are missing, these bones must then have turned abruptly downwards if they were to meet the squamous parts of the temporal bones. This can clearly be seen on the more complete right side of the cranium. The sagittal suture is very largely fused but can still be traced. This condition is somewhat surprising in an individual whose third molars were barely erupted and not yet in occlusion. It suggests that the eruption of the third molars in early hominids based on analogy with modern man may not be a reliable indication of age.

(3) The occipital bone. A large part of this bone is well preserved, especially on the right side. There is enough of the nuchal area intact as well as continuous contact from lambda to opisthion to make a reasonable reconstruction of the upper half of the occipital and it is possible to estimate, with a fair degree of accuracy, the lambda–opisthion arc and cord: these measure 87.5 mm and 71.0 mm respectively. The arc/cord index (Martin's index 125)[5] is 81.14. By doubling the measurement from the right asterion to the midline of the occipital it is also possible to estimate the bi-asterionic width, which is approximately 99 mm. The occipital index (Martin's index 129) is approximately 72.0.

664

表 2. 对第 24 号奥杜威原始人类牙齿的测量结果（单位：mm）

左侧	颊–舌宽	近中–远中长
P³	(12.0)	9.0
P⁴	(12.5)	9.1
M¹	(13.0)	12.6
M³	(14.5)	12.0

（1）额骨。右侧的眶上区和大部分眉间区都几乎完好无损。左眶上区的大部分也被保存了下来，但并未一直延伸到眶外角那么远。在左眶上区破片和眉间区之间还有一小块缺失的部分。右侧眶外角是完整无缺的，并且与颧骨眶突的连接也是正常的。作为一个整体，眶上区虽然向前突出，但并不算很粗大。眉间与鼻骨在鼻根处的衔接部位被保存了下来，鼻根恰好位于突出的眉间之后。在眶上区后面有一个凹陷处，该处在眉间之上比在两侧更明显。在被保存下来的这些部分中，额骨以一条低曲线从上述的凹陷处升向前囟。由现有的额骨足以合理地确定出眉间 – 前囟的长度，大约为 90 mm。

头骨右侧紧挨着眶外角和眶上圆枕后面的区域保存状况很好。这一区域的左侧也被保存了下来，因而可以比较准确地估计出最小前额宽度。该数值为 75 mm。

（2）顶骨。尽管两块顶骨都不完整，但是整条矢状缝被保存了下来，因此可以相当准确地测量出前后囟索和前后囟弓来：它们分别是 76.5 mm 和 81.0 mm。在矢状缝的两侧，顶骨以一条稍微有一点向下弯曲的曲线向侧面横向延伸了约 50 mm。尽管两块顶骨的侧面部分都丢失了，但是如果这些骨头与颞骨的鳞状部分会合的话，那么它们的走向肯定是突然向下的。从该头骨保存得比较完整的右侧部位可以清楚地看到这一点。大部分矢状缝融合在了一起，但仍然可以看到它的痕迹。在第三臼齿几乎没有萌出且尚不能咬合的个体中出现这种情况的确有点令人吃惊。这说明按照与现代人相似的方法用第三臼齿的萌出来推断早期原始人类的年龄可能是不太可靠的。

（3）枕骨。大部分枕骨保存完好，尤其是右侧部分。完整的项区以及从后囟点到枕后点间的连续衔接部位的长度已经足够，由此可以正确地复原枕骨的上半部分，而且可以相当精确地估计出后囟 – 枕后弓和后囟 – 后索的长度：测量结果分别是 87.5 mm 和 71.0 mm。弓 / 索指数（马丁指数 125）[5] 为 81.14。采用将从枕骨右星点到中线的测量尺寸加倍的方法还有可能估计出两侧星点间的宽度，所得结果约为 99 mm。枕骨指数（马丁指数 129）约为 72.0。

Viewed in profile, when the skull is orientated in the Frankfurt plane, the occipital region is seen to project far beyond a vertical line through the external auditory meatus, a feature seen in *Homo* but not in *Australopithecus*. The occipital condyles lie between the external auditory meati and the foramen magnum is elongate. The basi-occipital projection is short.

(4) The sphenoid bone. Nearly all the sphenoid is preserved including the pterygoid plates but not the pterygoid hamuli. In general appearance this bone is very similar to that seen in *Homo*, but this area requires detailed study in order to elucidate its significance taxonomically.

(5) The temporal bones. In the right temporal only the superior portion of the squamosal and part of the zygomatic process are missing. The mandibular fossa is perfectly preserved and is deep and narrow. The external auditory meatus is large and rather parallel-sided. The posterior part of the tympanic plate rises steeply to separate the meatus from the mastoid region. The tip of the mastoid process is broken off and the original size can only be estimated approximately from the preserved part. The zygomatic process is slenderly built and lacks the wide lateral shelf and outward flaring generally seen in *Australopithecus*.

The greater part of the left temporal bone is missing except for a small fragment in the medial region of the mandibular fossa.

(6) The face and palate. (*a*) The nasal bones. Both nasal bones are preserved with only the tips of the lateral processes on either side slightly damaged. The contact of the two bones in the midline is marked by a distinct keel which continues almost to the end of the nasal area. The margins of the pyriform aperture are not quite intact, but at its widest point it measures approximately 25 mm. The nasal length from nasion to the left lateral lip of the nasal aperture is 42.5 mm and nasion to nasospinale 36.0 mm. The nasal index (Martin's index 148) is 69.4, that is hyperchamaerrhine. There is a well developed anterior nasal spine at the center of the pyriform aperture and from this point a very distinct keel runs downwards in the mid-line on the naso-alveolar clivus. (*b*) The zygomatic bones. The right zygomatic bone is reasonably well preserved; only the zygomatic process and a chip from the frontal process are missing. The root of the zygomatic arch lies approximately above a point between the first and second molars. The left zygomatic bone is missing. (*c*) The maxillae. The right maxilla is almost complete; parts of the alveolar process are missing, particularly in the region of M^2, and at the canine jugum the bone is also missing. The left maxillary bone is less complete, the zygomatic process, part of the nasal surface, and much of the posterior part of the alveolar process are missing. At the incisor sockets the alveolar margin seems to be preserved lingually but is broken labially. At present the margin runs straight across between the two canine alveoli and is not curved; but it is difficult to assess the original form on account of the damage. The whole of the median palatal suture is preserved. The right side of the bony palate has been displaced posteriorly by approximately 2 mm. The palate is seen to be reasonably deep (depth of alveolar processes at the first molars is approximately 15.0 mm). (*d*) The palatine bones.

从侧面看来，当头骨被定位在法兰克福平面上时，就可以看到枕骨区明显突出于穿过外耳道的垂直线之外，这是一个存在于人属中的特征，南方古猿并不具备。枕髁位于外耳道之间，枕骨大孔呈细长形状。枕骨底部的突出很短。

（4）蝶骨。除翼钩外，包括翼板在内的绝大部分蝶骨被保存了下来。从整体外观来看，这个蝶骨与在人属中见到的很相似，但是要想阐明它在分类学上的意义，尚需要详细的研究。

（5）颞骨。在右侧颞骨中，只缺少鳞部的上部和颧突的一部分。深且窄的下颌窝部分保存完好。外耳道很大，并且侧边几乎是平行的。鼓板后部急剧上升将耳道与乳突区分开。乳突顶端断裂，只能根据保存下来的部分对其原来的尺寸进行粗略的估计。颧突细长而缺少宽阔的侧面支架和外部扩口，这种特征通常是南方古猿所具有的。

左侧颞骨的绝大部分丢失，仅剩下下颌窝中间区的一小块破片。

（6）面部和上腭。（a）鼻骨。两块鼻骨都保存了下来，只是每一侧外侧突起的尖端稍微有点损伤。中线上两块骨头衔接处以一条明显的龙骨状突起为标志，龙骨状突起几乎延伸到接近于鼻区的末端。梨状孔的边缘并不十分完整，但是在最宽处测量得到的值大约为 25 mm。鼻部从鼻根到鼻孔的左外侧唇的长度为 42.5 mm，从鼻根到鼻棘点的长度为 36.0 mm。鼻指数（马丁指数 148）是 69.4，属于超阔鼻型。在梨状孔中部有一个很发达的鼻前棘，另一个非常明显的龙骨状突起从此处开始沿处于中线的鼻齿槽斜坡向下延伸。（b）颧骨。右颧骨保存得相当好；只缺少颧突和额突上的一个薄片。颧弓根部大致位于第一和第二臼齿间的某点之上。左侧颧骨缺失。（c）上颌骨。右上颌骨基本上是完整的；齿槽突有部分丢失，尤其是 M^2 区，犬齿隆突处的骨头也找不到了。左上颌骨不太完整，缺少颧突、部分鼻表面以及齿槽突后部的很大一部分。门齿槽上的近舌侧齿槽边缘看似被保存了下来，但是近唇侧部分断掉了。目前齿槽边缘笔直地从两颗犬齿的齿槽之间穿过，毫不弯曲；但是由于发生了损坏，因而很难估计出其原来的形式。整个腭中缝都保存了下来。硬腭右侧向后错位了约 2 mm。上腭看起来非常深（第一臼齿处的齿槽突深度约为 15.0 mm）。（d）腭骨。腭骨是完整的，它们与上颌粗隆间以及与蝶骨间的衔接部位都完好地保存了下来。

The palatine bones are intact and the areas of their contact with the maxillary tuberosities and with the sphenoid are well preserved.

(7) The teeth (see Table 2) present in the cranium as now reconstructed are as follows; (*a*) The crown of the left M³. This is slightly broken on the distal aspect. The occlusal surface is undamaged and is very wrinkled with no sign of wear. (*b*) The left M¹ is intact and is firmly rooted in the maxilla. The enamel of the crown shows a degree of flat wear and the dentine is only exposed in a very small area on the protocone. (*c*) The left P⁴ is complete. Its bucco-lingual width is less than that of M¹ and it is rather rectangular in form. (*d*) The left P³ is partially preserved, the mesio-lingual area is broken away. (*e*) the right M³ is partially preserved, the paracone and part of the protocone are broken away. The tooth compares closely with the intact left M³. (*f*) The right M² is incomplete; it is broken

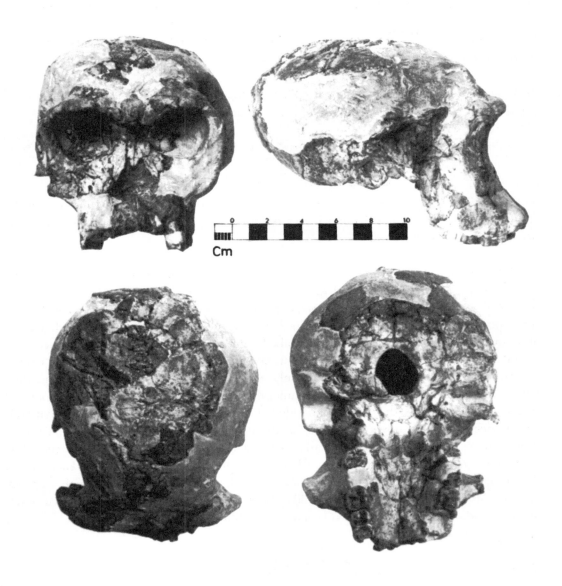

（7）现存于复原头骨上的牙齿（见表 2）情况如下：(a) 左 M³ 的齿冠。其远端面有轻微的破裂。咬合面没有破损，因为没有磨损，所以齿冠面上褶皱得很厉害。(b) 左 M¹ 完整，牢固地植根于上颌骨中。齿冠的珐琅质出现了某种程度的磨平，齿质仅仅暴露于上原尖上的一个很小的区域内。(c) 左 P⁴ 完整。其颊舌宽度比 M¹ 的要小，且外形非常接近于矩形。(d) 左 P³ 仅有部分被保存了下来，近中舌侧区断掉了。(e) 右 M³ 仅有部分被保存了下来，上前尖和部分上原尖已经断掉。该牙与保存完整的左 M³ 非常相像。(f) 右 M² 不完整；它在沿对角线方向发生了断裂，所以近舌侧

diagonally so that the lingual and distal area is missing. (*g*) The right M¹ is nearly complete, only the protocone is missing. Its wear and structure are like those of the left first molar.

In addition to these teeth several fragments of molars and premolars were also recovered during sieving. It has not yet been possible to fit these fragments on to the cranium.

(8) *Cranial capacity.* It is not possible at this stage to give a close estimate of cranial capacity but preliminary determinations give a figure in the order of 560 cm³.

(9) *Endocranial region.* Considerable parts of the endocranial morphology are preserved.

Comparisons with Other Hominids

There is still some evidence of distortion in the reconstruction. This has resulted in the vault of the skull being lower than it was originally and the backward projection of the occipital is now exaggerated.

The frontal bone does not exhibit the marked post-orbital constriction that is seen in the australopithecines from South and East Africa, nor does the supra-orbital element of the frontal bone curve backwards to the same extent. Seen in both lateral and vertical views the supra-orbital torus and glabellar region form a more or less straight line whereas in all known species of *Australopithecus* the glabella tends to project further forward with the lateral edges of the supra-orbital torus swinging backward. The parietal bones extend outwards from the sagittal suture with only a slight downward curve at first, and then bend steeply downwards to meet the squamosal parts of the temporal bones. The parietal region of the brain is thus more expanded than in *Australopithecus*, where the parietals usually begin to curve downwards close to the mid-line. Even allowing for the backward distortion of the occipital region this area of the skull extends further behind a vertical line through the external auditory meatus, when the cranium is in the Frankfurt plane, than in the australopithecines. The mandibular fossae are deep and very similar morphologically to those of *Homo sapiens* and wholly unlike those seen in *Australopithecus*. The nasal bones are long and slender with a marked keel in the mid-line.

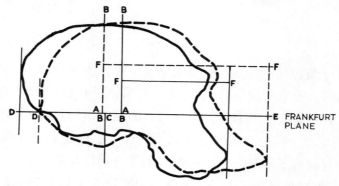

Fig. 3. Profile of Olduvai Hominid 24 (solid line) superimposed on that of *Australopithecus africanus* ST. 5 (broken line).

和远端区域都不见了。（*g*）右 M¹ 基本上是完整的，只有上原尖缺失。其磨损程度和结构都与左侧的第一臼齿类似。

除这些牙齿外，在筛查过程中还发现了一些臼齿和前臼齿的破片。现在想把这些破片复原到头骨上还不太可能。

（8）颅容量。现阶段还不可能准确地估计出颅容量的大小，不过，初步确定的结果给出的数量级为 560 cm³。

（9）颅腔区。颅腔区的大部分形态仍保持原状。

与其他原始人类的比较

在复原过程中仍能发现一些变形的迹象。这导致头骨顶部低于原来的位置，同时夸大了枕骨的向后突出。

额骨并未表现出向眶后明显收缩的现象，在南非和东非的南方古猿类中可以看到这种现象，额骨的眶上区部分也没有发生同等程度地向后弯曲。从侧面和垂直角度来看，眶上圆枕和眉间区域几乎形成了一条直线；但在所有已知的南方古猿种中，眉间都倾向于更加向前突出，而眶上圆枕的侧面边缘则向后摆动。顶骨从矢状缝处向外延伸，起初只是稍微有一点儿向下弯曲，而后则急剧地向下弯曲而与颞骨的鳞部会合。因此，第 24 号奥杜威原始人类脑子的顶骨区比南方古猿的要大，南方古猿的顶骨通常在接近中线处开始向下弯曲。当头骨位于法兰克福平面时，即便考虑到枕骨区的向后变形，第 24 号奥杜威原始人类头骨的这部分区域也比南方古猿类在更大程度上延伸到了穿过外耳道的垂直线之后。下颌窝很深，在形态上非常类似于智人，而完全不同于在南方古猿中看到的情形。鼻骨又长又细，在中线处有一个明显的龙骨状突起。

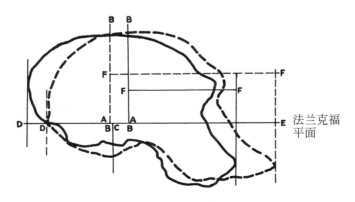

图 3. 第 24 号奥杜威原始人类的头骨侧面图（实线）与 ST. 5 号南方古猿非洲种的头骨侧面图（虚线）叠加在一起的效果图。

The discovery of this skull, which is clearly a member of the genus *Homo* as defined in 1964[6], although it has certain primitive morphological features, raises an important issue. Although it is clearly not an australopithecine it nevertheless differs in certain important respects from the incomplete type of *Homo habilis* (Olduvai H. 7). Yet it resembles the paratype from Bed II (Olduvai H. 13) in both cranial and dental characters. At the same time, the dentition of the type of *Homo habilis* shows considerable resemblances to that of Olduvai H. 16, from lower Bed II, Maiko Gully, although differing in some respects. The problem therefore is whether or not there are two forms of *Homo* in Beds I and II or whether the differences between the two groups can be accounted for on the basis of individual variation and sexual dimorphism.

Although only part of the upper dentition is preserved in the cranium from DK, there are other specimens from Beds I and II which have a comparably small or even smaller tooth size and are morphologically similar. These clearly belong within the same group. They include a complete upper molar (Olduvai H. 6) from the site of *Australopithecus boisei* and an isolated molar (Olduvai H. 21), also probably from Bed I.

In Olduvai H. 24 from DK and in H. 13 from MNK certain important diagnostic characters of the skull are preserved, including the area of the temporal bones around the external auditory meatus and most of the occipital bones. These features, together with the morphology of the teeth, clearly indicate that both specimens belong within the genus *Homo*.

Although the occipital bone of the type specimen of *Homo habilis* (Olduvai H. 7) is not preserved it is evident from the structure of the parietal bones, and especially the form of the lambdoid suture, that the occipital bone must have been morphologically similar to that of *Homo erectus*, that is to say, the lambdoid suture is in the form of a low, wide arch and not V-shaped. This form is also seen in the skull of Olduvai H. 16 from lower Bed II. In contrast, the form of this suture in both Olduvai H. 24 from DK and Olduvai H. 13 from MNK and, indeed, the whole form of the occipital bone, is very similar to that seen in *Homo sapiens* today: the line of the suture descends sharply from lambda in the form of an inverted V. There are thus two types of occipital morphology, one represented by Olduvai H. 24 and Olduvai H. 13 and the second by the type of *Homo habilis* and Olduvai H. 16.

The teeth of Olduvai H. 7 and H. 16 are megadont and within the size range of *Australopithecus africanus*; yet, in other respects, they display a number of morphological differences, especially in the premolars.

Distinct differences from the australopithecines are also evident in the cranial morphology, particularly in the parietals. Although the frontal bone of the type of *Homo habilis* is missing, a large part of this bone is preserved in Olduvai H. 16. Both the minimum frontal width and the width between the temporal crests is greater than in any known australopithecine.

672

尽管该头骨具有一定的原始形态特征，但其显然是 1964 年被定名的人属的一个成员 [6]，这一发现引出了一个重要问题。虽然它显然不是南方古猿类中的一种，但是在某些重要方面，它又与能人的不完整类型（第 7 号奥杜威原始人类）有所区别。而它的头骨和牙齿特征类似于在第 II 层中发现的能人副型（第 13 号奥杜威原始人类）。与此同时，虽然能人类型的齿系与在第 II 层下部舞子沟中发现的第 16 号奥杜威原始人类在某些方面有差异，但二者之间毕竟存在着很多相似之处。因此，问题就变成了在第 I 层和第 II 层中发现的是否是两种形式的人属，或者，这两个组群之间的差异是否可以用个体差异和两性异形来解释？

尽管 DK 遗址出土的头骨中只有部分上齿系保存了下来，但在第 I 层和第 II 层中还发现了其他标本，这些标本有相对较小或更小的牙齿，并且在形态上是相似的。它们显然属于同一组群。其中包括一枚完整的上臼齿（第 6 号奥杜威原始人类）和一枚单独的臼齿（第 21 号奥杜威原始人类），前者是从南方古猿鲍氏种遗址得到的，后者也可能来自于第 I 层。

在 DK 遗址出土的第 24 号奥杜威原始人类和 MNK 遗址出土的第 13 号奥杜威原始人类的头骨中，某些可用于鉴定的重要特征仍保存至今，包括外耳道周围的颞骨区和大部分枕骨。这些特征以及牙齿的形态都明确显示上述两个标本可归入人属。

尽管能人模式标本（第 7 号奥杜威原始人类）的枕骨没有被保存下来，但是从顶骨的结构，尤其是人字缝的形式就可以清楚地得到以下结论：能人的枕骨肯定在形态上与直立人的枕骨相似，也就是说，人字缝的形式是低而宽的弓形而非 V 字形。这种形式也见于在第 II 层下部发现的第 16 号奥杜威原始人类的头骨。相比之下，DK 第 24 号奥杜威原始人类和 MNK 第 13 号奥杜威原始人类的人字缝的形式，确切地说，是枕骨的整体形式，都与在今天智人中看到的情况非常相似：缝线从人字点处以倒 V 字形急剧下降。因此，枕骨有两种类型的形态：一种以第 24 号奥杜威原始人类和第 13 号奥杜威原始人类为代表；另一种则以能人类型和第 16 号奥杜威原始人类为代表。

第 7 号奥杜威原始人类和第 16 号奥杜威原始人类的牙齿属于巨型齿，其牙齿的大小在南方古猿非洲种的牙齿尺寸变化范围之内；然而，另一方面，它们在形态上又存在着很多差异，尤其是前臼齿的特征。

与南方古猿类的显著差异也明显地表现在头骨的形态上，尤其是顶骨。尽管找不到能人类型的额骨，但在第 16 号奥杜威原始人类中还保存着大部分的额骨。其最小额宽和颞峭之间的间距都要大于任何已知的南方古猿。

Until the discovery of Olduvai H. 24 it was considered possible that the difference in morphology and in size between the cranial parts and dentition of the type of *Homo habilis* from Bed I and those of the paratype from Bed II (Olduvai H. 13) might have resulted from the elapse of a prolonged time interval. Because Olduvai H. 24 is chronologically near to the type of *Homo habilis* and yet more closely resembles the paratype from Bed II this explanation is no longer tenable. There remains the question of sexual dimorphism and it is possible that Olduvai H. 13 and H. 24 represent females of *Homo habilis* with the type and H. 16 representing the males. The difference in the morphology of the occipital region in the two groups, however, cannot be disregarded and suggests the possibility of taxonomic variation.

Beyond doubt, the new specimen represents the genus *Homo* as defined by Leakey, Tobias and Napier and differs fundamentally from the australopithecines. At the same time it is not entirely certain that it necessarily represents a female of *Homo habilis*.

We thank Dr. A. Walker of the University of Nairobi for checking the text and measurements and for most valuable comments.

(**232**, 308-312; 1971)

M. D. Leakey, R. J. Clarke and L. S. B. Leakey: Centre for Prehistory and Palaeontology, PO Box 30239, Nairobi.

Received April 2, 1971.

References:

1. Leakey, M. D., *Nature*, **223**, 754 (1969).

2. Curtis, G. H., and Hay, R. L., in *Calibration of Hominoid Evolution* (edit. by Bishop, W. W., and Miller, J.) (Scottish Academic Press for Wenner Gren Foundation for Anthropological Research, in the press).

3. Leakey, L. S. B., and Leakey, M. D., *Nature*, **202**, 3 (1964).

4. Leakey, M. D., in *Background to Evolution in Africa* (edit. by Bishop, W. W., and Clark, J. D.) (University of Chicago Press, Chicago and London, 1967).

5. Martin, R., *Lehrbuch der Anthropologie* (Fischer, Stuttgart, 1959).

6. Leakey, L. S. B., Tobias, P. V., and Napier, J. R., *Nature*, **202**, 5 (1964).

在发现第 24 号奥杜威原始人类以前，以下这一解释被认为是有可能成立的，即来自第 I 层的能人类型和来自第 II 层的副型（第 13 号奥杜威原始人类）在头骨部分和齿系方面存在的形态和尺寸差异是由于两者之间跨越了漫长的岁月。因为第 24 号奥杜威原始人类在年代上接近于能人类型，但却与来自第 II 层的副型更加相像，因而上述解释再也站不住脚了。那么就只剩下两性异形的问题了，也许第 13 号和第 24 号奥杜威原始人类代表的是女性能人，而第 16 号奥杜威原始人类则代表了男性能人。但不能忽视这两个组群在枕骨区形态上存在的差异，这种差异暗示了分类上变异的可能性。

毫无疑问，这个新标本属于利基、托拜厄斯和内皮尔所定义的人属，而与南方古猿类有着本质上的不同。同时，并不能完全确定它一定代表着一个女性的能人。

内罗毕大学的沃克博士对文章内容和测量结果进行了核查，并提出了非常有价值的意见，我们对此表示衷心感谢。

（刘皓芳 翻译；林圣龙 审稿）

Non-random X Chromosome Expression in Female Mules and Hinnies

J. L. Hamerton *et al.*

Editor's Note

Equine hybrids, such as mules (produced from a male donkey and a female horse) and hinnies (produced from a male horse and a female donkey), have proved useful in the study of developmental genetics. Here John L. Hamerton and colleagues use female hybrids to lend support to English geneticist Mary Lyon's hypothesis that one of the X chromosome copies in female mammals is inactivated early in development. The team used expression of species-specific glucose-6-phosphate dehydrogenase to show that, in any given cell, only one of two X chromosomes is functional. Today, the principle of X chromosome inactivation is well accepted.

THERE have been several studies of X chromosome DNA replication and the behaviour of X-linked genes in the female mule[1-6] but the results are not in agreement on the frequency with which the two parental X chromosomes (X^D and X^H) show late DNA replication. Here we present additional data on the expression of the X-linked glucose-6-phosphate dehydrogenase (*Gd*, E.C.1.1.1.49) locus in a female mule and two female hinnies. (The hinny is the reciprocal cross *Equus caballus* ♂×*E. asinus* ♀.) The mule and one hinny were less than one year old and the third animal was a 35 day old hinny foetus obtained by hysterotomy. All were bred at the Veterinary School and ARC Unit of Reproductive Physiology and Biochemistry, Cambridge, England.

Fibroblast cultures were established from the three animals by standard methods. The medium used was McCoy's 5a (modified) supplemented with 15% foetal calf serum (McFC15). Cloning of fibroblasts was carried out as follows[7]. Healthy exponentially growing fibroblast cultures were trypsinized, and the cell suspension was diluted as necessary to a final dilution of about thirty cells per ml. One drop of this suspension (0.03 ml.) was placed in each well of an appropriate number of Falcon Microtest II culture plates. (Each plate contains ninety-six wells of 0.5 ml. capacity. For each experiment five or six plates were seeded.) Then 0.2 ml. of McFC15 was added to each well and the plates were covered and incubated in a 100% humidity incubator in an atmosphere of 5% CO_2 in air. They were examined after 3 and 5 days and wells containing one colony were marked. The plating efficiency varied from 20–40%, which was similar to that obtained in conventional plating experiments using the same cell suspensions.

After 10–14 days, wells containing single colonies were trypsinized and the cell suspension transferred to 60 mm Falcon Petri dishes. When these dishes were confluent, the cells were either transferred to culture bottles to allow more extensive growth or, alternatively, the

母马骡和母驴骡的X染色体非随机表达

哈默顿等

编者按

马的杂交后代，如马骡（由公驴和母马杂交产生）和驴骡（由公马和母驴杂交产生），已被证实在发育遗传学研究方面是很有用处的。在本文中，约翰·哈默顿及其同事用雌性杂交动物证实了英国遗传学家玛丽·莱昂的假说，即雌性哺乳动物的两条X染色体副本中的一条会在发育的早期失活。该研究小组用物种特异的葡萄糖-6-磷酸脱氢酶的表达来说明：在任意给定的细胞中，两条X染色体中只有一条在发挥作用。时至今日，X染色体失活的理论已经得到了大家的普遍认可。

目前我们已经见到了几篇关于母马骡中X染色体DNA复制和X连锁基因行为方式的研究报告[1-6]，但是在关于两条亲本X染色体（X^D和X^H）上的DNA发生复制延迟的频率方面，所得结果之间并不一致。在本文中，我们将给出关于一匹母马骡和两匹母驴骡中X连锁的葡萄糖-6-磷酸脱氢酶（Gd, E.C.1.1.1.49）基因位点表达的一些额外数据。（驴骡是由公马和母驴互交得到的。）这匹马骡和其中一匹驴骡的年龄都不到一岁，另外一匹驴骡是通过子宫切开术得到的35天大的胚胎。所有这些动物都是由英国剑桥大学的兽医学院以及农业研究委员会生殖生理与生物化学研究室饲养的。

采用标准方法培养建立这三只动物的成纤维细胞系。所使用的培养基是添加了15%胎牛血清（McFC15）的（改良）麦科伊5a。成纤维细胞的克隆按以下步骤进行[7]。将健康的、指数生长的成纤维细胞培养物进行胰蛋白酶消化，首先根据需要将细胞悬浮液稀释至每ml约含30个细胞的终浓度。将这样的悬浮液加入到孔数适当的猎鹰牌微量测定 II 型培养板的各个孔中，每个孔中加一滴（0.03 ml）。（每个培养板含有96个孔，每个孔的容量为0.5 ml。每次实验需要用5到6块培养板来进行接种。）接着在每个孔中加入0.2 ml McFC15，然后盖上培养板，并在含5% CO_2的大气条件下于湿度为100%的恒温箱中进行培育。分别在3天和5天后检查培育情况，并对含有一个克隆体的孔进行标记。培养板的接种效率在20%~40%之间变化，这与用同一细胞悬浮液在常规平板接种实验中所得的结果类似。

10天~14天后，我们对含有一个克隆体的孔内的细胞进行胰蛋白酶消化，然后将细胞悬浮液转移至直径为60 mm的猎鹰牌皮氏培养皿中。当细胞铺满这些培养皿时，可以将它们转移至培养瓶中扩大培养，或者停止进一步培养而去检测皮氏培

G6PD types were determined on the cells in the Petri dishes without further passage. Cells from each original culture and from a number of clones were stored at -70 or $-196°C$ in a cryoprotective medium containing 15% glycerol. Lysates were prepared from both original cultures and clones by freezing and thawing in 0.015 M Tris-borate buffer (pH 7.8) containing 0.005 M EDTA, 0.02 g% "Triton X–100", 2 mg% NADP and 0.05% (v/v) 2-mercaptoethanol. Electrophoresis ("Cellogel", Chemetron, Milan) was carried out for 1.25 h at 4°C at a potential gradient of 45 V/cm and the gels were stained for glucose-6-phosphate dehydrogenase[5].

Gd is seen as a single band in both parental species. Gd^H moving slower than the Gd^D (refs. 2 and 8). The faint slower bands seen in both parental species and the hybrids after starch gel electrophoresis represent breakdown products. The earlier samples from animals 100 -196 were typed on starch as described earlier[2]. A number of other hybrid animals of both sexes as well as the parental species have been studied using both erythrocytes and fibroblasts without cloning. The Gd types are summarized in Table 1, and clearly confirm X-linkage of Gd in the Equidae. The parents of the three hybrids that were cloned are included in this table and show the expected Gd patterns. The interrelationship of the various hybrids which we have studied in detail is shown in Fig. 1. The hybrids, with one exception, develop a strong Gd^H band and either a faint or no Gd^D band. The exception (animal 192) has a stronger Gd^D band than Gd^H band. This inter-animal variation may explain the lack of agreement between different workers[3,4].

Table 1. Expression of Glucose-6-phosphate Dehydrogenase in Horses and Donkeys and Their Hybrids

Animal No.	Type	Material	Gd^D	Gd^H	Source
Female hybrids					
100	Mule	E	±	+	Cambridge*
		F	–	+	
138	Hinny	E	±	+	Portugal
139	Hinny	E	–	+	Portugal
143	Mule	E	–	+	Portugal
187	Hinny	E	±	+	Portugal
188	Hinny	E	±	+	Portugal
189	Hinny	E	±	+	Portugal
190	Hinny	E	±	+	Portugal
		F	–	+	
191	Hinny	E	–	+	Portugal
192	Hinny	E	+	±	Portugal
195	Mule (foetus)	F	–	+	Cambridge†
196	Mule (foetus)	F	–	+	Cambridge†
200	Hinny (foetus)	F	–	+	Cambridge†
202	Mule	E	–	+	Cambridge
		F	±	+	Cambridge

养皿中细胞的葡萄糖 –6– 磷酸脱氢酶（G6PD）的类型。将来自每个原始培养物和来自许多克隆体的细胞在 –70℃或者 –196℃下储存于含 15% 甘油的冷冻保护液中。通过对原始培养物和克隆体进行冷冻和融解来制备溶菌液，融解介质为 0.015 M 三羟甲基硼酸缓冲液（pH 值 7.8），其中含 0.005 M 乙二胺四乙酸、0.02 g%"曲拉通 X–100"（译者注：成分为聚乙二醇辛基苯基醚）、2 mg% 烟酰胺腺嘌呤二核苷酸磷酸和 0.05%（体积比）的 2– 巯基乙醇。以 45 V/cm 为电位梯度在 4℃下电泳 1.25 h（电泳介质为"醋酸纤维素凝胶"，米兰凯美创公司产品），然后对凝胶进行葡萄糖 –6– 磷酸脱氢酶染色[5]。

在两个亲代物种中都只能看到一条单一的 *Gd* 电泳条带，并且 *Gd*[H] 比 *Gd*[D] 移动得要慢（参考文献 2 和 8）。经过淀粉凝胶电泳之后，在亲代物种和杂交体中都能看到一些移动较慢的微弱条带，它们代表的是裂解的产物。我们对来自 100 号至 196 号实验动物的早期样品进行了淀粉凝胶电泳分析结果的归类，这已在以前发表的文章中描述过[2]。现在我们用未经克隆的红细胞和成纤维细胞对其他许多物种进行研究——不仅研究了其亲代，而且研究了包括雌雄两性的杂种。*Gd* 类型总结于表 1 中，由此显然可以证明马科动物中 *Gd* 的 X 连锁特性。三只被克隆的杂交动物的亲本都包括在这张表中，其结果都与预期的 *Gd* 类型一致。我们曾经仔细研究过的各个杂交动物之间的相互关系示于图 1。除一只以外，其他杂交动物都显示出一条很强的 *Gd*[H] 条带和一条或者很弱或者消失的 *Gd*[D] 条带。不过，也有例外者（编号为 192 的动物），其 *Gd*[D] 条带要比 *Gd*[H] 条带强。动物间的这种变异也许可以用来解释不同工作者的研究结果之间为什么并非完全一致[3,4]。

表 1. 葡萄糖 –6– 磷酸脱氢酶在马、驴和它们的杂交后代中的表达

动物编号	类型	原料	*Gd*[D]	*Gd*[H]	样品来源
雌性杂交体					
100	马骡	E	±	+	剑桥 *
		F	−	+	
138	驴骡	E	±	+	葡萄牙
139	驴骡	E	−	+	葡萄牙
143	马骡	E	−	+	葡萄牙
187	驴骡	E	±	+	葡萄牙
188	驴骡	E	±	+	葡萄牙
189	驴骡	E	±	+	葡萄牙
190	驴骡	E	±	+	葡萄牙
		F		+	
191	驴骡	E	−	+	葡萄牙
192	驴骡	E	+	±	葡萄牙
195	马骡（胚胎）	F	−	+	剑桥 †
196	马骡（胚胎）	F	−	+	剑桥 †
200	驴骡（胚胎）	F	−	+	剑桥 †
202	马骡	E	−	+	剑桥
		F	±	+	剑桥

Continued

Animal No.	Type	Material	Gd^D	Gd^H	Source
203	Hinny	F	±	+	Cambridge
		E	±	+	
217	Mule	E	±	+	Cambridge
Male hybrids					
	Mule (n=1 foetus)	F	−	+	Cambridge
	Mules (n=4)	E	−	+	Portugal and Cambridge
	Hinnies (n=7)	E	+	−	Portugal and Cambridge
Parental species					
Males	Donkeys (n=7)	E	+	−	Cambridge
	Horses (n=2)	E	−	+	Cambridge
Females	Donkeys (n=12)	E	+	−	Cambridge
	Horses (n=8)	E	−	+	Cambridge

* This animal (No. 100) reported by Hamerton *et al.*, 1969.

† 195   45D gestation
  196   60D gestation
  200   35D gestation   } All obtained by hysterotomy
  201 ♂ mule 35D gestation

+ Strong; ±, faint; −, absent; E, erythrocytes; F, fibroblasts.

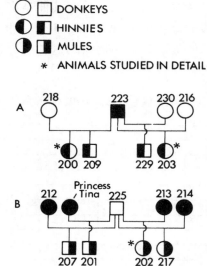

Fig. 1. Pedigree charts of the mules and hinnies studied. The numbers refer to numbers in Table 1. A, Hinnies; B, mules.

The *Gd* results obtained on 303 clones derived from three hybrids are given in Table 2. Two hundred and ninety-seven of these clones showed either the Gd^H or Gd^D band. Six clones were mixed (Gd^H/Gd^D), two of these were recloned, and 106 out of 107 of these sub-clones showed either Gd^H or Gd^D while one was again mixed (Table 3). In all animals,

续表

动物编号	类型	原料	Gd^D	Gd^H	样品来源
203	驴骡	F	±	+	剑桥
		E	±	+	
217	马骡	E	±	+	剑桥
雄性杂交体					
	马骡 (n=1, 胚胎)	F	−	+	剑桥
	马骡 (n=4)	E	−	+	葡萄牙和剑桥
	驴骡 (n=7)	E	+	−	葡萄牙和剑桥
亲代物种					
雄性	驴 (n=7)	E	+	−	剑桥
	马 (n=2)	E	−	+	剑桥
雌性	驴 (n=12)	E	+	−	剑桥
	马 (n=8)	E	−	+	剑桥

* 这只动物（编号为100）是由哈默顿等人在1969年报道的。

† 195： 怀孕45天 ⎫
  196： 怀孕60天 ⎬ 均通过子宫切开术获得
  200： 怀孕35天 ⎪
  201 公马骡：怀孕35天 ⎭

＋代表强，± 代表弱，－代表无；E 代表红细胞，F 代表成纤维细胞。

● ■ 马
○ □ 驴
◐ ◑ 驴骡
◑ ◐ 马骡

* 详细研究过的动物

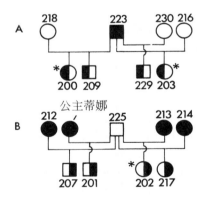

图1. 所研究的马骡和驴骡的谱系图。图中的编号指的是表1中的编号。A 为驴骡；B 为马骡。

由来自3只杂交动物的303个细胞克隆得到的 Gd 类型列于表2中。其中有297个克隆表现出 Gd^H 或者 Gd^D 条带。有6个克隆表现出混合条带（Gd^H/Gd^D），将其中两个再次进行克隆，结果在107个亚克隆中，有106个表现出 Gd^H 条带或者 Gd^D 条带，剩下的那一个仍然表现为混合条带（表3）。在所有实验动物中，不论杂交与否，这

681

irrespective of the cross, the frequency of the two types is significantly different from 50% ($P>0.0005$). This results from a deficiency of clones showing Gd^D.

Table 2. *Gd* Expression in Clones Derived from Fibroblasts from Three Equine Hybrids

Animal No.	Expt.	No. Gd^D	No. $Gd^D Gd^H$	Total	Proportion Gd^D
200 (Hinny ♀)	VIII	4	–	40	0.100
35 D Foetus	X	6	1	68	0.088
Total		10	1	108	0.093
202 (Mule ♀)	II	5	3	11	0.454
	IV	3	–	20	0.150
	VI	7	–	41	0.171
	XII	14	1	42	0.333
Total		29	4	114	0.254
203 (Hinny ♀)	VII	1	–	3	0.333
	IX	3	–	26	0.115
	XIII	8	1	52	0.154
Total		12	1	81	0.148
Grand total		51	6	303	0.168

Table 3. Expression of *Gd* Locus in Sub-clones from Two Mixed ($Gd^D Gd^H$) Clones from Animal 202

Clone	Expt.	No. Gd^D	No. $Gd^D Gd^H$	Total sub-clones	Proportion Gd^D
C1	XIV	9	1	58	0.155
C8	XV	8	–	49	0.163
Total		17	1	107	0.159

Recloning the two mixed clones at a later passage showed that the proportion of Gd^D sub-clones (0.16) is significantly lower than expected, if it is assumed that these mixed clones originated from two cells, one Gd^D and one Gd^H. This suggests powerful selective forces acting *in vitro*.

A number of conclusions can be drawn from these results. First, the mixed expression seen in the hybrids and some of the original cultures derived from them can be accounted for by the expression of one X chromosome only in any given cell and its descendants, as postulated by Lyon[9,10], and not from partial activity of both X chromosomes as postulated by Grüneberg[11] in his complemental X hypothesis. It could be argued, however, that the minor allele is expressed in less than 10% of the cells, in which case it would not be detected by the methods used here without sub-cloning. It seems unlikely that in a system where if the expression of an allele is equated to 100, all relative activities from 100:0 to 0:100 can reversibly occur for two alleles as suggested by Grüneberg[11], we would expect to find 81.7% of one type, 16.6% of the other and only 1.7% mixed, which are the results obtained here. Second, it can be concluded that active cell selection over a fairly short period of time occurs during *in vitro* fibroblast culture and that this selection

两种类型的发生频率明显偏离 50%（*P*>0.0005）。这一结果归因于表现为 *Gd*^D 的克隆数量不足。

表 2. *Gd* 在源于三匹马科动物杂交后代的成纤维细胞克隆中的表达

动物编号	实验	*Gd*^D 的数量	*Gd*^D*Gd*^H 的数量	总数	*Gd*^D 所占比例
200 （母驴骡） 35 天的胚胎	VIII	4	–	40	0.100
	X	6	1	68	0.088
共计		10	1	108	0.093
202 （母马骡）	II	5	3	11	0.454
	IV	3	–	20	0.150
	VI	7	–	41	0.171
	XII	14	1	42	0.333
共计		29	4	114	0.254
203 （母驴骡）	VII	1	–	3	0.333
	IX	3	–	26	0.115
	XIII	8	1	52	0.154
共计		12	1	81	0.148
合计		51	6	303	0.168

表 3. *Gd* 在源于 202 号动物两个混合（*Gd*^D*Gd*^H）克隆的亚克隆中的表达

克隆	实验	*Gd*^D 的数量	*Gd*^D*Gd*^H 的数量	亚克隆总数	*Gd*^D 所占比例
C1	XIV	9	1	58	0.155
C8	XV	8	–	49	0.163
共计		17	1	107	0.159

在后面的传代中再次克隆那两个表现出混合条带的克隆，结果 *Gd*^D 亚克隆的比例（0.16）明显低于预期，如果假设这些表现出混合条带的克隆是来自两个细胞（一个是 *Gd*^D，另一个是 *Gd*^H）的话。这表明有一种在体外发挥作用的强大选择力。

从这些结果中可以推出很多结论。首先，在杂交体和源于它们的一些原始培养物中观察到的混合表达可以用莱昂假说 [9,10] 来解释，即在任意一个给定的细胞及其后代中只表达了一条 X 染色体；而非格吕内贝格在他的 X 染色体补偿假说 [11] 中所提出的混合表达是来自两条 X 染色体的部分活性。然而，有人可能认为少数等位基因的表达发生在不超过 10% 的细胞中，在这种情况下，不采用亚克隆是无法用上述方法检测出来的。似乎不会像格吕内贝格所指出的那样 [11]：在一个体系中，如果一个等位基因的表达量为 100，那么从 100:0 到 0:100 之间的所有相对活性都可以在两个等位基因之间可逆地发生。我们预期能够发现一种类型为 81.7%，另一种类型为 16.6%，而混合类型只有 1.7%。这正是我们在本文中得到的结果。第二个可以得出结论的是：在体外成纤维细胞培养过程中，活性细胞的选择所经历的时间非常短，

would usually seem to be against those cells expressing Gd^D irrespective of whether the X^D is maternal or paternal in origin. This indicates that the maternal cytoplasm does not preferentially activate the maternal X chromosome or effect subsequent cell selection in these hybrids. Third, studies of X-linked loci using electrophoretic methods seem to demonstrate activity of a given locus only when it is expressed in more than 10% of the cell population. Original cultures from animals 202 and 203 both showed a minor fast band (Gd^D) at an early passage; this was subsequently lost during culture. In both these animals the frequency of Gd^D cells as demonstrated by the typing of clones was between 0.1 and 0.3 in different experiments. The original cultures from the foetus (200) never showed a fast Gd^D band; in spite of this, 9.0% of clones showed expression of Gd^D. These results are interesting in the light of the results reported by Sharman and his co-workers[12-14] on X-inactivation in marsupial hybrids in which they demonstrated preferential late replication of the paternal X chromosome and inactivation of the paternal Gd and phosphoglycerokinase (*PGK*) loci. Finally, the results obtained here agree with other data showing that the proportion of late replicating X^D ranged from 0.67–1.00 in six female mules and eight female hinnies[6]. If late replication of a given chromosome represents its genetic inactivation, then the autoradiographic results suggest that the proportion of cells expressing Gd^D should vary between 0.33 and zero which fits very closely to the results obtained here. Similar results have recently been reported for four mules by Cohen and Rattazzi[5].

These findings support the single active X hypothesis originally put forward by Lyon[9,10]. They demonstrate clearly activity of only one *Gd* allele in any given cell, which has also been shown for man[15,16]. Unfortunately, the other X-linked enzyme systems *PGK* and α-galactosidase which we have tested have failed as yet to show different mobilities in horse and donkey and so cannot be tested. Furthermore, these data demonstrate *in vitro* cell selection in favour of those cells carrying an active X^H. Examination of uncloned fibroblasts and erythrocytes from these animals also shows predominant expression of Gd^H (Table 1) suggesting that the proportion of cells with an active X^H *in vivo* are reflected in our *in vitro* results and that these are not therefore due to differential plating efficiencies of the two cell types. The one animal showing equal expression of the two types is unavailable for further study. Lyon[9,10] has postulated *in vivo* cell selection to account for variation in expression of sex linked loci in the mouse and man and the demonstration of such strong selective forces *in vitro* due to the activity or inactivity of a single X chromosome lends support to the hypothesis that similar selective forces may be acting *in vivo*. Finally, the close agreement between the autoradiographic data[2,4-6] and the genetic data presented here adds further support to the hypothesis that late replication is the cytological manifestation of genetic inactivity. A final proof of this would be provided by autoradiographic studies on the two clonal types derived here. These studies are at present in progress.

We thank Mrs. G. Anderson, Mrs. E. Cameron and Miss V. Niewczas-Late for technical assistance. This work was supported by a grant to J. L. H. from the Medical Research Council of Canada. Financial support from the Children's Hospital Research Foundation of Winnipeg is also gratefully acknowledged. W. R. A. is supported by the Thoroughbred

并且这种选择似乎总是不利于那些表达了 Gd^D 基因的细胞，不管 X^D 是来自母本或是父本。这表明：在这些杂交体中，母本细胞质并没有优先激活母本 X 染色体，也没有影响随后的细胞选择。第三，利用电泳法对 X 连锁基因位点的研究似乎说明：只有当一个给定基因位点在超过 10% 的细胞群中被表达时才能用电泳方法给出该位点的活性。来自 202 号和 203 号实验动物的原始培养物在早期阶段都表现出一条较小的快速条带（Gd^D）；在随后的培养过程中又消失了。根据克隆类型，这两只动物 Gd^D 细胞的发生频率在不同实验中得到的结果介于 0.1~0.3 之间。来自动物胚胎（编号 200）的原始培养物从未表现出快速的 Gd^D 条带；尽管如此，其克隆中仍有 9.0% 显示出 Gd^D 表达。这些结果在解释沙曼及其同事所报道的关于有袋动物杂交体中 X 染色体失活方面的研究成果 [12-14] 上很有意义，他们发现这些杂交体表现出父本 X 染色体的优先复制延迟以及父本的 Gd 和磷酸甘油酸激酶(PGK)位点的优先失活。最后，有数据显示：在 6 匹母马骡和 8 匹母驴骡中，X^D 复制延迟的比例在 0.67~1.00 之间 [6]，这与本文中得到的结果相符。如果一个给定染色体的复制延迟能反映出它的遗传失活，那么由放射自显影结果就可以给出表达 Gd^D 的细胞比例应该在 0~0.33 之间，这与本文中得到的结果非常吻合。最近，科亨和拉塔齐报道的有关 4 匹母马骡的结果 [5] 也与此类似。

上述发现支持了由莱昂最先提出的一条活性 X 染色体的假说 [9,10]。这些结果清楚地表明，在任一给定的细胞中只有一个 Gd 等位基因是具有活性的，人类中的情况也是如此 [15,16]。不幸的是，我们在对马和驴的其他 X 连锁酶系——PGK 系和 α- 半乳糖苷酶系进行测试时，并没有发现它们的迁移率有何不同，因而无法进行验证。此外，这些数据还表明：体外的细胞选择倾向于那些带有一个活性染色体 X^H 的细胞。我们对这些动物中未克隆的成纤维细胞和红细胞进行检测的结果也表明，占主导地位的是 Gd^H 基因的表达（表 1），这意味着体内带有一个活性染色体 X^H 的细胞比例与我们在体外的测试结果相符，因而在体外得到的结果不能用培养板对这两种细胞类型具有不同的接种效率来解释。进一步研究所需的、能等量表达这两种基因类型的单个动物是很难得到的。莱昂 [9,10] 曾提出，用体内细胞的选择可以解释小鼠和人类性别连锁基因位点在表达上的变化。发现由单一 X 染色体的活性或者失活在体外引起的强烈选择力也支持了如下假设：在体内可能同样存在着类似的选择力。最后，放射自显影数据 [2,4-6] 与本文提供的基因数据之间的严格一致进一步支持了复制延迟是基因失活的一种细胞学表现的假说。支持上述假说的最终证据将通过对源于本实验的两种克隆类型进行放射自显影研究得到。目前这些研究还在进行之中。

感谢安德森夫人、卡梅伦夫人和纽蔡斯－雷特小姐在技术上对我们的帮助。本工作是由加拿大医学研究委员会提供给哈默顿的一项经费支持的；温尼伯儿童医院研究基金会在经济上给予我们慷慨援助，谨此一并致谢。艾伦有幸受到了良种马饲

Breeders Association. Collection of material from some of the animals in Portugal was supported by a grant to J. L. H. and R. V. S. from the Wellcome Trust. We thank Dr. M. J. Freire and his veterinary colleagues for Portuguese samples.

(**232**, 312-315; 1971)

J. L. Hamerton, B. J. Richardson and Phyllis A. Gee: Department of Medical Genetics, Children's Hospital, Winnipeg, and Departments of Paediatrics and Anatomy, University of Manitoba.

W. R. Allen and R. V. Short: ARC Unit of Reproductive Physiology and Biochemistry, Animal Research Station, Huntingdon Road, Cambridge, and Department of Veterinary Clinical Studies, School of Veterinary Medicine, Madingley Road, Cambridge.

Received March 29; revised June 7, 1971.

References:

1. Mukherjee, B. B., and Sinha, A. K., *Proc. US Nat. Acad. Sci.*, **51**, 252 (1964).

2. Hamerton, J. L., Giannelli, F., Collins, F., Hallett, J., Fryer, A., McGuire, V. M., and Short, R. V., *Nature*, **222**, 1277 (1969).

3. Mukherjee, B. B., Mukherjee, A. B., and Mukherjee, A. B., *Nature*, **228**, 1321 (1970).

4. Hamerton, J. L., and Giannelli, F., *Nature*, **228**, 1323 (1970).

5. Cohen, M. M., and Rattazzi, M. C., *Proc. US Nat. Acad. Sci.*, **68**, 544 (1971).

6. Giannelli, F., and Hamerton, J. L., *Nature*, **232**, 315 (1971).

7. Cooper, J. E. K., *Texas Rep. Biol. Med.*, **28**, 29 (1970).

8. Trujillo, J. M., Walden, B., O'Niel, P., and Anstall, H. B., *Science*, **148**, 1603 (1965).

9. Lyon, M. F., *Ann. Rev. Genet.*, **2**, 31 (1968).

10. Lyon, M. F., *Phil. Trans. Roy. Soc.*, B, **259**, 41 (1970).

11. Grüneberg, H., *J. Embryol. Exp. Morphol.*, **22**, 145 (1969).

12. Sharman, G. B., *Nature*, **230**, 231 (1971).

13. Richardson, B. J., Czuppon, A. B., and Sharman, G. B., *Nature*, **230**, 154 (1971).

14. Cooper, D. W., Vandeberg, J. L., Sharman, G. B., and Poole, W. E., *Nature*, **230**, 155 (1971).

15. Davidson, R. G., Nitowsky, H. M., and Childs, B., *Proc. US Nat. Acad. Sci.*, **50**, 481 (1963).

16. Linder, D., and Gartler, S. M., *Amer. J. Human Genet.*, **17**, 212 (1965).

养者协会的资助，在葡萄牙搜集动物样本的工作则得益于维康基金会授予哈默顿和肖特的一项经费。感谢弗莱雷博士和他的兽医团队为我们提供了葡萄牙的动物样品。

（刘振明 翻译；梁前进 审稿）

Non-random Late Replication of X Chromosomes in Mules and Hinnies

F. Giannelli and J. L. Hamerton

Editor's Note

X chromosome inactivation—where one of the two copies of the X chromosome present in female mammals is silenced—had been proposed by geneticist Mary Lyon's several years earlier. But it was unclear which of the parental X chromosomes lost its function, and if the process was random. Here F. Giannelli and John L. Hamerton use autoradiographs of labelled cultured cells from female mules and hinnies to propose that donkey X chromosomes are more commonly inactivated than horse X chromosomes, regardless of the direction of the cross. This non-random inactivation was subsequently questioned by others who put the finding down to artefact, and today it is thought that X inactivation exists in two forms: random and imprinted.

THE process of DNA replication and genetic activity in X chromosomes of female mules and hinnies has been studied[1-6] without any agreement on the relative frequency with which the two parental X chromosomes (X^D and X^H) become late replicating and genetically inactive. Additional autoradiographic results on six female mules (*E. asinus* ♂ × *E. caballus* ♀) and eight female hinnies (*E. caballus* ♂ × *E. asinus* ♀) are presented here. One of the hinnies (No. 203) was bred in Cambridge[5], three of the mules (Nos. 27, 33, 100), subject of a preliminary communication[2], were obtained from various sources in Great Britain, while the remainder of the hybrids were from Portugal.

Lymphocyte and fibroblast cultures were established by standard methods[7,8]. Mixed lymphocyte cultures, using female donkey and horse blood were set up as controls, for the hybrid cultures. ^{3}H-Tdr (specific activity 5 Ci/mmol, Amersham) in a concentration 0.3–0.5 µCi/ml. was added to the leucocyte cultures 3–4 h before collection and colcemid was added 1.5 h before termination of the culture. Fibroblast cultures were labelled with 0.3 µCi/ml. 6 h before termination and colcemid was added 3 h later. Slides were prepared by air drying, stained lightly with lacto-acetic orcein and suitably spread metaphase plates were photographed. Autoradiographs were prepared by standard methods[2,9]. The cells which had previously been photographed were relocated and examined for a differentially labelled X chromosome. (This was defined as a medium sized chromosome which had at least twice as many autoradiographic grains as any other chromosome of similar size. This definition was adoped because the donkey has a submetacentric autosome much larger than the X and with a large heterochromatic paracentric region which is often densely labelled in late S.) The morphology of the differentially labelled X chromosome (DLX) was then determined by examination of the photographs taken before autoradiography. The two X chromosomes in the female hybrids are quite different, one (X^D) being

马骡和驴骡中X染色体的非随机复制延迟

詹内利，哈默顿

编者按

遗传学家玛丽·莱昂在几年之前就已经提出了 X 染色体失活假说——雌性哺乳动物体内两条 X 染色体中有一条发生沉默。但当时尚不清楚失活的是哪一条亲本 X 染色体，也不知道失活过程是否是随机的。在本文中，詹内利和约翰·哈默顿根据母马骡和母驴骡标记细胞培养物的放射自显影照片提出：驴 X 染色体要比马 X 染色体更经常发生失活的情况，而这与杂交的方向并无关系。这种非随机性失活的说法随即遭到了其他人的质疑，他们认为这一发现是人为因素造成的。而现在人们的看法是：X 染色体的失活存在两种形式——随机性的和印记性的。

目前已经有不少人研究过母马骡和母驴骡 X 染色体中的 DNA 复制过程和遗传活性 [1-6]，但在两条亲本 X 染色体（X^D 和 X^H）发生复制延迟和遗传失活的相对频率上还没有得到统一的结果。我们在本文中将会补充介绍一些有关 6 匹母马骡（公驴 × 母马）和 8 匹母驴骡（公马 × 母驴）的放射自显影结果。其中一匹驴骡（编号为 203）是在剑桥大学饲养的 [5]；3 匹马骡（编号分别为 27、33 和 100）是我们在先前的一篇文章中提到过的 [2]，它们源自英国的不同地方；而其余的杂交动物则来自葡萄牙。

淋巴细胞和成纤维细胞的培养物通过标准方法 [7,8] 制备。杂交体培养物的对照样品是用母驴和母马的血液制备的混合淋巴细胞培养物。在采样前 3 h~4 h，将浓度为 0.3 μCi/ml ~ 0.5 μCi/ml 的氚 - 胸腺嘧啶脱氧核苷（³H–Tdr）（比活度为 5 Ci/mmol，安玛西亚公司产品）加入白细胞培养物中；在终止培养前 1.5 h 加入秋水仙酰胺。成纤维细胞培养物在终止培养前 6 h 用 0.3 μCi/ml 的 ³H–Tdr 进行标记，3 h 后再加入秋水仙酰胺。采用空气干燥的方式制备载玻片样本，并用乳酸 - 醋酸地衣红进行轻微染色，然后对那些载有适当分散的分裂中期细胞的载玻片进行拍照。按照标准方法 [2,9] 制作放射自显影图。重新定位并检查先前被拍过照的细胞以搜索一条差异标记的 X 染色体。（对这个"差异"的界定是：中型大小染色体的放射自显影颗粒计数至少是任意其他相似大小染色体的 2 倍。采用上述定义的原因是：驴含有的近中着丝粒常染色体要比 X 染色体大很多，并且这个常染色体上有一大片异染色质着丝粒旁区域，在 S 期后期经常会被标记得很致密。）然后通过查看在放射自显影之前拍摄的照片来确定这个差异标记的 X 染色体（DLX）的形态。在雌性杂交体中的两条 X 染色体明显不相同：一条（X^D）是近中着丝粒的，而另一条（X^H）则是

submetacentric, while the other (X^H) is metacentric[1,2] (Fig. 1).

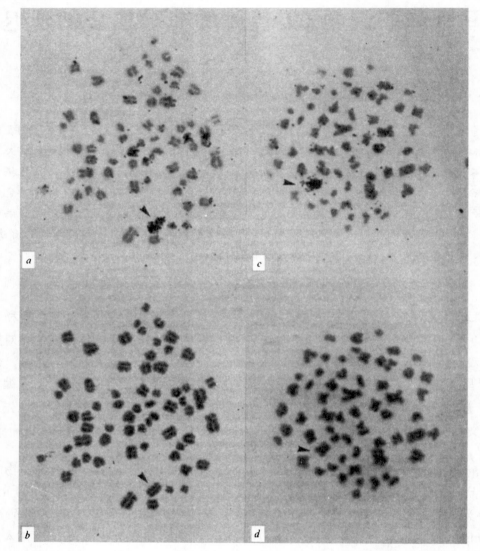

Fig. 1. Two metaphase plates from the same hybrid, the first showing (*a* and *b*) a submetacentric chromosome (arrowed) and the second (*c* and *d*) a metacentric chromosome (arrowed) differentially labelled. These chromosomes presumably represent, in order, the donkey and horse-derived X chromosomes.

Twenty-one suitable metaphase plates from each of two hinnies and one mule (Nos. 100, 188, 203) were selected for quantitative autoradiographic studies, and karyotypes prepared. The total autoradiographic grains for each cell and for each of the five longest medium sized submetacentric and metacentric chromosomes were then counted. Grain counts were also made on samples of cells from the mixed leucocyte cultures, selected either at random or for the presence of a differentially labelled X chromosome.

中央着丝粒的[1,2]（图1）。

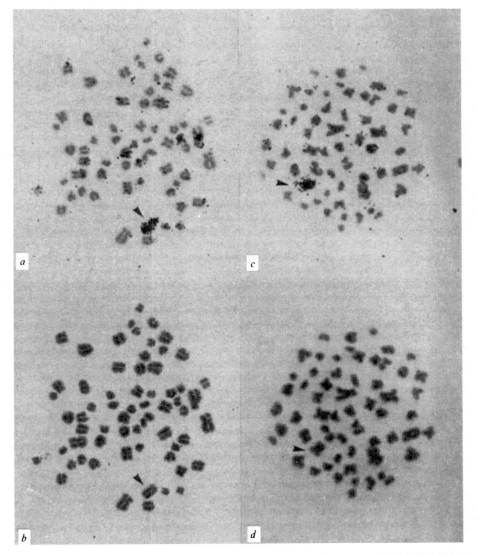

图 1. 两块来自同一杂交体的分裂中期细胞载玻片。第一块中（a 和 b）显示出一条近中着丝粒的染色体
（见箭头所指）；第二块中（c 和 d）显示出一条差异标记的中央着丝粒染色体。这两条染色体可能
依次代表了源自驴和马的 X 染色体。

将来源于两匹驴骡和一匹马骡（编号分别为 100、188 和 203）中每一个个体的
细胞培养物制成载玻片样本，从中选取 21 块适当分散的分裂中期细胞载玻片以进行
定量的放射自显影研究以及核型的制备。然后清点每个细胞中的放射自显影颗粒总
数以及中型大小近中着丝粒染色体和中央着丝粒染色体中 5 条最长的染色体的放射
自显影颗粒总数。此外还清点了来自混合白细胞培养物的细胞样本的放射自显影颗
粒数目，选择样本的方式或者是随机性的或者是针对那些存在差异标记 X 染色体的
样本。

The blood and skin cultures from the fourteen animals studied contained varying proportions of labelled cells and of cells with a differentially labelled X chromosome (Table 1). This did not influence the relative frequency of cells with a differentially labelled X^D or X^H. The relative frequencies differed significantly from 0.5 in every hybrid from which enough cells could be analysed and in each case there was an excess of DLX^D (Table 4). In the mixed leucocyte cultures, on the other hand, the number of horse cells which has a DLX was greater than the number of donkey cells with a DLX (Table 2).

Table 1. Autoradiographic Date from Six Mules and Eight Hinnies

Animal No.	Tissue cultured	No. of cells scored	Total No. of labelled cells	No. of cells with a DLX		No. of cells with a "very hot" DLX‡	
				Total	No. DLX^D	Total	No. DLX^D
Mules							
27	Skin	70	65	14	13	8	8
33	Blood*	1,000	35	27	24	19	18
	Skin	105	77	45	43	33	33
100	Blood*	755	453	68	60	55	50
	Blood†	15	9	3	3	2	2
	Skin	45	40	8	8	8	8
143	Blood*	12	2	1	1	1	1
	Blood†	18	16	7	7	5	5
144	Blood*	22	13	8	7	7	6
	Blood†	142	124	33	28	28	24
145	Blood*	12	7	1	1	0	0
	Blood†	17	14	2	2	2	2
Totals	Blood*	1,801	510	105	93	82	75
	Blood†	192	163	45	40	37	33
	Skin	220	182	67	64	49	49
Hinnies							
138	Blood*	9	5	2	2	1	1
	Blood†	3	2	0	0	0	0
139	Blood*	27	12	6	6	5	5
187	Blood*	172	155	28	22	21	18
	Blood†	17	16	0	0	0	0
188	Blood*	168	120	13	11	8	8
	Blood†	23	22	0	0	0	0
189	Blood*	326	133	18	12	14	10
190	Blood*	152	127	12	8	9	6
	Blood†	37	32	1	1	0	0
191	Blood*	159	135	5	5	3	3
	Blood†	32	30	4	3	3	2
203	Blood*	165	105	23	18	17	13
	Blood†	131	121	211	17	19	16
Totals	Blood*	1,178	792	107	84	78	64
	Blood†	243	223	26	21	22	18

* 3 h incubation with ³H-Tdr.

† 4 h incubation with ³H-Tdr.

‡ DLX with at least 2.2 times the grains counted over any other chromosome of similar size.

来自所有 14 匹马骡或驴骡的血液和皮肤培养物各自含有不同比例的标记细胞以及含有不同比例的含差异标记 X 染色体的细胞（表 1）。这并不影响含一个差异标记染色体 X^D 或者 X^H 的细胞的相对频率。在每一只有足够多细胞可供分析的杂交动物中都出现了相对频率明显偏离 0.5 的情况，并且每次都是 DLX^D 过量（表 4）。而另一方面，在混合的白细胞培养物中，含有一个 DLX 的马细胞数量要多于含有一个 DLX 的驴细胞数量（表 2）。

表 1.6 匹马骡和 8 匹驴骡的放射自显影数据

动物编号	培养的组织	记录的细胞数量	标记细胞的总数	含一个 DLX 染色体的细胞数量		含一个"过热"DLX 染色体‡的细胞数量	
				总数	含 DLX^D 的细胞数量	总数	含 DLX^D 的细胞数量
马骡							
27	皮肤	70	65	14	13	8	8
33	血液 *	1,000	35	27	24	19	18
	皮肤	105	77	45	43	33	33
100	血液 *	755	453	68	60	55	50
	血液 †	15	9	3	3	2	2
	皮肤	45	40	8	8	8	8
143	血液 *	12	2	1	1	1	1
	血液 †	18	16	7	7	5	5
144	血液 *	22	13	8	7	7	6
	血液 †	142	124	33	28	28	24
145	血液 *	12	7	1	1	0	0
	血液 †	17	14	2	2	2	2
总计	血液 *	1,801	510	105	93	82	75
	血液 †	192	163	45	40	37	33
	皮肤	220	182	67	64	49	49
驴骡							
138	血液 *	9	5	2	2	1	1
	血液 †	3	2	0	0	0	0
139	血液 *	27	12	6	6	5	5
187	血液 *	172	155	28	22	21	18
	血液 †	17	16	0	0	0	0
188	血液 *	168	120	13	11	8	8
	血液 †	23	22	0	0	0	0
189	血液 *	326	133	18	12	14	10
190	血液 *	152	127	12	8	9	6
	血液 †	37	32	1	1	0	0
191	血液 *	159	135	5	5	3	3
	血液 †	32	30	4	3	3	2
203	血液 *	165	105	23	18	17	13
	血液 †	131	121	211	17	19	16
总计	血液 *	1,178	792	107	84	78	64
	血液 †	243	223	26	21	22	18

* 用 ³H–Tdr 孵育 3 h。

† 用 ³H–Tdr 孵育 4 h。

‡ 显影颗粒数量至少是任何其他相似大小染色体的 2.2 倍的 DLX 染色体。

Table 2. Autoradiographic Data from Mixed Lymphocyte Cultures

Cell type	No. of cells scored	No. of labelled cells	Cells with a DLX		Difference in proportions	s.e.	P
			No.	Proportion			
Horse	158	144	33	0.2291	0.1205	0.0515	0.05>P>0.025
Donkey	96	92	10	0.1086			

The relative frequencies of DLX^D and DLX^H in cultures from individual mules or hinnies did not differ significantly from the overall frequencies for their own group (Tables 1 and 3). The hinnies behave in a similar fashion to the mules, but are possibly less homogeneous and seem to show a slightly higher frequency of DLX^H (Table 3).

Table 3. Observed Proportion of Cells with an X^D Differentially Labelled and Their 95% Confidence Limits

Hybrids		Tissue	Proportion DLX^D	95% Confidence limits
Type	No.			
Mules	27	S	0.928	0.661−0.998
	33	B	0.889	0.708−0.976
		S	0.955	0.848−0.995
	100	B	0.887	0.790−0.950
		S	1.00	0.631−1.00
	143	B	1.00	0.631−1.00
	144	B	0.854	0.708−0.944
	145	B	1.00	0.292−1.00
	Total	B	0.887	0.824−0.932
		S	0.955	0.875−0.991
Hinnies	138	B	1.00	0.158−1.00
	139	B	1.00	0.541−1.00
	187	B	0.786	0.590−0.917
	188	B	0.846	0.545−0.981
	189	B	0.667	0.410−0.867
	190	B	0.692	0.386−0.909
	191	B	0.889	0.517−0.997
	203	B	0.795	0.647−0.902
	Total	B	0.789	0.747−0.885
Total		B	0.841	0.801−0.853

S, Skin fibroblasts; B, lymphocytes.

In the sample of twenty cells selected at random from a mule and each of two hinnies (Table 4) the grain counts over the most densely labelled medium sized submetacentric and metacentric chromosomes showed the same regression line on the total cell grain counts, but the former chromosome had clearly higher grain counts than the latter. If these chromosomes are taken to represent respectively the X^D and X^H chromosome, these data seem to agree with the qualitative observation that the X^D chromosome is more frequently differentially labelled. Furthermore, the proportion of X chromosome grains counted over X^D seems to be very similar in the mule and the two hinnies.

表 2. 混合淋巴细胞培养物的放射自显影数据

细胞类型	记录的细胞数量	标记细胞的数量	含有一个 DLX 的细胞		比例之差	标准误差	概率
			数量	比例			
马	158	144	33	0.2291	0.1205	0.0515	0.05>P>0.025
驴	96	92	10	0.1086			

DLX^D 和 DLX^H 在每匹马骡或者驴骡细胞培养物中的相对频率与其在马骡或者驴骡所属群体中的总体频率并没有明显的差异(表 1 和表 3)。驴骡的表现与马骡很类似,但在均一性上可能要稍差一些,而且驴骡的 DLX^H 出现频率似乎比马骡的略高 (表 3)。

表 3. 含有一个差异标记的 X^D 染色体的细胞比例与它们的 95% 置信区间

杂交体		组织	DLX^D 的比例	95% 置信区间
类型	编号			
马骡	27	S	0.928	0.661 ~ 0.998
	33	B	0.889	0.708 ~ 0.976
		S	0.955	0.848 ~ 0.995
	100	B	0.887	0.790 ~ 0.950
		S	1.00	0.631 ~ 1.00
	143	B	1.00	0.631 ~ 1.00
	144	B	0.854	0.708 ~ 0.944
	145	B	1.00	0.292 ~ 1.00
	总计	B	0.887	0.824 ~ 0.932
		S	0.955	0.875 ~ 0.991
驴骡	138	B	1.00	0.158 ~ 1.00
	139	B	1.00	0.541 ~ 1.00
	187	B	0.786	0.590 ~ 0.917
	188	B	0.846	0.545 ~ 0.981
	189	B	0.667	0.410 ~ 0.867
	190	B	0.692	0.386 ~ 0.909
	191	B	0.889	0.517 ~ 0.997
	203	B	0.795	0.647 ~ 0.902
	总计	B	0.789	0.747 ~ 0.885
总计		B	0.841	0.801 ~ 0.853

S:皮肤成纤维细胞;B:淋巴细胞。

在一匹马骡和两匹驴骡中各随机抽取 20 个细胞样本 (表 4),对标记最致密的中型大小近中着丝粒染色体和中央着丝粒染色体的放射自显影颗粒进行计数,在用计数结果对全部细胞显影颗粒计数进行回归分析时得到了相同的回归线,但前者染色体的显影颗粒计数明显高于后者。如果认为这些染色体分别代表了 X^D 和 X^H 的话,那么上述数据似乎与定性观察结果相吻合,即 X^D 染色体在差异标记中出现得更频繁。此外,这匹马骡和这两匹驴骡的 X^D 染色体显影颗粒所占的比例似乎非常接近。

Table 4. Comparisons between the Grain Counts over the Most Densely Labelled X^D and X^H-like Chromosomes) $?X^D$, $?X^H$) in a Random Sample of Cells from Mule 100 and the Hinnies 188 and 203

Hybrid No.	No. of cells analysed	Comparison of mean grain counts over $?X^D$ and $?X^H$	Comparison of the regression coefficients of the logarithm of $?X^D$ and $?X^H$ grain counts on TGC*	Comparison of the contribution (D) of $?X^D$ to the grains counted over the presumptive X chromosomes in the mule and the two hinnies
100	21	$\overline{Y}_1 = 12.85$ $\overline{Y}_2 = 9.00$ $\overline{Y}_1 - \overline{Y}_2 = 3.85$ s.e. $(\overline{Y}_1 - \overline{Y}_2) = 1.35$ $P<0.02$	$b_1 = 0.000956$ $b_2 = 0.001864$ $b_1 - b_2 = -0.000908$ s.e.$(b_1 - b_2) = 0.000869$ $P>0.3$	$D_m = 0.5882$
188	20	$\overline{Y}_1 = 8.40$ $\overline{Y}_2 = 6.10$ $\overline{Y}_1 - \overline{Y}_2 = 2.30$ s.e.$(\overline{Y}_1 - \overline{Y}_2) = 0.964$ $P<0.05$	$b_1 = 0.00209$ $b_2 = 0.00199$ $b_1 - b_2 = 0.00010$ s.e.$(b_1 - b_2) = 0.00077$ $P>0.9$	$D_h = 0.5892$ $D_m - D_h = -0.0010$
203	18	$\overline{Y}_1 = 15.61$ $\overline{Y}_2 = 10.61$ $\overline{Y}_1 - \overline{Y}_2 = 5.00$ s.e. $(\overline{Y}_1 - \overline{Y}_2) = 2.25$ $P<0.05$	$b_1 = 0.00102$ $b_2 = 0.00205$ $b_1 - b_2 = -0.00103$ s.e.$(b_1 - b_2) = 0.000613$ $P>0.1$	s.e.$(D_m - D_h) = 0.023$ $P>0.8$

* Scatter diagrams have shown that the regressions of the logarithms of the $?X$ chromosomes grain counts on the total complement grain counts (TGC) are linear.
1, $?X^D$; 2, X^H; m, mule; h, hinny.

Finally, in the mixed leucocyte cultures the regression of the grains counted over the differentially labelled X chromosomes, or over the most densely labelled X-like chromosomes, on the total cell grain counts was very similar in the horse and donkey cells. The covariance analysis (Table 5) showed that the grain counts over the X^H and X^D were very similar after allowance had been made for the labelling over the rest of the complement.

Table 5. Comparison by Covariance Analysis of the Grain Counts over Differentially Labelled X Chromosomes (A) or the Most Densely Labelled X-like Chromosomes (B) in Horse–Donkey Mixed Blood Cultures

Analysis	A chromosome		B chromosome	
	X^D	X^H	$?X^D$	$?X^H$
No. cells analysed	10	33	20	20
Mean grain counts	$\overline{Y}_1 = 30.21$	$\overline{Y}_2 = 26.00$	$\overline{Y}_1 = 25.65$	$\overline{Y}_2 = 19.95$
Adjusted mean	$\overline{Y}_1^1 = 29.55$	$\overline{Y}_2^1 = 28.17$	$\overline{Y}_1^1 = 22.90$	$\overline{Y}_2^1 = 22.70$
Difference	$\overline{Y}_1^1 - \overline{Y}_2^1 = 1.38$		$\overline{Y}_1^1 - \overline{Y}_2^1 = 0.20$	
s.e. of difference	1.88		2.55	
Probability	$0.5>P>0.4$		$0.95>P>0.90$	

Scatter diagrams were made before these analyses. These have shown a linear relationship between the presumptive X chromosome grain counts and the counts over the rest of the complement. The variance of Y was fairly constant over the range of total grain counts used and this was similar in the two samples compared. The regression coefficients of the individual samples used in this comparison were significantly different from zero, but did not differ significantly from each other.

These results show that in both crosses irrespective of the direction of the cross, X^D is

表 4. 在 100 号马骡以及 188 号和 203 号驴骡的细胞随机抽样中标记最致密的类 X^D 和类 X^H 染色体（$?X^D$ 和 $?X^H$）之间的颗粒计数对比

杂交动物编号	被分析细胞的数量	对比 $?X^D$ 和 $?X^H$ 的平均颗粒计数	对比 $?X^D$ 和 $?X^H$ 的颗粒计数 log 值对 TGC* 的回归系数	对比 $?X^D$ 在这匹马骡和这两匹驴骡中类 X 色体的颗粒计数上的贡献（D）
100	21	$\overline{Y}_1 = 12.85$ $\overline{Y}_2 = 9.00$ $\overline{Y}_1 - \overline{Y}_2 = 3.85$ 标准误差 = 1.35 $P<0.02$	$b_1 = 0.000956$ $b_2 = 0.001864$ $b_1-b_2 = -0.000908$ 标准误差 = 0.000869 $P>0.3$	$D_m = 0.5882$
188	20	$\overline{Y}_1 = 8.40$ $\overline{Y}_2 = 6.10$ $\overline{Y}_1 - \overline{Y}_2 = 2.30$ 标准误差 = 0.964 $P<0.05$	$b_1 = 0.00209$ $b_2 = 0.00199$ $b_1-b_2 = 0.00010$ 标准误差 = 0.00077 $P>0.9$	$D_h = 0.5892$ $D_m-D_h = -0.0010$
203	18	$\overline{Y}_1 = 15.61$ $\overline{Y}_2 = 10.61$ $\overline{Y}_1 - \overline{Y}_2 = 5.00$ 标准误差 = 2.25 $P<0.05$	$b_1 = 0.00102$ $b_2 = 0.00205$ $b_1-b_2 = -0.00103$ 标准误差 = 0.000613 $P>0.1$	标准误差 =0.023 $P > 0.8$

* 散点图显示 $?X$ 染色体颗粒计数的 log 值对全部标记物颗粒计数（TGC）的回归是呈线性的。

1 代表 $?X^D$；2 代表 X^H；m 代表马骡；h 代表驴骡。

最后，在混合白细胞培养物中，用差异标记的 X 染色体或者标记最致密的类 X 染色体的颗粒计数对全部细胞显影颗粒计数进行回归分析的结果显示：马的细胞与驴的细胞非常相近。在考虑了剩余标记物对标记的影响后，协方差分析结果（表 5）显示染色体 X^H 和 X^D 的显影颗粒计数非常接近。

表 5. 马 – 驴混合血液培养物中差异标记 X 染色体（A）和标记最致密的类 X 染色体（B）的颗粒计数协方差分析结果对比

分析结果	A 染色体		B 染色体	
	X^D	X^H	$?X^D$	$?X^H$
被分析细胞的数量	10	33	20	20
平均颗粒计数	$\overline{Y}_1 = 30.21$	$\overline{Y}_2 = 26.00$	$\overline{Y}_1 = 25.65$	$\overline{Y}_2 = 19.95$
校正后的平均计数	$\overline{Y}_1^1 = 29.55$	$\overline{Y}_2^1 = 28.17$	$\overline{Y}_1^1 = 22.90$	$\overline{Y}_2^1 = 22.70$
偏差	$\overline{Y}_1^1 - \overline{Y}_2^1 = 1.38$		$\overline{Y}_1^1 - \overline{Y}_2^1 = 0.20$	
标准误差	1.88		2.55	
概率	$0.5>P>0.4$		$0.95>P>0.90$	

在进行这些分析之前先制作散点图。散点图表明了类 X 染色体的颗粒计数与剩余标记物颗粒计数之间的线性关系。方差 Y 在所用的全部颗粒计数范围内是相当稳定的，并且这种情况在用于对比的两个样品中都是类似的。在上述对比分析中用到的单个样品的回归系数显然不是 0，但各个回归系数之间并没有明显的差异。

上述结果表明：在两种杂交体中，不论杂交的方向如何，X^D 在差异标记中的出

consistently more often differentially labelled than X^H. This differs from the findings of Mukherjee and his co-workers[1,3] but is in broad agreement with the observation of Cohen and Rattazzi[6].

Mukherjee and Sinha[1] used both longer labelling and colchicine times for blood cultures, while for skin cultures Mukherjee *et al.*[3] used a shorter labelling time than ours. Their results, however, differ in the same direction in both culture systems from those reported here; this suggests that the discrepancy cannot be explained by a variation in labelling procedure.

In the present study the DLX was defined as the chromosome of compatible morphology which had at least twice as many grains as any other chromosome of a similar size. This is in agreement with the illustration of Mukherjee and Sinha[1] who did not discuss their criteria in detail, but is less strict than that used in their later article[3] in which the DLX is defined as the chromosome with a grain count of at least 50% the total grain count over the whole complement.

In our opinion, this definition is too strict because of the difficulty of counting fifty grains or more over an X-like chromosome, which means that all cells with a total grain count of 100 or more over the remainder of the complement would have to be rejected. To see whether a more strict definition of DLX could affect the results presented here, however, all cells in which the grain counts over the DLX were not greatly in excess of twice that over any chromosome of similar size were rejected, leaving only those cells with a "very hot" DLX available for analysis. This procedure did not alter the ratio of DLX^H to DLX^D (Table 1). It seems reasonable to conclude from this that the way in which the DLX is defined is unlikely to account for the differences observed. Could any peculiarity or intrinsic difference in the labelling of X^D and X^H, not associated with the process of facultative heterochromatinization of the X chromosome, for example, a higher rate of DNA synthesis in X^D than in X^H at some stage of late S, be responsible for the difference which we have observed between the frequency of differentially labelled X^D and X^H in the hybrids' cultures?

Data from the control cultures suggest that this is not so. The mixed lymphocyte cultures showed that the horse lymphocytes have a G_2 similar to that of the donkey and have a differentially labelled X chromosome at least as frequently. Admittedly a mixed lymphocyte culture is not a perfect control for cultures from hybrids in which each chromosome must be compared with the haploid sets from both parental species. But covariance analysis of grain counts over the DLX in the mixed lymphocyte cultures shows that, when account is taken of the labelling over the rest of the complement, DLX^D and DLX^H label in a similar fashion during the part of S studied. This is confirmed by the similarity of the regression of grain counts over the presumptive X^D and X^H on total complement grain counts

现频率始终比 X^H 高。这与慕克吉及其同事的发现 [1,3] 不相符，但与科恩和拉塔齐的观察结果 [6] 在很大程度上一致。

在对血液培养物进行标记和用秋水仙碱处理时，慕克吉和辛哈 [1] 用的时间比我们用的时间长；但在皮肤培养物中，慕克吉等人 [3] 在标记时用的时间比我们的短。然而，他们在这两个培养系统上得到的结果与本文中报道的结果之间存在着同一方向上的偏差；这表明结果上的这种差异并不能用标记过程的不一致来解释。

在本研究中，DLX 被定义为符合下述形态特征的染色体：显影的颗粒计数是具有相似大小的任何其他染色体的至少 2 倍。这与慕克吉和辛哈的描述 [1] 一致，他们没有对自己的这个标准进行详细的论述。但这个标准不及他们在后续文章 [3] 中所用的标准那么严格。在后面的文章中，他们把 DLX 定义为颗粒计数占整个标记物全部颗粒计数的至少 50% 的染色体。

我们认为，这种定义过于严格，因为在一个类 X 染色体上清点 50 个或者更多的颗粒数目是有一定困难的，这意味着我们将不得不放弃那些剩余标记物的总颗粒计数达到 100 或 100 以上的所有细胞。不管怎样，为了了解对 DLX 染色体的一个更严格的定义是否会对本文报道的研究结果产生影响，我们将不考虑那些在 DLX 染色体上的颗粒计数没有远远大于任何相似大小染色体上的颗粒计数 2 倍的所有细胞，那么就只剩下那些含有一个"过热"DLX 染色体的细胞可供分析了。这种研究方式并没有改变 DLX^H 与 DLX^D 的比值（表 1）。由此似乎可以很合理地得到如下结论：观察到的差异不可能用定义 DLX 染色体的方式不同来解释。标记染色体 X^D 和 X^H 时存在的独特性或者固有差异——这种独特性或者固有差异与 X 染色体的功能异染色质化过程无关，例如：在 S 期后期的某一阶段，X^D 染色体中的 DNA 合成速率比 X^H 染色体的要高——能否解释我们在杂交动物培养物中观察到的差异标记 X^D 和 X^H 染色体的出现频率之间的差异？

从对照培养物中得到的数据表明答案是否定的。混合淋巴细胞培养物的结果显示：马的淋巴细胞具有与驴的淋巴细胞相似的 G_2 期，并且至少经常会含有一条差异标记的 X 染色体。诚然，混合淋巴细胞培养物并不是杂交体培养物的最佳对照物，因为我们需要将杂交体中的每一条染色体与来自两个亲本物种的单倍体组进行对比。但是对混合淋巴细胞培养物中 DLX 染色体的颗粒计数的协方差分析结果显示：在考虑了剩余标记物对标记的影响后，染色体 DLX^D 和 DLX^H 在 S 期的部分阶段表现出相似的标记方式。这一观点得到了以下事实的证实：在我们用于定量研究的 3 匹杂交骡子上，对类 X^D 和类 X^H 染色体的颗粒计数进行基于全部标记物颗粒

(TGC) in the three animals studied quantitatively (Table 4). Furthermore, an analysis of lymphocyte cultures from the hybrids shows that with an increase in labelling time the proportion of labelled cells increases and that of cells with a DLX decreases, while the relative frequency of DLX^D and DLX^H remains the same (Tables 1 and 6).

Table 6. Analysis of the Tendency for the Proportion of DLX^D to Vary According to the Proportion of Labelled Cells in Blood Cultures of Mules and Hinnies

Type of hybrid	Regression coefficient	SS due to regression	χ^2	P
Mules	−0.5341	352.4	0.429	>0.5
Hinnies	−1.033	1,531	1.86	>0.1
All*	−1.189	3,777	4.6	<0.05

This analysis was conducted using the angular transformation method[11].

* Since the proportion of DLX^D in the hinnies is lower than that of mules and their cell samples contribute chiefly to the class with a relatively high proportion of labelled cells the data regarding both types of hybrid together are not very meaningful.

Finally, can these results be explained on the basis of an error in the identification of the X^D due to the presence of a morphologically similar late replicating autosome which mimics the behaviour of the DLX? Our definition of the DLX precludes this explanation unless the DLX^H had less than half the grains counted over this autosome much more often than the DLX^D. This could occur either if the DLX^H usually had lower grain counts than the DLX^D or if it was in the differentially labelled state less often. The data presented do not fit the first of these alternatives so that it seems reasonable to accept the second.

A further possibility which might account for our results is biased selection of cells or chromosome identification. To avoid this, the analysis of autoradiographs was conducted as independently as possible of the morphological chromosome analysis (a chromosome was classified as differentially labelled before analysis of the unlabelled photographs, and karyotypes were made by an individual who was unaware of the autoradiographic results). It is difficult, however, completely to exclude bias in an analysis of this type. The most serious cause of observer bias is the *a priori* expectations. In the study described here our intention was to investigate the relationship between differential labelling and genetic inactivity of one X chromosome, and it was expected that a 1:1 relationship would be found between the DLX^H and DLX^D in accordance with earlier findings[1]. Preliminary observations on differential labelling in cells with three mules[2] showed this was not so and it was considered a tentative hypothesis that the reciprocal cross might show the reverse, namely a greater frequency of DLX^H than DLX^D. On both counts therefore the results reported here are contrary to *a priori* expectations and lead to the conclusion that X^D is significantly more often differentially labelled than X^H in both mules and hinnies.

These results must now be considered in relation to the Lyon hypothesis (LH). In contrast to the suggestion of others[1,3] the mule may not provide a simple cytological test of random inactivation for reasons which have already been discussed[4]. These hybrids are, however, useful in studying the relationship between differential labelling of one X chromosome

700

计数（TGC）的回归分析，所得的结果是相似的（表4）。此外，关于杂交体的淋巴细胞培养物的一项分析结果显示：随着标记时间的增长，被标记细胞的比例增加，而含 DLX 染色体的细胞比例却降低，尽管 DLX^D 和 DLX^H 的相对频率保持不变（表1和表6）。

表 6. 马骡和驴骡血液培养物中 DLX^D 所占比例随标记细胞所占比例的变化而变化的趋势分析

杂交动物类型	回归系数	回归的离均差平方和	χ^2	P
马骡	−0.5341	352.4	0.429	>0.5
驴骡	−1.033	1,531	1.86	>0.1
所有 *	−1.189	3,777	4.6	<0.05

这项分析是采用角变换法进行的 [11]。

* 因为驴骡中 DLX^D 染色体的比例要低于马骡，并且它们的细胞样品主要是对标记细胞所占比例比较高的类别有贡献，所以合并两种杂交类型的数据并没有太大的意义。

最后，能否用在识别 X^D 染色体时的一个错误来解释这些结果呢？出现错误的原因是：存在形态上类似且延迟复制的常染色体，它可以表现出类似于 DLX 染色体的行为。我们对 DLX 染色体的定义即可排除上述解释，除非 DLX^H 染色体出现颗粒计数少于这种常染色体的一半的情况总是多于 DLX^D 染色体。如果 DLX^H 染色体的颗粒计数通常比 DLX^D 的低，或者 DLX^H 染色体在差异标记中的出现频率低，那么上述情况就有可能出现。本文提供的数据并不符合两种假设中的第一种，因而第二种似乎可以被合理地接受。

还有一种可能性，即细胞或者染色体识别上的偏差性选择，或许可以解释我们的分析结果。为避免发生这种情况，我们在进行放射自显影分析的时候尽可能做到不依赖于染色体的形态学分析（先把一个染色体归入差异标记类，然后再对未标示的照片进行分析；并让一位不知道放射自显影分析结果的研究人员来确定核型）。然而，要想在这类分析中完全不出现偏差是十分困难的。观察者产生偏差的最重要的原因是先验的预期。我们进行这项研究的目的是检查染色体的差异标记与一条 X 染色体在遗传性状上表达失活之间的联系，根据早先的报道 [1]，我们预计染色体 DLX^D 和 DLX^H 之间应存在 1:1 的关系。在 3 匹马骡的细胞中观察差异标记的初步结果 [2] 显示情况并非如此，于是我们便提出了一个尝试性假说，认为反交也许会表现出结果上的扭转，也就是说染色体 DLX^H 的出现频率要比染色体 DLX^D 的高。因此，在两者的计数上，本文报道的结果与先前的预期是相反的，由本文中的结果可以推出：在马骡和驴骡中，染色体 X^D 在差异标记中的出现频率显然高于染色体 X^H。

现在必须认为这些结果影响到了莱昂假说。与其他人的结论 [1,3] 相反，由于先前已经讨论过的原因 [4]，由马骡给出的简单细胞学检测结果可能说明不了随机失活。然而，这些杂交体在研究单一 X 染色体的差异标记与遗传失活之间的联系方面

and genetic inactivation. Data on glucose-6-phosphate dehydrogenase (Gd)[5] show that the frequency with which Gd^D is expressed in fibroblast clones derived from three hybrids is in almost exact inverse proportion to the frequency with which X^D is observed to be differentially labelled in both lymphocytes and fibroblasts. Furthermore, qualitative data on expression of Gd^D show that, with the exception of one animal, it is expressed far more weakly than Gd^H in all the hybrids studied[10]. Cohen and Rattazzi[6] have reported a close correlation between the frequency of DLX^D and the expression of Gd^D in four further female mules. In each animal the X^D was more frequently late replicating and, correlated with this, Gd^D was the minor component. Hook and Brustman[10] have studied Gd expression in organs from 37 female mules. They found that in most tissues (blood, pancreas, brain, cervical cord, kidney and parotid gland) Gd^H is preferentially expressed. In thyroid and lung there appeared to be random expression while in the liver Gd^D seemed to be preferentially expressed.

The excellent correlation observed in our studies and those of Cohen and Rattazzi[6] between differential labelling and the expression of an X-linked locus implies a definite relationship between these two phenomena; proof of such a relationship will be provided by autoradiographic studies on the clones discussed in the previous article[5]. These are in progress. A comparison of X chromosome behaviour and Gd espression in both the mule and the hinny suggests that neither the maternal cytoplasm nor the maternal environment is important in determining which X chromosome becomes genetically inactive and differentially labelled in the female hybrids or in determining which cell type proliferates preferentially.

The significant excess of cells with an inactive and differentially labelled X^D is most easily explained by a difference between the two X chromosomes either in respect to the mechanism of "induction" of facultative heterochromatin or to the increased fitness which an active X^H confers on the hybrid cells resulting in selection in their favour. There are at least two alternatives which might account for a difference between X^D and X^H in regard to the mechanism of heterochromatinization; first, that X^D is simply more prone to become heterochromatic, or, second, that heterochromatinization commences earlier in the donkey than in the horse and that this is retained in the hybrids and so leads to an earlier involvement of X^D compared with X^H. The studies reported in the previous article[5] on fibroblast clones suggest *in vitro* cell selection in favour of cells with an active X^H; studies by Hook and Brustman[10] suggest that *in vivo* cell selection occurs in different organs.

Our finding of one animal (No. 192)[5] with a preponderance of Gd^D, on which unfortunately autoradiographic studies were not possible, suggests that there may be inter-animal variation in the expression of Gd. Inter-animal variation could perhaps account also for the discrepancy between our autoradiographic results and those of Mukherjee and his colleagues[1,3].

Our data and those of Cohen and Rattazzi[6], however, clearly show that X^D tends to be more often heterochromatic than X^H in the tissues of female horse-donkey hybrids which have been available for study.

702

还是有用处的。有关葡萄糖 –6– 磷酸脱氢酶（*Gd*）的数据 [5] 显示，在源于 3 个杂交体的成纤维细胞克隆中 *Gd* 的表达频率与在淋巴细胞和成纤维细胞中观察到的染色体 X^D 差异标记的频率几乎精确成反比。而且，关于 *Gd*^{D} 表达的定性数据表明：除了一只动物以外，*Gd*^{D} 在所有研究过的杂交动物中的表达远远弱于 *Gd*^{H} 的表达 [10]。科恩和拉塔齐 [6] 曾报道过在另外 4 匹母马骡中染色体 DLX^D 的频率与 *Gd*^{D} 表达之间的密切关系。在每只动物中，染色体 X^D 都表现出更频繁的延迟复制，与此相关的是，*Gd*^{D} 成为了一种较少的成分。胡克和布鲁斯特曼 [10] 已经在 37 匹母马骡的器官中研究了 *Gd* 的表达。他们发现：在绝大多数组织（血液、胰腺、脑、颈髓、肾脏和腮腺）中，*Gd*^{H} 是优先表达的。在甲状腺和肺中看似为随机表达，而在肝脏中优先表达的似乎是 *Gd*^{D}。

我们与科恩、拉塔齐 [6] 在研究中观察到的差异标记与 X 连锁基因表达之间的良好相关性暗示着这两种现象之间存在着一定的联系；证明这种联系的证据可以通过对在先前文章中讨论过的克隆体 [5] 进行放射自显影研究得到。这些实验仍在进行中。对比马骡和驴骡中 X 染色体的行为与 *Gd* 的表达的结果表明：在决定雌性杂交体中哪条 X 染色体会发生遗传失活和差异标记，或者在决定哪种细胞类型会优先增殖上，母系的细胞质或者母系的环境都不重要。

那些含有失活和差异标记的 X^D 染色体的细胞出现显著过量现象很容易用两条 X 染色体之间的差异来解释，或者是因为功能异染色质的"诱导"机制，或者是因为活性 X^H 染色体赋予了杂交细胞更强的适应度，从而产生了有利于自身的选择。从异染色质化机制的角度来看，至少有两种解释可以说明染色体 X^D 和 X^H 之间的差异。第一，染色体 X^D 更容易发生异染色质化；或第二，异染色质化发生在驴身上比发生在马身上更早，并在杂交体上保留下来，于是就产生了染色体 X^D 发生异染色质化要早于 X^H 的结果。我们在以前文章 [5] 中报道的关于成纤维细胞克隆体的研究结果表明：体外细胞的选择偏向于含活性染色体 X^H 的细胞；胡克和布鲁斯特曼的研究结果 [10] 表明：体内的细胞选择会发生在各种器官中。

我们发现有一只动物（编号为 192）[5] 中 *Gd*^{D} 占多数，这表明 *Gd* 的表达也许存在动物的个体间差异，可惜我们无法对其进行放射自显影研究。动物的个体间差异或许还可以用于解释我们的放射自显影结果与慕克吉及其同事的结果 [1,3] 之间为什么有差别。

然而，我们的数据与科恩、拉塔齐的数据 [6] 显然说明：在曾被用于研究的母马 – 驴杂交体的组织中，染色体 X^D 倾向于比 X^H 更经常出现异染色质化。

We thank Drs. R. V. Short, W. R. Allen and M. J. Freire, with his colleagues in Portugal, for samples of material. Collection of Portuguese samples was supported by grants to J. L. H. from the Wellcome Trust. During this work J. L. H. and F. G. were supported by the Spastics Society. J. L. H. also acknowledges support from ARC and the Canadian Medical Research Council. We also thank Mrs. F. F. Collins, Mrs. J. Hallett, Miss A. Fryer, Miss V. M. McGuire and Mr. L. Grixti for technical assistance.

(**232**, 315-319; 1971)

F. Giannelli: Paediatric Research Unit, Guy's Hospital Medical School, London SEI.

J. L. Hamerton: Department of Genetics, Children's Hospital, Winnipeg, and Departments of Paediatrics and Anatomy, University of Manitoba.

Received May 7, 1971.

References:

1. Mukherjee, B. B., and Sinha, A. K., *Proc. US Nat. Acad. Sci.*, **51**, 252 (1964).

2. Hamerton, J. L., Giannelli, F., Collins, F., Hallett, J., Fryer, A., McGuire, V. M., and Short, R. V., *Nature*, **222**, 1277 (1969).

3. Mukherjee, B. B., Mukherjee, A. B., and Mukherjee, A. B., *Nature*, **228**, 1321 (1970).

4. Hamerton, J. L., and Giannelli, F., *Nature*, **228**, 1322 (1970).

5. Hamerton, J. L., Richardson, B. J., Gee, P. A., Allen, W. R., and Short, R. V., *Nature*, **232**, 312 (1971).

6. Cohen, M. M., and Rattazzi, M. C., *Proc. US Nat. Acad. Sci.*, **68**, 544 (1971).

7. Hsu, T. C., and Kellogg, jun., D. S., *J. Nat. Cancer Inst.*, **25**, 221 (1960).

8. Moorhead, P. S., Howell, P. C., Mellman, W. J., Battips, D. M., and Hungerford, D. A., *Exp. Cell Res.*, **20**, 613 (1960).

9. Giannelli, F., *Human Chromosomes DNA Synthesis, Monographs in Human Genetics*, 5 (edit. by Beckman, L., and Hauge, M.) (Karger, Basel and New York, 1970).

10. Hook, E. B., and Brustman, L. D., *Genetics*, **64**, 2, Part 2 (abstract, 1970).

11. Fisher, R. A., and Yates, F., *Statistical Tables for Biological, Agricultural and Medical Research*, fifth ed. (Oliver and Boyd, Edinburgh, 1957).

感谢肖特博士、艾伦博士、弗莱雷博士及其葡萄牙同事为我们提供了动物样本。在葡萄牙搜集动物样本的工作得益于维康基金会对哈默顿的资助。在这项研究中，哈默顿和詹内利得到了痉挛协会的支持，哈默顿还得到了英国农业研究委员会和加拿大医学研究委员会的支持。柯林斯夫人、哈利特夫人、弗吕耶小姐、麦圭尔小姐和格里克斯蒂先生为我们提供了技术上的帮助，在此一并表示感谢。

（刘振明 翻译；梁前进 审稿）

Evidence for Selective Differences between Cells with an Active Horse X Chromosome and Cells with an Active Donkey X Chromosome in the Female Mule

E. B. Hook and L. D. Brustman

Editor's Note

Conflicting evidence meant that researchers were unsure whether X-inactivation, the process in females where one copy of the X chromosome is silenced during embryonic development, was random or not. Here Ernest B. Hook and Loretta D. Brustman look at the contribution of paternal and maternal X chromosomes in different tissues from female mules and find there are two organ types: "those in which the horse phenotype was usually predominant, and those in which expression was not significantly different from what would be expected on a random basis." If X-inactivation were non-random, they argue, the favoured allele should be found in all tissues. Any discrepancies between previous studies, they conclude, probably reflect sampling differences.

THE glucose-6-phosphate dehydrogenase (G6PD) locus is known to be X-linked in the horse and donkey[1,2]. The female mule, an interspecific hybrid of these two species, is an obligatory heterozygote for two electrophoretically distinguishable G6PD alleles[1,2].

Studies of the DNA replication patterns of the chromosomes of two female mules by Mukherjee et al.[3,4] have shown that, in about half the cells investigated in each animal, the X chromosome derived from the female parent (the horse X) was late replicating and the X chromosome derived from the male parent (the donkey X), was early replicating; the reverse pattern obtained in the other half of the cells. Hamerton et al.[5] found in three female mules, however, that most lymphocytes and fibroblasts had a late replicating donkey X chromosome and early replicating horse X chromosome. The distribution was significantly different from the roughly equal representation of cell types noted by Mukherjee et al. In the only cell line studied electrophoretically by Hamerton et al. horse G6PD was preferentially expressed, consistent with the hypothesis that the early replicating mammalian X chromosome in females is the active one[6]. The observations of the latter workers suggest that in some female mules, either (1) the donkey X chromosome is preferentially inactivated early in development, or (and) (2) cells with an active horse X chromosome have a selective advantage in at least some tissues during ontogeny.

We have investigated this question by studying the G6PD phenotypes of samples from tissues and organs of fifty-four female mules. The results for representative organs are

母马骡中含马活性X染色体的细胞和含驴活性X染色体的细胞之间选择差异的证据

胡克，布鲁斯特曼

编者按

由于所获得的证据间互相矛盾，研究人员难以确定在雌性动物中发生的 X 染色体失活（X 染色体的一个拷贝在胚胎发育过程中被沉默）过程是否是随机的。在本文中，欧内斯特·胡克和洛蕾塔·布鲁斯特曼考察了母马骡不同组织中父本 X 染色体和母本 X 染色体的贡献并发现存在两种器官类型："在一种类型中马的表型通常占主要地位，而在另一种类型中表型表达却与随机抽样所得的结果没有明显区别。"他们认为，如果 X 染色体失活是非随机的，那么应该在所有组织中都能发现优势等位基因。他们推断：在先前的研究结论之间所存在的任何偏差有可能都只是采样差异的反映。

众所周知，马和驴的葡萄糖 –6– 磷酸脱氢酶（G6PD）位点都是 X 连锁的 [1,2]。作为这两个物种种间杂交体的母马骡必然是一个有两条电泳清晰可辨的 G6PD 等位基因的杂合子 [1,2]。

慕克吉等人 [3,4] 曾对两匹母马骡染色体的 DNA 复制模式进行过研究，结果显示：在每匹母马骡的细胞中，大约有一半会出现母本 X 染色体（马 X 染色体）发生延迟复制而父本染色体（驴 X 染色体）发生早期复制的现象；而在另一半细胞中会出现相反的复制方式。然而，哈默顿等人 [5] 发现在三匹母马骡中绝大多数淋巴细胞和成纤维细胞会含有一条发生延迟复制的驴 X 染色体和一条发生早期复制的马 X 染色体。这种分布情况与慕克吉等人提出的两个细胞类型表现大致相等的说法显然不符。在哈默顿等人用电泳研究的唯——个细胞系中，优先表达的是马的 G6PD，这与在雌性哺乳动物中发生早期复制的 X 染色体具有活性的假说相符 [6]。后期的研究者通过观察发现，在一些母马骡中：（1）在发育初期，优先失活的是驴的 X 染色体；或者（并且）（2）在个体发育中，至少某些组织内带有马活性 X 染色体的细胞会具有选择上的优势。

为了探索这一问题，我们对 54 匹母马骡的组织和器官样品中的 G6PD 表型进行了研究。表 1 中列出的是几种典型器官的结果。表型结果的实例以及对应的解释示

listed in Table 1. Examples of patterns and their interpretation are illustrated in Fig. 1.

Table 1. G6PD Phenotypes of Female Mules

Predominant phenotype	Cervical cord	Pancreas	Parotid	Liver	Lung	Thyroid
H>D	20 (18)	19 (12)	23 (15)	9 (6)	8 (8)	8 (6)
H≅D	1 (1)	4 (4)	4 (3)	12 (7)	11 (5)	12 (9)
D>H	2 (2)	4 (3)	3 (3)	13 (8)	6 (4)	9 (5)

The number of animals with the observed phenotypes are listed. Not all organs from every animal could be investigated, but in twenty-two of the fifty-four animals at least five of the six organs listed in the table were studied. The results for these twenty-two animals are listed in parentheses. The patterns were scored independently by E. B. H. and L. D. B. and the sample rerun if there was a discrepancy or uncertainty (see Fig. 1). Examination of blood samples revealed that the horse band was the usual predominant one here also. Mixing experiments with variable proportions of donkey and horse blood samples with known activity indicated that, when the bands of approximately equal intensity were observed, there was at least 35% activity of the major component in the mixture. In a mule in which expression of donkey and horse phenotype was close to equality, there was no observed difference in the proportion of parental phenotype between reticulocyte-rich and reticulocyte-poor preparations, although there was less activity in the latter. Similarly, there was no observed difference between fresh and stored cells in the proportion of parental phenotype, although activity was lower in stored cells. The specific activities of G6PD in peripheral blood of a young donkey and of a young horse were within 10% of each other. Earlier studies[8] suggested that the donkey phenotype was preferentially expressed in liver, but this no longer seems likely.

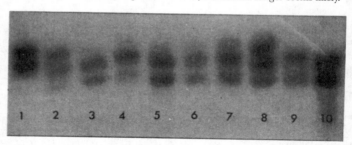

Fig. 1. The bands in the slots at extreme left (1) and right (10) illustrate donkey (D) and horse (H) patterns respectively. The other samples, from pancreas and parotid, were interpreted from left to right as follows: (2) D>H, (3) H>D, (4) ?, (repeat), (5) H>D, (6) H>D, (7) ?H≅D, (repeat), (8) D>H, (9) H>D. All organs were studied using starch gel electrophoresis in EBT buffer with standard methods[9] at pH 8.6. Almost all animals were relatively old. Organ samples were collected at the abattoir on dry ice about 60–120 min after death and exsanguination. Blood was obtained in citrate about 5–15 min after death and stored at 4°C.

There were two organ types: those in which the horse phenotype was usually predominant, and those in which expression was not significantly different from what would be expected on a random basis. In none of the organs studied was the donkey phenotype the usual predominant one. If X inactivation were non-random, and occurred at the early stage usually hypothesized in the mammalian female embryo, representation of the favoured allele should be relatively uniform in all derived tissues, unless cell selection in particular organs had also occurred. Since X inactivation is thought to occur at about the blastocyst stage[7], before observable organ differentiation, it seems unlikely that preferential

于图 1。

表 1. 母马骡的 G6PD 表型

主要表型	颈髓	胰腺	腮腺	肝脏	肺脏	甲状腺
马 > 驴	20 (18)	19 (12)	23 (15)	9 (6)	8 (8)	8 (6)
马 ⋚ 驴	1 (1)	4 (4)	4 (3)	12 (7)	11 (5)	12 (9)
驴 > 马	2 (2)	4 (3)	3 (3)	13 (8)	6 (4)	9 (5)

表中列出的是与观察到的表型相对应的动物数量。不能保证每只动物的全部器官都能用于研究，不过在 54 只动物中，我们对其中 22 只动物列于表中的 6 个器官中的至少 5 个进行了研究。这 22 只动物的研究结果列在圆括号中。表型结果（见图 1）是由欧内斯特·胡克和洛蕾塔·布鲁斯特曼分别得到的，如果两个人的结果之间存在不一致或者不确定的情况，那么样品实验就需要重复进行。对血液样品的检测结果显示：在这里马的显带仍然是普遍显著的。对已知活性的驴和马的血液样品进行不同比例混合实验，结果表明，当观察到显带的强度大致相同时，混合物中主要成分的活性至少可达 35%。在一匹驴和马的表型接近相等的马骡中，并没有观察到在富含和缺乏网织红细胞的培养物之间存在亲本表型比例上的差异，尽管在后者中活性会更低一些。同样地，在新鲜的细胞和储存的细胞之间也没有观测到亲本表型比例上的差别，尽管在储存的细胞中活性更低。在一匹幼驴和一匹幼马的外周血中，两者的 G6PD 比活性相差不到 10%。我们早先的研究结果 [8] 表明：在肝脏中优先表达的是驴的表型，但现在看来这是不可能的。

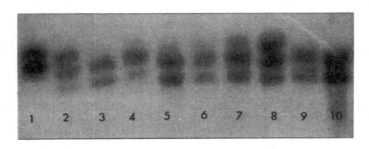

图 1. 电泳槽中的显带：最左边（1）和最右边（10）的显带分别代表驴（D）和马（H）的表型。其他样品均来自于胰腺和腮腺，从左到右依次为：(2) D>H，(3) H>D，(4) ?，(重复)，(5) H>D，(6) H>D，(7) ? H ⋚ D，(重复)，(8) D>H，(9) H>D。对所有器官的研究都是按照标准方法 [9] 在 pH 值 8.6 的 EBT 缓冲液（译者注：即 EDTA– 硼酸 –Tris 缓冲系统）中利用淀粉凝胶电泳进行的。几乎所有的动物年龄都相当大。在屠宰场收集已经死亡并被放血约 60 分钟~120 分钟后的动物的器官样本，放置在干冰上；在动物死亡约 5 分钟~15 分钟后取血并溶于柠檬酸盐中，然后 4℃储存。

我们发现有两种器官类型：一种是马的表型通常占主要地位的类型，另一种是表型表达与随机抽样所得结果没有明显区别的类型。在研究过的所有器官中，从未发现过任何一个驴的表型通常会占主要地位的器官。如果 X 染色体的失活是非随机的，并且按照通常的假设是发生在哺乳动物雌性胚胎生长的早期阶段，那么那些优势等位基因应该在所有的衍生组织中都表现出相对的一致性，除非在某些特殊器官中还会发生细胞选择。因为 X 染色体的失活大约发生在囊胚阶段 [7]，即在可观察到

inactivation has occurred just in the cell precursors of particular organs. It seems more probable that X-linked alleles of the donkey and horse have had different effects during development and maturation, with a relative selective advantage for cells with an active horse X chromosome in organs such as the parotid gland. But preferential expression of the horse X chromosome in these latter organs did not occur in all animals studied, indicating that the observed phenomenon represents a trend rather than a uniform developmental event in the female mule. Thus discrepancies between studies such as those of Hamerton *et al.* and Mukherjee *et al.* seem likely to reflect sampling differences in animals studied.

An alternative explanation for the observed distribution should be mentioned. Unknown organ specific factors may have differentially suppressed (or enhanced) expression of a particular parental G6PD phenotype (for example, perhaps inhibiting expression of the donkey band in cervical cord, pancreas and so on). Although this seems unlikely, it cannot be completely excluded. But when samples of pancreas with horse phenotype were mixed with samples of other organs which expressed the donkey phenotype, there was no evidence for an inhibiting factor.

(**232**, 349-350; 1971)

Ernest B. Hook and Loretta D. Brustman: Birth Defects Institute, New York State Department of Health, and Department of Pediatrics, Albany Medical College of Union University, Albany, New York 12208.

Received February 18, 1971.

References:

1. Trujillo, J. M., Walden, B., O'Neil, P., and Anstall, H. B., *Science*, **148**, 1603 (1965).

2. Mathai, C. K., Ohno, S., and Beutler, E., *Nature*, **210**, 115 (1966).

3. Mukherjee, B. B., Mukherjee, A. B., and Mukherjee, A. B., *Nature*, **228**, 1321 (1970).

4. Mukherjee, B. B., and Sinha, A. K., *Proc. US Nat. Acad. Sci.*, **51**, 252 (1964).

5. Hamerton, J. L., Gianelli, F., Collins, F., Hallett, J., Fryer, A., McGuire, V. M., and Short, R. V., *Nature*, **222**, 1277 (1969).

6. Lyon, M. F., in *Adv. Teratol.*, **1** (edit. by Woolam, D. H. M.) (Logos Press, London, 1966).

7. Kinsey, J. D., *Genetics*, **55**, 337 (1967).

8. Hook, E. B., and Brustman, L. D., *Genetics*, **64**, 530 (1970).

9. Motulsky, A. G., and Yoshida, A., in *Biochemical Methods in Red Cell Genetics* (edit. by Yunis, J. Y.), 51 (Academic Press, New York, 1969).

的器官分化出现之前，所以染色体优先失活刚好发生在某些特殊器官的细胞前体中似乎是不大可能的。可能性更大的似乎是：驴和马的 X 连锁等位基因在胚胎发育阶段和成熟阶段所起的作用不同，它们对腮腺等器官中含有马活性 X 染色体的细胞具有相对的选择性优势。但是在腮腺等器官中，马 X 染色体被优先表达的现象并没有发生在所有研究过的母马骡上，这说明观察到的现象所代表的只是一种倾向，而不是母马骡中始终如一的发育事件。因此，诸如哈默顿等人和慕克吉等人研究结果之间的差异，看起来很可能是被研究动物的采样差异的反映。

应该指出，还有一种能说明所观测到的分布规律的解释。器官中一些未知的特殊因子也许会差异性地抑制（或者增强）某种特定的亲本 G6PD 表型的表达（例如，也许会在颈髓、胰腺等器官中抑制驴的显带的表达）。尽管这看上去可能性不大，但也不能被完全排除。然而，当把带有马的表型的胰腺样品与带有驴的表型的其他器官样品混合在一起时，就找不到任何有关抑制因子的证据了。

（刘振明 翻译；梁前进 审稿）

Bomb ^{14}C in the Human Population

R. Nydal *et al.*

Editor's Note

Understanding the cycling of carbon between the atmosphere, oceans and biosphere (owing mostly to the uptake of carbon dioxide in photosynthesis) is essential for predicting how anthropogenic greenhouse gases affect climate. This paper from scientists at the Norwegian Institute of Technology shows how interest in the carbon cycle was already burgeoning in the early 1970s. It is expressed within the context of its time: it focuses on how the radioactive isotope carbon-14 (^{14}C), released into the atmosphere by nuclear weapons tests, will increase in the human body, which was considered a potential health risk. Strikingly, this increase is very short-lived, because the bomb ^{14}C is rapidly diluted by carbon dioxide released from fossil-fuel burning—today considered a much greater hazard.

IN the atmosphere ^{14}C occurs principally as ^{14}CO$_2$ and is usually produced by nuclear reactions between cosmic ray neutrons and the nitrogen atoms of the air. The natural equilibrium between production and disintegration of ^{14}C determines a part of the natural background radiation to the human population. From 1955 there has been a gradual increase of ^{14}C in the atmosphere, the land biosphere and the ocean, as a result of nuclear tests. Although ^{14}C was initially not regarded as an important hazard to man[1], it was later pointed out[2-4] that ^{14}C could be a source of appreciable genetic hazard in the world's population, because of its long half life (5,700 yr).

At this laboratory we have studied the ^{14}C concentration in the human body[5]. The correspondence between ^{14}C in the atmosphere and in the human body, mediated as it is by photosynthesis, has been confirmed in 6 yr of measurements[6-8].

Since 1955, about two-thirds of the total nuclear energy liberated in nuclear tests has resulted from tests carried out in the atmosphere at high northern latitudes in 1961 and 1962 (ref. 9). The subsequent transfer of ^{14}C down to the troposphere, the biosphere and the ocean has been followed in detail[10-16]. The ^{14}C excess[16] (δ^{14}C) in the northern troposphere (Fig. 1) is representative chiefly of the region between 30°N and 90°N, although the curve for the southern troposphere is representative of the region from the equator to 90°S.

进入人体的核弹 ^{14}C

尼达尔等

编者按

了解碳在大气、海洋和生物圈中的循环（主要归因于生物体在光合作用中对 CO_2 的吸收）对于预测人类活动所产生的温室气体将怎样影响气候相当重要。这篇由挪威技术研究所的科学家们所撰写的文章使我们了解到，在 20 世纪 70 年代早期人们是如何开始注意到碳循环的。本文反映了那个年代的焦点问题：由核武器试验释放到大气中的放射性同位素碳–14（^{14}C）在人体中的含量将会增加，这在当时被认为是一种潜在的健康威胁。显然，^{14}C 含量的增加是非常短暂的，因为核弹产生的 ^{14}C 很快就会被矿物燃料燃烧释放的 CO_2 所稀释，现在人们认为后者才是人类将要面临的更大威胁。

大气中 ^{14}C 主要以 $^{14}CO_2$ 的形式存在，通常由宇宙射线中子和大气中的氮原子通过核反应而产生。^{14}C 在产生和衰变之间的自然平衡决定了人类所受到的一部分天然本底辐射的大小。由于核试验的原因，从 1955 年起，大气层、陆地生物圈和海洋中的 ^{14}C 开始逐步增加。虽然起初人们并不认为 ^{14}C 会对人类造成重大危害[1]，但后来有人指出[2-4]：由于 ^{14}C 的半衰期很长（5,700 年），因而它对人类基因造成一定程度危害的可能性还是存在的。

在本实验室中，我们研究了人体内的 ^{14}C 浓度[5]。经过 6 年时间的测试，我们已证实大气中的 ^{14}C 与人体中的 ^{14}C 是相互关联的，它们之间的媒介是光合作用[6-8]。

自 1955 年起到现在，从核试验中释放出来的全部核能的 2/3 左右来自于 1961 年和 1962 年人们在北纬高纬度地区大气层中所进行的试验（参考文献 9）。有不少人对 ^{14}C 接下来向对流层、生物圈和海洋中的转移进行了详细的报道[10-16]。北半球对流层中 ^{14}C 的过量值[16]（$\delta^{14}C$）主要针对从北纬 30° 到北纬 90° 之间的区域（图 1），而南半球对流层曲线所代表的区域则是从赤道到南纬 90° 之间。

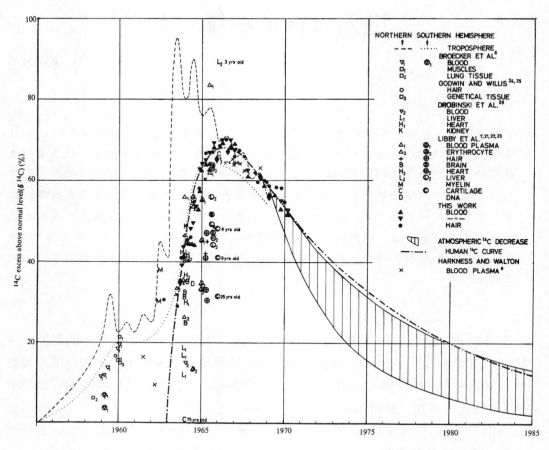

Fig. 1. Radiocarbon in the troposphere and human body.

The model for CO_2 exchange between the various reservoirs is shown in Fig. 2, in which the CO_2 in the troposphere is in exchange with CO_2 in the stratosphere, the land biosphere and the ocean. For CO_2 exchange between the troposphere and the biosphere we share the view of Münnich (for discussion, see ref. 17), who divided the biosphere into two parts. The first (b_1), which consists of leaves, grass, branches, and so on, is in rapid exchange with the troposphere and is combined with this reservoir, but the larger part of the vegetation (b_2) has a much slower exchange rate and is combined with the humus layer.

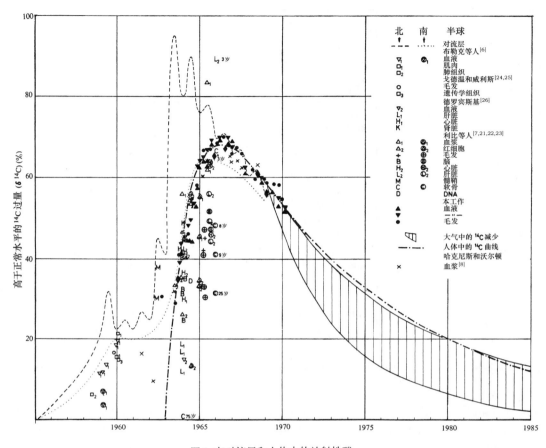

图 1. 在对流层和人体中的放射性碳。

CO$_2$ 在不同碳库之间的交换模型如图 2 所示。从图中可以看出，对流层中的 CO$_2$ 会与平流层、陆地生物圈和海洋之中的 CO$_2$ 发生交换。就 CO$_2$ 在对流层和生物圈之间的交换而言，我们赞同明尼希的观点，即认为生物圈可以被分为两个部分（讨论过程见参考文献 17）。第一部分（b_1）由树叶、草、树枝等组成，这部分与对流层之间发生着快速的交换并且与之结合；但相当多的植物属于第二部分（b_2），这部分与对流层之间的交换速率很慢并且是和腐殖质层结合在一起的。

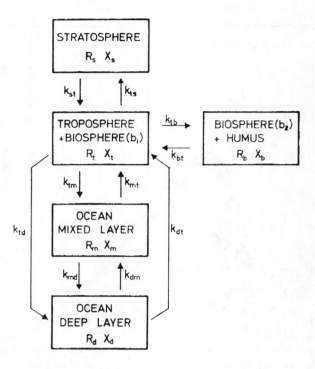

Fig. 2. Exchangeable carbon reservoirs, where: R_t, total carbon amount; X_t, ^{14}C excess; k_{ij}, exchange coefficients; i, j, t, b, m, d $(i \neq j)$.

The ocean is divided into two reservoirs, the mixed layer and the deep ocean. The exchange of CO_2 between the troposphere and the ocean occurs chiefly in the mixed layer, but according to Craig[18] there is also the possibility of a direct exchange with the deep ocean. The ^{14}C concentration in the mixed layer of the ocean is now 10 to 15% above normal[19,20].

Using the model of Fig. 2, we have treated the decrease of δ^{14}C in the troposphere in a previous article[20]. We showed that the measured variation of δ^{14}C (x_t) in the troposphere is approximately reproduced by the following two-term exponential function:

$$x_t = A_1 e^{-k_1 t} + A_2 e^{-k_2 t} \tag{1}$$

in which the parameters A_1, A_2, k_1 and k_2 depend on the various exchange coefficients. Because the errors on some of these coefficients are large, the extrapolation is uncertain and is given in the shaded area of Fig. 1.

The amount of bomb-produced ^{14}C in the atmosphere has increased the total natural amount of ^{14}C in nature by about 3%. According to Harkness *et al.*[8], the production of CO_2 from fossil fuel would lower the natural ^{14}C concentration in the atmosphere to about 16% below normal at the end of this century. It is thus reasonable that the ^{14}C excess caused by the atomic bomb will be more than compensated for by the dilution of inactive

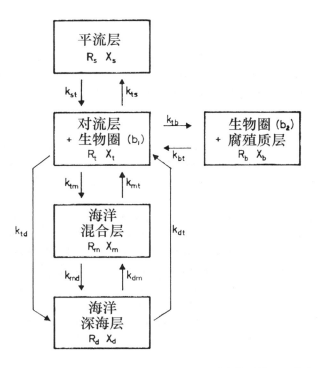

图 2. 可进行交换的碳库，其中：R_t 为总碳量；X_t 为 [14]C 过量；k_{ij} 为交换系数；i、j 代表 t、b、m、d $(i \neq j)$。

海洋被分成两个碳库，分别是混合层和深海层。CO_2 在对流层和海洋之间的交换主要发生在混合层，但根据克雷格的说法 [18]，直接交换也可能会发生在对流层和深海层之间。目前在海洋混合层中的 [14]C 浓度要高出正常值 10% ~ 15% [19,20]。

在之前发表的一篇文章中 [20]，我们利用图 2 的模型讨论了对流层中 δ^{14}C 的下降。我们认为，对流层中 δ^{14}C（x_t）测量值的变化可大致由以下这个包含两项指数函数的式子来模拟：

$$x_t = A_1 \mathrm{e}^{-k_1 t} + A_2 \mathrm{e}^{-k_2 t} \tag{1}$$

其中，参数 A_1、A_2、k_1 和 k_2 由不同的交换系数决定。因为其中有一些系数误差很大，所以外推结果有一定的变化范围，在图 1 中用阴影部分表示。

核弹在大气中产生的 [14]C 已使自然界中 [14]C 的天然总含量增加了约 3%。根据哈克尼斯等人的说法 [8]：到本世纪末，由矿物燃料产生的 CO_2 将使大气中的天然 [14]C 浓度下降到比正常值低大约 16% 的水平。因此，我们可以合理地推出，非放射性碳的稀释作用完全可以补偿由核弹引起的 [14]C 过量（苏斯效应）。

carbon (the Suess effect).

The transfer of ^{14}C into the human body depends on the following three factors: (1) the time between the photosynthesis in vegetational food and its consumption; (2) the diet, particularly the amount of vegetational food, and (3) the residence time of the carbon in the constituents of human tissue.

Broecker et al.[6] (Fig. 1) found that it took 1 and 1.8 yr before the ^{14}C concentration in blood and lung tissue, respectively, reached that in the atmosphere. They also found that the δ^{14}C value of blood had a maximum time lag of 6 months behind food.

Berger and collaborators[7,21-23] (Fig. 1) studied chiefly the metabolic turnover time of the constituents of human tissue. For this they used samples from persons who had travelled from the southern to the northern hemisphere. One result of their work was that the incorporation in these people of ^{14}C in brain protein and lipids, liver, heart, plasma protein and erythrocyte protein was very similar to, and reflected, the atmospheric ^{14}C content present several months earlier. Collagen of cartilage was found to be metabolically inert in older persons. The concentration of ^{14}C in the human body has been studied by other workers (refs. 8, 24-26) who obtained values shown in Fig. 1.

At our laboratory the transfer of ^{14}C into the human body was studied by following the time-variation of δ^{14}C in blood and hair for three persons[5,27] (Tables 1–3). No separation between blood plasma and erythrocyte protein was performed, and the measured ^{14}C activity is thus a mean value for the total blood samples. Fig. 1 shows that there is excellent agreement between data obtained for the blood and for the hair samples. The values of the ^{14}C concentration in blood plasma obtained by Harkness and Walton[8] are slightly lower than ours.

Table 1. Carbon in Neck Hair, from a Boy (K.N.) Born in 1962

Time of collection		δ^{14}C %	δ^{13}C/‰	Δ^{14}C %
November	1962	30.7±1.3		
June	1963	29.2±0.8	−19.7	26.7
October	1963	41.0±1.0	−19.2†	39.3
March	1964	46.0±1.0	−18.9	44.2
July	1964	54.8±1.0	−19.2†	52.9
October	1964	58.0±0.8	−18.6	55.9
February	1965	66.9±1.0	−19.2†	64.9
July	1965	67.2±1.0	−18.6	64.5
February	1966	68.7±1.0	−19.2	66.7
May	1966	70.0±0.9	−19.2†	68.0
December	1966	65.9±0.9	−19.2†	63.9
February	1967	67.5±1.1	−19.2†	65.4
July	1967	65.9±0.9	−19.2†	63.9
February	1968	61.5±0.9	−19.2†	59.6

^{14}C 向人体内的迁移过程取决于以下三个因素：（1）从植物性食物进行光合作用到它被人类食用之间的时间；（2）饮食结构，尤其是植物性食物所占的比重；（3）碳在人体组织各组成成分中的滞留时间。

布勒克等人 [6]（图 1）发现：要使血液和肺组织中的 ^{14}C 浓度达到大气中的浓度分别需要 1 年和 1.8 年的时间。他们还发现，从进食到血液中出现 δ^{14}C 之间的最大时间滞后可达 6 个月。

伯杰及其合作者 [7,21-23]（图 1）重点研究了人体组织各组成成分的新陈代谢周转时间。他们为此选用的样本均来自于那些有过从南半球到北半球旅行经历的人。他们获得的一项研究成果显示：^{14}C 与这些人的脑蛋白以及脂类、肝、心、血浆蛋白和红细胞蛋白的结合情况非常接近于数月前大气中的 ^{14}C 含量，可以认为它能够反映数月前大气中的 ^{14}C 含量。他们发现老年人软骨组织中的胶原蛋白具有新陈代谢惰性。图 1中还显示出了一些由其他研究者（参考文献 8 及 24~26）得到的人体中的 ^{14}C 浓度值。

在我们的实验室，对 ^{14}C 进入人体的研究是通过跟踪 3 个人血液和毛发中 δ^{14}C 随时间的变化来进行的 [5,27]（表 1 ~ 表 3）。因为没有对血液中的血浆和红细胞进行分离，所以测得的 ^{14}C 放射性是整个血样的平均值。从图 1 中可以看出，由血样得到的数据和由毛发样本得到的数据吻合得非常好。哈克尼斯和沃尔顿测得的血浆中的^{14}C 浓度数据 [8] 略微低于我们测得的值。

表 1. 颈部毛发中的碳，来自于一个 1962 年出生的男孩（K.N.）

采集时间	δ^{14}C %	δ^{13}C /‰	Δ^{14}C %
1962 年 11 月	30.7±1.3		
1963 年 6 月	29.2±0.8	−19.7	26.7
1963 年 10 月	41.0±1.0	−19.2†	39.3
1964 年 3 月	46.0±1.0	−18.9	44.2
1964 年 7 月	54.8±1.0	−19.2†	52.9
1964 年 10 月	58.0±0.8	−18.6	55.9
1965 年 2 月	66.9±1.0	−19.2†	64.9
1965 年 7 月	67.2±1.0	−18.6	64.5
1966 年 2 月	68.7±1.0	−19.2	66.7
1966 年 5 月	70.0±0.9	−19.2†	68.0
1966 年 12 月	65.9±0.9	−19.2†	63.9
1967 年 2 月	67.5±1.1	−19.2†	65.4
1967 年 7 月	65.9±0.9	−19.2†	63.9
1968 年 2 月	61.5±0.9	−19.2†	59.6

Continued

Time of collection		δ^{14}C %	δ^{13}C/‰	Δ^{14}C %
May	1968	60.2±1.1	−19.2†	58.2
August	1968	61.8±1.2	−19.2†	59.9
November	1968	59.7±1.1	−19.2†	57.7
January	1969	58.7±1.2	−19.2†	56.7
April	1969	58.2±1.2	−19.2†	56.5
May	1969	58.3±1.2	−19.2†	56.6
July	1969	58.1±1.1	−19.2†	56.4
October	1969	54.9±0.9	−19.2†	53.1
December	1969	54.7±1.1	−19.2†	52.9

† Not measured (mean value).

Table 2. Carbon in Blood Samples, from a Woman (I.N.), 26 Yr Old in 1963

Time of collection		δ^{14}C %	δ^{13}C/‰	Δ^{14}C %
September	1963	34.9±1.1	−22.0	34.0±1.1
October	1963	39.3±0.8	−22.2	38.5±0.8
November	1963	43.6±0.8	−22.7	42.9±0.9
February	1964	45.6±1.1	−22.0	44.7±1.2
April	1964	48.1±1.1	−21.7	47.1±1.1
June	1964	49.6±1.1	−21.7†	48.6±1.1
July	1964	53.7±1.0	−22.1	52.8±1.1
November	1964	62.9±0.9	−19.8	61.2±0.9
January	1965	64.2±0.9	−19.7	62.4±0.9
March	1965	65.0±0.9	−20.5	63.5±1.0
May	1965	67.1±1.0	−21.1	65.6±1.0
September	1965	69.1±0.9	−22.0	67.9±1.0
November	1965	65.6±0.9	−21.4	64.2±1.0
March	1966	69.7±0.9	−22.3	68.7±0.9
July	1966	67.6±1.1	−21.2	66.2±1.1
September	1966	69.8±1.0	−21.5	68.6±1.1
December	1966	67.4±1.0	−21.9	66.3±1.0
September	1967	62.5±0.9	−21.7†	61.4±0.9
June	1968	60.6±0.9	−21.7†	59.5±1.0
August	1968	59.9±0.9	−21.7†	58.8±1.0
January	1969	56.0±0.7	−21.7†	55.0±0.7
September	1969	55.5±1.2	−21.7†	54.5±1.2
March	1970	52.6±1.2	−21.7†	51.6±1.2

† Not measured (mean value).

Table 3. Carbon in Blood Samples, from a Woman (A.L.), 26 Yr Old in 1963

Time of collection		δ^{14}C %	δ^{13}C/‰	Δ^{14}C %
September	1963	35.2±0.8	−21.6	34.2±0.8
November	1963	41.5±0.6	−21.7†	40.6±0.7

续表

采集时间	δ^{14}C ‰	δ^{13}C /‰	Δ^{14}C ‰
1968 年 5 月	60.2 ± 1.1	−19.2†	58.2
1968 年 8 月	61.8 ± 1.2	−19.2†	59.9
1968 年 11 月	59.7 ± 1.1	−19.2†	57.7
1969 年 1 月	58.7 ± 1.2	−19.2†	56.7
1969 年 4 月	58.2 ± 1.2	−19.2†	56.5
1969 年 5 月	58.3 ± 1.2	−19.2†	56.6
1969 年 7 月	58.1 ± 1.1	−19.2†	56.4
1969 年 10 月	54.9 ± 0.9	−19.2†	53.1
1969 年 12 月	54.7 ± 1.1	−19.2†	52.9

† 未测量（平均值）。

表 2. 血样中的碳，来自于一位在 1963 年时年龄为 26 岁的妇女（I.N.）

采集时间	δ^{14}C ‰	δ^{13}C/ ‰	Δ^{14}C ‰
1963 年 9 月	34.9 ± 1.1	−22.0	34.0 ± 1.1
1963 年 10 月	39.3 ± 0.8	−22.2	38.5 ± 0.8
1963 年 11 月	43.6 ± 0.8	−22.7	42.9 ± 0.9
1964 年 2 月	45.6 ± 1.1	−22.0	44.7 ± 1.2
1964 年 4 月	48.1 ± 1.1	−21.7	47.1 ± 1.1
1964 年 6 月	49.6 ± 1.1	−21.7†	48.6 ± 1.1
1964 年 7 月	53.7 ± 1.0	−22.1	52.8 ± 1.1
1964 年 11 月	62.9 ± 0.9	−19.8	61.2 ± 0.9
1965 年 1 月	64.2 ± 0.9	−19.7	62.4 ± 0.9
1965 年 3 月	65.0 ± 0.9	−20.5	63.5 ± 1.0
1965 年 5 月	67.1 ± 1.0	−21.1	65.6 ± 1.0
1965 年 9 月	69.1 ± 0.9	−22.0	67.9 ± 1.0
1965 年 11 月	65.6 ± 0.9	−21.4	64.2 ± 1.0
1966 年 3 月	69.7 ± 0.9	−22.3	68.7 ± 0.9
1966 年 7 月	67.6 ± 1.1	−21.2	66.2 ± 1.1
1966 年 9 月	69.8 ± 1.0	−21.5	68.6 ± 1.1
1966 年 12 月	67.4 ± 1.0	−21.9	66.3 ± 1.0
1967 年 9 月	62.5 ± 0.9	−21.7†	61.4 ± 0.9
1968 年 6 月	60.6 ± 0.9	−21.7†	59.5 ± 1.0
1968 年 8 月	59.9 ± 0.9	−21.7†	58.8 ± 1.0
1969 年 1 月	56.0 ± 0.7	−21.7†	55.0 ± 0.7
1969 年 9 月	55.5 ± 1.2	−21.7†	54.5 ± 1.2
1970 年 3 月	52.6 ± 1.2	−21.7†	51.6 ± 1.2

† 未测量（平均值）。

表 3. 血样中的碳，来自于一位在 1963 年时年龄为 26 岁的妇女（A.L.）

采集时间	δ^{14}C ‰	δ^{13}C /‰	Δ^{14}C ‰
1963 年 9 月	35.2 ± 0.8	−21.6	34.2 ± 0.8
1963 年 11 月	41.5 ± 0.6	−21.7†	40.6 ± 0.7

Continued

Time of collection		δ^{14}C ‰	δ^{13}C/‰	Δ^{14}C ‰
February	1964	40.5±0.6	−20.9	39.3±0.7
March	1964	44.4±0.8	−22.5	43.5±0.9
April	1964	44.2±0.7	−23.2	43.6±0.7
June	1964	44.2±1.0	−22.1	43.3±1.0
August	1964	53.4±0.8	−21.9	52.4±0.9
November	1964	57.6±0.9	−20.7	56.2±0.9
January	1965	62.4±0.9	−19.1	60.5±0.9
March	1965	64.3±0.7	−20.1	62.6±0.7
May	1965	63.9±0.9	−21.0	62.5±1.0
September	1965	68.4±0.9	−22.0	67.3±1.0
November	1965	65.9±0.7	−21.4	64.4±0.8
March	1966	69.6±1.0	−22.0	68.5±1.1
July	1966	67.5±1.0	−21.2	66.2±1.1
September	1966	68.3±1.0	−20.9	66.9±1.0
December	1966	69.0±0.9	−20.8	67.6±1.0
September	1967	60.9±0.9	−21.7†	59.8±0.9
June	1968	61.4±0.9	−21.7†	60.3±0.9
August	1968	58.8±0.9	−21.7†	57.7±0.9
January	1969	56.6±0.7	−21.7†	55.6±0.7
May	1969	56.4±1.0	−21.7†	55.4±1.0
September	1969	53.0±1.0	−21.7†	52.0±1.0
March	1970	51.6±1.1	−21.7†	50.6±1.1

† Not measured (mean value).

The blood and hair data are almost representative for persons living in the northern hemisphere. Because δ^{14}C in the southern troposphere at present lags behind that of the northern troposphere by about 1 yr, there should also be a similar lag for δ^{14}C in the human populations of the respective hemispheres. After about 1970, the ^{14}C concentrations in people in the northern and southern hemispheres will be similar, and equal to those in the troposphere. Fig. 1 shows that δ^{14}C (x_H) in the human body appears as a pulse, delayed with respect to that of the atmosphere. The observed values for x_H can be fitted reasonably well by the following two-term exponential function:

$$x_H = 108 \left(e^{-0.1t} - e^{-0.75t} \right) \tag{2}$$

The coefficients in this function were determined by a least mean squares method, using the upper limits of the measured values for ^{14}C in the human body in the period from 1963 to 1970, and extrapolated values in the troposphere in the period from 1970 to 2000. The upper limit values were chosen because there was some excess ^{14}C before 1963 which should also be considered. There is also a tendency for the blood and hair data during the last 2 yr to correspond with the upper limit of the shaded area in Fig. 1. Function (2) was simplified by assuming that all previous nuclear tests occurred within a short time interval, and that the ^{14}C increase in the human population started in about January 1963.

采集时间	δ^{14}C ‰	δ^{13}C /‰	Δ^{14}C ‰
1964 年 2 月	40.5 ± 0.6	−20.9	39.3 ± 0.7
1964 年 3 月	44.4 ± 0.8	−22.5	43.5 ± 0.9
1964 年 4 月	44.2 ± 0.7	−23.2	43.6 ± 0.7
1964 年 6 月	44.2 ± 1.0	−22.1	43.3 ± 1.0
1964 年 8 月	53.4 ± 0.8	−21.9	52.4 ± 0.9
1964 年 11 月	57.6 ± 0.9	−20.7	56.2 ± 0.9
1965 年 1 月	62.4 ± 0.9	−19.1	60.5 ± 0.9
1965 年 3 月	64.3 ± 0.7	−20.1	62.6 ± 0.7
1965 年 5 月	63.9 ± 0.9	−21.0	62.5 ± 1.0
1965 年 9 月	68.4 ± 0.9	−22.0	67.3 ± 1.0
1965 年 11 月	65.9 ± 0.7	−21.4	64.4 ± 0.8
1966 年 3 月	69.6 ± 1.0	−22.0	68.5 ± 1.1
1966 年 7 月	67.5 ± 1.0	−21.2	66.2 ± 1.1
1966 年 9 月	68.3 ± 1.0	−20.9	66.9 ± 1.0
1966 年 12 月	69.0 ± 0.9	−20.8	67.6 ± 1.0
1967 年 9 月	60.9 ± 0.9	−21.7†	59.8 ± 0.9
1968 年 6 月	61.4 ± 0.9	−21.7†	60.3 ± 0.9
1968 年 8 月	58.8 ± 0.9	−21.7†	57.7 ± 0.9
1969 年 1 月	56.6 ± 0.7	−21.7†	55.6 ± 0.7
1969 年 5 月	56.4 ± 1.0	−21.7†	55.4 ± 1.0
1969 年 9 月	53.0 ± 1.0	−21.7†	52.0 ± 1.0
1970 年 3 月	51.6 ± 1.1	−21.7†	50.6 ± 1.1

† 未测量（平均值）。

来自血液和毛发的数据基本上代表了生活在北半球的所有人。因为南半球对流层的 δ^{14}C 值比北半球对流层滞后大约 1 年，所以居住在两个半球的人体内的 δ^{14}C 值也应该存在类似的滞后。大致到 1970 年之后，^{14}C 在南北半球的人体内的浓度将会趋于持平，并等于对流层中的 ^{14}C 浓度。从图 1 中可以看出：人体内部的 δ^{14}C（x_H）值就像一个落后于大气中 δ^{14}C 值的脉冲。用以下这个包含两项指数函数的式子可以很好地拟合 x_H 的观测值：

$$x_H = 108 \left(e^{-0.1t} - e^{-0.75t} \right) \tag{2}$$

函数式中的系数是通过最小均方法得到的，用到了在 1963 年～1970 年间测得的人体中 ^{14}C 的上限值，以及将对流层的数据外推到 1970 年～2000 年时的数据。选择上限值是因为还应当考虑到 1963 年以前的一些 ^{14}C 过量。在最近两年内得到的血液和毛发数据趋向于与图 1 阴影部分的上限值相符。化简式（2）的依据是以下两个假设：假设之前所有的核试验都集中发生在一个很短的时间间隔内，并且假设人体中 ^{14}C 含量开始增加的时间大约在 1963 年 1 月。

The first term in the brackets of equation (2) indicates that the excess ^{14}C in the human body has a mean lifetime of about 10 yr and the second term that ^{14}C enters the human body with a mean delay time of about 1.4 yr after production in the atmosphere. The latter value is probably accurate to within 30% and agrees with previous estimates[6,7].

The hazard to the human population from artificial radiocarbon arises largely from inventory radiation of the body. Natural ^{14}C contributes with a certain dose rate, r_0, as a result of its decay rate of about fourteen disintegrations per min per gram of carbon. The average value of r_0 is about 1.06 mrad/yr[9]. The dose from natural ^{14}C is distributed as follows: 1.64 mrad/yr in the bones, 1.15 mrad/yr in the cells lining bone surfaces and 0.71 mrad/yr in bone marrow and soft tissue. Applying function (2), the dose D_1 absorbed in the human body during a time t can be calculated from the formula:

$$D_1 = 1.08 \, r_0 \int_0^t (e^{-0.1t} - e^{-0.75t}) \, dt \qquad (3)$$

For a period of about 30 yr the total radiation dose from this source will be $9r_0$. We thus obtain a total radiation dose of 16 mrad to bone, 11 mrad to cells lining bone surfaces and 7 mrad to bone marrow and soft tissue. The genetic hazard is caused by the latter. That dose constitutes about 10% of the total gonad dose from all radioactive fallout. Purdom[4] pointed out, however, that the actual gonad dose is somewhat larger because of a transmutation process in the DNA molecule, in which the decaying ^{14}C atoms are replaced by nitrogen atoms. Purdom assumed that the biological damage from the transmutation was equal to that from β-radiation.

The amount of artificial ^{14}C in the human body at about the year AD 2000 will constitute about 3% of the total amount of ^{14}C. This isotope has a half-life of 5,700 yr, and several scientists[2,3,9,28] think that it would therefore cause a most serious genetic threat. The long term radiation dose can be calculated from the formula

$$D_2 = 0.03 \, r_0 \int_0^t e^{-0.000125t} \, dt \qquad (4)$$

The total radiation doses $(D_1 + D_2)$ which will be received by the bone cells, the cells lining bone surfaces, and the bone marrow and soft tissue in the next 10,000 yr will be 410, 290 and 180 mrad, respectively. These doses, which are in agreement with values given in a United Nations report[9] (page 45), are more important than those from all other radioactive fallout. We question, however, the value of the long term radiation dose (D_2) because, as previously mentioned, the use of fossil fuel might reduce the ^{14}C concentration in man below normal. We are of the opinion that the only ^{14}C hazard from previous tests which should be taken into account is attributable to a total genetic dose (D) of the order of 10 mrad, received in a period of about 30 yr. This dose is, however, negligible compared with the dose received from natural sources, which constitutes about 100 mrad per yr.

式（2）括号内的第一项表明，人体内过量 14C 的平均寿命大约为 10 年；第二项表明，14C 从在大气中产生到进入人体之间会有平均 1.4 年左右的时间滞后。滞后值的精确度大约可以达到 30% 以内，并与以前文献中的估计值相符 [6,7]。

人造放射性碳对人类造成的危害主要来源于人体内的辐射量。天然 14C 的剂量率 r_0 是一个固定值，由它的衰变速率——每克碳每分钟衰变约 14 次——决定。r_0 的平均值大致是 1.06 毫拉德 / 年 [9]。天然 14C 的剂量是这样分布的：在骨骼中为 1.64 毫拉德 / 年，在骨骼表层细胞中为 1.15 毫拉德 / 年，在骨髓和软组织中为 0.71 毫拉德 / 年。根据函数式（2），人体在 t 时间内吸收的剂量 D_1 可由下式计算：

$$D_1 = 1.08\, r_0 \int_0^t (e^{-0.1t} - e^{-0.75t})\, dt \qquad (3)$$

在大约 30 年内，来自该辐射源的总辐射剂量将为 $9r_0$。因此我们的骨骼所接受的辐射剂量为 16 毫拉德，骨骼表层细胞为 11 毫拉德，骨髓和软组织为 7 毫拉德。7 毫拉德的剂量会对基因造成危害。这一剂量大致等于生殖腺从所有放射性尘埃中所吸收的总剂量的 10%。但珀德姆 [4] 指出：实际上生殖腺所接收到的辐射剂量还要更大一些，因为 DNA 分子会发生嬗变，在嬗变过程中产生衰变的 14C 原子被替换成了 N 原子。珀德姆认为该嬗变过程对生物造成的伤害就相当于 β 辐射对生物的伤害。

到大约公元 2000 年时，人体中的人造 14C 量将占到 14C 总量的 3% 左右。这种同位素的半衰期为 5,700 年，因而有几位科学家 [2,3,9,28] 认为它将对人类基因造成严重的威胁。长期的辐射剂量可由下式计算：

$$D_2 = 0.03\, r_0 \int_0^t e^{-0.000125t}\, dt \qquad (4)$$

在未来的 10,000 年里，由骨骼细胞、骨骼表层细胞以及骨髓和软组织所吸收的总辐射剂量（D_1+D_2）分别为 410、290 和 180 毫拉德。这些剂量与一份联合国报告 [9]（第 45 页）中给出的值一致，它们比所有其他的放射性尘埃都更重要。然而，我们对长期辐射剂量（D_2）有所怀疑，因为正如我们之前曾经提到的，矿物燃料的使用可能会导致人体中的 14C 浓度降低至正常水平以下。我们认为：在大约 30 年内，由以前有足够规模的核试验所造成的 14C 危害对总遗传剂量（D）的贡献只有 10 毫拉德数量级。而从天然源中吸收的剂量约为 100 毫拉德 / 年，可见，与天然源相比，人工源的剂量是不值一提的。

We thank Norges Almenvitenskapelige Forskningsråd for financial support.

(**232**, 418-421; 1971)

Reidar Nydal, Knut Lövseth and Oddveig Syrstad: Radiological Dating Laboratory, Norwegian Institute of Technology, Trondheim, Norway.

Received November 10, 1969; revised August 24, 1970.

References:

1. Libby, W. F., *Science*, **123**, 657 (1956).

2. Pauling, L., *Science*, **128**, 3333 (1958).

3. Sakharow, A. D., *Soviet Scientists on the Danger of Nuclear Tests*, 39 (Foreign Languages Publishing House, Moscow, 1960).

4. Purdom, C. E., *New Scientist*, **298**, 255 (1962).

5. Nydal, R., *Nature*, **200**, 212 (1963).

6. Broecker, W. A., Schulert, A., and Olson, E. A., *Science*, **130**, 331 (1959).

7. Libby, W. F., Berger, R., Mead, J. F., Alexander, G. V., and Ross, J. F., *Science*, **146**, 1170 (1964).

8. Harkness, D. D., and Walton, A., *Nature*, **223**, 1216 (1969).

9. *Rep. UN Sci. Comm. Effect of Atomic Radiation*, No. 14 (A/5814) (United Nations, New York, 1964).

10. Münnich, K. O., and Roether, W., *Proc. Monaco Symp.*, 93 (Vienna, 1967).

11. Bien, G., and Suess, H., *Proc. Monaco Symp.*, 105 (Vienna, 1967).

12. Rafter, T. A., *NZ J. Sci.*, **8**, 4, 472 (1965).

13. Rafter, T. A., *NZ J. Sci.*, **11**, 4, 551 (1968).

14. Young, J. A., and Fairhall, A. W., *J. Geophys. Res.*, **73**, 1185 (1968).

15. Lal, D., and Rama, *J. Geophys. Res.*, **71**, 2865 (1966).

16. Nydal, R., *J. Geophys. Res.*, **73**, 3617 (1968).

17. Nydal, R., *Symp. on Radioactive Dating and Methods of Low-Level Counting, UN Doc. SM 87/29* (International Atomic Energy Agency, Vienna, 1967).

18. Craig, H., *Second UN Intern. Conf. on the Peaceful Uses of Atomic Energy*, A/CONF. 15/P/1979 (June 1958).

19. Rafter, T. A., and O'Brien, B. J., *Proc. 12th Nobel Symp.* (Almquist and Wiksell, Uppsala, 1970).

20. Nydal, R., and Lövseth, K., *CACR Symp.* (Heidelberg, 1969); *J. Geophys. Res.*, **75**, 2271 (1970).

21. Berger, R., Fergusson, G. J., and Libby, W. F., *Amer. J. Sci., Radiocarbon Suppl.*, 7, 336 (1965).

22. Berger, R., and Libby, W. F., *Amer. J. Sci., Radiocarbon Suppl.*, 8, 467 (1966).

23. Berger, R., and Libby, W. F., *Amer. J. Sci., Radiocarbon Suppl.*, 9, 477 (1967).

24. Godwin, H., and Willis, E. H., *Amer. J. Sci., Radiocarbon Suppl.*, 2, 62 (1960).

25. Godwin, H., and Willis, E. H., *Amer. J. Sci., Radiocarbon Suppl.*, 3, 77 (1961).

26. Drobinski, jun., J. C., La Gotta, D. P., Goldin, A. S., and Terril, jun., J. G., *Health Phys.*, **11**, 385 (1965).

27. Nydal, R., and Lövseth, K., *Nature*, **206**, 1029 (1965).

28. Pauling, L., *Les Prix Nobel*, 296 (1963) (Nobelstiftelsen, Stockholm, 1964).

感谢挪威自然和人文科学研究理事会为我们提供了经费上的支持。

（邓铭瑞 翻译；刘京国 审稿）

Statistical Mechanics and Quantum Mechanics

G. E. Uhlenbeck

Editor's Note

Nature here reprints a notable address given by physicist George Uhlenbeck in a ceremony awarding him the Lorentz Medal of the Royal Netherlands Academy of Science. Uhlenbeck describes his long-standing interest in fundamental questions of statistical mechanics, and notes that while the foundational problems of quantum theory had occupied theorists for decades, phase transitions—such as the abrupt gas-liquid transition—and related phenomena continued to pose many unsolved problems. Uhlenbeck also claims that the idea of a generally apparent frontier of science—separating the known from the unknown—is mostly a romantic illusion. Instead, he suggests, there are always many frontiers, and they usually become identified whenever there is an advance, not the other way around.

ARE the problems of statistical mechanics truly fundamental? I have often changed my opinion and now I would like to elaborate on it. When I was a young student, kinetic theory of matter seemed to me an example of a theory which truly explains something. With much care and effort I worked my way through the *Lectures on Gas Theory* by Boltzmann and the *Elementary Principles of Statistical Mechanics* by Gibbs. Much escaped me and became clear only after I read the famous encyclopaedia article by the Ehrenfests. It was a revelation, not only because of its great clarity but also because it contained a careful summing up of the series of more than twelve *lacunae* in the work of the masters. These were like frontier posts and a young student could thereby learn where the real problems lay. How difficult it is to find this out nowadays. The present pollution of the scientific literature makes the finding of clear water, the fundamental concepts, an extremely time consuming occupation. This is true not only for the new student but for anyone who tries to learn something outside his own speciality, as I well know by experience.

Though I passed my examinations successfully, I knew very little of quantum theory and even less of the theory of spectra. I learned that, with Goudsmit's help, when I returned from Rome in 1925 and became Ehrenfest's assistant. I shall not elaborate on the collaboration with Goudsmit, which I shall never forget and which led to the discovery of electron spin. Both Goudsmit and I have often related our memories of this unforgettable period and I mention it only because at that time my conception of statistical mechanics changed completely. I considered it to be clearly on a secondary level. Quantum mechanics on the other hand provided a foundation from which everything should follow, including the behaviour of gases, liquids and solids. This seemed to be confirmed by the success of the electron theory of metals. Pauli and Sommerfeld (both recipients of the Lorentz Medal) showed how all difficulties disappeared as soon as one applied the true quantum statistics. A few riddles remained, such

统计力学和量子力学

乌伦贝克

编者按

《自然》杂志在这里转载了物理学家乔治·乌伦贝克在接受荷兰皇家学会授予他洛伦兹奖的仪式上发表的一篇著名演讲。乌伦贝克谈到自己长期以来一直对统计力学中的一些基本问题很感兴趣，并且提到：量子理论的基本问题在数十年内吸引了众多理论工作者，与此同时，相变（例如突发的气－液转换）以及相关的现象也不断引发许多尚待解决的问题。乌伦贝克还指出：那种认为科学存在大致明显的前沿（将未知领域与已知领域分开）的观点多半是一种浪漫的幻象。相反，他认为：科学中总有很多前沿，它们往往是在科学产生进展的时候才被意识到，而不是反过来。

　　统计力学的问题真是基本性的吗？在这个问题上我自己的观点也经常改变，现在我想详细讲述一下。当我是一名年轻学生的时候，关于物质的动力学理论对我来说似乎是一种真正能够解释一些事物的理论。我花了很大工夫去钻研玻尔兹曼的《气体理论讲义》以及吉布斯的《统计力学的基本原理》。很多东西我当时并没有领会，只是在读完埃伦费斯特夫妇的那篇著名的百科全书文章（译者注：是应《数学科学百科全书》主编的要求撰写的）后才豁然开朗。那篇文章极具启发性，不仅因为清楚明了，而且因为它包括了对大师工作中一系列**缺陷**（超过 12 个）的仔细总结。这些著作就像边境站一样，可以让年轻学生了解到真正的问题所在。现在要了解这些问题是非常困难的。当前科学文献的污染使人们要花费很长时间才能找到一泓清泉，也就是那些基本概念。不仅对新学生是如此，对于任何想在自己专业之外了解一些知识的人也是一样，这一点我深有体会。

　　尽管能成功通过多次考试，但实际上我对量子理论知之甚少，对谱理论就更缺乏了解了。我是在 1925 年从罗马回来并成为埃伦费斯特的助手时，在古德斯密特的帮助下才认识到这点的。与古德斯密特的那段合作令我终生难忘，在合作中我们发现了电子的自旋，但在这里我不打算详述那段合作。古德斯密特和我经常谈起那段难忘的时光，我在这里提起它只是因为我对统计力学的观念在那段时间发生了彻底的改变。我本来认为它显然处于第二级的地位。另一方面，量子力学则提供了一个一切事物，包括气体、液体和固体的行为，必须遵循的基本原则。这似乎已被金属电子理论的成功所证实。泡利和索末菲（都是洛伦兹奖的获得者）曾揭示过所有的困难是怎样在应用了真正的量子统计之后迎刃而解的。目前还剩下几个未解之谜，

as superconductivity, but in our optimism we felt sure that all would be straightened out eventually. My dissertation in 1927 about statistical methods in quantum theory was therefore a kind of optimistic synthesis of the encyclopaedia article of the Ehrenfests and the new quantum mechanical ideas. The number of unproved assumptions was reduced to three.

Later in Ann Arbor, the beautiful experiments of N. H. Williams on thermal noise and shot noise aroused my interest in the theory of Brownian motion, one of the nicest applications of statistical mechanics. I thought it very interesting but of course it was not fundamental. I remember very well that when I told Pauli about it he called it "desperation physics". I didn't like this but I really agreed with him. For a physicist of the quantum mechanics generation to which I also belonged, the fundamental problems of the 1930s were the theory of the positron, quantum electrodynamics and the developing theories of nuclear structure and beta radioactivity; these were the things on which to work.

Let me say at this juncture that the image of progress in science as a kind of conquest of an unknown domain with a definite "frontier" and successive "breakthroughs" seems to me more and more to be only a romantic illusion. This picture was clearly inspired by the great breakthrough of quantum mechanics and it has influenced my judgment for a long time. I might even say that I was afflicted by it.

My opinion about the fundamental character of statistical mechanics began to change in 1937 to 1938 when I, together with Boris Kahn, became involved in the so called condensation theory. The question why a gas condenses below a sharply determined critical temperature at a sharply determined density has never been called to attention since Van der Waals and the proper understanding of it seemed difficult to us. During the lively discussion about this question at the Van der Waals Congress in 1938 it was even doubted whether the basic assumptions of statistical mechanics contained the answer even in principle. This doubt was not justified, but it made a deep impression on me. As long as such common phenomena as the equilibrium between liquid and vapour and the existence of a critical temperature were not truly understood, the field was not yet conquered, not everything had been explained in principle and thus there existed fundamental aspects of statistical mechanics which I had not appreciated.

(When I showed Pauli the article by Kahn and myself on condensation theory he looked at it and said, "Yes, one should read this". He did so and ridiculed somewhat the quasi-mathematical rigour of our work but I believe that he appreciated the fundamental character of the problem.)

After the war, I continued to follow the new developments in quantum electrodynamics and the theory of beta radioactivity, and from time to time I contributed a little. But my interest moved more and more towards the fundamental questions of statistical mechanics. In the 1950s I began to write a book on statistical mechanics with my pupil and friend, the late T. H. Berlin. I hoped that it would become a modernized and expanded version of the encyclopaedia article which had made such an impression on me. I hoped that we could determine the foundations

如超导电性，但是我们从乐观的角度来看，最终所有难题必将得到解决。因此，我在 1927 年的那篇关于量子理论中统计方法的博士学位论文，便成为埃伦费斯特夫妇的百科全书文章与新的量子力学概念的一种乐观综合。未经证实的假设数目被减少到 3 个。

之后在安阿伯市，威廉姆斯关于热噪声和散粒噪声的漂亮实验引起了我对布朗运动理论的兴趣。布朗运动理论是统计力学最好的应用之一，我觉得它非常有意思，但显然布朗运动理论并非基本性的问题。我记得非常清楚，当我和泡利谈起布朗运动理论时，他称其为"绝望物理学"。虽然我不喜欢这样的表述，但很同意泡利的观点。对于一位量子力学代的物理学家（我也属于这一代）来说，20 世纪 30 年代的基本问题是正电子理论、量子电动力学和正在发展的核结构理论、β 放射性理论；这些才是当务之急。

在这个关键时刻，我想说：把科学进步看成是对有清楚"前沿"并能不断被"突破"的未知领域的一种征服，对我来说越来越像一个浪漫的幻象。这个图景显然是由量子力学的伟大突破激发产生的，它在很长一段时间里影响了我的判断。我甚至可以说它曾折磨着我。

在 1937 年到 1938 年间我对统计力学基本特征的看法开始改变，那时候我和鲍里斯·卡恩在合伙研究所谓的凝聚理论。为什么一种气体在严格确定的临界温度之下以严格确定的密度凝聚，这个问题自范德瓦尔斯之后从未引起过人们的注意，而我们要想正确理解它似乎并不容易。在 1938 年范德瓦尔斯会议上与会者们对这个问题的热烈讨论中，有人甚至怀疑统计力学的基本假设在原理上是否能够解答这个问题。这个怀疑没有根据，但是给我留下了深刻的印象。只要像液体和气体之间的平衡以及临界温度的存在这类常见现象尚未被真正理解，这个领域就还没有被征服，就不能说所有的事情都已经从原理上得到了解释，因而统计力学中还存在着一些基本问题是我没有意识到的。

（当我把卡恩和我所写的关于凝聚理论的文章给泡利看的时候，他看了一下说："嗯，这个值得一读。"他确实读了，还取笑了我们文章中半吊子数学的严格性，但是我相信他理解这个问题的基本性。）

战后，我继续关注量子电动力学和 β 放射性理论的新进展，并不时发表一些自己的成果。但是我的兴趣越来越偏重于统计力学中的基本问题。在 20 世纪 50 年代，我开始和我的学生也是我的朋友——已故的伯林一起撰写一部关于统计力学的书。我希望这部书能够成为那篇曾让我留下深刻印象的百科全书文章的一个现代扩充版

of the theory in the same critical way as the Ehrenfests, and that we could make clear the nature of the still unsolved basic problems. In short, I hoped that we could discover the "structure" of statistical mechanics.

We worked hard on it but did not get very far and the sudden death of Ted Berlin in 1962 makes it doubtful that our plan will ever be realized. I have learned a lot from it, however, and I have the feeling that I more or less understand the structure of classical statistical mechanics at least. I believe that one always has to keep in mind that the task of statistical mechanics is to study the relationship between the macroscopic description of physical phenomena and the microscopic molecular description. These two pictures are in a certain sense independent; moreover, they are, so to speak, on a different level and are therefore, even qualitatively, totally different. If one sticks to this idea, one can see that Boltzmann, Gibbs, Einstein, Ehrenfest and Smoluchowski have formulated the true basis on which one has to build further. One sees also that there are still many unsolved problems, such as condensation and other so called phase transitions, on which much work is being done. All these problems are very difficult but they are, as a mathematician would say, *bien posés* and therefore one can work on them.

In my opinion the situation is somewhat different for quantum theory. The relationship between the classical and quantum mechanical descriptions of molecular phenomena is rather clear, but this is not so for quantum mechanics and the macroscopic theory. I am aware that this opinion is not shared by most of my colleagues. I believe that the most widespread opinion is that quantum mechanics can be "grafted" onto the classical statistical mechanics of Boltzmann and Gibbs and that therefore quantum mechanics does not require anything essentially new. I had thought so earlier too, but I have slowly retreated from that conviction. The recent discoveries of so called macroscopic quantization and interference phenomena in liquid helium and superconductors have had a great influence on my ideas. They seem to me to show that the existing theories of superconductivity and superfluidity do not provide a complete explanation and that the true macroscopic description of the superfluids has not yet been found. It would be no surprise to me that this is so because the foundations of quantum statistical mechanics have not yet been sufficiently clarified. One only needs to think of the persistent currents to feel doubt about the general validity of the ergodic theorems in quantum theory. Questions like these make low temperature physics so fascinating for me; they have had a rejuvenating effect on me and I am convinced that there is still much to be done on this "frontier" of physics and that profound surprises are possible.

Because I use the word "frontier" let me finally return to the romantic image of advances in science which I sketched earlier. I do not believe in it any longer. There are many frontiers and it comes down to the fact that in science one can only sometimes talk of progress. Whenever there is an advance there is a frontier, not the other way around. As to the direction of the advance, every investigator follows his own nose and does what he can. In my opinion this applies equally to space travel and to high energy physics and radio astronomy. These pursuits exist because they are possible and as long as the expense does not become too exorbitant one must, of course, continue them. But I think that one must oppose all fashion and prestige arguments. There is no natural hierarchy of problems and moreover, as Poincaré remarked

本。我希望我们能够像埃伦费斯特夫妇那样批判性地确定理论的基础，并能够弄清楚那些仍未解决的基本问题的本质。简言之，我希望我们能够发现统计力学的"架构"。

为此我们努力工作，但没有取得太大的进展，加之 1962 年特德·伯林突然离世，使得我们的计划能否最终实现都成了问题。但是我还是弄清了很多东西，并且感觉自己至少或多或少地理解了经典统计力学的架构。我相信一个人必须时刻记住，统计力学的任务是研究物理现象的宏观描述和微观分子描述之间的关系。这两个图景从某种意义上说是各自独立的；甚至可以说它们是在不同的层次上，因此即使定性地说也是完全不同的。如果坚持这个观点，就可以看出玻尔兹曼、吉布斯、爱因斯坦、埃伦费斯特和斯莫鲁霍夫斯基已经构造了真正的基础以供后人进一步发展。还可以看出仍然存在很多没有解决的问题，比如凝聚以及其他很多人正在研究的所谓相变过程。所有这些问题都非常艰涩，但是正如一位数学家所说的，它们是适定的，因此人们可以努力去解决它们。

按照我的观点，量子力学的情况会有所不同。分子现象的经典力学描述和量子力学描述之间的关系相当清楚，但是量子力学和宏观理论之间就另当别论了。我知道我的大部分同事都不同意这个观点。我相信最被广泛接受的观点是量子力学可以"嫁接"到玻尔兹曼和吉布斯的经典统计力学上，因此量子力学并不需要任何本质上是新的东西。以前我也这么认为，但慢慢地就不那么有信心了。最近，在液氦和超导体中发现的所谓宏观量子化以及干涉现象对我的观点影响很大。在我看来，这些发现都表明现有的超导电性和超流体性理论不能提供一个完整的解释，并且对超流体的真正宏观描述至今仍没有找到。对此我并不感到奇怪，因为量子统计力学的基础还没有被充分阐明。只要想想持续电流，就会对量子理论中遍历定理的普遍适用性产生怀疑。类似这样的问题使我感到低温物理非常有趣；它们使我精神振奋，我相信在物理学的这个"前沿"上仍有许多工作有待完成，并且还可能会有意义深刻的意外发现涌现出来。

既然使用了"前沿"这个词，让我最后回头再来看看前面简要提到的科学发展的浪漫图景。我已经不再相信它了。前沿有很多，但是归根结底的事实是，在科学中一个人只能不时地谈发展。每当有了一个进步就会出现一个前沿，而不是反过来。至于前进的方向，每位研究者都可以按自己的主意尽力而为。在我看来，这种情况对太空旅行和对高能物理学、射电天文学都同样适用。这些研究之所以存在，是因为它们有可能实现，只要代价不是太过昂贵，当然就应该继续下去。但是我觉得应该反对所有关于时髦和地位的争论。问题并无天然的等级之分，而且正如庞加莱很

long ago, a problem is never completely but always only more or less solved.

It seems better to me to view progress in science as the expansion of different circles of investigation, each autonomous and often apparently entirely independent of the others. The deep problems are to determine how these areas hang together, and how one can arrive at a larger unity. Biology and physical–chemical research, for example, form two such large circles. Their interrelationship seems to me to represent one of the deepest questions man can ask, a real *mysterium tremendum*. On a much smaller scale macroscopic and molecular physics form two such circles and statistical mechanics attempts to fathom their relationship.

(**232**, 449-450; 1971)

G. E. Uhlenbeck: Rockefeller University, New York.

久以前所指出的：一个问题永远不可能被彻底解决，只能或多或少被解决。

　　我更愿意把科学的发展看作是向许多不同研究领域的扩展，每个领域都是自主的，而且经常表现得完全独立于其他领域。深层次的问题是确定如何使这些领域互相结合在一起，且如何达到更广泛的统一。举例来说，生物学和物理－化学研究就是两个这样的大领域。在我看来，它们之间的相互关系是人类能够提出的最有深度的问题之一，是一个真正令人敬畏的奥秘。在小得多的尺度上，宏观物理和分子物理组成了两个这样的领域，统计力学则试图去探究它们之间的关系。

（何钧 翻译；李军刚 审稿）

Lithium in Psychiatry

I. B. Pearson and F. A. Jenner

Editor's Note

The medicinal uses of lithium salts far predate their current application to treat the psychiatric illness manic depression (bipolar disorder). But as psychiatrists I. B. Pearson and F. A. Jenner say in this overview, such uses were often over-optimistic and heedless of side-effects. The modern psychotropic application stemmed from a chance finding of mood alteration in 1949 by Australian doctor John Cade. Perhaps it is understandable that only two decades of use had not yet shed much light on the mode of action, but little more is known today. Pearson and Jenner hint that lithium might interfere with some aspect of brain metabolism; it now seems likely that it regulates production of a key neutrotransmitter, but the details remain unclear.

LITHIUM salts have been used medicinally in various ways for more than a century, and their history has been one of mistaken enthusiasm. Garrod recommended them for the treatment of kidney stones, gout and other rheumatic conditions in 1859[1], but without appreciable success. Subsequently lithium bromide was given as an anticonvulsant in the treatment of epilepsy, but it was no more effective than other bromides. At the end of the nineteenth century lithium salts were first tried in the treatment of mental illness, Lange[2] considered that lithium was helpful in mental depression, but fifty years were to elapse before further and more extensive psychiatric uses developed. More recently lithium salts have been offered as a substitute for sodium chloride in patients requiring a restricted sodium intake, but there were fatalities, and it is now recognized that cardiac and renal decompensation are both indications that the use of lithium should be avoided. Psychiatric interest was revived after work reported by Cade in 1949[3] when, following an accidental observation of a sedative effect on guinea-pigs, lithium was found to be helpful in controlling mania. The modern psychotropic use of lithium dates from that time, but dissemination has been slow and probably reflects a natural caution after the earlier fatalities, combined with the introduction of many new and effective psychoactive compounds.

During the past two decades lithium has been used increasingly in the treatment of manic-depressive illnesses in which the mood of the patient is elevated in mania and lowered in depressions. Results so far suggest that lithium salts have considerable potential in the treatment of manic depressive illnesses, although it is far from clear how they exert their effects.

Very occasionally the patient's mood changes in a regular clock-like manner, but it is more usual to find only occasional brief episodes of mania interspersed in a series of depressive episodes. The remarkably regular patients, though very rare, offer unusual opportunities to prove that lithium salts have a psychopharmacological effect. This has been done, but the relevance of such findings to the more usual clinical studies requires a more complicated

锂在精神病学中的应用

皮尔逊，詹纳

编者按

锂盐在被人们用于治疗躁狂抑郁症类精神病（双向障碍）之前早已作为药物使用。但正如精神病学家皮尔逊和詹纳在这篇综述中所指出的，人们过去对锂的应用总是过于乐观，毫不在意副作用。1949 年，澳大利亚医生约翰·凯德偶然发现了锂在改变情绪上的作用，从此开创了锂在现代精神类药物中的应用。也许 20 年的使用时间还不足以让人们认识锂的作用机制，但直到现在我们也几乎不比那个时候知道得更多。皮尔逊和詹纳指出锂可能干扰了脑内部分新陈代谢；现在看来它也可能控制着一种重要神经递质的产生，但具体细节尚不清楚。

一个多世纪以来，锂盐一直被人们用作各种形式的药物，其发展史已属于一种错误的狂热。1859 年，加罗德曾推荐用锂盐治疗肾结石、痛风以及其他风湿性疾病，可是并没有获得令人称道的成功 [1]。随后，溴化锂被用作一种治疗癫痫的抗惊厥药，但其疗效仅与其他溴化物相当。19 世纪末期，锂盐第一次被尝试用于治疗精神类疾病。朗厄 [2] 提出锂有助于治疗精神抑郁，但直到 50 年后，人们才把它更多、更广泛地用于治疗精神类疾病。最近，有人提出锂盐可以作为氯化钠的替代物用于那些需要限制钠摄入量的病人，但这种做法是致命的；因而现在人们认识到，为了防止心脏代偿和肾代偿失调，应该避免使用锂。在 1949 年凯德偶然观察到锂对豚鼠具有镇定作用 [3] 之后，人们发现锂有助于控制躁狂症，随后对锂在精神病治疗方面的研究兴趣又开始恢复。从那时起到现在，锂一直被用作治疗精神病的药物，但普及过程十分缓慢，可能是早期致死事件之后人类本能产生的谨慎以及许多高效精神类新药物的出现所致。

在过去的 20 年里，锂越来越多地被用于治疗躁狂抑郁性精神病，患有这种病的病人在躁狂时情绪激动，在抑郁时情绪又低落。目前的研究结果表明，锂盐在治疗躁狂抑郁性精神病方面具有很可观的疗效，但很难说清产生这种作用的机理到底是什么。

病人情绪的变化极少遵守严格的规律性，更常见的情况是，在一系列抑郁周期之中只会偶尔出现短暂的躁狂阶段。虽然定期发作的病人很少，但我们仍然从他们身上获得了一些能证明锂盐具有精神药理学效用的难得机会。这一工作已经完成，但上述结果与更普遍的临床研究之间的相关性还需要通过更为复杂的统计学方法来

statistical approach, taking proper account of the variable natural history of the condition.

It is difficult to classify these illnesses since unipolar affective disorders are much commoner that the bipolar type, and patients who have recurrent episodes of depression for several years may then have a manic episode. Depressions also merge into anxiety and other psychiatric states. The natural history and heterogeneity of the clinical group studied present all sorts of obvious difficulties to the investigator, and it is these types of problem which have influenced much of the debate about lithium in psychiatry. Schou, who produced a useful guide to the literature in 1968[4], has been the most active and assiduous student in this field.

The effectiveness of lithium in the treatment of mania is now well recognized, and has been confirmed by controlled studies. But this treatment requires daily doses of the order of 1.5–2 g of lithium carbonate, when therapeutic and toxic levels closely approximate. In recent years the prophylactic use of lithium has been advocated, using rather smaller doses in the range 0.75 to 1 g daily of lithium carbonate, when toxic effects are reduced. The efficacy of lithium salts in the prophylaxis of manic depressive illness has been the subject of some debate. It has been claimed that when effective, lithium salts diminish the change in mood and in addition reduce the frequency of relapse in affective illness. Angst *et al.*[5] have demonstrated a natural tendency in manic depressive illness for the frequency of episodes to increase, but the pattern of relapse in affective illness is variable, although it does tend to show a progression of increasing frequency which is greater in bipolar illness than in recurrent depressive illness.

Blackwell and Shepherd[6] properly challenged some of the earlier favourable reports, pointing out that with such patients seen at a time of frequently recurring illness, a reduced rate of relapse might be accounted for solely by chance, and certainly this could be so with patients having frequent episodes, even if there is an overall tendency for the cycles to shorten. They suggested that the prophylactic value of lithium could only be determined by a comparative trial. Subsequently several clinical studies have been reported, including double blind trials, and most of them support the original conclusion that prophylactic lithium is of value. In general it seems that the frequency of relapse is appreciably reduced and that the natural trend of increasing frequency is reversed.

Lithium belongs to the group of alkali metals which includes sodium and potassium and it shares several properties with the other members of this group, but Birch has pointed out that in certain respects it resembles magnesium and calcium to which it bears a diagonal relationship in the periodic table[7]. It is absorbed promptly and virtually completely from the gastro-intestinal tract, and this is independent of whether lithium is given as carbonate, citrate or acetate. Lithium is not bound to plasma proteins, but is distributed freely in the tissues, and equilibration occurs, although this is somewhat slower in bone and brain. Distribution in the tissue differs sharply from that of sodium and potassium since lithium is more evenly divided between intracellular and extracellular compartments. Concentrations in the serum reflect those in tissue and can be used satisfactorily to monitor treatment. Lithium salts are largely excreted by the kidneys, and only small amounts are lost in faeces and sweat. Renal lithium excretion is proportional to the plasma concentration over a wide range; renal clearance is of

确定，同时要适当考虑这种疾病的病程极易发生变化。

很难给这些精神病归类，因为单向情感性疾病比双向情感性障碍更为普遍，在几年内反复出现抑郁期的病人随后可能会表现出一个躁狂发作期。抑郁症也会合并焦虑和其他精神病症状。临床上的病程和异质性给研究者造成了各种各样显而易见的困难，也正是这些困难左右了很多关于锂用于精神病治疗的讨论。舒尔在 1968 年发表了针对这些文献的指南 [4]，他堪称这个领域内最活跃和最勤奋的研究者。

现在人们已经承认了锂在治疗躁狂症方面的有效性，这一点已经被对照实验所证实。但治疗需要每天服用 1.5 克 ~ 2 克碳酸锂，治疗所需剂量与中毒剂量非常接近。近年来，大家都倡导将锂作为预防用药，当每天服用碳酸锂的量降低至 0.75 克 ~ 1 克时，其毒性就会降低。锂盐在预防躁狂抑郁症方面的效果已经成为众多争论的焦点。有人指出：当锂盐发挥功效时，它能减少情绪上的变化并且能降低情感性疾病的复发频率。昂斯特等人 [5] 已经证明躁狂抑郁症的一个自然趋势是发病频率不断增加，而情感性疾病的复发模式却是变化无常的，不过后者也会表现出一种发病频率逐渐增加的趋势，但双向性疾病的发病频率比复发性抑郁症的发病频率增加得更快。

布莱克韦尔和谢泼德 [6] 彻底挑战了早期的一些支持锂具有预防作用的报道。他们指出：对于那些处于疾病反复发作时期的病人，复发频率的下降可能只是偶然出现的现象，频繁发病的病人显然也会发生类似的情况，即使整体趋势是周期在缩短。他们认为，锂的预防作用只能用对比试验来确定。随后，又有几项临床研究的成果被发表出来，包括一些双盲试验，这些结果大多支持最初的结论，即锂作为预防性药物是有效的。在通常情况下，锂似乎会使复发频率明显下降，而发病频率自然增加的趋势也会被逆转。

锂和钠、钾一样都属于碱金属，它的一些性质与碱金属中的其他成员相同，但伯奇指出，在某些方面，钾也类似于在元素周期表中与它呈对角线关系的镁和钙 [7]。无论锂的存在形式是碳酸锂、柠檬酸锂还是醋酸锂，它都会立刻被胃肠道完全吸收。锂没有与血浆蛋白结合，而是自由地分布于组织中，并会达到分布平衡，不过这种平衡在骨和脑中出现的速度比较慢。锂在组织中的分布与钠和钾完全不同，因为锂在细胞内结构和细胞外结构中的分布更平均。血清中的含量可以反映出组织中的含量，因而能够满意地用于监测治疗效果。大部分锂盐由肾排泄，只有很少量从粪便和汗液排出。从肾排出的锂在很宽的范围内正比于血浆浓度，肾清除率的数量级为 15 毫升 / 分钟 ~ 30 毫升 / 分钟，但会随着年龄的增长而下降，在老年人中低至

the order of 15–30 ml./min, but decreases with age, and values of 10–15 ml./min are not uncommon in elderly people. Lithium excretion decreases when sodium intake is restricted.

The principal disadvantage of lithium therapy lies in the narrow safety margin between therapeutic and toxic doses. Therapeutic plasma concentrations are usually considered to be between 0.8 and 1.6 mequiv./l.; at these concentrations only minor side effects occur. The commonest of these effects are gastro-intestinal disturbances, muscular weakness, tremor, drowsiness and a dazed feeling. When plasma concentrations are higher, serious toxic effects are liable to ensue, and poisoning results in coma, hyperreflexia, muscle tremor, attacks of hyperextension of the limbs and convulsions; fatalities have occurred. Haemodialysis is the most effective treatment if available but where this is not possible patients should be treated by forced diuresis. Long term treatment may give rise to small goitres and hypothyroidism but these usually respond to modest doses of thyroxine. Teratogenic effects have now been reported in two out of forty patients who received lithium during pregnancy[8]. Clearly lithium should be used with care, and concentrations in the blood should be monitored regularly.

Mode of Action

The mode of action of lithium in affective illness remains obscure, and most theories have related to interference in electrolyte metabolism or to effects on the metabolism of brain amines. More recently evidence has been adduced to suggest a specific effect of lithium on the limbic system of the brain, an area known to be associated with emotion[9]. These uncertainties about the action of lithium reflect the unsatisfactory state of understanding of the biological disturbance associated with manic-depressive illness.

When the fundamental importance of sodium and potassium for neuronal activity is considered together with the similarity of their ions to those of lithium, the suggestion that lithium interferes with the metabolism of these ions seems to be reasonable. Evidence is accumulating that disturbance of electrolyte and water balance accompanies manic-depressive illness although it is not clear whether this is causal or consequential. It has been shown that the administration of lithium leads to changes in the body water spaces, and this observation is supported by the natriuresis following the intake of lithium, which is more striking in normal people than in manic-depressive patients. More lithium is retained by patients than by normal people, and the retention is greater in mania and in patients who respond to lithium therapy. In addition a proportion of patients taking lithium develop persisting polyuria and thirst. This may be explained by the fact that lithium ions specifically and reversibly inhibit the action of the antidiuretic hormone on the kidney. Conceivably the consequences of this inhibition are relevant to the therapeutic effects.

Further work on this particular action has demonstrated that lithium probably blocks the action of the cyclic AMP released by vasopressin[10]. This raises the possibility that inhibition of the effect of vasopressin is just one example of an action on the effects of all hormones releasing cyclic AMP in target cells. In addition to its action on cyclic AMP, lithium also inhibits adenyl cyclase necessary for the production of cyclic AMP from ATP, but in the kidney this only occurs with high doses[11].

10 毫升 / 分钟 ~ 15 毫升 / 分钟的情况并不少见。当钠的摄入量受限时，锂的排泄也会下降。

锂作为治疗药物的主要缺点在于治疗剂量和中毒剂量之间的安全范围太窄。一般认为血浆治疗的浓度在 0.8 毫当量 / 升 ~ 1.6 毫当量 / 升之间，在这样的浓度范围内，只会出现很有限的副作用。其中最常见的是胃肠道障碍、肌肉无力、颤抖、嗜睡和晕眩。当血浆中的药物浓度更高时，很可能会随即出现严重的中毒反应，中毒的后果是昏迷、反射亢进、肌肉颤动、肢体伸展过度发作和痉挛，以至于致命。如果有条件，血液透析是最有效的治疗手段；但在条件不允许的情况下，必须对病人采用强迫利尿的治疗方法。长期治疗可能会引起甲状腺腺体缩小和甲状腺功能减退，但在通常情况下保留了对适度的甲状腺素的反应。在 40 例怀孕期间接受过锂治疗的病人中，目前已报道出现 2 例致畸 [8]。显然在使用锂时应格外小心，并且要定期检测其在血液中的浓度。

作 用 机 制

现在还不清楚锂在治疗情感性疾病方面的作用机制，大多数理论认为它与干扰电解质的代谢或者与影响脑胺的代谢有关。最近有人证明，锂可以对与情感相关的区域——大脑边缘系统产生特定的影响 [9]。关于锂作用机制的这些不确定性说明，人们在理解与躁狂抑郁症有关的生物失调方面还不能令人满意。

当把钠和钾对神经元活动的重要性同它们的离子类似于锂离子联系起来考虑的时候，就会认为锂干扰这些离子新陈代谢的观点是有道理的。不断积累的证据表明电解质和水平衡的紊乱与躁狂抑郁症有关联，但现在还不清楚两者之间是因果关系还是继发关系。有人指出服用锂会导致体内水区发生变化，而且这一发现也被摄入锂后出现的尿钠排泄所支持，这种症状在正常人身上的表现比在躁狂抑郁症患者身上更明显。在病人体内锂潴留比正常人更多，尤其是躁狂症病人和对锂治疗有反应的病人。另外，有一部分服用锂的病人会持续出现多尿和口渴的症状。这也许可以用以下论点来解释：锂离子通过特异性和可逆的方式抑制了肾脏内抗利尿激素的作用。或许可以认为这种抑制作用与疗效有关。

有人对这种特异性作用进行了深入的研究。结果表明，锂可能抑制了由抗利尿激素引起的环磷酸腺苷的释放 [10]。这就引出了这样一种可能性，即抗利尿激素的作用受到抑制仅仅是锂对靶细胞中所有能导致释放环磷酸腺苷的激素的其中一种作用。除了能对环磷酸腺苷产生影响之外，锂还能抑制由三磷酸腺苷生成环磷酸腺苷所需的腺苷酸环化酶，但在肾脏中这种抑制只有在高剂量的情况下才会出现 [11]。

Perhaps a more exciting observation is an increase of α-ketoglutaric acid (shown by Bond *et al.*) in the urine of patients receiving lithium. This observation, although unequivocally established, still requires explanation. Dose lithium, for example, inhibit enzymes in the tricarboxylic acid cycle and so cause a build-up of α-ketoglutaric acid? Is it a response to alkalosis and does it occur in brain? This, like many other questions, is being actively explored. It could also be relevant to Delgado and DeFeudis's observation[9] that lithium leads to an increased level of brain glutamate.

Inhibition of several enzyme systems could be the result of effects of lithium on tissue magnesium and calcium which have now been observed. As these changes may also occur in brain, possible hypotheses of the consequences are legion.

The work of Smith, Balagura and Lubran[12] demonstrates an apparently direct action of lithium on the lateral nuclei of the hypothalamus. There is stimulates drinking behaviour and presumably thirst. Application of lithium ions directly to the hippocampus and amygdala of monkeys[9] evoked rather specific EEG effects which could be associated with the reduction of aggression reported in man, rodents and fish[13-15]. These are among the few reported direct effects of lithium on nervous tissue, and it is not surprising that neural function can be altered in this way, but the significance of these observations in relation to the therapeutic actions of lithium is not entirely clear.

Lithium does, however, have very clear effects on the electroencephalogram in man. In particular, it increases the amplitude of the alpha rhythm and causes slow waves to appear. After quite usual doses of lithium carbonate have been discontinued, the effects on the electroencephalogram persist for up to 6 weeks.

Lithium, like so many other agents which have therapeutic uses, is like a heavy spanner in a delicate piece of machinery. Like electroconvulsive therapy, it changes so many things that clues to as what is relevant are difficult to assess. Among other effects which require further study, one must include inhibition of carbohydrate transport[16-18] across various membranes including the inhibition of the accumulation of myoinositol by the lens[19] and kidney[20]. The latter substance may well have a special role in the central nervous system.

The most popular current theories suggest that brain monoamine metabolism is altered in manic-depressive illness, but again, as with electrolytes, it is uncertain whether this is cause or effect; moreover, it is not clear which of the amines is related to changes in mood. Lithium has effects on brain monoamine metabolism, but these are confined to noradrenaline and the function of noradrenergic neurones. Noradrenaline metabolism is shifted from O-methylation to intraneuronal deamination with an increase in noradrenaline destruction; noradrenaline uptake by synaptosomes is increased and the release of synaptic neurotransmitters may be inhibited. Unfortunately these findings do not easily fit into models developed to account for the actions of psychotropic drugs, since such drugs change mood in one direction only, whereas lithium restricts mood swing in both directions. One school of thought, however, considers mania as a more profound form of depression[21].

一个更令人兴奋的发现也许是，在病人服用锂后其尿液中的 α- 酮戊二酸含量会有所增加（邦德等人的研究成果）。尽管没有人怀疑这个结果的真实性，但仍需要对其进行解释。例如：锂是否会在三羧酸循环中抑制酶的作用从而使 α- 酮戊二酸得以积聚？这是碱中毒的一个反应吗？会不会在大脑中出现？就像对许多其他问题一样，人们一直在积极探索这个问题的答案。德尔加多和德费乌迪斯的观察结果也与此相关 [9]，他们发现锂会导致脑谷氨酸水平的提高。

几个酶系统之所以被抑制可能是由于最近观察到的锂对组织镁和组织钙所起的作用。因为这些变化也可能会出现在脑中，所以对后果的假设不胜枚举。

史密斯、巴拉古拉和卢布兰 [12] 通过研究证明：锂会直接作用于下丘脑的外侧核。这样就会刺激人去饮水，可能是因为感到了口渴。将锂离子直接作用于猴的海马区和杏仁核 [9] 会引发特异性很强的脑电效应，这种脑电效应可能与人类、啮齿动物及鱼类的攻击性下降有关 [13-15]。关于锂可以对神经组织产生直接影响的报道寥寥无几，以上列举了其中的几个，它们无疑会使神经功能发生变化，但目前还不完全清楚这些发现对于解释锂的疗效有什么帮助。

然而，锂确实对人类的脑电图有很明显的影响，尤其是它可以增加 α 节律的波幅，进而导致慢波的出现。在停止使用常规剂量的碳酸锂之后，它对脑电图的作用还能持续长达 6 周。

如同许多其他用于治疗的药物一样，锂所起的作用也类似于一台精密机器中的重型扳手。和电痉挛治疗一样，锂改变的要素太多以至于很难评估到底哪一个与它的疗效相关。在其他一些需要深入研究的效应中，我们应该把抑制碳水化合物穿过不同生物膜的转运 [16-18] 考虑在内，其中包括晶状体 [19] 和肾脏 [20] 对肌醇堆积的抑制。因为肌醇在中枢神经系统中很可能起着特殊的作用。

当前最流行的理论认为，躁狂抑郁症病人脑内的单胺代谢会发生变化，但和电解质代谢一样，我们还是不清楚这到底是致病原因还是患病后的结果，而且也不清楚哪一种胺与情绪改变有关。锂对脑内的单胺代谢确实有影响，但影响范围只限于去甲肾上腺素和去甲肾上腺素能神经细胞的功能。随着去甲肾上腺素被破坏程度的增加，去甲肾上腺素代谢从 O-甲基化转变到神经细胞内的脱氨基作用；突触体对去甲肾上腺素的摄取也在增加，而突触神经递质的释放可能会减少。不幸的是，这些发现不太容易适用于那些解释神经药物作用机制的模型，因为这些药物只在一个方向上改变了情绪，而锂对情绪波动的限制是双向的。然而，有一个学派认为可以把躁狂症看作是抑郁症的一种深度发展的形式 [21]。

The pharmacological actions of lithium salts are curiously complex, and knowledge about them is far from complete, Indeed, there is ample room for further research designed to increase our understanding of the effects of lithium, which may in turn shed more light on the biological mechanisms possibly involved in manic-depressive illnesses.

(**232**, 532-533; 1971)

I. B. Pearson: University Department of Psychiatry, Sheffield S10 3TL.

F. A. Jenner: MRC Unit for Metabolic Studies in Psychiatry, University Department of Psychiatry, Sheffield S10 3TL.

References:

1. Garrod, A. B., *Gout and Rheumatic Gout* (Walton and Maberly, London, 1859), cited by Ottosson, J. O., *Acta Psychiat. Scand.*, Suppl. 207 (1969).

2. Lange, C., *Bidrag til urinsyrediates ens klinik. Hospitalstidende*, **5**, 1 (1897), cited by Ban, T., *Psychopharmacology* (Williams and Wilkins, 1969).

3. Cade, J. F. J., *Med. J. Austral.*, **36**, 349 (1949).

4. Schou, M., *J. Psychiat. Res.*, **6**, 67 (1968).

5. Angst, J., Weis, P., Grof, P., Baastrup, P. C., and Schou, M., *Brit. J. Psychiat.*, **116**, 604 (1970).

6. Blackwell, B., and Shepherd, M., *Lancet*, i, 968 (1968).

7. Birch, N. J., *Brit. J. Psychiat.*, **116**, 461 (1970).

8. Schou, M., and Amdisen, A., *Lancet*, i, 1391 (1970).

9. Delgado, J. M. R., and DeFeudis, F. V., *Exp. Neurol.*, **25**, 255 (1969).

10. Harris, C. A., and Jenner, F. A., *J. Pharmacol.* (in the press, 1971).

11. Dousa, T., and Hechter, O., *Life Sci.*, **9**, 1, 765 (1970).

12. Smith, D. F., Balagura, S., and Lubran, M., *Physiol. Behav.*, **6**, 209 (1971).

13. Sheard, M. H., *Nature*, **230**, 113 (1971).

14. Sheard, M. H., *Nature*, **228**, 284 (1970).

15. Weischer, M. Z., *Psychopharmacologia*, **15**, 245 (1969).

16. Bhattacharya, G., *Biochim. Biophys. Acta*, **93**, 644 (1964).

17. Bihler, I., and Adamic, S., *Biochim. Biophys. Acta*, **135**, 466 (1967).

18. Bosackova, J., and Crane, B. K., *Biochim. Biophys. Acta*, **102**, 423 (1965).

19. Varma, S. D., Chakrapani, B., and Reddy, V. N., *Invest. Ophthal.*, **9**, 794 (1970).

20. Margolis, R. U., and Heller, A., *Biochim. Biophys. Acta*, **98**, 438 (1965).

21. Coppen, A., and Shaw, D. M., *Lancet*, ii, 805 (1967).

　　锂盐的药理作用极其复杂，目前人们在这方面的知识还远远不够。确实，为了增加对锂作用机制的了解，我们还需要进行广泛的研究，这也许会有助于揭开隐藏在躁狂抑郁症背后的生物学机制。

（刘霞 翻译；陈建国 审稿）

Formation of New Connexions in Adult Rat Brains after Partial Deafferentation

P. D. Wall and M. D. Egger

Editor's Note

Here Patrick D. Wall and M. David Egger provide dogma-challenging evidence that the adult mammalian central nervous system contains some capacity to reorganize itself functionally after injury. The researchers severed part of a neuronal pathway linking leg to brain in the rat, and found to their surprise that "leg-responsive" brain cells began responding to "arm" stimulation after the surgery. The most likely explanation, they conclude, is that undamaged neurons grew new projections that formed connexions with their damaged neighbours. Such "plasticity", where the brain reorganizes neural pathways based on new experiences, is now well documented after brain injury, and is known to play an important role in learning and memory.

BRAIN damage in adult mammals may be followed by remarkable recovery or by a depressingly permanent defect. Any understanding of this sometime plasticity would be important not only for therapy but also for understanding how the central nervous system adjusts to its environment during development and learning. During experiments designed for a different purpose, we came across evidence that a group of cells which had been deprived of their major input began to respond to quite novel stimuli after a few days. In these experiments, the cell bodies of the normal major input had been destroyed. The one class of explanation which cannot be invoked is true regeneration in which cells had divided and replaced the destroyed cells. In the mammalian adult central nervous system (CNS) there is no evidence for nerve cells which are still capable of division, growth and differentiation: following destruction of nerve cells, non-neural elements divide and migrate into the region of damage, phagocytosing the wreckage and replacing it with an impenetrable scar. Even if the cell bodies are intact but their axons are severed, there is no evidence of successful regeneration of axons within the CNS.

Our experiments involved the dorsal columns, through which cutaneous sensory afferents travel from the hind limbs to terminate on cells of nucleus gracilis. From this nucleus, axons decussate and project to the ventral posterior nucleus of the thalamus (VPL). Similar projection systems pass from the forelimb by way of the cuneate nucleus and from the face through the trigeminal nucleus. Within this region of the thalamus, the entire contralateral body surface is represented in an exact somatotopic map (Fig. 1). Recent experiments have suggested that discriminative cutaneous sensation survives the destruction of the dorsal columns[1]. One explanation for this lack of effect is that other systems converge onto the thalamic nucleus and transmit the necessary afferent information by alternative pathways. To test this hypothesis, experiments were in progress to examine the response of cells

部分传入神经阻滞后
成年大鼠脑内新联系的形成

沃尔，埃格

编者按

在本文中，帕特里克·沃尔和戴维·埃格提供了挑战传统观点的证据，该证据证明成年哺乳动物的中枢神经系统在受损后，具有部分功能重组的能力。研究者切断了大鼠身上连接后肢和脑的那部分神经通路，他们惊奇地发现：原先"对后肢产生应答"的脑细胞在术后开始对"前肢"所受刺激作出反应。他们总结出的最可能的解释是：未损坏的神经元长出新投射，与已受损的相邻神经元之间产生联系。如今，脑在受损后基于新经验重组神经通路的这种"可塑性"已被很好地证明，这种"可塑性"也在学习和记忆中扮演重要的角色，此观点已成为共识。

成年哺乳动物脑损伤后可能会奇迹般地恢复，或者成为悲剧性的永久缺陷。对这一偶然发生的可塑性的任何理解不仅仅对治疗来说非常重要，而且对于理解中枢神经系统在发育和学习过程中如何适应它周围的环境也同样重要。在为另一个目的而设计的实验中，我们偶然发现了以下现象：一组已经失去自身主要输入的细胞，在几天后开始对全新的刺激产生应答。在这些实验中，具有正常主要输入的细胞体已被破坏掉。有一类解释是我们不能接受的，即发生了真正的再生，在再生过程中细胞进行分裂并取代了被破坏的细胞。在成年哺乳动物的中枢神经系统（CNS）中，没有证据表明神经细胞仍然能够分裂、生长和分化：在神经细胞遭到破坏后，非神经细胞就会分裂并移入受损区域，吞噬神经细胞残片并用一个难以穿过的伤疤替代它。即使细胞体未受损而只是它们的轴突被切断，也没有证据能证明中枢神经系统中的轴突可以成功再生。

我们的实验涉及背柱，来自后肢的皮肤感觉传入经过它到达终端薄束核的细胞。轴突从这一神经核起交叉成十字形并投射到丘脑腹后外侧核（VPL）。类似的投射系统转为前肢的话，将经过楔束核；而来自面部的类似投射系统将经过三叉神经核。在丘脑的这一区域内，全部对侧身体表面可反映在一张准确的躯体位置图上（图1）。最近的实验表明，具有辨别能力的皮肤感觉在背柱破坏后仍能幸存[1]。对于这种免受影响现象的一种解释是：其他系统汇聚到丘脑神经核团并通过替代的通路来传输必要的传入信息。为了检验这种假说，我们正在进行一系列实验，以检测背柱内侧丘系系统被破坏之前和之后丘脑腹后外侧核细胞的反应。分别在切断 11 只大鼠胸背

in VPL before and after part of the dorsal column-medial lemniscus system had been destroyed. Responses had been recorded in VPL immediately before and after section of thoracic dorsal columns in eleven rats, and after destruction of one nucleus gracilis in eight rats. We suspected that the full potentiality of the cells might not be revealed immediately after deafferentation and therefore decided to leave the animals for various times after the lesion before examining the thalamus. We encountered the unexpected result that cells in VPL which normally respond to leg stimulation began to respond to arm stimuli some time after destruction of nucleus gracilis. We shall report elsewhere the effect of acute and chronic deafferentation on the response of VPL cells to leg and body stimulation. Here we concentrate on those cells whose receptive fields switched from leg to arm.

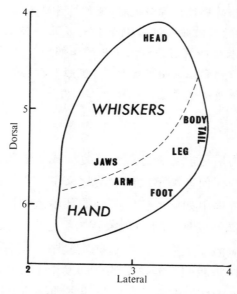

Fig. 1. Diagram of the representation in rat thalamus of the contralateral body surface. The region in which arm, trunk, leg and tail is represented in nucleus ventralis-posterior-lateralis. Maps are produced by placing microelectrodes successively at many locations in a single transverse plane in the region. For each recording point, the face and body surface is mechanically stimulated. Cells close to the recording electrode respond to a small area of skin. A combination of the receptive fields for all the points provides a map of the entire skin surface. The transverse plane is 4.5 mm rostral to external auditory meatus and the areas show distances in mm lateral to the midline and vertically below the cortical surface.

Recordings were made in seventy-seven adult rats, ASH–CSE strain, weighing 200–400 g, under urethane (25%) anaesthesia, 0.65 ml./100 g. The head was held in a stereotactic machine with the lambda vertically above the ear bars in which position the centre of VPL is A 4.5, L 3.0 and 5.0 mm below cortical surface. The nucleus is crescent shaped in cross section and extends 1.4 mm rostrocaudally and mediolaterally. Thalamic recordings were made with glass-covered platinum microelectrodes whose impedance was 600–800 kohms at 1,000 Hz. When marking of electrode sites was required, recording was first carried out with silver plated steel microelectrodes followed by electrolytic deposition of iron which was later located by the prussian blue reaction. Cortical unit recordings were made with

柱之前和之后，以及在破坏 8 只大鼠的一个薄束核后，立刻记录丘脑腹后外侧核的反应。我们怀疑在传入神经刚刚被阻滞之后细胞可能还没有发挥出全部的潜能，于是决定在损伤后把实验动物放养不同的时间然后再检验其丘脑。我们得到了出乎意料的结果：在薄束核受损一段时间之后，通常应该对来自后肢的刺激产生反应的丘脑腹后外侧核细胞开始对来自前肢的刺激有反应了。我们将在别处报道在急性和慢性传入神经阻滞后丘脑腹后外侧核细胞对来自后肢和躯干的刺激的反应。这里我们将把精力集中在那些感受野从后肢转换到前肢的细胞上。

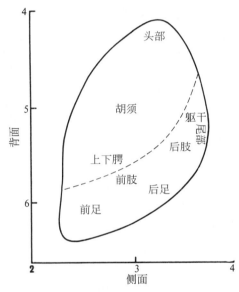

图 1. 对侧身体表面在大鼠丘脑中的映射图。前肢、躯干、后肢和尾部传入投射到丘脑腹后外侧核上的对应代表区域。这类映射图是通过在该区域单一横断面上多个位置陆续放置微电极得到的。每个记录点都是对动物面部和身体表面进行机械刺激的结果。记录电极周边的细胞对皮肤的一小块区域作出反应。所有这些点提供的感受野组合在一起就拼成了整个皮肤表面的映射图。横断面位于外耳道喙侧 4.5 mm 处，该区域到中线的距离为 mm 级，并垂直地位于皮层下方，距离也是 mm 级。

取 77 只 ASH–CSE 品种的成年大鼠，每只体重 200 g ~ 400 g，每 100 g 体重注射 0.65 ml 乌拉坦（25%）来实现麻醉，然后进行记录。将头部固定在脑立体定位仪中，使人字缝尖垂直高于耳夹，在这种定位中，丘脑腹后外侧核的中心在皮层表面之下，距离腹面 4.5 mm，距离侧面分别为 3.0 mm 和 5.0 mm。该神经核在横断面上为新月形，并向喙尾侧和中间外侧延伸 1.4 mm。用玻璃包裹的在 1,000 Hz 时电阻为 600 kΩ ~ 800 kΩ 的铂微电极记录丘脑信号。当电极位点需要标记时，先用镀银的钢微电极记录信号，接下来进行铁电解沉积，稍后用普鲁士蓝反应定位。皮层单元信号用充满

glass microelectrodes filled with 3 M KCl with impedance of 2–4 M ohms. When latencies were required, electrical stimuli were applied to the cutaneous receptive field of the unit through intradermal 30 gauge needles. Chronic lesions of nucleus gracilis or dorsal columns were made in sterile conditions with the animal anaesthetized with "Equithesin". With the head fully flexed and the cisterna magna open, nucleus gracilis can be observed directly without further dissection. The nucleus was destroyed by repeated maceration with honed jeweller's forceps. At various times after this lesion, thalamus or cortex was mapped and then the extent of the lesion was determined from serial frozen sections stained with darrow red–luxol fast blue. Only those animals with the lesion restricted to gracile nucleus are reported. In some, the extreme caudal end of the nucleus was spared.

Distribution of Receptive Fields

The distribution of receptive fields of cells in VPL was mapped in sixteen intact animals. In a further thirty-five animals maps were made of the intact VPL on one side so that these maps could be compared with those from the opposite VPL which had been partially deafferented by nucleus gracilis destruction. Successive recording points were distributed in a regular grid separated by 100 μm vertically and 200 or 250 μm rostrocaudally and mediolaterally. For each station on this three dimensional grid, the entire body surface was brushed with medium pressure and the position was noted of any area of skin which evoked unit responses with an amplitude greater than 50 μV.

In the normal VPL individual cells had small discrete receptive fields. Neighbouring cells recorded at a single electrode site had overlapping receptive fields restricted to some small area of the contralateral body surface. In 35% of the recording sites, cells responded to stimulation of trunk or proximal portions of the limbs or tail and these cells lie in the dorsolateral part of the nucleus. Twenty-four percent responded to lower hind leg or feet or toes and lie ventrolaterally. Forty-one percent responded to lower forearm or hands or fingers and are located ventromedially. The ventral surface of the nucleus is made up of a lamina about 200–400 μm thick which contains cells that respond to passive movement of the limbs. Ventral to the arm area these cells respond to arm movements and the cutaneous leg zone has leg movement cells ventral to it.

Cross-sectional maps were made first of one side and then continued across the midline to investigate the opposite nucleus. Fifty-seven pairs of maps were made in twenty animals at various stages after destruction of n. gracilis. Five variables were compared in the normal nucleus and its partner which had lost afferents: (1) the stereotactic coordinates of areas responding to particular parts of the body; (2) the ratio of the number of points on each side which responded to certain stimulus sites; (3) the monopoly by hind limb cells of the rostral pole of the normal nucleus; (4) the map in the ventral lamina of movement detection cells, which was unaffected by gracilis lesions and therefore provided another marker; (5) the receptive fields and latencies of selected single cells.

In rats mapped 1 or 2 days after destruction of the n. gracilis the picture is the same as immediately after the lesion (Fig. 2). The lower arm–hand–finger area is unchanged. In the leg–foot–toe region, there is an almost complete disappearance of sites where stimuli evoked activity. We shall describe the nature of these scattered responses to leg stimuli and

3 M KCl 的电阻为 2 MΩ ～ 4 MΩ 的玻璃微电极记录。当需要测量反应时间时，可以用 30 号皮内针对与该单元对应的皮肤感受野进行电刺激。腹腔注射"Equithesin"（译者注：0.6% 戊巴比妥钠和水合氯醛混合物）麻醉动物，在无菌条件下慢性损坏薄束核或背柱。使头部充分弯曲，打开小脑延髓池，不用进一步解剖就能直接观察到薄束核。用精巧珠宝镊反复浸离，破坏该神经核。在这种损伤后的不同时间点，绘制丘脑或皮层映射图，接下来用达罗红 – 罗克沙尔固蓝对连续冷冻切片进行染色，以确定损伤范围。我们只报道了那些损伤限制在薄束核内的动物的实验结果。在一些实验动物中，该神经核的极尾端没有被破坏。

感受野的分布

作 16 只正常动物的丘脑腹后外侧核细胞的感受野分布图。再作另外 35 只动物未受损一侧的丘脑腹后外侧核的感受野分布图，在此基础上，可以与对侧的因薄束核损伤导致部分传入神经阻滞的丘脑腹后外侧核感受野分布图进行比较。连续记录点分布在规则网格上，垂直间距为 100 μm，喙尾侧和中间外侧间距为 200 μm 或 250 μm。对于这一三维网格的每一记录点，用中等压力刷遍体表，标出能够引起单元反应幅度超过 50 μV 的任意皮肤区域。

在正常的腹后外侧核中，个别细胞具有小的离散感受野。由单电极位点记录的邻近细胞具有重叠的感受野，这些感受野都局限在对侧身体表面的小区域内。在 35% 的记录位点中，细胞对来自躯干或四肢最接近躯干部分或尾部的刺激有反应，这些细胞分布在该神经核的背外侧部分。在 24% 的记录位点中，细胞对来自后肢下部或后足或后爪的刺激有反应，这些细胞分布在该神经核的腹外侧部分。在剩下 41% 的记录位点中，细胞对来自前肢下部或前足或前爪的刺激有反应，这些细胞位于该神经核腹正中。该神经核的腹部表面由 200 μm ～ 400 μm 厚的单一薄层组成，薄层里含有对四肢的被动运动有反应的细胞。在前肢反应区腹侧的这些细胞对前肢运动有反应，而对后肢运动有反应的细胞位于皮肤的后肢映射带腹侧。

先完成一侧的横断面映射图，然后继续越过中线研究对侧的神经核。取 20 只动物，在破坏薄束核后的不同阶段作出了 57 对映射图。比较正常神经核和它对侧失去传入功能的神经核的 5 个变量：（1）对身体特定部位作出反应的区域的立体定位坐标；（2）两侧对确定刺激位点能产生反应的点的数量比；（3）正常神经核喙极对应后肢的细胞单独支配的区域；（4）由运动感知细胞构成的腹侧薄层中的对应图，它不受薄束损伤的影响，因此提供了另一标记；（5）被选单细胞的感受野和反应时间。

薄束核破坏 1 到 2 天后再对大鼠的反应作映射图，得到的图和损伤后立即作的图相同（图 2）。前肢下部 – 前足 – 前爪区域没有发生改变。在后肢 – 后足 – 后爪区域，由刺激能够引起活性的位点几乎完全消失。仅存在一些对后肢和躯干区域刺激产生

those in the body region in another paper. In eight of nine animals mapped 3–17 weeks after the lesion, responses to stimuli on trunk, tail and hind leg remained essentially the same as in the acute and short survival animals but there was an expansion of the arm area into regions normally responding to leg stimuli. Sites responding to body and proximal limb stimuli averaged 25% fewer than normal, those for leg averaged 87.5% fewer but the number of arm points increased by 24%. Examination of the maps in detail shows that this expansion is produced by a lateral movement of the lateral edge while the medial part remains unchanged (Fig. 3). This lateral zone subserves the lower arm and wrist and these sites increased by an average of 132%. The change was most marked at the rostral pole where the zone normally monopolized by leg cells was now occupied by arm cells. Arm cells now lay dorsal to cells which responded to leg movement. The 16 and 17 week survival animals showed no greater expansion than the 3 week survivors. In no animal was the entire area which normally responded to hind limb invaded by the forelimb area. In a ninth animal with 3 week survival there were signs of expansion of the body area.

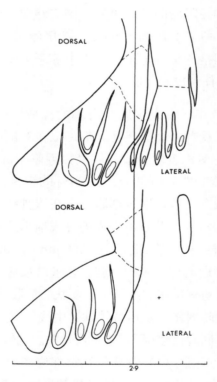

Fig. 2. Transverse map of distribution of receptive fields in VPL in rat 1 day after destruction of nucleus gracilis on one side. The map above shows the distribution in the thalamus supplied by the intact dorsal column nuclei with the forelimb representation medial, leg lateral, and body dorsolateral. The dotted lines mark the elbow and wrist on arm and the ankle on leg. The face area is not mapped. The map below shows the result of continuing the transverse search plane directly across the midline to the opposite thalamus which is not receiving an input from nucleus gracilis. The arm–hand–finger area is very similar in both maps. The leg area contained no responding cells in this plane with one exception marked by a cross. The horizontal axis marks 200 μm intervals in the mediolateral direction. The vertical line marks electrode tracks 2.9 mm from the midline penetrating both left and right thalamic maps. These tracks passed through the lateral arm region in each thalamus and show how similar the two arm regions are.

752

的零散反应，我们将在其他文章中描述这些反应的性质。在损伤 3 周～ 17 周后作映射图，9 只动物中有 8 只对于来自躯干、尾部和后肢的刺激的反应本质上与急性短期存活的动物一样，但是前肢区域会扩展到通常对后肢刺激有反应的区域。对来自躯干和四肢接近躯干部分的刺激产生反应的位点平均比正常动物少 25%，对后肢产生反应的位点平均比正常动物少 87.5%，但对前肢产生反应的位点数量增加了 24%。仔细检查映射图，发现这一扩展是由侧面边缘的侧向运动产生的，而中间部分仍维持原样（图 3）。这个侧面带促进了前肢下部和腕部，这些位点平均增长了 132%。这种变化大多集中在喙极，这一区域通常只分布着对后肢产生反应的细胞，现在却被对前肢产生反应的细胞所占据。对前肢产生反应的细胞现在位于对后肢运动产生反应的细胞的背侧。破坏 16 周和 17 周后依然存活的动物与破坏 3 周后的存活动物相比，扩展区没有进一步扩大。没有一只动物表现出通常对后肢产生反应的区域完全被对前肢产生反应的区域所占领的行为。在存活 3 周的动物中，有九分之一存在躯体区域扩展的迹象。

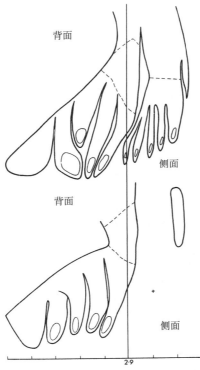

图 2. 单侧薄束核破坏 1 天后大鼠丘脑腹后外侧核中感受野的分布横断面图。上图显示了由未受损伤的背柱神经核提供的丘脑分布，中间代表前肢、侧面代表后肢以及背侧代表躯干。虚线标出了前肢的肘部和腕部所在处以及后肢的踝关节所在处。面部区域没有标示到图上。下图显示的是直接越过中线，对没有接收来自薄束核输入的对侧丘脑继续横向搜索断面的结果。前肢 – 前足 – 前爪区域在两幅图中非常相似。在这一断面上后肢区域不含有反应的细胞，有一个例外，用十字表示。水平轴沿中间外侧方向，刻度间隔 200 μm。垂线标出了电极轨迹，距离中线2.9 mm，贯穿丘脑图的左右两侧。这些轨迹穿过每一丘脑的前肢区域侧面，并显示出两个前肢区域有多相似。

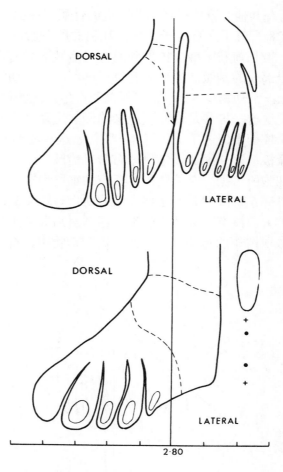

Fig. 3. Transverse map of distribution of receptive fields in intact VPL (above) and the map produced
by continuing the mapping plane across the midline into the opposite VPL studied 7 weeks after
destruction of the n. gracilis which projected to this nucleus (below). The vertical line marks
an electrode track 2.8 mm from the midline which samples a similar region of the thalamus on
the intact side to the vertical line shown in Fig. 2. The thalamus on the medial side of the line
contains a similar map on both the intact and deafferented side. But the region representing
the arm, especially the lower arm, has expanded on the operated side to invade a region which
responds to leg on the intact side. At the lateral edge of the nucleus four cells were encountered
which responded to body or leg stimulation but most cells in this region failed to respond to any
peripheral stimuli.

Time Course and Nature of the Change

The simplest explanation for the expansion would be the shrinking of deafferented
cells with a simple moving over of the neighbours. In this case there would be no
new connexions and the cortical somatotopic map would not be distorted. Successful
maps were completed of the arm and leg area of main sensory-motor cortex on both
sides in animals 2, 5 and 6 week after destruction of one n. gracilis. The animals were
anaesthetized with urethane and the body surface stimulated as in the thalamic recording
experiments. In order to obtain a sufficiently detailed map it was necessary to record the

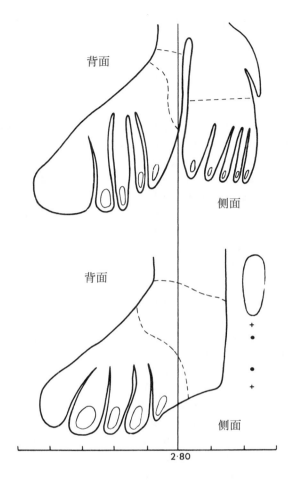

图 3. 未受损伤的丘脑腹后外侧核中感受野的分布横断面图（上图）；在投射到这一核团的薄束核被破坏7 周后进行研究，将断面继续绘至越过中线到对侧丘脑腹后外侧核，得到对应的映射图（下图）。垂线标出了电极轨迹，距离中线 2.8 mm，在丘脑未受损一侧垂线上的取样与图 2 中的垂线相同。垂线内侧的丘脑在未受损一侧和传入神经阻滞一侧的映射图类似。但是代表前肢的区域，尤其是代表前肢下部的区域，在手术一侧发生扩展，侵入到未受损一侧对后肢产生反应的区域。在该神经核侧面边缘找到 4 个对来自躯干或后肢的刺激产生反应的细胞，但这一区域中的大多数细胞对外周刺激不产生反应。

变化的时间进程和本质

对于这种扩展，最简单的解释可能是：传入阻滞的细胞发生萎缩，于是相邻细胞移动过来，简单地覆盖了萎缩细胞。在这种情况下，不会产生新联系，而且皮层躯体位置图也不会变形。分别在破坏一个薄束核 2 周、5 周和 6 周后，我们成功地绘制出动物两侧主要感觉-运动皮层前后肢对应区的映射图。用乌拉坦麻醉动物，并以在丘脑记录实验中所用的方式刺激体表。为了得到足够详细的映射图，需要记

receptive fields of cortical units by penetrating 500 μm into cortex with glass, 2–4 Mohms, KCl filled microelectrodes. Maps were constructed from a grid of recording points separated by 500 μm. In all three animals, the arm area had expanded into the leg area and it must therefore be concluded that thalamic cells projecting to cortex had changed their peripheral receptive fields.

The simplest explanation for the appearance of new receptive fields would be that the deafferentation had unmasked existing afferents which are normally inhibited. This is unlikely because in this type of preparation even massive electrical stimuli to arm in the intact animal fail to excite cells with discrete receptive fields on leg. Furthermore, there is a time delay in the switching of receptive fields. During this period when the former leg cells fail to respond to peripheral stimuli, ongoing activity continues in them at at least the frequency of normally connected cells showing that the deafferented cells themselves do not go through a period of lowered excitability.

To postulate the formation of new connexions, it is necessary first to discover the time course of their development. Eleven animals were examined 1–7 days after the lesion. At 1 and 2 days there was no significant change. At 3 days, two of three animals showed some expansion but without invasion of the rostral pole. At 4 days one animal showed both expansion and rostral invasion while a second showed no change. Of two animals at 5 days, one showed the full picture of expansion and the other some expansion. A 6-day survivor was inconclusive but the 7-day animal showed the same full picture as those examined after 3 weeks. We conclude that the changeover begins at 3 days and is fully established between 1 and 3 weeks. The cell bodies of the changed cells lay 200–400 μm from the original boundary of the normal area but one must remember that the dendrites of the innervated and deafferented cells might be intermingled so that any shift of connexion might be over very small distances.

It is conceivable that the stimulus for the change of connectivity is not the degeneration of the terminals but the absence of the normal afferent impulses which bombard the thalamic cells. This possibility was ruled out by sectioning the dorsal columns just caudal to n. gracilis leaving the nucleus itself intact. The section of the fibres was made to spare the more lateral component of dorsal columns which supplies the cuneate nucleus. Thalamic maps from this animal taken 7 days after the lesion showed no signs of expansion of the arm area into the silent region which no longer responded to leg stimuli. It is true that the thalamus would still be bombarded by the ongoing activity of the deafferented nucleus gracilis but this is presumably slight by comparison with that transmitted in the normal freely moving animal.

A possible explanation for the newly effective connexion is that a background of ineffective fibres from the cuneate nucleus lie scattered through the area normally innervated by n. gracilis and that these fibres mature and successfully stimulate the cells vacated by degenerating axons. The change could be either presynaptic or postsynaptic. If such a diffuse system of fibres existed, one might expect the receptive fields of the newly

录皮层单元的感受野，方法是用电阻为 2 MΩ ～ 4 MΩ 的充满 KCl 的玻璃微电极插入皮层下 500 μm。用间隔 500 μm 的记录点组成的网格构建映射图。在所有 3 只动物中，前肢区域都扩展到了后肢区域，因而我们只能认为丘脑投射到皮层的细胞已经改变了它们的外周感受野。

对于新感受野的出现，最简单的解释就是：传入阻滞使现存的、正常情况下被抑制的传入暴露出来。这种解释不太可能，因为在这类实验中，即使对未损伤动物的前肢施加强大电刺激，也无法激发后肢的离散感受野细胞。此外，感受野的转换还有一段时间延迟。在此前对后肢刺激有反应的细胞无法响应外周刺激的这段时间里，这些细胞中延续着持续的活性，至少维持正常联系细胞的频率，这说明传入阻滞的细胞本身并没有经历一个兴奋性降低的时期。

为了假定新联系的形成，首先需要揭示它们发育的时间进程。取 11 只动物，分别在损伤 1 天 ～ 7 天后加以检验。第 1 天和第 2 天没有明显的变化。在第 3 天，三分之二的动物显现出一些扩展，但是没有喙极的侵入。到第 4 天，有一只动物同时出现了扩展和喙极侵入，另一只仍没有显现出变化。在第 5 天，两只动物中的一只显现出完整的扩展图，另一只出现了一些扩展。一只损伤 6 天后的幸存动物结果不明确，但是损伤 7 天后的动物显示出了与那些损伤 3 周后才用于检查的动物一样完整的图。我们得出的结论是：转换过程在损伤后 3 天内开始，在损伤后 1 周到 3 周之间完全建立。转变后细胞的细胞体位于距离正常区域的原始边界 200 μm ～ 400 μm处，但是必须注意到，受神经支配的和传入阻滞的细胞的树突有可能会混在一起，因此联系的任何改变也许仅跨越了非常小的距离。

有人认为：使连通性发生改变的刺激并不是终端的退化，而是冲击丘脑细胞的正常传入脉冲的缺失。通过切断紧靠薄束核尾侧的背柱同时保证其神经核完好无损的方法，可排除这种可能性。将纤维切断时需保留给楔束核提供信号的背柱更外侧部分。从损伤 7 天后的动物得出的丘脑映射图来看，不存在前肢区域扩展进入已不再对后肢刺激产生反应的沉默区的迹象。事实上，丘脑仍然会被传入阻滞的薄束核的持续活性所冲击，但是比起能够自由活动的正常动物的传入，大概变得很轻微。

关于新的有效联系的一个可能解释是：来自楔束核的无效纤维的背景分布零星穿过了通常由薄束核神经所支配的区域，且这些纤维发育成熟并成功地对由于轴突不断退化而空出的细胞产生刺激。这一变化可能发生在突触前，也可能发生在突触后。如果存在这样的一个纤维扩散系统，就可以预期新联系起来的细胞的感受野将不同

connected cells to differ from those in the established part of the nucleus. In fact we were unable to differentiate the receptive fields of cells in the presumably newly invaded region from those medial to them either in terms of field size or threshold. It is a particularly suitable region for examining receptive fields because many cells respond to movement of one or more of the long whisker-like hairs protruding from the rat's volar wrist. Cells with precisely this type of receptive field seemed to be duplicated in the new territory. Another possible mechanism is that the cells respond to an indirect input perhaps by way of cortex rather than by way of axons originating in cuneate nucleus. This seems unlikely because the latency of response of the switched cells was identical to that in the unchanged zone.

Collateral Sprouting

Probably the most likely explanation is that sprouts have grown from the terminal arborization of intact axons from cuneate nucleus and have established successful contact with deafferented neighbours. Collateral sprouting and new contact formation have been shown to occur in the periphery both in denervated muscle[2] and in sympathetic ganglia[3]. In the central nervous system, light microscope evidence of sprouting into denervated regions has been provided for dorsal root fibres[4] and for optic nerve fibres[5]. Raisman[6] has shown clear electron microscope evidence for sprouting and end knob formation in the partially denervated septal nuclei of adult rat. But in the case of collateral sprouting, one must still explain the small receptive fields of the newly connected cells. The distance over which the sprouts would have to extend is not known, because although the cell bodies of the switched cells can be as much as 400 μm from the intact area it may be that the dendritic fields of the denervated cells overlap with those of the intact cells. If a sprout had only to grow a few μm to occupy a new cell, a pioneer sprout might lay down a pathway along which its neighbours could grow. Another way in which a restricted receptive field might be formed would be if the fibres which fire together grow together. This would require a mechanism by which the presence of more or less coincident impulse traffic in terminals would exaggerate the growth of terminals which sensed impulses in themselves and their neighbours.

Clearly an explanation of the phenomenon reported here will have to await an electron microscope examination of morphological changes in the region of changed response. In assessing the significance of the phenomenon of new connexions, one must give certain warnings. These observations were made in the rat, an animal which continues to grow throughout adult life, perhaps therefore retaining certain embryological characteristics. The distance over which new connexions could be established is evidently limited since there were no signs of occupation of vacant cells in the lateral edge of the nucleus. The new connexions do not represent recovery from the original lesions because information from arms is now channelled into a system presumably specialized to handle leg information. However, one might speculate that if scattered single cells were destroyed, as

于神经核已建立部分的那些细胞的感受野。事实上，我们无法区分假设新被入侵区域中的细胞的感受野与位于它们内侧的细胞的感受野，无论是在感受野的大小方面还是在阈值方面。有一个特别适合作感受野检查的区域，因为很多细胞对大鼠腕掌部突出来的一根或更多胡须状长毛的运动有反应。恰好具有这种类型感受野的细胞看上去在这个新领域中发生了复制。另一可能的机制是：细胞可能对经由皮层的间接输入有反应，而不是对经由源于楔束核的轴突的间接输入有反应。这一机制似乎不太可能，因为已转换细胞的反应时间与那些未变化带中细胞的反应时间完全相同。

侧 索 生 芽

也许最有可能的解释是：源自楔束核的未受损轴突的分支终端长出新芽，并与传入阻滞的相邻细胞之间成功地建立起联系。侧索生芽和新联系的形成已被证明可以发生在外周的去神经肌肉 [2] 和交感神经节 [3] 中。光学显微镜提供的证据表明：在中枢神经系统中，生芽进入去神经区发生在背根神经纤维 [4] 和视神经纤维 [5]。雷斯曼 [6] 已经给出明确的电子显微镜证据，该证据证明在成年大鼠体内，部分去神经的隔核中存在生芽和形成尾结的现象。但是，在侧索生芽的例子中，还需要解释新联系起来的细胞的小感受野。芽不得不延伸跨越的距离仍属未知，因为虽然已转换细胞的细胞体距离未受损区域可达 400 μm，但是去神经细胞的树突野也有可能和那些未受损细胞的树突野发生重叠。如果一个芽为了占领新细胞，只需长几 μm，那么一个先导芽可能会铺好一条通路，它邻近的细胞可以沿着这条通路生长。形成受限感受野的另外一种可能方式是，同时产生神经冲动的纤维一起生长。这就要求有一种机制能使终端有几乎同时产生的神经冲动发生，这会促进能感受到自身和相邻细胞冲动的终端的生长。

显然，要想给出此现象的一个解释，还需要等待用电子显微镜对反应发生改变区域中的形态学变化的检查结果。在评价新联系现象的意义时，必须给出某些提醒。这些观察结果是从大鼠身上得到的，大鼠是一种在整个成年期中持续生长的动物，也许因此保留了一些胚胎学特征。可以建立新联系的跨越距离显然有限，因为没有发现该核团侧面边缘中空闲细胞被占领的迹象。新联系并不代表从原来的损伤中康复，因为来自前肢的信息现在被导入到一个被认为专门处理来自后肢的信息的系统。虽然如此，我们可以推测，如果零星分布的单细胞被破坏，就像患脑膜炎时那样，

in an encephalitis, sprouting from associated collaborating neighbours might provide some functional advantage.

(**232**, 542-545; 1971)

P. D. Wall and M. D. Egger: MRC Cerebral Functions Research Group, Department of Anatomy, University College, Gower Street, London WCIE 6BT.

Received April 8; revised July 30, 1971.

References:

1. Wall, P. D., *Brain*, **93**, 505 (1970).

2. Edds, jun., Mac V., *Quart. Rev. Biol.*, **28**, 260 (1953).

3. Guth, L., and Bernstein, J., *J. Exp. Neurol.*, 4, 59 (1961).

4. Liu, C. N., and Chambers, W. W., *Arch. Neurol.*, **79**, 46 (1958).

5. Goodman, D. C., and Horel, J. A., *J. Comp. Neurol.*, **127**, 71 (1966).

6. Raisman, G., *Brain. Res.*, **14**, 25 (1969).

那么从相邻的有关合作细胞上生芽也许会带来某些功能上的益处。

（毛晨晖 邓铭瑞 翻译；刘力 审稿）

Change in Methylation of 16S Ribosomal RNA Associated with Mutation to Kasugamycin Resistance in *Escherichia coli*

T. L. Helser *et al.*

Editor's Note

The ribosome is the central component of the protein-manufacturing machinery found in all cells, and is made up of a large and small subunit. In this paper, James E. Dahlberg and colleagues suggest that a change in chemical modification (methylation) of a small subunit constituent (16S rRNA) causes resistance to the antibiotic kasugamycin in *Escherichia coli* bacteria. The mutation, they suggest, is linked with a change in methylation of a specific nucleotide sequence close to one end of the 16S rRNA. Several years later it was found that such a sequence participates directly in the initiation of protein synthesis by forming base pairs with messenger RNA.

GENES which code for proteins of both the 50S and 30S ribosomal subunits of *E. coli* seem to be clustered on the linkage map between minutes 62 and 64[1]. Mutations which affect proteins of the 30S subunit (streptomycin[2] and spectinomycin[3] resistances), those which affect proteins of the 50S subunit (erythromycin resistance[4]), and those in the translocation factor G (fusidic acid resistance[5-7]), all map in this region, as do several other 30S and 50S proteins[8,9]. In contrast, resistance to the aminoglycoside antibiotic kasugamycin (ksg), which is known to interact with the 30S subunit[10], maps close to minute 1[10-12]. Kasugamycin also inhibits the binding of fMet-tRNA to the mRNA-ribosome initiation complex in the presence of β,γ-methylene-guanosine triphosphate (GMPPcP), which indicates a different mode of action from the other aminoglycosides[11,13]. In this article we show that resistance to kasugamycin is determined by the properties of the 16S ribosomal RNA and that the mutation is associated with a change in the methylation of a specific nucleotide sequence close to the 3´ end of the 16S RNA[14,15].

Ribosomal Component Conferring Kasugamycin Sensitivity

The work of Sparling[10] has determined the site of action of kasugamycin as the 30S ribosome subunit. We have further localized its action using 30S subunits reconstituted from "core particles" and "split proteins" (obtained from cesium chloride density centrifugation of 30S subunits[16]) and find that sensitivity or resistance to kasugamycin is a property of the "core particles" (Table 1). 30S subunits reconstituted from pure 16S RNA and total protein[17] were then tested for sensitivity or resistance to kasugamycin in an *in vitro* polypeptide synthesizing system. The results with several different preparations of 16S RNA and total 30S proteins were all essentially the same: the particles containing 16S RNA from *ksg*ˢ strains were always more susceptible than particles containing 16S RNA from *ksg*ʳ strains (Table 2). Furthermore, we have analysed the proteins obtained from 30S

大肠杆菌中春日霉素抗性突变与16S 核糖体RNA的甲基化变化相关

赫尔泽等

编者按

核糖体在所有细胞中都是蛋白质合成体系中的核心成分，它由一大一小两个亚基构成。在这篇论文中，詹姆斯·达尔伯格和他的同事们指出，小亚基中成分（16S 核糖体 RNA）的化学修饰的变化（甲基化）会引起大肠杆菌对一种抗生素——春日霉素的抗性。他们还指出，突变是与靠近 16S 核糖体 RNA 一端的某一特定核苷酸序列的甲基化变化联系在一起的。几年后人们发现，这些序列通过与信使 RNA 形成碱基对直接参与了蛋白质合成的启动。

编码大肠杆菌 50S 和 30S 核糖体亚基蛋白质的基因看上去聚集在连锁图上 62 min 和 64 min 之间 [1]。影响 30S 亚基蛋白的突变（链霉素 [2] 和壮观霉素 [3] 抗性），以及那些影响 50S 亚基蛋白的突变（红霉素抗性 [4]）和那些易位因子 G 中的突变（夫西地酸抗性 [5-7]），都位于这一区域，其他几种 30S 和 50S 蛋白也是如此 [8, 9]。相反，对氨基糖苷类抗生素春日霉素（ksg）的抗性，已知是和 30S 亚基 [10] 发生相互作用，却位于靠近 1 min 的位置 [10-12]。在 β, γ– 亚甲基 – 鸟苷三磷酸盐（GMPPcP）存在的条件下，春日霉素也会抑制甲酰甲硫氨酸 – 转运 RNA 与信使 RNA– 核糖体启动复合物的结合，这显示出一种和其他氨基糖苷类不同的作用方式 [11, 13]。在本文中，我们将证明：对春日霉素的抗性是由 16S 核糖体 RNA 的性质决定的，并且突变与靠近 16S RNA 3′ 末端的某一特定核苷酸序列的甲基化变化有关 [14, 15]。

赋予春日霉素敏感性的核糖体成分

斯帕林 [10] 的工作已经确定春日霉素的作用位点是 30S 核糖体亚基。我们用由"核心粒子"和"脱落蛋白"（由 30S 亚基的 CsCl 密度离心获得 [16]）重组的 30S 亚基进一步定位了春日霉素的作用位点，并发现对春日霉素的敏感性或抗性是"核心粒子"的性质（表 1）。用纯 16S RNA 和全蛋白重组 30S 亚基 [17]，然后在体外多肽合成系统中测试它对春日霉素的敏感性或抗性。由 16S RNA 和全 30S 蛋白制备的几种不同产物都能得到基本一致的结果：含有来自春日霉素敏感性（ksg^s）品系的 16S RNA 的粒子通常比含有来自春日霉素抗性（ksg^r）品系的 16S RNA 的颗粒更易受影

subunits of *ksg*[s] and *ksg*[r] strains for chemical differences by one dimensional polyacrylamide gel electrophoresis, and by co-chromatography of ^{3}H-labelled "sensitive" proteins and ^{14}C-labelled "resistant" proteins on carboxymethylcellulose columns. We have found that the sensitive and resistant strains seem to have complete and identical complements of 30S ribosomal proteins.

Table 1. Reconstitution of 30S Ribosomes from Split Proteins and Core Particles

Reconstituted 30S ribosomes		Incorporation—c.p.m. (% of control c.p.m.)		
Split protein	Core particle	Concentration of ksg (μg/ml.)		
		0	20	100
S	S	19,230 (100)	12,100 (63)	5,800 (30)
R	S	16,200 (100)	10,430 (64)	5,700 (35)
S	R	17,900 (100)	16,400 (92)	13,260 (74)
R	R	16,100 (100)	13,240 (82)	10,800 (67)

Analysis of CsCl "split" and "core" fractions for ksg sensitivity and resistance. 30S subunits were reconstituted from the appropriate split protein and core particle preparations using the methods of Traub and Nomura[16] and assayed for poly UG-directed ^{14}C-valine incorporation. In a volume of 100 μl., the reactions contained from 1.1 to 1.3 A_{260} units of reconstituted 30S and 1.5 A_{260} units of 50S from the resistant strain, 10 μg of poly UG (2:1—U:G input), and magnesium acetate at a final concentration of 7.5 mM. ^{14}C-valine (25 μCi/μmol) and other components were added as described by Nirenberg[27]. Reactions were incubated for 30 min at 37°C and terminated by the addition of 1 ml. of 10% trichloroacetic acid. After collection, the precipitates were counted in a Packard scintillation counter using a toluene-based fluid.

Table 2. Reconstitution of 30S Ribosomes from Total Protein and 16S RNA

Reconstituted 30S ribosomes		Incorporation—c.p.m. (% of control c.p.m.)		
Total protein	16S RNA	Concentration of ksg (μg/ml.)		
		0	20	100
S	S	681 (100)	346 (51)	188 (28)
R	S	761 (100)	389 (51)	191 (25)
S	R	634 (100)	400 (63)	260 (41)
R	R	471 (100)	329 (70)	300 (64)

30S subunits were reconstituted from the appropriate total protein preparation (urea–lithium chloride extracted) and 16S RNA (phenol extracted) using the methods of Traub and Nomura[17]. They were assayed as in Table 1 using from 0.86 to 1.0 A_{260} units of reconstituted 30S and 0.9 A_{260} units of 50S from the resistant strain.

16S Ribosomal RNA Structures

With this evidence implicating 16S ribosomal RNA as the determinant of kasugamycin sensitivity or resistance we have compared the RNA sequences by the "fingerprint" analysis technique of Sanger and co-workers[18,19] using radioactively labelled ribosomal RNA obtained from *ksg*[s] and *ksg*[r] strains.

Initial experiments were performed on ^{32}P-labelled 16S RNA obtained from resistant and sensitive cells. The RNAs were digested with RNAase T$_1$ plus alkaline phosphatase and the resulting oligonucleotides were separated, as described in Fig. 1. The fingerprints of these RNAs are shown in Fig. 1*a* and Fig. 1*b*.

响（表2）。此外，我们还使用一维聚丙烯酰胺凝胶电泳法和联合色谱法（用羟甲基纤维素色谱柱分离 ^3H 标记的"敏感"蛋白和 ^{14}C 标记的"抗性"蛋白）来分析从 ksg^s 品系和 ksg^r 品系的 30S 亚基获得的蛋白，以寻找它们间的化学差异。我们发现，敏感性品系和抗性品系的 30S 核糖体蛋白成分似乎是完全相同的。

表 1. 来自脱落蛋白和核心粒子的 30S 核糖体的重组

重组的 30S 核糖体		重组后的 c.p.m.（占对照 c.p.m. 的百分比）		
		春日霉素浓度（µg/ml）		
脱落蛋白	核心粒子	0	20	100
敏感性	敏感性	19,230 (100)	12,100 (63)	5,800 (30)
抗性	敏感性	16,200 (100)	10,430 (64)	5,700 (35)
敏感性	抗性	17,900 (100)	16,400 (92)	13,260 (74)
抗性	抗性	16,100 (100)	13,240 (82)	10,800 (67)

春日霉素敏感性和抗性的"脱落"和"核心"片段的 CsCl 离心法分析。采用特劳布和野村法 [16] 用合适的脱落蛋白和核心粒子制剂重组 30S 亚基，并化验多聚 UG 指导的 ^{14}C– 缬氨酸的掺入。在 100 µl 体积内，反应物含有 1.1 A_{260} ～ 1.3 A_{260} 单位的重组 30S 和 1.5 A_{260} 单位来自抗性品系的 50S、10 µg 多聚 UG（输入 U:G 为 2:1）和终浓度为 7.5 mM 的醋酸镁。^{14}C– 缬氨酸（25 µCi/µmol）和其他成分按尼伦伯格所述添加 [27]。反应在 37℃ 下进行 30 min，加入 1 ml 10% 的三氯乙酸终止反应。收集后，沉淀物使用测量溶液为甲苯的帕卡德闪烁计数器计数。

表 2. 来自全蛋白和 16S RNA 的 30S 核糖体的重组

重组的 30S 核糖体		重组后的 c.p.m.（占对照 c.p.m. 的百分比）		
		春日霉素浓度（µg/ml）		
全蛋白	16S RNA	0	20	100
敏感性	敏感性	681 (100)	346 (51)	188 (28)
抗性	敏感性	761 (100)	389 (51)	191 (25)
敏感性	抗性	634 (100)	400 (63)	260 (41)
抗性	抗性	471 (100)	329 (70)	300 (64)

采用特劳布和野村法 [17] 由 16S RNA（苯酚提取）与合适的全蛋白制剂（尿素 – 氯化锂提取）重组得到 30S 亚基。用如表 1 注所述的方式分析它们，使用 0.86 A_{260} ～ 1.0 A_{260} 单位的重组 30S 和 0.9 A_{260} 单位来自抗性品系的 50S。

16S 核糖体 RNA 的结构

上述证据表明，16S 核糖体 RNA 是春日霉素敏感性和抗性的决定因素。采用桑格及其同事 [18,19] 发明的"指纹"分析技术，用放射性标记取自 ksg^s 和 ksg^r 品系的核糖体 RNA，我们比较了 RNA 序列。

最初的实验是在 ^{32}P 标记的取自抗性和敏感性细胞的 16S RNA 上进行的。用加入碱性磷酸酶的 T_1 核糖核酸酶消化这些 RNA，分离得到寡核苷酸，具体过程参见图 1 注中的描述。这些 RNA 的指纹如图 1a 和图 1b 所示。

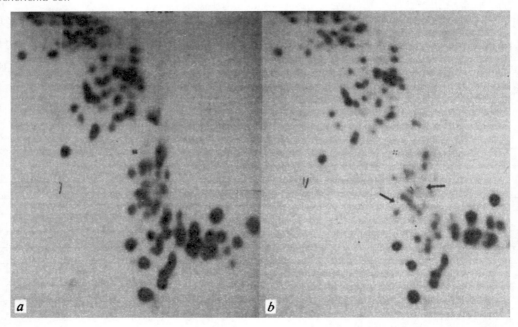

Fig. 1. RNAase T₁ plus phosphatase fingerprints of ³²P-labelled 16S RNA isolated from *ksg* sensitive (*a*) and resistant (*b*) *E. coli*. The arrows in *b* indicate the positions of oligonucleotides which are present in only one or the other digest. The strains were labelled by growth in 1% "Bactotryptone", 0.5% yeast extract, 0.3% glucose medium from which inorganic phosphate had been removed by MgCl₂ precipitation at *p*H 9 before sterilization. ³²P-Phosphate (1 mCi) was added to 25 ml. of the above medium (*p*H 7.8). Cells were grown to late log phase, collected, washed by centrifugation and lysed by lysozyme/EDTA treatment. Total RNA was extracted with phenol and purified on a 5–20% sucrose gradient. The 16S RNA peaks were collected and ethanol-precipitated to remove EDTA. 20 µg (~10⁶ c.p.m.) of each RNA was digested with 1 µg RNAase T₁ (Sankyo) plus 2 µg bacterial alkaline phosphatase (Worthington, BAP–F) in 2 µl. of 0.05 M Tris Cl, *p*H 7.7, 0.0001 M ZnCl₂ for 30 min at 37°C. Electrophoresis from right to left was on a 90 cm Oxoid cellulose acetate strip in *p*H 3.5 pyridine acetate containing 8 M urea for 3 h at 5 kV. Ionophoresis in the second dimension (from top to bottom) was on a 40×80 cm DEAE cellulose paper (Whatman) in 7% formic acid for 16 h at 1 kV. The autoradiogram was exposed for 1 day.

A comparison of the two fingerprints reveals only two differences, which are indicated by the arrows in Fig. 1*b*. Oligonucleotide No. 71 (using the numbering system of Fellner *et al.*[14,20]) is absent from the digest of RNA from the resistant cells, and a different oligonucleotide, No. p-71, is present. Oligonucleotide 71 has the sequence $m_2^6Am_2^6ACCUG$, while oligonucleotide p-71 is probably its unmethylated precursor and has the sequence AACCUG[21]. Thus, mutation from kasugamycin sensitivity to resistance could be accompanied by the inability of the cells to convert adenine in oligonucleotide p-71 to dimethyl adenine.

This inference was confirmed by fingerprint analysis of ¹⁴C-methyl-labelled 16S RNAs. These fingerprints (Fig. 2) show that an oligonucleotide with the mobility of $m_2^6Am_2^6ACCUG$ (No. 71) is present only in the RNA from the sensitive cells (2*a*). It is clear that no other methylation changes in the 16S RNA fragments can be detected (the

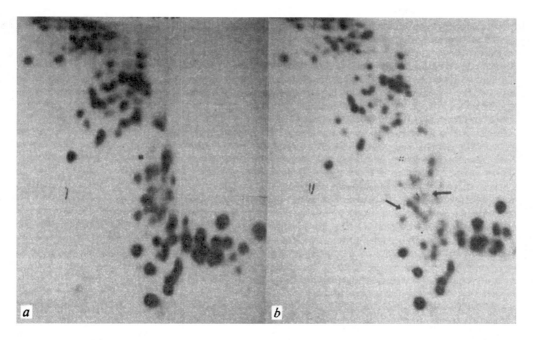

图 1. 从春日霉素敏感性（a）和抗性（b）大肠杆菌中分离 ^{32}P 标记的 16S RNA，并经加入磷酸酶的 T_1 核糖核酸酶消化后的指纹图。图 b 中箭头指示存在只被一种（或另一种）酶消化的寡核苷酸的位置。配制含 1% "细菌用胰蛋白胨"、0.5% 酵母提取物和 0.3% 葡萄糖的培养基，灭菌前在 pH 9 条件下用 $MgCl_2$ 沉淀除去无机磷酸盐。用这种培养基培养大肠杆菌品系，从而标记它。加入 ^{32}P 标记的磷酸盐（1 mCi），使上述培养基（pH 7.8）的体积达到 25 ml。细胞在这种培养基中生长到对数期后期，收集，用离心法洗涤，再用溶菌酶 / EDTA 溶液处理以溶解细胞。用苯酚提取全 RNA，并经 5% ~ 20% 蔗糖梯度纯化。在 16S RNA 峰值收集，并用乙醇沉淀除去 EDTA。每 20 μg(~10^6 c.p.m.) RNA 在 2 μl pH 值为 7.7 的 0.05 M Tris-HCl 和 0.0001 M $ZnCl_2$ 中，用 1 μg T_1 核糖核酸酶（三共）加上 2 μg 细菌碱性磷酸酶（沃辛顿，BAP–F）消化，在 37℃ 下反应 30 min。电泳从右到左是在一个长 90 cm 的奥克欧德牌醋酸纤维素带上进行的，电泳液为 pH 3.5 含有 8 M 尿素的吡啶醋酸盐溶液，在 5 kV 条件下电泳 3 h。离子电泳作用在第二维上，（从上到下）是在一个 40 cm × 80 cm 的二乙氨基乙基纤维素纸（沃特曼）上进行的，电泳液为 7% 的甲酸，在 1 kV 条件下电泳 16 h。放射自显影照片的曝光时间为 1 天。

　　两幅指纹图的比较只显示出两处不同，如图 1b 中的箭头所示。当消化的是来自抗性细胞的 RNA 提取物时，71号寡核苷酸（采用费尔纳等人制订的编号系统 [14,20]）没有出现，但出现了一个与之不同的寡核苷酸 p–71号。71号寡核苷酸具有序列 $m_2^6Am_2^6ACCUG$，而 p–71号寡核苷酸很有可能是它的非甲基化前体，具有序列 $AACCUG$[21]。因此，从春日霉素敏感性到抗性的突变可能伴随着细胞能力的缺失——不能将 p–71号寡核苷酸中的腺嘌呤转化为二甲基腺嘌呤。

　　对 ^{14}C– 甲基标记的 16S RNA 进行指纹分析的结果证实了这一推论。这些指纹图（图 2）显示，一种具有 $m_2^6Am_2^6ACCUG$ 迁移率的寡核苷酸（71 号）只存在于敏感性细胞的 RNA 中（图 2a）。目前已清楚的是，在 16S RNA 片段中没有检测到其

additional spots visible in the resistant fingerprint (2*b*) are due to contamination with 23S RNA).

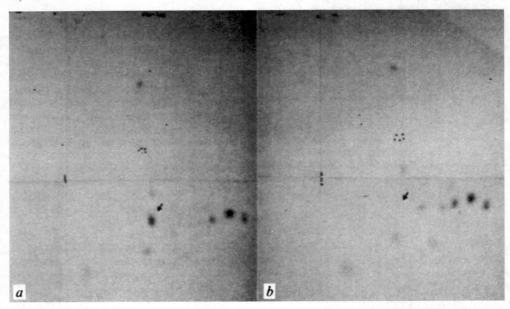

Fig. 2. RNAase T₁ plus phosphatase fingerprints of ¹⁴C-methyl labelled 16S RNA isolated from *ksg* sensitive (*a*) and resistant (*b*) *E. coli*. The RNAs were isolated as described in the legend to Fig. 1 from cells which had been grown on Tris minimal medium[28] supplemented with 50 μg/ml. each of threonine, leucine, cytidine, thymidine, and uridine. ¹⁴C-methyl-L-methionine was added (25 μCi/10.5 μmol in 25 ml. of medium) and the cells were allowed to grow for one generation, when unlabelled methionine (2 μg/ml.) was added. The cells were collected in late log phase. The enzymatic digestion and fingerprinting were performed as described in the legend to Fig. 1 except that 40 μg of each RNA (~2×10⁴ c.p.m. ¹⁴C) were digested with 2 μg RNAase T₁ and 4 μg phosphatase in a volume of 4 μl. The autoradiogram was exposed for 12 days.

Significance of Methylation

Until recently, the only mutations known to affect ribosome structure and function have been those in which a ribosomal protein was altered. The phenotypes of these mutations have been antibiotic resistance, ribosome ambiguity, or ribosome assembly[22,23]. Lai and Weisblum, however, have reported that the induced appearance of erythromycin resistance in *Staphylococcus aureus* is accompanied by methylation of the 23S ribosomal RNA, consistent with the fact that erythromycin resistance is a property of the 50S subunit of the ribosome[24]. Kasugamycin resistance also seems to be an example of a change in ribosomal RNA, since we find that the kasugamycin sensitive and resistant phenotypes are determined by the source of the 16S RNA in reconstitution experiments. The change from kasugamycin-sensitivity to resistance is apparently associated with a failure to methylate a specific sequence in this RNA. We have yet to establish, however, a direct cause and effect relationship between the presence of the m$_2^6$Am$_2^6$ACCUG sequence and the sensitive phenotype, or between the AACCUG sequence and the resistant phenotype.

他甲基化变化（抗性指纹图（2b）中的一些额外的可视点是由 23S RNA 的污染所致）。

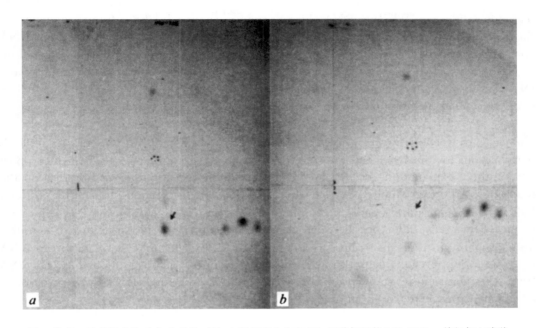

图 2. 从春日霉素敏感性（a）和抗性（b）大肠杆菌中分离 ^{14}C– 甲基标记的 16S RNA，并经加入磷酸酶的 T$_1$ 核糖核酸酶消化后所得的指纹图。向三羟甲基氨基甲烷（Tris）基础培养基 [28] 中分别加入 50 μg/ml 的苏氨酸、亮氨酸、胞嘧啶、胸腺嘧啶和尿嘧啶，以此培养细胞，从这些细胞中分离 RNA 的方法见图 1 注。加入 ^{14}C– 甲基 –L– 甲硫氨酸（每 25 ml 培养基中加入 25 μCi/10.5 μmol），允许这些细胞生长一代，然后加入未标记的甲硫氨酸（2 μg/ml）。在对数期后期收集这些细胞。按照图 1 注所述进行酶消化和指纹实验，不同之处是用每份 40 μg RNA（~2 × 10^4 c.p.m. ^{14}C）在体积为 4 μl 含 2 μg T$_1$ 核糖核酸酶和 4 μg 磷酸酶的体系中消化。放射自显影照片的曝光时间为 12 天。

甲基化的意义

截止到最近，已知能影响核糖体结构和功能的突变都是那些使核糖体蛋白发生改变的突变。这些突变的表型具有抗生素抗性、核糖体双关性或核糖体组装 [22,23] 的特点。虽然如此，莱和韦斯布卢姆曾报道称：伴随 23S 核糖体 RNA 的甲基化，金黄色葡萄球菌出现被引发的红霉素抗性表象，这与红霉素抗性是核糖体 50S 亚基性质的事实一致 [24]。春日霉素抗性看上去也是核糖体 RNA 变化的一个例子，因为我们发现，春日霉素敏感性和抗性表型是由重组实验中 16S RNA 的来源决定的。从春日霉素敏感性到抗性的转化显然和该 RNA 中特定序列的甲基化失败有关。虽然如此，我们至今也还没有在 m$_2^6$Am$_2^6$ACCUG 序列的存在和敏感性表型之间，或在 AACCUG 序列和抗性表型之间，建立起直接的因果关系。

Assuming that a cause and effect relationship does exist, there are at least three possible mechanisms which could result in failure to dimethylate the adenylic acid residues in oligonucleotide p-71 of 16S RNA. First, a minor change in the primary sequence of the RNA, which may not be detectable by fingerprint analysis, could modify the RNA conformation so that it would no longer be a good substrate for a methylase. Second, an as yet undetected change in the structure of one of the ribosomal proteins could prevent methylation of oligonucleotide p-71 during maturation. Third, a specific RNA methylase could be altered by mutation.

No clear distinction between these possibilities can be made at present. In diploids heterozygous for the ksg_A locus, the sensitive phenotype is dominant, which might support any of these explanations (ref. 12 and Helser, unpublished observations). Studies on the mapping of the ribosomal RNA genes by DNA–RNA hybridization indicate that at least half of these genes are located near minute 74 of the *E. coli* chromosome[25,26]. Since we cannot detect any difference between the ribosomal proteins of kasugamycin sensitive and kasugamycin resistant strains, we suggest that the ksg_A locus is the gene for an RNA methylase. Support for this proposal would come from the demonstration that 16S RNA from a kasugamycin resistant strain can be converted to "sensitive" RNA by methylation *in vitro*. Such experiments are in progress.

Fingerprinting of the 23S RNA and total soluble RNA fractions (unpublished observations) has provided two other points of interest. First is the fact that, in the kasugamycin-resistant strain in which dimethylation of adenine does not occur, monomethylation of the N-6 position of adenine in 23S RNA does occur. Thus it is very likely that different enzymes are responsible for monomethylation and dimethylation of adenine residues in RNA. Second, one oligonucleotide from a RNAase T_1 and phosphatase digest of low molecular weight RNA (approximately 4S) is unmethylated in the resistant strain. If this sequence is from a distinct tRNA species, it would indicate the absence of dimethylated adenine in the only two species of RNA in *E. coli* that normally contain this base. But because this oligonucleotide seems to have the same sequence as oligonucleotide 71 from 16S RNA, this apparent tRNA fragment could have come from degradation of the 16S RNA during isolation.

This work was supported by a grant from the National Institutes of Health and the National Science Foundation. The Graduate School, University of Wisconsin, provided funds for the purchase of zonal centrifugation equipment. J. E. D. holds an NIH research career development award. T. L. H. was a recipient of NIH training grant support, awarded to the Department of Biochemistry. Kasugamycin was provided by Dr. M. J. Cron of Bristol Laboratories. We thank Dr. B. Weisblum for interest and comments.

(*Nature New Biology*, **233**, 12-14; 1971)

假设因果关系确实存在，那么至少存在三种可能的机制，均会使 16S RNA 的 p–71 号寡核苷酸中的腺苷酸残基二甲基化失败。第一，RNA 初级序列的一个小变化，可能用指纹分析法检测不到，但会改变 RNA 的构象，使它不再是甲基化酶的有效底物。第二，某一核糖体蛋白可能发生了到目前为止未能检测到的结构变化，这种变化会阻止 p–71 号寡核苷酸在成熟过程中的甲基化。第三，一种特异的 RNA 甲基化酶通过突变发生了改变。

目前还不知道如何明确区分这几种可能性。在具有 ksg_A 基因座的二倍体杂合子中，敏感性表型为显性，这可能支持上述解释中的任何一条（参考文献 12 和赫尔泽尚未发表的观察结果）。通过 DNA–RNA 杂交研究核糖体 RNA 基因的图谱，结果表明这些基因中至少有一半位于大肠杆菌染色体 74 min 附近 [25,26]。由于我们未能检测到春日霉素敏感性和春日霉素抗性品系的核糖体蛋白间的任何区别，我们提议，ksg_A 基因座是对 RNA 甲基化酶产生反应的基因。对这一提议的支持将来自于下述证据：在体外能够通过甲基化将来自春日霉素抗性品系的 16S RNA 转化为"敏感性"RNA。这样的实验正在进行中。

23S RNA 和全部可溶 RNA 片段的指纹图（尚未发表的观察结果）提供了另外两点值得关注之处。第一点，在没有发生腺嘌呤二甲基化的春日霉素抗性品系中，的确存在 23S RNA 中腺嘌呤的 N–6 位置被单甲基化的现象。因此非常有可能由不同的酶负责 RNA 中腺嘌呤残基的单甲基化和二甲基化。第二，在抗性品系中发现，小分子量（大约 4S）RNA 经 T_1 核糖核酸酶和磷酸酶消化后得到的一个寡核苷酸产物是未甲基化的。如果该序列来自另一种转运 RNA 类型，那么将说明：在大肠杆菌中，所有两种通常含有这一碱基的 RNA 类型都存在二甲基化腺嘌呤缺失的现象。但因为该寡核苷酸看上去和来自 16S RNA 的 71 号寡核苷酸具有相同的序列，所以这一貌似转运 RNA 的片段可能来自分离时降解的 16S RNA。

本工作得到了美国国立卫生研究院和美国国家科学基金会的拨款支持。用于购买区带离心设备的资金是由威斯康星大学研究生院提供的。朱利安·戴维斯获得了美国国立卫生研究院的研究事业进步奖金。特里·赫尔泽是美国国立卫生研究院授给生化系的培训基金资助的获得者。春日霉素由布里斯托尔实验室的克龙博士提供。感谢韦斯布卢姆博士对我们的关注和评价。

（邓铭瑞 翻译；陈新文 陈继征 审稿）

Change in Methylation of 16S Ribosomal RNA Associated with Mutation to Kasugamycin Resistance in *Escherichia coli*

Terry L. Helser and Julian E. Davies: Department of Biochemistry, College of Agricultural and Life Sciences, University of Wisconsin, Madison, Wisconsin 53706.

James E. Dahlberg: Department of Physiological Chemistry, University of Wisconsin, Madison, Wisconsin 53706.

Received June 4; revised July 12, 1971.

References:

1. Flaks, J. G., Leboy, P. S., Birge, E. A., and Kurland, C. G., *Cold Spring Harbor Symp. Quant. Biol.*, **31**, 623 (1966).

2. Ozaki, M., Mizushima, S., and Nomura, M., *Nature*, **222**, 333 (1969).

3. Bollen, A., Davies, J., Ozaki, M., and Mizushima, S., *Science*, **165**, 85 (1969).

4. Takata, R., Osawa, S., Tanaka, K., Teraoka, H., and Tamaki, M., *Mol. Gen. Genet.*, **109**, 123 (1970).

5. Bernardi, A., and Leder, P., *J. Biol. Chem.*, **245**, 4263 (1970).

6. Kuwano, M., Schlessinger, D., Rinaldi, G., Felicetti, L., and Tocchini-Valentini, G. P., *Biochem. Biophys. Res. Commun.*, **42**, 441 (1971).

7. Tanaka, N., Kawano, G., and Kinoshita, T., *Biochem. Biophys. Res. Commun.*, **42**, 564 (1971).

8. Dekio, S., Takata, R., and Osawa, S., *Mol. Gen. Genet.*, **109**, 131 (1970).

9. O'Neil, D. M., Baron, L. S., and Sypherd, P. S., *J. Bact.*, **99**, 242 (1969).

10. Sparling, P. F., *Science*, **167**, 56 (1968).

11. Helser, T. L., and Davies, J. E., *Bact. Proc.*, P82 (1971).

12. Sparling, P. F., *Bact. Proc.*, P81 (1971).

13. Okuyama, A., Machiyama, N., Kinoshita, T., and Tanaka, N., *Biochem. Biophys. Res. Commun.*, **43**, 196 (1971).

14. Ehresman, C., Fellner, P., and Ebel, J. P., *FEBS Lett.*, **13**, 325 (1971).

15. Bowman, C. M., Dahlberg, J. E., Ikemura, T., Konisky, J., and Nomura, M., *Proc. US Nat. Acad. Sci.*, **68**, 964 (1971).

16. Traub, P., and Nomura, M., *J. Mol. Biol.*, **34**, 575 (1968).

17. Traub, P., and Nomura, M., *Proc. US Nat. Acad. Sci.*, **59**, 777 (1968).

18. Sanger, F., Brownlee, G. G., and Barsell, B. G., *J. Mol. Biol.*, **13**, 373 (1965).

19. Brownlee, G. G., and Sanger, F., *J. Mol. Biol.*, **23**, 337 (1967).

20. Fellner, P., Ehresman, C., and Ebel, J. P., *Nature*, **225**, 26 (1970).

21. Lowry, C. V., and Dahlberg, J. E., *Nature New Biology*, **232**, 52 (1971).

22. Nomura, M., *Bact. Revs.*, **34**, 228 (1970).

23. Weisblum, B., and Davies, J., *Bact. Revs.*, **32**, 493 (1968).

24. Lai, C. J., and Weisblum, B., *Proc. US Nat. Acad. Sci.*, **68**, 856 (1971).

25. Yu, M. T., Vermeulen, C. W., and Atwood, K. C., *Proc. US Nat. Acad. Sci.*, **67**, 26 (1970).

26. Birnbaum, L. S., and Kaplan, S., *Proc. US Nat. Acad. Sci.*, **68**, 925 (1971).

27. Nirenberg, M. W., in *Methods in Enzymology* (edit. by Colowick, S. P., and Kaplan, N. O.), **6**, 17 (Academic Press, New York, 1964).

28. Grossman, L., in *Methods in Enzymology* (edit. by Grossman, L., and Moldave, K.), **12A**, 700 (Academic Press, New York, 1967).

Problems of Artificial Fertilization

R. G. Edwards

Editor's Note

With *in vitro* fertilization (IVF) capable of producing 6-day old human embryos, IVF pioneer Robert Edwards describes the practical and social problems related to his technique. He highlights the need to use pre-ovulatory eggs, and suggests that ovulation-inducing compounds such as clomiphene may prove superior and less costly than gonadotrophin injections—a debate that continues today. Successful IVF, he argues, could give some infertile couples their own children so "comments about overpopulation seem to be highly unjust to such an underprivileged minority." Much of the debate so far, with its constant references to nuclear cloning and survival of the family unit, are "unreal", and Edwards urges for rational discussion of the emerging social issues related to IVF.

UNTIL recently, opportunities for scientific and clinical studies on human conception have been extremely limited, largely because of the inaccessibility of the ovary and the difficulty in obtaining preovulatory oocytes. One egg per month was a discouraging target and experience had shown that even this single egg was difficult to recover because ovulation could not be predicted with any degree of accuracy. In the past two or three years, considerable progress has been made with the clinical and scientific problems associated with the study of human fertilization and cleavage. The opening came with the discovery that human oocytes would undergo their final stages of maturation—those occurring just before ovulation—when removed from their follicles and placed in a suitable culture medium. These stages could be timed with considerable accuracy, and the availability of this human material provided opportunities for studies on meiosis, ovulation and fertilization[1]. Oocytes matured *in vitro* thus provided the material for studies on human fertilization *in vitro*, which was achieved two years ago.

Patients Involved

When fertilization had been accomplished using these oocytes, the emphasis of the work changed to include studies on patients in order to realize the potential of these studies for human infertility. There were various reasons for this extension into clinical studies. While oocytes matured *in vitro* provide good material for fertilization, they are unsuitable for studies on cleavage because observations in animals has shown that the resulting embryos fail to develop normally[2]. For normal development to full term, oocytes must be collected after completing, or almost completing, their maturation in the ovary (see Fig. 1). Endocrine methods were thus needed to induce follicular growth and oocyte maturation in the patients, the preovulatory growth of oocytes had to be timed exactly from the estimates made from cultures and surgical methods had to be developed for the collection of the oocytes just before ovulation. The achievement of these objectives has opened

关于人工受精的几个难题

爱德华兹

编者按

在本文中，体外受精技术（IVF）的先驱者罗伯特·爱德华兹描述了与这项技术相关的实际操作问题和社会问题，那时他已经能够运用该项技术获得 6 天大的人类胚胎。他强调了使用排卵前卵子的必要性，并指出可诱导排卵的化合物如克罗米酚等可能比注射促性腺激素更有效而且更便宜——关于两者效用对比的讨论至今仍在继续。他指出，体外受精技术的成功可使一些不孕夫妇拥有自己的孩子，所以"和这些生育能力低下的少数群体谈论人口过剩问题似乎是很不公平的"。迄今为止，那些不断提及核克隆和家庭维持问题的大量讨论是"毫无意义"的，并且爱德华兹极力主张人们要对由 IVF 技术引发的社会问题进行理性的讨论。

直到最近，进行人类受孕的科学和临床研究一直受到很大的限制，主要是因为很难从卵巢中获得排卵前的卵母细胞。人每月只能排出一个卵子已经够令人沮丧的了，但以往的经验告诉我们：即使是这样一个卵子也很难取得，因为我们无法准确地预测出排卵时间。最近两三年间，人们已经在与人类受精和卵裂研究相关的临床和科学难题上取得了重要突破。首先是发现将人类卵母细胞从卵泡内取出并置于适当的培养基中之后，它们能够发育到成熟的最后阶段——与即将排卵时相对应的阶段。这样就可以非常精确地确定取出卵子的时间，而人体中卵子的获得为研究减数分裂、排卵和受精提供了可能 [1]。因此，体外成熟的卵母细胞就为两年前已取得成功的人类体外受精研究提供了原材料。

临 床 研 究

在实现对这些卵母细胞的受精后，工作重点转移到了包括对患者的研究方面，以便了解将这些研究成果运用于治疗人类不孕症的可能性。将研究扩展到临床领域的原因有很多。虽然体外成熟的卵母细胞为受精实验提供了良好的材料，但它们却不适合用于研究卵裂，因为在动物实验中发现由此得到的胚胎不能正常发育 [2]。为了使胚胎能正常发育到妊娠足月，就必须等到卵母细胞在卵巢内发育成熟或接近发育成熟时再进行收集（见图 1）。因而需要用内分泌法来诱导患者体内的卵泡生长和卵母细胞成熟，并且需要根据体外培养得出的预测结果精确地确定排卵前卵母细胞的生长进程，同时还必须发展外科技术以保证刚好在即将排卵之前收集到卵母细胞。

the possibility of growing and analysing cleaving embryos in culture, replacing them in the mother, and studying the processes of implantation. Each of these projects opens fundamental opportunities for the study of human conception. What progress has been made in these various areas of investigation?

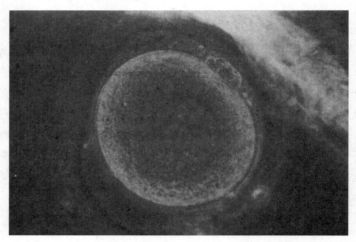

Fig. 1. Human pronucleate stage.

The surgical methods for collecting human oocytes are perhaps almost as refined by now as they ever will be. Laparoscopy has proved to be a simple and very safe procedure permitting the necessary manipulations to be carried out on the ovary[3]. Oocytes are collected from more than one-half of the available Graafian follicles, and although the proportion could be improved the loss of one-half of the oocytes in this way is not holding up further developments in any serious manner. The timing of oocyte maturation and ovulation are also under fine control. None of the many patients so far examined has ovulated before the expected time, and many of the oocytes were fertilized soon after collection, showing that they were certainly preovulatory. The major problems in the initiation of follicular growth and oocyte maturation concern the response of the patients to the endocrine treatments, which are based on the use of human menopausal gonadotrophins on amenorrhoeic women[4]. Some of the patients have few or no preovulatory follicles after the treatment.

There are well known difficulties with the method—for example, the great variation between patients or even between successive treatments of the same patient[5]. Three or four preovulatory follicles are the minimum required to provide sufficient oocytes to work with. Measurements of the excretion of oestrogen in the urine of the patients during treatment provides some indication of their response to the treatment, particularly as a safeguard against overstimulation, but its usefulness as a measure of the growth of preovulatory follicles remains to be decided. There is some scope for improvements in the hormone treatment. The amount of gonadotrophin being administered to the patients is modest in comparison with that use for the treatment of amenorrhoea, partly because the patients have a normal menstrual cycle which might heighten their response. Simply raising the

这些目标实现后，我们就有可能在培养基中培养和分析分裂中的胚胎，然后将其置回母体内，并对植入过程进行研究。所有这些科研项目都为研究人类受孕带来了重要的机遇。那么，在这些不同的研究领域中我们取得了哪些进展呢？

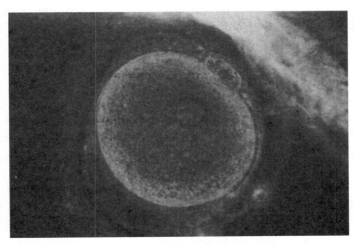

图 1. 原核期的人类胚胎

现在我们用于收集人类卵母细胞的外科方法或许已经几近完善了。腹腔镜手术已被证明是一种既简单又十分安全的处理方式，我们可以利用它在卵巢内进行必要的操作 [3]。卵母细胞是从超过一半的可利用格拉夫卵泡中收集到的，并且尽管这个比例还可以再提高，但是以此种方式损失一半的卵母细胞并不会严重影响进一步的发育。卵母细胞成熟和排卵的时间点也在我们的精确控制之中。迄今为止，在参与研究的众多患者中没有一人在预期时间之前排卵，并且相当多的卵母细胞在收集后不久便受精成功，这表明它们的确处于排卵前的状态。对于接受内分泌治疗的患者——这种内分泌治疗是基于给闭经患者使用人绝经期促性腺激素 [4]，需担心的主要问题是：卵泡生长初期和卵母细胞成熟过程中患者对内分泌治疗的反应。治疗后，有些患者只产生了很少或者根本不产生排卵前的卵泡。

此种方法遇到了一些众所周知的难题——例如：在不同患者之间，甚或同一患者的连续治疗期间也存在着很大的差异 [5]。为给人工受精提供足够的卵母细胞，至少需要 3 ~ 4 个排卵前的卵泡。在治疗期间检测患者尿液中的雌激素浓度可提供了解患者对治疗的反应的某些指征，特别是可以作为一种安全指征，以预防过度刺激；但将这一检测作为排卵前卵泡发育情况的量度的有效性仍需进一步确证。激素治疗法还有进一步改善的余地。给患者服用的促性腺激素的剂量与用于治疗闭经的剂量相比并不算大，在一定程度上是因为月经周期正常的患者可能会对药物有更强烈的反应。简单地加大促性腺激素的剂量将使大多数患者产生更重大的药物反应。

dosage of gonadotrophins should induce a greater response in most patients. Alternatively, the use of compounds such as clomiphene, to induce the release of endogenous hormones, might prove superior, cheaper, and more acceptable than the injection of gonadotrophins. Clomiphene is widely used in the treatment of female hypopituitarism, and should work well with cyclic patients. The recent purification of the gonadotrophin releasing hormones of the hypothalamus could well offer another alternative, provided that the dosage and response can be controlled.

Human Ova

Studies on the fertilization of mammalian ova *in vitro* have moved quickly in the past two or three years after a decade of uncertainty. Belief in the necessity of uterine spermatozoa had become almost dogmatic as a result of experiments involving mostly rabbit ova. Even the demonstration that hamster ova could be fertilized *in vitro* by epididymal spermatozoa[6] had scarcely shaken this fixed belief. When the conditions needed in the culture medium for hamster fertilization were defined, the work was extended to human material, using oocytes matured *in vitro* and washed, ejaculated spermatozoa. Fertilization was established using the same criteria defined for studies with animal ova[7]. Moreover, similar studies are now being extended to other species such as the mouse and cow, and even in rabbits spermatozoa have now been found to penetrate through the membranes of the ova. The culture media are simple: a basic Tyrode's solution is supplemented with bovine serum albumin, pyruvate, and bicarbonate to a pH of 7.6. Pyruvate is obviously an energy source, and the albumin presumably serves as a source of nitrogen or to stabilize cell membranes. The significance of the high pH, or of the contributions of the cumulus cells surrounding the ova, remain unexplained.

Media suitable for fertilization and for cleavage are rarely identical. The development of media to support the cleavage of human ova has not relied on experiments with mammalian ova to nearly the same degree. Simple defined media had been developed for the cleavage of mouse ova, following the recognition of the importance of pyruvate as an energy source during these early embryonic stages[8]. The initial attempts to culture human embryos utilized these media, but cleavage progressed only to the 8-celled stage[9] (Fig. 2). More complex media developed for routine tissue culture have proved much more successful. A medium composed of Ham's F10 supplemented with calf or human serum, at a pH of 7.3 under a gas phase of 5% O_2, 5% CO_2 and 90% N_2, has supported development to the blastocyst stage[10]. Several blastocysts, each having 100 or more nuclei and several mitoses, have been grown under these conditions (Fig. 3). The inner cell mass, trophoblast and blastocoelic cavity were well defined, and some blastocysts expanded in culture. The blastocoel appeared to form from the secretions of large cells that accumulated at one pole of the morula. Modified body fluids are also reported to support the cleavage of human embryos[11]. According to one report, oocytes matured *in vitro* had to be fertilized by human spermatozoa previously incubated in the uterus of a monkey[12]; the abortive cleavage of the embryos might have been a consequence of maturation *in vitro* or some other cause.

另一种方案是：或许可以证明使用诸如克罗米酚这样的化合物来诱导内源性激素的释放会比注射促性腺激素的效果更好、更经济和更容易被接受。克罗米酚被广泛用于治疗女性垂体功能减退，并且对周期性患者应该有很好的疗效。最近从下丘脑中得到了提纯的促性腺激素释放激素，如果在临床上可对这种激素的剂量和用药后的效应加以调控，则很可能会为治疗提供另一种选择。

人 类 卵 子

经过十年的困惑期之后，关于哺乳动物卵子体外受精的研究在近两三年内发展得很迅速。根据主要基于兔卵子的实验结果，人们曾认为在实验中必须使用从子宫内取出的精子，这一结论几乎成了金科玉律。即使发现仓鼠卵子可与附睾精子在体外受精[6]这样的证据也几乎没能动摇这一固有的观念。在使仓鼠受精所需的培养基条件确定之后，研究工作随即扩展到包括体外成熟的卵母细胞和清洗过的射出精子在内的人类材料。在设定人类体外受精条件时采用了从动物卵子的研究中得到的标准[7]。此外，类似的研究如今已经扩展到了其他物种，如小鼠和牛，现在甚至发现兔精子也可以穿透卵子的细胞膜。所用的培养基非常简单：在一种碱性台罗德氏溶液中加入牛血清白蛋白、丙酮酸和碳酸氢盐并将 pH 值调至 7.6。丙酮酸显然是一种能量来源，而白蛋白可能作为氮源或者起稳定细胞膜的作用。现在我们还不能解释这一高 pH 值的重要性以及卵子周围的卵丘细胞所起的作用。

适合于受精和适合于卵裂的培养基各不相同。研制能促进人卵子分裂的培养基并不完全依赖于哺乳动物的卵子实验。在认识到丙酮酸作为胚胎早期阶段能量来源的重要性之后[8]，目前已研制出了用于小鼠卵子分裂的、配方明确的简单培养基。在最初尝试培养人类胚胎时曾使用过这些培养基，可惜分裂只能进行到 8 细胞期[9]（图 2）。现已证明，更为复杂的用于常规组织培养的培养基可更成功地用于人类胚胎培养。使用由哈姆氏 F 10 组成，并添加小牛或人血清及校正 pH 值为 7.3 的培养基，在 5% O_2、5% CO_2 和 90% N_2 的气相条件下，可使细胞发育到囊胚阶段[10]。在这种条件下培养出了好几个囊胚，每个囊胚都有 100 或更多个细胞核和若干个有丝分裂（图 3）。内细胞团、滋养层和囊胚腔之间界限分明，有些囊胚还在培养过程中发生了膨胀。囊胚腔似乎是由累积在桑葚胚一极的大细胞分泌形成的。另有报道称改良的体液也能维持人类胚胎的分裂[11]。据报道，体外成熟的卵母细胞只能用事先在猴子子宫中孵育过的人类精子受精[12]；胚胎分裂的失败或许是由体外成熟或其他一些原因造成的。

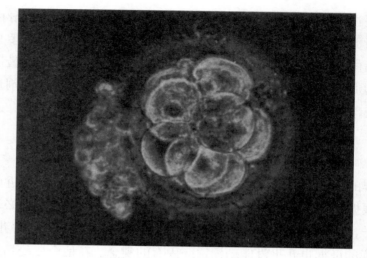

Fig. 2. Human eight-celled embryo.

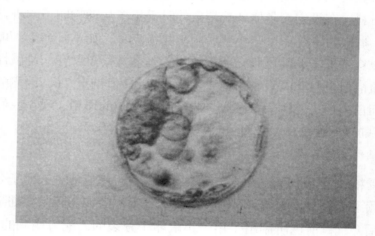

Fig. 3. Human blastocyst.

Where Next?

Further development beyond the blastocyst stage must surely be the next study. This raises the question of whether the embryos will be able to implant in the mother, that is, if the uterus has been sufficiently stimulated by the endocrine treatments used to induce follicular maturation. Another question concerns the capacity of the embryos to implant. The indications are good: the pronounced differentiation of many embryos in culture augurs well for their continued development. Conditions in the mother also seem to be satisfactory: most patients have had a secretory endometrium, excreted suitable amounts of pregnanediol, and their induced cycle has resembled a natural cycle[3].

What is known of the capacity of the embryos for normal development? The criteria for cleavage are now well recognized, and provide the first safeguard. Several of the embryos have possessed a chromosome complement that appeared to be diploid, thus excluding

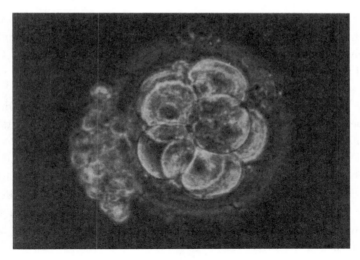

图 2. 人类的 8 细胞期胚胎

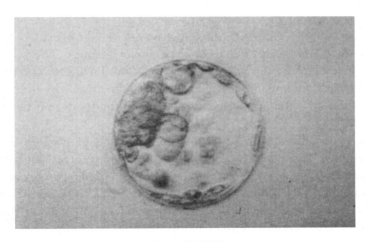

图 3. 人类的囊胚

下一步的目标?

下一步要研究的当然是囊胚阶段以后的发育过程。这就引出了这样一个问题：这些胚胎能否被移植到母体中？更确切地说，子宫能否被用以诱导卵泡成熟的内分泌治疗充分刺激。另一个问题是要考虑胚胎的植入能力。目前的迹象是好的：许多培养的胚胎出现了显著的分化，这预示着它们将会有良好的进一步发育。母体中的情况似乎也很令人满意：大多数患者的子宫内膜能够分泌适量的孕二醇，并且它们的诱导周期接近于自然周期[3]。

人们对胚胎正常发育能力的认识都有哪些呢？现在，人们对分裂的标准已经有了很深入的了解，这就提供了第一道安全保障。有几个胚胎拥有一套看似是二倍体

the possibility of triploidy. Trisomy has not been excluded. Yet the more that is learnt about natural human pregnancy, the more obvious becomes the conclusion that many embryos conceived naturally are trisomics, triploids or mosaics destined to perish in the first trimester. The possibility of trisomy in cultured embryos thus becomes less important, and especially since Down's syndrome can be identified in foetuses by amniocentesis. Nor should the problem of teratogenic development present undue difficulties, because widespread experience in animals and man has shown that agents known to be teratogenic in later stages of pregnancy are lethal to preimplantation embryos.

The immediate social consequences of the successful reimplantation of human embryos would be the cure of some forms of infertility, notably where the wife has occluded oviducts or the husband is oligospermic. There should be no criticism in giving these couples their own children: comments about overpopulation seem to be highly unjust to such an underprivileged minority.

The next development could well be the sexing of embryos before transfer. Rabbit blastocysts were sexed from the presence or absence of sex chromatin in small pieces of trophoblast excised by microsurgery[13]; the embryos recovered after a few hours in culture and some of them developed to full term in recipient females. The sex of all foetuses had been predicted correctly; this was the first occasion that the secondary sex ratio had been controlled in any mammal. Most efforts in this direction had been devoted to the attempted separation of X and Y spermatozoa, so far without any convincing success.

Improvements are now needed in the methods for sexing blastocysts. Two approaches are currently feasible: the identification of enzyme activity or of antigens determined by sex-linked genes. The activity of glucose-6-phosphate dehydrogenase (G6PD) and hypoxanthine-guanine phosphoribosyl transferase (HGPRT) have been studied in mouse embryos; it is not yet certain that these genes are sex-linked in mice as they are in man. Assuming that they are sex-linked, female embryos might be expected to possess twice the activity of male embryos. Unfortunately, levels of G6PD were dominated by the massive amounts of maternal enzyme "inherited" from the oocyte, and which declined steadily during cleavage[8,14]. The activity of HGPRT in embryos increased after fertilization, indicating that this enzyme was being synthesized during these early stages and, perhaps more important, that the sex chromosomes are active at this time[15]. This enzyme might thus be present in different amounts in male and female embryos. Evidence for sex-linked antigens is restricted to one report showing that the sex ratio of mouse offspring can be altered by interfering with the normal immunological processes of pregnancy[16]. Sexing blastocysts would be an excellent approach to the control of sex-linked mutant genes in man by avoiding the birth of affected boys. Strict control would have to be exerted over sexing if it could be demonstrated that widespread parental choice would seriously disturb the sex ratio in human populations.

Studies on human conception open new approaches to human problems including preventive medicine and family planning. More knowledge about the growth of ovulatory

的染色体组，这样就排除了三倍性的可能性。但三体性并没有被排除。人们对人类自然受孕的了解越多，就越清楚地看到以下这一点，即许多自然受孕的胚胎是在前三个月内注定要死亡的三体、三倍体或嵌合体。这样，在培养的胚胎中可能会出现三体性就变得不那么重要了，尤其是在利用羊水诊断就能知道胎儿是否患有唐氏综合征之后。解释畸形发育问题也不会有太大的难度，因为从动物和人身上得到的大量经验表明，怀孕后期能致畸的化学物质对于植入子宫前的胚胎来说是致命的。

成功再植入人类胚胎的直接社会效应将是可以治疗某些类型的不育症，尤其是女方输卵管堵塞或者男方精子太少的情况。让这样的夫妻拥有自己的子女不该受到人们的指责；和这些生育能力低下的少数群体谈论人口过剩问题似乎是很不公平的。

下一步的研究方向很可能是移植之前的性别判断。兔囊胚的性别可以通过检查由显微外科手术切除得到的小片滋养层细胞是否具有性染色质来判断[13]；胚胎在培养几小时后回收，有一些胚胎可在雌性受体内发育到足月。所有胎儿的性别都已被正确地预测出来；这是人们对哺乳动物出生性别比进行控制的首次尝试。以前朝这个方向的努力大多集中于尝试分离 X 精子和 Y 精子，不过至今尚未取得令人信服的成果。

目前我们还需要改进判断囊胚性别的方法。现在有两种方法是可行的：一种是鉴定酶的活性，另一种是鉴定由性连锁基因决定的抗原。我们已经在小鼠胚胎中研究了葡萄糖–6–磷酸脱氢酶（G6PD）和次黄嘌呤–鸟嘌呤磷酸核糖转移酶（HGPRT）的活性；目前还不能确定这些在人身上表现为性连锁的基因是否在小鼠身上也是性连锁的。假设这些基因是性连锁的，那么雌性胚胎中的酶活性应该是雄性胚胎中的两倍。但遗憾的是，G6PD 的水平主要以卵母细胞"遗传"的大量母源酶为主，而这些母源酶会在分裂过程中不断减少[8,14]。胚胎中 HGPRT 的活性在受精后有所增加，这表明此酶是在早期阶段合成的，也许更重要的是可以表明性染色体在这时是活跃的[15]。因此，HGPRT 在雄性胚胎和雌性胚胎中可能有不同的量。目前仅有一篇文献与性连锁抗原有关，该文指出，小鼠后代的性别比例可以通过干扰怀孕时的自然免疫过程来改变[16]。囊胚性别鉴定将是一种通过避免患病男婴出生从而控制性连锁突变基因的绝好方法。如果有证据表明父母们的普遍意愿会严重干扰人口的性别比例，那么就必须对性别鉴定进行严格的控制。

人类受孕研究开辟了解决包括预防医学和计划生育在内的人类问题的新途径。更多地了解关于排卵卵泡生长、囊胚分泌以及精子获能成分方面的知识也许会使我

follicles, the secretions of the blastocyst or the components of capacitation could lead to the development of novel methods of contraception. Rational discussion is needed about the emerging social issues involved in these studies. Much of the debate so far has been unreal in the sense of being far removed from the actual clinical problems involved: constant reference to nuclear cloning is an example. Earlier remonstrations about the disposal of tiny blastocysts appear almost irrelevant when foetuses of four months' gestation or older are being aborted for social reasons. Alleviating infertility has even been criticized because more consideration is needed about the survival of the family unit in our society! Realization of the benefits that could accrue to many people should lead to more rational discussion and conclusions.

(**233**, 23-25; 1971)

References:

1. Edwards, R. G., *Lancet*, ii, 926 (1965).

2. Chang, M. C., *J. Exp. Zool.*, **128**, 379 (1955).

3. Steptoe, P. C., and Edwards, R. G., *Lancet*, i, 683 (1970).

4. Hack, M., Brish, M., Serr, D. M., Insler, V., and Lunenfeld, B., *J. Amer. Med. Assoc.*, **211**, 791 (1970).

5. Crooke, A. C., *Brit. Med. Bull.*, **26**, 17 (1970).

6. Yanagimachi, R., and Chang, M. C., *J. Exp. Zool.*, **156**, 361 (1970).

7. Edwards, R. G., Bavister, B. D., and Steptoe, P. C., *Nature*, **221**, 632 (1969).

8. Brinster, R. L., Chap 17 in *Biology of the Blastocyst* (edit. by Blandau R. J.) (University of Chicago Press, 1971).

9. Edwards, R. G., Steptoe, P. C., and Purdy, J. M., *Nature*, **227**, 1307 (1970).

10. Steptoe, P. C., Edwards, R. G., and Purdy, J. M., *Nature*, **229**, 132 (1971).

11. Shettles, L. B., *Nature*, **229**, 343 (1971).

13. Gardner, R. L., and Edwards, R. G., *Nature*, **218**, 346 (1968).

14. Brinster, R. L., *Biochem. J.*, **101**, 161 (1966).

15. Epstein, C. J., *J. Biol. Chem.*, **245**, 3289 (1970).

16. Lappe, O. O., and Schalk, M. J., *Transplantation*, **11**, 491 (1971).

们找到避孕的新方法。关于由这些研究引发的社会问题尚需要通过理性的讨论来解决。迄今为止的讨论大多因为远远脱离了实际临床问题而显得毫无意义：经常被引用的核克隆就是一个例子。当怀孕四个月或者更大的胎儿因社会原因而被流产时，早先人们对丢掉小囊胚的抗议也就显得无关紧要了。缓解不孕症一度曾受到了批评，因为当前需要更多考虑的是家庭单元在现实生活中是否能维持下去！在认识到人工受精会使众多的民众受益之后，人们才会进行更理性的讨论，并作出结论。

（冯琛 翻译；郑家驹 审稿）

Tyrosine tRNA Precursor Molecule Polynucleotide Sequence

S. Altman* and J. D. Smith

Editor's Note

Biologist Sidney Altman had previously isolated the transcript of the gene for tyrosine transfer RNA (tRNA), the small RNA molecule that transfers the amino acid tyrosine to the growing polypeptide chain during protein translation. Here Altman and his colleague John D. Smith report the discovery of extra nucleotides at both ends of the transcribed precursor tRNA molecule. When the precursor tRNA was mixed with an extract of *Escherichia coli*, it became apparent that enzymes in the cell extract could cleave off the "extra" nucleotides yielding mature tRNA. The researchers demonstrated that the RNA itself had catalytic properties: it is a so-called ribozyme. Altman went on to isolate the enzyme responsible, ribonuclease P, earning himself a Nobel Prize.

RIBOSOMAL RNAs in bacterial and mammalian cells are transcribed in units longer than the functional final product[1-4]. Transfer RNA in mammalian cells is also thought to be made through precursor molecules[4,5]. Although the biological role of the extra pieces in these transcription products is not known, they may contain sequences affecting the level of production of the final product. The isolation of precursor molecules to one species of *E. coli* tyrosine transfer RNA, which is amenable to total nucleotide sequence analysis and specific mutant selection, was recently described[6]. We now report (*a*) the nucleotide sequence of the new segment of one of these precursor molecules and verify the absence of the usual nucleotide modifications from this molecule; (*b*) that a mutation[7] (A2P) that increases the amount of mature tRNA produced by tyrosine tRNA-mutant A2 is located in the precursor segment close to the usual 5′ end of the tRNA sequence, and (*c*) that a nuclease activity, present in crude extracts of *E. coli*, specifically cleaves the mature tRNA sequence from the precursor *in vitro*.

The sequence that we describe is characteristic of a class of single base change mutants of tyrosine tRNA and differs from the wild type precursor in a few nucleotides at the 3′ end of the molecule. The newly defined segment at the 5′ end of the precursor molecule can, in principle, assume different configurations. We will briefly discuss a kinetic model of tRNA biosynthesis in which secondary structure of precursor plays an important role.

---

* Present address: Department of Biology, Yale University, New Haven, Connecticut.

酪氨酸转运RNA前体分子的多聚核苷酸序列

奥尔特曼[*]，史密斯

编者按

生物学家西德尼·奥尔特曼之前曾分离出了酪氨酸转运 RNA（tRNA）基因的转录本。tRNA 是一种小 RNA 分子，在蛋白质翻译过程中可以将酪氨酸转运到延伸中的多肽链上。在本文中，奥尔特曼和他的同事约翰·史密斯报道称，他们发现在转录的 tRNA 前体分子两端存在额外的核苷酸。当 tRNA 前体与大肠杆菌提取物混合时，很明显地，细胞提取物中的酶可以切掉"多余"的核苷酸，产生成熟的 tRNA。研究人员证明：RNA 自身具有催化活性，它是一种核酶。奥尔特曼接着分离出了这个起作用的酶——核糖核酸酶 P，并因此获得了诺贝尔奖。

细菌和哺乳动物细胞中的核糖体 RNA 在转录时的长度比功能性终产物更长[1-4]。哺乳动物细胞中的 tRNA 也被认为是经过前体分子而形成的[4,5]。尽管现在还不清楚这些转录产物多余片段的生物学功能，但猜测它们可能含有影响终产物产生水平的序列。前不久曾报道过已分离得到一种大肠杆菌酪氨酸 tRNA 的前体分子[6]，用它可以进行总核苷酸序列分析和特异性突变筛选。我们现在要报道的是：(a) 这些前体分子之一的新片段核苷酸序列，并证实这一分子中缺少常见的核苷酸修饰；(b) 有一个突变[7]（A2P）能增加由酪氨酸 tRNA–突变体 A2 产生的成熟 tRNA 的数量，这个突变在前体片段中的位置很靠近 tRNA 序列的常见 5′ 端；(c) 大肠杆菌粗提物的核酸酶活性可以在体外特异性地将成熟 tRNA 从前体中切割出来。

我们所描述的核苷酸序列是酪氨酸 tRNA 的一类单碱基改变突变体所特有的，它与野生型前体相比在分子 3′ 端存在少数几个核苷酸的区别。原则上讲，新确定的前体分子的 5′ 末端片段能够呈现不同的立体结构。我们将简要讨论一种有关 tRNA 生物合成的动力学模型，在该模型中，前体的二级结构起着重要的作用。

---

* 现在的地址：康涅狄格州纽黑文市耶鲁大学生物系。

Isolation and Nucleotide Sequence of Precursor

[32]P-labelled precursor tRNA was isolated after pulse labelling of *E. coli* infected with φ80 phage carrying a mutant *su*III gene specifying tyrosine tRNA with a single base substitution[6]. This type of mutant gives a much higher yield of precursor than the original *su*[+]III gene. We used mutant A25 whose tRNA has a G→A substitution at residue 25[7]. All the phage mutants used here yielded a precursor band identical to band Y of ref. 6, migrating just behind 5S RNA in acrylamide gels.

The T[1] and pancreatic ribonuclease fingerprints of A25 precursor tRNA are shown in Fig. 1. The unlabelled nucleotides correspond to those found in digests of mature tRNA and the numbered nucleotides are derived from the additional segments of precursor tRNA. Their sequences are given in Table 1. All the nucleotides derived from the tRNA portion of the precursor were identified by further enzymatic or alkaline digestion as previously described[8]. This analysis showed that the precursor contained the complete primary tRNA sequence. Comparison with mature tRNA, however, showed two important differences: (1) those bases which are normally modified were almost completely unmodified, and (2) the T[1] and pancreatic digestion products derived from the 5′ and 3′ termini of mature tRNA were absent in digests of precursor.

Table 1. Additional Products of Enzymatic Digestion of Precursor tRNA

T[1] ribonuclease No. in Fig. 1a	Pancreatic ribonuclease No. in Fig. 1b
1 CCAG	1 AGGC
2 AUAAG	2 AAAAGC
3 UAAAAG	3 GAU
4 CUUCCCG	4 AGU
5 CAUUACCCG	5 GGU
6 pppGp	6 AAGGGAGC
7 AAUCCUUCCCCCACCACCAUCU[OH] CAG AG UG	7 pppGC AC AU (2 moles) GU

All products are in molar yield except where indicated. Sequences were derived from the products of T[1], pancreatic or U[2] ribonuclease digestion. CUUCCCG was determined by partial digestion of the dephosphorylated nucleotide with snake venom diesterase. Overlap data from larger fragments were used for AAGGGAGC.

前体分离及其核苷酸序列

su$_{III}$ 突变基因可特异性地使酪氨酸 tRNA 的单个碱基发生替换，利用携带 *su$_{III}$* 突变基因的 φ80 噬菌体感染大肠杆菌，并对感染后的大肠杆菌进行脉冲标记，最后将 ^{32}P 标记的 tRNA 前体分离出来[6]。与原始的 *su$^+_{III}$* 基因相比，由这类突变基因得到的前体产量要高很多。我们采用了 A25 突变体，该突变体的 tRNA 在第 25 位残基处有一个 G → A 的替换[7]。在此使用的所有噬菌体突变都能产生与参考文献 6 中的 Y 条带完全一致的前体条带，这个条带在丙烯酰胺凝胶电泳中的迁移距离紧跟在 5S RNA 后面。

图 1 是 A25 tRNA 前体的 T$_1$ 核糖核酸酶和胰核糖核酸酶指纹图。未标记的核苷酸与那些在成熟 tRNA 酶解物中发现的核苷酸一致，有数字编号的核苷酸是由 tRNA 前体的额外片段产生的。表 1 给出了相应核苷酸的序列。前体中 tRNA 部分的所有核苷酸都用以前描述过的酶解或碱溶法进行了鉴定[8]。分析结果表明前体具有完整的初级 tRNA 序列。但与成熟 tRNA 相比，有以下两点重要的不同：（1）那些通常情况下被修饰的碱基几乎完全未被修饰；（2）源于成熟 tRNA 5′ 和 3′ 末端的 T$_1$ 核糖核酸酶和胰核糖核酸酶酶解产物在前体的酶解物中不存在。

表 1．tRNA 前体酶解的额外产物

T$_1$ 核糖核酸酶 按图 1a 中的编号	胰核糖核酸酶 按图 1b 中的编号
1 CCAG	1 AGGC
2 AUAAG	2 AAAAGC
3 UAAAAG	3 GAU
4 CUUCCCG	4 AGU
5 CAUUACCCG	5 GGU
6 pppGp	6 AAGGGAGC
7 AAUCCUUCCCCCACCACCAUCU$_{OH}$	7 pppGC
CAG	AC
AG	AU (2 mol)
UG	GU

除非特别标注，所有产物的产量均以摩尔为单位。这些序列均源于 T$_1$ 核糖核酸酶、胰核糖核酸酶或 U$_2$ 核糖核酸酶的酶解产物。CUUCCCG 由蛇毒二酯酶对去磷酸化的核苷酸的部分酶解作用所确定。AAGGGAGC 由较大片段的重叠数据所确定。

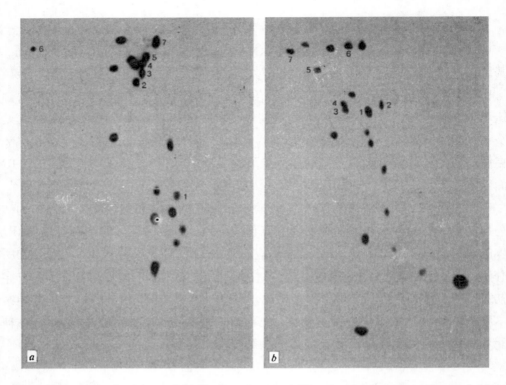

Fig. 1. Fingerprints of products of (a) T_1 ribonuclease and (b) pancreatic ribonuclease digests of A25 precursor tRNA. The numbered spots are those not found in digests of A25 tRNA (Table 1). Autoradiographs of two dimensional separations: right to left, electrophoresis on cellulose acetate in pyridine-acetate pH 3.5 containing 7 M urea and 0.002 M EDTA; top to bottom, electrophoresis on DEAE paper in 7% v/v formic acid. In b nucleotide 1 (AGGC) is not separated from GAGC.

Su_{III} tyrosine tRNA contains seven modified nucleoside residues[8], which are (numbered from the 5′ end) 4-thiouridines, 8 and 9; 2′O-methyl guanosine, 17; 2-thiomethyl, 6-isopentenyl adenosine, 38; pseudouridines, 40 and 64; and thymine riboside, 63. In the precursor tRNA G17 and A38 are unmodified and uridine replaces ψ40 and T63. Residue 64 (present as ψ in the TψCG sequence of the mature tRNA) is partly modified in the precursor; about 10% was isolated as ψ and 90% as U. We have not measured the extent of modification of the thiolated residues 8 and 9.

It has been argued from hybridization experiments that the common CCA_{OH} terminal sequence of mature tRNA is not part of the tRNA gene[9]. So it is important to know whether this sequence is present in the precursor tRNA.

The 3′ terminus of tyrosine tRNA gives the T_1 ribonuclease product $AAUCCUUCCCCCACCACCA_{OH}$. This is absent in digests of precursor tRNA but the entire sequence is present in nucleotide 7 occupying a different position on the fingerprint (Fig. 1). Nucleotide 7 contains the 3′ terminus of the tRNA with three additional nucleotides at the 3′ end (Table 1). Since it does not contain G this is the 3′ terminus of the precursor and all the other extra nucleotides in the digests must be part of the 5′ additional segment.

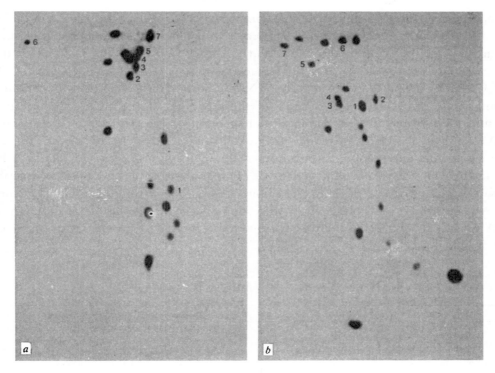

图 1. A25 tRNA 前体的（*a*）T₁ 核糖核酸酶酶解产物和（*b*）胰核糖核酸酶酶解产物的指纹图。图中有数字编号的点是在 A25 tRNA 酶解物中找不到的点（表 1）。二维分离的放射自显影图：从右至左，电泳液为含有 7 M 尿素和 0.002 M EDTA 的 pH 3.5 的醋酸哌啶溶液，在醋酸纤维素膜上进行电泳检测；从上至下，电泳液为体积比为 7% 的甲酸溶液，在二乙氨基乙基纤维素纸上进行电泳检测。图 *b* 中的第 1 号核苷酸（AGGC）与 GAGC 没有分开。

*su*ₘ酪氨酸 tRNA 含有 7 个修饰的核苷酸残基 [8]，这些残基分别是（从 5′端开始编号）：4–硫尿核苷，8 和 9；2′–O–甲基鸟苷，17；2–甲硫基–6–异戊烯基腺苷，38；假尿苷，40 和 64；胸腺嘧啶核苷，63。在 tRNA 前体中，G17 和 A38 未发生修饰，并且尿苷代替了 ψ40 和 T63。第 64 位残基（成熟 tRNA 的 TψCG 序列中出现的 ψ）在前体中被部分修饰：分离出来的残基约有 10% 为 ψ，90% 为 U。我们还没有测定硫醇化残基 8 和 9 的修饰情况。

从杂交实验角度看，通常情况下成熟 tRNA 的 CCA_OH 末端序列并不是 tRNA 基因的一部分 [9]。因此了解该序列是否存在于 tRNA 前体中很重要。

由酪氨酸 tRNA 3′末端给出的 T₁ 核糖核酸酶酶解产物的序列为 AAUCCUUCCCCCACCACCA_OH。在 tRNA 前体的酶解物中不存在这一序列，但整个序列存在于第 7 号核苷酸中，在指纹图里出现在另一个不同的位置上（图 1）。第 7 号核苷酸包含 tRNA 的 3′末端，在 3′端有 3 个额外的核苷酸（表 1）。因为第 7 号核苷酸不包含 G，所以是前体的 3′末端；酶解物中所有其他多余核苷酸一定是 5′端额外片段的一部分。

Comparisons of the 3′ terminus of A25 precursor (nucleotide 7 in Fig. 1 and Table 1) with that of A25 mature tRNA showed: (1) pancreatic ribonuclease digests of precursor contained 1 mol AU in addition to the AAU, AC, C and U found both in precursor and mature tRNA; (2) U_2 ribonuclease digests[10] gave CCUUCCCCCA, AA, A, CCA and as expected from mature tRNA and an extra nucleotide only containing U and C. CCA_{OH} was absent. Because of the repetition of the CCA sequence at the terminus of tyrosine tRNA (Table 2) determination of the sequence at the terminus of A25 precursor-tRNA depended on the yield of CCA in the U_2 digest. To avoid reliance on this measurement we examined the 3′ terminus of precursor tRNA in a mutant in which C80 was changed to U. (This mutant A2 U41 U80 P is described below.) Analysis of the 3′ terminal T_1 ribonuclease product from this mutant precursor tRNA is illustrated in Table 2. As U_2 digestion gives equal molar yields of UCA and CCA we can conclude that the precursor contains the tRNA terminal sequence CCA. This is linked to a U residue.

Table 2. Sequence of the 3′ Terminus of Precursor tRNA

	3′ terminus isolated after T_1 ribonuclease digestion
A25 tRNA	AAUCCUUCCCCCACCACCA $_{OH}$
A2 U80 U41 P tRNA	AAUCCUUCCCCCAUCACCA $_{OH}$
A2 U80 U41 P precursor	AAUCCUUCCCCCAUCACCAUCU $_{OH}$
A25 precursor	AAUCCUUCCCCCACCACCAUCU $_{OH}$

Identified products from U_2 ribonuclease digestion are defined by a line above the sequence, those from pancreatic ribonuclease digests by a line below.

The 5′ terminus of tyrosine tRNA is pGGU—which gives pGp with T_1 ribonuclease and pGGU with pancreatic ribonuclease. Both of these products are absent from digests of precursor. The additional pancreatic ribonuclease product GGU is the only sequence which could contain the 5′ terminus of the tRNA itself, suggesting that this is joined to the additional 5′ segment as pyr.GGU. This was confirmed by the sequence analysis.

We have examined the precursor from four different base substitution mutants A25[7], A15, A17 and A31[11] and all give the same additional T_1 and pancreatic ribonuclease digestion products shown in Table 1. Quantitative analysis of the nucleotides from the digests showed that those unique to the precursor tRNA sequence are present in approximately molar yield and that the dinucleotides and trinucleotides listed are also present in the additional segment. The identification of pppGp and pppGC defines the 5′ terminus of the precursor and we conclude that the initial transcript is intact at this end.

The sequence of the 5′ segment was determined by analysis of products of partial digestion with T_1 ribonuclease[8,12] and is shown in Fig. 2. Examination of T_1 ribonuclease partial digestion products which include portions of the tRNA shows that they all correspond to the fragments isolated from similar digests of tyrosine tRNA[8]. This suggests that the secondary structure of the tRNA portion of precursor is similar to that of mature

比较 A25 前体的 3′ 末端序列（图 1 和表 1 中的第 7 号核苷酸）与 A25 成熟 tRNA 的 3′末端序列，结果如下：（1）前体的胰核糖核酸酶酶解物除了含有在前体和成熟 tRNA 中都能找到的 AAU、AC、C 和 U 之外，还含有 1 mol AU；（2）前体 U_2 核糖核酸酶酶解物 [10] 中含有 CCUUCCCCCA、AA、A 和 CCA（成熟 tRNA 产物中也有这些序列），而且还含有一个仅由 U 和 C 组成的多余核苷酸；不存在 CCA_{OH}。因为酪氨酸 tRNA 末端具有重复的 CCA 序列（表 2），所以 A25 tRNA 前体末端的序列是不是 CCA 取决于 U_2 核糖核酸酶酶解物中 CCA 的生成量。为了避免单独依靠这种测定方法，我们检测了一个 tRNA 前体突变体的 3′ 末端序列，在这个突变体中，第 80 位的 C 转变成了 U（关于该突变体 A2 U41 U80 P 的描述见下文）。对此 tRNA 前体突变体的 3′ 末端的 T_1 核糖核酸酶酶解物进行分析，结果见表 2。由于 U_2 核糖核酸酶的酶解物中 UCA 和 CCA 的摩尔数相等，因此我们可以推断该前体含有 tRNA 的末端序列 CCA。这个 CCA 序列与一个 U 残基相连。

表 2. tRNA 前体的 3′ 末端序列

	T_1 核糖核酸酶酶解后分离出的 3′ 末端序列
A25 tRNA	AAUCCUUCCCCCACCACCA OH
A2 U80 U41 P tRNA	AAUCCUUCCCCCAUCACCA OH
A2 U80 U41 P 前体	AAUCCUUCCCCCAUCACCAUCU OH
A25 前体	AAUCCUUCCCCCACCACCAUCU OH

序列上方有线代表是由 U_2 核糖核酸酶酶解鉴定出的结果，序列下方有线代表是由胰核糖核酸酶酶解鉴定出的结果。

酪氨酸 tRNA 的 5′ 末端是 pGGU——使得 T_1 核糖核酸酶酶解物具有 pGp，胰糖核酸酶酶解物具有 pGGU。这两种产物在前体酶解物中都不存在。胰核糖核酸酶酶解的额外产物 GGU 是唯一可能含有 tRNA 自身 5′ 末端的序列，这说明该序列可以以吡啶 GGU 的形式连接到 5′ 端的额外片段上。上述结论已通过基因序列分析确认。

我们检测了来自 4 个不同碱基替换突变体 A25[7]、A15、A17 和 A31[11] 的前体，所有这些前体在 T_1 核糖核酸酶和胰核糖核酸酶酶解后都生成了完全相同的额外产物，结果见表 1。对酶解物中核苷酸的定量分析结果显示：那些为 tRNA 前体所特有的核苷酸序列的产量都达到了摩尔水平，表 1 中列出的二核苷酸和三核苷酸在额外片段中也存在。通过鉴别 pppGp 和 pppGC 可以确定前体的 5′ 末端，而且我们断定此末端的初期转录本是完整的。

通过对 T_1 核糖核酸酶部分酶解的产物进行分析确定 5′ 端片段的序列 [8,12]，结果如图 2 所示。对含有 tRNA 部分的 T_1 核糖核酸酶的部分酶解产物进行检测，结果发现它们与从酪氨酸 tRNA 的类似酶解物中分离出来的片段完全一致 [8]。这表明前体分子中 tRNA 部分的二级结构与成熟 tRNA 中的类似。假设 tRNA 部分具有三叶草形二

tRNA. Assuming the tRNA portion has the clover leaf secondary structure and is not interacting with the 5′ segment, a possible secondary structure for the latter is shown as structure II (Fig. 2).

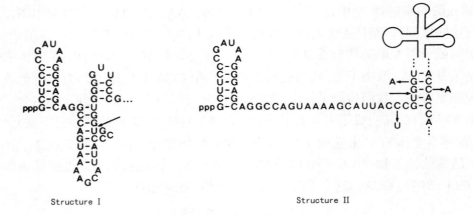

Structure I   Structure II

Fig. 2. Possible configuration for tyrosine precursor. The hydrogen-bonded loops shown are stable according to the approximate criteria cited in ref. 20. The arrows pointing towards the sequence indicate the beginning of the 5′ end of the tRNA moiety and a cleavage point. In the mature tRNA, none of the last four nucleotides shown at the 3′ end of structure II are involved in hydrogen bonding. The arrows pointing outward indicate the positions of certain mutants: P (C → U); A2 (G → A); and A81 (C → A), all mentioned in the text.

Mutant Sequence in Precursor Segment

Mutation A2P increases the production of a particular mutant (A2) tyrosine tRNA[7]. As P does not change the sequence of the mature tRNA it must lie outside this portion of the gene, so we examined the possibility that it produced a sequence change in the additional parts of the gene transcribed as part of the precursor. This could not be determined directly because both A2 and A2P, unlike base substitution tRNA mutants such as A25, do not lead to accumulation of precursor. Several hydroxylamine induced su⁻ mutants of A2 and A2P also failed to accumulate precursor, so it seemed that the apparent rapid *in vivo* degradation of precursor might be due to the change in tRNA structure resulting from the A2 mutation. We therefore examined derivatives of A2P in which the base pairing between residues 2 and 80 was restored by the mutation C80→U.

These derivatives also had a third base substitution within the tRNA so as to be analogous to the base substitution mutants of the type A25 which accumulate precursor tRNA. The *su*III multiple mutant A2 U80 U41 P was isolated starting with *E. coli* MB93 *su*III A2P and using selection techniques previously described[7]. This was obtained as φ80 psu A2 U80 U41 P. Two other completely independent isolations yielded φ80 psu A2 U80 U54 P and φ80 psu A2 U80 A46 P. These were identified by tRNA sequence analysis. Cells infected with each of these phages accumulated precursor tRNA in ³²P pulse-label experiments.

The T₁ ribonuclease fingerprint of precursor from cells infected with φ80 psu A2 U80 U41 P showed the altered products resulting from the three mutations in the tRNA portion of

级结构，并且与 5′ 端的序列不发生相互作用，则后者可能的二级结构如结构 II 所示
（图 2）。

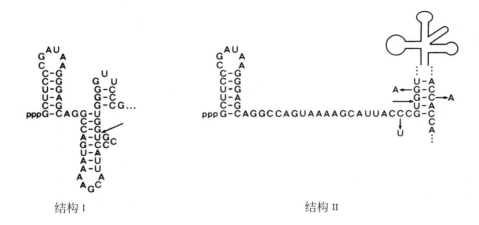

结构 I   结构 II

图 2. 酪氨酸前体的可能结构。根据参考文献 20 中的大概标准，图中氢键环是稳定的。指向序列的箭头
表示 tRNA 组分 5′ 端的起始点，同时也是一个切割点。在成熟 tRNA 中，结构 II 中 3′ 端的最后 4
个核苷酸都不含氢键。指向序列外的箭头表示发生突变的位置：P（C → U）；A2（G → A）；A81（C → A），
这些突变都在文中被提到过。

前体片段的突变序列

突变 A2P 增加了一种特定突变体（A2）酪氨酸 tRNA 的产量 [7]。既然 P 不改变
成熟 tRNA 的序列，它一定存在于该段基因的外部，因而我们检测了如下可能性，
即 P 会在前体部分转录的基因的额外部分产生序列改变。这一点不能直接进行检测，
因为 A2 和 A2P 与 tRNA 的碱基替换突变体（例如 A25 突变体）不同，它们都不能
导致前体积累。A2 和 A2P 的几个羟胺诱导的 su⁻ 突变体同样不能积累前体，因此前
体在体内迅速降解可能是由于 A2 突变引起 tRNA 的结构变化所致。所以我们检测了
A2P 的几种衍生物，在这些衍生物中，第 2 位残基和第 80 位残基之间的碱基配对由
于第 80 位的 C 突变为 U 而得到了恢复。

这些衍生物在 tRNA 内部还有第三个碱基发生替换，以便与能够积累 tRNA 前
体的 A25 型碱基替换突变体类似。从大肠杆菌 MB93 *su*$_{III}$ A2P 步开始，采用以前
描述过的筛选技术 [7]，将 *su*$_{III}$ 多重突变体 A2 U80 U41 P 分离出来。得到了 φ80 psu
A2 U80 U41 P。另外两种完全独立的分离过程则产生了 φ80 psu A2 U80 U54 P 和
φ80 psu A2 U80 A46 P。这些产物通过 tRNA 序列分析得以鉴别。在 ³²P 脉冲标记的
实验中，被所有这些噬菌体感染的细胞都能积累 tRNA 前体。

从感染 φ80 psu A2 U80 U41 P 的细胞中提取的前体 T₁ 核糖核酸酶指纹图显示：
前体的 tRNA 部分的 3 个突变造成了酶解产物的改变；A2 产生 AUG 而不是 UG；

the precursor; A2 gives AUG instead of UG; U80 gives a 3′ terminus product with altered mobility; U41 changes the mobility of the anticodon-containing fragment. In addition nucleotide 5 (CAUUACCCG) (Fig. l*a*), part of the precursor segment, is absent and replaced by a nucleotide in a position corresponding to a C→U change. Sequence analysis of this nucleotide identified it as CAUUACUCG. In this precursor tRNA the 5′ segment is altered by a C→U change at the position indicated in Fig. 2. As all three *su*$_{III}$ mutants derived from A2P showed the same change we consider this is specified by the P mutation.

Precursor Cleavage *in vitro*

We have detected a nucleolytic activity, which may produce tRNA from its precursor, in extracts of *E. coli* MRE 600. After incubation of purified A25 precursor with cell extracts, there are three major products (Fig. 3): (*a*) a band migrating near the position of mature tRNA (band B in Fig. 3); (*b*) a much faster moving band (band C in Fig. 3); and (*c*) two diffuse bands moving with the salt front, which consist primarily of 5′ mononucleotides but also containing a small percentage of dinucleotides and trinucleotides.

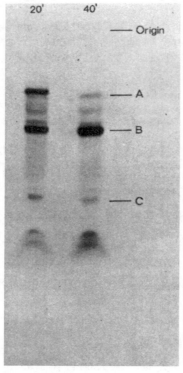

Fig. 3. Autoradiogram of acrylamide gel separation of precursor cleavage products. Purified ^{32}P-labelled A25 precursor was incubated at 37°C in siliconized glass tubes containing 5 mM MgCl$_2$, 0.1 mM beta-mercaptoethanol, 0.1 mM EDTA, 10 mM Tris (hydroxymethyl) amine, *p*H 8, an excess (approximately 1.5 A$_{260}$ units) of cold carrier *E. coli* tRNA and 5 A$_{260}$ units of a 30,000*g* supernatant of *E. coli* MRE 600 extract (a gift of Dr. H. D. Robertson) in a final volume of 0.4 ml. At the times indicated, 20 μl. of 0.4 M EDTA, *p*H 9.4 was added to 0.2 ml. of the reaction mixture which was then evaporated to dryness. Each sample was resuspended in 35 μl. 40% sucrose made 0.04 M in EDTA, and containing 2 μl. of a saturated bromphenol blue solution, and was then layered on a 10% acrylamide gel. Electrophoresis was for approximately 16 h at 400 V and 4°C. In separate experiments we have observed that mature tRNA marker runs in the same position as band B.

U80 产生的是迁移率发生变化的 3′末端产物；U41 则改变了含反密码子片段的迁移率。此外，作为前体片段一部分的第 5 号核苷酸（CAUUACCCG）（图 1a）缺失了，取而代之的是一个在相应位置由 C 变为 U 的核苷酸。这个核苷酸经过序列分析鉴定被确定为 CAUUACUCG。在这个 tRNA 前体中，5′端片段因图 2 所示位置上 C → U 的变化而发生了改变。因为源于 A2P 的所有 3 种 su_{III} 突变体都表现出相同的改变，所以我们认为这种特异性是由 P 突变引起的。

前体的体外切割

我们已经从大肠杆菌 MRE 600 的提取液中检测到了核溶解活性，该活性可能使前体产生 tRNA。用细胞提取液孵育纯化的 A25 前体之后，得到 3 种主要产物（图 3）：（a）成熟 tRNA 位置附近的条带（图 3 中的 B 带）；（b）迁移速度非常快的条带（图 3 中的 C 带）；以及（c）两条随着盐缘移动而移动的弥散带，这两条弥散带主要由 5′端的单核苷酸组成，但也含有很小比例的二核苷酸和三核苷酸。

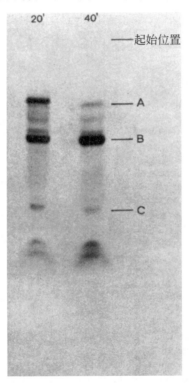

图 3. 前体切割产物的丙烯酰胺凝胶电泳分离放射自显影图。将纯化了的 ^{32}P 标记的 A25 前体置于硅玻璃管中，并在 37℃ 下孵育，硅玻璃管中含有 5 mM $MgCl_2$、0.1 mM β– 巯基乙醇、0.1 mM EDTA、pH 值为 8 的 10 mM Tris、过量（大约 1.5 个 A_{260} 单位）的冷大肠杆菌 tRNA 载体和 5 个 A_{260} 单位的经 30,000g 离心的大肠杆菌 MRE 600 提取液（罗伯逊博士捐赠）的上清液，最终混合溶液的体积为 0.4 ml。在图中所标的时间内，将 20 μl、pH 值为 9.4 的 0.4 M EDTA 加入到 0.2 ml 的反应混合物中，然后将混合物蒸发至干燥。每个样品被重悬于 35 μl、40% 含有 0.04 M EDTA 和 2 μl 饱和溴酚蓝的蔗糖溶液中，然后加样于 10% 的丙烯酰胺凝胶中。在 400 V 电压和 4℃ 下持续电泳约 16 h。在另外几个独立的实验中，我们观察到成熟 tRNA 标准品迁移到了与 B 条带相同的位置。

Specific *in vitro* cleavage of the precursor is established because a two dimensional fingerprint of a pancreatic ribonuclease digest of band B shows that the 5´ end is pGGU—as expected for the mature tRNA and the additional 5´ segment of the precursor has been completely removed. A fingerprint of the T_1 ribonuclease digest of band B (Fig. 4) is also identical to that of mature A25 tRNA except that two spots derived from the 3´ terminus are present. One of these has the same mobility as the precursor 3´ oligonucleotide. The other, nearby in the fingerprint, is present in about 20% yield and lacks at least the two terminal nucleotides, presumably due to the action of another nuclease in the cell extract. The yield of the modified 3´ end is dependent upon the time of incubation of the reaction mixture. Prolonged electrophoresis can resolve band B into two bands, the faster moving of which contains exclusively the modified 3´ end.

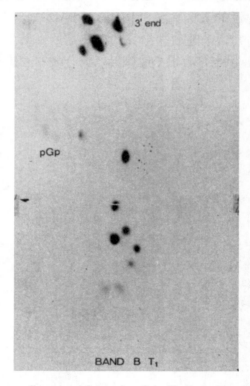

Fig. 4. Autoradiogram of a two dimensional fingerprint of the T_1 ribonuclease digestion products of A25 precursor cleavage product. Band B of Fig. 3 was eluted from the gel, digested with T_1 ribonuclease and the products separated by two dimensional electrophoresis. The newly generated 5´ end is indicated on the autoradiogram as is the position of the precursor 3´ terminal oligonucleotide and a nearby spot in molar yield near the position of the usual 3´ terminal oligonucleotide of mature tyrosine tRNA. These products are discussed further in the text.

Band C contains the extreme 5´ end of the precursor molecule reading in to the sequence…AGGCC(A). Presumably the rest of the precursor sequence at this end of the molecule has been degraded to mononucleotides.

Precursor exposed to cell extract (band A in Fig. 3), but still retaining its original mobility

前体的特异性体外切割已得到确认，因为 B 条带的胰核糖核酸酶酶解物的二维指纹图显示 5′ 末端是 pGGU——与成熟 tRNA 一样，且前体的 5′ 端额外片段已被完全移除。除了源于 3′ 末端的两个点以外，B 条带的 T_1 核糖核酸酶酶解物的指纹图（图 4）也与成熟 A25 tRNA 的指纹图相同。其中一个点的迁移率与前体 3′ 端寡核苷酸的迁移率相同。而另一个点，在指纹图上该点的附近，呈现出大约 20% 的产量，并且至少缺失了两个终端核苷酸，我们猜测是因为细胞提取液中其他核酸酶的作用所致。修饰的 3′ 端的产量依反应混合物的孵育时间而定。延长电泳时间能使 B 条带分解成两个条带，迁移较快的条带仅含有修饰的 3′ 端。

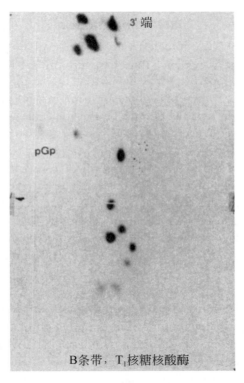

图 4. A25 前体切割产物 T_1 核糖核酸酶酶解物的二维电泳分离放射自显影图。从凝胶中洗脱出图 3 中的 B 条带，然后用 T_1 核糖核酸酶进行酶解，最后用二维电泳法分离产物。放射自显影图中显示出了新产生的 5′ 端以及前体 3′ 端寡核苷酸的位置，在成熟酪氨酸 tRNA 的常见 3′ 端寡核苷酸的位置附近还有一个产量为摩尔水平的斑点。对这些产物的讨论详见正文。

C 条带含有前体分子 5′ 端的序列，其序列为…AGGCC(A)。我们猜测分子这一端的前体序列的其余部分已经被降解成单核苷酸了。

虽然前体被浸没在细胞提取液中（图 3 中的 A 条带），但孵育后它仍能在凝胶

in gels after incubation, does not have any interruptions in the nucleotide sequence.

Residual endonucleolytic activity on ribosomes washed twice in 2 M NH$_4$Cl (given by D. Ish-Horowicz) can carry out the maturation reaction in a standard mixture lacking requirements for nucleotide modification[13-15]. It seems likely, therefore, that addition of isopentyl, methyl or thio groups or pseudouri-dylation is not necessary for cleavage *in vitro* (One indication of the lack of dependence on modification is the absence of spots containing 2'O methyl G from the two dimensional fingerprints of band B in Fig. 3) The enzyme does not degrade mature tRNA. A more complete description of the novel endonucleolytic activity will be given (S. A., H. D. Robertson, and J. D. S., in preparation).

tRNA Biosynthesis

In vitro transcription products are initiated with 5'-triphosphate purine nucleotide residues at their 5' end[16,17] and there is evidence that these also initiate RNA *in vivo*[18]. As the tRNA precursor begins with 5' pppGp..., it is likely that this is the start of a transcriptional unit unless some complex 5' pyrophosphate or triphosphate addition reaction is active *in vivo*. We cannot conclude that the 3' end of the molecule is the appropriate bacterial transcription termination sequence.

Although we have studied the precursor transcribed from a tRNA inserted in a phage chromosome, transcription is likely to be the same when the gene is on the bacterial chromosome. In particular, the tRNA gene on the phage chromosome still responds to relaxed-stringent control as do other bacterial tRNAs in φ80 infected cells[19] and in this respect differs from phage messages. Therefore, certain characteristics of the tyrosine tRNA precursor which we will discuss may be of general significance for other bacterial tRNAs.

First, as nucleotide modification seems to be unnecessary for *in vitro* cleavage of precursor, the rare nucleotides are probably important in the function of the individual tRNA in the translational machinery rather than in the biosynthesis of tRNA itself. Second, our results regarding the presence of the—CCA sequence at the 3' end of the molecule suggest that this triplet is part of the transcriptional unit, in contrast to earlier published work[9]. We have not yet determined the sequence of the 3' terminal oligonucleotide of wild type tRNA precursor. Preliminary experiments indicate that this precursor is a longer molecule and differs from mutant precursor only at the 3' end.

Lastly, we consider the significance of the lengthy 5' segment of the precursor. While the specificity for cleavage may be entirely governed by structural factors, it seems more likely that recognition of a specific nucleotide sequence is also very important. This is apparent from considering the mutation P, four nucleotides from the cleavage point, which alters greatly the level of production of mature tRNA *in vivo* when compared with its parent. It is possible that this mutation simply changes the binding constant of the enzyme to a

中保持原有的电泳迁移率，没有对核苷酸序列造成任何干扰。

将核糖体用 2 M NH₄Cl（由伊什－霍罗威茨提供）清洗两次后，残留在其上的核酸内切酶活性能在一个缺少核苷酸修饰所需条件的标准混合物中完成成熟反应 [13-15]。因此，添加异戊基、甲基、硫代基团或者假尿苷化可能对于体外切割是不必要的（不依赖修饰的一个迹象是：在图 3 中 B 条带的二维指纹图中缺少含有 2′–O–甲基鸟苷的斑点）。这种酶不降解成熟 tRNA。今后我们将对这种奇特的核酸内切酶活性进行更加完整的描述（奥尔特曼、罗伯逊和史密斯，完稿中）。

tRNA 的生物合成

体外的转录产物是从 5′ 端以 5′－ 三磷酸嘌呤核苷酸残基开始的 [16,17]，有证据证明体内 RNA 也是从这个位置起始的 [18]。由于 tRNA 前体起始于 5′ pppGp…，很可能这就是一个转录单位的起点，除非体内发生了某种复杂的 5′ 焦磷酸或者三磷酸加成反应。我们不能断定分子的 3′ 端就是细菌合适的转录终止序列。

虽然我们研究的是由插入到噬菌体染色体中的 tRNA 转录得到的前体，但是细菌染色体上的基因的转录过程很可能是一样的。特别是，噬菌体染色体上的 tRNA 基因仍然对松弛－紧密控制有反应，就像其他被 Φ80 感染的细胞里的细菌 tRNA 一样 [19]，在这方面不同于噬菌体信息。因此，我们将要讨论的酪氨酸 tRNA 前体的某些特点有可能对于其他细菌 tRNA 来说是有普遍意义的。

首先，因为核苷酸修饰对于前体的体外切割而言看起来是不必要的，所以稀有核苷酸对单个 tRNA 的功能的重要意义很可能体现在翻译机制而非 tRNA 自身的生物合成方面。其次，与前人发表的研究结果 [9] 相反，我们关于前体分子 3′ 端存在一CCA 序列的结果暗示这一三联体是转录单位的一部分。我们尚未确定野生型 tRNA 前体的 3′ 端寡核苷酸序列。初步实验表明：野生型前体有较长的分子，而且仅在 3′ 端与前体突变体不同。

最后，我们来考虑冗长的前体 5′ 端片段的意义。尽管切割的特异性可能完全由结构因素决定，但似乎更有可能的是对特定核苷酸序列的识别也同样非常重要。显然，同其母体相比，与切割点距离 4 个核苷酸的突变体 P 极大地改变了体内成熟 tRNA 的产量。有可能这种突变仅仅改变了某种特定 RNA 酶的结合常数。突变体 A2 和 A81 都能产生少量的 tRNA[7]，并且都不能在体内积累前体。这些突变位于（在序列

particular stretch of RNA. Mutants A2 and A81 both produce low levels of tRNA[7] and do not accumulate precursor *in vivo*. These mutations are located in the finished tRNA molecule very close (in the sequence or in space) to the cleavage point (Fig. 2) and may also effect "precursor-endonuclease" binding in an undetermined fashion such that breakdown of precursor to products other than tRNA is enhanced. The phenotype of other mutants (A15, A25, A17 and A 31) distant from the cleavage point in the molecule suggests that a structural factor is also important in precursor endonuclease activity.

We think it plausible that, as precursor synthesis proceeds from the 5′ to the 3′ end of the molecule, it may first assume a structure similar to structure I (Fig. 2) in which the total sequence near the cleavage point is involved in a hydrogen-bonded structure. In this model, when transcription of the entire molecule is completed, the clover leaf configuration is assumed, as shown in structure II (Fig. 2), since it is an energetically favoured configuration[20]. Structure II, we propose, may be more susceptible than structure I to precursor-endonuclease attack. If the transition from I to II is inhibited by the inability to form certain hydrogen bonds in the tRNA moiety, precursor effectively has a longer half-life and should accumulate *in vivo*. This is what we observe for A15, A17, A25 and A31, single base change mutants all involved in breaking hydrogen bonds normally present in the wild type tRNA. An alternative kinetic scheme, in which the rate of transition of precursor from I to II is unchanged in the mutants, but the rate of production of tRNA from mutant structure II is decreased relative to wild type, is also feasible. In either case, secondary as well as primary structure of the precursor is likely to be important in determining the kinetics of tRNA biosynthesis.

It should be noted that precursor we isolate is susceptible to precursor endonuclease attack *in vitro* suggesting, according to our model, that if it accumulates as structure I *in vivo*, it can rapidly assume structure II *in vitro*. Furthermore, to explain the low level of mature tRNA produced by these mutants, it is necessary to postulate an additional pathway of degradation not producing tRNA *in vivo*.

Our experiments with φ80 carrying a single tRNA gene have yielded the first sequence analysis of a tRNA precursor. Similar data regarding T4-induced tRNAs in *E. coli* will be presented (W. H. McClain, personal communication). No direct evidence is available yet regarding the nature of transcription of tRNAs from the *E. coli* chromosome.

We thank our colleagues, especially Dr. H. D. Robertson for helpful discussions, and Miss E. Higgins and Mr. T. V. Smith for technical assistance.

Note added in proof. Although the last residue of fragment 7 in Table 1 has been written as U_{OH}, its identity has not been conclusively established.

(*Nature New Biology*, **233**, 35-39; 1971)

或者空间上）距切割点非常近的已形成的 tRNA 分子中（图 2），它们也可能以一种未知的方式影响"前体－内切酶"的结合，以使前体分解成产物，但产物并不是成熟 tRNA。分子中远离切割点的其他突变体（A15、A25、A17 和 A31）的表型说明，结构因素对于前体的内切酶活性也很重要。

因为前体的生物合成是从分子的 5′ 端开始向 3′ 端延伸，我们认为以下模型似乎是合理的，即可以首先假设一个与结构 I（图 2）相类似的结构，其中靠近切割点的全部序列都以某种氢键结构相结合。在这个模型中，当整个分子完成转录时，就可以假设形成了如结构 II 所示的三叶草结构（图 2），因为三叶草结构是能量最低的结构[20]。我们建议，结构 II 可能比结构 I 更容易受到前体内切酶的攻击。如果因为在 tRNA 部分不能形成某种氢键而阻碍了从结构 I 转换到结构 II 的过程，那么前体就会拥有更长的半衰期，并在体内可以积累。这正是我们观察 A15、A17、A25 和 A31 时所发现的，单碱基改变突变体都会使通常存在于野生型 tRNA 中的氢键断裂。在另一种动力学模型中，突变体前体从结构 I 转换到结构 II 的比例没有变化，但从突变体的结构 II 生成 tRNA 量的比例相对野生型来说减少了，这也是有可能的。在以上两种模型中，前体的二级结构和一级结构一样，都可能对确定 tRNA 生物合成的动力学起着重要作用。

需要注意的是：根据我们的模型，我们分离出的前体在体外很容易受到前体内切酶的攻击这一点表明，如果前体以结构 I 的形式在体内积累，那么在体外它就会快速转换为结构 II 的形式。此外，为了解释由这些突变体产生的成熟 tRNA 产量低的原因，还需要假设在体内存在着另外一条降解而非生成 tRNA 的途径。

我们用只携带一个 tRNA 基因的 Φ80 噬菌体进行实验，得到了 tRNA 前体的第一个序列分析结果。关于大肠杆菌中 T4 诱导的 tRNA 的类似数据（麦克莱恩，个人交流）也将被报道。到目前为止还没有直接的证据能证明大肠杆菌染色体中 tRNA 的转录本质。

感谢我们的同事，特别是罗伯逊博士与我们进行了多次有益的讨论，还要感谢希金斯小姐和史密斯先生给我们提供了技术支持。

附加说明：尽管表 1 中第 7 号片段的最后一个残基被写作 U_{OH}，但现在还没有完全证实这一点。

（邓铭瑞 翻译；李素霞 审稿）

S. Altman and J. D. Smith: MRC Laboratory of Molecular Biology, Hills Road, Cambridge CB2 2QH.

Received June 21; revised July 26, 1971.

References:

1. Hecht, N. B., and Woese, C. R., *J. Bact.*, **95**, 986 (1968).

2. Adesnik, M., and Levinthal, C., *J. Mol. Biol.*, **46**, 281 (1969).

3. Forget, B. G., and Jordan, B., *Science*, **167**, 382 (1970).

4. Darnell, jun., J. E., *Bact. Rev.*, **32**, 262 (1968).

5. Burdon, R. H., Martin, B. T., and Lal, B. M., *J. Mol. Biol.*, **28**, 357 (1967).

6. Altman, S., *Nature New Biology*, **229**, 19 (1971).

7. Smith, J. D., Barnett, L., Brenner, S., and Russell, R. L., *J. Mol. Biol.*, **54**, 1 (1970).

8. Goodman, H. M., Abelson, J., Landy, A., Zadrazil, S., and Smith, J. D., *Europ. J. Biochem.*, **13**, 461 (1970).

9. Daniel, V., Sarid, S., and Littauer, U. Z., *Science*, **167**, 1682 (1970).

10. Arima, T., Uchida, T., and Egami, F., *Biochem. J.*, **106**, 609 (1968).

11. Abelson, J. N., Gefter, M. L., Barnett, L., Landy, A., Russell, R. L., and Smith, J. D., *J. Mol. Biol.*, **47**, 15 (1970).

12. Brownlee, G. G., and Sanger, F., *Europ. J. Biochem.*, **11**, 395 (1969).

13. Abrell, J. W., Kaufman, E. E., and Lipsett, M. N., *J. Biol. Chem.*, **246**, 294 (1971).

14. Bartz, J. K., Kline, L. K., and Söll, D., *Biochem. Biophys. Res. Commun.*, **40**, 1481 (1970).

15. Johnson, L., and Söll, D., *Proc. US Nat. Acad. Sci.*, **67**, 943 (1970).

16. Maitra, U., Novogrodsky, A., Baltimore, D., and Hurwitz, J., *Biochem. Biophys. Res. Commun.*, **18**, 801 (1965).

17. Bremer, H., Konrad, M. W., Gaines, K., and Stent, G. S., *J. Mol. Biol.*, **13**, 540 (1965).

18. Jorgensen, S. E., Buch, L. B., and Nierlich, D. P., *Science*, **164**, 1067 (1969).

19. Primakoff, P., and Berg, P., *Cold Spring Harbor Symp. Quant. Biol.*, **35**, 391 (1970).

20. Tinoco, jun., I., Uhlenbeck, O. C., and Levine, M. D., *Nature*, **230**, 362 (1971).

Poly A Sequences at the 3' Termini of Rabbit Globin mRNAs

H. Burr and J. B. Lingrel

Editor's Note

Here Henry Burr and Jerry B. Lingrel report the presence of polyadenylic acid (poly A) "tails" at one end of two different rabbit globin messenger RNAs. They speculate that the sequences may have been conserved during evolution, and may play a role in messenger RNA maturation after transcription. Conserved, non-translated regions in RNAs which direct peptide synthesis had already been observed in certain RNA viruses, raising the possibility that they may be acting as regulators of gene expression. It is now accepted that polyadenylation (the addition of a poly A tail to an RNA molecule) plays a role in gene expression, forming part of the process that yields mature messenger RNA for translation into protein.

THE 9S RNA fraction of reticulocyte polyribosomes includes the mRNAs for the α and β-chains of haemoglobin and rabbit 9S RNA directs the synthesis of rabbit α and β-chains when added to either an *E. coli*[1] or guinea-pig reticulocyte cell-free system (Jones and Lingrel, unpublished results). Similarly, mouse 9S RNA directs the synthesis of mouse β-chains in the rabbit cell-free systems[2] as well as α and β-globin chains in the guinea-pig and duck reticulocyte cell-free systems[3].

We report the isolation of 3' terminal fragments of rabbit globin mRNAs produced by T_1 and pancreatic RNAases, and the base sequence of the pancreatic RNAase fragments.

T_1 RNAase Fragments

Milligram quantities of the haemoglobin mRNA were prepared using procedures described previously[4,5] except that RNAs were separated by zonal rotor. The mRNA is well resolved from the other RNAs and gives a single band in acrylamide gel electrophoresis.

The 3' terminal nucleoside of the RNA was labelled using the periodate oxidation-tritiated borohydride reduction technique[6,7] and, as tritium is incorporated only at the 3' terminus, this method assured identification of the terminal fragments. T_1 and pancreatic RNAase digestion products of ^{3}H-mRNA and carrier RNA were fractionated by "DEAE-Sephadex" chromatography according to the number of their phosphate groups[6].

Two major 3' terminal fragments are resolved when the mRNA is digested with T_1 RNAase (Fig. 1). Considerable radioactivity in early fractions is not derived from the RNA because it was present in undigested samples. Furthermore, when digests are appropriately chromatographed on "DEAE-Sephadex A-25", no radioactivity is present in nucleoside

兔球蛋白信使RNA 3′末端的
多聚腺苷酸序列

伯尔，林格里尔

编者按

在本文中，亨利·伯尔和杰里·林格里尔报道了在两种不同的兔球蛋白信使 RNA 分子同一末端存在多聚腺苷酸"尾巴"。他们推测这类序列在进化过程中可能是保守的，并且可能在信使 RNA 转录后的成熟过程中发挥着某种作用。在某些 RNA 病毒中已经观察到指导肽合成的 RNA 非翻译保守区域，这就增加了它们是基因表达调控者的可能性。多聚腺苷酸化（将多聚腺苷酸尾巴加到一个 RNA 分子上）在基因表达中的作用现在已经被普遍接受，它构成产生蛋白质翻译所需成熟信使 RNA 的过程的一部分。

网状细胞多聚核糖体的 9S RNA 部分包含血红蛋白 α 链和 β 链的信使 RNA（mRNA）。将兔 9S RNA 加入到大肠杆菌 [1] 或豚鼠网状细胞的无细胞体系中时，它能指导兔 α 链和 β 链的合成（琼斯和林格里尔，尚未发表的结果）。与此类似，小鼠 9S RNA 既能在豚鼠和鸭网状细胞的无细胞体系中指导小鼠 α 球蛋白链和 β 球蛋白链的合成 [3]，也能在兔的无细胞体系中指导小鼠 β 链的合成 [2]。

我们报告的是通过 T₁ 核糖核酸酶和胰核糖核酸酶产生的兔球蛋白 mRNA 3′ 末端片段的分离，以及胰核糖核酸酶片段的碱基序列。

T₁ 核糖核酸酶片段

除了 RNA 是通过区带转头离心机分离外，毫克级血红蛋白 mRNA 是按以前描述过的程序 [4,5] 制备的。mRNA 与其他 RNA 的分离很彻底，在丙烯酰胺凝胶电泳中只有单一条带。

因为氚元素只与 3′ 末端结合，所以我们使用过碘酸盐氧化-氚标记的硼氢化物还原技术来标记 RNA 的 3′ 末端核苷 [6,7]，这种方法能确保识别出末端片段。利用"二乙氨基乙基-葡聚糖"色谱柱将 ³H-mRNA 和载体 RNA 的 T₁ 核糖核酸酶和胰核糖核酸酶酶解产物按照磷酸基团的数量分离成不同的组分 [6]。

当 mRNA 被 T₁ 核糖核酸酶酶解时，两个主要的 3′ 末端片段被分离出来（图 1）。因为在未酶解的样品中出现放射现象，所以早期洗脱组分的大量放射性并非来自于 RNA。此外，当用"二乙氨基乙基-葡聚糖 A-25"色谱柱对酶解物进行适当分离时，

derivatives or mononucleotides. This non-RNA radioactivity has been observed by other workers[6,8,9] and is probably labelled side-reaction products which are not completely removed from the RNA by purification[7]. Approximately 90% of this tritium label could be removed by an MAK column, but this procedure was not used because the RNA appeared to be somewhat resistant to enzymatic digestion.

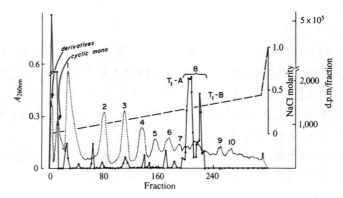

Fig. 1. T_1 RNAase digest of terminally labelled globin mRNA. 200 μg of globin mRNA, with rabbit reticulocyte 18S RNA as ultraviolet-carrier, was digested with T_1 RNAase (E.C. 2.7.7.26, Sigma) for 1 h at 37°C in 0.02 M Tris buffer (pH 7.0) containing 2 mM EDTA. These conditions were essentially identical to those used by other workers[34,35]. Carrier nucleoside derivatives[6] and monophosphates were added as markers for numbering the peaks and the digest was made 7 M in urea and applied to a 0.9×23 cm "DEAE Sephadex A-25" column previously equilibrated with 7 M urea in 0.02 M Tris (pH 7.6). Elution was carried out using a 3 litre gradient of 0.0–0.45 M NaCl in Tris (pH 7.6) and 7 M urea. The column was stripped with a 100 ml. gradient of 0.45–1.0 NaCl in the same buffer. Samples of 3 ml. of each fraction with 1 ml. H_2O were counted in 10 ml. of "Insta-Gel" (Packard) at approximately 12% efficiency. Globin mRNA was labelled using a procedure similar to that of DeWachter and Fiers[6]. RNA was dissolved in 1 ml. of 0.01 M sodium phosphate buffer (pH 6.0) and 0.05 ml. of 0.1 M $NaIO_4$ was added and allowed to stand in the dark. After 1 h, 0.05 ml. of 1 M ethylene glycol was added and allowed to stand 30 min. Next, 1 ml. of 0.5 M sodium phosphate buffer (pH 7.0) was added an mixed. NaB^3H_4 (502 mCi/mM, Amersham-Searle, crystalline solid) was dissolved in cold 1 N NaOH so that 0.1 ml. contained 10 mCi; this level of radioactivity was used routinely. Reduction was allowed to proceed for 2 h at room temperature. The RNA was precipitated two or three times with cold ethanol and further purified from excess ^3H by sedimentation through one or two sucrose gradients 5–20% (w/w) in the Spinco SW-27 rotor for 24 h at 2°C with additional precipitation between sedimentations. The 3′-terminal nucleoside after oxidation and reduction is referred to as a nucleoside derivative in this paper. These steps removed much of the extraneous label; however, some counts not derived from RNA can be seen in the first fractions of this figure and Fig. 2. (See text.) Peaks are designated according to the number of negative charges in the fragments; beyond seven the numbering is somewhat arbitrary. ——, Radioactivity; . . . . ., absorbance at 260 nm; - - - - -, NaCl gradient.

The T_1 fragment elutes in the region of eight phosphate groups inferring that it comprises nine bases as the terminal fragment lacks the phosphate on the 3′ terminus, but this is only tentative as base composition begins to influence the elution pattern of longer oligonucleotides[6,10]. The first guanosine nucleotide would be at position ten, counting from the 3′ end. This may be an underestimate as DeWachter and Fiers have isolated a fragment from MS2 bacteriophage RNA which elutes as though it contained eight

核苷衍生物或单核苷酸中都没有表现出放射性。这种不是来自 RNA 的放射性已被其他研究者观察到 [6,8,9]，很可能是被标记的副反应产物在提纯时没有完全从 RNA 中移走产生的 [7]。大约 90% 的氚标记物能通过一个 MAK 柱去除，但是这样做似乎会使 RNA 对酶解作用有一定程度的抗性，因此我们没有使用这个步骤。

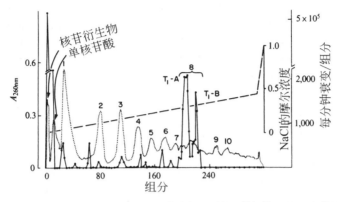

图 1. 末端标记的球蛋白 mRNA 的 T_1 核糖核酸酶酶解产物。用兔网状细胞 18S RNA 作为紫外辐射载体，200 μg 球蛋白 mRNA 在含 2 mM EDTA 的 0.02 M Tris（pH 值为 7.0）中用 T_1 核糖核酸酶（E.C. 2.7.7.26，西格马公司）在 37℃ 下分解 1 h。这些条件与其他研究者采用的条件 [34,35] 基本一致。为了给这些峰编号，我们加入核苷衍生物载体 [6] 和单磷酸盐作为标准物，在尿素中将酶解物调至 7 M，然后使用被 7 M 尿素的 0.02 M Tris 溶液（pH 值为 7.6）预先平衡过的 0.9 cm×23 cm "二乙氨基乙基 – 葡聚糖 A-25" 色谱柱进行分离。用 Tris（pH 值为 7.6）和 7 M 尿素溶液配制浓度梯度为 0.0 M ~ 0.45 M 的 3 L NaCl 溶液以进行洗脱。色谱柱用同一缓冲液配制的浓度梯度为 0.45 M ~ 1.0 M 的 100 ml NaCl 溶液彻底洗脱。从每个组分中取 3 ml 样品加入 1 ml H_2O，然后置于 10 ml 大约 12% 效能的 "英斯达凝胶"（帕卡德公司）中进行计数。用与德瓦赫特和菲耶尔所采用的类似步骤 [6] 来标记球蛋白 mRNA。将 RNA 溶解于 1 ml 0.01 M 的磷酸钠缓冲液（pH 值为 6.0）中，再加入 0.05 ml 0.1 M $NaIO_4$，在黑暗中静置 1 h，然后加入 0.05 ml 1 M 的乙二醇并静置 30 min。接下来，加入 1 ml 0.5 M 的磷酸钠缓冲液（pH 值为 7.0）并混合均匀。将 NaB^3H_4（502 mCi/mM，安玛西亚 – 瑟尔公司，结晶固体）溶解于冷的 1 N NaOH 中，这样每 0.1 ml 含有 10 mCi；这就是常规情况下使用的放射性水平。还原反应在室温下持续进行 2 h。用冷乙醇沉淀 RNA 2 到 3 次，然后按照下述方法从过量的 ^3H 中进一步提纯：在斯平科 SW-27 离心机中，通过 1 到 2 个 5% ~ 20%（重量比）蔗糖浓度梯度在 2℃ 条件下离心 24 h，得到从两次沉淀中提纯的新沉淀。经过氧化和还原的 3′ 末端核苷在本文中被认为是核苷衍生物。上述步骤能除去大量外来的标记物；然而，在本图和图 2 的第一个组分中可以看到一些并非来自 RNA 的计数（见正文）。根据片段中负电荷的数量命名波峰；编号超过 7 则有一定的主观性。——：放射性；……：在 260 nm 处的吸光度；- - -：NaCl 梯度。

　　由于末端片段缺少 3′ 末端的磷酸基团，根据 T_1 片段在 8 个磷酸基团区域被洗脱下来可以推断出它包含 9 个碱基。但上述推断只是我们的假设，因为碱基组成开始影响较长寡聚核苷酸的洗脱曲线 [6,10]。从 3′ 端开始计数，第一个鸟苷酸将出现在第 10 个核苷酸的位置。这个数字也许被低估了，因为德瓦赫特和菲耶尔曾经从 MS2 噬菌体 RNA 中分离出一个片段，洗脱出来它似乎含有 8 个碱基，而最终测序

bases while the final sequence revealed ten[6]. As a 3′ terminal G would not be cleaved enzymatically, the terminal base of the T_1-A fragment was determined by paper chromatography[6] of a KOH digest. Radioactivity was found only in adenine residue.

Sequence of Pancreatic RNAase Fragments

Chromatography of the pancreatic RNAase digest (Fig. 2) shows a pattern similar to that with T_1 RNAase. These fragments are five and six bases long, indicating that there are no pyrimidine bases in the terminal five or six nucleotides of the α and β-chain mRNAs with the exception of the 3′ terminal base. End-group analysis carried out as before on both pancreatic RNAase fragments indicated only A again.

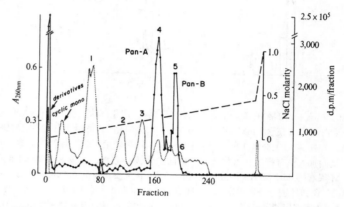

Fig. 2. Pancreatic RNAase digest of terminally labelled globin mRNA. Conditions of digestion and fragment separation were identical to those described in the legend to Fig. 1. Bovine pancreatic RNAase (E.C. 2.7.7.16) was obtained from Worthington Biochemical Corp. ——, Radioactivity; . . . . ., absorbance at 260 nm; - - - - -, NaCl gradient.

Therefore, there is no guanosine in the last nine bases, and no pyrimidines in the last five to six bases. Consequently, the α and β-chain mRNAs must terminate in a sequence of five to six adenine nucleotides. Consistent with this conclusion is the finding that chromatography of each fragment on the basis of base composition (DEAE cellulose, pH 3.5) produced only one peak. Electrophoretic immobility of T_1 and pancreatic RNAase fragments at pH 3.0 suggested to Hunt and Laycock that the 3′ terminal fragments might be enriched in adenylic acid[11].

The fragments from both RNAase digests occur in a 2:1 ratio with the smaller one predominating. This would not be anticipated if each fragment originated from a different globin chain mRNA; indeed, one would expect, *a priori*, that the quantities of α and β-chain mRNAs would be reflected by the amount of each chain found in a reticulocyte. The unequal amounts of the two fragments could be the result of several anomalies: (1) labelling difficulties due to secondary structure in the RNA, base preference in reaction, addition of ³H label elsewhere in the RNA, esterification of 3′-OH, (2) incomplete digestion, (3) contamination with ribosomal RNAs.

显示的碱基数是 10 个 [6]。由于 3′ 末端鸟苷酸不能用酶切开，因此 T$_1$–A 片段的末端碱基用 KOH 分解的纸层析法 [6] 测定。放射性只在腺嘌呤残基中被发现。

胰核糖核酸酶片段的序列

胰核糖核酸酶酶解产物的色谱图（图 2）所显示的洗脱曲线类似于 T$_1$ 核糖核酸酶酶解产物的色谱图。酶解产物片段有 5 到 6 个碱基长，这表明：除了 3′ 末端碱基外，在 α 链和 β 链 mRNA 末端的 5 个或 6 个核苷酸中没有嘧啶碱基。跟之前一样，对两个胰核糖核酸酶片段进行末端基团分析，结果显示还是只有腺苷酸。

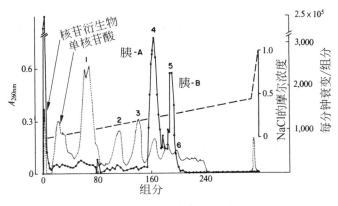

图 2. 末端标记的球蛋白 mRNA 的胰核糖核酸酶酶解产物。分解条件和片段分离条件与图 1 注中所描述的完全一样。牛胰核糖核酸酶（E.C.2.7.7.16）来自于沃辛顿生物化学公司。——：放射性；……：在 260 nm 处的吸光度；- - -：NaCl 梯度。

因此，在最后 9 个碱基中没有鸟苷，并且在最后 5 到 6 个碱基中也不会有嘧啶。所以，α 链和 β 链 mRNA 一定是以 5 到 6 个腺嘌呤核苷酸序列结束的。每个片段用色谱法（二乙氨基乙基纤维素，pH 值为 3.5）分析碱基组成都只产生一个峰，该分析结果符合上述结论。T$_1$ 核糖核酸酶和胰核糖核酸酶片段在 pH 值为 3.0 时的电泳停滞使亨特和莱科克认为 3′ 末端片段可能富含腺苷酸 [11]。

两种核糖核酸酶酶解产物的片段以 2:1 的比率产生，其中较小片段占多数。无法判断两者是否分别来自于球蛋白链不同的 mRNA；的确，我们会先验地认为，α 链和 β 链 mRNA 的量可以通过在一个网状细胞中发现的每种链的数量来反映。两种片段在数量上的不相等可能由以下几种异常造成：（1）因 RNA 二级结构、碱基在反应上的偏好性、RNA 的其他位置被 ^{3}H 标记和 3′–OH 的酯化作用而导致的标记困难；（2）分解不完全；（3）被核糖体 RNA 污染。

The efficiency of periodate oxidation-borohydride reduction of RNA is known to be variable and lower as the size of the RNA increases[6,8,12], because of the increased secondary structure of the larger molecules[9]. Our labelled preparations have had specific activities indicating a range of 5 to 44% of ends labelled if each end carries two tritium atoms. As both preparations digested gave essentially the same fragment patterns, secondary structure does not seem to be influencing the type of end available for labelling. The chemical specificity and apparent absence of base specificity have been shown by others[7,13,14]. Separation of KOH hydrolysis products revealed tritium in only the derivatives, showing that label is not in the rings or ribose of bases other than the one at the 3′ terminus.

Addition of label to the 3′ end does not occur unless the mRNA is previously oxidized, indicating that there is a *cis* diol on the terminal ribose. The known variability of labelling efficiency and requirement for previous oxidation make it doubtful that a substantial proportion of molecules are esterified. We cannot conclude, however, that all molecules in the 9S RNA fraction are not esterified.

Enzymatic digestion at different enzyme substrate ratios (1:100 and 1:20) for different times (30 min and 16 h) revealed no differences in elution patterns. Acrylamide gel electrophoresis of the mRNA used in this study showed no contamination by any of the intact ribosomal RNAs.

Consequently, we feel that these results are a realistic reflexion of the molecular composition of the globin mRNA fraction and that both globin mRNAs terminate in a region of poly A which does not correlate with the known amino-acid sequence of either of the globin chains. These results are consistent with the presence of a UAA chain terminating triplet.

Terminal Fragments and Globin Synthesis

Each terminal fragment is derived from one of the messengers. A pool of α-chains in rabbit reticulocytes[15-17] and the finding that nascent α-chain appear on smaller polysomes[18] are compatible with an excess of α-chain mRNA. It seems reasonable, then, the smaller fragment might be derived from the α-messenger and the larger fragment from the β-mRNA. Hunt and co-workers, however, have found that α-chain synthesis is substantially faster[19], and at present the data do not permit assignment of α or β-mRNA to either fragment. Both globin mRNAs may be represented in only one of the fragments while the other fragment is derived from some other mRNA. The fact that the two fragments differ by only one adenine nucleotide might be explained by the addition of a nucleotide as has been found elsewhere[20].

Terminal Sequences and mRNA Synthesis

The current models of eukaryotic gene expression view mRNA synthesis in terms of a high molecular weight, rapidly labelled, nuclear RNA (HnRNA)[21,22]. Synthesis of a large

已经知道 RNA 的过碘酸盐氧化–硼氢化物还原的效能是可变的——随着 RNA 分子的增大而降低 [6,8,12]，这是因为较大分子的二级结构更复杂 [9]。如果每个末端都能带上 2 个氚原子，那么由我们标记的制剂的放射性比活度大小可以说明 5% ~ 44% 的末端被标记。由于两种酶解产物制剂给出了基本相同的片段图谱，因此二级结构似乎不影响标记的末端类型。其他研究者已证明存在化学特异性但显然不存在碱基特异性 [7,13,14]。KOH 水解产物的分离结果表明氚只存在于衍生物中，这说明不是在碱基环或核糖上而是在 3′ 末端标记。

除非预先对 mRNA 进行氧化处理，否则不能在 3′ 端添加标记，这表明在末端核糖中存在着顺式二醇。前文已提及的标记效能的可变性和对前期氧化的需要使得有多少比例的分子发生酯化变得不确定。然而，我们不能断定 9S RNA 部分的所有分子都没有被酯化。

不同酶底物比（1∶100 和 1∶20）在不同作用时间（30 min 和 16 h）下得到的酶解产物在洗脱曲线上没有显示出任何差别。丙烯酰胺凝胶电泳结果显示，本研究中所用的 mRNA 没有被任何完整的核糖体 RNA 所污染。

因此我们认为，这些结果真实地反映了球蛋白 mRNA 组分的分子组成，并认为两种球蛋白 mRNA 都终止于多聚腺苷酸区域，该多聚腺苷酸区域与两种球蛋白链上的已知氨基酸序列都不相关。这些结果与 UAA 链终止三联体的存在相符合。

末端片段和球蛋白合成

每一个末端片段都源自于一个 mRNA。兔网状细胞中的 α 链库 [15-17] 以及新生 α 链在较小的多聚核糖体上出现的发现[18] 都与 α 链 mRNA 的过量相一致。因此，较小片段可能源于 α 链 mRNA 而较大片段源于 β 链 mRNA 的推断似乎是合理的。然而，亨特和他的同事们曾发现，α 链的合成实际上更快一些 [19]，而且目前的数据没有将 α 链 mRNA 或 β 链 mRNA 与两个片段中的任何一个对应起来。两种球蛋白 mRNA 也许都仅对应于两个片段中的一个，而另一个片段则源于其他的 mRNA。仅由一个腺嘌呤核苷酸造成两个片段不同的事实可以通过添加一个核苷酸得到解释，这种情况曾在别处发现过 [20]。

末端序列和 mRNA 的合成

真核生物基因表达的当前模型是从高分子量、快速标记、核 RNA（HnRNA）方面来考虑 mRNA 的合成 [21,22]。大前体 mRNA 的合成意味着要在切除以及可能的后

pre-mRNA implies recognition of the messenger region for excision and perhaps further processing. The possible precursor-product relationship between HnRNA and polysomal mRNA has been indicated recently by the finding that both RNAs contain A-rich sequences[23-25].

Lim and Canellakis have isolated an A-rich fragment approximately fifty to seventy bases long (70% A) from the purified rabbit globin mRNA fraction[26]. Our calculations of the maximum percentage of A which could be present in a fragment of this size, if it were derived from within the globin coding region, indicate that the large A-rich fragment must have originated from outside the peptide-coding region and therefore must be located in one of the termini. To relate our results to those mentioned above, it seems that the small poly A sequence at the 3' terminus of both globin mRNAs represents a small part of a longer, untranslated A-rich region, which may play a role in post-transcriptional processing.

Untranslated A-rich regions may be common to many or all mRNAs with the result that their dT-rich complements are reiterated in the DNA. Williamson et al.[27] have hybridized purified mouse globin mRNA fraction and obtained very interesting results. The DNA was not saturated until the RNA/DNA input ratio was three; yet at each RNA input, the time needed for maximum binding was only 10 min. These results are compatible with the presence of a component in the RNA which is hybridizing to reiterated DNA sequences. Kedes and Birnstiel, however, have hybridized sea urchin histone mRNA fraction with a large excess of DNA and failed to demonstrate a rapidly hybridizing RNA component which would be expected if binding were due to a sequence common to all messengers and were uniformly distributed throughout the genome[28]. It is not clear whether the A-rich regions found in crude mRNA fractions and globin mRNA are actually transcribed from DNA or are added later by another mechanism[29].

An alternative interpretation of our results has as its basis the idea that different proteins have emerged during evolution through gene duplication, followed by independent mutation of each gene[30]. Ingram[31] used this idea to explain the remarkable similarity of the different globin chains. This would produce identical regions in the mRNAs coding for the proteins, and we cannot exclude the possibility that the results reported here are due to such a process. Should this be the explanation of our results, the terminal sequences seem to have been conserved during evolution at least as well as the non-variable globin-coding regions.

Conserved, non-translated regions in RNAs which direct peptide synthesis have also been observed in RNA bacteriophages[32,33] and may be a general feature of informational RNAs. Immunity from mutational pressure implies a rather strict requirement for the region. Since these regions are apparently not translated, they become likely candidates for regulators in the complicated, highly specific process of gene expression.

续处理过程中对 mRNA 区域进行识别。HnRNA 和多聚核糖体 mRNA 之间可能具有的母核–产物关系最近已经通过两种 RNA 都富含腺苷酸序列这一发现得到了证明 [23-25]。

利姆和卡耐尔拉基斯曾从纯化的兔球蛋白 mRNA 组分中分离出一个大约长 50 ～ 70 个碱基（70% 腺苷酸）的富含腺苷酸的片段 [26]。假设富含腺苷酸的片段源于球蛋白编码区域内部，我们所计算出的腺苷酸可能存在于这一大片段上的最大百分率表明富含腺苷酸的大片段一定源于多肽编码区域之外，因此必定位于其中一个末端。将我们的结果和上述内容联系起来，两种球蛋白 mRNA 3′ 末端的小多聚腺苷酸序列似乎代表了一个较长的、非翻译的富含腺苷酸区域的一小部分，这个区域在转录后的加工过程中可能起作用。

对许多或者全部 mRNA 来说，非翻译的富含腺苷酸区域也许很常见，其结果是：与它们互补的富含胸腺嘧啶脱氧核苷酸的区域在 DNA 中重复出现。威廉森等人 [27] 曾将纯化的小鼠球蛋白 mRNA 组分进行杂交并得到了一些非常有趣的结果。在 RNA/DNA 的加入比例等于 3 之前，DNA 是不饱和的；然而对于每个加入的 RNA，达到最大键联所需的时间只有 10 min。这些结果与 RNA 中存在一个与重复 DNA 序列杂交的组分是一致的。然而，基德斯和比恩施蒂尔曾将海胆组蛋白 mRNA 组分与大量过量的 DNA 杂交，却没有发现一种能快速杂交的 RNA 组分。如果键联是基于所有 mRNA 所共有的序列，且均匀地分布在整个基因组中，这种 RNA 组分应该能找得到 [28]。在天然 mRNA 组分和球蛋白 mRNA 中发现的富含腺苷酸区域确实是由 DNA 转录而来还是由其他机制后来加上去的，至今还不是很清楚 [29]。

我们所得结果的另一种解释基于以下理论，即在通过基因复制的进化过程中出现了不同的蛋白质，而后每个基因都发生了独立的突变 [30]。英格拉姆 [31] 用这个理论解释了不同球蛋白链间惊人的相似性。这将在编码蛋白质的 mRNA 中产生完全一样的区域，我们不能排除本文报告的结果源于这一过程的可能性。如果这就是对我们所得结果的解释，那么末端序列在进化过程中被保留下来的程度至少会和未发生变化的球蛋白编码区域一样好。

在 RNA 噬菌体中也发现了指导肽合成的 RNA 非翻译保守区域 [32,33]，这或许是带有信息的 RNA 的一个普遍特征。未受突变压力的影响意味着对该区域有更加严格的要求。这些区域显然并没有被翻译，因而它们很可能在复杂的、高度特异的基因表达过程中成为候选的调控者。

This work was supported by research grants from the American Cancer Society, USPHS National Institutes of Health, and the National Science Foundation. J. B. L. is a career development awardee of the USPHS National Institutes of Health.

(*Nature New Biology*, **233**, 41-43; 1971)

Henry Burr and Jerry B. Lingrel: Department of Biological Chemistry, University of Cincinnati College of Medicine, Cincinnati, Ohio 45219.

Received May 24; revised July 26,1971.

References:
1. Laycock, D. G., and Hunt, J. A., *Nature*, **211**, 1118 (1969).

2. Lockard, R. E., and Lingrel, J. B., *Biochim. Biophys. Res. Commun.*, **37**, 204 (1969).

3. Lingrel, J. B., in *Methods in Protein Biosynthesis*, Methods in Molecular Biology Series (edit. by Laskin, A. E., and Last, J. A.), **2** (Dekker, New York, in the press).

4. Evans, M. J., and Lingrel, J. B., *Biochemistry*, **8**, 829 (1969).

5. Evans, M. J., and Lingrel, J. B., *Biochemistry*, **8**, 3000 (1969).

6. DeWachter, R., and Fiers, W., *J. Mol. Biol.*, **30**, 507 (1967).

7. RajBhandary, U. L., *J. Biol. Chem.*, **243**, 556 (1968).

8. Glitz, D. G., and Sigman, D. S., *Biochemistry*, **9**, 3433 (1970).

9. Glitz, D. G., Bradley, A., and Fraenkel-Conrat, H., *Biochim. Biophys. Acta*, **161**, 1 (1968).

10. Robinson, W. E., Tessman, I., and Gilham, P. T., *Biochemistry*, **8**, 483 (1969).

11. Hunt, J. A., and Laycock, D. G., *Cold Spring Harbor Symp. Quant. Biol.*, **34**, 579 (1969).

12. Leppla, S. H., Bjoraker, B., and Bock, R. M., in *Methods in Enzymology* (edit. by Grossman, L., and Moldave, K.), **12B**, 236 (Academic Press, New York, 1968).

13. Schmidt, G., in *Methods in Enzymology* (edit. by Grossman, L., and Moldave, K.), **12B**, 230 (Academic Press, New York, 1968).

14. Khym, J. X., and Cohn, W. E., *J. Amer. Chem. Soc.*, **82**, 6380 (1960).

15. Baglioni, C., and Campana, T., *Europ. J. Biochem.*, **2**, 480 (1967).

16. Shaeffer, J. R., Trostle, P. K., and Evans, R. F., *Science*, **158**, 488 (1967).

17. Tavill, A. S., Grayzel, A. I., London, I. M., Williams, M. K., and Vanderhoff, G. A., *J. Biol. Chem.*, **243**, 4987 (1968).

18. Hunt, R. T., Hunter, A. R., and Munro, A. J., *Nature*, **220**, 481 (1968).

19. Hunt, T., Hunter, A., and Munro, A., *J. Mol. Biol.*, **43**, 123 (1969).

20. Kamen, R., *Nature*, **221**, 321 (1969).

21. Scherrer, K., and Marcaud, L., *J. Cell. Physiol.*, **72**, supp. **1**, 181 (1968).

22. Georgiev, G. P., *J. Theoret. Biol.*, **25**, 473 (1969).

23. Darnell, J. E., Wall, R., and Tushinski, R. J., *Proc. US Nat. Acad. Sci.*, **68**, 1321 (1971).

24. Lee, S. Y., Mendecki, J., and Brawerman, G., *Proc. US Nat. Acad. Sci.*, **68**, 1331 (1971).

25. Edmonds, M., Vaughan, M. H., and Nakazato, H., *Proc. US Nat. Acad. Sci.*, **68**, 1336 (1971).

26. Lim, L., and Canellakis, E. S., *Nature*, **227**, 710 (1970).

27. Williamson, R., Morrison, M., and Paul, J., *Biochem. Biophys. Res. Commun.*, **40**, 740 (1970).

28. Kedes, L. H., and Birnstiel, M. L., *Nature New Biology*, **230**, 165 (1971).

29. Twu, J. S., and Bretthauer, R. K., *Biochemistry*, **10**, 1576 (1971).

30. Lewis, E. B., *Cold Spring Harbor Symp. Quant. Biol.*, **16**, 159 (1951).

31. Ingram, V. B., *Nature*, **189**, 704 (1961).

32. DeWachter, R., Vanbenberghe, A., Merregaert, J., Contreras, R., and Fiers, W., *Proc. US Nat. Acad. Sci.*, **68**, 585 (1971).

33. Cory, S., Spahr, P. F., and Adams, J. M., *Cold Spring Harbor Symp. Quant. Biol.*, **35**, 1 (1970).

34. Sanger, F., Brownlee, G. G., and Barrell, B. G., *J. Mol. Biol.*, **13**, 373 (1965).

35. Brownlee, G. G., and Sanger, F., *J. Mol. Biol.*, **23**, 337 (1967).

　　这项工作的研究经费来自于美国癌症协会、美国公共卫生署国立卫生研究院和美国国家科学基金会。杰里·林格里尔是美国公共卫生署国立卫生研究院颁发的职业发展奖的获得者。

（邓铭瑞 翻译；李素霞 审稿）

On the Mechanism of Action of *lac* Repressor

B. Chen *et al.*

Editor's Note

The *E. coli lac* operon is a set of genes responsible for the breakdown of lactose into sugars used for metabolism. In the cell's default state, a repressor molecule prevents gene expression by binding to a control region of bacterial DNA. But when lactose enters the cell and binds to the repressor, the repressor is released and RNA polymerase can begin transcription of the operon. Here Robert R. Perlman and colleagues show that the *lac* repressor and RNA polymerase bind independently to *lac* DNA *in vitro*, but that a mutation in the promoter can lead to competitive binding between repressor and polymerase. The *lac* operon was the first genetic regulatory mechanism to be described in detail, and remains a textbook classic.

THE expression of the *lac* operon is controlled by a specific repressor which prevents transcription of the operon, as well as by cyclic AMP and a cyclic AMP receptor protein (CRP) which stimulate transcription[1,2]. The *lac* repressor is a protein and binds to *lac* DNA at the operator locus[2]. It could repress transcription by interfering with one of several steps in DNA transcription: (*a*) it may prevent binding of RNA polymerase to *lac* DNA; (*b*) it may act subsequent to the binding of RNA polymerase, but before the formation of the first nucleotide bond; or (*c*) it may act after the formation of the first nucleotide bond. We have described a purified system capable of transcribing the *lac* operon and controlled by *lac* repressor[3]. We have used this system and rifampicin, which inhibits RNA polymerase, to establish whether repressor prevents binding of RNA polymerase to the *lac* promoter or acts at a subsequent step in the transcription process. We find that for the wild type *lac* operon, *lac* repressor does not inhibit the binding of RNA polymerase. A mutation in the *lac* promoter which increases the expression of the operon both *in vivo* and *in vitro* (*lac p*[s])[7], however, also alters the operon so that the polymerase and repressor compete for binding.

Wild Type *lac* DNA

When λh80d*lac* DNA containing a normal *lac* promoter is preincubated with CRP and RNA polymerase in the presence of cyclic AMP, a complex is formed which is resistant to inhibition by rifampicin. In the presence of the drug, transcription of the *lac* operon is thought to begin at this "preinitiation complex" and terminate after a single round of transcription is completed[3,4]. *Lac* transcription is repressed by adding the *lac* repressor to the preincubation mixture; repression is observed whether repressor is added after or before the addition of CRP and RNA polymerase (Table 1, lines 1, 2 and 4). In each case, repression is overcome by the later addition of the inducer, IPTG, together with rifampicin (lines 3 and 5). These results indicate that (*a*) repressor will bind effectively and

关于乳糖操纵子阻遏物的作用机理

陈等

编者按

大肠杆菌乳糖操纵子是一套基因，负责将乳糖降解成能用于新陈代谢的糖。细胞处于默认状态时，阻遏物分子可以通过结合到细菌 DNA 的控制区域上而阻遏基因的表达。但在乳糖进入细胞并与阻遏物结合之后，如果阻遏物被释放，RNA 聚合酶就能开始操纵子的转录。在本文中，罗伯特·帕尔曼及其同事们证明：在体外，乳糖操纵子阻遏物和 RNA 聚合酶可以独立地结合到乳糖操纵子 DNA 上，但启动子上发生的某一突变可以导致阻遏物和聚合酶之间出现竞争性结合。乳糖操纵子是第一个被详尽描述的遗传调控机制，至今仍是教科书中的经典。

乳糖操纵子的表达被一个能阻止操纵子转录的特异阻遏物所控制，同时也受到能促进转录的环磷酸腺苷（AMP）和环磷酸腺苷受体蛋白（CRP）的影响 [1,2]。乳糖操纵子阻遏物是一种蛋白质，并且结合在乳糖操纵子 DNA 的操纵基因位点上 [2]。它能通过干扰 DNA 转录过程的几个步骤中的一个来抑制转录：(a) 它可能阻止 RNA 聚合酶和乳糖操纵子 DNA 的结合；(b) 它可能在 RNA 聚合酶结合之后、第一个核苷酸键形成之前发挥作用；或者 (c) 它可能在第一个核苷酸键形成之后对其进行干扰。我们曾描述过一个能使乳糖操纵子进行转录的纯化系统，这一系统受乳糖操纵子阻遏物的调控 [3]。我们使用这套系统和能够抑制 RNA 聚合酶的利福平来证实：阻遏物到底是通过阻止 RNA 聚合酶与乳糖启动子之间的结合发挥作用，还是在转录过程的后续步骤中发挥作用。我们发现，对于野生型乳糖操纵子，阻遏物并未抑制 RNA 聚合酶的结合。然而，乳糖启动子中的一个无论在体内还是在体外都能增强操纵子表达的突变（$lac\ p^s$）[7]，也同时造成了聚合酶与阻遏物之间对操纵子的竞争性结合。

野生型乳糖操纵子 DNA

在环 AMP 存在的情况下将含有一个正常乳糖启动子的 λh80d 乳糖操纵子 DNA 与 CRP 和 RNA 聚合酶预孵育后，形成了一个能抵抗利福平抑制作用的复合体。在有这种药物存在的条件下，乳糖操纵子的转录过程被认为是从这个"起始前复合体"开始，并在一轮转录完成后终止 [3,4]。通过往预孵育混合物中加入阻遏物，乳糖操纵子转录受到抑制；不管加入阻遏物是在添加 CRP 和 RNA 聚合酶之前还是之后，都能观察到阻遏现象（表 1，第 1、2 和 4 行）。在每种情况中，阻遏都能被之后与利福平一起加入的诱导剂——异丙基–β–D–硫代半乳糖苷（IPTG）所逆转（第 3 行和

reversibly to the *lac* operator when a preinitiation complex exists, and (*b*) RNA polymerase will bind to a *lac* DNA–repressor complex. This last conclusion assumes that free RNA polymerase does not bind to *lac* DNA and form a preinitiation complex in the presence of rifampicin. We have determined this directly by showing that free RNA polymerase is inactivated by rifampicin in less than 10 s, whereas the binding of RNA polymerase to the *lac* promoter has a half-life of 80 s. In the presence of 10^{-2} M IPTG the *lac* operator–*lac* repressor complex has a half-life too fast to be measured by existing techniques[5], whereas rifampicin inactivates RNA polymerase bound to the *lac* promoter with a half-life of 90 s. Our experimental conditions therefore prevent the binding of active RNA polymerase to *lac* DNA after the addition of rifampicin, while permitting the dissociation of the repressor DNA complex at a rate much faster than the inactivation of the preinitiation complex by rifampicin. We conclude therefore that with λh80d*lac* DNA containing a normal *lac* promoter, RNA polymerase and *lac* repressor bind independently.

Table 1. Repressor Action with λh80d*lac* DNA

Time of addition (min)			Experiment	
0	5	10	I	II
CRP+RNP	—	Rif+XTP	4.0	3.6
CRP+RNP	Repressor	Rif+XTP	1.6	1.6
CRP+RNP	Repressor	Rif+XTP+IPTG	4.5	3.5
Repressor	CRP+RNP	Rif+XTP	1.9	1.2
Repressor	CRP+RNP	Rif+XTP+IPTG	5.3	—

Each reaction mixture of 0.15 ml. contained 0.02 M Tris-HCl, pH 7.9, 0.01 M MgCl$_2$, 0.06 M KCl, 1×10^{-4} M dithiothreitol, 4.6 µg λh80d*lac* DNA, 0.75 µg rho, 1×10^{-4} M cyclic AMP, 1.2 µg repressor, 1.7 µg CRP, 3.6 µg RNA polymerase (350 U/mg), 0.15 mM each of ATP, GTP and UTP and 0.075 mM CTP (20 Ci/mmol). DNA, cyclic AMP and the basic salt solution were mixed together at 0°C and then brought to 30°C (zero time). Then CRP together with RNA polymerase or *lac* repressor were added at 5 min intervals as indicated. Five minutes after the addition of the last component, rifampicin and nucleotides were added and the samples incubated for another 15 min before the reaction was stopped and samples prepared for hybridization as previously described[3]. IPTG at 10^{-2} M was added as indicated with rifampicin and nucleotides. In the absence of cyclic AMP and CRP a background of 1.3–1.7% *lac* mRNA was obtained and subtracted from the values shown. In a typical experiment with λh80d*lac* or λh80d*lac* p^s DNA, 1.6×10^6 c.p.m. of RNA was made. This value was not affected by the presence of cyclic AMP, CRP or repressor.

Preparation of the components of the *in vitro* transcription system for the *lac* operon has already been described. DNA from λh80t68d*lac* or λh80t68d*lac* p^s was used as template. *Lac*-specific transcription was detected by prehybridization of the RNA to λc*I857*S*am7* DNA followed by hybridization of the unannealed RNA to the separated DNA strands of λc*I857*S*am7*p*lac5*[3]. The latter phage was prepared from λc*I857* p*lac5* (gift of J. Beckwith).

Mutant *lac* p^s DNA

We described a mutation of the *lac* operon, p^s, which results in increased synthesis of β-galactosidase both *in vivo* and *in vitro*[6]. DNA containing the *lac* p^s mutation serves as a

第 5 行）。这些结果说明：（a）当起始前复合体存在时，阻遏物能有效并可逆地同乳糖操纵子的操纵基因结合；（b）RNA 聚合酶将同乳糖操纵子 DNA-阻遏物复合体结合。后一个结论假设游离的 RNA 聚合酶在利福平存在的条件下不能与乳糖操纵子 DNA 结合而形成起始前复合体。我们通过下列结果直接证实了上述假设，即：利福平在不到 10 秒的时间内就能使游离 RNA 聚合酶灭活，而 RNA 聚合酶与乳糖启动子的结合则具有 80 秒的半衰期。在浓度为 10^{-2} M IPTG 存在的条件下，乳糖操纵基因 – 阻遏物复合体的半衰期非常短以至于用现有的技术还无法对其进行测量 [5]，而经利福平灭活的 RNA 聚合酶结合乳糖启动子的半衰期则为 90 秒。因此在加入利福平之后，我们的实验条件阻止了活性 RNA 聚合酶与乳糖操纵子 DNA 之间的结合，而允许阻遏物 –DNA 复合体发生分离，其速度远远超过利福平使起始前复合体灭活的速度。因此我们的结论是：对于含一个正常乳糖启动子的 λh80d 乳糖操纵子 DNA 来说，RNA 聚合酶和乳糖操纵子阻遏物在与它的结合上是独立的。

表 1. 阻遏物与 λh80d 乳糖操纵子 DNA 的作用

加入时间（分钟）			实验	
0	5	10	I	II
CRP+RNA 聚合酶	—	利福平 + XTP	4.0	3.6
CRP+RNA 聚合酶	阻遏物	利福平 + XTP	1.6	1.6
CRP+RNA 聚合酶	阻遏物	利福平 + XTP + IPTG	4.5	3.5
阻遏物	CRP+RNA 聚合酶	利福平 + XTP	1.9	1.2
阻遏物	CRP+RNA 聚合酶	利福平 + XTP + IPTG	5.3	—

每 0.15 ml 反应混合物包含：pH 值为 7.9 的 0.02 M Tris-HCl, 0.01 M 氯化镁, 0.06 M 氯化钾, 1×10^{-4} M 二硫苏糖醇, 4.6 μg λh80d 乳糖操纵子 DNA, 0.75 μg rho, 1×10^{-4} M 环 AMP, 1.2 μg 阻遏物, 1.7 μg CRP, 3.6 μg RNA 聚合酶（三磷酸胞苷, 350 U/mg), ATP（三磷酸腺苷）、GTP（三磷酸鸟苷）、UTP（三磷酸尿苷）各 0.15 mM 以及 0.075 mM CTP（20 Ci/mmol)。将 DNA、环 AMP 和基础盐溶液在 0℃ 下混合后升温至 30℃（记为 0 时）。接下来以 5 分钟为间隔按表中所述加入 CRP 和 RNA 聚合酶或者乳糖操纵子阻遏物。加入最后成分后再过 5 分钟，加入利福平和核苷酸（XTP），在反应停止前再孵育样品 15 分钟，按以前描述过的方法准备样品以便进行杂交 [3]。如表中所述在利福平和核苷酸中加入 10^{-2} M IPTG。在缺乏环 AMP 和 CRP 的条件下，获得背景为 1.3% ~ 1.7% 的乳糖信使 RNA 并从显示值中扣除。在 λh80d 乳糖操纵子或 λh80d 乳糖操纵子 p^s DNA 的典型实验中，生成了 1.6×10^6 放射性计数 / 分钟的 RNA。该值不受环 AMP、CRP 或阻遏物影响。

乳糖操纵子体外转录系统的成分制备已经叙述。用 λh80t68d 乳糖操纵子 DNA 或 λh80t68d 乳糖操纵子 p^s DNA 作为模板。通过将 RNA 和 λcI857Sam7 DNA 预杂交后接着对未退火的 RNA 和分离自 λcI857Sam7plac5[3] 的 DNA 条带进行杂交，来对乳糖操纵子特异转录进行检测。后一种噬菌体是由 λcI857plac5（由贝克威思赠送）制备的。

乳糖操纵子突变型 p^s DNA

我们曾描述过乳糖操纵子的一种突变 p^s，它在体内体外都能导致 β– 半乳糖苷酶合成加速 [6]。在体外纯化系统中，与母本乳糖操纵子 DNA 相比，含有乳糖操纵子

better template for *lac* RNA synthesis in a purified *in vitro* system than the parental *lac* DNA[3]. As some single mutations in the *lac* operon affect both promoter and operator function (Smith and Sadler, personal communication), it was of particular interest to test the action of repressor on this mutant. Our first experiments failed to demonstrate any difference between wild type and the mutant. The *in vivo* synthesis of β-galactosidase from the *lac p^s* operon is fully repressible as is the *in vitro lac* RNA synthesis. Furthermore, the wild type and mutant operons seem to be equally sensitive to repressor; the repressor concentration required for 50% inhibition of *lac* transcription is approximately the same for both templates (data not shown). Nevertheless, the action of repressor on the mutant operon is, at least in part, different from its action on the wild type operon (Table 2). These results show that (*a*) *lac p^s* DNA is a more effective template for *lac* transcription than normal *lac* DNA (compare Table 2, line 1, with Table 1, line 1); (*b*) the addition of repressor after formation of the preinitiation complex produces only partial repression, which is removed by the addition of IPTG (lines 2 and 3); (*c*) the addition of repressor before RNA polymerase produces complete repression (line 4), and partially interferes with the binding of RNA polymerase since subsequent addition of IPTG produces only a partial reversal of inhibition (lines 1 and 5).

Table 2. Repressor Action with λh80d*lac p^s* DNA

Time of addition (min)			Experiment	
0	5	10	I	II
CRP+RNP	—	Rif+XTP	7.7	6.4
CRP+RNP	Repressor	Rif+XTP	4.6	4.4
CRP+RNP	Repressor	Rif+XTP+IPTG	6.6	6.1
Repressor	CRP+RNP	Rif+XTP	1.6	1.4
Repressor	CRP+RNP	Rif+XTP+IPTG	3.4	2.6

The experiment was performed as in Table 1. In the absence of cyclic AMP and CRP, a background of 1–2% *lac* mRNA was made which was subtracted from the values shown.

Although the addition of IPTG and rifampicin does not restore *lac* transcription to unrepressed levels, prolonged incubation with inducer before addition of rifampicin does (Fig. 1). RNA polymerase was added to a repressor–DNA complex in the presence of CRP and cyclic AMP. After 5 min of incubation, IPTG was added and the incubation continued. At various times, rifampicin and the four ribonucleoside triphosphates were added, and the amount of *lac* transcription measured after additional incubation. Following an initial lag of about 1 min, transcription gradually returns to unrepressed levels in 3–4 min, probably because of the binding of free RNA polymerase. Independent experiments have shown that RNA polymerase required 5 min to reach maximal binding to available *lac* promoters.

p^s 突变的 DNA 是合成乳糖操纵子 RNA 的更好的模板 [3]。由于乳糖操纵子中的一些单突变能同时影响启动子和操纵基因的功能（史密斯和萨德勒，个人交流），因此我们对测试阻遏物对这种突变体的作用特别感兴趣。我们最初的实验结果显示野生型和突变体之间没有任何区别。来自 p^s 乳糖操纵子的 β- 半乳糖苷酶的体内合成同体外发生的乳糖操纵子的 RNA 合成一样受到完全阻遏。此外，野生型操纵子和突变体操纵子似乎对阻遏物具有同等的敏感度；对于两种模板来说，要使对乳糖操纵子转录的抑制率达到 50% 所需要的阻遏物浓度是近乎一样的（数据未给出）。尽管如此，阻遏物对突变体操纵子的作用，至少在某种程度上，与它对野生型操纵子的作用是不同的（表 2）。这些结果表明：(a) 乳糖操纵子 p^s DNA 是比普通乳糖操纵子 DNA 更有效的乳糖转录模板（对比表 2 的第 1 行和表 1 的第 1 行）；(b) 在起始前复合体形成之后加入阻遏物只能产生部分阻遏，其阻遏作用可在加入 IPTG 后去除（第 2 和第 3 行）；(c) 在 RNA 聚合酶之前加入阻遏物能产生完全的阻遏（第 4 行），并对 RNA 聚合酶的结合造成部分干扰，因为随后加入的 IPTG 只部分逆转了抑制效应（第 1 行和第 5 行）。

表 2. 阻遏物与 λh80d 乳糖操纵子 p^s DNA 的作用

加入时间（分钟）			实验	
0	5	10	I	II
CRP+RNA 聚合酶	—	利福平 + XTP	7.7	6.4
CRP+RNA 聚合酶	阻遏物	利福平 + XTP	4.6	4.4
CRP+RNA 聚合酶	阻遏物	利福平 + XTP + IPTG	6.6	6.1
阻遏物	CRP+RNA 聚合酶	利福平 + XTP	1.6	1.4
阻遏物	CRP+RNA 聚合酶	利福平 + XTP + IPTG	3.4	2.6

实验按表 1 中描述的步骤进行。在缺乏环 AMP 和 CRP 的条件下，获得背景为 1% ~ 2% 的乳糖信使 RNA，该值已经从显示值中扣除。

尽管加入 IPTG 和利福平并没有使乳糖操纵子转录恢复到未受阻遏时的水平，但在加入利福平之前延长与诱导剂一起孵育的时间却能做到（图 1）。在 CRP 和环 AMP 存在的条件下将 RNA 聚合酶加入到阻遏物 –DNA 复合体中。孵育 5 分钟后，加入 IPTG 继续孵育。选择不同的时间将利福平和 4 种核苷三磷酸盐加入，在附加的孵育过程结束之后测量乳糖操纵子转录的数量。在大约 1 分钟的起始滞后期之后，大概是因为游离 RNA 聚合酶结合的原因，转录在 3 分钟 ~ 4 分钟之内逐渐恢复到未受阻遏时的水平。另有一些独立的实验显示，RNA 聚合酶需要 5 分钟时间才能与可结合的乳糖启动子达到最大程度的结合。

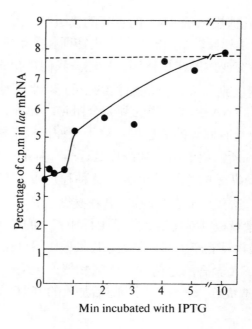

Fig. 1. Kinetics of repressor dissociation by IPTG. Incubation medium was the same as in Table 1. DNA, CRP and *lac* repressor were mixed at 0°C. After RNA polymerase was added the temperature was brought to 30°C for 5 min. Then IPTG (10^{-2} M) was added followed at the times indicated in the figure by rifampicin and nucleotides. — — —, *lac* RNA synthesis in the absence of IPTG; - - -, *lac* RNA synthesis in the absence of repressor.

Both the preinitiation and repressor–DNA complexes are stable (Fig. 2). When repressor is added after formation of the preinitiation complex, the level of inhibition does not increase beyond the initial (~50%) level even if incubation is continued for 30 min. A five-fold increase in the concentration of repressor also does not produce further inhibition (data not shown). Similarly, only background levels of *lac* RNA are made when CRP and RNA polymerase are added after formation of a repressor–DNA complex, even when the mixture is incubated for 30 min. The addition of a five-fold excess of CRP and RNA polymerase does not overcome repression (data not shown). The stability of the *lac* repressor–*lac* DNA complex has already been described by Bourgeois and Riggs[7], who measured the binding of repressor to radioactively labelled *lac* DNA.

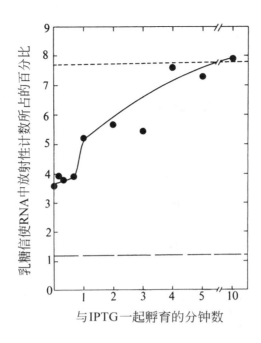

图 1. IPTG 使阻遏物发生解离的动力学曲线。孵育环境和表 1 中的一样。在 0℃ 下混合 DNA、CRP 和
乳糖操纵子阻遏物。加入 RNA 聚合酶后升温至 30℃ 并持续 5 分钟。此时添加 IPTG（10^{-2} M），随
后按照图中所标示的时间加入利福平和核苷酸。— — — 表示在缺少 IPTG 条件下的乳糖操纵子
RNA 合成；-------- 表示在缺少阻遏物条件下的乳糖操纵子 RNA 合成。

起始前复合体和阻遏物–DNA 复合体都很稳定（图 2）。如果在起始前复合体形
成后加入阻遏物，那么即使孵育时间持续 30 分钟，抑制水平的增加也未能超过刚开
始时的水平（约 50%）。阻遏物的浓度增至 5 倍亦不能产生更强的抑制（数据未给出）。
同样，如果在阻遏物–DNA 复合体形成后才加入 CRP 和 RNA 聚合酶，即使混合物
孵育时间长达 30 分钟，也只会产生背景水平的乳糖操纵子 RNA。加入 5 倍过量的
CRP 和 RNA 聚合酶也不能消除阻遏（数据未给出）。布儒瓦和里格斯已经对乳糖操
纵子阻遏物–乳糖操纵子 DNA 复合体的稳定性进行过描述 [7]，他们曾经测量过阻遏
物与放射性标记的乳糖操纵子 DNA 的结合情况。

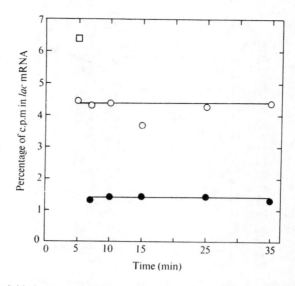

Fig. 2. Stability of preinitiation complex. The experiments were performed as described in Table 1. ○, CRP and polymerase added before repressor; ●, repressor added before CRP and polymerase; □, control, no repressor added.

CRP has an affinity for DNA which is greatly increased by cyclic AMP[8]. We believe that CRP acts by binding to the *lac* promoter, altering the promoter in a manner which allows RNA polymerase to bind. Unlike CRP plus RNA polymerase, CRP alone does not compete with repressor for binding to the *lac p^s* template. Previous incubation of the *lac p^s* DNA with CRP and cyclic AMP does not prevent repressor from exerting maximal inhibition of *lac* transcription (Table 3).

Table 3. Effect of the Order of Addition of CRP, RNA Polymerase and Repressor on *lac* RNA Synthesis with *lac p^s* DNA

Time of addition (min)			Experiment
0	5	10	% *lac* mRNA
CRP	RNP	Rep	6.0
CRP	Rep	RNP	2.8
CRP	RNP	—	9.4
RNP	—	—	1.5
Repressor	CRP	RNP	2.8

Conditions were similar to those of Table 1 except that *lac p^s* DNA was used. All the initial components were preincubated at 0°C, the temperature raised to 30°C and the various additions made at 5 min intervals. Five minutes after the last addition, rifampicin and nucleotides were added. The background *lac* mRNA synthesis was not subtracted.

We have presented evidence based on *in vitro* transcription studies which indicates that the mechanism by which the *lac* repressor inhibits transcription in a wild type *lac* operon is different from its mechanism of action in a *lac* "promoter" mutant, *lac p^s*. With normal

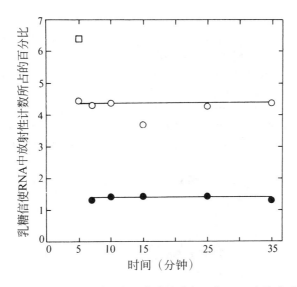

图 2. 起始前复合体的稳定性。实验按表 1 描述的步骤进行。○：CRP 和聚合酶在阻遏物之前加入；
●：CRP 和聚合酶在阻遏物之后加入；□：对照，未加入阻遏物。

　　CRP 对 DNA 具有亲和力，且这种亲和力在环 AMP 存在的情况下显著增强[8]。我们认为 CRP 的作用方式是通过结合乳糖操纵子的启动子，从而在某种程度上改变启动子以使 RNA 聚合酶能结合到操纵子上。与 CRP 和 RNA 聚合酶共同作用时不同，单独的 CRP 并不与阻遏物竞争与乳糖操纵子 p^s 模板的结合。用 CRP 和环 AMP 与乳糖操纵子 p^s DNA 的预孵育也不能阻止阻遏物最大程度地发挥对乳糖操纵子转录的抑制（表 3）。

表 3. CRP、RNA 聚合酶和阻遏物的加入顺序对用乳糖操纵子 p^s DNA 的 RNA 合成的影响

加入时间（分钟）			实验
0	5	10	% 乳糖信使 RNA
CRP	RNA 聚合酶	阻遏物	6.0
CRP	阻遏物	RNA 聚合酶	2.8
CRP	RNA 聚合酶	—	9.4
RNA 聚合酶	—	—	1.5
阻遏物	CRP	RNA 聚合酶	2.8

除了使用的是乳糖操纵子 p^s DNA 外，其他条件和表 1 所述相似。所有初始成分都在 0℃ 下预孵育，然后升温至 30℃，各种添加成分以 5 分钟为间隔加入。在加入最后一个成分后再过 5 分钟加入利福平和核苷酸。背景的乳糖信使 RNA 合成没有被扣除。

　　我们已经提出了基于体外转录研究的证据，该证据说明：在野生型乳糖操纵子中阻遏物抑制转录的机理和它在乳糖操纵子的"启动子"突变体（lac p^s）中的作用机理不同。在正常乳糖操纵子 DNA 里，阻遏物在 RNA 聚合酶–乳糖操纵子 DNA *lac* DNA, *lac* repressor exerts its inhibitory action at a stage subsequent to formation of the RNA polymerase–*lac* DNA preinitiation complex, because repressor is unable to prevent formation of this complex, but is able to prevent polymerase once bound to DNA from transcribing the *lac* operon. Thus, RNA polymerase and the *lac* repressor must bind independently of one another (Fig. 3*a*). With *lac p^s* DNA, on the other hand, previous incubation of the DNA with repressor partially prevents the formation of the preinitiation complex, and transcription from preinitiation complexes already formed in the absence of repressor is partially inhibited by the subsequent addition of repressor.

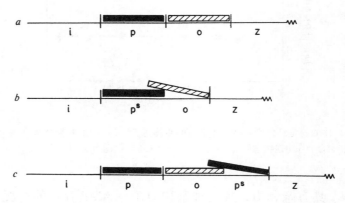

Fig. 3. Mechanism of action of *lac* repressor. RNA polymerase is represented by solid bar and *lac* repressor by striped bar. *a*, Normal *lac* DNA; *b* and *c*, *lac p^s* DNA.

Previous experiments on the mechanism of action of the *lac*, *gal*, *bio* and λ repressors do not present a conclusive or consistent picture. Reznikoff *et al.*[9] found that *lac* repressor binding *in vivo* to the *lac* operator could partially block transcription initiated at a distal promoter. They suggested that repression could occur subsequent to RNA chain initiation. Buttin (personal communication) found that induction of a λ lysogen in which λ DNA synthesis cannot occur results in synthesis of *gal* enzymes in the presence of the *gal* repressor. This "escape synthesis" seems to be caused by transcriptional read-through into *gal* by an RNA polymerase initiating at a λ promoter. Escape synthesis of the dethiobiotin synthetase on induction of a λ prophage can also be explained by a similar mechanism (K. Krell, M. Gottesman, J. Parks, M. Eisenberg, in preparation; A. Campbell, personal communication). The λ repressor seems to inhibit the binding of RNA polymerase to λ DNA (Hayward and Green[10]; Wu *et al.*[11]). Wu *et al.* found also that λ repressor could inhibit λ transcription even when added after RNA polymerase. This is in apparent contradiction to the findings of Chadwick *et al.*[12] who found that the binding of labelled λ repressor was inhibited by previous binding of RNA polymerase to DNA.

Our findings, in agreement with previous genetic studies, suggest that the promoter and operator binding sites may overlap in the *lac p^s* mutant. Ordal[13] finds that some virulent (*o^c*) mutants map on each side of a promoter mutant in the x region of λ. Smith and Sadler (personal communication), who have studied a large number of *lac* operator and promoter mutants, concluded that a single mutation could show both operator–constitutive and

起始前复合体形成之后的某个阶段发挥它的抑制作用，原因是阻遏物无法阻止这种复合体的形成，但能阻止已结合到 DNA 上的聚合酶转录乳糖操纵子。因此，RNA 聚合酶和乳糖操纵子阻遏物一定是独立地与 DNA 结合的（图 3a）。另一方面，在乳糖操纵子 p^s DNA 中，阻遏物与 DNA 的预孵育可以部分阻止起始前复合体的形成，而由形成于无阻遏物存在条件下的起始前复合体开始的转录也会被随后加入的阻遏物部分抑制。

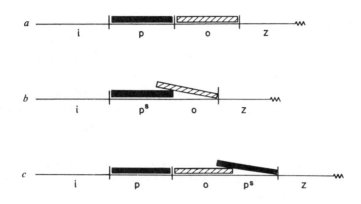

图 3. 乳糖操纵子阻遏物的作用机理。RNA 聚合酶用实心条表示，乳糖操纵子阻遏物用斜线条表示。a，
　　　正常乳糖操纵子 DNA；b 和 c，乳糖操纵子 p^s DNA。

以前关于乳糖、半乳糖、生物素和 λ 阻遏物作用机理的实验都没有给出一个结论性或一致性的描述。列兹尼科夫等人 [9] 发现：在体内，阻遏物与乳糖操纵子操纵基因的结合能够部分地抑制开始于一个远端启动子的转录。他们认为阻遏作用能够在 RNA 链起始后发生。比坦（个人交流）发现：在 λ DNA 无法合成的情况中，λ 溶素原的诱导将导致半乳糖酶的合成发生在半乳糖操纵子阻遏物存在时。这种"逃避合成"似乎是由起始于一个 λ 启动子的 RNA 聚合酶引起的转录通读到半乳糖操纵子所致。由 λ 前噬菌体诱导的脱硫生物素合成酶的逃避合成也能用相似的机理来解释（克雷尔、戈特斯曼、帕克斯、海森伯格，完稿中；坎贝尔，个人交流）。λ 阻遏物似乎能抑制 RNA 聚合酶与 λ DNA 的结合（海沃德和格林 [10]，以及吴等 [11]）。吴等人还发现，甚至在 RNA 聚合酶之后加入 λ 阻遏物也能抑制 λ 转录。这明显与查德威克等人 [12] 的发现相冲突，后者发现 RNA 聚合酶和 DNA 结合后会对标记的 λ 阻遏物的结合产生抑制。

与以前基于基因水平的研究一致，我们的研究结果表明，在乳糖操纵子 p^s 突变体中启动子和操纵基因的结合位点可能是部分重叠的。奥德尔 [13] 发现一些毒性突变体（o^c）出现在 λ 的 x 区域中某个启动子突变的两边。史密斯和萨德勒曾研究过大量乳糖操纵子的操纵基因和启动子突变体（个人交流），他们得出的结论是：一个单

promoter phenotypes; the predominance of one phenotype depends on the location of the mutation.

Our biochemical data for transcription from a wild type *lac* DNA template fail to demonstrate any overlapping of operator and promoter regions (Fig. 3*a*). With *lac p^s* DNA, however, the non-competitive situation characteristic of the wild type *lac* operon has been converted to a partially competitive one. Two models for the molecular basis of this conversion are presented below.

(*a*) The *lac p^s* mutation is a deletion which brings the promoter and operator closer together, causing partial overlapping of the repressor and RNA polymerase binding sites (Fig. 3*b*). Similarly, a point mutation might produce functional interference between the two sites. This hypothesis, however, does not explain the biochemical observation that inhibition of transcription from a *lac p^s*–RNA polymerase preinitiation complex by the subsequent addition of repressor is only 50% effective and is independent of repressor and CRP and RNA polymerase concentration over a five-fold range.

(*b*) The new promoter hypothesis, *lac p^s*, is a mutation creating a promoter site near the operator (Fig. 3*c*). RNA polymerase bound to this site is no longer repressible, although repressor-binding to the operator and inhibition of transcription at the normal promoter still occur. If repressor is bound first to the promoter site, RNA polymerase can no longer bind to the new promoter, although binding at the normal site is unaffected. This model explains the observed partial inhibition and competition by invoking two promoter sites. It also supposes that a cyclic AMP–CRP-dependent promoter has been translocated close to the *lac* operator or that a mutation can create a new promoter in a very small region of the *lac* operon which is still repressible by *lac* repressor and still cyclic AMP–CRP-dependent. No examples of such a mutation are known.

Studies are now in progress to resolve these models by fine structure genetic mapping.

We thank T. Platt and W. Gilbert for *lac* repressor, J. Beckwith for λp*lac*, P. Nissley and J. Parks for helpful discussion, and F. Herder for technical assistance.

(*Nature New Biology*, **233**, 67-69; 1971)

Beatrice Chen, Benoit De Crombrugghe, Wayne B. Anderson, Max E. Gottesman and Ira Pastan: Laboratory of Molecular Biology, National Cancer Institute, National Institutes of Health, Bethesda, Maryland 20014.
Robert L. Perlman: Clinical Endocrinology Branch, National Institute of Arthritis and Metabolic Diseases, National Institutes of Health, Bethesda, Maryland 20014.

Received July 13, 1971.

突变能同时显示出操纵基因组成型表型和启动子表型；突变发生的位置决定了有一种表型会占主导。

我们以野生型乳糖操纵子 DNA 为模板进行转录而得到的生化数据不能证明操纵基因区域和启动子区域之间有任何重叠（图 3a）。然而，在乳糖操纵子 p^s DNA 中，野生型乳糖操纵子所特有的无竞争环境转化成了部分竞争环境。描述这一转化的两种分子基础的模型如下所述。

（a）乳糖操纵子 p^s 突变是导致启动子和操纵基因挨得更近的缺失突变，这使得阻遏物和 RNA 聚合酶的结合位点部分重叠（图 3b）。与此类似，一个点突变也可能会导致两个位点间的功能性干扰。然而，这个假设并不能解释如下的生化观察结果：后来加入的阻遏物对源自乳糖操纵子 p^s-RNA 聚合酶起始前复合体的转录的抑制效用只有 50%，而且在 5 倍的浓度范围内，这种效应与阻遏物、CRP 和 RNA 聚合酶的浓度无关。

（b）新的启动子假说认为：乳糖操纵子 p^s 突变在操纵基因附近产生了一个启动子位点（图 3c）。尽管阻遏物与操纵基因的结合以及对正常启动子转录的抑制依然会发生，但是 RNA 聚合酶对新启动子位点的结合不再受到阻遏。如果是阻遏物首先与这种启动子位点结合，那么 RNA 聚合酶就不能再结合这种新型启动子了，但在正常位点的结合不受影响。这个模型通过引入两个启动子位点解释了观察到的部分抑制和竞争现象。它还假定环 AMP-CRP 依赖的启动子被转移到靠近乳糖操纵基因的位置；或者说一个突变在乳糖操纵子的一个非常小的区域创造了一个新启动子，这个新启动子同样受到乳糖操纵子阻遏物的阻遏，并且仍为环 AMP-CRP 依赖。目前还没有发现一例这样的突变。

通过精细结构遗传图来解析这些模型的研究目前正在进行中。

感谢普拉特和吉尔伯特为我们提供乳糖操纵子阻遏物，感谢贝克威思提供 λplac，感谢尼斯利和帕克斯与我们进行了有益的讨论，还要感谢赫德的技术支持。

（邓铭瑞 翻译；金城 审稿）

References:

1. Pastan, I., and Perlman, R. L., *Science,* **169**, 339 (1970).

2. Gilbert, W., and Muller-Hill, B., *Proc. US Nat. Acad. Sci.*, **56**, 1891 (1966).

3. de Crombrugghe, B., Chen, B., Anderson, W., Nissley, P., Gottesman, M., Perlman, R., and Pastan, I., *Nature New Biology,* **231**, 139 (1971).

4. Bautz, E. F. K., and Bautz, F. A., *Nature,* **226**, 1219 (1970).

5. Riggs, A. D., Newby, R. F., and Bourgeois, S., *J. Mol. Biol.*, **51**, 303 (1970).

6. de Crombrugghe, B., Chen, B., Gottesman, M., Pastan, I., Varmus, H. E., Emmer, M., and Perlman, R. L., *Nature New Biology,* **230**, 37 (1971).

7. Riggs, A. D., Suzugi, H., and Bourgeois, S., *J. Mol. Biol.*, **48**, 67 (1970).

8. Pastan, I., de Crombrugghe, B., Chen, B., Anderson, W., Parks, J., Nissley, P., Straub, M., Gottesman, M., and Perlman R., *Proc. Miami Winter Symp.* (North Holland, Amsterdam, 1971).

9. Reznikoff, W. S., Miller, J. H., Scaife, M. J., and Beckwith, J. R., *J. Mol. Biol.*, **43**, 201 (1969).

10. Hayward, W. S., and Green, M. H., *Proc. US Nat. Acad. Sci.*, **64**, 962 (1969).

11. Wu, A., Ghosh, S., and Echols, H., *Fed. Proc.*, **30**, 1529 (1971).

12. Chadwick, P., Pirrotta, V., Steinberg, R., Hopkins, N., and Ptashne, M., *Cold Spring Harbor Symp. Quant. Biol.*, **35**, 283 (1970).

13. Ordal, G., in *The Bacteriophage Lambda* (edit. by the Cold Spring Harbor. Lab., Cold Spring Harbor, New York) (in the press).

Functional Organization of Genetic Material as a Product of Molecular Evolution

T. Ohta and M. Kimura

Editor's Note

Motoo Kimura's influential neutral theory of molecular evolution states that, at the molecular level, evolutionary changes are caused by the random drift of selectively neutral mutants. The theory was based on constancy in rates of amino-acid change seen in proteins seen over time, most of which, Kimura argued, had no influence on individual fitness. Here Tomoko Ohta and Kimura calculate that an average of 8 amino-acid substitutions occur in the human genome every year, and conclude that, since base substitutions have no effect, a large part of an organism's DNA must be non-essential. Although some viewed Kimura's theory as an argument against Darwinian evolution, Kimura argued that the two theories could coexist, with natural selection and genetic drift both influencing evolution.

MOLECULAR evolution consists of a sequence of events in which originally rare molecular mutants (DNA changes) spread into the species. Two important classes of mutations are nucleotide (or amino-acid) replacement and gene duplication.

From comparative studies of the protein sequences of related organisms, we now have some information on the rate of amino-acid substitution in evolution. The rate is different from protein to protein, but for each particular molecule, such as haemoglobin α or cytochrome c, it is remarkably uniform per year in diverse lines over geological times[1]. This constitutes very strong evidence for the hypothesis[1-3] that most nucleotide substitutions in evolution are the result of random fixation of selectively neutral or near neutral mutants. Furthermore, the rate at which neutral mutant genes are substituted in the population per generation is equal to the rate of occurrence of such mutants per gamete[5].

There are significant differences in evolutionary rates among proteins. The highest rate (fibrinopeptides) is some 1,500 times greater than the lowest rate (histones)[4]. This means that the rate depends on the functional requirement of the molecule (refs. 1 and 3 and unpublished work of M. K. and T. O.). The greater the chance that the mutations are deleterious, the lower the evolutionary rate. The uniformity of evolutionary rate for each molecule implies that the fraction of neutral mutations among all mutations in each cistron remains constant per year.

The average rate of amino-acid substitutions estimated using nine proteins is about 1.6×10^{-9}/amino-acid site/yr[3]. If the difference of evolutionary rates among proteins

功能性遗传物质是分子进化过程中的产物

太田朋子，木村资生

编者按

木村资生颇具影响力的分子进化中性理论认为：在分子水平上，进化的改变是由选择性中性突变的随机漂移导致的。该理论是基于观察到蛋白质中氨基酸的变化速率在很长时间内保持恒定，木村资生认为大多数这种变化对个体适应度并无影响。在本文中，太田朋子和木村资生计算出人类每个基因组平均每年会发生 8 次氨基酸替换，他们得出结论：因为碱基替换没有产生任何影响，所以生物体中的 DNA 一定有很大一部分是非必需的。虽然有人提出木村资生的理论有悖于达尔文的进化论，但木村本人认为这两种理论是可以共存的，自然选择和遗传漂变都对进化过程有影响。

分子进化由一连串事件构成，在这些事件中，最初稀少的分子突变（DNA 变化）逐渐扩散到各物种中。其中有两类重要的突变，即核苷酸(或氨基酸)替换和基因重复。

通过对相关生物体蛋白质序列的对比研究，现在我们已经得到了关于进化过程中氨基酸替换速率方面的一些信息。每一种蛋白质都有不同的氨基酸替换速率，但是对于每个特定的分子而言，例如血红蛋白 α 或细胞色素 c，处于不同地质时代的各种生物世系在每一年中的变化速率却非常一致 [1]。这为以下假说 [1-3] 提供了非常有力的证据：进化过程中的大部分核苷酸替换是选择性中性突变或近中性突变随机固定的结果。此外，每一代群体的中性突变基因发生替换的速率都与每个生殖细胞发生这种突变的速率相同 [5]。

各种蛋白质之间的进化速率存在显著差异。最高速率（血纤维蛋白肽）是最低速率（组蛋白）的 1,500 倍左右 [4]。这意味着该速率取决于蛋白质分子的功能性需求（参考文献 1、3 以及木村资生和太田朋子尚未发表的研究结果）。有害突变发生的机会越多，进化速率就越慢。每个分子都具有同样的变化速率说明：在每个顺反子的所有突变中，中性突变的比例每年都保持恒定。

有人用 9 种蛋白质估算出氨基酸替换的平均速率——每个氨基酸位点每年约为 1.6×10^{-9} [3]。如果蛋白质进化速率的差异是由于功能性需求上的差异而非它们的

is due to the difference in functional requirement rather than the difference in their mutation rate, we should expect that for any cistron the frequency of mutation at the time of occurrence is equal to that of the fibrinopeptides showing the highest substitution rate. This allows us to estimate the true mutation rate at the molecular level.

From the atlas of Dayhoff[6] we sampled seven organisms for which the complete amino-acid sequences of fibrinopeptides A, B and cytochrome c are given, from which to calculate the regression of substitution rate of the fibrinopeptides on that of cytochrome c for which the rate of substitution is well known. We therefore chose the rapidly evolving parts corresponding to the amino-acid positions four to seven in fibrinopeptide A and nine to twenty in fibrinopeptide B (alignment 9 of Dayhoff[6]). The remaining amino-acid positions not only evolve much more slowly but also show some non-randomness with respect to the pattern of substitution. We have therefore excluded these slowly evolving parts from our calculation. Fig. 1 illustrates the regression based on all the pairs of comparisons between seven organisms (human, rhesus monkey, rabbit, dog, horse, pig and kangaroo) with observed values shown by dots. The abscissa gives the number of substitutions in terms of $-\log_e (1-p_d)$ for cytochrome c while the ordinate gives that for fibrinopeptides, where p_d is the fraction of different amino-acids. (For the rationale of using such a logarithmic scale, see ref. 1.) The regression is about 22.4, suggesting that the true mutation rate is 22.4 times the substitution rate of cytochrome c, which is about 0.37×10^{-9}/amino-acid site/yr in mammalian evolution. The resulting mutation rate becomes

$$0.37\times10^{-9}\times 22.4 \approx 8.3\times10^{-9}$$

per amino-acid site/yr. This is roughly five times the average rate of substitutions of the nine proteins and agrees with the conclusion of Corbin and Uzzell[7], and with the conventional mutation rate per locus per generation of $10^{-5}\sim10^{-6}$ if the average cistron codes for the protein of several hundred amino-acids long and if the average generation time is not much different from 1 yr.

突变率差异，那么我们就可以认为任何顺反子发生突变的频率都与替换速率最高的血纤维蛋白肽的突变频率相等。这使我们能够估计出分子水平上的真实突变率。

　　从戴霍夫[6]的图集中，我们抽取了 7 种生物，这 7 种生物的血纤维蛋白肽 A、B 和细胞色素 c 的完整氨基酸序列均已给出，由这些序列出发，根据细胞色素 c 的已知替换速率对血纤维蛋白肽替换速率的回归系数进行计算。为此我们选择了一些快速进化的部分，即与血纤维蛋白肽 A 中氨基酸位点 4 到 7 及血纤维蛋白肽 B 中氨基酸位点 9 到 20 对应的部分（戴霍夫比对 9[6]）。其余的氨基酸位点不仅在进化速率上要慢很多，而且替换模式还具有一些非随机性。因此我们在计算中没有将这些进化缓慢的部分考虑进去。图 1 中绘出了对 7 种生物（人类、恒河猴、兔、狗、马、猪和袋鼠）的所有配对进行比较得到的回归结果，观察值用点表示。横坐标给出了以 $-\log_e(1-p_d)$ 表示的细胞色素 c 的替换数目，而纵坐标则给出了血纤维蛋白肽的替换数目，式中 p_d 代表不同氨基酸所占的比例。（关于使用这种对数标尺的基本原理，请参见参考文献 1。）得出的回归系数约为 22.4，这说明真实突变率是细胞色素 c 的替换速率的 22.4 倍，在哺乳动物的进化中，细胞色素 c 的替换速率大致为每个氨基酸位点每年 0.37×10^{-9}。于是真实突变率为每个氨基酸位点每年：

$$0.37 \times 10^{-9} \times 22.4 \approx 8.3 \times 10^{-9}$$

这大概是那 9 种蛋白质的平均替换速率的 5 倍，与科尔宾和尤泽尔[7]得到的结果一致。如果平均而言顺反子编码的蛋白质长度达到几百个氨基酸，并且如果平均世代时间大约等于一年，那么这个值也与每个基因座每世代 $10^{-5} \sim 10^{-6}$ 的公认突变率一致。

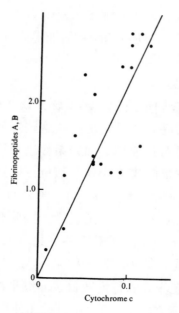

Fig. 1. The regression of the rate of amino-acid substitution of fibrinopeptides (actually their rapidly evolving parts) on that of cytochrome c. In each coordinate, the number of different amino-acid sites between two homologous proteins is expressed in terms of $-\log_e(1-p_d)$ where p_d is the fraction of differing sites. Dots represent twenty-one observed values (of which two sets of values coincide) from paired comparisons involving seven organisms (human, rhesus monkey, rabbit, dog, horse, pig and kangaroo). The estimated regression coefficient is 22.4.

If a large fraction of mutations are deleterious as discussed above, every higher organism must suffer a heavy genetic load. According to the Haldane–Muller principle[5] the mutation load of equilibrium populations is equal to one to two times the total deleterious mutation rate depending on the degree of dominance of mutations[8]. Recent investigations in *Drosophila* have shown that the detrimental mutations have a fairly high degree of dominance[9,10]. The mutation load must therefore be nearly twice the total mutation rate, although epistatic (synergistic) interaction in fitness among the loci may reduce the load somewhat[10,11].

Various species of mammals have about the same amount of DNA. The human haploid genome consists of about 3×10^9 nucleotide sites[12,13], equivalent to 10^9 amino-acid sites: thus the total mutation rate due to base replacement per genome per year amounts to

$$8.3 \times 10^{-9} \times 10^9 \approx 8$$

If the mutation rate is strictly proportional to chronological time, the rate per generation is probably twenty times this figure in man but half as large in mouse. In the main course of mammalian evolution, the average generation time was probably 2~3 yr, so we tentatively equate 1 yr with one generation in mammals. If most of these mutations are deleterious, any mammalian species must suffer an intolerable mutation load: Muller argued[14] that

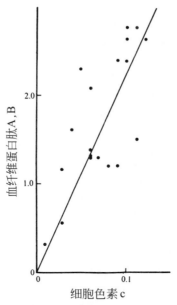

图 1. 根据细胞色素 c 的氨基酸替换速率对血纤维蛋白肽（实际上是其中快速进化的部分）的氨基酸替
换速率进行回归分析得到的结果。在每个坐标上，两个同源蛋白质之间的不同氨基酸位点的数目
以 $-\log_e(1-p_d)$ 来表示，式中 p_d 表示不同位点所占的比例。图中的点代表 7 种生物（人类、恒河猴、
兔、狗、马、猪和袋鼠）配对比较的 21 个观察值（其中有两组数据是重叠的）。回归系数的估计
值为 22.4。

如上所述，如果大部分突变是有害变异的话，那么每种高等生物都必须承受非
常大的遗传负荷。根据霍尔丹－马勒原理 [5]，平衡群体的突变负荷依突变显性程度
的不同而相当于总有害突变率的 1 ～ 2 倍 [8]。对果蝇的最新研究结果显示，有害突
变的显性度相当高 [9,10]。因此，尽管基因座间存在适当大小的上位（协同）相互作用
也许会在某种程度上减轻这种负荷 [10,11]，但突变负荷肯定接近于总突变率的 2 倍。

不同种类哺乳动物所含的 DNA 数目大致相同。人类的单倍体基因组由大约
3×10^9 个核苷酸位点构成 [12,13]，相当于 10^9 个氨基酸位点，因此由每个基因组每年
的碱基替换速率导致的人类基因组的总突变率为：

$$8.3 \times 10^{-9} \times 10^9 \approx 8$$

如果突变率严格与年代时间成正比的话，那么人类每世代的突变率可能是这一数字
的 20 倍，而小鼠的突变率则仅为这一数字的 2 倍。在哺乳动物的主要进化路线中，
平均世代时间可能为 2 年～ 3 年，所以我们试探性地将哺乳动物的一个世代定为 1 年。
如果这些突变中的大部分是有害的，那么任何一个哺乳动物物种肯定都承受着无法

the total rate for detrimental mutations in man is at most 0.5 per generation. What does such great discrepancy signify? We conclude that a large part of DNA in the genome is not essential for the life of the organisms in that base substitutions have no effects[3]. If we compare the above estimate of the total mutation rate with Muller's maximum detrimental mutation rate we are led to the conclusion that only 0.5/8 or 6% of the total DNA are as important in function as the cistrons such as those coding for cytochrome c or haemoglobins. If the estimated total mutation rate per generation is twenty times that per year and the total detrimental mutation rate is 1.0 (taking into account the "viability polygenes" of Mukai)[15], then the fraction becomes 0.6%. Although we conclude, with Muller[16], that the total number of "genes" in man is about 3×10^4, whereas he assumes a large gene size (corresponding to 30,000 amino-acids), we assume that the genes are much smaller in size (corresponding to several hundred amino-acids on average) but a large fraction of DNA is not "informational".

Mammalian DNA is about 1,000 times larger than bacterial DNA, so that the genetic material duplicated some ten times on average ($2^{10}=1,024$) in the course of evolution from a unicellular organism to the mammals[17]. After each fixation of duplication in the species, irrespective of whether the duplicated part is a whole chromosome or a tiny fraction, the duplicated genes must have differentiated from the original genes through nucleotide substitution. It is possible that in this process many mutations which would have been deleterious before duplication become harmless (selectively neutral) if they occurred after duplication, for one set of genes provides the essential function of the organism. The originally deleterious mutants will spread into the population by random drift, so that there will be degeneration in many duplicated genes. The possibility of DNA degeneration after gene duplication has been pointed out by Ohno et al.[18] and Nei[17]. The probability of such degenerated parts acquiring new functions might be quite small. Some duplicated genes will acquire new functions, establishing themselves as important genes of the organism. But mutation is a random event, so that the chance that duplicated genes will acquire a new function must be much smaller than that they will become inert. Thus, we should expect that higher organisms have much non-informational (inert) DNA in their genome.

In this case, the rate of nucleotide substitution must be very rapid within those parts, for all the mutations are neutral. We estimate this rate approximately as $1/3 \times 8.3 \times 10^{-9}$/yr/nucleotide site, which is one-third of the estimated rate per amino-acid sites in rapidly evolving portions of the fibrinopeptides. We further multiply this by 1.2 to give total nucleotide substitution rate by taking account of the synonymous mutations[19]. The resulting rate is 0.33×10^{-8}/yr/nucleotide site. This is about five times as high as the rate estimated from the average proteins.

Recent investigations using DNA hybridization techniques indicate that the differentiation of DNA in mammalian evolution is very rapid. Laird et al.[20] estimated that the rate of DNA evolution is about three times as fast in artiodactyls and thirty times in rodents as the corresponding rate inferred from haemoglobins. Walker[21] estimated that the differentiation

忍受的突变负荷：马勒认为 [14] 人类的有害突变率每世代总计至多为 0.5。如此大的差异意味着什么？我们推测基因组中的大部分 DNA 并不是生物体维持生命所必需的，因而碱基替换没有产生任何影响 [3]。如果我们将上述总突变率的估计值与马勒的最大有害突变率相比较，就可以得到以下结论：在全部 DNA 中，只有 0.5/8 或 6% 与顺反子（如编码细胞色素 c 或血红蛋白的顺反子）在功能上具有同等的重要性。如果估计出的每世代总突变率是每年突变率的 20 倍，且总有害突变率是 1.0（考虑到向井辉美的"活性多基因"）[15]，那么上述比例就变成了 0.6%。尽管我们和马勒 [16] 都确信人类"基因"的总数目大概是 3×10^4，不过他认为基因很大（含 30,000 个氨基酸），而我们认为基因的大小要小很多（平均只含几百个氨基酸），但大部分 DNA 是非"编码"的。

哺乳动物的 DNA 大约是细菌 DNA 的 1,000 倍，所以在从单细胞生物进化到哺乳动物的过程中，遗传物质平均要复制 10 次左右（$2^{10}=1,024$）[17]。在每次对物种中的复制进行固定之后，不论复制的部分是一整条染色体还是一个微小的片段，复制的基因都必然是通过核苷酸替换从最初的基因分化而来的。在这一过程中，许多复制之前是有害的突变在发生复制之后可能反而变成无害了（选择中性），这是因为其中有一套基因为生物体提供了必要的功能。原来有害的突变体将通过随机漂移扩散到整个群体之中，因此在许多基因副本中会出现退化现象。大野乾等人 [18] 和根井正利 [17] 曾经指出，基因复制之后可能会出现 DNA 退化现象。这些退化部分获取新功能的概率可能会非常小。有些基因副本获得了新功能，成为了生物体的重要基因。但突变是一个随机事件，因而基因副本获取新功能的概率一定会比它们变成无义突变的概率小很多。因此，我们应当认为高等生物的基因组中有很多非编码（无义）的 DNA。

在这种情况下，由于非编码 DNA 部分的所有突变都是中性的，所以它们的核苷酸替换速率一定很快。我们估计这个速率大致为每个核苷酸位点每年 $1/3 \times 8.3 \times 10^{-9}$，该值是血纤维蛋白肽快速进化部分每个氨基酸位点的替换速率估计值的 1/3。考虑到同义突变 [19]，我们再将该值乘以 1.2 以给出总的核苷酸替换速率。最终得到的速率为每个核苷酸位点每年 0.33×10^{-8}。这大概是从几种蛋白质估计出的平均速率的 5 倍。

最近使用 DNA 杂交技术进行的研究表明，在哺乳动物的进化过程中 DNA 发生分化的速率很快。莱尔德等人 [20] 根据从血红蛋白突变速率推导出的相应速率估计出：哺乳动物 DNA 的进化速率大概是偶蹄动物的 3 倍，是啮齿类动物的 30 倍。沃

of DNA of rodents is fifteen times as fast as that of known proteins. It is possible that the evolutionary rate of total DNA is more nearly proportional to generations rather than to chronological time. More recently, Kohn[22], who has summarized these results, emphasizes that the substitution rate in DNA of mammalian genome is proportional to generations. He concludes that the number of nucleotide substitutions in non-repeated DNA is roughly five per genome per generation, and the total rate of substitutions is probably two to four times greater. It is interesting that his figure is roughly equal to our estimate, that is, eight substitutions per genome per year.

We thank Dr. Kazutoshi Mayeda for reading out manuscript and correcting the English.

(**233**, 118-119; 1971)

Tomoko Ohta and Motoo Kimura: National Institute of Genetics, Mishima, Shizuoka-ken, 411.

Received December 2, 1970; revised March 17, 1971.

References:

1. Kimura, M., *Proc. US Nat. Acad. Sci.*, **63**, 1181 (1969).
2. Kimura, M., *Nature*, **217**, 624 (1968).
3. King, J. L., and Jukes, T. H., *Science*, **164**, 788 (1969).
4. McLaughlin, P. J., and Dayhoff, M. O., in *Atlas of Protein Sequence and Structure 1969* (edit. by Dayhoff, M. O.), 39 (National Biomedical Research Foundation, Silver Spring, Maryland, 1969).
5. Crow, J. F., and Kimura, M., *An Introduction to Population Genetics Theory* (Harper and Row, New York, 1970).
6. Dayhoff, M. O., *Atlas of Protein Sequence and Structure* (National Biomedical Research Foundation, Silver Spring, Maryland, 1969).
7. Corbin, K. W., and Uzzell, T., *Amer. Nat.*, **104**, 37 (1970).
8. Kimura, M., *Jap. J. Genet.*, **37** (Suppl.), 179 (1961).
9. Crow, J. F., in *Population Biology and Evolution* (edit. by Lewontin, R.), 71 (Syracuse University Press, New York, 1968).
10. Mukai, T., *Genetics*, **61**, 749 (1969).
11. Kimura, M., and Maruyama, T., *Genetics*, **54**, 1337 (1966).
12. Muller, H. J., *Bull. Amer. Math. Soc.*, **64**, 137 (1958).
13. Vogel, F., *Nature*, **201**, 847 (1964).
14. Muller, H. J., *Amer. J. Human Genet.*, **2**, 111 (1950).
15. Mukai, T., *Genetics*, **50**, 1 (1964).
16. Muller, H. J., in *Heritage from Mendel* (edit. by Brink, R. A.), 419 (University of Wisconsin Press, Madison, 1967).
17. Nei, M., *Nature*, **221**, 40 (1969).
18. Ohno, S., Wolf, U., and Atkin, N. B., *Hereditas*, **59**, 169 (1968).
19. Kimura, M., *Genet. Res.*, **11**, 247 (1968).
20. Laird, C. D., McConaughy, B. L., and McCarthy, B. J., *Nature*, **224**, 149 (1969).
21. Walker, P. M. B., *Nature*, **219**, 228 (1968).
22. Kohn, D. E., *Quart. Rev. Biophys.*, **3** (3), 327 (1970).

克 [21] 估计啮齿类动物的 DNA 分化速率是已知蛋白质的 15 倍。总 DNA 的进化速率可能更接近于与世代时间成正比，而非与年代时间成正比。就在前不久，总结出上述结果的科恩 [22] 强调指出：哺乳动物基因组的 DNA 替换速率与世代成正比。他推测：在非重复 DNA 中，核苷酸替换的数目大概为每个基因组每世代 5 次，总的替换速率可能是这一数值的 2～4 倍。有趣的是，他得到的数值与我们的估计值大致相等，即每个基因组每年发生 8 次替换。

感谢前田和俊（译者注：音译）博士通读了我们的手稿并对英文进行了修改。

（刘皓芳 翻译；陈新文 陈继征 审稿）

Covalently Linked RNA–DNA Molecule as Initial Product of RNA Tumour Virus DNA Polymerase

I. M. Verma *et al.*

Editor's Note

A year earlier, Nobel laureate David Baltimore co-discovered the enzyme reverse transcriptase, which converts messenger RNA into DNA and thus enables RNA-encoded viruses to integrate with the host genome. Baltimore and his coworkers show here that the same enzyme from an avian tumour virus converts RNA into a chemically bound DNA–RNA species, which they suggest contains a small RNA "primer" molecule. The primer, they correctly speculate, is a host-encoded transfer RNA. The study hinted that primers could be used to kick start the production of genes from messenger RNAs in the laboratory, a reaction that was to prove important to the development of the biotechnology industry.

THE DNA polymerase found in virions of the RNA tumour viruses[1,2] can be assayed in two ways. If disrupted virions are incubated without addition of a template, the endogenous viral RNA is copied by the DNA polymerase[3-5]. If exogenous templates are provided, often these are copied at a much higher rate than the endogenous RNA[6-12]. With exogenous templates, however, the DNA polymerase requires the presence of a homologous polynucleotide primer to initiate polymerization of nucleotides[10]. The primer, which can be as short as a tetranucleotide[11,12], is physically incorporated into the product (Smoler, Molineaux and Baltimore, submitted for publication). The primer requirement of the enzyme, demonstrated with exogenous polynucleotide templates, suggests that in the absence of such templates, when the enzyme copies the endogenous 60–70S viral RNA, a primer might also be present to initiate polymerization.

The initial reaction product formed when the virion DNA polymerase copies the endogenous viral RNA consists of small pieces of DNA attached to the 60–70S RNA[3,4,13-15]. Analysis by buoyant density in Cs_2SO_4 indicated that the DNA product could be released from the viral RNA by procedures which disrupt hydrogen bonds[3].

Further analysis of the product released from the viral RNA by heat treatment has now revealed that the material is not free DNA. After 30 min or less of reaction the product contains molecules which behave like DNA–RNA duplexes even after heat denaturation. One interpretation of this result is that the initial product of the reaction might be a covalently linked DNA–RNA molecule and that the primer for initiation of synthesis might be an RNA species.

The initial observation was with Moloney mouse leukaemia virus (MLV). After 20 min of incubation, the product of the virion DNA polymerase reaction was extracted with

844

RNA肿瘤病毒DNA聚合酶的初产物是通过共价键连接的RNA-DNA分子

维尔马等

编者按

一年前，诺贝尔奖获得者戴维·巴尔的摩和其他研究者各自独立发现了逆转录酶，这种酶能将信使 RNA 转化为 DNA，由此使得 RNA 病毒基因能够整合到宿主基因组。巴尔的摩和他的同事在本文中展示了一种来自禽肿瘤病毒的逆转录酶，这种酶可以将 RNA 转化为通过化学键连接的 DNA-RNA 分子，他们认为此 DNA-RNA 分子含有一个小的 RNA "引物" 分子。巴尔的摩等人正确地推测出此引物是一个宿主编码的转运 RNA。本项研究暗示，在实验室中这些引物可以用于启动从信使 RNA 开始的基因生产，此反应在生物科技产业发展中的重要性现已被证实。

可以通过两种途径检测出在 RNA 肿瘤病毒的病毒体中发现的 DNA 聚合酶[1,2]。如果破裂的病毒体在没有额外模板的条件下培养，那么内源病毒 RNA 就会通过这种 DNA 聚合酶进行复制[3-5]。如果提供外源模板，通常这些模板的复制速率会远高于内源 RNA[6-12]。虽然如此，在提供外源模板时，DNA 聚合酶仍需在同源多聚核苷酸引物存在的条件下才能启动核苷酸聚合[10]。该引物最小为 4 个核苷酸[11,12]，它会与聚合产物物理混合在一起（斯莫勒、莫里纽克斯和巴尔的摩，已提请出版）。此酶对引物的需求表明：在没有外源多聚核苷酸模板的条件下，当酶复制内源 60–70S 病毒 RNA 时，可能也存在引物以启动聚合反应。

当病毒体 DNA 聚合酶复制这些病毒内源性的 RNA 时，会形成许多附在 60–70S RNA 上的小片段 DNA，这就是最初的反应产物[3,4,13-15]。Cs_2SO_4 溶液浮力密度分析结果显示，DNA 产物可以通过切断氢键的过程从病毒 RNA 里释放出来[3]。

通过热处理对从病毒 RNA 中释放的产物作进一步分析，现已揭示该物质不是自由 DNA。经过 30 min 或者更短时间的反应，产物中含有表现得很像 DNA-RNA 双链体的分子，即使经过热变性处理，这种情况仍然存在。对这个结果的一种解释是：此反应的初产物也许是一个通过共价键连接的 DNA-RNA 分子，用于启动该合成的引物可能是一种 RNA。

最初的观测基于莫洛尼氏小鼠白血病病毒（MLV）。培养 20 min 后，用"肌氨酰"提取病毒体 DNA 聚合酶反应的产物，再用"葡聚糖凝胶 G-50"柱提纯，煮沸使二

"Sarkosyl", purified on a "Sephadex G-50" column, boiled to denature the secondary structure and centrifuged to equilibrium in a Cs_2SO_4 gradient. The principal component of the boiled product banded at a density slightly greater than denatured P22 phage DNA (Fig. 1a). Some material of greater density was also evident. After treatment with alkali (Fig. 1b), ribonuclease in low salt (Fig. 1c) or ribonuclease in 0.3 M NaCl plus 0.3 M Na citrate (Fig. 1d), the product DNA banded coincidentally with the denatured P22 DNA although the polymerase product formed a much wider band than the marker. The effects of alkali and ribonuclease indicate that RNA was attached to the product DNA even after boiling and was causing the DNA to band at a higher density than the marker phage DNA.

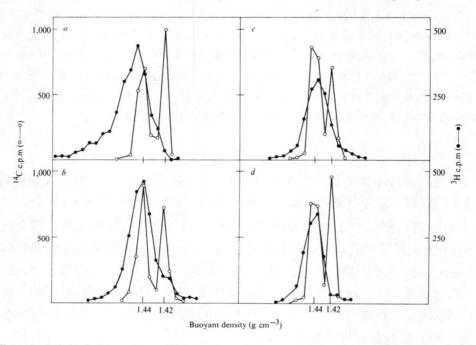

Fig. 1. Analysis in Cs_2SO_4 gradients of the product of the mouse leukaemia virus DNA polymerase. A 20 min reaction was carried out in standard conditions[13] with virions of Moloney mouse leukaemia virus and ^{3}H-TTP. The fast sedimenting fraction was separated on sucrose gradients, collected by precipitation with ethanol, and dissolved in 0.01 M Tris-HCl (pH 7.6), 0.01 M NaCl. Portions were placed in a boiling water bath for 5 min and chilled. Parts of the heated samples were treated for 10 min at 37°C in 0.4 ml. with 16 μg of pancreatic ribonuclease (Worthington) plus 3 μg of T_1 ribonuclease (Calbiochem, 5,000 U/mg) contained either in 0.01 M Tris-HCl (pH 7.6), 0.01 M NaCl (low salt) or 0.3 M NaCl, 0.03 M Na citrate (high salt). A separate portion of the product was adjusted to 0.3 M NaOH and placed in a boiling water bath for 5 min, chilled and neutralized with HCl. For analysis, the treated samples were mixed with 1.40 ml. of 0.01 M Tris-HCl (pH 7.4), 0.001 M EDTA saturated at 24°C with Cs_2SO_4 and enough Tris-EDTA buffer to make 3.0 ml. The samples were placed in polyallomer tubes, a cushion of 0.15 ml. of saturated Cs_2SO_4 was carefully placed at the bottom and the top was covered with "Nujol". The solutions were centrifuged for 65–70 h at 33,000 r.p.m. and 23°C in a Spinco SW 50.1 rotor in a model L ultracentrifuge. All the gradients contained ^{14}C-labelled heat-denatured and native P22 DNA as standard markers with buoyant densities of 1.44 and 1.42 respectively[13]. Three to five drop fractions were collected from the bottom of the tube, acid-precipitated, collected on filters as previously described[13] and counted in a mixture of 5 g PPO and 100 g naphthalene in 1 l. of p-dioxane. a, Boiled product; b, alkali-treated product; c, boiled product after ribonuclease treatment in low salt; d, boiled product after ribonuclease treatment in high salt.

级结构变性，然后用 Cs₂SO₄ 密度梯度离心达到平衡。煮沸后产物的主要成分在密度略高于变性后 P22 噬菌体 DNA 的地方形成条带（图 1a）。存在某种密度更高的物质也是显而易见的。用碱液处理（图 1b）、用溶于低浓度盐溶液的核糖核酸酶处理（图 1c）或用溶于 0.3 M NaCl 外加 0.3 M 柠檬酸钠溶液的核糖核酸酶处理之后（图 1d），产物 DNA 恰好与变性 P22 噬菌体 DNA 聚集在一起，不过聚合酶产物形成的条带要比标志基因宽很多。碱液和核糖核酸酶的作用结果表明：即使在煮沸后，RNA 仍与产物 DNA 结合在一起，并使 DNA 在比标志物噬菌体 DNA 密度更高的地方形成条带。

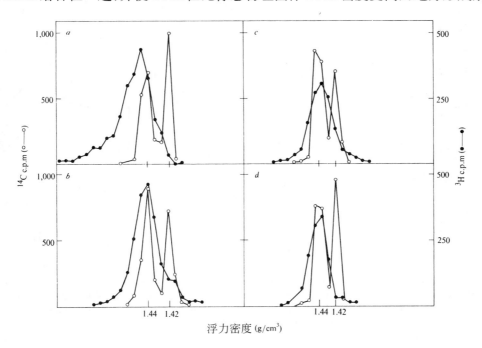

图 1. 用 Cs₂SO₄ 梯度分析小鼠白血病病毒 DNA 聚合酶的反应产物。在标准条件下[13]，莫洛尼氏小鼠白血病病毒的病毒体和 ³H– 胸腺嘧啶核苷三磷酸反应 20 min。用蔗糖梯度法分离快速沉降级分，再用乙醇沉淀法收集这些级分，然后溶解在 0.01 M Tris-HCl（pH 7.6）和 0.01 M NaCl 溶液中。取部分置于沸水浴中 5 min，随后快速冷却。在 37℃ 条件下，将两份加热后的样品分别加入到 0.4 ml 含有 16 μg 胰核糖核酸酶（沃辛顿）外加 3 μg T₁ 核糖核酸酶（卡尔生物化学公司，5,000 U/mg）的 0.01 M Tris-HCl（pH 7.6）、0.01 M NaCl（低盐）溶液或 0.3 M NaCl、0.03 M 柠檬酸钠（高盐）溶液中处理 10 min。将独立的一份产物调整到 NaOH 浓度为 0.3 M 并置于沸水浴中 5 min，然后快速冷却并用 HCl 中和。为了分析，将处理过的样品同 1.40 ml 0.01 M Tris-HCl（pH 7.4）、24℃下 Cs₂SO₄ 饱和的 0.001 M EDTA 溶液以及足量 Tris-EDTA 缓冲液混合，以使溶液体积达到 3.0 ml。将样品放置在异质同品聚合物管里，小心地将 0.15 ml 饱和 Cs₂SO₄ 垫在管底部，顶部用"纽加尔"美国药典矿物油覆盖。将溶液置于 L 型超速离心机的斯平科 SW 50.1 转子中，在 23℃ 下以每 min 转数 33,000 的速度离心 65 h ～ 70 h。所有梯度中都含有 ¹⁴C 标记的经热变性处理的 P22 噬菌体 DNA 和原生 P22 噬菌体 DNA，这两种 DNA 作为标准标志，浮力密度分别为 1.44 和 1.42[13]。从管底部收集 3 到 5 滴级分，用酸沉淀，以之前发表的文章中描述过的过滤器[13] 进行收集，然后在含 5 g 多酚氧化酶和 100 g 萘混合物的 1 L 对二氧杂环己烷中计数。a，煮沸过的产物；b，碱液处理过的产物；c，在低盐条件下用核糖核酸酶处理的煮沸产物；d，在高盐条件下用核糖核酸酶处理的煮沸产物。

To confirm and extend these data the reaction product of the avian myeloblastosis virus (AMV) DNA polymerase was investigated because larger amounts of this virus were available. The endogenous product formed after 2, 5, 10, 15 and 30 min of reaction was banded in Cs_2SO_4 in its native state, after boiling and after alkali treatment.

The native products consisted of some DNA banding coincidentally with an RNA marker, at a density of 1.65 (Fig. 2a). Increasing amounts of DNA banding at lower density appeared as incubation time increased. These complexes have been described previously[3,4,13-15].

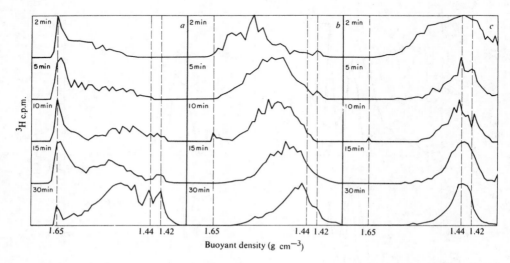

Fig. 2. Analysis in Cs_2SO_4 gradients of the product of the avian myeloblastosis virus DNA polymerase after various times of reaction. The products were prepared using the following 0.2 ml. reaction mixture: 50 mM Tris-HCl (pH 8.3), 6 mM magnesium acetate, 20 mM dithiothreitol, NaCl, 1 mM dATP, 1mM dGTP, 1 mM dCTP, 6.5 μM ^{3}H-dTTP (6,000 c.p.m./pmol), 0.2% "Nonidet P-40" and 1–2 mg of AMV protein in purified virions[10]. Samples were incubated at 37°C for the given length of time and the reaction terminated by the addition of an equal volume of 3% sodium dodecyl sarcosinate. The samples were further incubated for 5 min at 37°C. Portions were withdrawn from the samples to measure acid-insoluble material. The 2, 5, 10, 15 and 30 min products in a typical experiment had 51,000, 165,000, 280,000, 400,000 and 500,000 total c.p.m. respectively. The products were then separated from low molecular weight material by chromatography on "Sephadex G-50" columns using 0.1 M NH_4HCO_3 buffer, pH 8.0, for elution. The recovery of the purified product was over 70%. For heat denaturation, 0.01–0.05 ml. of the product was diluted to 0.5 ml. with 0.01 M Tris-HCl, pH 7.6, and 0.01 M NaCl, placed in a boiling water bath for 5 min and cooled rapidly. For alkaline hydrolysis, portions in the same buffer containing 0.3 M NaOH were placed in a boiling water bath for 5 min, chilled and neutralized with HCl to pH 7.0. Cs_2SO_4 gradients containing 8,000–12,000 c.p.m. of products were prepared and analysed as in Fig. 1. ^{14}C-18S ribosomal RNA was also included as a marker. Recoveries from the gradients containing native material were 20–50% and from the other gradients were 55–80%. Drops from the gradient tubes were collected directly into scintillation fluid. a, Native products; b, boiled products; c, alkali-treated products.

The heat-denatured product after 2 min of incubation (Fig. 2b) banded heterogeneously with most of the DNA heavier than 1.5 g/ml. which is the density of a 1:1 DNA·RNA

为了确认和扩展这些数据，我们对禽成髓细胞瘤病毒（AMV）DNA 聚合酶的反应产物进行了研究，因为可以很方便地获得更多量的这种病毒。将反应 2 min、5 min、10 min、15 min 和 30 min 后形成的内源产物，分别以原生、经过煮沸和经过碱液处理的状态放入 Cs₂SO₄ 溶液中，聚集成条带。

原生产物中含有某种 DNA，这种 DNA 碰巧与一种 RNA 标志物聚集在一起，在密度为 1.65 处形成条带（图 2a）。随着培养时间的增加，聚集在低密度处的 DNA 的数量看上去也在增加。前人已经在文章中描述过这些复合物 [3,4,13-15]。

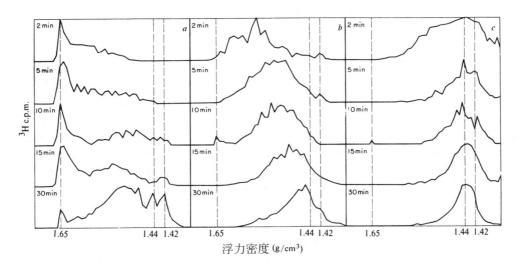

图 2. 用 Cs₂SO₄ 梯度分析不同反应时间段禽成髓细胞瘤病毒 DNA 聚合酶的产物。使用 0.2 ml 的以下反应混合物制备产物：50 mM Tris-HCl（pH 8.3）、6 mM 醋酸镁、20 mM 二硫苏糖醇、NaCl、1 mM 脱氧腺苷三磷酸、1 mM 脱氧鸟苷三磷酸、1 mM 脱氧胞苷三磷酸、6.5 μM ³H– 脱氧胸苷三磷酸（6,000 c.p.m./pmol）、0.2% "诺乃洗涤剂 P-40" 和 1 mg ~ 2 mg 提纯病毒体中的 AMV 蛋白 [10]。在 37℃ 条件下按给定时长培养样品，加入等体积的 3% 十二烷基肌氨酸钠终止反应。接下来样品在 37℃ 继续培养 5 min。从样品中取出一部分用于测量不溶于酸的物质。反应 2 min、5 min、10 min、15 min 和 30 min 后的产物在典型实验中的总 c.p.m. 值分别为 51,000、165,000、280,000、400,000 及 500,000。使用 "葡聚糖凝胶 G-50" 柱层析，用 0.1 M NH₄HCO₃ 缓冲液（pH 8.0）洗脱，从而将产物从低分子量物质中分离出来。纯化产物的回收率超过 70%。热变性处理：取 0.01 ml ~ 0.05 ml 产物用 0.01 M pH 为 7.6 的 Tris-HCl 和 0.01 M NaCl 稀释至 0.5 ml，置于沸水浴中 5 min，然后迅速冷却。碱水解：将部分产物置于含 0.3 M NaOH 的同种缓冲液中，沸水浴 5 min，快速冷却后用 HCl 中和至 pH 为 7.0。按图 1 中的方法制备和分析含 c.p.m. 为 8,000 ~ 12,000 的产物的 Cs₂SO₄ 梯度。¹⁴C 标记的 18S 核糖体 RNA 也被包含在其中作为标志物。含有原生物质的梯度的回收率为 20% ~ 50%，其他梯度的回收率为 55% ~ 80%。将梯度管中的滴液直接收集到闪液中。a，原生产物；b，煮沸过的产物；c，碱液处理过的产物。

培养 2 min 后，热变性产物（图 2b）与大多数密度比 1.5 g/ml 高的 DNA 聚集在一起形成异质性条带，其密度与 DNA 和 RNA 按 1:1 比例以氢键结合的双链体相同 [16]。

hydrogen-bonded duplex[16]. With increasing time of incubation, the heterogeneous band moved to lighter positions in the gradient. By 30 min the product resembled that seen after 20 min of reaction by the MLV DNA polymerase.

Treatment of the DNA polymerase products with alkali in conditions which hydrolyse all RNA caused them to band in Cs_2SO_4 at a lower average density than the boiled product (Fig. 2c). The bands were quite broad, indicating a low molecular weight. The samples from later times of incubation gave a sharper band which centred at a density slightly lighter than the denatured P22 phage DNA. The earliest sample gave an especially board band but still the alkali-treated product was on the average less dense than the boiled product.

To show that the boiled product did not spontaneously renature, the effect of the single-strand-specific nuclease from *Neurospora** was investigated. A portion of the boiled product from a 15 min incubation of AMV was treated with *Neurospora* nuclease in previously specified conditions which only degrade single stranded regions of nucleic acids[13]. The treated material was then centrifuged to equilibrium in Cs_2SO_4 as was an equivalent amount of boiled but undigested material. The nuclease-treated product contained only 4% of the radioactivity of the untreated product and this was distributed heterogeneously. Therefore, after the boiling treatment, almost all of the DNA remains in a single stranded state.

To see if the 60–70S viral RNA contained an RNA primer, the reaction of purified AMV DNA polymerase with isolated 60–70S AMV RNA was studied. A reaction was carried out for 15 min and portions of the product were centrifuged to equilibrium in Cs_2SO_4 either without any treatment, after boiling, or after alkaline hydrolysis. As with the early endogenous product, most of this product banded with RNA at $\rho = 1.65$ g cm^{-3} before treatment (Fig. 3a). Boiling converted it to material banding between RNA and DNA (Fig. 3b) and alkaline hydrolysis caused it to form a wide band centring slightly lighter than the P22 denatured DNA (Fig. 3c). The product formed when purified enzyme is allowed to copy 60–70S viral RNA therefore behaves similarly to the product of the endogenous reaction, supporting the idea that these two systems are comparable.

---

* In a previous paper[13] this enzyme was called the *Neurospora* endonuclease and was thought to be identical to the enzyme prepared by Linn and Lehman[20]. Dr. M. Fraser, who prepared the nuclease used in the previous studies, has informed us that the nuclease is a different enzyme from the Linn and Lehman enzyme. It is an exonuclease combined with some endonuclease activity but has very high specificity for single stranded regions of nucleic acid like the Linn and Lehman enzyme. Using a modification of the procedure of Rabin, Preiss and Fraser[21], we have isolated the enzyme used in the present experiments and have confirmed its high specificity for single stranded nucleic acid as previously reported[13].

随着培养时间的增加，这个异质性条带移动到梯度中更轻的位置。培养 30 min 的产物类似于用 MLV DNA 聚合酶反应 20 min 后观察到的产物。

经碱液处理水解掉所有 RNA 后，DNA 聚合酶产物在 Cs_2SO_4 中平均密度比煮沸产物低的位置形成条带（图 2c）。这些条带非常宽，说明分子量很小。培养后期的样品给出了一个更窄的条带，其中心在密度比变性 P22 噬菌体 DNA 略低的位置。培养最早期的样品所给出的条带特别宽，但平均看来，碱液处理产物的密度依然低于煮沸产物。

为了说明煮沸产物并没有自发复性，我们对来自脉孢菌 * 的单链特异性核酸酶的效应进行了研究。取一份培养了 15 min 的 AMV 的煮沸产物，在此前只降解核酸单链区的指定条件下 [13] 用脉胞菌核酸酶处理。之后将这些处理过的物质和一份等量的煮沸过但未经消化的物质分别在 Cs_2SO_4 中离心至达到平衡。核酸酶处理过的产物只具有未处理产物 4% 的放射性，并且分布也是异质的。因此，在煮沸处理后，几乎所有的 DNA 仍保持在单链状态。

为了检验 60–70S 的病毒RNA 中是否包含 RNA 引物，我们对提纯的 AMV DNA 聚合酶与分离的 60–70S AMV RNA 的反应进行了研究。反应 15 min 后，将未经过任何处理的、煮沸后的或经过碱液水解的各份产物分别在 Cs_2SO_4 中离心达到平衡。因为混有早期内源产物，所以在处理前，大多数这种产物都与 RNA 一起在密度为 1.65 g/cm^3 处形成条带（图 3a）。煮沸使得这种产物转变为条带位于 RNA 和 DNA 之间的物质（图 3b），碱液水解使它形成一条宽带，其中心在比 P22 变性 DNA 略轻的位置上（图 3c）。用提纯过的酶复制 60–70S 病毒 RNA 时所形成的产物表现得类似于内源反应产物，该事实支持了外源系统与内源系统具有相似性的观点。

---

* 在之前的一篇论文中 [13]，这种酶被称为脉孢菌核酸内切酶，并被认为与林和莱曼 [20] 制备的酶相同。此前研究中使用的这种核酸酶是由弗雷泽博士提供的，他告诉我们这种核酸酶与林和莱曼制备的酶并不相同。这是一种带有一些核酸内切酶活性的核酸外切酶，但对核酸单链区具有非常高的特异性，这一点与林和莱曼制备的酶类似。通过改进雷宾、普赖斯和弗雷泽提出的步骤 [21]，我们已经分离出现有实验中使用的这种酶，并已证实它与以前所报道的 [13] 一样，都对单链核酸具有很高的特异性。

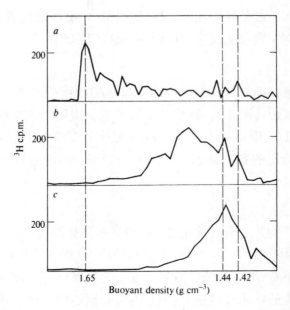

Fig. 3. Analysis in Cs₂SO₄ gradients of the product of purified avian myeloblastosis virus DNA polymerase copying 60–70S viral RNA. The polymerase was purified by disruption of the virions with 0.2% "Nonidet–P40", chromatography on "DEAE–Sephadex" and then chromatography on phosphocellulose. A yield of 44% of the initial activity was obtained using poly(C) · (dG)₁₄ as template-primer[10] and a purification of fifty times was achieved (I. M. V. and D. B., unpublished results). The 60–70S RNA was isolated by centrifugation through a sucrose gradient of purified avian myeloblastosis virus[10] disrupted with sodium dodecyl sulphate. The RNA was identified by absorbance at 260 nm and ethanol precipitated. Two μg of DNA polymerase and 5 μg of viral RNA were incubated at 37°C for 15 min in the reaction mixture described in Fig. 2, lacking detergent and virus. The product was purified as in Fig. 2 and contained 25,000 c.p.m. of ³H label. Portions were treated as in Fig. 2 and analysed as in Fig. 1. *a*, Native product; *b*, heat-denatured product; *c*, alkali-treated product.

These date indicate that the initial product of the endogenous DNA polymerase reaction of both MLV and AMV and of the reaction of purified AMV polymerase with AMV 60–70S RNA is a covalently bonded DNA–RNA molecule. Covalent bonding is indicated by the resistance of the product to boiling. The sensitivity of the boiled product to *Neurospora* nuclease and the change of density of the product after treatment with ribonuclease in 0.3 M NaCl indicate that little or no RNA remains hydrogen-bonded to the product DNA after heat denaturation. The ability of alkali and ribonuclease to convert the boiled product to material banding coincidentally with DNA indicates that RNA and not some other material was responsible for the density of the boiled product being greater than that of free DNA. The decreasing density of the boiled product with time of incubation (Fig. 2*b*) coupled with the increasing size of the DNA product indicated by its decreasing band width (Fig. 2*c*) suggest that a constant size piece of RNA is attached to a growing DNA strand.

The RNA in the product presumably acts as a primer for the endogenous reaction. Experiments utilizing the inhibition of the polymerase reaction by dideoxythymidine

852

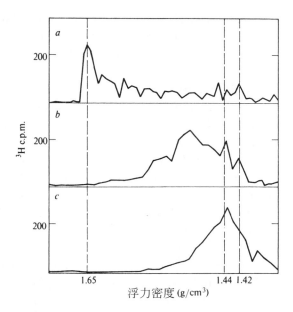

图 3. 用 Cs_2SO_4 梯度分析经提纯的禽成髓细胞瘤病毒 DNA 聚合酶复制 60–70S 病毒 RNA 的产物。先用 0.2%"诺乃洗涤剂 –P40"破坏病毒体，再经"DEAE– 葡聚糖"层析，最后用磷酸纤维素层析，以提纯聚合酶。使用聚（C)·(dG)₁₄作为模板引物[10]，获得的活性为初活性的 44%，并达到 50 倍的提纯（英德尔·维尔马和戴维·巴尔的摩，尚未发表的结果）。先用十二烷基硫酸钠破坏经提纯的禽成髓细胞瘤病毒[10]，再通过蔗糖梯度离心分离 60–70S RNA。通过 260 nm 紫外吸光率鉴别 RNA，再用乙醇使 RNA 沉淀。2 μg DNA 聚合酶和 5 μg 病毒 RNA 在 37℃条件下培养 15 min，反应混合物中的成分如图 2 注中所述，只是缺少洗涤剂和病毒。产物用图 2 描述的方法提纯，其中含有的 ³H 标记为 25,000 c.p.m.。按图 2 中的方式处理各份产物，并按图 1 的方法进行分析。a，原生产物；b，热变性的产物；c，碱液处理的产物。

这些数据表明：MLV 和 AMV 与内源 DNA 聚合酶反应的初产物，以及经提纯的 AMV 聚合酶与 AMV 60–70S RNA 反应的初产物，都是一种以共价键结合的 DNA–RNA 分子。产物对煮沸的耐受力说明它们是共价结合的。煮沸后产物对脉孢菌核酸酶的敏感性，以及用溶于 0.3 M NaCl 的核糖核酸酶处理后产物密度的变化，都说明：在热变性处理后，很少或几乎没有 RNA 能保持以氢键与产物中的 DNA 相结合。碱液和核糖核酸酶能使煮沸产物变成碰巧与 DNA 共同形成条带的物质，这说明：使煮沸产物的密度大于自由 DNA 的是 RNA，而不是其他物质。随着培养时间的增加，煮沸产物的密度不断减小（图 2b），加之不断变窄的带宽反映出 DNA 产物的体积在不断增加（图 2c），这些都说明有一条大小不变的 RNA 附着在一条持续增长的 DNA 链上。

产物中的 RNA 很可能在内源反应中作为引物。用双脱氧胸苷三磷酸抑制聚合酶反应的实验（斯莫勒、莫里纽克斯和巴尔的摩，已提请出版）表明，DNA 附着在

triphosphate (Smoler, Molineaux and Baltimore, submitted for publication) indicate that the DNA is attached to the 3′-OH of the primer RNA. Experiments are in progress to determine whether unique nucleotides in the DNA and RNA are linked.

The nature of the attached RNA is under investigation. Two models seem most likely. One is that the 60–70S bends back on itself to form a "hair pin" and that DNA synthesis is initiated on an end of 60–70S RNA. The sensitivity of boiled product to the *Neurospora* nuclease argues against this model because a "hair pin" structure should renature spontaneously. The second model invokes a small RNA primer and we favour this idea at present. The existence of transfer RNA species in the 60–70S RNA complex[17] suggests that they might serve this function. Previous evidence that multiple DNA molecules are formed from a single region of viral RNA[13] argues that multiple primer molecules may exist attached to the viral RNA.

The use of an RNA primer for initiating DNA synthesis might occur in systems other than the RNA tumour viruses. For example, an RNA molecule might serve the function of the postulated initiator in bacterial DNA synthesis[18,19]. Such an initiator molecule could be synthesized from a DNA template or could be formed by specific enzymes in the absence of a template.

This work was supported by a grant from the American Cancer Society and a contract from the Special Virus Cancer Program of the National Cancer Institute. I. M. V. was a fellow of the Jane Coffin Childs Memorial Fund for Medical Research, K. F. M. was a fellow of, and D. B. was a faculty research awardee of, the American Cancer Society.

(*Nature New Biology*, **233**, 131-134; 1971)

Inder M. Verma, Nora L. Meuth, Esther Bromfeld, Kenneth F. Manly and David Baltimore: Department of Biology, Massachusetts Institute of Technology, 77 Massachusetts Avenue, Cambridge, Massachusetts 02139.

Received August 19, 1971.

References:

1. Baltimore, D., *Nature*, **226**, 1209 (1970).

2. Temin, H., and Mizutani, S., *Nature*, **226**, 1211 (1970).

3. Spiegelman, S., Burny, A., Das, M. R., Keydar, J., Schlom, J., Travnicek, M., and Waston, K., *Nature*, **227**, 563 (1970).

4. Rokutanda, M., Rokutanda, H., Green, M., Fujinaga, K., Ray, R. K., and Gurgo, C., *Nature*, **227**, 1026 (1970).

5. Duesberg, P. H., and Canaani, E., *Virology*, **42**, 783 (1970).

6. Spiegelman, S., Burny, A., Das, M. R., Keydar, J., Schlom, J., Travnicek, M., and Watson, K., *Nature*, **227**, 1029 (1970).

7. Spiegelman, S., Burny, A., Das, M. R., Keydar, J., Schlom, J., Travnicek, M., and Waston, K., *Nature*, **228**, 430 (1970).

8. Mizutani, S., Boettiger, D., and Temin, H. M., *Nature*, **228**, 424 (1970).

9. Riman, J., and Beaudreau, G. S., *Nature*, **228**, 427 (1970).

10. Baltimore, D., and Smoler, D., *Proc. US Nat. Acad. Sci.*, **68**, 1507 (1971).

11. Baltimore, D., and Smoler, D., *Proc. Third Annual Miami Winter Biochemistry Symp.* (in the press).

引物 RNA 的 3′–OH 端。用以测定 DNA 和 RNA 中相连接的是否是某些特定核苷酸的实验正在进行中。

目前正在研究附着的 RNA 的性质。看起来有两个模型可能性最大。一个模型认为 60–70S 自身会弯曲，形成"发卡"，并且 DNA 合成始于 60–70S RNA 的一端。煮沸产物对脉孢菌核酸酶的敏感性不支持这一模型，因为"发卡"结构应该自发复性。第二个模型引入了一个小的 RNA 引物，目前我们更倾向于这种提法。在 60–70S RNA 复合体中存在转运 RNA 类型 [17] 说明转运 RNA 也许具有这一功能。此前有人发现多种 DNA 分子从病毒 RNA 的某一单区形成 [13]，这一证据表明，也许存在多种附着在病毒 RNA 上的引物分子。

使用 RNA 引物来启动 DNA 合成也许还会发生在除 RNA 肿瘤病毒以外的系统内。比如，在细菌的 DNA 合成中 [18,19]，或许就可以认为 RNA 分子具有启动子的功能。这种启动子分子能由 DNA 模板合成，在模板缺失的条件下也可以通过特异的酶合成。

这项工作得到了美国癌症协会的拨款并与国家癌症研究所特殊癌症病毒项目签订了合同。英德尔·维尔马是简·科芬·蔡尔兹医学研究纪念基金学院的成员，肯尼思·曼利是美国癌症协会的会员，戴维·巴尔的摩是美国癌症协会的一名教授研究奖的获得者。

（邓铭瑞 翻译；陈新文 陈继征 审稿）

12. Baltimore, D., Smoler, D., Manly, K. F., and Bromfeld, E., in Ciba Foundation Symp. *The Strategy of the Viral Genome* (Churchill, London, in the press).

13. Manly, K., Smoler, D. F., Bromfeld, E., and Baltimore, D., *J. Virol.*, 7, 106 (1971).

14. Fujinaga, K., Parsons, J. T., Beard, J. W., Beard, D., and Green, M., *Proc. US Nat. Acad. Sci.*, 67, 1432 (1970).

15. Garapin, A.-C., McDonnell, J. P., Levinson, W. E., Quintrell, N., Fanshier, L., and Bishop, J. M., *J. Virol.*, 6, 589 (1970).

16. Chamberlain, M., and Berg, P., *J. Mol. Biol.*, 8, 297 (1964).

17. Erikson, E., and Erikson, R. L., *J. Virol.* (in the press).

18. Jacob, F., and Brenner, S., *CR Acad. Sci.*, 256, 298 (1963).

19. Jacob, F., Brenner, S., and Cuzin, F., *Cold Spring Harbor Symp. Quant. Biol.*, 28, 329 (1963).

20. Linn, S., and Lehman, I. R., *J. Biol. Chem.*, 240, 1287 and 1294 (1965).

21. Rabin, Preiss and Fraser, *Preparative Biochemistry* (in the press).

Titration of Oral Nicotine Intake with Smoking Behaviour in Monkeys

S. D. Glick *et al.*

Editor's Note

By the 1970s, research had hinted that orally administered nicotine could decrease the desire to smoke, and Stanley D. Glick and colleagues had shown that monkeys trained to inhale cigarette smoke puffed less when treated with the nicotinic antagonist mecamylamine. Here Glick's team confirm this effect, and go on to show that combining oral nicotine with mecamylamine induces a profound drop in smoking behaviour. The results raised interesting questions about the role of nicotine in smoking, and the authors suggest nicotinic blockade rather than activation makes large doses of oral nicotine unpleasant. Blockage of nicotinic activating, presumably rewarding, actions of nicotine by mecamylamine would then allow non-rewarding blocking actions to predominate.

SEVERAL studies have indicated that nicotine is an incentive in smoking. Johnston[1] found that heavy smokers reported a pleasurable sensation when given nicotine, whereas nonsmokers reported an unpleasant effect. Lucchesi *et al.*[2] showed that intravenous administration of nicotine diminished the number of cigarettes smoked by heavy smokers. Jarvik *et al.*[3] found that oral nicotine administration produced a very small but significant decrease in the number of cigarettes smoked but because humans were used, they[3] were not able to use large doses of nicotine which might have produced larger decrements in smoking. Previous work in this laboratory with monkeys trained to puff cigarette smoke showed that mecamylamine, a nicotinic-blocking agent, reduced their smoking[4], and the work reported here was conducted to establish more definitely that orally administered nicotine could substitute for nicotine derived from smoking.

Four mature rhesus monkeys were trained to puff cigarette smoke. Only one (Phoebe) had served as a subject in the previous study with mecamylamine. Puffing behaviour was instilled initially by making the monkeys suck on a tube in order to drink. The mouthpiece of a cigarette smoking apparatus[5] was then substituted for the water tube. The smoking apparatus allowed a monkey to smoke lit cigarettes by automatically lighting each cigarette, spacing the cigarettes over time, and sensing changes in pressure as the monkey puffed. When the monkeys had learned to puff, they were so trained that they had to puff but were allowed to choose between smoke and air[6]. This procedure was developed to reduce the large variability from subject to subject inherent in free puffing.

A smoking apparatus was attached to a "Plexiglas" panel covering a 36 cm square opening in the door of each monkey's home cage. Two tubes, one delivering cigarette smoke and a "dummy" tube with access only to air, were also mounted on the panel. A water solenoid

口服尼古丁的摄入量与猴子的吸烟行为

格利克等

编者按

到 20 世纪 70 年代时，研究工作已经暗示，口服尼古丁有可能会降低烟瘾。斯坦利·格利克及其同事曾指出：在给予四甲双环庚胺这种尼古丁拮抗剂之后，受过香烟烟雾吸入训练的猴子会减少吸烟。在本文中，格利克的研究小组确认了上述效应，并进一步证实，口服尼古丁与注射四甲双环庚胺相结合会导致吸烟行为的显著下降。这些结果提出了关于尼古丁在吸烟中所起作用的有趣问题，本文作者认为是尼古丁的阻滞作用而非激活作用使口服大剂量尼古丁时产生不快的感受。尼古丁的激活作用可能是有快感的，在它被四甲双环庚胺阻断之后，就会让没有快感的阻滞作用占了上风。

　　一些研究指出，尼古丁是吸烟的一种诱因性刺激。约翰斯顿[1] 发现：重度吸烟者在接受了尼古丁之后会产生一种愉悦的感觉，而不吸烟者则报告说有不舒服的效果。卢凯西等人[2] 指出，静脉注射尼古丁可以减少重度吸烟者的吸烟量。亚尔维克等人[3] 发现，口服尼古丁可以使吸烟的支数发生很小但有意义的减少。尽管加大尼古丁剂量可能会造成更大的吸烟量减少，但因为是以人为实验对象，所以他们[3] 不能使用大剂量的尼古丁。本实验室以前用受过香烟烟雾吸入训练的猴子进行过实验，结果表明，一种尼古丁阻断剂——四甲双环庚胺可以减少猴子的吸烟量[4]。本文所报告的工作旨在更确切地证实口服尼古丁能够替代由吸烟摄入的尼古丁。

　　通过训练使四只成年恒河猴学会吸香烟的烟雾。其中只有一只（菲比）曾作为实验对象用于之前的四甲双环庚胺研究。这些猴子之所以养成了吸烟的习惯，是因为起初它们只能通过吸管才能喝到水。然后用吸烟装置的烟嘴[5] 来替代吸水管。为了让猴子吸到点着的烟，吸烟装置每间隔一定时间就自动点燃一支香烟，并能感知猴子吸气时的压力变化。如果猴子已经学过吸气，就要训练它们必须去吸，但可以选择是吸烟还是吸空气[6]。发展这种方法是为了减少个体与个体之间生来就具有的在自主吸气上的巨大差异。

　　在每只猴笼的门上开一个面积为 36 cm² 的洞口，吸烟装置就装在覆盖于洞口上的一个"普列克斯玻璃"面板上。面板上还装有两根管子，一根管子释放香烟产生的烟雾，另一根为"虚构"管，仅与空气连通。在吸烟管和空气管之间有一个控制

was mounted between the smoke and air tubes. A puff on either the smoke or air tubes preset the solenoid and would release a small amount of water when the monkey touched the solenoid spout. A light mounted above the solenoid signalled the availability of water. A fixed ratio (FR) contingency was added, so that a monkey could be required to puff a specific number of times to obtain water.

The monkeys received all their water during a daily 4 h puffing session. Thirty cigarettes were loaded into the smoking apparatus each morning and the test was started at 1030 h. A new cigarette was automatically lit every 7.5 min. The positions of the smoke and air tubes were interchanged each morning so that side preferences would not develop. Initially, water could be won with a single puff on either the smoke or air tube. The number of puffs for a reward of water was then increased to five, ten, twenty and finally to thirty. The FR 30 schedule was then maintained. Puffs were recorded on Sodeco counters.

All four monkeys preferred smoke to air; that is, although they could get water by puffing on either the smoke or the air tubes, they reliably took more puffs on the smoke tube than on the air tube. When puffing rates on the FR 30 schedule stabilized, the nicotine experiment was begun (except for the monkey used in the previous mecamylamine experiment[4]; the present experiment was started 2 months after completion of the previous experiment).

Various quantities (50 mg to 200 mg) of nicotine tartrate were dissolved in the water which each monkey obtained through puffing. The amount of nicotine on a given day was always dissolved in 700 ml. of water although the monkeys would usually consume only 300–400 ml. during a puffing session. Increasing dosages of nicotine were self-administered in this way with at least 4 days between successive nicotine trials. Each dose was repeated two or three times before starting a higher dose.

The results obtained from such oral nicotine administration are shown in Table 1. The data on days immediately preceding oral nicotine days were used as control data in paired t tests. For each monkey, doses of oral nicotine were found which significantly decreased and in some cases reversed the smoke–air preference without significantly affecting the overall puffing rate.

Table 1. Changes in Smoke Preference Induced by Oral Nicotine

Dose (mg)	Phoebe		Alex		Ivan		Dot	
	Total puffs	% pref.	Total puffs	% pref.	Total puffs	% pref.	Total puffs	% pref.
Control	6,103	88.7	4,844	86.4	2,786	87.2	4,322	91.1
50	6,509	87.5			2,594	87.0	3,666	88.3
75	6,466	91.0	5,191	90.0	3,465	87.0	4,437	86.0
100	6,400	92.0			3,453	75.0	4,754	81.5
125	5,784	64.1*	4,798	91.9	2,589	41.7*	4,308	14.8*
175			4,973	75.0				
225			4,623	56.7*				

* Significantly less than control at $P<0.05$.

进水的螺线管。不管是用吸烟管吸气还是用空气管吸气，都会使螺线管具有预设值，并在猴子触及螺线管的喷水口时释放出一小股水。螺线管上方的指示灯可以显示是否有水。还要引入事件发生的某个固定比值（FR），要求猴子需要吸特定的次数才能喝到水。

每天安排一个 4 小时的吸水时段，让猴子获取它们一天所需的所有水量。每天早上将 30 支香烟装入吸烟装置中，测试开始的时间是上午 10 点 30 分。吸烟装置每隔 7.5 分钟会自动点燃一支新的香烟。每天早上都要交换吸烟管和空气管的位置以防形成对某一侧的偏好。起先，吸一口吸烟管或空气管后都能得到水。随后为了喝到水需要吸的次数逐渐增加至 5 次、10 次、20 次，最后达到 30 次。然后维持 FR 比值在 30 次。用索迪科计数器记录吸的次数。

所有四只猴子都更愿意吸烟而不是吸空气；也就是说，尽管它们既可以通过吸吸烟管也可以通过吸空气管来获得水，但它们确实会多吸吸烟管，而不是空气管。一旦为喝到水猴子需要吸的次数稳定在 FR 值 30 次，尼古丁实验就可以开始了（除了那只先前曾用于四甲双环庚胺实验的猴子 [4]；本项实验在四甲双环庚胺实验结束 2 个月后开始）。

让每只猴子通过吸气获得溶解于水中的不同量的尼古丁酒石酸盐（50 mg ～ 200 mg）。在某一天所给予的一定剂量的尼古丁总是被溶于 700 ml 水中，不过猴子在一个吸水时段内通常只能消耗 300 ml ～ 400 ml 水。用这种方式让猴子自主服用剂量逐渐增加的尼古丁，两次尼古丁实验之间至少间隔 4 天。针对每个剂量都会重复 2 ～ 3 次实验，然后才开始使用更高的剂量。

由这样的口服尼古丁实验得到的结果见表 1。在配对 t 检验中，用口服尼古丁之前一天的数据作为对照数据。从表中的数据可以看出：对每只猴子来说，都存在一个口服尼古丁的剂量，这个剂量能明显降低甚至在某些情况下会逆转猴子对香烟 - 空气的偏好，而不显著影响猴子的总吸入量。

表 1. 口服尼古丁引起的吸烟偏好的变化

剂量	菲比		亚历克斯		伊万		多特	
	总吸入量	偏好率 %	总吸入量	偏好率 %	总吸入量	偏好率 %	总吸入量	偏好率 %
对照	6,103	88.7	4,844	86.4	2,786	87.2	4,322	91.1
50	6,509	87.5			2,594	87.0	3,666	88.3
75	6,466	91.0	5,191	90.0	3,465	87.0	4,437	86.0
100	6,400	92.0			3,453	75.0	4,754	81.5
125	5,784	64.1*	4,798	91.9	2,589	41.7*	4,308	14.8*
175			4,973	75.0				
225			4,623	56.7*				

* 显著低于对照组，$P<0.05$。

One additional drug trial was conducted with one of the monkeys. Because previous work had shown that mecamylamine inhibited monkeys' smoking, it was of interest to determine whether mecamylamine would antagonize the inhibition of smoking by orally administered nicotine, that is, whether the combination would depress smoking behaviour less than either treatment alone. For this purpose, the monkey used in the previous mecamylamine experiment as well as the more recent oral nicotine experiment was used again. A dose of 125 mg of nicotine tartrate was administered orally as already described. In addition, a dose of 0.8 mg/kg of mecamylamine was given intramuscularly 15 min before the beginning of the same puffing session. This combination was repeated twice. Thereafter, two administrations of the mecamylamine alone were conducted. The results are shown in Table 2. All three treatments—oral nicotine alone, mecamylamine alone and the combination—produced significant inhibition of smoking behaviour. Only mecamylamine alone and the combination significantly decreased overall puffing. Most surprising, however, was the finding that the inhibition of smoking produced by the combination was significantly greater ($P<0.05$) than that produced by either drug treatment alone.

Table 2. Changes in Smoke Preference of Phoebe induced by Oral Nicotine (125 mg) and/or Mecamylamine (0.8 mg/kg)

	Total puff	% pref.
Control	6,055	88.2
Nicotine	5,784	64.1*
Mecamylamine	4,842*	65.5*
Nicotine+mecamylamine	3,358*	33.5*

* Significantly less than control at $P<0.05$.

These results raise interesting questions about the role of nicotine in smoking. If oral nicotine depressed smoking by providing a greater than optimal level of nicotine, such that additional nicotine derived from smoking was aversive, then mecamylamine should have antagonized rather than potentiated this effect. However, different central actions of nicotine may have been responsible. Perhaps the aversiveness produced by the large oral nicotine doses was a function of nicotinic blockade rather than of activation.[7] Blockage of nicotinic activating, presumably rewarding, actions of nicotine by mecamylamine would then allow non-rewarding blocking actions to predominate. Clinical studies are being conducted in this laboratory to evaluate the therapeutic significance of this hypothesis.

This work was supported by grants from the US National Institute of Mental Health and the American Cancer Society.

(**233**, 207-208; 1971)

S. D. Glick*, B. Zimmerberg and M. E. Jarvik: Department of Pharmacology and Psychiatry, Albert Einstein College of Medicine, 1300 Morris Park Avenue, Bronx, New York 10461.

Received June 21, 1971.

* Present address: Department of Pharmacology, Mount Sinai School of Medicine, New York, NY, 10029.

　　我们还对其中一只猴子进行了额外的药物实验。因为之前的实验结果已经表明四甲双环庚胺会抑制猴子吸烟，所以我们很想知道四甲双环庚胺会不会拮抗口服尼古丁对吸烟的抑制，也就是说，这两种处理相结合对吸烟行为的抑制作用是否会比单独给予任意一种时更小。出于这个目的，那只在以前的实验中接受过四甲双环庚胺并在最近的实验中口服过尼古丁的猴子被再次使用。按照前述方法，让这只猴子口服 125 mg 的尼古丁酒石酸盐。另外，在开始同一吸烟实验之前 15 分钟时，给猴子肌肉注射剂量为 0.8 mg/kg 的四甲双环庚胺。这种联合用药的方式被重复了两次。然后再让猴子只注射四甲双环庚胺两次。实验结果见表 2。三种处理方式——仅口服尼古丁、仅注射四甲双环庚胺和两者同时使用都产生了对吸烟行为的显著抑制作用。只有在单独使用四甲双环庚胺和同时使用两者时会显著减少总吸入量。然而，最令人惊讶的是，我们发现在两者合用时所产生的对吸烟的抑制作用要远远大于（$P<0.05$）仅使用其中某一种处理时的效果。

表 2. 口服尼古丁（125 mg）和 / 或四甲双环庚胺（0.8 mg/kg）引起的猴子菲比的吸烟偏好变化

	总吸入量	偏好率 %
对照	6,055	88.2
尼古丁	5,784	64.1*
四甲双环庚胺	4,842*	65.5*
尼古丁 + 四甲双环庚胺	3,358*	33.5*

* 显著低于对照组，$P<0.05$。

　　这些结果提出了关于尼古丁在吸烟中所起作用的有趣问题。如果口服尼古丁对吸烟的抑制作用是由于提供了超过最佳水平的尼古丁，因而通过吸烟得到的额外的尼古丁就会使人产生不快的感觉，那么四甲双环庚胺应该是拮抗而不是加强了这种作用。然而，尼古丁的其他重要功用也有可能是产生原因。或许由口服大剂量尼古丁所产生的不快的感觉代表的是尼古丁的阻滞作用而不是激活作用 [7]。尼古丁的激活作用可能是有快感的，在它被四甲双环庚胺阻断之后，就会让没有快感的阻滞作用占了上风。为了评估这个假设对治疗烟瘾的意义，本实验室正在进行临床研究。

　　美国国立精神健康研究所和美国癌症协会为这项研究提供了经费上的支持。

（董培智 翻译；顾孝诚 审稿）

References:
1. Johnston, L. M., *Lancet*, ii, 742 (1942).
2. Lucchesi, B. R., Schuster, C. R., and Emley, G. S., *Clin. Pharmacol. Ther.*, **8**, 789 (1967).
3. Jarvik, M. E., Glick, S. D., and Nakamura, R. K., *Clin. Pharmacol. Ther.*, **11**, 574 (1970).
4. Glick, S. D., Jarvik, M. E., and Nakamura, R. K., *Nature*, **227**, 969 (1970).
5. Pybus, R., Goldfarb, T., and Jarvik, M. E., *Exp. Anal. Behav.*, **12**, 88 (1969).
6. Glick, S. D., Canfield, J. L., and Jarvik, M. E., *Psychol. Rep.*, **26**, 707 (1970).
7. Goodman, L. S., and Gilman, A., *The Pharmacological Basis of Therapeutics*, 585 (Macmillan, London, 1965).

Redistribution and Pinocytosis of Lymphocyte Surface Immunoglobulin Molecules Induced by Anti-Immunoglobulin Antibody

R. B. Taylor *et al.*

Editor's Note

Here Roger Taylor and colleagues use fluorescent-labelled antibodies to visualize immunoglobulin molecules on the surface of lymphocytes. In a normal cell the molecules are diffusely scattered, but when the antibody binds, the immunoglobulin molecules gather over one pole of the cell and are then brought inside. This rapid clearing of immunoglobulin from the cell surface provided an explanation for "antigenic modulation", where cell-surface antigens "disappear" following incubation with antibodies. A similar mechanism has since been implicated in the control of many cell-surface receptors following the binding of their extracellular ligand. The paper also suggested that cell membranes are two-dimensional fluids that can traffic molecules around, changing the way researchers thought about membrane structure and function.

IMMUNOGLOBULIN (Ig) determinants, presumably functioning as antigen receptors, can be demonstrated on the surface of lymphocytes in various ways[1]. The distribution of Ig determinants on the cell surface, when living lymphocytes have been studied in suspension with fluoresceinated anti-Ig antibodies, has been variably reported as diffuse and patchy, giving a spotted or ring-like appearance[2] (Fig. 1a), or polar, giving a crescent or cap-like appearance over one pole of the cell[3,4] (Fig. 1b). Immunoferritin electron microscopy showed that the difference in distribution was temperature dependent and that the former pattern was seen when cells were studied at $0°C$, while the latter was seen at $20°C$ (S. de P. and M. C. R., unpublished work). Using immunofluorescence, we demonstrate here that the distribution on resting lymphocytes is diffuse, while the polar distribution is induced by the interaction of the anti-Ig antibodies with the Ig molecules of the cell membrane. Following this redistribution the Ig molecules are pinocytosed. This sequence of events is temperature dependent and suggests an explanation for antigenic modulation, a possible mechanism for lymphocyte triggering by antibody, mitogens and antigen, and raises important questions about the structure of mammalian cell membranes.

抗免疫球蛋白抗体诱导的淋巴细胞表面免疫球蛋白分子的重分布和胞饮现象

泰勒 等

编者按

这里，罗杰·泰勒和同事们利用荧光素标记的抗体来观察淋巴细胞表面的免疫球蛋白分子。在正常细胞中，这类分子呈现为弥散分布；然而当与抗体结合时，免疫球蛋白分子就会聚集到细胞的一极，并被带到细胞内部。这种免疫球蛋白分子从细胞表面快速清除的现象为"抗原调变"提供了解释。"抗原调变"指的是：在细胞与抗体孵育之后，细胞表面的抗原会"消失"。在结合细胞外配体后，很多细胞表面受体的调制也牵涉到了与之相似的机制。这篇论文还提示细胞膜是可以转运分子使之移动的二维液体，这改变了以往研究者考虑膜结构及其功能的思维方式。

免疫球蛋白决定簇，其功能很可能如抗原受体一样，能在淋巴细胞表面以多种方式表现出来 [1]。当用荧光素标记的抗免疫球蛋白抗体研究悬浮液中的活淋巴细胞时，所报道的关于免疫球蛋白决定簇在细胞表面的分布并不一致。一种是弥散或斑块分布，显示为点状或环状 [2]（图 1a）；另一种是极性的，显示为集中在细胞一极的新月状或冠状 [3,4]（图 1b）。采用免疫铁蛋白技术在电子显微镜下观察，结果显示分布的不同是由温度决定的，前一种分布是在 0℃ 下研究的细胞中被发现的，而后一种是在 20℃ 下被观察到的（斯特凡内洛·德·彼得里斯和马丁·拉夫，尚未发表的研究结果）。利用免疫荧光的方法，我们在此展示了它在静止淋巴细胞上的分布是弥散的，而极性分布是由抗免疫球蛋白抗体与细胞膜上的免疫球蛋白分子之间的相互作用引起的。随着这种重分布，免疫球蛋白分子被胞饮掉。这一系列依赖于温度的现象暗示了对抗原调变的一种解释（抗原调变是淋巴细胞在抗体、促细胞分裂剂和抗原作用下被激发出的一种可能的机制），并提出了若干关于哺乳动物细胞膜结构的重要问题。

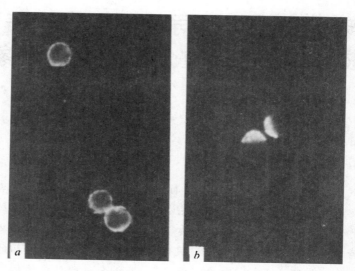

Fig. 1. Pattern of immunofluorescence in mouse spleen cells incubated in R anti-MIg-Fl in VBS for 30 min, (*a*) at 0°C ("ring" pattern), (*b*) at room temperature ("cap" pattern). The cells were washed and examined at room temperature in the presence of 3×10^{-3} M sodium azide.

Most of these studies were carried out independently in two laboratories. Since the results were in complete agreement we publish them here together.

CBA spleen cell suspensions were prepared by teasing in veronal buffered saline with 0.1% bovine serum albumin (VBS), Leibovitz medium[5] with 10% foetal calf serum (L-15) or phosphate-buffered balanced salt solution (BSS)[6]. Anti-Ig sera were prepared, fractionated, conjugated with fluorescein and sometimes purified, as previously described[3,4]. The sera used and the preparation of univalent Fab fragments are described in Table 1. Anti-θC3H (anti-θ), anti-H-2[k] and anti-lymphocyte serum (ALS) were prepared as previously described[7,8]. Direct and indirect immunofluorescent staining was carried out, using 25 μl. of live spleen cells (10–20×10[6] cells/ml.) and 25 μl. of antiserum at concentrations indicated in Table 1, unless otherwise specified[3]. Cells were examined in suspension under coverslip with ultraviolet or blue-violet light, and the percentage of leucocytes stained and those showing "caps" and "ring" staining was determined. Cells were counted as "caps" if the fluorescence was at one pole and occupied one half or less of the surface. Cells were counted as "rings" when fluorescence occupied the entire surface or was broken up into patches without obvious polar distribution.

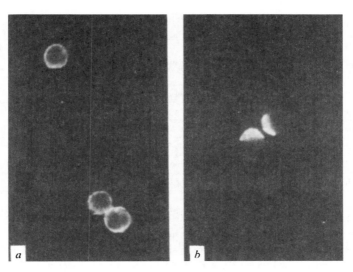

图 1. 在 VBS 中与兔抗鼠免疫球蛋白荧光标记物共孵育 30 min 后小鼠脾细胞的免疫荧光检测结果，(a)
在 0℃时（呈"环状"分布），(b) 在室温下（呈"冠状"分布）。对细胞的冲洗和检测是在室温下、
有浓度为 3×10⁻³ M 叠氮化钠存在的情况下进行的。

这些研究大多是在两个实验室中独立进行的。由于结果完全一致，我们在此将
其一并公布。

将撕碎的脾浸泡在由巴比妥缓冲的含 0.1% 牛血清白蛋白的生理盐水（VBS）或
含 10% 胎牛血清的莱博维茨培养基（L-15）[5] 或由磷酸盐缓冲的平衡盐溶液（BSS）[6]
中，制得 CBA 脾细胞悬浮液（译者注：CBA 是一种小鼠品系，这种品系具有较低
的肿瘤发生率）。按已描述过的方法 [3,4] 制备抗免疫球蛋白血清、层析、与荧光素结
合，有时还需要提纯。使用的血清和单价抗原结合片段的制备方法如表 1 所述。按
照以前描述过的方法 [7,8] 准备好抗 θC3H（抗 θ）、抗 H-2ᵏ 和抗淋巴细胞血清（ALS）。
如果没有特别说明，用 25 μl 活脾细胞（每 ml 含 10×10⁶ ~ 20×10⁶ 个细胞）和 25 μl
如表 1 所示浓度的抗血清直接或间接进行免疫荧光染色 [3]。盖上盖玻片用紫外光或
蓝紫光照射。对处于悬浮状态的细胞进行检验，分别测定染上色的、显现出"冠状"
和"环状"染色的白细胞的百分比。如果荧光集中在一极并占据了一半或更少的表面，
那么对应的细胞就被计入"冠状"。当荧光占据了整个细胞表面或破散成没有明显极
性分布的斑点时，则被计入"环状"。

Table 1. Properties of Antisera

Antiserum	Fluoresceinated	Abbreviation	Protein used	Usual concentration used (mg/ml.)	
				Protein	Antibody
Rabbit anti-mouse Ig	+	R anti-MIg-Fl	γG*	5	–
Rabbit anti-mouse Ig	–	R anti-MIg	γG*	6.1	0.21
Rabbit anti-mouse Ig	–	Fab R anti-MIg	Fab- γG†	5.7	0.19
Goat anti-mouse Ig	+	G anti-MIg-Fl	Purified antibody‡	0.08	~0.05
Goat anti-mouse Ig	+	Fab G anti-MIg-Fl	Fab-purified antibody§	0.08	~0.05
Goat anti-rabbit Ig	+	G anti-RIg-Fl	γG*	1	–

* Prepared by fractionation on DEAE–cellulose (in 0.02 M phosphate buffer and 0.01 M NaCl at pH 7.5) after precipitation with 50% saturated ammonium sulphate.

† The R anti-MIg γG was digested by papain (one part papain to 100 parts γG (w/w)) in the presence of 0.01 M mercaptoethanol for 18 h at 37°C and the Fab fragments were separated on "Sephadex G-100".

‡ G anti-MIg or G anti-MIg-Fl was purified by elution from "Sepharose" immunoabsorbent columns[33].

§ Purified G anti-MIg was digested as above in the presence of 0.005 M dithiothreitol for 4 h. The Fab fragments were separated as above and conjugated as previously described[3].

Direct and indirect immunofluorescence testing gave similar results except where indicated, and results using various anti-MIg sera and various media were not significantly different. Although we only illustrate representative experiments in the tables and figures, each type of experiment was done at least twice and gave consistent results.

Redistribution of Surface Ig Determinants

As previously reported[3], approximately 30–50% of spleen cells could be demonstrated to have surface Ig by immunofluorescence. When cells were treated at 0°C, surface fluorescence was entirely ring-like (Fig. 1a). If the procedure was carried out at room temperature, or 37°C, the percentage of stained cells was the same, but most showed cap fluorescence (Fib. 1b). Cap staining frequently overlaid a foot-like projection of the cell; the uropod[9]. Ring cells which had been stained at 0°C transformed into cap cells when warmed (Fig. 2). The transformation from ring-staining to cap-staining was rapid at 37°C (50% by 1.5 min) and considerably slower at 24°C (50% by 4 min). Increasing the concentration of BSA to 5% slowed cap formation to some extent (50% by 5 min at 24°C), but even in neat foetal calf serum, cap formation occurred rapidly. Transformation to caps could be observed in individual ring-staining cells when they were warmed under a coverslip.

表 1. 抗血清的性质

抗血清	是否荧光染色	缩写	使用的蛋白质	通常使用浓度 (mg/ml)	
				蛋白质	抗体
兔抗鼠免疫球蛋白	+	R 抗 –MIg–Fl	γ 球蛋白 *	5	—
兔抗鼠免疫球蛋白	–	R 抗 –MIg	γ 球蛋白 *	6.1	0.21
兔抗鼠免疫球蛋白	–	Fab R 抗 –MIg	抗原结合片段 –γ 球蛋白 †	5.7	0.19
山羊抗鼠免疫球蛋白	+	G 抗 –MIg–Fl	纯化抗体 ‡	0.08	~ 0.05
山羊抗鼠免疫球蛋白	+	Fab G 抗 –MIg–Fl	纯化抗体的抗原结合片段 §	0.08	~ 0.05
山羊抗兔免疫球蛋白	+	G 抗 –RIg–Fl	γ 球蛋白 *	1	—

* 用 50% 饱和硫酸铵沉淀后，经二乙氨基乙基纤维素（洗脱剂为 pH 值 7.5 的 0.02 M 磷酸盐缓冲液和 0.01 M 氯化钠）层析制得。

† 将兔抗鼠免疫球蛋白 γ 球蛋白在 37℃、0.01 M 巯基乙醇存在的条件下用木瓜蛋白酶（1 份木瓜蛋白酶 对应 100 份 γ 球蛋白（重量比））消化 18 h，得到的抗原结合片段在"葡聚糖 G-100"上分离。

‡ 山羊抗鼠免疫球蛋白或山羊抗鼠免疫球蛋白荧光标记物经"琼脂糖"免疫吸附柱洗脱提纯 [33]。

§ 提纯后的山羊抗鼠免疫球蛋白按如上条件在 0.005 M 二硫苏糖醇存在的条件下消化 4 h。抗原结合片 段的分离方法如上所述并照以前描述过的方法结合 [3]。

除另有说明的以外，直接和间接的免疫荧光检验都给出了相似的结果；当使用多种抗鼠免疫球蛋白血清和多种培养基时，结果也没有表现出显著差异。虽然我们在图表中只举例说明了具有代表性的实验，但每种实验都至少重复过一次且都给出了一致的结果。

表面免疫球蛋白决定簇的重分布

根据之前发表的报告 [3]，大约有 30% ~ 50% 的脾细胞可以被免疫荧光检验法证实拥有表面免疫球蛋白。当细胞在 0℃ 下被处理时，表面荧光为完整的环状（图 1 a）。如果这个过程是在室温或 37℃ 下进行的，则虽然被染色细胞的百分比没有变化，但大多数表现为冠状荧光（图 1b）。冠状染色经常覆盖在细胞的一个足状凸出物上，即尾足 [9]。0℃ 时被染色的环状细胞，在加热的情况下会转变为冠状细胞（图 2）。这种由环状染色变为冠状染色的转化在 37℃ 时相当迅速（50% 需要 1.5 min），而在 24℃ 时则要慢得多（50% 需要 4 min）。增加牛血清白蛋白的浓度至 5% 可以在一定程度上减缓冠状染色的形成（50% 在 24℃ 时需要 5 min），但即使是在纯胎牛血清中，冠状形成也会很快发生。在盖玻片下加热时，可以观察到单个的环状染色细胞转化为冠状细胞。

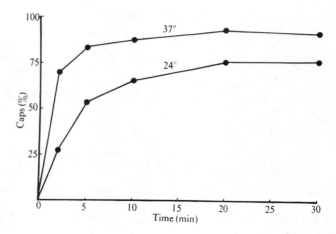

Fig. 2. Rate of cap formation at 37°C and 24°C. Cells were incubated in R anti-MIg-Fl in VBS for 30 min at 0°C, washed at 0°C and then warmed to 37°C or 24°C in a water bath. After the specified time the cells were cooled, 3×10^{-2} M sodium azide was added and the percentage of staining cells which showed cap formation was determined.

When spleen cells were treated with ferritin-labelled anti-MIg and examined by electron microscopy the same phenomenon was observed (unpublished work of S. de P. and M. C. R.). At 0°C the ferritin labelling was patchy and diffusely distributed over the cell surface. At 20°C the labelling was confluent and located over one pole of the cell, which contained the Golgi apparatus when this was visible in the section. As the total surface ferritin labelling was approximately the same at 0°C and at 20°C, cap formation must be the result of a redistribution of labelled Ig determinants which tend to gather over the Golgi pole of the cell.

Mechanism of Cap Formation

As Fig. 3 shows, cap formation was completely inhibited at 20°C by sodium azide; the inhibition was dose-dependent and readily reversible. At 37°C inhibition was 97% at 10^{-2} M and complete at 3×10^{-2} M. Dinitrophenol also inhibited cap formation and inhibition was complete at 10^{-3} M at 20°C, but was still reversible at 10^{-2} M. Thus, cap formation is a metabolically dependent active process. As cells warmed at 37°C and then treated with anti-MIg-Fl in the presence of azide showed only ring-staining, cap formation must be induced by the interaction of the anti-Ig antibody with the Ig molecules of the surface membrane, and not by increased temperature alone.

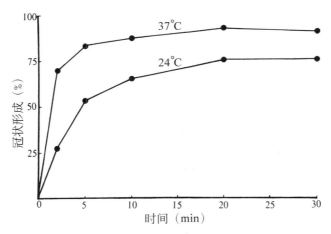

图 2. 37℃和 24℃下冠状形成的比例。将浸泡在 VBS 中的细胞在 0℃下与兔抗鼠免疫球蛋白荧光标记物
共孵育 30 min，在 0℃下冲洗后，再用水浴加热到 37℃或 24℃。等细胞经过一定时间的自然冷却后，
加入浓度为 3×10^{-2} M 的叠氮化钠并测定呈冠状染色的细胞的百分比。

当脾细胞用铁蛋白标记的抗鼠免疫球蛋白处理后，在电子显微镜下也能观察到同样的现象（斯特凡内洛·德·彼得里斯和马丁·拉夫，尚未发表的研究结果）。0℃时，铁蛋白标记在细胞表面表现为斑点和弥散分布。在 20℃时，标记汇合于细胞的一极，当这种情况出现时从剖面图可以看到这个位置包含有高尔基体。因为在 0℃和 20℃时表面上铁蛋白标记的总数大致相同，所以冠状形成必定是带有标记的免疫球蛋白决定簇重分布的结果，这种重分布趋向于集中在细胞含高尔基体的一极。

冠状形成的机理

如图 3 所示，冠状形成在 20℃时完全被叠氮化钠抑制；这种抑制是剂量依赖的并且很容易逆转。在 37℃时 10^{-2} M 叠氮化钠对冠状形成的抑制率达到 97%，浓度为 3×10^{-2} M 时完全抑制。二硝基酚也会抑制冠状形成，20℃时 10^{-3} M 就可以达到完全抑制，但在浓度为 10^{-2} M 时抑制依然是可逆的。因此，冠状形成是一个取决于新陈代谢的活性过程。因为细胞在 37℃加热后再在叠氮化物存在的条件下用抗鼠免疫球蛋白荧光标记物处理只显示出了环状染色，所以冠状形成必须由抗免疫球蛋白抗体和膜表面的免疫球蛋白分子之间的相互作用诱导，而不能仅由温度的增加诱导。

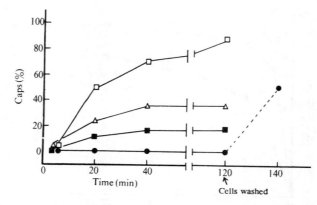

Fig. 3. Reversible inhibition of cap formation by sodium azide. Cells were incubated in sodium azide in
BSS for 15 min at 20°C before G anti-MIg-Fl was added. Cells were sampled at specified times and
the percentage of staining cells which showed cap formation was determined. After 2 h the cells in
10^{-3} and 10^{-2} M azide were washed and reincubated in BSS for another 20 min. Concentrations of
sodium azide were 10^{-3} M (●), 10^{-4} M (■), 10^{-5} M (△), control (□). Experimental points at
10^{-2} M were coincident with those at 10^{-3} M.

Univalent Fab fragments (prepared by digesting G anti-MIg with papain[10] and labelling
with fluorescein (Table 1)) stained the same percentage of spleen cells as undigested G
anti-MIg-Fl but did not induce cap formation (Table 2). Also, ring fluorescence with the
Fab antibody was invariably smooth and complete and never showed the granular or
patchy distribution seen with bivalent antibody. When unlabelled Fab R anti-MIg was
used as a middle layer in indirect testing with G anti-RIg-Fl, where the final staining with
the latter reagent was done at 0°C in the presence of azide, no caps were formed, but the
rings were generally granular. However, if the G anti-RIg-Fl was added without azide
at 37°C, then caps were induced (Table 2). It seems likely that multivalent binding and
lattice formation at the cell surface are required for cap formation. The lack of patchy
fluorescence seen with Fab G anti-MIg-Fl suggests that the patchy distribution of surface
Ig determinants may also be induced by multivalent binding of the anti-Ig antibody and
demands caution in the interpretation of patchy distribution of other surface antigens
such as H-2 when observed with multivalent labelled antibodies[11].

Table 2. Failure of Cap Formation with Fab-anti-Ig

Experiment No.	Type of immunofluorescence testing	Type of anti-MIg	% cells stained	% caps
1	Direct at 20°C*	G anti-MIg-Fl	25	75
		Fab G anti-MIg-Fl	23	0
2	Indirect with† development at 0°C	R anti-MIg	43	70
		Fab R anti-MIg	45	0
3	Indirect with† development at 37°C	Fab R anti-MIg	46	52

* Cells were incubated at 20°C for 40 min. The Fab-G anti-MIg-Fl was tested over a wide range of
concentrations (0.001 to 1 mg/ml.) with similar results.

† Cells were incubated in R anti-MIg for 20 min at 37°C, washed and incubated with G anti-RIg-Fl at
0°C for 30 min or 37°C for 20 min. Undigested anti-MIg and Fab fragments were used at an antibody
concentration of about 0.2 mg/ml.

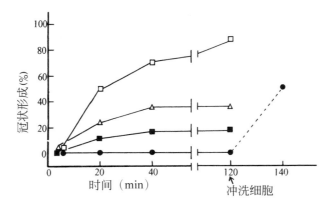

图 3. 叠氮化钠对冠状形成的可逆抑制。在加入山羊抗鼠免疫球蛋白荧光标记物之前将细胞置于 20℃ 下的含叠氮化钠的 BSS 中孵育 15 min。在特定时间抽取细胞样本并对染色细胞中出现冠状形成的百分比进行测定。2 h 后对用 10^{-3} M 和 10^{-2} M 叠氮化物处理的细胞进行冲洗并再一次在 BSS 中孵育 20 min。叠氮化钠的浓度为 10^{-3} M（●）、10^{-4} M（■）、10^{-5} M（△）和对照（□）。用 10^{-2} M 叠氮化钠处理得到的实验点与 10^{-3} M 的点重合。

与未经消化的山羊抗鼠免疫球蛋白荧光标记物相比，单价抗原结合片段（制备方法是：用木瓜蛋白酶消化山羊抗鼠免疫球蛋白[10]并进行荧光标记（表 1））可以使同样百分比的脾细胞染色，但没有引起冠状形成（表 2）。此外，由该抗原结合片段抗体染色导致的环状荧光总是很平滑，完全不会出现由二价抗体染色时表现出的颗粒状或斑点状分布。当在间接免疫荧光检验中用未标记的兔抗鼠免疫球蛋白的抗原结合片段作为中间层、然后用山羊抗兔免疫球蛋白荧光标记物作染色剂进行检测时，在 0℃ 且有叠氮化物存在的条件下，无冠状形成，但环状荧光一般为颗粒状。然而，如果山羊抗兔免疫球蛋白荧光标记物是在 37℃、没有叠氮化物的情况下加入的，则会引起冠状现象（表 2）。这似乎表明冠状形成需要多价结合和在细胞表面形成晶格结构。用山羊抗鼠免疫球蛋白抗原结合片段荧光标记物进行染色时未发现斑点荧光，这说明表面免疫球蛋白决定簇的斑状分布可能也是由抗免疫球蛋白抗体的多价结合引起的，在用多价标记抗体进行观察时，需要注意对诸如 H-2 等其他表面抗原引起的斑状分布的解释[11]。

表 2. 用抗免疫球蛋白抗原结合片段不能导致冠状分布的形成

实验编号	免疫荧光检验法的类型	抗鼠免疫球蛋白的类型	染色的细胞%	冠状形成%
1	在 20℃ 下进行，直接 *	山羊抗鼠免疫球蛋白荧光标记物	25	75
		山羊抗鼠免疫球蛋白抗原结合片段荧光标记物	23	0
2	在 0℃ 下进行，间接 †	兔抗鼠免疫球蛋白	43	70
		兔抗鼠免疫球蛋白抗原结合片段	45	0
3	在 37℃ 下进行，间接 †	兔抗鼠免疫球蛋白抗原结合片段	46	52

＊ 将细胞在 20℃ 下孵育 40 min。用山羊抗鼠免疫球蛋白抗原结合片段荧光标记物在宽浓度范围内（0.001 mg/ml ~ 1 mg/ml）检验时所得的结果类似。

† 将细胞在 37℃ 下用兔抗鼠免疫球蛋白孵育 20 min，冲洗并在 0℃ 下用山羊抗兔免疫球蛋白荧光标记物孵育 30 min 或在 37℃ 下孵育 20 min。未经消化的抗鼠免疫球蛋白和其抗原结合片段的抗体使用浓度大约为 0.2 mg/ml。

If cap formation depends on lattice formation, inhibition of cap formation would be expected with increasing concentrations of anti-MIg (prozone effect), as in immunoprecipitation reactions. As Fig. 4 shows, cap formation decreased in the presence of high concentrations of anti-MIg.

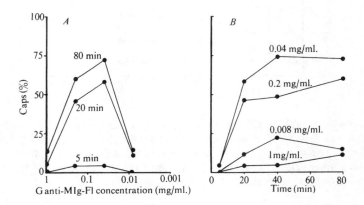

Fig. 4. Effect of anti-MIg concentration on the rate of cap formation. Cells were incubated at 20°C with various concentrations of G anti-MIg-Fl (purified antibody) for 5, 20, 40 and 80 min. Cells were washed at 4°C and examined immediately. The percentage of stained cells showing cap formation is plotted against antibody concentration (A) to emphasize the prozone effect with high antibody concentration, and against time (B) to illustrate the effect of protein concentration on the rate of cap formation. About 48% of the cells were stained at the antibody concentration of 1 mg/ml., 35% at 0.2 and 0.04 mg/ml., and 26% at 0.008 mg/ml.

In view of the frequent association of the caps with the lymphocyte uropod, it seemed possible that cap formation was somehow associated with membrane flow and cell motility. Cytochalasin B, which is claimed to specifically inhibit a contractile microfilament system responsible for cell movement[12], consistently inhibited cap formation, but only partially, even at high concentrations, and the effect was reversible (Table 3). After treatment with colcemid the cells looked very irregular but cap formation was not affected, suggesting that micro-tubular activity is not involved[13] (Table 3). To determine if cells free in suspension, without contact with substrate, could form caps, cells were kept in suspension at a concentration of 1.5×10^6/ml. by continuous stirring in the presence of R anti-MIg-Fl and then washed in the presence of azide. No significant inhibition of cap formation could be demonstrated. Pre-incubating cells at room temperature or at 37°C for 30 min in calcium-free medium in the presence of up to 4 mM of ethylene glycol-*bis* (2-amino ethyl ether)-tetra-acetic acid (EGTA), or calcium and magnesium-free medium in the presence of up to 4 mM ethylene diamino-tetra-acetic acid (EDTA) (at an estimated[14] free Ca^{2+} concentration of less than $1-5 \times 10^{-8}$), and treating and washing cells in the same conditions did not significantly inhibit cap formation.

如果冠状形成依靠晶格结构的形成，那么就会如同在免疫沉淀反应中一样，可以期望通过增加抗鼠免疫球蛋白的浓度而达到对冠状形成的抑制（前带效应）。如图4所示，在抗鼠免疫球蛋白浓度较高时冠状形成有所减少。

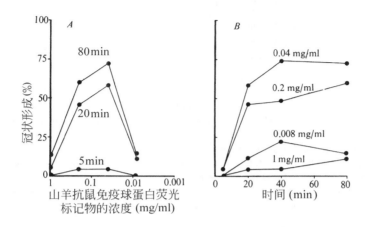

图 4. 抗鼠免疫球蛋白浓度对冠状形成比例的影响。将细胞在 20℃ 下用多种浓度的山羊抗鼠免疫球蛋白荧光标记物（纯化抗体）孵育 5 min、20 min、40 min 和 80 min。在 4℃ 下冲洗细胞并立即进行检验。将染色细胞中出现冠状形成的百分比对抗体浓度作图（*A*）以突出由高浓度抗体带来的前带效应，并对时间作图（*B*）以说明蛋白质浓度对冠状形成比例的影响。大约 48% 的细胞在抗体浓度为 1 mg/ml、35% 的细胞在 0.2 mg/ml 和 0.04 mg/ml 以及 26% 的细胞在 0.008 mg/ml 时被染色。

从冠状现象和淋巴细胞尾足经常会同时出现这一角度考虑，冠状形成看起来同膜流动性和细胞运动性之间可能存在着某种关系。细胞松弛素 B 被认为可以特异性破坏与细胞运动有关的、有收缩性的微丝系统 [12]，它能持续地抑制冠状形成，但只是部分抑制，甚至在高浓度下这种影响也是可逆的（表 3）。在用秋水仙酰胺处理后，细胞看起来十分不规则，但冠状形成并没有受到影响，说明这同微管活性无关 [13]（表 3）。为了弄清在悬浮液中自由存在、与培养基不接触的细胞是否会出现冠状形成，我们对细胞浓度为 1.5×10^6/ml 的悬浮液在有兔抗鼠免疫球蛋白荧光标记物存在的条件下不停搅拌，然后再在叠氮化物中冲洗，结果证明没有显著的冠状形成抑制现象发生。用含浓度可达 4 mM 的乙二醇双 (2– 氨基乙醚) 四乙酸（EGTA）的无钙培养基或用含浓度可达 4 mM 的乙二胺四乙酸（EDTA）的无钙镁（估计 [14] 自由钙离子浓度低于 $1 \times 10^{-8} \sim 5 \times 10^{-8}$）培养基在室温或 37℃ 下预孵育细胞 30 min，然后在相同条件下处理和冲洗细胞，结果发现冠状形成并未受到显著的抑制。

Table 3. Effect of Cytochalasin B and Colcemid on Cap Formation

Experiment No.	Drug	Concentration (µg/ml.)	% caps	
			With drug	After recovery
1*	Cytochalasin B†	0	84	—
	Cytochalasin B†	10	67	—
	Cytochalasin B†	30	55	—
	Cytochalasin B†	50	52	75
2‡	Cytochalasin B†	0	90	—
	Cytochalasin B†	20	34	—
	Colcemid	20	91	—

* After preincubation at 2×10^6 cells/ml. in cytochalasin B in L-15 for 30 min at 37°C, cells were incubated with R anti-MIg for 15 min at 37°C washed in cytochalasin B and incubated with G anti-RIg-Fl at 0°C in 3×10^{-2} M azide for 30 min.

† Cytochalasin B (Imperial Chemical Industries, Alderley Park) was dissolved in dimethyl sulphoxide (DMSO) (10 µl./mg). The final DMSO concentration was the same in experimental and control samples and was 0.3% in experiment 1 and 1% in experiment 2.

‡ After preincubation at 10^6 cells/ml. in drug in VBS for 30 min at 37°C, cells were treated with R anti-MIg-Fl at 0°C for 15 min and then warmed up in drug to 37°C for 20 min.

Thus, Ig cap formation is an active, temperature-dependent process possibly involving contractile microfilament activity that is induced by multivalent binding of anti-Ig at the cell surface, and which seems not to require extracellular calcium or magnesium. The actual mechanism is unclear but we favour the possibility that surface Ig molecules are immobilized by cross-linking of the anti-Ig antibodies while the rest of the membrane can move or flow forward, resulting in the Ig molecules gathering over the trailing tail of the lymphocyte; the uropod. A more detailed discussion of possible mechanisms will be presented elsewhere (S. de P. and M. C. R. in preparation).

Antigenic Modulation

Cap formation is rapidly followed by pinocytosis of the Ig determinants. This could be seen when spleen cells were incubated with anti-MIg-Fl at 0°C, washed and then kept at 37°C. Cap formation occurred rapidly (Fig. 2) and, after 5 min, pinocytosis of the fluorescent label was seen and was marked by 10 min. By 30 min most of the label seemed to be inside the cells. No visible pinocytosis occurred, however, when cells were stained at 0°C in the presence of azide with univalent Fab anti-MIg-Fl. Spleen cells stained with ferritin-labelled anti-MIg at 20°C and examined by electron microscopy not only showed cap localization of the ferritin labelling but invariably contained ferritin-lined pinocytotic vesicles near the Golgi area, underlying the cap. Such vesicles were not seen when the cells were treated at 0°C.

To study further the disappearance of surface Ig, spleen cells were incubated with unlabelled R anti-MIg at 37°C. After 10 min or after 3 h, cells were washed and treated with G anti-RIg-Fl in azide at 0°C (Table 4). At 10 min, 40–50% of the cells were stained; most showed cap fluorescence. At 3 h, only 20–30% of the cells stained, and many of these had only a few fluorescent spots at one pole (Table 4). When the 3-h cells

表 3. 细胞松弛素 B 和秋水仙酰胺对冠状形成的影响

实验编号	药物	浓度 (μg/ml)	冠状形成%	
			用药	恢复后
1*	细胞松弛素 B†	0	84	—
	细胞松弛素 B†	10	67	—
	细胞松弛素 B†	30	55	—
	细胞松弛素 B†	50	52	75
2‡	细胞松弛素 B†	0	90	—
	细胞松弛素 B†	20	34	—
	秋水仙酰胺	20	91	—

* 37℃ 下将浓度为 2×10^6/ml 的细胞在 L-15 中与细胞松弛素 B 预孵育 30 min，再将其在 37℃ 下用兔抗鼠免疫球蛋白孵育 15 min，在细胞松弛素 B 中冲洗并在 0℃、有 3×10^{-2} M 叠氮化物存在的条件下用山羊抗兔免疫球蛋白荧光标记物孵育 30 min。

† 将细胞松弛素 B（帝国化学工业公司，奥尔德利公园）溶解在二甲基亚砜（DMSO）（10 μl/mg）中。实验组中和对照样本组中 DMSO 的最终浓度是一致的，在实验 1 中是 0.3%，在实验 2 中是 1%。

‡ 37℃ 下将浓度为 10^6/ml 的细胞在 VBS 中与药物预孵育 30 min，再将其在 0℃ 下用兔抗鼠免疫球蛋白荧光标记物处理 15 min，然后在药物中加热至 37℃ 并维持 20 min。

　　因此，免疫球蛋白冠状形成是一个活性的、依赖于温度的过程，可能牵涉到由细胞表面的抗免疫球蛋白的多价结合引起的微丝收缩活性，并且这个过程似乎不依赖于细胞外的钙和镁。明确的机理还不清楚，但我们支持如下这种可能性：表面免疫球蛋白分子被抗免疫球蛋白抗体的交联所固定，而膜的其余部位仍能向前移动或流动，导致免疫球蛋白分子集中在淋巴细胞拖后的尾部，即尾足。对几种可能机理的更详细的讨论将在其他地方发表（斯特凡内洛·德·彼得里斯和马丁·拉夫，完稿中）。

抗 原 调 变

　　冠状形成之后迅速发生免疫球蛋白决定簇的胞饮。在 0℃ 下将脾细胞用抗鼠免疫球蛋白荧光标记物孵育、冲洗然后保存于 37℃ 时，就能观察到这种现象。冠状形成迅速发生（图 2），5 min 后能观察到荧光标记的胞饮现象并在 10 min 时非常显著。到 30 min 时看起来大多数标记已处于细胞内。然而，如果细胞是在叠氮化物和抗鼠免疫球蛋白单价抗原结合片段荧光标记物存在的条件下于 0℃ 时染色的，则没有可见的胞饮现象发生。当用电子显微镜观察 20℃ 下用铁蛋白标记的抗鼠免疫球蛋白染色的脾细胞时，不仅能在冠状形成中找到铁蛋白标记物，还总能在冠状染色下方的高尔基区附近发现包含有铁蛋白的胞饮泡。在 0℃ 下处理细胞时观察不到这样的小泡。

　　为了进一步研究细胞表面免疫球蛋白的消失现象，将脾细胞在 37℃ 下用未标记的兔抗鼠免疫球蛋白孵育。分别在 10 min 和 3 h 后冲洗细胞，并于 0℃ 下用含叠氮化物的山羊抗兔免疫球蛋白荧光标记物处理这些细胞（表 4）。10 min 时，40% ~ 50% 的细胞被染上色；大多数显示出冠状荧光。3 h 时，只有 20% ~ 30% 的细胞被染色，许多被染色的细胞在细胞的一极只有少量荧光斑（表 4）。如果在 0℃ 的叠氮

were treated with anti-MIg-Fl in azide at 0°C instead of the G anti-RIg-Fl, only a few cells stained and all of these showed weak cap staining (Table 5). Thus, Ig determinants have been largely cleared off the cell surface by treatment with unlabelled anti-MIg for 3 h at 37°C, the process of removal appearing to be complete in 50% of Ig-bearing cells. However, when the 3-h cells were tested with ALS or anti-H-2 serum by indirect immunofluorescence in azide at 0°C, they showed normal intensity ring staining suggesting that only Ig determinants had been removed by the anti-Ig antibody (Table 5). When the spleen cells were incubated for 3 h at 37°C with unlabelled Fab-anti-MIg and then stained with G anti-RIg-Fl in azide at 0°C, 40–50% of the cells stained with ring fluorescence and there was no obvious loss of intensity of staining. Thus Fab fragments were unable to cause the disappearance of surface Ig molecules. Although cytochalasin B, at a concentration of 30 μg/ml., only partially inhibited cap formation (Table 3), it completely inhibited visible pinocytosis and markedly inhibited the disappearance of Ig determinants induced by anti-Ig. In the absence of extracellular calcium and in the presence of 3 mM EGTA, pinocytosis and Ig disappearance occurred normally.

Table 4. Disappearance of Ig Determinants*

Type of anti-MIg	Time (min)	% cells stained	% caps†		% rings
			Large	Small	
R anti-MIg	20	44	75	9	16
R anti-MIg	150	28	8	85	7
Fab-R anti-MIg	20	48	0	0	100
Fab-R anti-MIg	150	43	2	0	98

* 2×10^6 cells were incubated at 37°C in 0.25 ml. of R anti-MIg in L-15; cells were sampled at 20 and 150 min and stained with G anti-RIg-Fl for 30 min at 0°C in 3×10^{-2} M azide.

† Caps were considered "large" if estimated to occupy at least one-quarter of the cell surface and "small" if occupying less than this. Many of the small caps consisted of several fluorescent spots at one pole of the cell.

Table 5. Specificity of Ig Disappearance*

Anti-MIg-treated cells re-treated with		% cells stained	% caps	% rings
First layer	Second layer			
R anti-MIg-Fl	—	14 (faint)	0	100
R anti-MIg	G anti-RIg-Fl	25 (faint)	0	100
Anti-H-2^k (1:2)	R anti-MIg-Fl	100	0	100
ALS (1:100)	G anti-RIg-Fl	100	0	100

* Cells were from the same cell preparation as reported in Table 4, which were treated with R anti-MIg for 150 min at 37°C. They were then washed and subjected to direct or indirect testing as indicated at 0°C in 3×10^{-2} M sodium azide.

化物中用抗鼠免疫球蛋白荧光标记物替换山羊抗兔免疫球蛋白荧光标记物来处理孵育 3 h 的细胞，则只有少量细胞被染色，并且全都显示出微弱的冠状染色（表 5）（译者注：表 5 可能有误，前两行数据似应为冠状形成 100%）。因此，在 37℃ 下用未标记的抗鼠免疫球蛋白处理 3 h 就可以把大多数免疫球蛋白决定簇从细胞表面清除掉，这个清除过程看似在 50% 表面带有免疫球蛋白的细胞中是完全的。然而，当孵育了 3 h 的细胞在 0℃ 下的叠氮化物中通过间接免疫荧光法用 ALS 或抗 H-2 血清作测试时，它们会显示出正常强度的环状染色，这说明只有免疫球蛋白决定簇被抗免疫球蛋白抗体清除掉了（表 5）。将脾细胞在 37℃ 下用未标记的抗鼠免疫球蛋白抗原结合片段孵育 3 h，再在 0℃ 的叠氮化物中用山羊抗兔免疫球蛋白荧光标记物染色，这时 40%～50% 的细胞染色显示出环状荧光且未出现染色强度的明显降低。因此，抗原结合片段并不能引起表面免疫球蛋白分子的消失。虽然细胞松弛素 B 在浓度为 30 μg/ml 时只能部分抑制冠状形成（表 3），但它能完全抑制可见的胞饮现象并能显著抑制由抗免疫球蛋白引起的免疫球蛋白决定簇的消失。在细胞外缺少钙和有 3 mM EGTA 存在的条件下，胞饮和免疫球蛋白消失的现象仍能正常发生。

表 4. 免疫球蛋白决定簇的消失现象*

抗鼠免疫球蛋白的类型	时间 (min)	染色的细胞%	冠状形成%†		环状形成%
			大	小	
兔抗鼠免疫球蛋白	20	44	75	9	16
兔抗鼠免疫球蛋白	150	28	8	85	7
兔抗鼠免疫球蛋白抗原结合片段	20	48	0	0	100
兔抗鼠免疫球蛋白抗原结合片段	150	43	2	0	98

* 37℃ 下将 2×10^6 个细胞在 L-15 中与 0.25 ml 兔抗鼠免疫球蛋白共孵育；分别在 20 min 和 150 min 时采集细胞样本并将采集的样本在 0℃、存在 3×10^{-2} M 叠氮化物的条件下用山羊抗兔免疫球蛋白荧光标记物染色 30 min（译者注：第 879 页最后一段中提到的采样时间分别是 10 min 和 3 h）。

† 如果冠状荧光染色区域至少占据了细胞表面的四分之一就被认为是"大"，如果小于四分之一则被认为是"小"。许多小冠状染色由细胞一极的若干荧光小斑点组成。

表 5. 免疫球蛋白消失现象的特异性*

经抗鼠免疫球蛋白处理的细胞的再处理		染色的细胞%	冠状形成%	环状形成%
第一层	第二层			
兔抗鼠免疫球蛋白荧光标记物	—	14（模糊）	0	100
兔抗鼠免疫球蛋白	山羊抗兔免疫球蛋白荧光标记物	25（模糊）	0	100
抗 H-2^k（1:2）	兔抗鼠免疫球蛋白荧光标记物	100	0	100
ALS（1:100）	山羊抗兔免疫球蛋白荧光标记物	100	0	100

* 细胞来源于表 4 中报道的细胞制备物，是在 37℃ 下用兔抗鼠免疫球蛋白处理 150 min 后得到的。随后进行冲洗并在 0℃、存在 3×10^{-2} M 叠氮化钠的条件下进行直接或间接的荧光检测。

The disappearance of surface Ig determinants induced by anti-Ig antibody is analogous to antigenic modulation described for the thymus-leukaemia (TL) antigens[15]. When TL-positive cells, particularly some lymphomas, are exposed to anti-TL antibody *in vivo* or *in vitro*, they rapidly lose their sensitivity to the cytotoxic action of anti-TL serum and complement. TL modulation does not occur at $0°C$ or in the presence of actinomycin D[15] but is said to occur with univalent Fab anti-TL[16]. Recently, Takahashi has observed similar modulation by anti-Ig antibody of Ig determinants on the surface of some murine myeloma cells and normal spleen cells[17]. The mechanism of antigenic modulation has remained a mystery, although the possibility of it being pinocytosis has recently been raised by Takahashi[17]. Our findings strongly suggest that modulation, of surface Ig determinants at least, is the result of antibody induced pinocytosis, preceded by the gathering of the determinants over the Golgi area. It is unclear why Fab fragments modulate TL but fail to modulate Ig. It will be important to see if cytochalasin B inhibits modulation of the TL antigens.

Anti-Ig sera are being widely used to inhibit the function and antigen-binding ability of lymphocytes[1]. The assumption has been that the anti-Ig inhibits lymphocyte antigen-binding by blocking or by steric hindrance[1]. Our findings, and those of Takahashi, suggest that modulation of the Ig receptors may sometimes be operating. If so, one might expect the inhibition due to modulation to be more effective than steric inhibition, which may explain the prozone effect that has been observed with increasing concentrations of anti-Ig[18], where cap formation would be inhibited.

Cap Formation with Anti-θ

The theta (θ) alloantigen is present on mouse thymocytes[19] and thymus-derived (T) lymphocytes[20,21]. One of us (M. C. R.) previously reported that anti-θ serum used in indirect immuno-fluorescence testing produced only ring-like staining of thymocytes and T cells, and that the morphology of the fluorescence could thus be used to distinguish θ-bearing T cells from non-θ-bearing B cells, since the latter showed mainly cap-like staining with anti-MIg-Fl[4]. To exclude the possibility that cap formation was unique for Ig determinants and/or B cells, we attempted to induce cap formation with thymocytes using various dilutions of anti-θ serum followed by a constant concentration of anti-MIg-Fl. When anti-θ was used at high concentrations (as was the case in the experiments previously reported), only rings were seen (Fig. 5), but when lower concentrations were used, cap formation occurred. In experiments where thymus cells were treated with dilute anti-θ at $37°C$ and anti-MIg-Fl used at $0°C$, no cap formation occurred (Fig. 5), indicating that anti-θ alone did not induce caps during the 30 min incubation. When thymus cells were treated with dilute anti-θ, then with unlabelled R anti-MIg at $37°C$ for 20 min or 2 h, followed by G anti-RIg-Fl at $0°C$, the caps were smaller after 2 h than at 20 min, suggesting that some disappearance had occurred. Our preliminary studies with anti-H-2[k] serum gave similar results. Takahashi has recently found that anti-H-2 alone did not cause H-2 modulation, but anti-H-2 plus anti-Ig did modulate if the anti-H-2 was used in low concentrations[17].

由抗免疫球蛋白抗体引起的表面免疫球蛋白决定簇的消失现象与描述胸腺白血病（TL）抗原时的抗原调变[15]类似。当 TL 阳性细胞，尤其是一些淋巴瘤，在体内或体外暴露于抗 TL 抗体时，它们会迅速失去对抗 TL 血清和补体的细胞毒性作用的敏感性。尽管 TL 抗原调变在 0℃时或者在有放线菌素 D[15]存在的条件下不发生，但有报道称在与抗 TL 单价抗原结合片段在一起时会发生[16]。近来，高桥在一些鼠骨髓瘤细胞和正常脾细胞中观察到，由免疫球蛋白决定簇的抗免疫球蛋白抗体也能引起细胞表面发生类似的调变[17]。虽然高桥最近提出它由胞饮作用引起的可能性[17]，但抗原调变的机理至今仍是个谜。我们的发现显然表明：表面免疫球蛋白决定簇的调变现象，至少是由抗体引起的胞饮现象的结果，并发生在决定簇聚集在高尔基区之后。抗原结合片段能调变 TL 抗原但不能调变免疫球蛋白的原因尚不清楚。观察细胞松弛素 B 是否会抑制 TL 抗原的调变将是一件很重要的事。

抗免疫球蛋白血清被广泛用于抑制淋巴细胞的功能及其与抗原结合的能力[1]。之前的假说是，抗免疫球蛋白通过阻塞或位阻抑制了淋巴细胞与抗原的结合[1]。我们的发现以及高桥的发现都暗示，免疫球蛋白受体的调变可能会在有些情况下起作用。如果是这样的话，就可以预期由调变引起的抑制要比由位阻引起的抑制更有效，这样就可以解释在增加抗免疫球蛋白浓度从而使冠状形成受到抑制时观察到的前带效应[18]。

与抗 θ 有关的冠状形成

θ 同种异体抗原出现在小鼠胸腺细胞[19]和源于胸腺的（T）淋巴细胞[20,21]中。我们中的一位作者（马丁·拉夫）之前曾报道过，抗 θ 血清在间接免疫荧光检验中只产生了胸腺细胞和 T 细胞的环状染色，因而可以用荧光形状来区分带有 θ 的 T 细胞和不带 θ 的 B 细胞，因为后者在用抗鼠免疫球蛋白荧光标记物染色时主要表现出冠状染色[4]。为了排除冠状形成是免疫球蛋白决定簇和（或）B 细胞所特有的可能性，我们先用具有不同稀释度的抗 θ 血清，然后用某一恒定浓度的抗鼠免疫球蛋白荧光标记物来处理胸腺细胞，以期诱导出该细胞的冠状形成。当使用高浓度的抗 θ 时（如同之前报道的实验），只有环状染色出现（图 5）；但当使用较低浓度的抗 θ 时，冠状形成发生。在 37℃时用稀释的抗 θ 和 0℃时用抗鼠免疫球蛋白荧光标记物处理胸腺细胞的实验中，冠状形成没有发生（图 5），这表明在仅有抗 θ 的条件下孵育 30 min 并不能引起冠状形成。如果用稀释的抗 θ 处理胸腺细胞，再用未标记的兔抗鼠免疫球蛋白在 37℃下孵育 20 min 或 2 h，接着在 0℃下用山羊抗兔免疫球蛋白荧光标记物处理，则孵育 2 h 的冠状染色要小于孵育了 20 min 的，这说明发生了一些消失现象。我们用抗 H-2[k] 血清所作的初步研究也给出了相似的结果。高桥最近发现：仅用抗 H-2 不能引起 H-2 调变，但如果使用的是低浓度的抗 H-2，则抗 H-2 加上抗免疫球蛋白就确实能导致调变[17]。

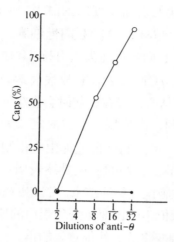

Fig. 5. Cap formation with anti-θ C3H in indirect immuno-fluorescence with CBA thymocytes. Cells were incubated in dilutions of anti-θ in VBS for 20 min at 37°C, washed and incubated with R anti-MIg-Fl for 30 min at 37°C (○) or 0°C (●). In all cases 100% of the cells stained.

The selective segregation and disappearance of specific surface determinants induced by specific antibody imply that at least some membrane components can move relative to one another. The significance of this in terms of membrane structure will be considered in more detail elsewhere and has recently been discussed by Frye and Edidin[22] who studied the movement of histocompatibility antigens on the surface of newly formed heterokaryons.

Immunological Significance

Are cap formation and pinocytosis involved in triggering lymphocyte transformation and/or tolerance induction? Although there is no direct evidence for this, there are a number of observations that are consistent with it. Our failure to induce cap formation or pinocytosis with univalent Fab anti-Ig mirrors the failure of Fab anti-Ig to transform rabbit lymphocytes or of Fab anti-mouse lymphocyte serum to activate mouse lymphocytes, where divalent $F(ab')_2$ did so[23,24]. Mitogens such as concanavalin A[25] and phytohaemagglutinin (PHA)[26] give cap staining localized over the uropod when surface binding was detected by immunofluorescence and concanavalin A binding was followed by pinocytosis[25]. In addition, pinocytosis in the area of the uropod has been observed during mixed lymphocyte reactions[27]. Cytochalasin B, which partially inhibits cap formation and markedly inhibits pinocytosis[28], has been found to inhibit PHA transformation, as well as the transformation of lymphocytes responding to PPD and allogeneic cells (unpublished work of D. Webster and A. C. Allison). Prozone effects observed when lymphocytes are stimulated with increasing concentrations of PHA or ALS[29] or anti-Ig[30] could possibly reflect prozones in inducing cap formation.

If cap formation or pinocytosis play an important physiological role in lymphocyte stimulation or tolerance induction, it should be possible to demonstrate that they can

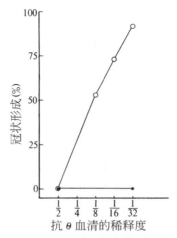

图 5. 用抗 θ C3H 对 CBA 胸腺细胞进行间接免疫荧光染色时的冠状形成。37℃ 下将细胞在 VBS 中与不同稀释度的抗 θ 共孵育 20 min，冲洗后在 37℃（〇）或 0℃（●）下用兔抗鼠免疫球蛋白荧光染色物孵育 30 min。在各种稀释度下染色细胞所占的比例均为 100%。

选择性隔离和由特异抗体引起的特定表面决定簇的消失现象表明，至少有一些膜组分能够发生相互之间的移动。我们将另辟文章详细讨论这在膜结构方面的意义；最近，研究新形成异核体表面的组织相容性抗原运动的弗赖伊和埃迪登 [22] 也探讨过这个问题。

免疫学意义

冠状形成和胞饮现象是否牵涉到引起淋巴细胞转化和（或）耐受性诱导？虽然没有直接的证据表明如此，但是有一大堆观察结果与此相符。我们用抗免疫球蛋白单价抗原结合片段未能引起冠状形成或胞饮现象，这反映出抗免疫球蛋白抗原结合片段不能用来转化兔淋巴细胞或不能用抗鼠淋巴细胞血清中的抗原结合片段来激活鼠淋巴细胞，而二价抗原结合片段则能做到 [23,24]。当通过免疫荧光法检测表面结合时，促分裂素原，如伴刀豆球蛋白 A[25] 和植物凝血素（PHA）[26]，能在尾足处形成冠状染色，并且在伴刀豆球蛋白 A 结合后发生胞饮现象 [25]。除此之外，在混合淋巴细胞反应 [27] 中也观察到了尾足区域的胞饮现象。有人发现，能部分抑制冠状形成和显著抑制胞饮现象的细胞松弛素 B[28] 也能抑制 PHA 的转化以及淋巴细胞为应对结核菌素（PPD）和同种异体细胞而发生的转化（韦伯斯特和艾利森，尚未发表的研究结果）。在用浓度不断增加的 PHA 或 ALS[29] 或抗免疫球蛋白 [30] 刺激淋巴细胞时观察到的前带效应有可能反映了在诱导冠状形成时的前带。

如果冠状形成或胞饮现象在淋巴细胞刺激或耐受性诱导中起着重要的生理学作用，那就应该可以证明它们是通过与表面免疫球蛋白受体相结合的多价抗原来诱导

be induced by multivalent antigens binding to surface Ig receptors. Most lymphocyte antigen binding studies have been carried out at 0°C, often in the presence of azide, and cap-like polar binding has not been reported. In preliminary studies of antigen binding cells (demonstrated by exposing spleen cells to DNP_1BSA, DNP_8BSA, DNP_5BGG and $DNP_{23}BGG$ and staining with purified fluorescent antibodies against the carrier) we have found that at 37°C DNP_1BSA formed only rings, while all multivalent conjugates formed mainly caps.

The increasing evidence for the importance of matrix formation and multivalent binding at the lymphocyte surface for the induction of immunity (reviewed in refs. 18 and 31) and tolerance[32] could possibly reflect the need for multivalent binding in cap formation and pinocytosis. It should be possible to determine this by using *in vitro* models of induction and tolerance together with methods for purification of antigen-sensitive cells, to study the relationship between the pattern of antigen binding to lymphocytes and the induction-tolerance decision.

We thank Mr. M. R. Young for taking the micrographs used in Fig. 1, and Mr. J. Singh for technical assistance. M. C. R. was supported by a postdoctoral fellowship of the US National Multiple Sclerosis Society and S. de P. by a fellowship of the European Molecular Biology Organization (EMBO).

(*Nature New Biology*, **233**, 225-229; 1971)

Roger B. Taylor and W. Philip H. Duffus: MRC Immunobiology Group, University of Bristol, and Department of Pathology, Medical School, Bristol.

Martin C. Raff and Stefanello de Petris: National Institute for Medical Research, Mill Hill, London.

Received August 18; revised September 20, 1971.

References:

1. Greaves, M. F., *Transplant. Rev.*, **5**, 45 (1970).
2. Pernis, B., Forni, L., and Amante, L., *J. Exp. Med.*, **132**, 1001 (1970).
3. Raff, M. C., Sternberg, M., and Taylor, R. B., *Nature*, **225**, 553 (1970).
4. Raff, M. C., *Immunology*, **19**, 637 (1970).
5. Leibovitz, A., *Amer. J. Hyg.*, **78**, 173 (1963).
6. Mishell, R. I., and Dutton, R. W., *J. Exp. Med.*, **126**, 423 (1967).
7. Raff, M. C., *Nature New Biology*, **229**, 182 (1971).
8. Levey, R. H., and Medawar, P. B., *Ann. New York Acad. Sci.*, **129**, 164 (1966).
9. McFarland, W., Heilman, D. H., and Moorhead, J. P., *J. Exp. Med.*, **124**, 851 (1966).
10. Porter, R. R., *Biochem. J.*, **73**, 119 (1959).
11. Cerrottini, J.-C., and Brunner, K. T., *Immunology*, **13**, 395 (1967).
12. Wessells, N. K., Spooner, B. S., Ash, J. F., Bradley, M. O., Luduena, M. A., Taylor, E. L., Wrenn, J. T., and Yamada, K. M., *Science*, **171**, 135 (1971).
13. Tilney, L. G., *J. Cell Sci.*, **3**, 549 (1968).
14. Portzehl, H., Caldwell, P. C., and Rüegg, J. C., *Biochim. Biophys. Acta*, **79**, 591 (1964).
15. Old, L. J., Stockert, E., Boyse, E. A., and Kim, J. H., *J. Exp. Med.*, **127**, 523 (1968).
16. Lamm, M. E., Boyse, E. A., Old, L. J., Lisowska-Bernstein, B., and Stockert, E., *J. Immunol.*, **101**, 99 (1968).
17. Takahashi, T., *Transpl. Proc.* (in the press).

的。大多数有关淋巴细胞抗原结合的研究是在 0℃、通常有叠氮化物存在的条件下进行的，从未有人报道过有冠状极性结合的现象。在对抗原结合细胞的初步研究中（通过将脾细胞暴露于 DNP_1BSA、DNP_8BSA、DNP_5BGG 和 $DNP_{23}BGG$ 并用提纯过的抗载体荧光抗体染色来证明），我们发现 37℃时 DNP_1BSA 只形成了环状，而所有多价结合则主要形成冠状。

越来越多的证据表明淋巴细胞表面的基质建造和多价结合对诱导免疫（见参考文献 18 和 31）和耐受性 [32] 具有重要意义，这有可能反映出冠状形成和胞饮现象是需要多价结合的。我们或许可以通过体外诱导模型和体外耐受性模型以及用提纯抗原敏感细胞的方法来确定上述结论，以便研究抗原结合淋巴细胞的方式和诱导－耐受决定之间的关系。

感谢扬先生为我们拍摄了图 1 中所用的显微照片，还要感谢辛格先生为我们提供技术支持。马丁·拉夫是美国国家多发性硬化症协会的博士后奖学金的获得者，斯特凡内洛·德·彼得里斯受到了欧洲分子生物学组织（EMBO）提供的奖学金的资助。

（邓铭瑞 翻译；秦志海 审稿）

18. Mitchison, N. A., *In vitro* (in the press).

19. Reif, A. E., and Allen, J. M. V., *J. Exp. Med.*, **120**, 413 (1964).

20. Schlesinger, M., and Yron, I., *Science*, **164**, 1412 (1969).

21. Raff, M. C., *Nature*, **224**, 378 (1969).

22. Frye, L. D., and Edidin, M., *J. Cell Sci.*, 7, 319 (1970).

23. Fanger, M. W., Hart, D. A., Wells, V. J., and Nisonoff, A., *J. Immunol.*, **105**, 1484 (1970).

24. Riethmüller, G., Riethmüller, D., Stein, H., and Hansen, P., *J. Immunol.*, **100**, 969 (1968).

25. Smith, C. W., and Hollers, J. C., *J. Reticuloendothel. Soc.*, **8**, 458 (1970).

26. Osunkoya, B. O., Williams, A. I. O., Adler, W. H., and Smith, R. T., *Afr. J. Med. Sci.*, **1**, 3 (1970).

27. McFarland, W., and Schechter, G. P., *Blood*, **34**, 832 (1969).

28. Allison, A. C., Davies, P., and dePetris, S., *Nature New Biology*, **232**, 153 (1971).

29. Foerster, J., Lamelin, J.-P., Green, I., and Benacerraf, B., *J. Exp. Med.*, **129**, 295 (1969).

30. Sell, S., and Gell, P. G. H., *J. Exp. Med.*, **122**, 423 (1965).

31. Mitchison, N. A., *Immunopathology*, **6**, 52 (1971).

32. Diener, E., and Feldmann, M., *J. Exp. Med.*, **132**, 31 (1970).

33. Wofsy, L., and Burr, B., *J. Immunol.*, **103**, 380 (1969).

抗免疫球蛋白抗体诱导的淋巴细胞表面免疫球蛋白分子的重分布和胞饮现象

Immunoglobulin E (Reagin) and Allergy

D. R. Stanworth

Editor's Note

In 1921, Carl Prausnitz showed it was possible to induce allergic sensitivity in non-allergic people by injecting them with sera from an allergic person. That landmark paper demonstrated that immediate hypersensitivity was mediated by a some tissue-sensitizing factor, which in 1966, Japanese couple Teruko and Kimishige Ishizaka identified as the antibody immunoglobulin E (IgE). Here British immunologist Denis R. Stanworth charts the progress from Prausnitz to present day, speculating that improved understanding of IgE's mode of action could lead to the development of new preventative therapies.

FIFTY years ago Prausnitz showed that it was possible to sensitize sites on his forearms by the intradermal injection of serum from one of his allergic patients (Küstner) who was hypersensitive to fish[1]. The injection of fish extract into the same sites 24 h later evoked immediate weal and erythema reactions similar to those shown by the patient himself (and by other fish-sensitive individuals) in response to the direct intradermal injection of fish extract.

This observation was a historic "landmark" in a field which has not always been noted for objectivity. Besides demonstrating that human hypersensitivity of this immediate-type could be transferred to normal tissue, outside the influence of the allergic individual, it meant that a passively induced reaction could be restricted to a localized area of the skin with minimal discomfort to the non-allergic recipient. Of even greater significance, however, was the inference that immediate hypersensitivity (unlike that of the delayed type, of which tuberculin sensitivity is an example) was mediated by a humoral factor.

There soon followed similar demonstrations of the local transfer of human hypersensitivity to many common inhalants (such as grass pollens, animal danders and house dusts); the Prausnitz–Küstner (P–K) test, as it is known, being used as an alternative to direct skin testing in the diagnosis of hay fever and allergic asthma. Its principal application, however, has been in the experimental study of immediate-type hypersensitivity; where, until a few years ago, it offered the only satisfactory means of assay. Consequently attempts to characterize the skin sensitizing factor more fully have been seriously handicapped.

Early investigations showed this serum constituent to resemble antibodies which appear in the circulation of humans and animals in response to conventional immunization procedures. But it seemed to lack certain properties commonly associated with immune antibodies, such as the capacity to form a precipitate and to fix complement when

免疫球蛋白E（反应素）与过敏反应

斯坦沃思

编者按

1921 年，卡尔·普劳斯尼茨指出向非过敏者体内注入过敏者的血清可能诱导其产生过敏性敏感。他在那篇具有里程碑意义的论文中证实，速发型超敏反应是由某种组织致敏性因子介导的。1966 年，日本夫妇石坂照子和石坂公成将其鉴定为抗体免疫球蛋白 E（IgE）。在本文中，英国免疫学家丹尼斯·斯坦沃思描绘了自普劳斯尼茨至今的研究进展，他推断对 IgE 作用方式的更好理解可能会引导人们发现新的预防疗法。

50 年前，普劳斯尼茨通过皮内注射将一个对鱼过敏的患者（屈斯特纳）的血清注入自己的前臂中，他发现注射部位可能会因此而变得敏感[1]。24 小时后向这个部位注射鱼的提取物可以立即引发斑痕和红斑反应，这些反应与该过敏患者本人（以及其他对鱼过敏的患者）直接接受皮内注射鱼提取物后产生的症状相似。

这一观察结果对这个一向缺乏客观性的领域具有历史性的"里程碑"意义。除了证明人的这种速发型超敏反应可以被转移到受过敏患者影响以外的正常组织中之外，这一结果还显示出这种被动导入的过敏反应仅限于皮肤的局部区域，且给非过敏的接受者带来的不适很小。然而，更重要的意义在于，可以由此推断出速发型超敏反应（与对结核菌素等过敏的迟发型超敏反应不同）是由体液中的一种因子介导的。

之后很快有类似的发现称，人类对许多常见吸入物（如草的花粉、动物的皮屑和房间里的灰尘）的超敏反应也可以被转移到局部区域；众所周知，在诊断枯草热和过敏性哮喘时，可以用普劳斯尼茨 – 屈斯特纳（P–K）试验取代直接的皮内试验。然而到目前为止，这种方法最重要的应用仍在于速发型超敏反应的实验研究，并且直到几年前它还是唯一令人满意的检测方法。随后在尝试对皮肤致敏因子进行更为详细的特征描述时却遇到了严重的障碍。

早期的研究显示这种血清中含有类似抗体的组分。在人和动物对常见的免疫过程作出应答时，其血液循环中会出现抗体。不过这一组分似乎并不具备免疫抗体的某些常见特性，例如：在体外实验中，它不能够在与特异性抗原结合时产生沉淀，

combined with specific antigens *in vitro*. For these reasons, some investigators[2] preferred to reserve judgment on its antibody status by terming it "atopic reagin" ("atopy" denoting a form of human hypersensitivity in which there was evidence of a hereditary predisposition, the sensitizing substances being referred to as "atopen"). The factor demonstrable in the serum of individuals with immediate hypersensitivity of the asthma–hay fever–urticaria type, has since been termed "reagin" and it has been customary to refer to the provoking agents (in inhalants, foods and so on) as "allergens".

P–K testing revealed that reagins become firmly "fixed" in normal isologous human skin where they are detectable (by subsequent allergen challenge) several weeks after the transfer of the allergic serum. In contrast, antibodies produced by the immunization of rabbits with allergenic substances (such as pollen extracts and egg protein) failed to fix to human skin; although unlike reagins, they could passively sensitize the skin of heterologous guinea-pigs for relatively short times. Human antibodies (γG type) against diphtheria toxoid likewise disappear rapidly when injected into isologous human skin (with a half-life of 12 h)[3], whereas reagins transferred isologously have been estimated[4] to have a "half-life" of 15 days.

Quantitative P–K testing[5] based on the accurate measurement of the areas of weals produced on the backs of normal recipients showed that a maximal skin response was achieved with a time interval of about 50 h between transfer of allergic serum and challenge with specific allergen. Once this was effected, however, a weal and erythema reaction developed rapidly with the weal approximately doubling in area during 10–20 min after introduction of the allergen. The susceptibility of reagins to relatively mild heat treatment was also confirmed[5]. Similar conditions are used in the destruction of the complement activity of immune sera, but the addition of fresh normal human serum to heated allergic serum fails to restore P–K activity[6] and other evidence indicates that reagins do not depend on the complement system for their activity.

Reagins were also found to differ from immune (7S type) antibodies in their inability to cross the placenta. This situation is obviously fortunate for the offspring of allergic women, as is the apparent absence of reagins from human colostrums. It has been attributed by some investigators to the macroglobulin (19S) antibody nature of the tissue sensitizing factor, which was thought to be of sufficiently large molecular size to be retained by the human placenta's supposed sieving mechanism. But extensive studies by Brambell and his associates[7], and others have indicated that the placental transmission of immunoglobulins is a highly selective process (controlled by sites located within their Fc regions).

The biological properties of reagins revealed by these early investigations, based principally on P–K testing, are summarized in Table 1. This was the position around 1940, when techniques of free-solution electrophoresis and ultracentrifugation were first applied to the fractionation of plasma proteins. Although such physico-chemical procedures offered better means of separating complex protein mixtures than had been

也不能结合补体。基于这些原因，一些研究人员 [2] 对它的抗体地位持保留态度，仍将其称为"特应性反应素"（"特应性"指的是人的一种超敏反应，有证据表明其具有遗传易感性，引起这种超敏反应的致敏物质被称为"特应原"）。在哮喘 – 枯草热 – 风疹类型的速发型超敏反应患者的血清中，与超敏有关的因子被称为"反应素"，而引发这些超敏反应的物质（在可吸入物或食物等中）则被习惯性地称为"过敏原"。

P–K 试验显示：反应素可以牢牢地"固定"到同源的正常人体的皮肤上，并且在过敏性血清移植实验后好几周仍能被检测到（即用过敏原刺激后会发生过敏反应）。与此相反，使用引起过敏的物质（如花粉提取物、鸡蛋蛋白）免疫兔子得到的抗体则不能固定到人的皮肤上；但与反应素不同，这种抗体可以使异源的豚鼠皮肤在相对较短的时间内被动致敏。人抗白喉类毒素抗体（γG 型）在以同样方式注射到同源人体的皮肤中之后很快便消失了（半衰期为 12 小时）[3]，但据估计 [4] 在同源间转移的反应素的"半衰期"可以达到 15 天。

定量 P–K 试验 [5] 是基于对正常接受者背部产生的斑痕面积的精确测量而进行的。其结果显示，在转移过敏性血清约 50 小时后再注入特定过敏原可引起最强烈的皮肤过敏反应。然而，即使马上接触过敏原，斑痕和红斑反应也会迅速发生，斑痕面积在引入过敏原之后 10 分钟~20 分钟内会增加一倍左右。此外，反应素对于比较温和的加热处理很敏感也得到了证实 [5]。类似的实验条件同样可以破坏免疫血清中补体的活性，而向经加热处理的过敏性血清中加入正常人的新鲜血清并不能恢复该血清的 P–K 活性 [6]，其他证据也证明反应素的活性并不依赖于补体系统。

人们还发现反应素与免疫（7S 型）抗体不同，它不能穿越胎盘。这一点对于过敏体质女性的后代来说显然是幸运的，在产妇的初乳中也明显不含有反应素。一些研究人员认为：组织中致敏因子的本质是巨球蛋白（19S），这些球蛋白的分子很大以至于不能够穿越血胎屏障而影响胎儿。不过布兰贝尔和他的同事们 [7] 以及其他一些研究者通过大量的研究证明，免疫球蛋白通过血胎屏障是一个高选择性的过程（由免疫球蛋白结晶片段（Fc）区上的某些位点控制）。

这些主要基于 P–K 试验的早期研究揭示出了反应素的生物学特性，表 1 中汇总了研究得到的所有生物学特性。在 1940 年前后，自由溶液电泳技术和超速离心技术首次被应用于分离血浆中的蛋白质组分。尽管这些物理化学方法在复杂蛋白质混合物的分离上比以前靠盐类和低温乙醇沉淀进行的分离更有效，但它们本质上仍是用

previously possible, by salt or low temperature-ethanol precipitation, they were essentially analytical tools. Nevertheless, electrophoretic analyses of the sera of animals before and after immunization provided the first evidence of the γ globulin nature of precipitating antibodies[8]; while corresponding ultracentrifugal studies indicated a size heterogeneity (antibody activity being associated with both 7S and 19S components).

Table 1. Main Biological and Physico-Chemical Properties of Reagins (γE-Antibodies)

(1) Bind firmly to isologous, and closely related heterologous, tissues
(2) Heat labile (destroyed by 56°C for 1 h)
(3) Not dependent on complement
(4) Fail to cross the placenta
(5) Move in the "fast γ" region on electrophoresis
(6) Sediment near to 8 S

It was naturally hoped that a similar approach would provide more convincing evidence of the antibody nature of reagins; but this was thwarted by practical difficulties. It was established, however, that reagins were electrophoretically faster than immune γ globulins, moving in the β region (where 19S type immune antibodies were also found). But this conclusion was very much an extrapolation, and the minute amount of skin sensitizing factor present in allergic sera could have been moving in the electric field in combination with a major constituent. More refined preparative fractionation procedures were required.

Physico-Chemical Characteristics

As in the characterization of many other minor active protein constituents of biological fluids, it was the advent of zone-fractionation procedures which gave the first definitive indication of the physico-chemical characteristics of the skin sensitizing factor. Thus, zone electrophoresis of allergic sera in starch blocks[9] confirmed that reagins moved in the "fast γ" (slow β) region; whilst zone-centrifugation in buffered sucrose gradients[10] showed clearly that they sedimented in the 7S region (and were not macroglobulins, as had been suggested to explain their failure to cross the placenta). There were, of course, limitations to this type of correlative approach because each of the major serum electrophoretic fractions, including the γ fraction, comprised several components. It was at this stage, however, that the application of highly-specific and sensitive immunological techniques began to compensate for the shortcomings of the physico-chemical procedures. Studies on the monoclonal γ globulins, isolated in large quantities from the sera of patients with multiple myelomatosis and Waldenström macroglobulinaemia, led to the production of specific antisera which distinguished three major immunoglobulin classes[11]: γG or IgG (previously referred to as 7S γ globulin): γM or IgM (previously referred to as 19S macroglobulin) and γA or IgA (a newly discovered third class[12], which when isolated from normal human serum by a zinc precipitation procedure was found to comprise a major 7S component, with minor amounts of polymerized material, and which migrated in the fast γ region on electrophoresis). It was established that the three major immunoglobulin classes then known possessed common light polypeptide chains, but distinctive heavy chains (Fig. 1).

于分析的手段。尽管如此，用电泳实验分析动物免疫前后的血清成分为证明沉淀出的抗体的本质是 γ 球蛋白提供了第一个证据[8]；而相应的超速离心研究则证明了抗体分子在大小上的不均一性（7S 和 19S 组分都与抗体活性有关）。

表 1. 反应素的主要生物学特性和物理化学特性（γE 型抗体）

(1) 与同源组织紧密结合，与异源组织也密切相关
(2) 热不稳定性（在 56℃ 下处理 1 小时后活性被破坏）
(3) 不依赖于补体
(4) 不能穿越血胎屏障
(5) 在电泳实验中位于"快 γ"区
(6) 沉降系数约为 8S

人们很自然地希望有一种类似的方法能提供更多令人信服的证据来证明反应素的本质是抗体；不过这种想法实行起来有难度。虽然反应素比 γ 免疫球蛋白的电泳速度更快，位于 β 区域（19S 型免疫抗体也位于这一区域），但这一结论在很大程度上只是一种推断：在电场作用下，过敏性血清中微量的皮肤致敏因子可能与血清中的某种主要成分结合而共同泳动。我们需要更精细的样品分离制备步骤。

物理化学特性

和表征生物液体样品中许多其他微量活性蛋白组分时一样，直到区带分离技术出现后人们才得以首次得到关于皮肤致敏因子的物理化学特性的决定性依据。例如：过敏性血清的淀粉区带电泳实验[9]证实，反应素在电泳中位于"快 γ"（慢 β）区；同时蔗糖密度梯度缓冲液的区带离心实验[10]显然说明，反应素的沉降系数位于 7S 区（也就是说它不是巨球蛋白，同时证明之前以反应素的分子太大为由来解释其不能穿越血胎屏障的说法是不成立的）。当然，这种关联法也有其局限性，因为各个主要的血清电泳组分，包括 γ 组分，都由数种成分组成。不过，在现阶段可以用高度特异性和敏感性的免疫学技术来弥补物理化学分析方法的不足。研究人员对从多发性骨髓瘤和瓦尔登斯特伦巨球蛋白血症患者血清中分离出来的大量单克隆 γ 球蛋白进行了分析，结果发现它是一种不同于三种主要免疫球蛋白类型的特殊抗血清[11]，即不同于 γG（或 IgG，之前称为 7S γ 球蛋白）、γM（或 IgM，之前称为 19S 巨球蛋白）和 γA（或 IgA，最新发现的第三种类型[12]，它是人们利用锌离子沉淀法从正常人的血清中分离出来的，主要由 7S 组分组成，含有少量的多聚物质，在电泳中位于快 γ 区）。已经确认目前已知的这三种主要类型的免疫球蛋白都具有相同的轻多肽链，但重链有所不同（图 1）。

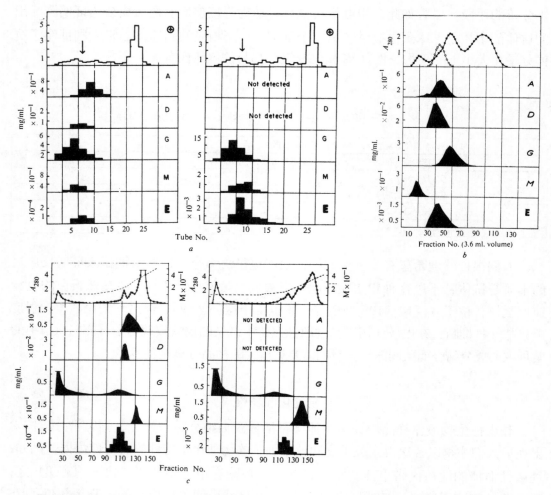

Fig. 1. A comparison of the physico-chemical properties of the five major human immunoglobulin classes. *a*, Zone electrophoresis; *b*, gel-filtration; *c*, ion-exchange chromatography on DEAE-"Sephadex" (reproduced from ref. 26, by courtesy of the authors).

The problem then was to show that skin sensitizing activity was a property of one (or perhaps more) of these antigenically distinguishable immunoglobulins. Antigenic and physico-chemical analysis of fractions of allergic human serum separated by chromatography on DEAE-cellulose (which provided a high degree of resolution of the various classes of immunoglobulin) revealed maximal P–K activity in a fraction in which only electrophoretically fast 7S γG globulin could be detected. As Fig. 1*c* shows, this was in an elution position well ahead of any detectable γM globulin; and even ahead of any γA globulin detectable by immunodiffusion analysis using specific antisera[13].

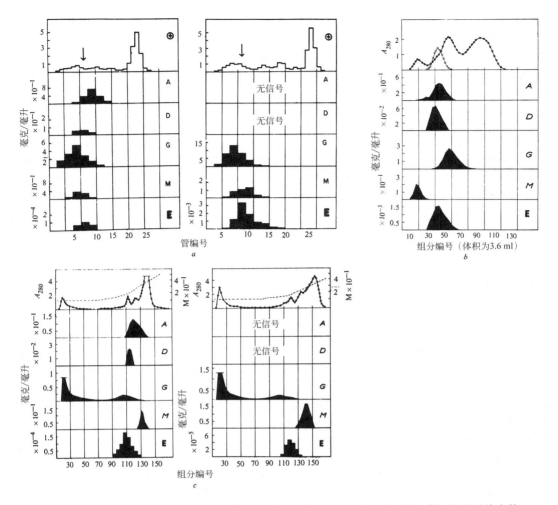

图 1. 五种主要类型人免疫球蛋白的物理化学性质比较。(a）区带电泳实验；(b）凝胶过滤实验；(c）二乙氨基乙基 – 葡聚糖凝胶柱离子交换层析（经作者允许，从参考文献 26 中复制）。

接下来的问题是要证明，皮肤致敏活性是一种（也可能是多种）抗原不同的免疫球蛋白的特性。研究人员对经过二乙氨基乙基 – 纤维素层析（具有很高的分辨率，可以区分开不同类型的免疫球蛋白）分离的过敏患者血清各组分的抗原特性和物理化学性质进行了分析，发现在其中一个组分中能检测到最高的 P–K 活性。在电泳中，只有该组分能迁移到快 7S γG 球蛋白区。如图 1c 所示，该组分的洗脱峰位于所有能检测得到的 γM 球蛋白的前面；甚至还在用特异性抗血清进行免疫扩散分析时能检测得到的任一 γA 球蛋白的前面[13]。

This latter observation was particularly significant, at a time when many claims were being made that reagins were γA globulins. These were based on such evidence as the recovery of P–K activity in highly purified γA globulin preparations[14], the removal of activity from allergic sera by absorption with specific sheep anti-human γA globulin antiserum[15] and the blockage of P–K reactions by normal human γA globulin or its isolated heavy chains[16]. They were of obvious teleological appeal as γA globulin had been found in high levels in nasal and other secretions, where it supposedly acted as a "front-line" defensive agent. But a lack of correlation was observed between reagin activity and γA globulin distribution in DEAE cellulose chromatorgraphic fractions of allergic sera[13]; and other studies[17] suggested that P–K activity was associated with a minor component of the sera of hypersensitive individuals, which had appeared as a contaminant in the supposedly pure γA globulin fractions investigated previously.

Were reagins a unique type of immunoglobulin (a prospect on which I had speculated in 1963 (ref. 18))? The discovery of a new human immunoglobulin class (IgD or γD)[19], which resembled γA globulin electrophoretically, seemed a possibility; but several independent investigations suggested this immunoglobulin did not possess skin sensitizing activity.

Reagins were found, however, to have unusual physico-chemical characteristics as well as distinctive biological properties (for antibodies). For example, the gel filtration of sera of people sensitive to ragweed (on "Sephadex G200"[20]) led to the recovery of maximal P–K activity slightly ahead of the 7S peak containing the γG and γA globulins, but well behind the 19S peak containing the γM globulin. Furthermore, reagins in such sera were found by density gradient ultracentrifugation[21] to possess a sedimentation coefficient of 7.7S (7.4–7.9S range)—significantly greater than human γG and γA globulins. It also seemed significant that the reagin-like antibodies, occurring naturally in some animals (such as the dog) and induced artificially in others (for example, rats and rabbits), had sedimentation coefficients greater than 7S but much less than 19S (Table 2).

Table 2. Sedimentation Characteristics of Reagin-Type Antibodies Formed in Various Mammalian Species (as Determined by Density Gradient Ultracentrifugation)

Species	Mode of antibody formation	Sed. coeff. (S°)
Human	Spontaneously	>7.4S–7.9S
Dog	Spontaneously	6.8S–10.1S
Rat	Experimentally	>7S, <<19S
Rabbit	Experimentally	>7S, <<19S

Further evidence that reagins were probably a unique class of immunoglobulins was obtained by Ishizaka and his associates[22], who isolated active preparations by application of a multistep procedure to the fractionation of pools of sera from individuals showing marked hypersensitivity to ragweed pollen and who developed highly sensitive

后一个观察结果非常重要，因为当时有很多人认为反应素就是 γA 球蛋白。这一观点的提出主要基于以下证据：由高纯度 γA 球蛋白制备物能够恢复 P–K 活性[14]；使用特异的绵羊抗人 γA 球蛋白的抗血清除去过敏性血清中的 γA 球蛋白后，其 P–K 活性也随之消失[15]；此外，使用正常人血清中的 γA 球蛋白或其分离的重链都可以抑制过敏性血清的 P–K 活性[16]。γA 球蛋白在鼻子和其他器官的分泌物中含量很高，这些分泌物被认为是抵御外来物质的"第一道防线"，基于此，人们很自然地把 γA 球蛋白和反应素联系在了一起。然而，在用二乙氨基乙基–纤维素层析分离得到的过敏性血清的各个组分中，人们发现含 γA 球蛋白的组分并不具有反应素的活性[13]；其他研究也表明 P–K 活性与超敏患者血清中的一种微量组分有关[17]，这说明在以前检测过的看似高纯度的 γA 球蛋白中很可能混入了这样的污染物。

反应素会不会是一种特殊类型的免疫球蛋白（在 1963 年我曾作过这样的推测，参考文献 18）呢？一种新发现的人免疫球蛋白类型（IgD 或 γD）[19] 具有与 γA 球蛋白相似的电泳特征，这似乎提供了一种可能性；不过，几项独立的研究结果显示，这种免疫球蛋白并不具有引起皮肤过敏的活性。

然而，人们发现（对于抗体来说）反应素具有不寻常的物理化学性质和与众不同的生物学特性。例如，用凝胶过滤（葡聚糖凝胶 G200[20]）对豚草过敏的人的血清后，发现稍早于含 γG 和 γA 球蛋白的 7S 洗脱峰的组分具有最大的 P–K 活性，但该组分远远晚于含有 γM 球蛋白的 19S 洗脱峰。此外，密度梯度超速离心实验[21]的结果显示，该血清中反应素的沉降系数为 7.7S（7.4S ～ 7.9S）——明显高于人 γG 和 γA 球蛋白。以下这一点显然也很重要：一些类似反应素的抗体在某些动物（例如狗）中会天然存在，而在另一些动物（如大鼠和兔子）中可以人为地诱导出来，它们的沉降系数都大于 7S 而远小于 19S（表 2）。

表 2. 形成于几种哺乳动物中的类反应素抗体的沉降特性（用密度梯度超速离心法测量）

物种	抗体形成方式	沉降系数（S°）
人	自发	>7.4S~7.9S
狗	自发	6.8S~10.1S
大鼠	实验诱导	>7S, «19S
兔子	实验诱导	>7S, «19S

石坂公成及其同事发现了证明反应素很可能是一种独特的免疫球蛋白类型的新证据[22]。他们采用一个多步过程从对豚草花粉高度过敏的患者血清中分离得到了活性组分，并且发展出一种高敏感性的放射性免疫扩散分析方法，在体外实验中这种

radioimmune-diffusion assays as *in vitro* alternatives to the P–K test for the measurement of the reagin in the isolated fractions. Reagin preparations thus obtained were used to produce anti-reagin antisera, which were rendered specific by absorption with the major classes of immunoglobulin and which were used in radio-immunoelectrophoresis to provide evidence that a radio-labelled ragweed allergen (E) preparation combined with the reagin isolated from ragweed-sensitive individuals' sera.

Ishizaka and associates[23] suggested that reagin activity was carried by a unique immunoglobulin which they tentatively termed "γE" (in view of its specific binding capacity for ragweed allergen E). Despite the evidence presented in support of this idea, however, some investigators felt that such claims were perhaps a little premature until chemical evidence was available to suggest the existence of a unique type of polypeptide chain.

Myeloma Protein

The final evidence that reagins were a unique class of immunoglobulins came with the isolation of an atypical myeloma protein (originally designated "IgND"), from the serum of a patient ("ND") with myelomatosis and Bence Jones proteinuria[24], which lacked the antigenic determinants characteristic of the heavy polypeptide chains of the then known immunoglobulin classes (γG, γM, γA and γD) while possessing similar light chain determinants (of sub-type L). Like myeloma γA and γD globulins, this atypical protein moved in the "fast γ" region on zone electrophoresis (Fig. 1); but it was eluted slightly ahead of these classes of immunoglobulin during chromatography on DEAE-"Sephadex". Of greater significance, however, was its elution position during gel-filtration on "Sephadex G100", where it emerged after the γA globulin but just ahead of the γG globulin. Furthermore, free solution ultracentrifugal analysis[25] showed the atypical myeloma protein (IgND) to possess a sedimentation coefficient (S°20, W) of 7.92S (and molecular weight 196,000 from Archibald analysis); a value very similar to that which had been assigned to the reagins in sera of ragweed-sensitive individuals on the basis of the observed rate of sedimentation of the P–K activity in buffered sucrose gradients.

This similarity in sedimentation coefficient between the new type of myeloma protein and reagin could have been fortuitous, but it seemed significant that the myeloma protein isolated from the serum of patient "ND" was the first known type of immunoglobulin to have similar size characteristics to the skin sensitizing factor. Other observations were beginning to suggest a relationship between the new class of immunoglobulin and reagin. For example, by means of a radio-immunosorbent technique based on the use of "Sephadex"-coupled antibody directed specifically against the new myeloma protein[24], a significantly elevated concentration (5,900 ng/ml.) of an antigenically similar protein was detected in the serum of an individual with allergy to dog dander; in comparison with the much smaller amounts (100–700 ng/ml.) found in normal sera. Later comparative studies[26] of the antigenic characteristics of the new myeloma globulin and the reagin-rich fraction (designated γE) isolated from sera of ragweed-sensitive individuals were to provide evidence of a close structural relationship between the two proteins.

方法可以代替 P–K 试验用以检测分离出来的各组分中的反应素。这样得到的反应素被用来制备抗反应素的抗血清。他们特异地去除了抗血清中几种主要的免疫球蛋白类型，然后用这个抗血清进行放射性免疫电泳实验，以此证明放射性标记的豚草过敏原（E）可以结合从对豚草过敏的患者血清中分离出来的反应素。

石坂及其同事 [23] 认为反应素活性源自于一种独特的免疫球蛋白，他们将其暂时命名为"γE"（因为它可以和豚草过敏原 E 特异地结合）。然而，尽管有上述证据支持石坂等人的观点，一些研究人员仍然认为，在找到化学证据证明存在这种独特的多肽链之前提出上述论断或许有点为时尚早。

骨髓瘤蛋白

最后一个能证明反应素是一种独特的免疫球蛋白类型的证据来自于从患有骨髓瘤病和本周蛋白尿症的患者（"ND"）血清中分离出来的非典型骨髓瘤蛋白（起初被命名为"IgND"）[24]。这种蛋白缺乏四种已知免疫球蛋白（γG、γM、γA 和 γD）类型的重肽链所特有的抗原决定簇，但有与它们类似的轻链决定簇（L 亚型）。与骨髓瘤 γA 和 γD 球蛋白类似，这种非典型蛋白在区带电泳中位于"快 γ"区（图 1）；但是它在二乙氨基乙基 – 葡聚糖凝胶层析中的洗脱峰略早于这两类免疫球蛋白。然而，如果使用葡聚糖凝胶 G100 进行凝胶过滤层析，其洗脱位置的意义更重大：这种蛋白的洗脱峰晚于 γA 球蛋白但略早于 γG 球蛋白。此外，自由溶液超速离心分析 [25] 显示，这种非典型骨髓瘤蛋白（IgND）的沉降系数（S°20，W）为 7.92S（并且通过阿奇博尔德分析测得其分子量为 196,000）；这一数值与豚草过敏患者血清中反应素的沉降系数非常接近，后者是基于在蔗糖梯度缓冲液中测定 P–K 活性的沉降速度而得到的。

也许这种新发现的骨髓瘤蛋白与反应素在沉降系数上的相似性是一种巧合，不过似乎值得注意的一点是，从患者"ND"的血清中分离出来的这种骨髓瘤蛋白是人们发现的第一个与皮肤致敏因子具有相似尺寸特征的免疫球蛋白类型。其他观察结果正开始预示这种新型免疫球蛋白和反应素之间的某种联系。例如，使用葡聚糖凝胶偶联抗体进行放射免疫吸附试验，可以特异地识别这种新的骨髓瘤蛋白 [24]，也可以显著提高一个对狗皮屑过敏的人的血清中一种有类似抗原性的蛋白的浓度（5,900纳克 / 毫升）。在正常血清中这种蛋白的浓度要低得多（100 纳克 / 毫升 ~ 700 纳克/ 毫升）。后来，有人对这种新的骨髓瘤球蛋白的抗原特性和从豚草过敏患者血清中分离得到的富含反应素组分（命名为 γE）的抗原特性进行了比较研究 [26]，从而为这两种蛋白在结构上的相近性提供了依据。

The most convincing evidence that the myeloma protein (IgND) was a pathological counterpart of reagin was obtained, however, from inhibition-P–K testing in a normal human recipient[27]. The intradermal injection of the myeloma protein mixed with, or 24 h before, the sensitizing serum (at a dosage of 5–50 times in excess of the level of reagin in the serum) completely inhibited a weal and erythema response on subsequent challenge with the specific allergen (isolated from horse dandruff). Thus not only was the myeloma protein (IgND) antigenically similar to reagin, it also seemed to have its striking affinity for isologous tissues. There was no evidence, however, that the myeloma protein could bind antigen (that is allergen). Thus it seemed to be a pathological counterpart of a new immunoglobulin class of which reagin was a normal representative, just as an over-production of monoclonal forms of the major immunoglobulin classes has often been seen in plasmocytic and lymphocytic neoplastic disorders.

Immunological and chemical studies[25] indicated that the myeloma protein IgND was a new class of immunoglobulin, with similar light chains to those in the other four classes, but distinctive heavy polypeptide chains somewhat larger (75,500 molecular weight) than those in the other immunoglobulins. Consequently at a meeting initiated by the World Health Organization in Lausanne in 1968 (ref. 28) it was decided that there was sufficient evidence to conclude that reagin was representative of this new class of immunoglobulin, which it was proposed should be designated "IgE" or "γE".

The availability of the myeloma protein offers a means of chemically characterizing reagins, and ultimately of explaining their unusual biological properties in structural terms. It has been calculated that the chance of finding a case of monoclonal production of γ globulin of the E type is about one in 50,000 that of finding a more common case of myelomatosis; so the protein isolated from the serum of the Swedish case has proved particularly valuable and highly sought after. Fortunately, however, a second case has been reported[29] in the United States, who has clinical manifestations similar to those seen in the case originally reported by Johansson and Bennich in Sweden.

Already the two γE myeloma proteins are providing important information about the role of the antibody (reagin) in immediate hypersensitivity reactions. For example, the myeloma IgE has been degraded into different types of polypeptide fragment by means of proteolytic and chemical cleavage procedures, and tested the ability of these to inhibit skin sensitization by the reagins (γE antibodies) in the sera of individuals sensitive to horse dandruff and grass pollen[30,31]. Of the various types of fragments tested (originating from the different parts of the IgE molecule as illustrated schematically in Fig. 2) only those incorporating the Fc region had the inhibitory activity of the parent molecule. Similar findings have resulted from inhibition studies in sub-human primates (for example, rhesus monkeys and baboons) which, like non-allergic humans, have proved receptive to sensitization by human γE antibodies but which (for obvious reasons) are now preferred as test recipients.

然而，有一个非常令人信服的证据能证明骨髓瘤蛋白（IgND）是反应素在病理上的对应物，该证据来自于正常受试者血清的抑制性 P–K 试验 [27]。将骨髓瘤蛋白与致敏性血清混合（以高于血清中反应素 5 倍～50 倍的剂量）或者在注射致敏性血清之前 24 小时进行皮内注射，都可以完全抑制随后由特定过敏原（从马的皮屑中分离得到）引起的斑痕和红斑反应。因此，这种骨髓瘤蛋白（IgND）不仅在抗原性上与反应素相似，它似乎还与同源组织具有很高的亲和力。然而，尚没有证据表明骨髓瘤蛋白可以与抗原（这里指过敏原）结合。如此看来，反应素似乎是这种新免疫球蛋白类型在体内的正常存在形式，而骨髓瘤蛋白则是其病理上的对应物，正如在患有浆细胞瘤和淋巴细胞瘤的人身上经常观察到的主要免疫球蛋白类型单克隆形式过度分泌的现象一样。

免疫学和化学研究 [25] 表明：骨髓瘤蛋白 IgND 是一种新型的免疫球蛋白，它具有与另外四种免疫球蛋白类型相似的轻链，但其重链（分子量为 75,500）却比其他类型的重链略大一些。因此，在 1968 年由世界卫生组织在瑞士洛桑举办的会议上（参考文献 28），大家一致认为有足够的证据可以证明反应素是这种新免疫球蛋白类型的代表，并建议把这种免疫球蛋白命名为"IgE"或者"γE"。

骨髓瘤蛋白的发现提供了一种用化学方法表征反应素的方式，这种方式可以使我们最终在结构水平上解释其独特的生物学特性。有人计算得出，找到一例 E 型单克隆 γ 球蛋白的几率大概是找到一例更典型的骨髓瘤蛋白的 1/50,000。因此，从这个瑞典患者的血清中分离出的这种蛋白是非常珍贵和难得的。然而，幸运的是，美国的研究人员已报道了第二个类似的例子 [29]。这个患者的临床症状与约翰松和本宁最初在瑞典报道的病例相似。

这两例 γE 骨髓瘤蛋白现已为研究抗体（反应素）在速发型超敏反应中的作用提供了重要的信息。例如，使用蛋白酶解和化学消化的方法可以将骨髓瘤 IgE 降解成不同类型的多肽片段，然后检测这些片段对于由马皮屑和草花粉过敏患者血清中反应素引起的皮肤敏感化的抑制能力 [30,31]。在检测的这些不同类型的片段中（如图 2所示，来自 IgE 分子中的不同部分），只有那些包含 Fc 区的片段具有对亲本分子的抑制活性。类似的抑制性结果在非人灵长类（例如恒河猴和狒狒）中也被发现。和人类相似，原本不过敏的动物在注射人 γE 抗体后也会变得对某种过敏原过敏，（由于显而易见的原因）人们更倾向于用非人灵长类动物作为测试的受体。

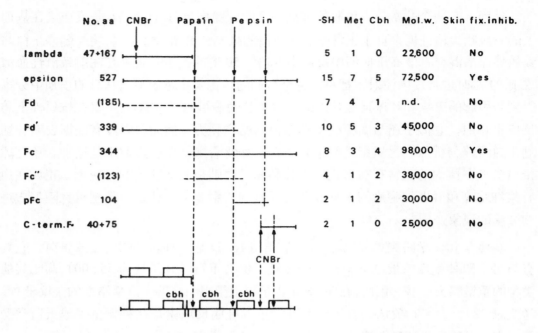

	No. aa	CNBr	Papain	Pepsin	-SH	Met	Cbh	Mol.w.	Skin fix. inhib.
lambda	47+167				5	1	0	22,600	No
epsilon	527				15	7	5	72,500	Yes
Fd	(185)				7	4	1	n.d.	No
Fd'	339				10	5	3	45,000	No
Fc	344				8	3	4	98,000	Yes
Fc''	(123)				4	1	2	38,000	No
pFc	104				2	1	2	30,000	No
C-term.F	40+75				2	1	0	25,000	No

Fig. 2. Working model for molecular structure of IgE indicating the disposition of antigenically and biologically active fragments, and carbohydrate (cbh) prosthetic groups. (Reproduced from ref. 62, by permission of the authors.)

Other inhibition sensitization tests in baboons[32], have involved myeloma IgE preparations which have been reduced to various extents with 2-mercaptoethanol, to ascertain the importance of the relatively large number of disulphide bridges in maintaining the conformational integrity of that part of the IgE molecule involved in tissue binding.

Binding of IgE

Inhibition tests with proteolytic cleavage fragments of myeloma IgE have led to important conclusions about the binding of antibody IgE to isologous (or closely related heterologous) tissue. They suggest that, like the myeloma protein molecules, the antibody (reagin) molecules similarly bind to the tissue receptors through sites within their Fc regions (Fig. 3). Sites within the Fab region of the cell-bound antibody molecules are thus free to react subsequently with antigen (allergen) in the usual manner. In contrast, the myeloma IgE molecules (like most myeloma forms of the other immunoglobulin classes) cannot combine with antigen (Fig. 3). If, on the other hand, combination with the target cells had been found to occur through the Fab regions of the antibody IgE molecule, it would have been necessary to infer that immediate-type hypersensitivity is an auto-immune phenomenon involving the production of antibody against self-cell surface antigen (as occurs, for example, in autoimmune haemolytic anaemia).

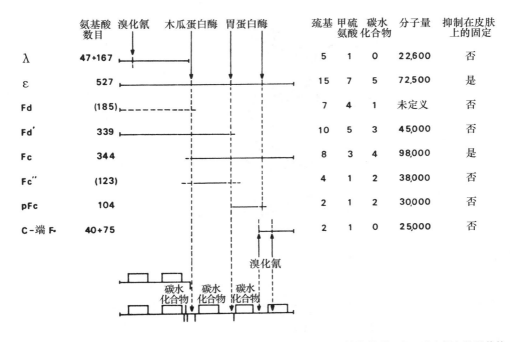

图 2. IgE分子结构的实用模型，图中显示出抗原结合活性和生物学活性的排列，以及碳水化合物辅基的位置。（征得各位原作者许可后，从参考文献62中复制。）

另一些抑制皮肤敏感化的试验是在狒狒中进行的[32]，试验中使用的骨髓瘤 IgE 样品被 2– 巯基乙醇不同程度地还原，目的在于确定相对较多的二硫键在维持 IgE 分子中与组织结合部分的构象完整性方面的重要性。

IgE 的 结 合

使用经蛋白酶解的骨髓瘤 IgE 片段进行抑制试验，得出一些关于 IgE 抗体可与同源组织（或比较接近的异源组织）相结合的重要结论。结论认为：和骨髓瘤蛋白类似,抗体(反应素)分子同样可以通过其 Fc 区中的位点与组织上的受体发生结合(图3)。随后细胞结合型抗体分子就可以通过其抗原结合片段（Fab）区中的位点自由地与抗原（过敏原）按照通常方式结合。与之相反，骨髓瘤 IgE 分子（与大多数其他免疫球蛋白类型的骨髓瘤蛋白类似）则不能与抗原结合（图 3）。另一方面，如果发现 IgE 抗体分子会通过其 Fab 区与靶细胞结合，那么就应该可以断定：速发型超敏反应是一种自体免疫现象，即身体产生了抗自身细胞表面抗原的抗体（正如在自体免疫性溶血性贫血症等中发生的一样）。

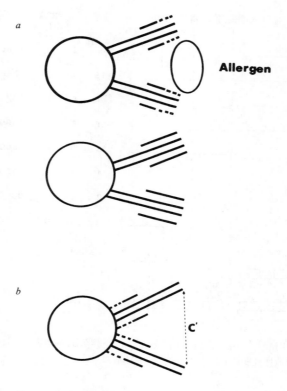

Fig. 3. *a*, Diagrammatic comparison of the properties of antibody and myeloma γE molecules, showing mode of attachment to target cells (this is by means of sites in the Fc regions). *b*, Mode of interaction of γG type cytolytic antibody molecules with target cells, showing subsequent interaction of complement (c′) with sites located in the Fc regions.

Thus it is now possible to start explaining how the immunological reactions occurring at tissue mast cell surfaces bring about the pharmacological manifestations characteristic of hypersensitivity reactions of the immediate-type. Whether such reactions are mediated by γE-type antibodies in passively sensitized human tissues (as, for example, in the classical P–K test), or by non-reaginic γG-type antibodies in the heterologous tissues of guinea-pigs passively sensitized with the serum of experimentally immunized animals, the sequence of events is remarkably similar. The antibody plays a crucial role, not only in the initial sensitization process (which, of course, occurs spontaneously in the allergic individual or the actively sensitized guinea-pig), but also in the manner in which it subsequently interacts with specific antigen (allergen) to activate the enzyme system supposedly responsible for effecting the release of histamine, 5-hydroxytryptamine and other pharmacologically active substances. The elucidation of the structural basis of these different, but complementary, function of tissue-sensitizing antibodies poses a problem of protein characterization. Moreover, it seems likely that studies along these lines on γE globulins will throw light on the mode of action of other classes of immunoglobulin fulfilling other roles on the surfaces of other types of cell (for example, receptor immunoglobulin or lymphocytes).

The emergence of *in vitro* alternatives to the P–K test in humans, and the PCA test in

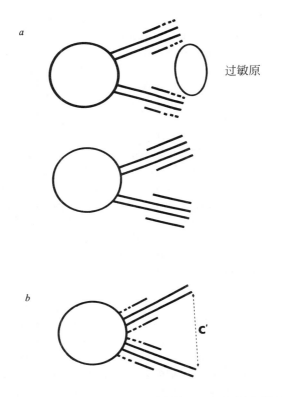

图 3. *a* 图，用示意图比较抗体分子和骨髓瘤 γE 分子的特性，画出了两者与靶细胞结合（通过 Fc 区的位点结合）的模式。*b* 图，溶细胞性 γG 抗体分子与靶细胞的相互作用模式，图中显示出补体（c′）随后与 Fc 区位点发生的相互作用。

这样我们就有可能来解释组织中肥大细胞表面发生的免疫反应是如何引起速发型超敏反应的药理学症状的。无论这些反应是由被动致敏的人体组织中的 γE 型抗体所介导（如在经典的 P–K 试验中），还是由豚鼠（由免疫动物的血清被动致敏）的异源性组织中的非反应素 γG 型抗体所介导，所发生的事件的顺序是非常相似的。不论是在致敏的起始阶段（当然，在过敏患者和主动致敏的豚鼠中会自发出现），还是在后续与特异的抗原（过敏原）结合并激活酶系统的过程中，抗体都起着关键性的作用。酶系统的激活被认为与组胺、5- 羟色胺以及其他药理活性物质的释放有关。要想从分子结构层面阐明这些组织致敏性抗体不尽相同但又互相补充的功能，目前还需要解决蛋白质表征方面的问题。此外，对 γE 型球蛋白的这些方面的研究可能会阐明其他类型的免疫球蛋白在其他类型细胞表面的作用方式（例如受体免疫球蛋白或淋巴细胞）。

人体外 P–K 试验的替代法的出现，以及非人灵长类中被动皮肤过敏反应（PCA）

sub-human primates, is facilitating the delineation of the biochemical events set in train by the combination of cell-bound γE antibody and allergen. Such systems are based on passive sensitization by γE antibodies of chopped human lung[33], normal human leucocytes[34], chopped monkey skin[35] or other suitable primate tissue. The histamine released from the washed sensitized cells or tissues as a result of interaction with specific allergen can be measured accurately (down to levels of a few nanograms) by bioassay using isolated guinea-pig ileum, but a spectrofluorometric procedure involving coupling with ophthalaldehyde[36] has been adopted as a satisfactory chemical alternative. These indirect procedures have obvious advantages over the previous pharmacological approach to the study of immediate hypersensitivity reactions, which involved the direct assay *in situ* of the histamine liberated on presentation of the specific antigen to the actively sensitized tissue set up in an organ bath. Their application has provided convincing evidence[37,38] that the allergen-induced release of histamine and other mediations of immediate-type hypersensitivity reactions is accomplished by a multi-step, energy-requiring process to which the glycolytic pathway is essential. There are precise pH and temperature requirements, and a dependence on calcium and magnesium ions.

It is important, however, to distinguish this process from cytolytic reactions in which destruction of the cell membrane is effected through the combined agency of anti-cell antibody and complement. In contrast, γE-mediated histamine release has been shown (from K^+ efflux studies[38]) to be an active secretory process which is not intrinsically injurious to the target cell. Thus, there is a fundamental difference in the release mechanism initiated by sensitizing antibodies (for example of the γE type), in the absence of complement, and those more drastic processes induced by cytolytic antibodies (for example of the γG type) with the aid of the complement system. As I have already implied (Fig. 3), the type of process evoked depends on the manner in which the antibody is presented to the cell. Antibodies of the γE type seem particularly suited to binding to histamine-containing cells through sites on their Fc regions, and to possess within their own structures sites capable of direct action on the target cell membrane (or other cell constituents). On the other hand, cytolytic antibodies (whether directed against cell membrane antigen, or coating antigen) react initially through sites within their Fab regions, a subsequent intermolecular interaction between their free Fc regions[39] supposedly leading to the activation of the complement system responsible for the ensuing lysis.

Tertiary and Quaternary Structure

The problem now is to establish how the interaction of the cell-bound γE antibody (reagin) with allergen triggers off the events outlined, which seem (from microscopic studies of viable cell preparations) to be associated with characteristic morphological changes[40] in the target cells, involving the release of their histamine-containing granules. The amino-acid sequencing in progress on the two myeloma IgE preparations should provide important information as might the characterization of the relatively large carbohydrate (11.7%) prosthetic group. Furthermore, studies of the inhibitory capacity of proteolytic cleavage fragments of the myeloma IgE (mentioned earlier) are being extended to smaller and smaller fragments, with the hope of isolating a readily characterizable low molecular weight peptide retaining tissue-binding activity. It is becoming increasingly obvious, however, that the peculiar biological properties of γE antibodies (as well as those of the

试验的建立，使得人们更容易描述细胞结合型 γE 抗体与过敏原结合时发生的生化过程。这些体系是基于由以下组织中的 γE 抗体引起的被动致敏而建立的，这些组织包括：捣碎的人肺组织 [33]、正常人白细胞 [34]、捣碎的猴皮肤组织 [35] 或其他合适的灵长类组织。当清洗后的致敏细胞或组织与特异性抗原发生相互作用后，便会释放出组胺。组胺的浓度可以通过生物测定法用分离的豚鼠回肠来精确测定（最小值在几纳克水平），不过后来人们采用邻苯二甲醛 [36] 和荧光光谱相结合的方法作为一种令人满意的化学替代检测法。与先前研究速发型超敏反应的药理学方法相比，这些间接的检测方法具有明显的优势。过去的方法需要在器官浴中使用特定的抗原激活组织，并对释放的组胺进行直接原位检测。新方法的应用为以下论点提供了具有说服力的证据 [37,38]，即过敏原引起的组胺释放以及速发型超敏反应中其他中间产物的释放都是由一个多步骤的耗能过程完成的，在这个过程中糖酵解途径是必需的。这个过程对 pH 值和温度有着精确的要求，并且依赖于钙离子和镁离子。

不过，重要的是要把组胺的释放与细胞溶解反应区分开来。在细胞溶解反应中，由溶细胞性抗体和补体的结合中间体导致了细胞膜的破裂。与此相反，γE 抗体介导的组胺释放（通过钾离子外流实验 [38]）是一个主动分泌的过程，对于靶细胞来讲也没有本质上的伤害。因此，不需要补体参与的、由致敏性抗体（如 γE 型抗体）引发的组胺释放过程和需要补体系统参与的、由溶细胞性抗体（如 γG 型抗体）引发的更为剧烈的过程之间存在着根本的区别。正如我在前面曾暗示过的那样（图 3），所激发过程的类型取决于细胞中存在的抗体种类。γE 抗体似乎特别适合通过它们的 Fc 区位点与含有组胺的细胞结合，并且其自身结构中含有能够与靶细胞膜（或其他细胞组分）发生直接作用的位点。另一方面，溶细胞性抗体（不管直接识别的是细胞膜表面抗原还是包被抗原）起初通过它们 Fab 区域的位点与细胞结合，之后在它们自由的 Fc 区之间会发生分子间相互作用 [39]，这种相互作用可能激活了补体系统，从而导致细胞的溶解。

三级结构和四级结构

现在的问题在于细胞结合型 γE 抗体（反应素）与过敏原的相互作用是如何引发下游事件的，这似乎（根据用显微镜对活细胞进行的观察）与靶细胞的特征性形态改变有关 [40]，同时伴随着含有组胺的颗粒物的释放。对两个骨髓瘤 IgE 的正在进行的氨基酸序列分析和对较大（占分子量 11.7%）的碳水化合物辅基的表征应该能够提供一些重要的信息。此外，用蛋白酶解的方法将骨髓瘤 IgE 抗体降解成越来越小的片段，并对这些片段的抑制活性进行分析（之前曾提到过），以期分离出一个具有组织结合活性且可进行表征的最小分子量的肽段。然而，日益明显的是，γE 抗体（以及在实验动物中产生的低效率致敏性 γG 抗体）的这种罕见的生物学功能是由其非

less efficient γG type sensitizing antibodies produced in experimental animals) will be explicable in terms of unusual tertiary and quaternary structural characteristics. It seems likely (as discussed fully elsewhere[41]) that the two structural features which will prove to distinguish sensitizing antibodies will be an ability to bind strongly to complementary tissue sites with no accompanying loss in the conformational integrity of their Fc region (which can soon occur as a result, for example, of relatively mild heat treatment); and the possession of sufficient flexibility within the "hinge regions" to permit the transmission of a critical allosteric change resulting from combination of allergen with sites in the Fab regions of adjacent cell-bound molecules.

There is evidence[42] that antigen-induced conformational changes can occur in free solution, in rabbit antibody directed against commonly used antigens such as bovine serum albumin and horse ferritin, and these lead to the exposure of new antigenic determinants within the Fc regions. It seems reasonable to conclude, therefore, that similar conformational changes could occur in γE-type antibody molecules in combination with specific allergen (as already proposed[43]). Moreover, if the γE antibody is already anchored to the target cell surfaces, through sites within its Fc region, newly exposed side chains could be brought into critical juxtaposition with points on the cell where activation of the appropriate enzyme system would occur (Fig. 4). Indeed there is evidence (from inhibition studies with aggregated IgE) that association of IgE molecules might lead to the formation of "tissue activation sites" which are distinct from the tissue binding sites in monomeric (antibody and myeloma) IgE molecules; and it is possible that activation sites are similarly formed in the Fc regions of adjacent cell-bound sensitizing antibody molecules as a result of the bridging by specific allergen, for which there is increasing evidence[45,46] and which presumable involves the cross-linking of sites within the antibody Fab regions (Fig. 4). The critical question then to be answered is whether groups exposed from the Fc regions of the cross-linked antibody molecules act cooperatively to form the activation site. In this event, the activation site could be linked to the active site of an enzyme, which of course is usually contained within a single polypeptide chain. Alternatively, the side-chains which are supposedly exposed in the Fc regions of the sensitizing antibody molecules might be proved to exert an independent effect on the target cell.

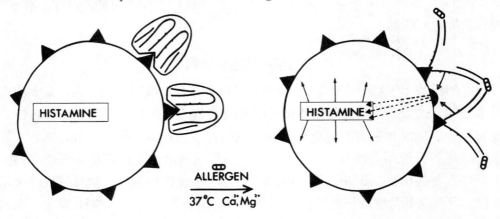

Fig. 4. Postulated mode of interaction between cell-bound γE antibodies and allergen leading to the triggering of release of vasoactive amines (modified from ref. 45).

同寻常的三级和四级结构所决定的。似乎是（正如我在另一篇文章中详细讨论的那样 [41]）这两种结构特点使得致敏性抗体不同于其他抗体，因而致敏性抗体可以在与互补的组织位点紧密结合的同时不影响其 Fc 区的构象完整性（例如在相对温和的热处理中很快会出现的现象）；"铰链区"充分的结构柔性也使得相邻细胞结合型抗体 Fab 区的某些位点与过敏原结合所需的构象改变可以实现。

有证据表明 [42]，由抗原引起的抗体构象改变可以在自由溶液中发生，兔抗体对牛血清白蛋白或马铁蛋白等常用抗原的识别会导致抗体 Fc 区暴露出新的抗原决定簇。因此我们似乎可以很合理地得出以下结论，当 γE 型抗体分子与特殊的过敏原结合时也会发生类似的构象改变（正如已经提出的那样 [43]）。此外，如果 γE 型抗体事先已经通过其 Fc 区中的位点锚定在靶细胞的表面，那么新暴露的侧链就有可能与细胞上相应酶系统的激活点处于严格并行的位置（图 4）。事实上，的确有证据（来自对聚集的 IgE 分子的抑制活性研究）表明：多个 IgE 分子的结合可能会导致"组织激活位点"的形成，这与单体（抗体或骨髓瘤）IgE 分子的组织结合位点是不一样的；并且有越来越多的证据表明 [45,46]，通过特异性过敏原的桥接作用，在相邻细胞结合型致敏抗体的 Fc 区有可能同样会形成激活位点，并且抗体 Fab 区的交联位点也可能参与其中（图 4）。于是，一个需要回答的重要问题是，从交联抗体分子 Fc 区暴露出的基团是否能互相协作形成激活位点？如果是的话，那么这个激活位点就可以连接到酶的活性位点了，当然这两个位点通常存在于同一条多肽链中。如果不是，也许我们能证明，致敏抗体分子 Fc 区中可能暴露出来的一些氨基酸侧链基团可以独立地对靶细胞施加某种作用。

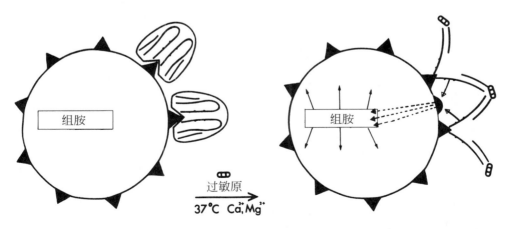

图 4. 细胞结合型 γE 抗体与过敏原相互作用引发血管活性胺释放的假想模式（根据参考文献 45 修改而成）。

In attempting to decide between these alternatives it is worth considering the results of studies designed to short-circuit the histamine release process initiated by reagin-allergen combination. These involve the use of alternative, artificial, ways of cross-linking the γE molecules, and seem to lead to pharmacological responses similar to those of classical immediate sensitivity reactions. Apart from the pre-aggregation of the γE molecule before presentation to the target cell (as already mentioned), it is possible to effect histamine release in human or monkey skin by bringing about the cross-linking of the cell-bound γE molecules with antibody directed specifically against determinants within their Fc regions. Thus, it can be demonstrated[46] that the intradermal injection of specific anti-human IgE antiserum induces an immediate oedematous and erythematous reaction similar to that observed in the P–K test.

Tissue Activation Sites

It is suggested that, as in the classical reagin-allergen mediated reaction, the exposure of tissue activation sites within the Fc region of the γE molecule triggers the release of the pharmacologically active mediators. But the cross-linking process which induces the required conformational change is less efficient than that effected by the cross-linking of the Fab regions of the γE antibody molecules by allergen. This might be expected by reference to the model shown in Fig. 5, which suggests that a force applied at position A (at maximum distance from the fulcrum) would be the most effective way of forming the activation site at position S; but application of a force at position B would accomplish the same effect in a less efficient manner. This analogy could offer an explanation of the skin reactions effected by the action of anti-IgE antibody, as well as that elicited by other agents such as protein A (an antigenic component of *Staphylococcus aureus*) which has an unusual capacity for combination with the Fc regions of immunoglobulins[47] and which presumably acts too by cross-linking cell-bound γE molecules[48].

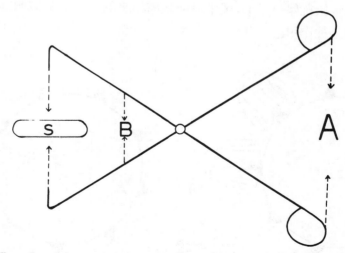

Fig. 5. Model illustrating various methods of inducing an allosteric transformation within cell-bound γE antibody molecules.

　　当我们试图从这些可能性中作出判断的时候，应该考虑旨在缩短由反应素 – 过敏原结合引起的组胺释放过程的研究结果。这些实验使用了一些使 γE 分子发生交联的人为替代方法，看似可以得到与经典的速发型过敏反应相似的药理反应。除了在暴露于靶细胞之前将 γE 抗体分子预聚集之外（如前所述），利用可以特异性识别 Fc 区中抗原决定簇的抗体与细胞结合型 γE 抗体分子的交联也有可能在人或猴子的皮肤中引起组胺的释放。由此可以证明 [46]，皮内注射特异性抗人 IgE 抗血清所引发的速发型水肿和红斑反应与 P–K 试验中所观察到的现象类似。

组织激活位点

　　有人认为：和反应素 – 过敏原介导的经典反应一样，γE 抗体 Fc 区中的组织激活位点一旦暴露出来就会引发药理活性因子的释放。不过，与引起必要构象改变的交联过程相比，由过敏原引起的 γE 抗体 Fab 区的交联过程效率更高。这一点可以参照图 5 中所示的模式推测得出。在这个模式图中，作用于 A 处（离支点最远的点）的力是在 S 处形成激活位点的最有效的方法，而如果在 B 处施加一个力，则要达到同样效果就会效率降低。以此类推，这一模式也可以解释由抗 IgE 抗体以及由蛋白 A（金黄色葡萄球菌的抗原成分）等其他试剂引起的皮肤反应。蛋白 A 具有一种能与免疫球蛋白 Fc 区相结合的不同寻常的能力 [47]，并且有可能也起着交联细胞结合型 γE 抗体的作用 [48]。

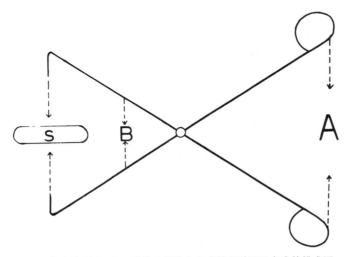

图 5. 引起细胞结合型 γE 抗体分子构象改变的两种不同方式的模式图。

Alternatively, it seems likely that the conformational changes necessary for the formation of tissue activation sites can also occur in non-specifically aggregated IgE (brought about, for example, by lyophilization of monomeric myeloma IgE). As already mentioned, IgE treated in this way is also capable of effecting an immediate release of histamine on injection into human or monkey skin[46]. Thus, perhaps surprisingly, in spite of the non-specific nature of the aggregation process, a conformational change seems to be induced within the Fc regions similar to that resulting from antigen-mediated association of the γE molecules. This is directly analogous, however, to the situation with regard to the association of human (and rabbit) γG molecules where biological activities (for example heterologous skin reactivity and complement fixability), and new antigenic determinants (similar to those formed on specific antigen-antibody combination) are induced by non-specific denaturation treatments. Moreover, recent studies[49] on the nature of the structural changes shown by γG globulins as a result of physical or chemical treatments suggest that here too association is initiated by preliminary (non-covalent) interaction between the Fab regions of the molecule but in this case, of course, without the agency of the antigen. This, it seems, leads to an unfolding of the Fc regions, similar to that occurring in antibody γG molecules on combination with antigen, thereby providing scope for intermolecular Fc interaction with formation of the sites of the various biological activities shown by aggregated γG globulins. Thus what might be expected to be a random aggregation process seems to be a highly ordered polymerization, directed presumable by the initial intermolecular reactions of the Fab regions of the monomer molecules.

The complete characterization of these crucial tertiary and quarternary structural changes could have an important bearing on the explanation of other immunological phenomena. As far as immediate hypersensitivity is concerned, the need now is to characterize the "tissue activation sites" formed in γE globulin molecules on association, and to elucidate the nature of their "substrate" located on the target cells. Various possibilities are being considered. For example, could it be that reagin-allergen combination on the cell surface activates a phospholipase responsible for hydrolysis of membrane phospholipid[50]; or perhaps an esterase is activated, in a similar manner to that implicated in complement mediated cytolytic reactions[51]. Another possibility[52] is the stimulation of the adenyl-cyclase system, which is located on the inner surface of cell membranes (where it catalyses the conversion of ATP to cyclic AMP) and which has been shown to be involved in the action of certain hormones[53]. It could be more than fortuitous that certain polypeptide hormones (such as ACTH) which act in this manner are also potent histamine liberators[54]. It will, however, be important to exclude the simpler possibility that the primary triggering mechanism is a physical shearing of the cell membrane ("rigidification", as one investigator[44] has termed it), brought about by the association of surface-bound γE antibody molecules.

Future Tasks

Although the initiative is now passing to biochemists and biophysicists, many other aspects of the behaviour of γE antibodies require immunological investigation. For example, with the aid of specific antisera prepared against the myeloma proteins, it is possible to

或者，形成组织激活位点所需的构象改变也可能在非特异聚集的 IgE（例如，由骨髓瘤 IgE 单体在冻干时导致）中发生。如前所述，当把这种 IgE 注射到人或猴的皮肤中时，也会立即引起组胺的释放[46]。因此，尽管这种聚集的过程是非特异的，但令人惊奇的是，在这些抗体的 Fc 区也发生了与结合了抗原的 γE 抗体类似的构象变化。这与人（或兔）γG 抗体分子的结合情况很相似，即非特异性的变性处理可以引起生物学活性（如异源皮肤反应和补体固定）和新抗原决定簇（与特异的抗原－抗体结合所形成的抗原决定簇类似）的产生。此外，最近对 γG 球蛋白在经物理或化学方法处理后发生结构变化的研究[49]也表明：这种结合是由抗体分子 Fab 区之间的初级（非共价结合）相互作用引起的，但在这种情况下当然不可能由抗原介导。这种结合似乎会导致 Fc 区的解折叠，这和抗体 γG 分子与抗原结合时所发生的变化相似。因此，在发生聚集的 γG 球蛋白中，这种结合为分子间 Fc 区发生相互作用从而形成各种生物活性位点提供了可能。因而看似应当为随机过程的分子聚集似乎是一个高度有序的聚合反应，这很可能是由单体分子 Fab 区的初始分子间反应引起的。

完整表征这些三级和四级结构的重要变化对于解释其他免疫学现象具有重大的意义。就速发型超敏反应来说，现在需要做的是表征 γE 球蛋白分子在结合时所形成的"组织激活位点"并阐明位于靶细胞上的"底物"的类别。需要考虑到各种可能性。例如，反应素－过敏原在细胞表面的结合能否激活可以水解细胞膜中磷脂的磷脂酶[50]；或者是否会通过与补体介导的细胞溶解反应相似的途径引起酯酶的激活[51]。另一种可能性[52]是，分布于细胞膜内表面的腺苷酸环化酶系统被激活（在这里它催化 ATP 转变为环化 AMP），该系统已被证明与某些激素的功能有关[53]。某些与腺苷酸环化酶系统相关的多肽类激素（例如 ACTH）同时又是有效的组胺释放者[54]，这一点并非偶然。然而，排除下面这种更为简单的可能性是很重要的，即认为最初的启动来源于表面结合型 γE 抗体分子在结合时所引起的细胞膜的物理剪切（有一位研究人员[44]称之为"硬化"）。

今后的任务

尽管目前研究的主动权已经转移到了生物化学家和生物物理学家的手里，但 γE 抗体的许多其他方面的行为仍需要免疫学角度的研究。例如，借助于抗骨髓瘤蛋白

begin to identify the sites of binding of γE antibodies on their target cells; as well as their sites of synthesis in human lymphoid tissues. Immunofluorescence studies[55] have provided evidence that γE antibodies are formed locally in the respiratory and gastro-intestinal tract where they probably become involved in allergic states affecting these organs. In any studies of γE antibody synthesis it will be important to answer the fundamental question about the definition of the factors which govern the production of sensitizing rather than immunizing antibodies. Here the use of animal models[56] is particularly revealing, because it is becoming apparent that the reagin-like antibodies produced in species like the rat, the rabbit and the mouse closely resemble the human γE antibodies. The chemical nature of the allergen, and its form and mode of administration are proving important factors in deciding the nature of the resultant antibody response, as is the influence of other classes of antibody produced concomitantly. Through such investigations it is becoming possible to define the immunological basis of "desensitization" (that is hyposensitization), a prophylactic measure which has been practiced by clinical allergists for several years and which is thought to encourage the production of γG-type antibodies which bind allergen preferentially (besides producing effects at the cellular level).

Other possible new forms of prophylaxis are suggested by studies[57] on the prevention of the passive sensitization of baboons with allergic human serum by the systemic administration of myeloma IgE, where a refractory state persisting for about a week has been induced by the intravenous injection of about 10 mg protein/kg body weight. The ultimate aim of this approach would be the isolation of a low molecular weight peptide fragment of the myeloma IgE, which retained tissue-binding activity and which could be made available in large amounts by application of modern methods of polypeptide synthesis.

Another advantage to the clinical allergist resulting from the discovery of the myeloma proteins has been the development of methods of measuring IgE concentration which do not rely on tissue or leucocyte sensitization. For example, radioimmunosorbent assay procedures involving the use of anti-IgE[24] or specific allergen[58] coupled chemically to dextran (or some other suitable insoluble carrier such as a cellulose carbonate derivative)[59] have been used to determine the total, or antibody, IgE levels in the sera of patients, and the use of radiolabelled anti-antibody[59] has rendered the single radial diffusion test sufficiently sensitive to detect the relatively low levels of IgE in allergic sera by autoradiography.

It is important to recognize, however, that γE antibodies need not necessarily be deleterious, as suggested, for example, by studies[60] of the immune reactions occurring in the mucous membranes of the rat during the expulsion of an infecting nematode (*Nippostrongylus brasiliensis*). There is evidence of an association between a sharp rise in intestinal mast cells, an alteration of mucosal permeability (effected by vasoactive amines released from the mast cells) and the expulsion of the parasites. It is tempting to conclude, therefore, in this situation that γE antibodies are fulfilling a protective role (the so called "self-cure" mechanism[61]); and it may be significant that one of the few conditions (other

916

的特异性抗血清，人们有可能开始进行 γE 抗体在其靶细胞上的结合位点以及在人淋巴组织中的合成位点的鉴定。免疫荧光实验 [55] 证明：γE 抗体只在呼吸道以及胃肠道中形成，并且很可能与这些器官的过敏反应有关。在对 γE 抗体合成的研究中，对何种因子控制着产生致敏性抗体而不是免疫性抗体这一基本问题的解答很重要。在这一点上，基于多种动物模型的研究很有意义 [56]，因为人们逐渐明确了在大鼠、兔子和小鼠等物种中所产生的类似反应素的抗体与人类的 γE 抗体非常相似。已证明过敏原的化学本质、形式和注射方式是决定所产生的抗体反应的重要因素，同时出现的其他类抗体所产生的影响也很重要。通过这些研究，人们也许可以弄清"脱敏反应"（即消除过敏）的免疫学基础，这种预防性的方法已经被临床过敏症专科医师应用了很多年，它被认为能够刺激产生可以优先与过敏原结合的 γG 抗体（除了产生细胞水平上的效应之外）。

通过全身注射骨髓瘤 IgE 阻止由人过敏性血清引起狒狒被动致敏反应的研究 [57] 为预防过敏提供了另外一些可能的新形式。每千克体重静脉注射约 10 毫克蛋白可使受试者在一周左右的时间内维持耐受状态。这种方法最终的发展趋势将是从骨髓瘤 IgE 中分离出一个低分子量的多肽片段，该片段能保持组织结合活性并且可以通过现代的多肽合成方法被大规模地制备出来。

骨髓瘤蛋白的发现带给临床过敏症专科医师的另一个好处是，得到了不依赖于组织或白细胞敏感化的测量 IgE 浓度的方法。例如：在放射免疫吸附试验中使用抗 IgE 抗体 [24] 或通过化学方式连接到葡聚糖（或其他合适的不溶性载体，例如纤维素碳酸盐衍生物）[59] 上的特异过敏原 [58]，并用这样的放射免疫吸附法测定患者血清中总的或抗体性的 IgE 水平；使用放射性标记的抗抗体 [59] 使得单向扩散试验灵敏到可以借助放射自显影术检测到过敏性血清中含量相对较低的 IgE。

然而，意识到 γE 抗体并不一定都是有害的也很重要，正如在对大鼠黏膜排斥感染线虫（巴西日圆线虫）时产生的免疫反应的研究 [60] 中所揭示出的结果。有证据表明，在肠肥大细胞迅速增多、黏膜渗透性改变（由肥大细胞释放的血管活性胺引起）和排斥寄生虫之间存在着一种关联。因此，我们很容易得出这样一个结论，即 γE 抗体在这种情况下起到了一种保护作用（即所谓的"自愈"机制 [61]）；并且，在血清中可以检测到很高浓度 IgE 抗体的少数几种情况（除了哮喘－枯草热型超敏反应和

than a hypersensitivity of the asthma-hay fever type, and atopic eczema) where very high serum IgE levels have been recorded is in human (as well as animal) parasitic infections.

(**233**, 310-316; 1971)

D. R. Stanworth: Department of Experimental Pathology, University of Birmingham.

References:

1. Frausnitz, C., and Köstner, H., *Zentr. Bakteriol., Parasiteuk.,* Abt. I, **86**, 160 (1921).

2. Coca, A. F., and Grove, E. F., *J. Immunol.,* **10**, 445 (1925).

3. Kuhns, W. J., *Proc. Soc. Exp. Biol. Med.*, **108**, 63 (1961).

4. Augustin, R., in *Handbook of Experimental Immunology* (edit. by Weir, D. M.), 1076 (Blackwell, Oxford, 1967).

5. Stanworth, D. R., and Kuhns, W. J., *Immunology*, **8**, 323 (1965).

6. Stanworth, D. R., and Kuhns, W. J., quoted in Stanworth, D. R., *Adv. Immunol.*, **3**, 181 (1963).

7. Hemmings, W. A., and Brambell, F. W. R., *Brit. Med. Bull.*, **17**, 96 (1961).

8. Tiselius, A., and Kabat, E. A., *J. Exp. Med.*, **69**, 119 (1939).

9. Brattsten, I., Colldahl, H., and Laurell, A. H. F., *Acta Allergol.*, **8**, 339 (1955).

10. Stanworth, D. R., *Immunology*, **2**, 384 (1959).

11. Franklin, E. C., and Stanworth, D. R., *J. Exp. Med.*, **114**, 521 (1961).

12. Heremans, J. F., Heremans, M. T., and Schultze, H. E., *Clin. Chim. Acta*, **4**, 96 (1959).

13. Stanworth, D. R., *Intern. Arch. Allergy*, **28**, 71 (1965).

14. Vaerman, J. P., Epstein, W., Fudenberg, H., and Ishizaka, K., *Nature*, **203**, 1046 (1964).

15. Fireman, P., Vannier, W. E., and Goodman, H. C., *J. Exp. Med.*, **117**, 203 (1963).

16. Ishizaka, K., Ishizaka, T., and Hornbrook, M., *J. Allergy*, **34**, 395 (1963).

17. Ishizaka, K., and Ishizaka, T., *J. Allergy*, **37**, 169 (1966).

18. Stanworth, D. R., *Adv. Immunol.*, **3**, 181 (1963).

19. Rowe, D. S., and Fahey, J. L., *J. Exp. Med.*, **121**, 171 (1965).

20. Terr, A. I., and Bentz, J. D., *J. Allergy*, **35**, 206 (1964).

21. Andersen, B. R., and Vannier, W. E., *J. Exp. Med.*, **203**, 117 (1963).

22. Ishizaka, K., and Ishizaka, T., *J. Allergy*, **42**, 330 (1968).

23. Ishizaka, K., Ishizaka, T., and Hornbrook, M. M., *J. Immunol.*, **97**, 35 (1966).

24. Johansson, S. G. O., Bennich, H., and Wide, L., *Immunology*, **14**, 265 (1968).

25. Johansson, S. G. O., and Bennich, H., *Immunology*, **13**, 381 (1967).

26. Bennich, H., Ishizaka, K., Ishizaka, T., and Johansson, S. G. O., *J. Immunol.*, **102**, 826 (1969).

27. Stanworth, D. R., Humphrey, J. H., Bennich, H., and Johansson, S. G. O., *Lancet*, ii, 330 (1967).

28. Bennich, H., Ishizaka, K., Johansson, S. G. O., Rowe, D. S., Stanworth, D. R., and Terry, W. D., *Bull. World Health Org.*, **38**, 151 (1968).

29. Ogawa, M., Kochwa, S., Smith, C., Ishizaka, K., and McIntyre, O. R., *New Engl. J. Med.*, **281**, 1217 (1969).

30. Stanworth, D. R., Humphrey, J. H., Bennich, H., and Johansson, S. G. O., *Lancet*, ii, 17 (1968).

31. Stanworth, D. R., Housley, J., Bennich, H., and Johansson, S. G. O. (in preparation).

32. Stanworth, D. R., Housley, J., Bennich, H., and Johansson, S. G. O., *Immunochemistry*, **7**, 321 (1970).

33. Sheard, P., Killingback, P. G., and Blair, A. M. J. N., *Nature*, **216**, 283 (1967).

34. Van Arsdel, P. P., and Sells, C. J., *Science*, **141**, 1190 (1963).

35. Goodfriend, L., and Luhovy, J. I., *Intern. Arch. Allergy*, **33**, 171 (1968).

36. Shore, P. A., Burkhalter, A., and Cohn, U. H., *J. Pharmacol. Exp. Ther.*, **127**, 182 (1959).

37. Schild, H. O., in *Biochemistry of the Acute Allergic Reactions* (edit. by Austen, K. F., and Becker, E. L.), 99 (CIOMS Symp., 1968).

38. Lichenstein, L. M., in *Biochemistry of the Acute Allergic Reactions* (edit. by Austen, K. F., and Becker, E. L.), 153 (CIOMS Symp., 1968).

39. Stanworth, D. R., and Henney, C. S., *Immunology*, **12**, 1267 (1967).

40. Hastie, R., *Clin. Exp. Immunol.* (in the press).

41. Stanworth, D. E., *Immediate Hypersensitivity* (monograph, in preparation).

42. Henney, C. S., and Stanworth, D. R., *Nature*, **210**, 1071 (1966).

遗传性过敏性湿疹）之一是人（或动物）受到寄生虫感染时，这一点可能意义重大。

（张锦彬 翻译；刘京国 审稿）

43. Stanworth, D. R., *Clin. Exp. Immunol.*, **6**, 1 (1970).

44. Levine, B. B., *J. Immunol.*, **94**, 111, 121 (1965).

45. De Weck, A. L., and Schneider, C. H., in *Bayer Symp. on Problems in Allergy*, **1** (1969).

46. Ishizaka, K., and Ishizaka, T., *J. Immunol.*, **100**, 554 (1968).

47. Forsgren, A., and Sjöquist, J., *J. Immunol.*, **97**, 822 (1966).

48. Stanworth, D. R., Matthews, N., and Sjöquist, J. (in preparation).

49. Matthews, N., and Stanworth, D. R., *Proc. Eighteenth Bruges Symp. Protides of Biological Fluids* (in the press).

50. Fernö, O., Högberg, B., and Uvnäs, B., *Acta Pharmacol.*, **17**, 18 (1960).

51. Becker, E. L., and Austen, K. F., *J. Exp. Med.*, **124**, 379 (1966).

52. Lichenstein, L. M., *Proc. Eighth Symp. Collegium Intern. Allergologicum*, Switzerland (1970).

53. Catt, K. J., *Lancet*, i, 763 (1970).

54. Jaques, R., *Intern. Arch. Allergy*, **28**, 221 (1965).

55. Ishizaka, K., and Ishizaka, T., *Clin. Exp. Immunol.*, **6**, 25 (1970).

56. Patterson, R., *Prog. Allergy*, **13**, 332 (1969).

57. Stanworth, D. R., *Clin. Allergy*, **1** (in the press).

58. Vide, L., Bennich, H., and Johansson, S. G. O., *Lancet*, ii, 1105 (1967).

59. Rowe, D. S., *Bull. World Health Org.*, **40**, 613 (1969).

60. Miller, H. R. P., and Jarrett, W. F. H. (in the press).

61. Stewart, D. F., *Austral. J. Agric. Res.*, **4**, 100 (1953).

62. Bennich, H., and Johansson, S. G. O., *Vox Sang.*, **19**, 1 (1970).

Egg Transfer in Domestic Animals

L. E. A. Rowson

Editor's Note

Although the first successful egg transfer experiments were performed in the late nineteenth century, the technique was almost totally disregarded, both as a method of livestock improvement and as a tool for reproductive research, until after the Second World War. Here Tim Rowson describes the revival that subsequently ensued, which he based on his 1970 Hammond Memorial Lecture. Rowson, a pioneer in cattle embryo transfer, points out that egg transfer yields pregnancies in cows, but that the low success rates may be due to the surgical techniques used for their initial retrieval. The subsequent development of non-surgical methods in the mid-1970s was a major milestone towards the widespread application of embryo-transfer technology in cattle.

ALTHOUGH the first successful experiments on egg transfer were carried out by Walter Heape of Cambridge late in the nineteenth century, the technique was almost totally disregarded both as a method of livestock improvement and as a tool for reproductive research until after the Second World War. When one considers the enormous value of the technique in genetics and studies on reproductive physiology, this fact is quite astonishing. Egg transfer is, however, now used as a routine technique for research in many small mammals and during the past ten or fifteen years has been extensively used for studies in the larger domestic species, particularly the sheep, goat, pig and cow. In the polytocous species such as the small mammals and even the pig, it is not normally necessary to induce superovulation in order to provide the requisite number of eggs for experimentation but in most of the domestic species this is an important requirement.

Superovulation

Two chief sources of gonadotrophins have been used. In the small mammals and in some of the earlier work on the domestic species, gonadotrophins of pituitary origin were extensively used and were obtained either from the horse, pig or sheep. Their use in the larger animals was, however, rather expensive and to obtain optimum results it was usually necessary to give repeated injections during the follicular phase of the cycle. The alternative source, gonadotrophins obtained from the serum of mares pregnant between 50 and 80 days (PMSG), is readily obtainable more cheaply and is effective when administered as a single injection. The follicular response to such gonadotrophins was consistently satisfactory but the ovulatory response often left a great deal to be desired. Many animals developed large numbers of follicles of which either only a few or none at all ovulated and this phenomenon seemed to vary with differing batches of PMSG; some

家畜卵移植

罗森

编者按

虽然第一次成功的卵移植实验早在 19 世纪晚期就已经实现，但是直到第二次世界大战结束之前这项技术几乎被人们完全遗忘了，不论是作为改良家畜的方法，还是作为研究繁殖的工具。蒂姆·罗森在本文中描述了这项技术在第二次世界大战之后的复兴，文章取材于 1970 年他在哈蒙德纪念讲座上发表的讲话。作为牛胚胎移植的先驱者，罗森指出卵移植可以使母牛怀孕。但成功率很低，这可能与最初用于回收卵子的外科手术有关。随后在 20 世纪 70 年代中叶，非外科手术方法的推广成为牛胚胎移植技术得以广泛应用的一个重要里程碑。

虽然第一次成功的卵移植实验早在 19 世纪晚期就已经由剑桥大学的沃尔特·希普实现，但是直到第二次世界大战结束之前这项技术几乎被人们完全遗忘了，不论是作为改良家畜的方法，还是作为研究繁殖的工具。就遗传学技术和生殖生理学研究的巨大价值而论，这一事实非常令人迷惑不解。虽然在过去的 10 年或 15 年中，卵移植一直被广泛地用于研究较大的家畜，特别是绵羊、山羊、猪和牛，但是现在它已成为研究多种小型哺乳动物的常规技术。对于多胎的家畜，例如小型哺乳动物，甚至包括猪，要提供实验所需的卵数一般不需要诱导其超数排卵。但对于大多数家畜来说，这是一个很重要的必备条件。

超 数 排 卵

目前使用过的促性腺激素主要有两种来源。来自于马、猪或绵羊的垂体促性腺激素被广泛应用于小型哺乳动物和对家畜进行的一些早期研究中。然而，在研究较大的动物时使用促性腺激素成本就会很高，并且为了得到最佳结果通常需要在卵泡期内反复注射。促性腺激素也可以从怀孕 50 天 ~ 80 天的母马血清中获得（PMSG），这不仅很容易通过较为便宜的方式得到，而且单次注射也能有效。卵泡对这类促性腺激素的反应一向是令人满意的，但是排卵反应通常还有很大的改善空间。很多动物能产生大量的卵泡，其中只有几个排卵或者全部不排卵，这种现象似乎随着 PMSG 批次的不同而变化；其中一些不仅可以非常高效地诱发卵泡反应，还可以诱发排卵，而另一些则只能诱发卵泡反应。这一问题至今尚未得到彻底解决，不过现

induced both follicular response and ovulation very efficiently but others induced only the first of these. This problem has not yet been completely solved, but it is beginning to look as though the ratio of the two components of PMSG (that is, the follicle stimulating hormone (FSH) and the luteinizing hormone (LH)) may be important. It is well known that a proportion of both cattle and sheep injected with PMSG do not exhibit oestrus at the expected time or, even if they do, the eggs are in some cases unfertilized. It has also been clear for several years that the injection of such gonadotrophins may cause the premature ovulation of a follicle which is present in the ovary at the time of injection and it seems likely that this effect is related to the LH content of the injected gonadotrophin. In such circumstances either the animal would not exhibit oestrus or the effect of the FSH component would cause sufficient follicular response for oestrus to occur but the progesterone secreted by the newly ovulated follicle might adversely affect fertilization. This effect could be explained in a number of ways, including failure of capacitation or failure of sperm transport to the site of fertilization. It is quite common in these conditions to find an absence of spermatozoa in the zona pellucida of the ovulated eggs.

Once a satisfactory batch of PMSG has been indentified, however, it is very efficient, provided that the animal is not overstimulated. In the cow and sheep, for example, it is inadvisable to stimulate the animal to produce more than about twenty ovulations because stimulation beyond this point seems to upset completely the physiological mechanisms of the reproductive tract and the proportion of unfertilized eggs increases rapidly. It is usual, therefore, to aim at an ovulation rate of about ten eggs per animal in these species. The response also varies from species to species; for example, a dose of 1,200 IU of PMSG given to a medium to large sheep will produce a response similar to a dose of 2,000 IU given to a cow weighing six or seven times as much. In most species it is unnecessary to give exogenous LH to obtain ovulation if normal oestrus is exhibited.

Recovery of Eggs

To obtain optimum results after egg transfer it is necessary to transfer the egg to a site where it would be expected to be in normal physiological conditions; because transfer to the uterus is simpler than transfer to the oviduct, it is usual to attempt to recover the eggs at a time when they have entered or are just about to enter the uterus. The timing of this will vary with the species, but is usually 4 to 5 days from the onset of oestrus in the cow and sheep and rather earlier for the pig. A surgical approach is necessary if maximum recovery of egg is to be achieved. This involves a simple laparotomy; the introduction of a fine cannula into the ovarian end of the oviduct and the injection of the flushing fluid into the ovarian portion of the uterus. The eggs are collected in special cups which can be placed directly under the microscope without further manipulation; the state of cleavage of the recovered eggs can then be identified. In the horse and pig there is a valve-like structure at the utero-tubal junction and it is not always possible to carry out retrograde flushing; in such cases it is usual to clamp off the top portion of the uterus, flush the oviduct towards the clamp and insert the recovery tube in the tip of the uterus, so that the fluid containing the eggs can be milked back into the collecting cup. Although this

在人们开始注意到 PMSG 中两种组成成分（即促卵泡激素（FSH）和促黄体生成激素（LH））的比值可能是一个重要的参数。众所周知，有一定比例注射过 PMSG 的牛和绵羊在预期的时间内并没有发情表现，或者即使有发情表现，卵子在某些情况下也是未受精的。另外，几年前人们就已经知道注射这种促性腺激素可能会导致注射时存在于卵巢中的卵泡过早排卵，并且这种效应似乎很可能与注射的促性腺激素中的 LH 含量有关。在过早排卵的情况下，要么动物未显示发情，要么在 FSH 组分的作用下产生了足以导致发情的卵泡反应，但是如果因此排卵，由新排卵的卵泡分泌的孕酮可能会对受精起反作用。可以从很多方面来解释这一效应，包括精子获能的丧失或者精子未能移动到受精点。在这些情况下通常会发现在排出的卵细胞的透明带中并没有精子存在。

虽然如此，我们一度鉴定出了一批令人满意的 PMSG，在动物没有受到过度刺激的情况下它是非常有效的。例如，对于牛和绵羊来说，刺激它们一次排出多于 20 个卵子是不可取的，因为超过这种程度的刺激似乎会完全打乱其生殖系统的生理机能，并且未受精的卵的比例会迅速增加。因此，通常的目标是使每头牛和每只绵羊的排卵率约为 10 个卵子。对 PMSG 的反应也会随着物种的不同而有所不同；例如，给予大中型绵羊 1,200 IU 剂量的 PMSG 将与给予一头相当于绵羊体重 6 倍或 7 倍的牛 2,000 IU 剂量所产生的反应相似。对于大多数物种而言，如果已经表现出正常的发情，就没有必要再给予外源的 LH 来诱导排卵了。

取　卵

为了在卵移植之后得到最佳结果，有必要将卵移植到一个处于正常生理条件下的部位；因为移植到子宫比移植到输卵管更简单，所以通常在卵子已经进入或即将进入子宫时进行取卵。取卵时间会随物种的不同而有所变化，通常是在牛和绵羊发情开始后的 4 天~5 天，如果是猪则会更早些。要想使卵子的回收率达到最大就必须进行外科手术。为此需要实施一次简单的剖腹手术；将一根细管插入输卵管的卵巢端，并向子宫的卵巢端注射冲洗液。卵子被收集到特殊的杯子里，我们可以直接把这些杯子放在显微镜下观察而无需进行进一步的处理；由此可以识别出回收卵的卵裂状态。在马和猪的子宫输卵管交界处有一个类似于阀门的结构，此处并不总能实现反向冲洗；在这种情况下，通常需要夹住子宫的上半部分，同时在子宫顶端插入回收管并朝夹子的方向冲洗输卵管，这样就使含有卵子的液体像挤奶一样回流到回收杯里。虽然这项技术看上去比较原始，但是取卵的效果与直接冲洗法一样好。通常可

technique seems rather crude, egg recovery is as efficient as recovery by the direct flushing method. About 90% of the eggs shed can usually be collected. The most effective flushing medium varies with the species—for the sheep it is homologous serum, for the pig Tyrode plus a little albumen and for the cow TCM 199.

Transfer and Synchronization

The technique of egg transfer is simple—the egg is merely picked up in the medium selected, using a Pasteur pipette attached to a 2 ml. syringe, and the tip of the pipette stabbed through the uterine wall; the egg is then expelled directly into the lumen. A minimum of flushing medium is used, seldom more than 0.1 ml.

The stage of the cycle of the donor and recipient animals must be closely synchronized to obtain optimum pregnancy rates. The degree of variability which can be tolerated is known to be ±2 days in the sheep and ±1 day in the cow; the best results are obtained, however, when oestrus in donor and recipient occurs on the same day (Fig. 1).

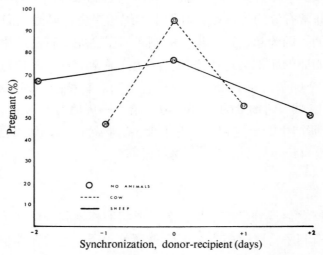

Fig. 1. The effect of varying the degree of synchronization of oestrus on fertility in cattle (- - -) and sheep (———). Numbers of animals are given in the figure.

The results obtained in cases of exact synchronization are remarkably good and are possibly influenced by the fact that any unfertilized, abnormal or retarded eggs are rejected and not transferred after egg recovery from the donor animal.

If the eggs are to be transferred on the day of recovery it is quite satisfactory to store them in the flushing medium in an incubator at 37°C. Sheep pregnancies have been achieved successfully after up to 72 h of storage at 8°C, but the percentage of successful transfers decreases rapidly after 24 h. It has also been shown that the transfer of fertilized eggs of the pig, cow and sheep to the oviduct of the rabbit will result in their continued normal development for longer periods; they can then be recovered and successfully retransferred

926

以收集到约 90% 的流出卵子。最有效的冲洗媒介随着物种的不同而有所不同——对于绵羊而言用的是同种血清，猪用的是加了少量蛋白的台罗德氏溶液，牛为组织培养基 199（TCM 199）。

移植和同步性

这种卵移植技术很简单——只需用与 2 ml 注射器相连的巴斯德吸管吸取选定媒介中的卵子，然后将吸管的尖端刺入子宫壁，这样卵子就可以直接排入到内腔。冲洗媒介的使用量越少越好，一般不会超过 0.1 ml。

为了获得最佳妊娠率，供体动物和受体动物的发情期必须保持基本同步。已知的允许误差是：绵羊为 ±2 天，牛为 ±1 天；然而，当供体动物和受体动物在同一天发情时我们得到的结果最好（图 1）。

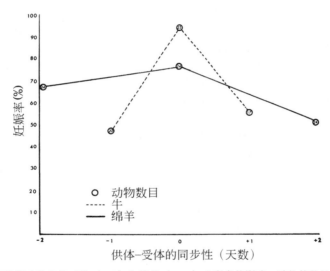

图 1. 发情同步程度的变化对牛（- - -）和绵羊（——）生育率的影响，动物的数目显示于图中。

精确同步时所得的结果非常好，但以下处理可能会对结果有影响，即在从供体动物中回收卵子之后进行移植之前去除了所有未受精的、异常的或发育迟缓的卵子。

如果卵子在回收的当日进行移植，则将它们储存在被置于 37℃ 恒温箱中的冲洗媒介里就很合适。利用在 8℃ 下储存达 72 h 的卵子曾使绵羊成功怀孕，但移植的成功率在 24 h 后迅速下降。研究还发现：将猪、牛和绵羊的受精卵移植到兔子的输卵管中会使它们在较长的时间内继续正常生长；随后可将它们回收并成功地再次移植

to suitable recipients. This shows that the requirements for culture of eggs of these species are not very specific and augurs well for *in vitro* culture of such eggs. The use of the rabbit as an incubator would permit the export of large numbers of eggs, for example, of cattle at very little cost, to various parts of the world. The transfer of such eggs after prolonged storage in the rabbit does, however, mean that development of the conceptus will only take place to a certain stage, after which it dies; the membranes are eventually expelled or resorbed. The ultimate solution to the problem of egg storage will lie in deep freezing.

Non-surgical Transfer

Most of the successful work carried out on egg transfer involves a laparotomy and the surgical recovery and transfer of the egg. Access to the uterus of the cow by way of the cervix is quite easy, but attempts to obtain pregnancies after the transfer of eggs in this way have been very disappointing. There are two reasons for this. First, the luteal phase uterus of the cow is very susceptible to infection and the introduction of any organism— very likely when the non-surgical approach is used—will cause pyometritis. Second, the insertion of a catheter, which might be used to introduce the egg, has a stimulating effect on the cervix and uterus so that uterine contractility is enhanced; eggs deposited in this way are frequently expelled and are found in the vagina within a few hours of their deposition. This effect is believed to be caused by the release of oxytocin from the pituitary as a result of the cervical and uterine stimulation, but we have so far been unable to confirm this. We are endeavouring to find an explanation of this phenomenon and to find ways in which the problem of egg expulsion can be overcome.

Reproductive Physiology

The technique of egg transfer has been used in the large domestic animals to study various fundamental and applied problems of reproductive physiology, One of the most interesting aspects has been the use of egg transfer in experiments on utero-ovarian-embryo relationships. The factors concerned with the initiation and formation of the cyclical corpus luteum are well known, but those associated with regression are far less clearly understood.

The uterus is known to be closely involved in the process because hysterectomy in the domestic animal results in persistence of the corpus luteum for prolonged periods and grafting of the removed endometrium between the flank muscles will restore cyclical behaviour and normal corpus luteum regression. The question which arises, therefore, is how the embryo overcomes the normal regression; it would seem from the repeated injection of embryo homogenates into the uterus that it acts in an anti-luteolytic manner. In an attempt to establish at what stage the presence of the embryo within the uterus is essential to prevent corpus luteum regression, eggs have been transferred at later and later stages until it is no longer possible to maintain the corpus luteum as one of pregnancy. In the sheep with a 16 to 17 day cycle the embryo must be present within the uterus by day $12\frac{1}{2}$, otherwise regression cannot be prevented. Similar requirements have not been worked out in detail for other domestic animals, but there are indications that a relatively earlier presence of the embryo within the uterus is necessary in the cow and pig.

到合适的受体中。这说明猪、牛和绵羊的卵子培养条件并不是很特殊，对这些卵子进行体外培养应该会有很好的前景。使用兔子作为恒温箱可以将大量卵子，例如牛卵子，以非常廉价的方式运往世界各地。但是，在用兔子体内长期储存的卵子进行移植时发现：孕体只能发育到某个特定阶段，在这个阶段之后孕体将会死亡；膜最终会被排出或者被再吸收。解决卵子储存问题的最终方法将是低温冷冻。

非手术移植

大多数成功的卵移植实验包括以下两步：先用剖腹和外科手术取卵，然后进行受精卵移植。从子宫颈很容易进入牛的子宫，但是用这种方式进行卵移植之后很难使牛怀孕。原因有两点。第一，牛子宫在黄体期时非常容易被感染，因而引入任何有机体都将导致脓性子宫炎——当使用非手术方式时很容易出现这种情况。第二，为了植入卵子有可能需要插入导管，这会刺激子宫颈和子宫导致宫缩增强。用这种方式放置的卵经常会被排出，在放置后几小时之内就会在阴道中发现这些卵。这种效应被认为是由于子宫颈和子宫受到刺激致使垂体释放催产素造成的，但迄今为止我们还不能证实这一点。我们正努力寻找对这一现象的解释，并在寻找可以克服卵排出问题的办法。

生殖生理学

人们已将卵移植技术应用于大型家畜以研究生殖生理学中的各种基本问题以及应用方面的问题。其中最有趣的一个方面是将卵移植应用于研究子宫－卵巢－胚胎之间关系的实验。那些影响周期性黄体产生和形成的因素已为人所共知，但是与黄体退化有关的因素却很少有人知晓。

一般认为子宫与此过程密切相关，因为切除家畜的子宫会导致黄体在很长时间内持续存在，并且如果把移去的子宫内膜移植到侧腹肌之间，则周期行为和黄体的正常退化就会得到恢复。因此产生了这样一个问题，即胚胎怎样才能克服正常的衰退；向子宫中反复注入胚胎匀浆似乎可以起到抑制黄体溶解的作用。为了确定妊娠建立的时间，即在什么阶段将胚胎植入子宫才能有效防止黄体退化，我们将卵子分批移植到受体子宫，一直到其不再能维持妊娠黄体为止。绵羊的周期为 16 天 ~17 天，因而在 12.5 天之内必须将胚胎置于子宫中，否则无法抑制黄体退化的发生。我们还未详细了解其他家畜的类似条件，但有迹象表明在牛和猪中有必要更早地将胚胎置于子宫内。

There is a remarkable unilateral utero-embryo-ovarian relationship in the cow and the sheep, which has been demonstrated by the use of egg transfer. If, for example, an egg is confined to the uterine horn adjoining the corpus luteum, the pregnancy continues normally; but if a similar egg is confined to the contralateral horn, pregnancy never occurs and the corpus luteum of the non-pregnant side regresses normally. This can be shown to be a unilateral luteolytic effect by removal of the non-pregnant horn adjoining the corpus luteum; the pregnancy will then continue normally. The situation is slightly modified in the case of the pig, for if a similar situation is created by confining embryos to one uterine horn, the lytic effect of the non-pregnant side will eventually result in regression of both sets of corpora lutea. The unilateral nature of these effects would suggest that it is the uterus itself rather than an indirect effect through some other gland which is responsible for lysis. It has been recently shown that radioactive material within the uterine vein is present in higher concentration in the ovarian artery, which runs in close apposition to it, than in other parts of the circulation; this suggests some form of direct transfer or communication between vein and artery although this has not been demonstrated anatomically and would involve a blood flow against the normal pressure differences.

Maturation and Culture

For the study of maturation and *in vitro* fertilization and for the satisfactory culture of eggs, laboratory techniques can only be a guide and it eventually becomes necessary to transfer eggs treated in this way to assess viability and the continuation of normal development. In experiments to assess the fertility of frozen semen it is often convenient to use the two oviducts separately, one as a control, to be injected with normal semen, and the other as a receiver for the experimental sample. Eggs transferred to each oviduct can then be examined and compared. The possibility of using the oviduct connected by fine tubes leading to the exterior as an *in vivo* means of fertilizing follicular eggs, both within and between species, is being investigated.

The demonstration that excellent pregnancy rates after transfer could be achieved with TCM 199 as a storage and flushing medium for cow eggs was followed by an attempt to increase production in this species by the introduction of two eggs into one uterine horn to produce twins. The first experiments were disappointing and only 12.5% produced twins. It was later found that when the two eggs were both deposited in a single uterine horn, migration of one egg did not occur and both implanted on the side; there was consequent competition for nutrients and death of one of the embryos frequently occurred. One egg was deposited in each horn during later experiments and a twinning rate of 73% was obtained. The economic implications of this finding are obvious and a vigorous attempt is being made to solve the problem of the reduced pregnancy rate obtained by non-surgical transfer of eggs so that the twinning technique can be put into practice.

Chimaerism in Cattle

Fusion of the foetal membranes occurs very early in pregnancy in many cattle twins and there is an interchange of haemopoietic and other types of cell between the embryos. The testes cells of the male in mixed sex twins contain many of the XX variety, but it is not

牛和绵羊中存在的子宫－胚胎－卵巢关系很显然具有单侧特性，这已经被卵移植实验所证实。举例来说，如果一个卵子被限制在与黄体相邻的子宫角内，则怀孕可以正常进行；但如果同样的卵子被限制在对侧角，则怀孕永远不会发生且未孕一侧的黄体会正常退化。在切除与黄体相邻的未孕角之后发现这里只有单侧的溶黄体作用；之后怀孕将正常进行。猪的情况略有不同，因为假如同样是将胚胎限制在一个子宫角，则未孕一侧的溶黄体作用将最终导致两部分黄体都退化。上述效应的单侧特性表明，产生溶解现象的原因是子宫本身而非其他一些腺体的间接作用。最近有研究表明：注入子宫静脉中的放射性物质出现在与该静脉紧挨着的并行卵巢动脉中的浓度要高于其出现在血液循环中其他部位的浓度；尽管尚未得到解剖学上的证明，并且这种血液流动可能会使压差不正常，但仍能说明在静脉和动脉之间存在着某种形式的直接迁移或连通。

成熟和培养

为了进行成熟研究和体外受精研究以及更好地培养卵子，实验室技术只能作为一个前导，最终还是需要移植以这种方式处理的卵子来评估它的成活能力以及继续正常发育的能力。在评估冷冻精子受精能力的实验中，一种常用的便利方法是：分别使用两个独立的输卵管，一个作为对照，注入正常精子，另一个注入实验样本。而后对移植到每个输卵管中的卵子进行检查和比较。人们正在研究是否有可能利用与导向体外的细管相连接的输卵管使体内的卵泡卵子受精，不管是在同一物种内部还是在不同物种之间。

在证明用 TCM 199 作为牛卵子的储存和冲洗媒介可以在移植后得到令人满意的妊娠率之后，我们尝试将两个卵子引入到一个子宫角中以产生双胞胎来提高牛的生育率。第一批实验没有得到令人满意的结果，只有 12.5% 产生了双胞胎。后来发现：当两个卵子都被置于同一个子宫角时，没有一个卵子会发生迁移，两个卵子都挤在这一端；随即出现两者对养分的竞争，结果常常导致其中一个胚胎的死亡。在后来的实验中，我们将两个卵子分别放到一个子宫角中，从而得到了 73% 的双胎率。这一发现的经济价值是显而易见的，人们正在积极尝试一些方案以解决用非手术方式移植卵子时妊娠率下降的问题，因此双胞胎技术是有可能会被付诸实践的。

牛的嵌合性

在多数双胞胎牛中，胎膜的融合发生在怀孕的最开始阶段，并且造血细胞或其他类型的细胞在两个胚胎之间存在互换现象。在混合性别双胞胎中，雄性的睾丸细

yet established whether germ cells of this type continue through to actual spermatozoa. It seems likely that such a situation would occur in the case of chimaeric male calves. If so, it would mean that a proportion of the offspring of one twin may genetically be by the brother and this could seriously interfere with the accuracy of progeny tests, in which such bulls are used for artificial insemination. The percentage of twins born is not high (usually about 2 to 3%), but from our earlier experiments it was obvious that one of a pair present within a single horn frequently died by day 60 of gestation; as fusion of membranes occurs well before this stage, the fact that a cow has a single calf does not, therefore, mean that it did not start life originally as a twin. Twin ovulations have been estimated to be as high as 11% in the cow by some workers.

Our experiments on twinning open up a simple method of determining whether one twin can sire his brother's offspring. We have been able to transfer the egg of one breed of cattle to one uterine horn and that of a different breed to the other, using breeds which would colour mark their offspring. The use of such twins to inseminate a fairly large number of females should establish with certainty whether the interchanged germ cells of the chimaeras are capable of carrying through spermatogenesis. The use of similar sets of females will also be of interest because one can determine if the mixture of blood types has any effect on milk production and quality by producing twins of widely differing production characteristics such as the Jersey and Friesian. Such chimaeras are also tissue tolerant, so it should also be possible reciprocally to interchange half of the udder and to study milk production at the cellular level with the blood supply remaining constant.

Larger Litters

Transplantation has been used quite extensively to investigate the possibility of increasing the litter size, particularly of the sheep and to some extent of the pig.

Initial experiments involving the transfer of either two or five eggs to recipient sheep indicated that the uterus had a severely limiting effect on the number of offspring which would continue development and it became obvious that the problem was not solely one of availability of sufficient eggs. Lawson has recently investigated this problem in breeds of sheep of normally high, medium and low fertility, by the transfer of five eggs from a common genetic source to each group. At the time of transfer the potential fertility of each group was obtained by counting the number of corpora lutea (indicating the number of eggs shed). This work showed that the high and medium fertility breeds were producing eggs at almost their maximum potential, but that the uterus of the low fertility breed was capable of carrying about twice the maximum number assessed by corpora lutea counts. The last of these is the chief breed of sheep in New Zealand and clearly selection on the basis of high ovulation is necessary if litter sizes are to be increased. Although the litter size of the pig can be increased to some extent, the same uterine limitations apply as described previously for the cow and sheep.

Selection for an overall increase in litter size does, therefore, involve many factors, and in the cow and sheep, for example, there are great variations in cotyledon numbers; these are obviously of importance in multiple births and an examination of their inheritance

胞包含很多 XX 变种，但直到现在仍不清楚这种类型的生殖细胞是否能继续分裂分化到生成实际的精子。也许这样的情况会发生在嵌合体雄性牛仔中。如果事实确实如此，那就意味着在双胞胎之一的后代中有一部分可能在遗传学上应该算是它兄弟的后代，这会严重干扰用后代公牛进行人工授精实验的准确性。双胞胎的出生比例并不高（通常约为 2%~3%），但从我们的早期实验中可以很明显地看到：被置于同一个子宫角的一对卵子中的一个通常会在妊娠 60 天之内死亡；因为膜的融合刚好在这一阶段之前发生，因此，一头母牛只生下一个单胞胎并不意味着它在生命刚开始的时候不是双胞胎。一些研究人员曾估计牛的双胞胎排卵率可高达 11%。

我们的双胞胎实验为确定一个双胞胎是否是它兄弟后代的种畜提供了一个简单的方法。我们已经能够把一个品种的牛的卵子移植到一个子宫角中，而把另一个品种的牛的卵子移植到另一个子宫角，可以用颜色来区别所选用品种的后代。用这种双胞胎对相当数量的母牛进行人工授精就可以明确地知道嵌合体中互换的生殖细胞是否能够实现精子发生。用类似系列的母牛进行实验也同样受到人们的关注，因为人们可以通过制造产奶能力完全不同的双胞胎，如泽西奶牛和弗里斯兰奶牛，来确定血型混合是否会对产奶量和品质有影响。这种嵌合体还具有组织耐受性，所以应该也可以互换一半乳房，并且可以让我们在保持其供血恒定的前提下从细胞水平上研究产奶量。

更多的产仔数

移植技术曾被非常广泛地用于研究增加产仔数的可能性，特别是绵羊和少数几个品种的猪。

最初的实验是将 2 个或者 5 个卵子移植到绵羊受体中，结果表明绵羊子宫对将在其中继续发育的后代的数量有严格的限制。显然，问题不仅仅在于要拥有足够多的卵子。最近劳森采用在正常情况下具有高、中和低生育率的绵羊品种对这一问题进行了研究，方法是把具有共同遗传来源的 5 个卵子分别移植到每个组中。在移植的时候可以通过计算黄体的数量（代表排出卵子的数量）来获得每个组潜在的生育率。这项研究表明：具有高、中等生育率的品种排出的卵子数几乎等于它们的最大潜在能力；而低生育率品种的子宫可以容纳的卵子数量是根据黄体数估计出的最大生育能力的两倍。后者是新西兰的主要绵羊品种，很明显，如果要增加产仔数，就必须在高排卵的基础上进行选择。虽然猪的产仔数可以有某种程度的增加，但是猪的子宫也有与前面介绍的牛和绵羊子宫相同的限制作用。

因此，为增加总产仔数而进行的选择确实与很多因素有关。例如，牛和绵羊在绒毛叶数量上的巨大差异；这些在多胎妊娠中显然是很重要的因素，因而有必要检

would be worthwhile. This can only be done at slaughter and would, therefore, require superovulation and removal of fertilized eggs from such animals so that they could be transferred to recipients if a high cotyledon count was found.

Identical Twins

Although identical twins are rarely produced by domestic animals, they are invaluable for research and the possibility of producing them artificially has been enhanced by work on small mammals and the pig. It has been shown that the removal of all but one blastomere of even a four or eight-cell egg can result in normal offspring after the transfer of that egg to a suitable recipient. In principle, therefore, the transfer of removed blastocysts to emptied zonae could lead to the production of identical offspring, but a number of problems have arisen, the chief one being that the blastomere injected into the new zona is very liable to be exuded through the crack made at the time of injection. Attempts are being made to overcome this loss by temporary transfer of such eggs to the rabbit oviduct which coats them with a layer of mucin (Fig. 2); these experiments are still in progress. An alternative approach which seems to be successful in the small mammals is to divide the blastocyst and then to culture the two halves before transfer until they become spherical again. Attempts to use this technique have not yet been made in the domestic animals.

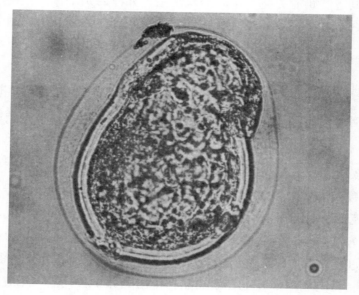

Fig. 2. A sheep blastocyst injected with cells (lower left) when at the eight cell stage and transferred to the rabbit oviduct to become sealed with a mucin coat.

It is clear that the value of egg transfer has only relatively recently been fully realized and there is little doubt that it will be extensively used as a tool for research in reproductive physiology in the future.

(**233**, 379-381; 1971)

L. E. A. Rowson: ARC Unit of Reproductive Physiology and Biochemistry, University of Cambridge, 307 Huntingdon Road, Cambridge.

查它们的遗传特征。这只能在屠宰的时候做到，因此需要超数排卵和从这些动物身上取出受精卵，这样它们才可以被移植到受体中，前提是绒毛叶数量很多。

同卵双胞胎

虽然家畜很少会产下同卵双胞胎，但它们在研究上无比珍贵。通过对小型哺乳动物和猪的研究，人工产生同卵双胞胎的可能性已经有所提高。结果表明：即使在4细胞卵或者8细胞卵的所有卵裂球中只剩下一个没有被去除，也会在将这个卵移植到合适的受体之后产生正常的后代。因此，在原则上，将移除的囊胚移植到空的透明带中是可以产生相同后代的；但会引发很多问题，其中一个主要的问题是，被注入新透明带中的卵裂球很容易从注射时留下的缝隙排出来。现在人们正在尝试利用暂时将这些卵移植到兔子的输卵管中以便使它们的表面裹上一层黏蛋白的方法来克服这种损失（图2）；这些实验仍在进行之中。另一种看似很适合小型哺乳动物的方法是分裂囊胚，然后在移植之前培养分开的两部分，直到它们再次成为球形。目前还没有人尝试过在家畜中使用这项技术。

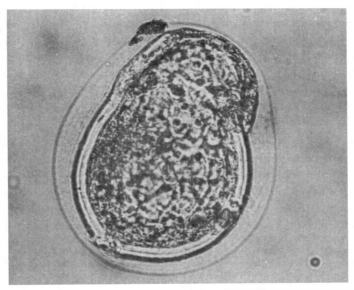

图2. 将处于8细胞阶段的细胞（左下方）注入绵羊囊胚中，并将该囊胚移植到兔子的输卵管中以便裹上一层黏蛋白。

很显然，卵移植的价值直到最近才被人们充分认识到；毫无疑问，在未来它将作为一种研究生殖生理学的工具而得到广泛的应用。

（董培智 翻译；曹文广 审稿）

In vitro Culture of Rabbit Ova from the Single Cell to the Blastocyst Stage

S. Ogawa *et al.*

Editor's Note

Although it was possible at this time to culture fertilized mouse eggs into early embryos, researchers were struggling to replicate their results in other mammalian species and suspected that the tissue culture media played an important role. Here Shyoso Ogawa and colleagues reveal their custom-made synthetic media mix which, they show, supports the *in vitro* development of fertilized rabbit eggs into early embryos. Sixty-five percent of their eggs developed into blastocysts, hollow embryonic structures consisting of around 100 cells, representing a significant increase in the technique's efficiency.

SEVERAL investigators have reported culturing two and four-celled mammalian ova to the blastocyst stage[1-5]. Although successful *in vitro* cultivation of eggs from the single cell to the blastocyst stage has been achieved in the mouse[6-8], few satisfactory methods have been devised for the culture of the ova, at this stage, of other mammalian species, apart from some experiments with human oocytes[9-10]. We now wish to report a higher rate of success with one-celled rabbit ova cultivated *in vitro* to the blastocyst stage, using a nutrient solution composed of several known synthetic media.

Preliminary trials showed that none of the usual chemically defined media were suitable for this work. The best results were obtained with the solution composed of $HamF_{12}$ solution[11] (Nissan 59% v/v); RPMI 1640[12] (Nissan 20% v/v); Eagle's solution[13] (Hanks' solution + Eagle's amino-acids and vitamins, Nissan 20% v/v); sodium caseinate solution (5 g milk casein dissolved slowly in 40–45 ml. of 0.1 N NaOH was centrifuged for 5 min at 3,000 r.p.m., and the supernatant was used as a sodium caseinate solution, 1% v/v).

The medium was adjusted to pH 7.5 with $NaHCO_3$, supplemented with 20% v/v calf serum and completed by adding 60 mg of kanamycin sulphate/1.

Ova were flushed with the medium from the oviducts of a rabbit 17–19 h after copulation. In most cases, Earle's flasks (10 ml.) containing 6 ml. of medium were used for cultivation. Two ova were placed in every flask and cultured for up to 4 days at 37˚C in a humidified incubator with a constant flow of 5% CO_2 in air. About half of the flasks were stoppered tightly with silicon bungs before being placed in the incubator. After incubation, ova were examined by phase contrast microscopy, and classified according to the final stage of development. The microcinephotographic microscope was also used, together with a specially designed cuvette (a flat slender-rectangular solid type, 3 mm internal depth, with 3–4 ml. volume) filled with the medium. The cleavage and behaviour of the embryonic cells could be recorded through the flat sides without distortion under the inverted

936

兔卵子从单细胞到囊胚阶段的体外培养

尾川昭三等

编者按

尽管小鼠受精卵已可以被培育成早期胚胎，研究人员仍在尝试将这项研究成果应用到其他哺乳动物中去，并猜测组织培养基在其中发挥了非常重要的作用。尾川昭三和他的同事们在本文中报道了一种特制的合成培养基混合物，他们的实验结果表明这种混合物有助于将受精的兔卵子体外培养至早期胚胎阶段。其中有65%的卵子发育成了囊胚。空心的胚胎结构包含了大约100个细胞，证明该技术的有效性比以往有了显著的提高。

有几位研究者曾报道过将 2 细胞或 4 细胞的哺乳动物卵子培养至囊胚阶段 [1-5]。尽管已经在小鼠身上成功地实现了从单个卵细胞到囊胚阶段的体外培养 [6-8]，但是除了人类卵母细胞的一些实验以外 [9-10]，人们目前还几乎没有设计出什么令人满意的方法能适用于培养其他哺乳动物的卵子。现在，我们要报道一种能够更成功地实现将单细胞兔卵子体外培养至囊胚阶段的方法，我们使用了一种由若干已知合成培养基组成的营养液。

初步试验显示，所有常用的成分确定的化学培养基都不适用于这项研究。最佳结果是用以下组成的混合溶液得到的：哈姆氏 F_{12} 溶液 [11]（尼桑 59% 体积比）；RPMI 1640[12]（尼桑 20% 体积比）；伊格尔氏溶液 [13]（汉克斯液 + 伊格尔氏氨基酸和维生素，尼桑 20% 体积比）；酪蛋白酸钠溶液（先将 5 克乳酪蛋白缓慢地溶解于40 毫升 ~ 45 毫升 0.1 摩尔 / 升的 NaOH 中，然后以 3,000 转 / 分的速度离心 5 分钟，得到的上清液就是我们所用的酪蛋白酸钠溶液，1% 体积比）。

用 $NaHCO_3$ 将培养基的 pH 值调至 7.5，添加占总体积 20% 的小牛血清，最后按每升体积 60 毫克的量加入硫酸卡那霉素。

在兔子交配后 17 小时到 19 小时之内，用培养基冲洗其输卵管得到卵子。通常用装入 6 毫升培养基的伊格尔氏培养瓶（容量为 10 毫升）进行培养。每个培养瓶中装有两个卵子，在 37℃ 下、CO_2 占空气的比例恒为 5% 的加湿培养箱中培养 4 天。在被放入培养箱之前，约有一半培养瓶用硅质的塞子密封。培养结束后，用相差显微镜检测卵子，并根据最终的发育阶段进行分类。我们还使用了带有显微摄影装置的显微镜和一个充满培养基的特制透明容器（一种扁平细长的矩形固体容器，内部深度为 3 毫米，体积为 3 毫升 ~ 4 毫升）。因此，胚细胞在 37℃ 微型培养容器中的卵

937

microcinemicroscope kept at 37°C within the microscopic incubator.

Fifty-eight of sixty-seven ova incubated appeared to have undergone normal cleavage to eight cell, morula, or to the blastocyst. Most of them developed to the blastocyst (65%) rather than the morula (24%). Table 1 summaries the results of the studies with either the open or closed system of cultivation.

Table 1. *In vitro* Development of Rabbit Ova from One-Celled Stage

Culture system	No. of eggs tested	No. of embryos at final stage of development				
		1~2-cell	8-cell	Morula	Early expanding blastocyst	Expanding blastocyst
Earle's flask						
Open	24	5	4	9	4	2
Closed	27	3	2	3	4	15
Flat cuvette						
Closed	16	1	0	2	4	9

There was a difference in the proportion of ova developing to the blastocyst in the two culture systems; in the open system more embryos remained at the morula stage than in the closed system. There were, however, some cases of the development to the blastocyst stage in the open system. The most advanced development was obtained when we used a closed flask of cuvette without a gas phase. Four consecutive experiments yielded twenty-four expanding blastocysts (56%), eight early expanding blastocysts (19%) and five morulae (12%) from forty-three ova.

Time lapse microcinephotographs (1–8 frames/2 min on 16 mm film under phase contrast) of the embryo which developed from the one-celled stage to the expanding blastocyst (Fig. 1) show a regular pattern of cleavage as the culture passed (two-cell, 20–25 h; eight-cell, 38–45 h; morula, 58–67 h, and early blastocyst, 75–170 h after copulation). This pattern seems to parallel that which can be expected in oviducts and uteri.

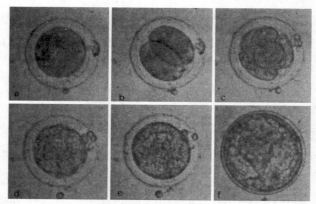

Fig. 1. The development of the rabbit ovum from one-cell to blastocyst stage *in vitro*. From a time-lapse film (16 mm) of an ovum isolated 18 h after mating (× *c*. 200). (*a*) 4.5 h after the start of culture; (*b*) two-cell stage, 6.5 h after (*a*); (*c*) eight-cell stage, 41 h after (*a*); (*d*) late morula to early blastocyst stage, 74 h after (*a*); (*e*) early blastocyst stage, 83.5 h after (*a*); (*f*) expanding blastocyst stage, 122 h after (*a*).

裂和运动状况可以用倒置显微摄像显微镜通过两个扁平端无失真地拍摄下来。

在培养的 67 个卵子中，有 58 个经历了正常的卵裂而达到 8 细胞以至桑葚胚，甚或囊胚的状态。它们中的大多数发育成了囊胚（65%）而不是桑葚胚（24%）。表 1 概述了在开放或密闭培养体系下得到的研究结果。

表 1. 兔卵子从单细胞阶段开始的体外发育

培养体系	检测的卵子数量	处于发育最终阶段的胚胎数量				
		1~2 细胞	8 细胞	桑葚胚	早期扩张的囊胚	扩张的囊胚
伊格尔氏培养瓶						
开放	24	5	4	9	4	2
密闭	27	3	2	3	4	15
扁平的透明容器						
密闭	16	1	0	2	4	9

在两种培养体系中，发育到囊胚阶段的卵子的比例是不同的：与密闭体系相比，在开放体系中会有更多的胚胎保持在桑葚胚状态。不过，在开放体系中还是有一些胚胎发育到了囊胚阶段。当我们使用一个无气相的密闭小型透明容器作为培养瓶时，所获得的胚胎发育进展最为显著。通过 4 个连续的实验，我们从 43 个卵子中培养出了 24 个扩张的囊胚（56%）、8 个早期扩张的囊胚（19%）和 5 个桑葚胚（12%）。

定时显微摄像记录（每 2 分钟 1 张 ~ 8 张，记录在相差为 16 毫米的电影胶片上）表明：从单细胞状态发育到扩张囊胚阶段的胚胎（图 1）随培养过程显示出常规的卵裂模式（2 细胞，交配后 20 小时 ~ 25 小时；8 细胞，交配后 38 小时 ~ 45 小时；桑葚胚，交配后 58 小时 ~ 67 小时；早期囊胚，交配后 75 小时 ~ 170 小时）。这种模式似乎与我们在输卵管和子宫内分析得到的结果一致。

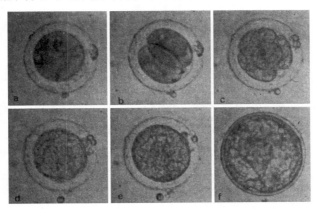

图 1. 兔卵子从单细胞到囊胚阶段的体外发育。交配后 18 小时分离的一个卵子的定时显微胶片（16 毫米）（放大约 200 倍）。(a) 培养开始后 4.5 小时；(b) 2 细胞阶段，(a) 之后 6.5 小时；(c) 8 细胞阶段，(a) 之后 41 小时；(d) 晚期桑葚胚到早期囊胚阶段，(a) 之后 74 小时；(e) 早期囊胚阶段，(a) 之后 83.5 小时；(f) 扩张囊胚阶段，(a) 之后 122 小时。

We have confirmed by microcinephotography the presence of rhythmical contraction and expansion, like those reported[14-16] in the mouse blastocyst, accompanying cleavage division of the cell mass in the embryo. The movement occurred at the transitional stage from late morula to early blastocyst and increasingly continued throughout the expanding blastocyst stage. The zona seemed to be thinner and elastic, its volume continuing to decrease, while the volume of the blastocoelic cavity continued to increase.

During the expanding stage, many intracellular particles moved up and down sometimes in a circular movement, within the blastocoelic cavity. The cell mass was finally fixed under the marginal expanding membrane of the blastocoelic cavity.

The composition of the culture medium *in vitro* is a critical factor in the cultivation of mammalian ova. Our medium can supply the necessary nutrients and environment to support a high rate of development of one-celled rabbit ova into early blastocysts. Furthermore, because a CO_2 incubator is not needed it seems to be convenient for the study of development of the rabbit ova *in vitro*. We think that this medium could also be used for the culture of the ova of other mammalian species *in vitro*.

This work was supported by a research grant from the Ministry of Education, Japan. We thank Mr. S. Etoh and N. T. Takatsuna for microcinephotography.

(**233**, 422-424; 1971)

Shyoso Ogawa, Kahei Satoh and Hajime Hashimoto: Department of Animal Reproduction, College of Agriculture and Veterinary Medicine, Nihon University, Setagaya-ku, Tokyo.

Received June 2; revised July 5, 1971.

References:

1. Brinster, R. L., *Exp. Cell Res.*, **32**, 205 (1963).

2. Brinster, R. L., *J. Reprod. Fert.*, **10**, 227 (1965).

3. Biggers, J. D., Moore, B. D., and Whittingham, D. G., *Nature*, **206**, 734 (1965).

4. Onuma, H., Maurer, R. R., and Foote, R. H., *J. Reprod. Fert.*, **16**, 491 (1968).

5. Kane, M. T., and Foote, R. H., *Biol. Reprod.*, **2**, 245 (1970).

6. Biggers, J. D., Gwatkin, R. B. L., and Brinster, R. L., *Nature*, **194**, 747 (1962).

7. Whitten, W. K., and Biggers, J. D., *J. Reprod. Fert.*, **17**, 399 (1968).

8. Mukherjee, A. B., and Cohen, M. M., *Nature*, **228**, 472 (1970).

9. Edwards, R. G., Steptoe, P. C., and Purdy, J. M., *Nature*, **227**, 1307 (1970).

10. Steptoe, P. C., Edwards, R. G., and Purdy, J. M., *Nature*, **229**, 132 (1971).

11. Ham, R. G., *Proc. US Nat. Acad. Sci.*, **53**, 288 (1965).

12. Moore, G. G., Gerner, R. E., and Addison, H. F., *J. Amer. Med. Assoc.*, **199**, 519 (1967).

13. Eagle, H., *Science*, **130**, 432 (1959).

14. Kuhl, W., and Friedrich-Freksa, H., *Zool. Anz., Suppl.*, **9**, 187 (1936).

15. Borghese, E., and Cassini, A., in *Cinemicrography in Cell Biology* (edit. by Rose, G. G.), 274 (Academic Press, New York, 1963).

16. Cole, R. J., and Paule, J., *Preimplantation Stages of Pregnancy*, Ciba Foundation Symp. (edit. by Wolstenholme, G. E. W., and O'Conner, M.), 82 (Little Brown, Boston, 1965).

显微摄影方法使我们确信：与那些对小鼠囊胚的报道一样 [14-16]，伴随胚胎中内细胞团的卵裂，存在着节律性的收缩和扩张。这种运动发生在从晚期桑葚胚到早期囊胚的过渡阶段，并且在整个扩张囊胚阶段持续增加。透明带似乎会变薄且有弹性，其体积持续减少，与此同时囊胚腔的体积却在不断扩大。

在扩张阶段，囊胚腔中的许多细胞内颗粒有时会沿着圆周轨迹来回移动。最后，内细胞团被固定在囊胚腔边缘扩张膜的下面。

体外培养基的成分是哺乳动物卵子培养的一个关键因素。我们的培养基可以提供必需的营养成分和环境，以保证单细胞兔卵子快速地发育到早期囊胚阶段。此外，因为不需要 CO_2 培养箱，所以对于研究兔卵子的体外发育是很方便的。我们认为这种培养基也能用于体外培养其他哺乳动物的卵子。

这项工作得到了日本教育省提供的科研经费的资助。还要感谢晴代先生和高纲先生在显微摄影方面为我们提供的帮助。

（吴彦 翻译；王晓晨 审稿）

Proposed Mechanism of Force Generation in Striated Muscle

A. F. Huxley and R. M. Simmons

Editor's Note

By the early 1970s, the filamentous sliding nature of muscle fibres was well established. It was known that myosin cross-bridges projected from the thick filaments and interacted with the thin ones, but it was not known how the tension between filaments was generated. Here biologists Andrew Fielding Huxley and Robert M. Simmons from University College London describe a series of experiments measuring the change in tension in striated muscle after a sudden change in length. Cross-bridges, they conclude, are elastic structures with ratchet-like properties: each cross-bridge has three stable positions with progressively lower potential energy. These features enable the cross-bridges to generate the force and movement between muscle filaments.

ONE approach to the elucidation of the kinetics of movement of the "cross-bridges" which are widely assumed to generate the relative force between the thick and thin filaments during contraction of a striated muscle fibre is to record and analyse the transient response of stimulated muscle to a sudden change either of tension or of length. Considerable progress has been made in this way by Podolsky and his colleagues[1-3] who recorded the time course of shortening after a sudden reduction in load. Similar responses have been recorded repeatedly in this laboratory but have not been published because we did not succeed in making the tension change sharply enough to distinguish the component of length change that is truly synchronous with the tension change from that which lags behind the tension change. We therefore turned[4] to the inverse type of experiment, in which the length of the fibre is suddenly altered (by ±0.1–1.5%) and the time course of the resulting tension change is recorded. The results have led to some fairly definite suggestions about the way in which the cross-bridges may actually produce the force between the thick and thin filaments.

All the experiments were carried out on isolated fibres from the semitendinosus muscle of the frog *Rana temporaria*, at 0°–4°C. Length changes, complete in less than 1 ms, were produced by means of a servo system[5], and tension was recorded with a capacitance gauge[6]. Compliance in the apparatus itself is small enough to be completely disregarded; precautions were taken to reduce the compliance in the tendon attachments to a minimum, and in some of the experiments it was eliminated altogether by using the "spot-follower" device[5], which continuously measures the length of a middle segment of the fibre.

横纹肌产生力量的建议机制

赫胥黎，西蒙斯

编者按

人们在20世纪70年代早期就已证实肌丝的滑动特性。那个时候人们就知道肌球蛋白横桥凸出于粗肌丝之上，并能与细肌丝发生相互作用，但尚不知道肌丝之间的张力是如何产生的。在本文中，伦敦大学学院的生物学家安德鲁·菲尔丁·赫胥黎和罗伯特·西蒙斯描述了一系列测量横纹肌在长度突然变化后发生张力改变的实验。他们得出的结论是：横桥是具有棘齿式特性的弹性结构——每个横桥都拥有三个势能逐渐降低的稳定位置。这些特性可以使横桥在肌丝之间产生力和运动。

大家普遍认为，“横桥”会在横纹肌纤维收缩时产生粗肌丝和细肌丝之间的相对推力，有一种方式可以解释横桥运动的动力学，那就是记录并分析受刺激肌肉在张力或长度突然变化时的瞬时反应。波多尔斯基及其同事[1-3]已经在这方面取得了相当大的进展，他们记录了在负载突然减少之后肌纤维收缩的时间进程。我们在实验室中也曾多次观察到类似的反应，但一直没有对外发表，因为我们不能使张力变化的速度快到足以将与张力变化真正同步的长度变化成分和滞后于张力变化的长度变化成分区分开来。因此，我们转而进行[4]相反类型的实验，即在纤维长度突然改变（±0.1%～1.5%）时将由此导致的张力变化的时间进程记录下来。根据这些记录结果，我们得到了一些非常确切的证据，这些证据说明横桥确实可以在粗细肌丝之间产生力。

所有实验都是在0℃～4℃下用林蛙半腱肌的分离纤维进行的。在不足1 ms的时间内通过一个伺服系统[5]产生长度变化，并用电容量表[6]记录张力。装置自身的柔量小到完全可以被忽略；还采取一定的措施使肌腱附着点的柔量减至最小，在其中一些实验中，我们使用了能连续观测纤维中间部分长度的“点跟踪”装置[5]以完全消除柔量的影响。

Responses to Stepwise Length Change

The general time course of tension in these experiments is shown in Fig. 1. This article is concerned only with the changes that occur simultaneously with the length change itself and during the first few milliseconds after it. As has already been briefly reported[4], these changes are of the kind shown in Fig. 2: the tension undergoes a relatively large alteration simultaneously with the step change of length, but recovers quickly towards a level closer to that which existed before the step. The final recovery to the original tension which has been seen by many earlier investigators[7-9] takes place on an altogether slower time scale. The early changes seen in Fig. 2 have only come to light through the improved time resolution of present-day apparatus.

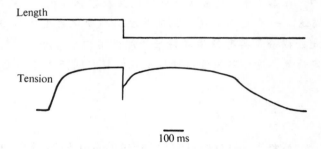

Fig. 1. Isometric tetanus of an isolated muscle fibre (frog, 4°C), with an imposed shortening step. This article is concerned with the tension changes during, and in the first few milliseconds after, the length step; these are shown on a fast time scale in Fig. 2.

The behaviour shown in Fig. 2 suggests the presence of two structural elements in series. One of these would be an elastic element whose length is altered simultaneously with the change of length that is applied to the whole fibre, thus producing the large initial change of tension. The other would be an element with viscous as well as elastic properties, whose length readjusts itself during the period of a few milliseconds immediately after the length change, as a result of the change in tension. As this readjustment proceeds, the imposed length change comes to be shared between the two structures, giving a tension intermediate between the values immediately before and immediately after the length change. At the time of our first note[4] about this quick initial tension recovery, we thought it likely that the recovery took place by sliding, with movement of the cross-bridges, but that the instantaneous elasticity was mostly in the filaments themselves. Since then we have measured these responses in fibres stretched so as to reduce the amount of overlap between thick and thin filaments. We found[10] that responses to a given absolute length change were altered only by a reduction in the scale of the tension changes, which varied in direct proportion to the amount of overlap and therefore also to the number of cross-bridges capable of contributing to tension. On these grounds we now believe that the instantaneous elasticity (or at least the greater part of it) resides in the cross-bridges themselves, as well as the structure responsible for the tension recovery.

对长度阶跃变化的反应

在上述实验中张力的一般时间进程示于图 1。本文中所涉及的仅仅是在长度发生变化的同时以及在随后几个毫秒内的变化。正如我们已经简要报道过 [4] 的那样，这些变化所属的类型如图 2 所示：在长度发生阶跃变化的同时，张力会出现相当大的改变，但会向接近于发生阶跃变化之前的水平快速恢复。虽然许多早期的研究者 [7-9] 已注意到张力最终会恢复到初始的状态，但从总体来看会发生在一个较慢的时间尺度上。图 2 所示的早期变化只有用时间分辨率较高的现代装置才能检测到。

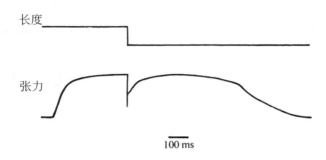

图 1. 一条分离的肌纤维（蛙，4℃）在外加长度阶跃缩短时的等长强直收缩。本文所涉及的是在长度发生变化的同时以及在随后几个毫秒内的张力变化；图 2 所示的就是在快时标上的变化。

图 2 所示的变化说明存在着两个串联的结构成分。其中一个是弹性成分，其长度随着整个纤维的长度变化同步改变，因而张力有很大的初始变化。另一个是同时具有黏性和弹性性质的成分，在长度变化之后的几个毫秒内，这个结构成分的长度会根据张力的变化不断调整。在这种不断调整的过程中，外加的长度变化分摊到两种结构成分上，因而给出的张力值将介于长度变化快要发生之前和长度变化刚好结束之后的数值之间。当我们第一次注意到 [4] 这种向初始张力快速恢复的现象时，我们认为：恢复很可能是通过滑动进行的，其中伴随着横桥的运动，但瞬时弹性主要发生在肌丝自身之中。此后，我们在伸长量达到可以减少粗细肌丝间交叠量的纤维中观测了上述反应。我们发现 [10]：对于给定的绝对长度变化，在反应上的不同仅仅是张力变化尺度有所下降，下降幅度与交叠量成正比，也正比于对张力有贡献的横桥的数量。基于这些结果，我们现在认为：瞬时弹性（或者至少是其中很大的一部分）不但存在于导致张力恢复的结构之中，还存在于横桥自身。

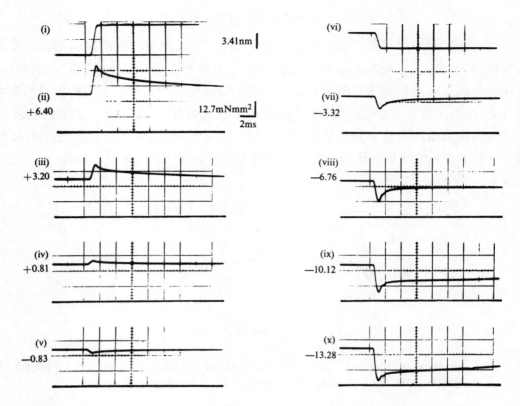

Fig. 2. Transient changes in tension exerted by stimulated muscle fibre when suddenly stretched (ii–iv) or shortened (v, vii–x); same experiment as Fig. 1, which shows the whole of the contraction during which record (ix) was taken. (i) and (vi): records of length change during tension records (ii) and (vii) respectively. The number by each tension record shows the amount of the length change per half-sarcomere, in nm.

The relations between length change and tension are illustrated in Fig. 3. The curve T_1 shows the extreme tension reached during the step change of length. It is somewhat non-linear, becoming stiffer with increasing tension as is commonly found in biological materials. This curve is the best experimental approach that we have to the instantaneous elasticity of the fibre, but it is clear from records such as viii–x in Fig. 2 that the tension drop in the larger shortening steps is cut down because the quick recovery has progressed to an appreciable extent before the length change is complete. The true curve of the instantaneous elasticity is therefore less curved on the shortening side than the curve of T_1 in Fig. 3; it is even possible that it is practically straight, as indicated by the broken line.

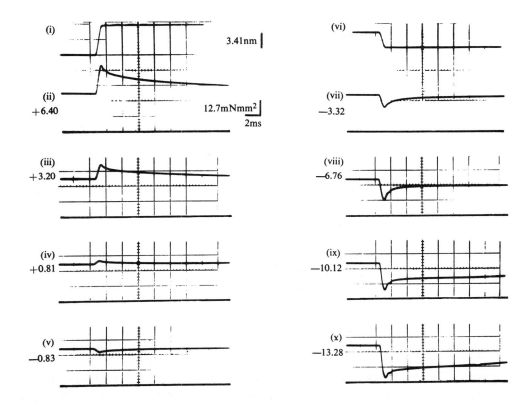

图 2. 受刺激的肌纤维在突然拉伸（ii~iv）或者突然收缩（v, vii~x）时产生的瞬时张力变化；与图 1 对应的实验相同，图 1 显示了记录（ix）中所对应的时间范围内的总长度缩短量。(i) 和 (vi)：分别为在张力记录（ii）和（vii）期间的长度变化记录。每幅张力记录图上的数字代表了每个半肌节的长度变化量，单位是 nm。

　　长度变化与张力之间的关系示于图 3。曲线 T_1 代表在长度发生阶跃变化的过程中所达到的张力极限值。它在某种程度上是非线性的，和大多数生物材料一样，在张力增加时就会变得更硬。这条曲线是我们由纤维瞬时弹性实验得到的最好结果，但是从一些记录，如图 2 的记录 viii~x 中可以清楚地看到，当长度发生较大的阶跃缩短时，张力的下降幅度变小了，因为快速恢复过程在长度变化完成之前就已经发展到了相当的程度。因此，与图 3 中的曲线 T_1 相比，瞬时弹性的真实曲线在阶跃缩短一侧的弯曲程度要小一点；曲线 T_1 在阶跃缩短一侧的部分甚至有可能是直的，如虚线所示。

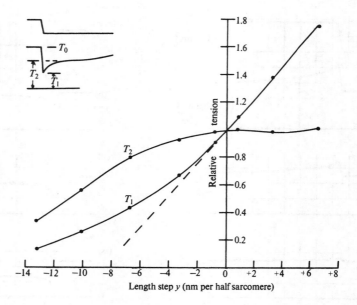

Fig. 3. T_1, Extreme tension reached during step, and T_2, tension approached during quick recovery phase, plotted against amount of sudden stretch (positive) or release (negative). Broken line: extrapolation of the part of the T_1 curve which refers to stretches and small releases. From records in Fig. 2.

In contrast to this straightforward behaviour of instantaneous elasticity, the quick tension recovery is highly nonlinear both in its extent and in its speed. The line T_2 in Fig. 3 shows the level approached at the end of the quick phase of recovery; for moderate amounts of shortening it has the unusual feature of being concave downwards, reflecting the fact that after a small length step the tension returns practically to its previous level (Fig. 2, iv, v). As regards the time course, it is evident from Fig. 2 that the early tension recovery is much more rapid in releases than in stretches, and that its speed varies continuously over a wide range with the size of the length step. The recovery is not exponential, but an estimate of the dominant rate constant can be obtained and is plotted against the size of the stretch or release in Fig. 4; it is roughly fitted by a curve of the form

$$r = \frac{r_0}{2}(1 + \exp -\alpha y) \tag{1}$$

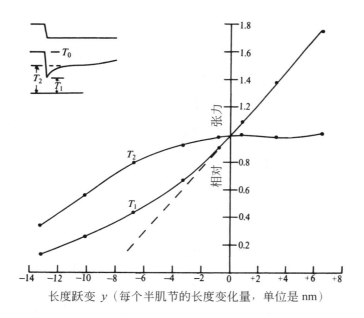

图3. T_1，在长度阶跃变化时达到的张力极限值；T_2，在快速恢复阶段的张力值，横坐标是突然拉伸（正）或释放（负）的量。虚线：从曲线T_1的拉伸和释放量较小部分外推得到的结果。依据是图2中的记录。

与瞬时弹性的这种简单特性相反，快速张力恢复在量上和速度上都是高度非线性的。图3中的曲线T_2显示出了快速恢复阶段末期所达到的水平；当阶跃缩短量适中的时候，它表现出向下凹陷的不寻常特征，这说明在小的长度跃变之后张力几乎可以恢复到原有的水平（图2，iv，v）。至于时间进程，从图2中可以清楚地看到：处于释放状态中的初期张力恢复比处于拉伸状态中的要快很多，并且恢复速度会在很宽的范围内随长度跃变的大小连续变化。恢复并不是指数型的，但可以估计出它的主要速率常数并对拉伸或释放的大小作图，见图4；拟合曲线的表达式大致为：

$$r = \frac{r_0}{2}(1 + \exp -\alpha y) \tag{1}$$

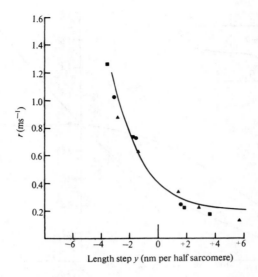

Fig. 4. Rate constant r of quick recovery phase following a length step of magnitude y (positive for stretch). Estimated as $(\ln 3)/t_{1/3}$ where $t_{1/3}$ is the time for recovery from T_1 to $(2T_2+T_1)/3$ (see Fig. 3). From three experiments using the "spot-follower" device; temperature $4°$C. The curve is $r = 0.2\,(1+\exp-0.5\,y)$.

All these features can be given at least a qualitative explanation if we assume that the force on a cross-bridge influences the length changes in that cross-bridge in the way that is assumed by Eyring and others[11,12] in their theory of the visco-elastic behaviour of high molecular weight polymers. The treatment presented in the following paragraphs is meant only to indicate the way in which these features would emerge from such a theory; a more complete treatment will be needed in order to test whether it is fully consistent with the data.

Assumptions

The key assumptions that have to be made are (1) that the movement by which a cross-bridge performs work during the period while it is attached takes place in a small number of steps, from one to the next of a series of stable positions with progressively lower potential energy, and (2) that there is a virtually instantaneous elasticity within each cross-bridge allowing it to shift from one of these stable positions to the next without a simultaneous displacement of the whole thick and thin filaments relative to one another.

These assumptions could be incorporated into some of the mechanisms that have been proposed for the action of the cross-bridges, for example, that of Davies[13], in which each cross-bridge shortens by folding at a number of points, or that of H. E. Huxley[14], in which the head of the myosin molecule (H, Fig. 5) rotates relative to the thin filament, acting as a lever which pulls the thick filament along by a link AB which is also part of the myosin molecule. Our assumptions fit very conveniently on to H. E. Huxley's proposals, and we shall discuss them on this basis in the way illustrated in Fig. 5. The features shown there which are additional to H. E. Huxley's scheme are as follows. (1) The link AB is not inextensible as in H. E. Huxley's proposal but contains the instantaneous elasticity which shows up as curve T_1 (Fig. 3). (2) The head has a small number s of combining sites

950

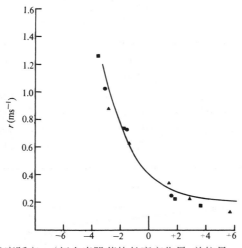

长度跃变 y（每个半肌节的长度变化量,单位是 nm）

图 4. 紧随幅度为 y（对于拉伸为正值）的长度跃变之后的快速恢复阶段的速率常数 r。估计其表达式为 $(\ln 3)/t_{1/3}$，其中 $t_{1/3}$ 是从 T_1 恢复到 $(2T_2 + T_1)/3$ 所需的时间（见图 3）。数据来自于使用"点跟踪"装置的三次实验；温度为 4℃。曲线为 $r = 0.2(1+\exp - 0.5 y)$。

如果我们假定横桥上的力能够像艾林和其他人 [11,12] 在高分子聚合物黏弹性行为理论中所设想的那样影响该横桥中的长度变化，那么就至少可以对上述所有特征给出一个定性的解释。在以下段落中所描述的处理方法只是为了说明怎样才能从我们的理论推导出上述特征；若要检验理论与数据是否完全相符，还需要更为全面的考量。

假 定

必须引入的两个关键假定是：（1）通过少数几个步骤就能产生使横桥在连接时实现其功能的运动,即从一系列势能逐渐降低的稳定位置中的一个转移到下一个。（2）每个横桥内部都存在着虚拟的瞬时弹性，使其可以从上述稳定位置中的一个转变成另一个，而不会同时出现整条粗肌丝和细肌丝相对于彼此的位移。

这些假定可以与某些曾被用于解释横桥作用的机制相结合。例如：在戴维斯提出的机制中 [13]，每个横桥的收缩是通过在许多点的折叠实现的；或者按照赫胥黎的说法 [14]，肌球蛋白分子头部（H，图 5）会相对于细肌丝旋转，就像一根杠杆一样沿着同样是肌球蛋白一部分的连接 AB 拉动粗肌丝。我们的假定很容易与赫胥黎的提法相契合，因而我们将在此基础上按照图 5 所描绘的方式来加以讨论。下面列出了一些在赫胥黎理论中没有提到的特征。（1）连接 AB 并非像赫胥黎所说的那样不能伸展，而是能够表现出如曲线 T_1（图 3）所示的瞬时弹性。（2）头部有数量为 s 的少量结合点（M_1、M_2 等，图 5），每个结合点都能与细肌丝中肌动蛋白分子上的

(M_1, M_2 and so on, in Fig. 5), each of which is capable of combining reversibly with a corresponding site (A_1, A_2 and so on) on an actin molecule in the thin filament. A single M–A attachment allows variation of θ (rotation in the plane of the diagram of Fig. 5) without hindrance, but no other degree of freedom of the myosin head relative to the actin molecule. (3) The affinity between these myosin and actin sites is smallest for M_1A_1, larger for M_2A_2 and so on. (4) The sites are placed so that the myosin head has $(s-1)$ stable positions, each of which allows two consecutive M and A sites to be attached simultaneously. (5) When the myosin head is in its $(s-1)$th stable position it can be detached from the thin filament by a process involving the hydrolysis of ATP.

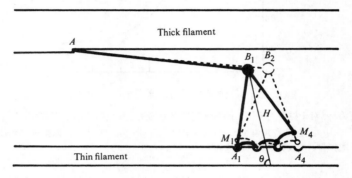

Fig. 5. Diagram showing assumed cross-bridge properties. The myosin head H is connected to the thick filament by a link AB containing the undamped elasticity which shows up as T_1 (Fig. 3) in the whole fibre. Full line shows head in position where M_1A_1 and M_2A_2 attachments are made; broken lines show position where M_2A_2 and M_3A_3 attachments are made.

On this basis the quick tension recovery is due to the tendency for the myosin head to rotate to positions of lower potential energy, while the fact that the recovery occurs at a finite speed is a manifestation of the rate constant for movement of the system from one of the stable positions to the next.

Potential Energy Diagram of a Cross-Bridge

Curves i–iv in Fig. 6 show the potential energy diagrams for individual attachment sites (M_1A_1, M_2A_2 and so on) on a single cross-bridge. Each contains a flat-bottomed well extending over the range of myosin head positions where that particular attachment can exist. Curve v is the sum of curves i–iv, and therefore gives the total potential energy of the cross-bridge (in the absence of force in the link AB); it consists of a series of steps, separated by narrow troughs at the positions where two of the links are attached simultaneously. The depth of each trough will depend on the shapes, and on the exact positions, of the sides of the potential wells that contribute to it; it is assumed in Fig. 6 that these are such that the quantities E_1 and E_2 (v, Fig. 6) are the same for each of the troughs.

相应位置（A_1、A_2 等）可逆地结合。单独的一个 M–A 连接可以保证 θ 的变化（在图 5 所示平面内的旋转）不受阻碍，但是肌球蛋白头部相对于肌动蛋白分子没有其他的自由度。（3）上述肌球蛋白与肌动蛋白结合点之间的亲和性在 M_1A_1 处最小，在 M_2A_2 处要大于 M_1A_1 处，以此类推。（4）结合点的分布要能确保肌球蛋白头部具有（s − 1）个稳定位置，每个稳定位置允许两个顺序排列的 M 和 A 结合点同时连接。（5）当肌球蛋白头部位于它的第（s − 1）个稳定位置时，它可以借助一种有三磷酸腺苷水解介入的过程与细肌丝分离。

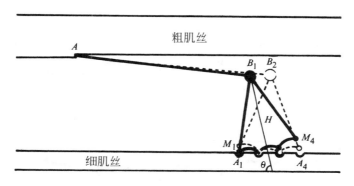

图 5. 假想中的横桥性质示意图。肌球蛋白头部 H 通过连接 AB 与粗肌丝相连，连接 AB 表现出的无阻尼弹性如整个纤维的 T_1 曲线（图 3）所示。实线显示的是当 M_1A_1 和 M_2A_2 发生连接时头部所处的位置；虚线是当 M_2A_2 和 M_3A_3 连接时头部所处的位置。

以此为基础可以认为：出现快速张力恢复的原因是肌球蛋白头部有旋转到势能较低位置的趋势，而以有限速度恢复这一事实是系统从一个稳定位置运动到另一个稳定位置所具有的速率常数的体现。

横桥的势能图

图 6 中的曲线 i~iv 描绘出单一横桥上每对连接点（M_1A_1、M_2A_2 等）的势能图。每条曲线都包含一个平底部分，这个平底部分的延伸范围代表了某个特定连接可以存在于其中的一系列肌球蛋白头部位置。曲线 v 是曲线 i~iv 的叠加，因此给出了横桥（在连接 AB 中不存在力时）的总势能；曲线 v 包含一系列阶跃，阶跃与阶跃之间的分界线是位于同时相连的两个连接处的狭窄凹点。每个凹点的深度取决于导致该凹点的势阱的边缘形状和边缘所在的具体位置；图 6 中假定 E_1 和 E_2 的值（曲线 v，图 6）对于每个凹点都是一样的。

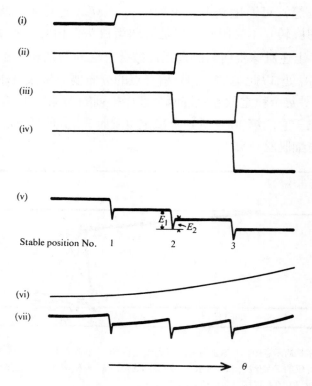

Fig. 6. Potential diagrams relating to the system illustrated in Fig. 5. i–iv, Diagrams for individual attachments M_1A_1, M_2A_2, M_3A_3, M_4A_4 respectively; in each the thick line corresponds to the range of θ within which the corresponding M and A sites are attached; v, sum of i–iv, giving potential energy of a system composed only of a myosin head and a thin filament; vi, potential energy due to stretching the elastic link AB; vii, total potential energy.

The total potential energy of an attached cross-bridge contains also the potential energy of stretching the elastic link AB. The latter term is shown in curve vi, and the total in curve vii.

Responses Expected Theoretically

In the mathematical section at the end of this article, we derive equations describing the response of a system of this kind to a step change of length. The system treated there is simplified by assuming that only two stable positions are available to each attached cross-bridge. The corresponding potential energy diagram is sketched in Fig. 7. This shows that B_2, the activation energy for transfer of a bridge from position 1 to position 2, contains a term W which depends on the force in the link AB, being increased by a stretch and reduced by a release. B_1, however, the activation energy for the reverse transfer, contains no such term and is independent of the force. It is this asymmetry which enables the theory to account for the way in which the rate constant of the quick tension recovery varies with the direction and magnitude of the length step: the theoretical result is expressed in equation (12) which is identical in form with equation (1), already shown (Fig. 4) to represent adequately the experimental data. The theory also leads to equation (16) for

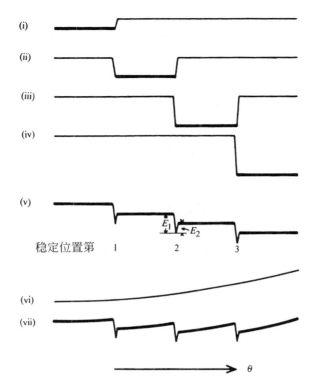

图 6. 与图 5 中所描述的系统相对应的势能图。i~iv 分别为单个连接 M_1A_1、M_2A_2、M_3A_3 和 M_4A_4 的示意图；在每幅图中，粗线代表在对应 M 点和 A 点连接时 θ 的范围；v（i~iv 的叠加）给出一个仅由一个肌球蛋白头部与一条细肌丝组成的系统的势能；vi，由拉伸弹性连接 AB 所产生的势能；vii，总势能。

一个处于连接状态的横桥的总势能还包括拉伸弹性连接 AB 所产生的势能。曲线 vi 代表的是后者，而曲线 vii 则显示了总势能。

从理论上推出的反应

在本文末尾处的数学部分中，我们推导出了一些可以描述这类系统对长度阶跃变化的反应的式子。为了简化要处理的系统，我们假设每个处于连接状态的横桥只有两个可能的稳定位置。对应的势能示意图绘于图 7。图 7 说明一个横桥从位置 1 转移到位置 2 的活化能 B_2 中包含着一个 W 项，该项取决于连接 AB 中的力，在拉伸时增加而在释放时减少。但逆向转移过程的活化能 B_1 却不包含这样的项，所以与该力无关。正是这种不对称性使得我们的理论可以解释快速张力恢复的速率常数随长度跃变方向和大小而变化的形式；理论结果用等式（12）来表示，等式（12）与表达式（1）的形式相同，式（1）已经被实验数据充分证明（图 4）。由我们的理论还可以推出快速恢复阶段末期所能达到的张力水平，即等式（16）；将其绘于图 8 之中，

the tension level approached at the end of the quick recovery phase; this is plotted in Fig. 8 which is seen to reproduce the main features of the experimental T_2 curve in Fig. 3.

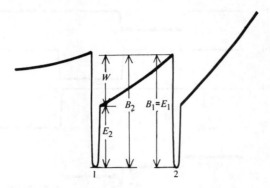

Fig. 7. Potential energy diagram equivalent to Fig. 6 (vii) but referring to the simplified system with only two stable positions.

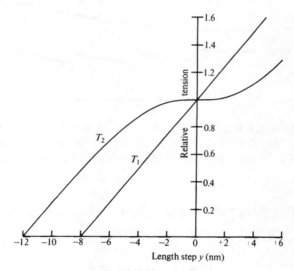

Fig. 8. Curves of T_1 and T_2 calculated from the simplified system, plotted on same scales as the experimental values in Fig. 3. T_2 curve: Equation (16) with $E_1-E_2=4kT$, $1/\alpha=2$ nm, $h=8$ nm.

The two striking features of the quick tension recovery are thus accounted for by this theory. The numerical values used in obtaining this degree of agreement are: E_1-E_2, the potential energy difference between the stable positions of attachment of a cross-bridge, is equal to 4 kT; h, the travel of point B between its two stable positions, is 8 nm; K, the stiffness of the link AB, is 2.5×10^{-4} N m^{-1}.

The following considerations show, however, that the assumption that the cross-bridge movement takes place in a single step is probably not correct.

Isometric force and number of bridges. Equations (4) and (7) show that the isometric force

956

可以看到它也具有在图 3 中由实验得到的曲线 T_2 的主要特征。

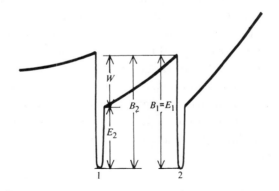

图 7. 与图 6（vii）所示相当的势能图，但所对应的是只有两个稳定位置的简化系统。

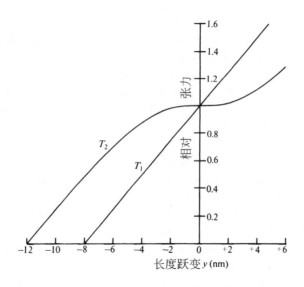

图 8. 由简化系统计算得到的 T_1 曲线和 T_2 曲线，用与图 3 中的实验值相同的标度画出。T_2 曲线：按等式（16）画出，其中 $E_1 - E_2 = 4\,kT$，$1/\alpha = 2\,nm$，$h = 8\,nm$。

因此，根据这一理论可以解释快速张力恢复的两个显著特征。达到这种吻合程度所要用到的数据是：E_1–E_2，一个横桥上两个稳定连接位置之间的势能差，其值等于 $4\,kT$；h，B 点在其两个稳定位置之间的行程，其值为 $8\,nm$；K，连接 AB 的刚度，其值为 $2.5 \times 10^{-4}\,N\,m^{-1}$。

然而，下面的论证过程说明假定横桥的运动仅通过单一步骤完成很可能是不正确的。

等长收缩力与桥的数目。 从等式（4）和（7）中可以看出：每个处于连接状态的横

per attached cross-bridge is $(E_1-E_2)/h$; with the values mentioned in the last section this amounts to 2.0×10^{-12} N. To reach a total force of 3×10^5 N m^{-2}, such as real fibres produce, would therefore need 1.5×10^{17} attached bridges m^{-2} in each half-sarcomere. This is about 1.5 times greater than the number of myosin molecules present. The discrepancy would be greater if the number of cross-bridges were equal to the number of projections on the thick filaments detected by low-angle X-ray diffraction since this appears to be about half the number of myosin molecules[15], and greater still if a substantial proportion of the cross-bridges were unattached during isometric contraction. (It is conceivable that each of the two heads on a myosin molecule should be counted separately; this would be appropriate only if the instantaneous elasticity existed within each of the heads, allowing them to shift independently.)

Work per attached cross-bridge. An upper limit to the external work done by the fibre per cross-bridge attachment will be given by the integral in equation (17), between the isometric point $y=0$ and the point ($y=-12.0$ nm) where $\varphi_2=0$. With the adopted values of α and h, this is 3.8 kT. This result is only about half the value which can be calculated as follows from the actual performance of frog muscle. Work can be as much as 40% of (work + initial heat)[16], and the latter quantity is about 11 kcalories/mol of phosphorylcreatine split[17], giving the work term as 4.4 kcalories/mol. This is equal to 7.3 kT per molecule, which will represent the work per cycle of attachment and detachment of a cross-bridge if it is assumed that the cycle is coupled (presumably through ATP) to the hydrolysis of one molecule of phosphorylcreatine.

Probable number of stable positions. The quantitative treatment just presented has thus led to low values for the force and work per cross-bridge. It is just possible that revised values for α and for the number of cross-bridges will resolve these discrepancies, but it seems to us more likely that it will be necessary to assume that the cross-bridge movement takes place not in a single step but in two or perhaps more. This would lead to proportional increases in the calculated force and work, but the expected time course and extent of the quick tension recovery, which are already in good agreement with the experimental results, would not be much altered if each step has the same height E_1-E_2 as has already been assumed and the value of h is reduced so as to keep the same total range of travel. Fig. 5 is drawn for the case where the number of steps is 2 (3 stable positions and 4 points of attachment), which at present seems the most probable number.

Relation to Earlier Theories

The idea of applying Eyring's theory of polymers to muscle is not new. A comprehensive theory of muscle was developed by Polissar[18], in which the shortening of links in actomyosin chains was influenced in this way by the load, but this theory lost its relevance when it became clear that major changes of length take place by sliding, not folding, of the filaments.

The proposal that the sliding movement is generated by the tendency of attachments between the filaments to move through a series of a few positions of progressively lower

桥的等长收缩力为 $(E_1-E_2)/h$；代入最后一部分中提到的数字，其值为 2.0×10^{-12} N。为了使总力和真实纤维中的情况一样达到 3×10^5 N m^{-2}，就需要在每个半肌节中有每平方米 1.5×10^{17} 个连接的横桥。这个值大概是现有肌球蛋白分子数量的 1.5 倍。如果横桥的数目等于用低角度 X 射线衍射法检测到的粗肌丝上的凸起数，那么两者之间的差异还会更大，因为由后者得到的结果似乎只有肌球蛋白分子数量的一半左右 [15]；而如果在等长收缩过程中有相当比例的横桥没有连接，那么这个差值还会再大一些。（有人认为应该分别计算一个肌球蛋白分子的两个头；只有当每个头中都存在瞬时弹性进而可以独立移动时，这样做才是恰当的。）

与每个处于连接状态的横桥相对应的功。每个横桥连接的纤维所做的外功上限可以由等式（17）中的积分给出，积分范围是从等长收缩点 $y = 0$ 到与 $\varphi_2 = 0$ 对应的点（$y = -12.0$ nm）。代入 α 和 h 的采用值，可以得到 $3.8\ kT$。这一结果只有按照以下方法从青蛙肌肉实际表现计算出来的数值的一半左右。功可以达到（功＋初始热量）的 40% [16]，（功＋初始热量）约为 11 kcal/mol，是由磷酸肌酸分解 [17] 得到的，由此计算出功的大小为 4.4 kcal/mol。这相当于每分子 $7.3\ kT$，如果假定连接与解连接的循环与一分子磷酸肌酸的水解偶联（可能是通过三磷酸腺苷），那么这个值就代表了与每个处于单一连接与解连接循环中的横桥相对应的功。

稳定位置的可能数目。由上述定量处理所得到的对应于每个横桥的力值和功值都偏低。虽然通过修正 α 值和横桥数目有可能会解决这个矛盾，但我们认为更有可能的情况是：应该假定横桥的运动不是通过单一步骤完成的，而是通过两步或者更多步完成的。这样会使计算出来的力和功成比例增长，但在每一步都和前述假定一样有同样高度的 $E_1 - E_2$ 且 h 值减少到足以保证总行程大致不变的情况下，已经与实验结果吻合得很好的时间进程和快速张力恢复程度却不会发生很大的变动。图 5 就是按照步骤数为 2 的情况（3 个稳定位置和 4 个连接点）绘制的，也是目前看来最有可能的数目。

与早期理论的关系

将艾林的聚合物理论应用于肌肉算不上新观点。波利萨 [18] 曾提出过一种较为完备的肌肉理论，其中肌动球蛋白链中连接的缩短就是以这种方式受负载影响的。但是当人们逐渐了解到长度的大部分变化是源自肌丝的滑动而非折叠的时候，波利萨理论的价值就不复存在了。

滑动运动的产生是由于肌丝之间的连接具有在一系列势能逐渐递减的若干位置

potential energy was made many years ago by H. H. Weber[19], who also pointed out that in this case the rate constants for shifting from one position to another would be affected by the force on the attachment. He discussed this idea purely on the basis of a translational movement of the thick relative to the thin filament, with a site rigidly fixed to one of the filaments transferring itself from one to the next of the sites on the other filament to which it could be attached. It is difficult to visualize a mechanism of this kind operating over the rather large distances—several nanometers—that the transient responses show to be involved, but the difficulty disappears if there is an elastic structure allowing one of the attachment sites to undergo substantial displacements relative to the filament to which it belongs.

On the kinetic side, the scheme discussed here combines the advantages of the proposals made by A. F. Huxley[20] in 1957 and by Podolsky et al.[3]. In each of these schemes the production of force was assumed to occur as an immediate consequence of the formation of a myosin–actin link. In A. F. Huxley's scheme, attachment was assumed to be the main rate-limiting factor in steady shortening, while detachment after the performance of work by a cross-bridge was relatively rapid; with these assumptions it is possible to fit A. V. Hill's relations between load, speed and heat production but not the transient responses discussed here. Podolsky et al. reversed the assumptions about the rate constants, making attachment rapid and breakage rate-limiting; in this way they were able to fit many aspects of transient responses but, as they recognized, not the thermal data. With appropriate rate constants for the initial attachment and final detachment of each cross-bridge, the present scheme can probably account for the force–velocity and thermal relationships in the same way as A. F. Huxley's 1957 scheme, while the rapid transfer between stable positions of the myosin head produces transient responses not unlike those which, on the theory of Podolsky et al., result from the rapid formation of new attachments. The present proposal is able to combine the successful aspects of both of these theories because it subdivides the force-generating event into distinct stages, one for attachment and others for stretching the cross-bridge, the latter being much more rapid than the former. This separation also removes another difficulty that both of the earlier theories would very likely have met in a fully quantitative treatment. They assumed that tension is already present in the cross-bridge when it attaches to the thin filament; thermal motion would so seldom bring the cross-bridge to such a large deflexion that it might be impossible to account in that way for the rapidity of contraction that some real muscles achieve.

Mathematical Section

Equations will be derived for the extent and time-course of the quick tension recovery to be expected from a system similar to that shown in Fig. 5 but with only two instead of three stable positions of the myosin head relative to the thin filament. The following additional simplifying assumptions are also made. (1) Actual detachment and re-attachment of cross-bridges are slow enough to be disregarded. (2) Filaments themselves are completely rigid. (3) Filaments undergo no sliding movements except when the total length of the fibre is being altered. (4) The elasticity of the link AB obeys Hooke's law. (5) The link AB is capable of exerting negative as well as positive tensions. (6) In the

上连续移动的趋势，这个建议是多年以前由韦伯[19] 提出的。他还指出，在这种情况下从一个位置移动到另一个位置时的速率常数将会受到连接处的力的影响。他对这一构想的讨论完全是基于粗肌丝相对于细肌丝的平移运动，运动方式是一个牢固地固定于某一条肌丝上的连接点从它能与之连接的另一条肌丝上的一个位置转移到下一个位置。很难想象这种机制会适用于有瞬时反应出现的较大距离（几个纳米），但如果有一种弹性结构能允许其中一个连接点相对于它所在的肌丝发生足量的位移，那么这个难题就会迎刃而解。

从动力学的角度来看，上述理论同时具备赫胥黎 1957 年的提议 [20] 与波多尔斯基等人的提议 [3] 所具有的优点。这些理论都假定力的产生是肌球蛋白-肌动蛋白之间形成连接的直接后果。在赫胥黎的理论中，连接被认为是稳态收缩中的主要限速因素，而横桥在产生力之后的解连接过程则要相对快一些；这些假定或许能与希尔所说的负载、速度和放热之间的关系相符合，但无法与本文所讨论的瞬时反应相符合。波多尔斯基等人颠倒了关于速率常数的假设，认为连接是快速的而解连接过程是限速的；由此他们可以解释瞬时反应的很多方面，但不包括热数据，这一点他们也承认。如果知道每个横桥初始连接和最终解连接的速率常数的确切数值，那么目前的理论就有可能可以利用与 1957 年赫胥黎理论相同的方式来解释力–速度与放热的关系，而由肌球蛋白头部在稳定位置之间的快速转移产生瞬时反应的观点也不会与波多尔斯基等人把瞬时反应看作是源自于新连接的快速形成的理论有什么不同。目前的提法能够结合这两种理论的成功之处，因为它把产生力的过程细分为不同的阶段，一个是连接阶段，其他几个是横桥的拉伸阶段，后者比前者快很多。这种细分的处理方法还回避了两种早期理论在纯定量处理中很可能会遇到的另一个困难。两种早期理论假定当横桥与细肌丝相接时，张力已经存在于横桥之中；热运动几乎不会使横桥产生如此巨大的偏转，因此用热运动难以解释某些真实肌肉中出现的快速收缩。

数 学 部 分

我们将从与图 5 所示类似但肌球蛋白头部相对于细肌丝只有两个而不是三个稳定位置的系统中导出几个有关快速张力恢复程度和时间进程的表达式。另外还需要作以下假设简化计算。（1）横桥中实际存在的解连接和重连接过程进行得很慢以至于可以忽略。（2）肌丝本身是完全刚性的。（3）只有在纤维总长度发生改变时，肌丝才产生滑动运动。（4）连接 AB 的弹性遵循胡克定律。（5）连接 AB 既能施加正张力，也能施加负张力。（6）在等长收缩的稳定状态下，每个处于连接状态的横桥在

isometric steady state, every attached cross-bridge spends equal amounts of time in each of the two available positions (this cannot be strictly true in real muscle because the spacings along the thick and thin filaments are not in any simple ratio, so the relative positions of the myosin and actin molecules must vary from one cross-bridge to another). (7) The time taken in transferring from one to the other of the two positions is negligible.

The following notation will be used; n_1: fraction of attached bridges in position 1; n_2 ($=1-n_1$): fraction of attached bridges in position 2; y: displacement of thick relative to thin filament when fibre is stretched or shortened (zero in isometric state before the applied length change; positive for stretch); y_0: extension of elastic link AB when bridge is midway between positions 1 and 2 (equal to amount of sudden sliding movement needed to bring tension to zero from the isometric state); h: increase in length of AB when bridge shifts from position 1 to position 2; K: stiffness of link AB (assumed to obey Hooke's law); F_1: tension in AB when bridge is in position 1; F_2: tension in AB when bridge is in position 2; φ : time average of F_1 and F_2.

From these definitions,

$$F_1=K(y+y_0-h/2) \text{ and } F_2=K(y+y_0+h/2) \tag{2}$$

and the time average of tension is

$$\begin{aligned} \varphi &=n_1F_1+n_2F_2 \\ &=K(y+y_0-h/2+hn_2) \end{aligned} \tag{3}$$

In the isometric state, $y=0$ and $n_2=1/2$, and this equation reduces to the expression for the isometric force per attached cross-bridge

$$\varphi_0=Ky_0 \tag{4}$$

The rate constants k_+ for transfer from position 1 to position 2, and k_- for transfer from 2 to 1, are governed by the energy barriers $B_2(=E_2+W)$ and B_1 $(=E_1)$ respectively (Fig. 7). W is the work done in stretching AB when the bridge transfers from position 1 to position 2, and is given by

$$\begin{aligned} W &= h\frac{F_1+F_2}{2} \\ &= Kh(y+y_0) \end{aligned} \tag{5}$$

from equations (2).

Assuming the ks proportional to $\exp -B/kT$, we have

$$\begin{aligned} k_+ &= k_- \exp (B_1-B_2)/kT \\ &= k_- \exp (E_1-E_2-W)/kT \\ &= k_- \exp (E_1-E_2-Kh(y+y_0))/kT \end{aligned} \tag{6}$$

两个可能位置上的逗留时间都相等（这在真实肌肉中是不可能严格正确的，因为沿着粗肌丝和细肌丝方向的分子排布间距不存在任何简单的比例关系，因此对每个横桥而言，肌球蛋白和肌动蛋白分子的相对位置都不一样）。（7）从两个位置中的一个向另一个转移时所需的时间是可以忽略的。

我们将使用下列符号。n_1：在位置 1 处连接的横桥所占的比例；n_2（$= 1 - n_1$）：在位置 2 处连接的横桥所占的比例；y：当纤维在外力作用下伸长或缩短时粗肌丝相对于细肌丝的位移（在施加长度变化前的等长收缩状态时为 0；对于拉伸为正）；y_0：当横桥处于位置 1 和位置 2 之间时弹性连接 AB 的长度（等于为使张力从等长收缩状态变为 0 所需的突然滑动运动的量）；h：当横桥从位置 1 移向位置 2 时 AB 的长度增量；K：连接 AB（假设其遵循胡克定律）的刚性系数；F_1：当横桥处于位置 1 时 AB 中的张力；F_2：当横桥处于位置 2 时 AB 中的张力；φ：F_1 和 F_2 的时间平均值。

根据上述定义，有：

$$F_1 = K\,(y + y_0 - h/2) \ \text{和} \ F_2 = K\,(y + y_0 + h/2) \tag{2}$$

而张力的时间平均值为：

$$\begin{aligned}
\varphi &= n_1 F_1 + n_2 F_2 \\
&= K\,(y + y_0 - h/2 + h n_2)
\end{aligned} \tag{3}$$

在等长收缩状态下，有 $y = 0$ 和 $n_2 = 1/2$，由此可以把上式化简为表示每个连接横桥的等长收缩力的式子：

$$\varphi_0 = K y_0 \tag{4}$$

从位置 1 转移到位置 2 时的速率常数 k_+ 和从位置 2 转移到位置 1 时的速率常数 k_- 分别由能垒 B_2（$= E_2 + W$）和 B_1（$= E_1$）决定（图 7）。W 为横桥从位置 1 转移到位置 2 时纤维拉伸 AB 所做的功，根据式（2）可以化简为：

$$\begin{aligned}
W &= h\frac{F_1 + F_2}{2} \\
&= Kh(\,y + y_0)
\end{aligned} \tag{5}$$

假定 k_+ 和 k_- 均与 $\exp{-B/kT}$ 成比例，我们有：

$$\begin{aligned}
k_+ &= k_-\exp{(B_1 - B_2)}\,/kT \\
&= k_-\exp{(E_1 - E_2 - W)}\,/kT \\
&= k_-\exp{(E_1 - E_2 - Kh\,(y + y_0))}\,/kT
\end{aligned} \tag{6}$$

where k_- is constant since B_1 is a fixed quantity independent of the tension in AB.

In the isometric state we have assumed $n_1=n_2$, so $k_+=k_-$; also $y=0$ since y is defined as a length change from the isometric state. It then follows from (6) that

$$E_1-E_2=Khy_0 \tag{7}$$

and (6) becomes

$$k_+=k_- \exp - yKh/kT \tag{8}$$

In the experiments we are considering, y is suddenly altered by imposing a length change on the muscle fibre, and is subsequently held constant. The transfer of myosin heads from one position to the other is then governed by the equation

$$\begin{aligned}
dn_2/dt &= k_+n_1 - k_-n_2 \\
&= k_+ - (k_+ + k_-)n_2
\end{aligned} \tag{9}$$

This equation represents an exponential approach, with rate constant r given by

$$r = k_+ + k_- \tag{10}$$

towards an equilibrium where

$$n_2 = k_+/(k_+ + k_-) \tag{11}$$

Substituting from (8) into (10) we have

$$r = k_- (1 + \exp - yKh/kT) \tag{12}$$

This has the same form as equation (1), and the equations become identical, giving approximate agreement with the experimental results in Fig. 4, if we take

$$Kh = \alpha kT \tag{13}$$

Equation (8) can therefore be written

$$k_+ = k_- \exp - \alpha y \tag{14}$$

and (11) becomes

$$n_2 = \frac{1}{2}\left(1 - \tanh\frac{\alpha y}{2}\right) \tag{15}$$

其中 k_- 为常数，因为 B_1 是不依赖于 AB 中张力的固定量。

我们曾假定在等长收缩状态下有 $n_1 = n_2$，所以 $k_+ = k_-$；且 $y = 0$，因为 y 被定义为从等长收缩状态开始的长度变化。因此由式（6）可以得到：

$$E_1 - E_2 = Khy_0 \tag{7}$$

而式（6）则变为：

$$k_+ = k_- \exp - yKh/kT \tag{8}$$

在所设想的实验中，我们通过对肌纤维施加一个长度变化而突然改变 y，随后令其保持恒定。因此，利用下式即可确定肌球蛋白头部从一个位置向另一个位置的转移：

$$\begin{aligned} \mathrm{d}n_2/\mathrm{d}t &= k_+ n_1 - k_- n_2 \\ &= k_+ - (k_+ + k_-) n_2 \end{aligned} \tag{9}$$

该式呈指数形式，其中由下式给出的速率常数 r

$$r = k_+ + k_- \tag{10}$$

指向的是下面的平衡态：

$$n_2 = k_+/(k_+ + k_-) \tag{11}$$

将（8）代入（10）后得到：

$$r = k_- (1 + \exp - yKh/kT) \tag{12}$$

上式与式（1）有相同的形式，若要与图 4 中的实验结果大体相符，则两个式子应该相等，如果我们令：

$$Kh = \alpha kT \tag{13}$$

那么就可以将式（8）写作：

$$k_+ = k_- \exp - \alpha y \tag{14}$$

而（11）则变成：

$$n_2 = \frac{1}{2}\left(1 - \tanh\frac{\alpha y}{2}\right) \tag{15}$$

The tension φ_2 at the end of the quick recovery (corresponding to T_2 in the whole fibre) is obtained by combining (3), (13) and (15) to give

$$\varphi_2 = \frac{\alpha kT}{h}\left(y_0 + y - \frac{h}{2}\tanh\frac{\alpha y}{2}\right)$$

(16)

The work done during shortening at a low enough speed so that n_2 always has its equilibrium value would be obtained by integrating (16):

$$\int\varphi_2 \, dy = kT\left(\frac{\alpha y}{h}\left(y_0 + \frac{y}{2}\right) - \ln\cosh\frac{\alpha y}{2}\right)$$

(17)

To match the points in Fig. 4, α is taken as 5×10^8 m^{-1}, the value used for the curve in that figure. (E_1-E_2) is shown by equations (7) and (13) to be equal to $\alpha y_0 kT$. From Fig. 3 (broken line), y_0 is about 8 nm, giving $E_1-E_2=4kT$. h has to be chosen to give the right shape for the curve of T_2 against y (equation 16). A value $4/\alpha$, or 8 nm, is used in Fig. 8; lower values give a less inflected curve and higher values give a curve with a region of negative slope.

Generation of Tension

The tension changes observed in the first few milliseconds after suddenly changing the length of an active muscle fibre suggest the following mechanism for the generation of tension or shortening by the cross-bridges. Each cross-bridge has three stable positions with progressively lower potential energies, in steps of about 4 times kT, separated by about 4 nm of travel. Transfer from one of these positions to the next is made possible, without simultaneous displacement of the whole filaments through an equally large distance, by the presence of elasticity associated with each individual cross-bridge. The tension generated in this way in the elastic element will show up as such if the muscle length is held constant, or will help to make the filaments slide past each other if shortening is permitted.

A simplified theoretical treatment is given; a more complete treatment will be presented later.

(**233**, 533-538; 1971)

A. F. Huxley and R. M. Simmons: Department of Physiology, University College London, Gower Street, London WC1.

Received August 25, 1971.

References:

1. Podolsky, R. J., *Nature*, **188**, 666 (1960).

2. Civan, M. M., and Podolsky, R. J., *J. Physiol.*, **184**, 511 (1966).

3. Podolsky, R. J., Nolan, A. C., and Zaveler, S. A., *Proc. US Nat. Acad. Sci.*, **64**, 504 (1969).

4. Huxley, A. F., and Simmons, R. M., *J. Physiol.*, **208**, 52P (1970).

5. Gordon, A. M., Huxley, A. F., and Julian, F. J., *J. Physiol.*, **184**, 143 (1966).

6. Huxley, A. F., and Simmons, R. M., *J. Physiol.*, **197**, 12P (1968).

7. Gasser, H. S., and Hill, A. V., *Proc. Roy. Soc.*, B, **96**, 398 (1924).

在快速恢复结束时的张力 φ_2（相当于整个纤维中的 T_2）可以通过联立（3）、(13) 和（15）得到：

$$\varphi_2 = \frac{\alpha kT}{h}\left(y_0 + y - \frac{h}{2}\tanh\frac{\alpha y}{2}\right) \tag{16}$$

在以足够低的速度收缩以使 n_2 始终保持其平衡值的过程中所做的功可以通过积分（16）得到：

$$\int \varphi_2 \, dy = kT\left(\frac{\alpha y}{h}\left(y_0 + \frac{y}{2}\right) - \ln\cosh\frac{\alpha y}{2}\right) \tag{17}$$

为了与图 4 中的点匹配，取 α 为 $5\times10^8 \, \text{m}^{-1}$，也是该图中的曲线所用的值。由式（7）和式（13）可以得到 $(E_1 - E_2)$ 等于 $\alpha y_0 kT$。根据图 3（虚线部分），y_0 约为 8 nm，这说明 $E_1 - E_2 = 4kT$。h 的取值必须能够保证以 y 为横坐标的曲线 T_2（式 16）有正确的形状。图 8 中 h 的取值是 $4/\alpha$ 或 8 nm；当 h 取值较低时得到的曲线会更平直一些，而取值较高时在得到的曲线中会出现一段负斜率区。

张力的产生

在突然改变一条活性肌纤维长度之后的最初几个毫秒内所观测到的张力变化意味着由横桥所导致的张力产生或收缩具有如下机制。每个横桥具有三个势能逐渐降低的稳定位置，能量差约为 kT 的 4 倍，之间大约相隔 4 nm。如果假设每个单独的横桥都存在弹性，那么从上述位置中的一个向另一个的转移过程就可以在整条肌丝不发生同样长度的同步位移的前提下实现。以这种方式在弹性成分中产生的张力会表现得如同肌肉长度没有变化一样，或者在允许收缩时有助于肌丝滑过彼此。

本文只给出了简化的理论处理过程；更详细的处理过程将在以后发表。

（王耀杨 翻译；刘京国 审稿）

8. Hill, A. V., *Proc. Roy. Soc.*, B, **141**, 104 (1953).

9. Jewell, B. R., and Wilkie, D. R., *J. Physiol.*, **143**, 515 (1958).

10. Huxley, A. F., and Simmons, R. M., *J. Physiol.*, **218**, 59P (1971).

11. Eyring, H., *J. Chem. Phys.*, 4, 283 (1936).

12. Burte, H., and Halsey, G., *Tex. Res. J.*, **17**, 465 (1947).

13. Davies, R. E., *Nature*, **199**, 1068 (1963).

14. Huxley, H. E., *Science*, **164**, 1356 (1969).

15. Huxley, H. E., *J. Mol. Biol.*, 7, 281 (1963).

16. Hill, A. V., *Proc. Roy. Soc.*, B, **127**, 434 (1939).

17. Wilkie, D. R., *J. Physiol.*, **195**, 157 (1968).

18. Polissar, M. J., *Amer. J. Physiol.*, **168**, 766, 782, 793 and 805 (1952).

19. Weber, H. H., *The Motility of Muscle and Cells*, 32 (Harvard University Press, Cambridge, Massachusetts, 1958).

20. Huxley, A. F., *Prog. Biophys.*, 7, 255 (1957).

Molecular Evolution in the Descent of Man

M. Goodman *et al.*

Editor's Note

Studies of human evolution had been about fossils until Morris Goodman's work showing how comparison of amino-acid sequences of proteins could be used to estimate evolutionary relationships and the rate of evolutionary change. This paper pioneered the idea that human beings shared a common ancestry with chimpanzees that excluded other apes, such as the gorilla. However, the view remained that the rate of change had decelerated among higher primates, allowing for a long ancestry of humans through *Australopithecus* and back to *Ramapithecus* more than 10 million years ago. Later work would suggest that the divergence between apes and humans had been in fact more recent—and palaeontology would show that *Ramapithecus* was more closely related to the orang-utan than humans.

IT is likely that the level of molecular organization in higher animals is now more complicated than would have been possible in the first life forms of three billion years or so ago. Even after the emergence of the genetic code and the biochemical apparatus of translation, natural selection would have had to act over long stretches of evolutionary time to produce the sophisticated structures and functions of the multichained proteins now found in living organisms. To begin with, almost any point mutation in a gene coding for a polypeptide chain would have been tolerable; with the evolution of higher levels of molecular organization, however, increasingly stringent functional restraints would have markedly decreased the number of acceptable mutations.

The notion that the level of molecular organization places restraints on how fast genes evolve is implicit in Ingram's hypothesis[1] that the genes for alpha globin have changed more slowly than those for beta globins. The same alpha chain combines with different types of beta chains in the several tetrameric haemoglobins which are synthesized during the life of a mammal. Since there are more restraints on variations of the alpha chains than of the beta chains, fewer mutations would be tolerated at an alpha locus than at a beta locus and alpha genes would not evolve as rapidly as beta genes. In the same way, there may be differences in the rates of evolution of the globin genes at earlier and later evolutionary stages. The original single-chained globin would no doubt have been recognizable by its three-dimensional structure and haem binding site, but it would yet have had to acquire specific sites for subunit combination, for binding diphosphoglycerate, for allosteric modulation of structure to promote the Bohr effect and for combining with the plasma protein haptoglobin. With these functions, natural selection tolerated fewer mutations in the globin genes. From this it follows that the primordial globin genes

人类起源过程中的分子进化

古德曼等

编者按

莫里斯·古德曼的这项工作展示了如何将蛋白质的氨基酸序列比较用于评估进化关系以及进化变化的速度，在此之前，人类进化的研究工作一直都是针对化石展开的。这篇文章率先提出人类和黑猩猩（不包括其他类人猿，例如大猩猩）拥有共同的祖先。虽然如此，在从南方古猿以及追溯到 1,000 多万年前的腊玛古猿来考虑人类的远祖之后，作者仍然认为在高等灵长类动物中变化的速度已经减慢。而后来的工作表明，类人猿与人类间分化的时间实际上离现在更近，并且古生物学后来证明腊玛古猿更接近于红毛猩猩，而不是人类。

现今高等动物中的分子组织水平很可能比约 30 亿年前的第一个可能的生命形态更复杂。甚至在遗传密码和翻译的生化装置出现以后，自然选择仍需要很长的进化时间才能形成现在活有机体中多链蛋白的复杂结构和功能。起先，在编码多肽链的基因中，几乎任何点突变都是可接受的；然而，随着分子组织向更高水平的进化，越来越严密的功能性抑制将使可接受突变的数量显著减少。

英格拉姆假说[1]中隐含着分子组织水平会对基因进化速度加以抑制的概念，该假说认为，α 球蛋白的相关基因比 β 球蛋白的相关基因变化得更慢。在哺乳动物生存期间合成的几种四聚体血红蛋白中，相同的 α 链结合了不同类型的 β 链。因为比起 β 链，针对 α 链变化的抑制会更多一些，所以 α 基因座比 β 基因座能容忍的突变少，并且 α 基因的进化速度也不可能与 β 基因一样快。在进化的更早和更晚阶段，球蛋白基因的进化速度同样可能存在差异。原始单链球蛋白无疑可以通过它的三维结构及血红素结合位点来识别，但它仍不得不获得一些特异位点以用于结合亚基、用于结合二磷酸甘油酸异构酯、用于结构的变构调整以促进玻尔效应以及用于与血浆蛋白中的触珠蛋白结合。由于这些功能，自然选择只允许球蛋白基因中发生很少的突变。由此得出的结论是，原始球蛋白基因的进化速度要高于后来脊椎动物的球蛋白基因

evolved more rapidly than the later globin genes of vertebrates, consonant with an earlier hypothesis that molecular evolution at a number of gene loci has decelerated, especially in the lineage leading to man[2-4].

This hypothesis, followed by others[5,6], attributes divergent evolution in proteins to selectively neutral mutations but also implies that more mutations were neutral in primitive organisms than in descendant species. Thus biochemical adaptations in human antecedents must have increased with the development of new organs such as the placenta and the cerebral neocortex and the extra functional restraints would then decrease the chances for fresh mutations to accumulate. An immunological mechanism could have further restricted the degree of genetic variability in higher primate populations, for the haemochorial placenta (with its intimate apposition of foetal and maternal blood circulations) and the long gestation period would have increased the risk to the foetus from maternal immunizations to foetal allotypes.

We present evidence in this article that molecular evolution has indeed been slower in higher primates than in other mammals. In particular, from a detailed analysis of the phylogeny of globin genes, we support Ingram's hypothesis that the evolution of alpha globin genes has been slower than that of the beta genes. Available data on proteins also bear on the cladistic relationships of man and other mammals.

The most penetrating view of the molecular changes in individual genes during the descent of man is provided by comparing the amino-acid sequences of human proteins with homologous proteins in other organisms. We have followed the approach of Fitch and Margoliash[7] in constructing gene phylogenetic trees from amino-acid sequence data and for this purpose have used three computer programs. The first program (MMUTD) calculates mutation distances for every pairwise comparison of aligned amino-acid sequences using a matrix based on the genetic code which gives for each amino-acid pair the minimum number of nucleotides that would need to be changed to bring about such a mutation. The second program[6] (UWPGM) produces from a dissimilarity matrix of the mutation distances a dendrogram of the gene species in the set. This dendrogram is an initial approximation to a cladogram, that is a graph which depicts the order of ancestral branching in the gene species set. The UWPGM builds the tree from the smallest to the largest branches in a series of pairwise clustering cycles, each time grouping together the two members of the set (either singleton species or joined species from a previous cycle) with the smallest mutation distance between them. If all the species in the set had evolved at a uniform, or nearly uniform, rate in their descent from a common ancestor, the dendrogram produced by the UWPGM would be the true cladogram[9]. But neither gene species nor animal species necessarily evolve at uniform rates. Thus, with the third computer program (DENDR) we construct alternative dendrograms. The DENDR

进化速度，这与早前的假说一致。早前的假说认为：很多基因座的分子进化已经发生了减速，特别是在进化成人类的这条支系中[2-4]。

这个假说，还有接下来的其他几个[5,6]，将蛋白质中的趋异进化归因于选择性的中性突变，但也暗示与后代物种相比，原始生物中存在更多的中性突变。因此，随着胎盘和大脑新皮层等新器官的发育，人类祖先的生化适应性必定有所增强，但额外的功能性限制接下来会减少新突变积累的机会。在高等灵长类种群中，有一种免疫机制可能会进一步限制基因变异的量，因为血绒膜胎盘（在这里胎儿血液循环和母体血液循环紧密接触）和长怀孕期增加了由母体免疫系统对胎儿同种抗免疫球蛋白的作用给胎儿带来的危险。

我们将在本文中提供证据证明，高等灵长类动物的分子进化速度确实比其他哺乳动物的分子进化速度慢。特别是，从对球蛋白基因系统发生的详尽分析结果来看，我们支持英格拉姆假说——α球蛋白基因的进化速度比β球蛋白基因的进化速度慢。由蛋白质的可用数据还可以得到人类与其他哺乳动物的进化枝关系。

最敏锐地检查人类起源过程中单独基因的分子变化的手段是比较人类蛋白质与其他生物体内同源蛋白质的氨基酸序列。我们按照菲奇和马格利亚什[7]的方法，由氨基酸序列数据来创建基因系统发生树，为了达到这一目的还使用了三个计算机程序。第一个程序（MMUTD）使用基于遗传密码的矩阵来计算由成对比较对齐的氨基酸序列而得到的突变距离，由此得出为了带来这一突变，每一氨基酸对所需变化的最少核苷酸数。第二个程序[6]（UWPGM）由突变距离的相异度矩阵绘制出该系列基因的系统树图。该系统树图是一个进化树的初级近似，图中描绘了该系列基因的祖先分枝的顺序。UWPGM 在一系列配对的聚类循环中建立起从最小到最大分枝的系统树，每次总是把系列中拥有最小突变距离的两个成员（不管是单件种类还是来自前一个循环的联合种类）分在一组。如果系列中所有种类的进化速度在一个共同祖先的后代中保持一致，或接近一致，那 UWPGM 绘制的系统树图就是真实的进化树[9]。但基因类型和动物物种都不一定会按均一的速度进化。因此，我们利用第三个计算机程序（DENDR）建立了若干个备选的系统树图。由 DENDR 程序计算出

program calculates the patristic mutation length* for each pair of adjacent nodes in a dendrogram, sums the patristic lengths through the sequence of nodes between species to calculate a reconstructed mutation distance for each pair of species in the set, and then compares the reconstructed mutation distances to the given mutation distances in the original dissimilarity matrix to calculate a coefficient for the entire dendrogram called "average percentage standard deviation" (APSD)[7]. Among the alternative dendrograms the one with least deviation between original and reconstructed mutation distances (that is, the lowest APSD coefficient) is considered the closest approximation of those tried to a true phylogenetic tree. This approach to finding the best fitting tree has proved capable of capturing the cladistic relationships among gene species even when markedly dissimilar amounts of mutational change characterize their descent from a common ancestor[10].

Globin Phylogenetic Tree

Table 1 is the matrix of mutation values from all possible pairing of sixty-eight metozoan globin chain sequences[11-47]. These chains range in size from 135 to 153 amino-acid residues. They include, apart from carp alpha, chicken alpha, and mammalian alpha and non-alpha haemoglobin chains, a globin of lamprey, myoglobins of horse and sperm whale, and a globin of the insect chironomus. The chicken alpha chain is the first non-mammalian tetrapod haemoglobin chain to be sequenced[17]. It diverges less from human (and chimpanzee) alpha than from any other mammalian alpha (Table 1). This is not due to any special relationship between chicken and man, but, as will be shown, results from the marked conservativism of higher primate alpha chains.

Table 1. Mutation Values from Pairwise Comparisons of Vertebrate Globin Sequences

Full name of globin species given in legend to Fig. 1. The half matrix lists minimum numbers of mutations interrelating pairs of polypeptide chains. These mutational values are converted into percentage mutational divergence

$$\left(\frac{\text{No. of mutations}}{\text{No. of shared amino-acids}} \times 100\right)$$

values, the mutation distances used for constructing the phylogenetic tree in Fig. 1. Alpha llama, sheep foetal beta, and goat A' beta are not completely sequenced. Hence their mutation values may not represent full mutation values.

---

*The patristic mutation lengths associated with any node, N, on a dendrogram are calculated as follows. Any node N divides the species of which it is the common ancestor into two sets: set A and set B. All remaining species under study comprise set C. Let D_{ab} be the average of dissimilarity values for pairs of species such that the first species is a member of set A and the second species is a member of set B, and let D_{ac} and D_{bc} be similarly calculated. The length from set A to node N is called a; the length from set B to node N is called b; and the length from set C to node N is called c. These lengths are calculated by the following formulas:

$$a = \frac{D_{ab} + D_{ac} - D_{bc}}{2}$$

$$b = \frac{D_{ab} + D_{bc} - D_{ac}}{2}$$

$$c = \frac{D_{ac} + D_{bc} - D_{ab}}{2}$$

For the special case that N is the apex of the tree (that is, the common ancestor of all species under study): $a = b = \dfrac{D_{ab}}{2}$. c is undefined.

系统树图中每对相邻节点的父系突变长度 *，沿着两物种间的一系列节点加和父系长度，以得到系列中每对物种的重组突变距离，然后比较重组突变距离与原始相异度矩阵中给出的突变距离，以计算出整个系统树图的系数，这个系数被称为"平均百分比标准偏差"（APSD）[7]。在备选的系统树图中，原始和重组突变距离之间具有最小偏差（即 APSD 系数最低）的那一个系统树图被认为最接近于真实的进化系统发生树。这种寻找最适树图的方法已被证明可以捕捉到在基因类型中存在的进化枝关系，甚至在来自一个共同祖先的后代具有迥然不同的突变变化总量时也是可行的 [10]。

球蛋白系统发生树

表 1 是 68 种后生动物球蛋白链序列的所有可能配对的突变值矩阵 [11-47]。在大小上这些链的范围是 135 个～153 个氨基酸残基。除包括鲤鱼 α 以外，还包括：鸡 α、哺乳动物 α 和哺乳动物非 α 血红蛋白链，七鳃鳗的某一球蛋白，马和抹香鲸的肌红蛋白，摇蚊属昆虫的某一球蛋白。鸡 α 链是第一条被测序的非哺乳类四足动物血红蛋白链 [17]。它偏离人类(和黑猩猩)α 链的程度要小于偏离其他哺乳类 α 链的程度(表1)。这并不是因为鸡和人之间存在着某种特殊关系，而是由下面将要讲到的高等灵长目动物 α 链的格外保守造成的。

表 1. 由成对比较脊椎动物球蛋白序列得到的突变值

图 1 两侧的说明文字给出了各类球蛋白的全称。该半矩阵列出了与各多肽链配对相关的最小突变数。这些突变值被转化成百分比形式的突变偏离值：

$$\left(\frac{\text{突变数}}{\text{共享的氨基酸数}}\right) \times 100$$

突变距离被用来构建图 1 中的系统发生树。对美洲驼 α、绵羊胚胎 β 和山羊 A′ β 的测序还不完全。因此它们的突变值也许不能代表完整的突变值。

---

* 计算与系统树图上任一节点 N 相关的父系突变长度的方法如下。任意节点 N 将以 N 为共同祖先的物种分为两组：A 组和 B 组。所有剩下的被研究物种组成 C 组。令 D_{ab} 为配对物种相异值的平均值，所以第一个物种是 A 组中的一个成员，第二个物种是 B 组中的一个成员。以同样的方式计算 D_{ac} 和 D_{bc}。从 A 组到节点 N 的长度称为 a；从 B 组到节点 N 的长度称为 b；从 C 组到节点 N 的长度称为 c。这些长度按下式计算：

$$a = \frac{D_{ab} + D_{ac} - D_{bc}}{2}$$

$$b = \frac{D_{ab} + D_{bc} - D_{ac}}{2}$$

$$c = \frac{D_{ac} + D_{bc} - D_{ab}}{2}$$

作为特例 N 为树顶（即所有被研究物种的共同祖先）：$a = b = \dfrac{D_{ab}}{2}$，未定义 c。

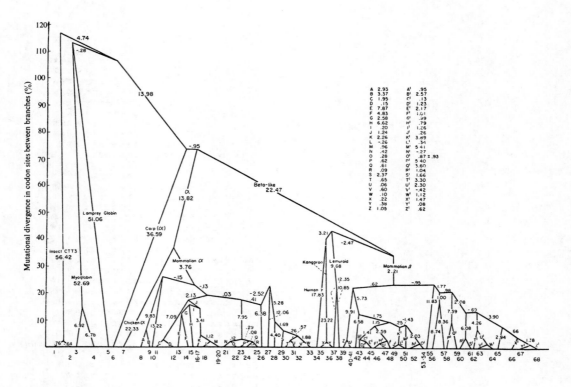

Fig. 1. Globin phylogenetic tree. 1, Insect CTT-3 (*Chironomus thummi*)[11]; 2, insect CTT-3 (sub)[11]—alternative amino-acids (39 Thr, 57 Ile) were used for ambiguous positions; 3, myoglobin sperm whale[13]; 4, myoglobin horse—sequence alignment as given in ref. 14; 5, globin lamprey[15]; 6, alpha carp[16]; 7, alpha chicken[17]; 8, alpha rabbit[18]; 9, alpha rabbit (sub)[18]—alternative amino-acids (29 Leu, 48 Leu, 70 Thr, 76 Val, 80 Ser, 113 His) were used for ambiguous positions; 10, alpha tree shrew[19]; 11, alpha mouse NB[20,21]; 12, alpha mouse C-57Bl[20,21]; 13, alpha sifaka (*Propithecus verreauxi*)[19]; 14, alpha lemur (*Lemur fulvus*)[19]; 15, alpha bush baby (*Galago crassicaudatus*)[19]; 16, alpha *Macaca mulatta*[22]; 17, alpha *Macaca fuscata* (G. Matsuda, unpublished); 18, alpha gorilla[23]; 19, alpha chimpanzee[24]; 20, alpha human[25,26]; 21, alpha donkey[27]; 22, alpha horse slow (24 Phe)[27]; 23, alpha horse fast (24 Phe)[27]; 24, alpha horse fast (24 Tyr)[27]; 25, alpha horse slow (24 Tyr)[28]; 26, alpha pig—sequence alignment as given in ref. 14; 27, alpha llama—sequence alignment as given in ref. 14; 28, alpha bovine[29]; 29, alpha goat II (non-allelic)[30]; 30, alpha goat B (allelic)[30]; 31, alpha goat A[30]; 32, alpha sheep D[31]; 33, alpha sheep A[32,33]; 34, gamma human[34]; 35, beta kangaroo[35]; 36, beta kangaroo-2 (2 Gln)[35]; 37, beta sifaka[19]; 38, beta lemur[19]; 39, beta mouse AKR[36]; 40, beta mouse Sec[36]; 41, beta mouse C-57Bl[36]; 42, beta rabbit[37]; 43, beta squirrel monkey (*Saimiri sciures*)[38]; 44, beta tamarin (*Saguinus nigricollis*)[38]; 45, beta spider monkey (*Ateles geoffroyi*)[38]; 46, delta squirrel monkey[38]; 47, delta tamarin[38]; 48, delta spider monkey[38]; 49, beta *Macaca fuscata*[39]; 50, beta *Macaca mulatta*[22]; 51, delta human[40]; 52, beta gorilla[23]; 53, beta chimpanzee[24]; 54, beta human[25]; 55, beta horse slow[42]; 56, beta pig—sequence alignment as given in ref. 14; 57, beta llama—sequence alignment as given in ref. 14; 58, beta bovine foetal[42]; 59, beta sheep foetal[43]; 60, beta bovine A[44]; 61, beta bovine B[44]; 62, beta sheep barbary C[45]; 63, beta goat C[47]; 64, beta sheep C[46]; 65, beta sheep B[46]; 66, beta sheep A[46]; 67, beta goat A[47]; 68, beta goat A' (allelic)[47].

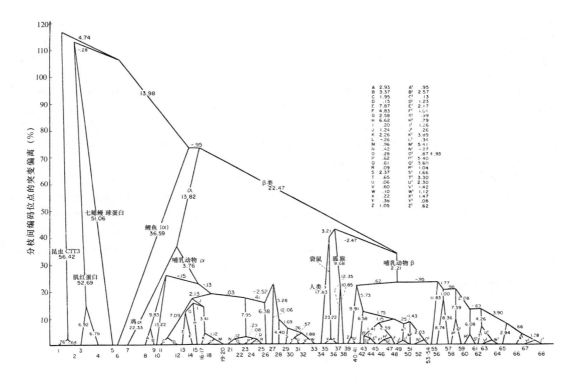

图1. 球蛋白系统发生树。1，昆虫CTT-3（吐氏摇蚊）[11]；2，昆虫CTT-3（侧枝）[11]——可替代氨基酸（39苏氨酸，57异亮氨酸）被用于发生替代的位置；3，肌红蛋白抹香鲸[13]；4，肌红蛋白马——序列比对见参考文献14；5，球蛋白七鳃鳗[15]；6，α鲤鱼[16]；7，α鸡[17]；8，α兔[18]；9，α兔（侧枝）[18]——可替代氨基酸（29亮氨酸，48亮氨酸，70苏氨酸，76缬氨酸，80丝氨酸，113组氨酸）被用于发生替代的位置；10，α树鼩[19]；11，α小鼠NB[20,21]；12，α小鼠C-57Bl[20,21]；13，α马达加斯加狐猴（维氏冕狐猴）[19]；14，α狐猴（褐狐猴）[19]；15，α丛猴（粗尾丛猴）[19]；16，α普通猕猴[22]；17，α日本猕猴（松田，尚未发表）；18，α大猩猩[23]；19，α黑猩猩[24]；20，α人[25,26]；21，α驴[27]；22，α马慢（24苯丙氨酸）[27]；23，α马快（24苯丙氨酸）[27]；24，α马快（24酪氨酸）[27]；25，α马慢（24酪氨酸）[28]；26，α猪——序列比对见参考文献14；27，α美洲驼——序列比对见参考文献14；28，α牛[29]；29，α山羊II（非等位基因）[30]；30，α山羊B（等位基因）[30]；31，α山羊A[30]；32，α绵羊D[31]；33，α绵羊A[32,33]；34，γ人[34]；35，β袋鼠[35]；36，β袋鼠-2（2谷氨酰胺）[35]；37，β马达加斯加狐猴[19]；38，β狐猴[19]；39，β小鼠AKR[36]；40，β小鼠Sec[36]；41，β小鼠C-57Bl[36]；42，β兔[37]；43，β松鼠猴（松鼠猴）[38]；44，β柽柳猴（黑须柽柳猴）[38]；45，β蜘蛛猴（黑掌蛛猴）[38]；46，δ松鼠猴[38]；47，δ柽柳猴[38]；48，δ蜘蛛猴[38]；49，β日本猕猴[39]；50，β普通猕猴[22]；51，δ人[40]；52，β大猩猩[23]；53，β黑猩猩[24]；54，β人[25]；55，β马慢[42]；56，β猪——序列比对见参考文献14；57，β美洲驼——序列比对见参考文献14；58，β牛胚胎[42]；59，β绵羊胚胎[43]；60，β牛A[44]；61，β牛B[44]；62，β巴巴里绵羊C[45]（译者注：一种北非产的大角羊）；63，β山羊C[47]；64，β绵羊C[46]；65，β绵羊B[46]；66，β绵羊A[46]；67，β山羊A[47]；68，β山羊A'（等位基因）[47]。

979

The best tree so far obtained depicting the phylogeny of the globins is given in Fig. 1. Fig. 2 shows the best of forty-one alternatives tried for the restricted set of tetrapod alpha chains, and Fig. 3 the best tree of forty-five alternatives tried for the restricted set of mammalian non-alpha or beta-like globin chains. The APSD coefficient was lowered from 15.11 for the alpha tree constructed by the UWPGM to 11.14 for the tree in Fig. 2, and from 11.32 for the beta-like tree by the UWPGM to 8.40 for the tree in Fig. 3. The original tree for the sixty-eight globin species constructed by the UWPGM had an APSD coefficient of 18.52. This was lowered by several points on trying a dendrogram which followed the branching order shown in Figs. 2 and 3, but which otherwise maintained the topology of the UWPGM tree. Shifting (a) the carp alpha branch from its UWPGM union with other alphas to a union with the line ancestral to both mammalian beta-like globins and tetrapod alphas, and (b) the lamprey globin branch from its UWPGM union with the branch ancestral to all the globin chains in vertebrate haemoglobins over to union with the myoglobin branch, lowered the APSD coefficient to 12.27 and produced the tree shown in Fig. 1. So far eighteen alternative configurations for the major branches of the large globin tree have been tried.

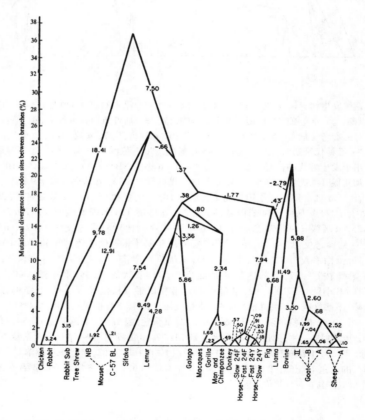

Fig. 2. Chicken and mammalian alpha globin phylogenetic tree.

图1给出了目前所能获得的描述球蛋白系统发生的最佳树图。图2显示的是就四足动物α链的有限系列进行尝试得到的41个备选树图中的最佳树图，而图3是就哺乳动物非α或称β类球蛋白链的有限系列进行尝试得到的45个备选树图中的最佳树图。APSD系数从由UWPGM程序构建的α树图的15.11下降到图2中树图的11.14，从由UWPGM建立的β类树图的11.32下降到图3中树图的8.40。68种球蛋白类型的原始树图是由UWPGM程序构建的，其APSD系数为18.52。在尝试按图2和图3所示的枝序作出系统树图时，这个值会有所下降，但整张图依旧保持着UWPGM树图的拓扑结构。（a）将鲤鱼α枝从含有其他α枝的UWPGM联合体置换到含哺乳动物β类球蛋白和四足动物α球蛋白共同祖先的支系联合体中，（b）将七鳃鳗球蛋白枝从含脊椎动物血红蛋白中所有球蛋白链的祖先分枝的UWPGM联合体置换到肌红蛋白枝的联合体中，将使APSD系数下降到12.27，建立的树如图1所示。到目前为止已尝试过这一大球蛋白树主要分枝的18种备选结构。

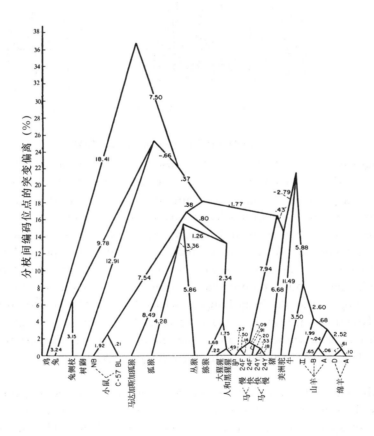

图 2. 鸡和哺乳动物的α球蛋白系统发生树。

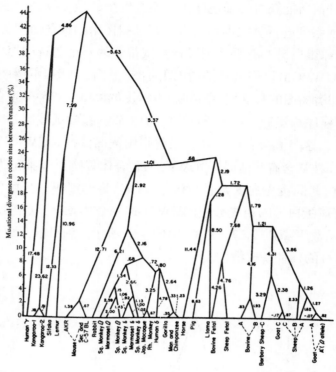

Fig. 3. Mammalian beta-like globin phylogenetic tree.

Course of Globin Evolution

The recognizable homologies between insect haem binding protein and vertebrate myoglobins and haemoglobins in codon sequence and in three-dimensional structure and functional properties[47] place the primordial globin gene deep in the Pre-Cambrian epoch before the protovertebrates had embarked on an independent course of evolution. Fig. 1 reveals that when man and lamprey still had a common ancestor, the primitive vertebrate genome already had more than one gene locus coding for globin chains; it was then that a gene duplication separated the ancestor of myoglobin genes from that of haemoglobin genes. Almost immediately after the myoglobin–haemoglobin duplication, the line leading to the globin in lamprey split off from the myoglobin side as a separate branch. Myoglobins are single chained proteins. Similarly, lamprey globins, including the one which has been sequenced, are single chained, although in certain physico-chemical conditions these lamprey globin chains form larger aggregates[45].

In the early bony fishes ancestral to the land vertebrates a haemoglobin gene duplicated to produce the split between the alpha and beta-like chain genes. This is depicted in Fig. 1 where the tetrapod alpha and beta-like lines separate from each other immediately after their separation from the carp alpha line. Much later in the lineage leading to therian mammals a gamma–beta chain gene duplicated to produce, on the one hand, the first separate ancestor of the genes for the kangaroo non-alpha chain, the human gamma chain (found in the haemoglobin of the human foetus) and the lemuroid non-alpha

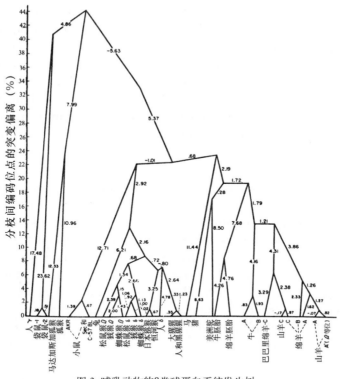

图 3. 哺乳动物的β类球蛋白系统发生树。

球蛋白进化过程

　　昆虫血红素结合蛋白和脊椎动物肌红蛋白、血红蛋白在编码序列和三维结构上可识别的同源性以及它们的功能特性[47]使原始球蛋白基因深藏在原始脊椎动物开始独立进化过程前的前寒武纪时代。图1表明：在人和七鳃鳗仍然拥有一个共同祖先时，原始脊椎动物的基因组中就已经有不止一个基因座来编码球蛋白链了；这时某一基因的复制使肌红蛋白基因的祖先从血红蛋白基因的祖先中分离出来。几乎紧随肌红蛋白-血红蛋白复制，七鳃鳗的球蛋白很快就从肌红蛋白的一侧分离而成为一条独立的分枝。肌红蛋白是单链蛋白。七鳃鳗球蛋白（包括那条已经测序的）同样也是单链的；但在某些特定的物理和化学条件下这些七鳃鳗球蛋白链会形成更大的聚集体[45]。

　　在陆地脊椎动物的祖先早期硬骨鱼中，一个血红蛋白基因的复制产生了α链和β类链基因间的分化。如图1所示：在从鲤鱼α支系分离后，四足动物α和β类支系很快就相互分开。很久之后，在向兽亚纲哺乳动物进化的支系中，一个γ-β链基因的复制：一方面产生了袋鼠非α链、人类γ链（在人类胚胎的血红蛋白中被发现）和狐猴非α链基因的第一个分离祖先，另一方面产生了哺乳动物β链基因的分离祖先。

chains and, on the other hand, the separate ancestor for the mammalian beta chain genes. The first separate ancestor of the lemuroid (lemur and sifaka) non-alpha globin chains may have been a gamma–beta hybrid produced by unequal homologous crossing over between originally linked gamma and beta genes. There are two residues (13 Ser, 21 Glu) in kangaroo, lemur and sifaka chains and three additional residues in the lemur and sifaka chains (9 Ala, 50 Ser, 52 Ser) which are homologous to human gamma chain. Furthermore, lemur and sifaka chains resemble more human gamma from the N-terminal end than human beta and resemble more human beta from the C-terminal end than human gamma.

At the nodes of Fig. 2 for the two most ancient branching points among mammalian alpha genes, ancestral rabbit and tree shrew genes diverged from each other immediately after their separation from the branch to all other mammalian alphas. Tree shrew alpha actually shows a greater mutation distance from rabbit, and rabbit from tree shrew, than either shows from other mammalian alpha chains (Table 1). This type of pattern, which resembles that of the human gamma, kangaroo and lemuroid non-alpha branch of the beta-like tree, suggests that alpha gene duplications had occurred in the early therian mammals producing ancestral rabbit and tree shrew genes and also the ancestor of other mammalian alphas. Recent duplications of alpha genes are known to occur in present day mammals, for example, in buffalo[50], horse[27], goat[52], macaques[54], mouse[56] and probably rabbit[18].

During eutherian phylogeny, beta chain genes duplicated independently in separate mammalian lines and certain of the descending duplicated genes ultimately coded for new proteins. For example, postnatal human blood contains in addition to its major haemoglobin (A) a minor haemoglobin (A$_2$) in which a different beta chain, called delta chain[1,57], combines with alpha chain. Similarly, the ceboid monkeys have a minor haemoglobin[38,58] with a beta chain (again called delta) different from the beta chain of the principal ceboid haemoglobin, Fig. 3 depicts in the early Anthropoidea, shortly after the branching apart of ceboids and catarrhine primates, two independent beta gene duplications: one on the catarrhine side coincided with the hominoid-cercopithecoid split to give rise to hominoid delta, and the other on the ceboid side produced the ancestor of ceboid deltas. Independent beta gene duplications also occurred during the evolution of the ruminants. Before the splitting apart of bovines and caprines, a descendant gene from a beta duplication in the early ruminant line began to code for the bovid foetal beta chain. The caprines (but not the bovines) have, like hominoids and ceboids, a second adult haemoglobin[45-47,59] (in this case, called haemoglobin C) normally present in negligible quantities, but synthesized in large amounts in animals under severe anaemic stress. In this second adult caprine haemoglobin, the beta C chain is found rather than the regular beta chain of caprine haemoglobin A. The ancestral A–C gene duplicated in the caprine line to give rise to the linked A and C gene loci shortly after the ancestral separation of bovines and caprines (Fig. 3).

Later in caprine evolution, at some point before the ancestral separation of sheep and goat, a mutation at the A locus produced the first separate ancestor of the present day sheep beta B gene. The period of separate evolution of sheep betas B and A seems to be

狐猴（狐猴和马达加斯加狐猴）非 α 球蛋白链的第一个分离祖先也许是一个由最初相连的 γ 和 β 基因之间的不等同源交叉产生的 γ–β 杂种。在袋鼠、狐猴和马达加斯加狐猴链中有 2 个氨基酸残基（13 丝氨酸，21 谷氨酸）；在与人类 γ 链同源的狐猴和马达加斯加狐猴链中还有 3 个额外的残基（9 丙氨酸，50 丝氨酸，52 丝氨酸）。此外，从 N 端看，狐猴和马达加斯加狐猴链与人类 γ 链的相似程度要高于与人类 β 链的相似程度；但从 C 端看，它们更像人类的 β 链而不是 γ 链。

图 2 中，在哺乳动物 α 基因中的 2 个最原始分枝节点上，兔和树鼩的祖先的基因在它们与所有其他哺乳动物 α 枝分离后很快就各自分开了。从树鼩 α 链到兔 α 链之间显示出的突变距离，实际上比这两者分别到其他任一哺乳动物 α 链的突变距离都要大（表 1）。这种模式很类似 β 类树中人 γ 枝以及袋鼠和狐猴非 α 枝的类型，这说明 α 基因复制发生在早期的兽亚纲哺乳动物中，由此产生了兔和树鼩祖先的基因以及其他哺乳动物 α 的祖先。已知最晚的 α 基因复制发生在现代哺乳动物中，例如水牛[50]、马[27]、山羊[52]、猕猴[54] 和小鼠[56]，还可能包括兔[18]。

在真兽次亚纲系统发生史中，β 链基因在分离的哺乳动物支系上独立复制，并且某些后来复制的基因还能最终编码新蛋白质。比如：初生婴儿的血液中除了包含主要的血红蛋白（A）外，还含有一种少量的血红蛋白（A₂），其中有一个不同质的 β 链（被称为 "δ 链"[1,57]）与 α 链相结合。悬猴也拥有一种含量少的血红蛋白[38,58]，其 β 链（仍被称为 δ）不同于悬猴主要血红蛋白的 β 链。图 3 描绘了在早期的类人猿亚目中，悬猴和狭鼻猴灵长类发生分离后，很快出现了 2 个独立的 β 基因复制：一个位于狭鼻猴那边，正好那时发生人科 – 猕猴科分离从而导致了人科 δ 链的形成；另一个位于悬猴那边，产生了悬猴 δ 链的祖先。独立的 β 基因复制也发生在反刍动物的进化中。牛和羊分离前，由早期反刍动物支系上的一个 β 基因复制的子代基因已经开始编码牛胚胎 β 链。羊（而不是牛）像人科动物和悬猴一样拥有第二种成体血红蛋白[45-47,59]（这里指血红蛋白 C），正常情况下只显示出可忽略的量，但在严重贫血压力下，动物体内会大量合成。在此第二种成体羊血红蛋白中发现了 β C 链而不是羊血红蛋白 A 中的普通 β 链。在牛和羊的祖先分离后不久，羊支系上的祖先 A–C 基因发生复制，产生了连锁的 A 和 C 的基因座（图 3）。

稍后在羊进化过程中，在绵羊和山羊的祖先发生分离前的某个点上，A 基因座上的一个突变产生了今天绵羊 β B 基因的第一个分离祖先。绵羊 β B 和 β A 分离进化的时期看上去比绵羊和山羊 β A 的进化时间更长。今天绵羊的 β B 与绵羊或山羊

greater than that of sheep and goat beta As. Present day sheep beta B differs from sheep or goat beta A by seven point mutations, whereas sheep beta A differs from goat beta A by four point mutations (Table 1). The sheep A and B-beta results illustrate that typical allelic proteins within a mammalian population can differ by several or more amino-acids. Bovine A and B beta alleles provide another example of such allelic variation; they differ by four point mutations (Table 1). Allelic human haemoglobins, on the other hand, differ from common human haemoglobin A mostly by only single point mutations.

The difference between bovid and human populations with respect to the kind of allelic variation expressed may be because the human foetus is at greater risk from maternal isoimmunizations than the bovid foetus. Bovids, like many mammals, have placentas of the epitheliochorial type[60] which separate the maternal and foetal vascular systems by several layers of tissue and thereby minimize the chance of maternal immune attacks on the foetus. In contrast the haemochorial placenta of the higher primates maximizes the opportunity for such attacks. Thus, the type of allelic beta chains with multiple differences in bovids, if found in man, could give rise to maternal immune reactions and be selected against. The first placentas to evolve in mammals were probably of the epitheliochorial type[60], so that the early mammals would not have been subjected to the immunological mechanism restricting genetic variability which we postulate for higher primate populations.

Rates of Globin Evolution

The patristic distance data, tabulated in Table 2, demonstrate that rates of evolution have varied markedly among vertebrate globin genes. The mammalian alpha genes diverge the least from the common vertebrate globin ancestor and the myoglobin genes; the group of non-alpha kangaroo, lemuroid, and human gamma genes diverge the most; lamprey globin, carp alpha, and chicken alpha each show more mutational change from this common ancestor than does any mammalian alpha (Fig. 1; Table 2, column 4).

Table 2. Percentage Mutational Divergence of Vertebrate Globins during Descent

Globin species	From ancestral eutherian mammal MMUTD†	From ancestral eutherian mammal PML	From ancestral Hb–Mb PML
Human alpha	6.3	6.13	39.34
Chimp alpha*	6.3	6.13	39.34
Gorilla alpha*	7.0	5.86	38.12
Mulatta alpha	7.1	5.57	41.68
Fuscata alpha	7.1	5.57	41.68
Mouse C57 alpha	8.5	8.50	39.75
Mouse NB alpha	10.6	10.21	41.65
Goat A alpha	10.6	8.96	36.26
Lemur alpha*	11.3	10.45	41.46
Bush baby alpha*	11.3	8.67	40.67

的 β A 的区别在于 7 个点突变,而绵羊 β A 与山羊 β A 的区别只有 4 个点突变(表 1)。绵羊 A 和 B β 的结果表明：在一个哺乳动物种群中，典型等位基因蛋白质之间会在几个或更多氨基酸上有所不同。牛 A 和 B β 等位基因为这类等位基因变异提供了另一个例子；它们的区别表现在 4 个点突变（表 1）。另一方面，等位的人血红蛋白与普通的人血红蛋白 A 相比，最多只在一个点突变上有所不同。

牛种群和人种群在表达的等位基因变异的类别上存在不同，这可能是因为人胚胎比牛胚胎更容易受到来自母体的同种免疫的威胁。和很多哺乳动物一样，牛拥有上皮绒膜类型的胎盘[60]，这使母体和胚胎的血管系统之间有几层组织相隔，因而最大程度地减小了母体免疫系统攻击胚胎的机会。反之，高等灵长类的血绒膜胎盘却使这类攻击的机会最大化。因此，在牛体内可以有存在多方面差异的等位 β 链基因类型，如果在人体内也是这样，就会引起母体免疫反应，从而被母体选择为敌对方。哺乳动物演变的第一个胎盘很可能属于上皮绒膜类型[60]，因此早期哺乳动物不会因为免疫机制而使基因变异受到限制，而我们假设在高等灵长类动物中是存在这一限制的。

球蛋白进化速度

列于表 2 中的父系长度数据表明，脊椎动物球蛋白基因的进化速度相互之间差异显著。哺乳动物 α 基因与脊椎动物球蛋白基因的共同祖先基因及肌红蛋白基因的偏离最少；袋鼠非 α、狐猴非 α 和人 γ 基因与祖先的偏离最多；七鳃鳗球蛋白、鲤鱼 α 和鸡 α 与任意其他哺乳动物 α 相比，都显示出了和共同祖先之间的更大突变变化（图 1；表 2，第 4 列）。

表 2. 脊椎动物球蛋白在进化过程中的突变变化百分比

球蛋白种类	自原始真兽次亚纲哺乳动物的MMUTD计算值†	自原始真兽次亚纲哺乳动物的父系突变长度	自祖先血红蛋白-肌红蛋白的父系突变长度
人 α	6.3	6.13	39.34
黑猩猩 α*	6.3	6.13	39.34
大猩猩 α*	7.0	5.86	38.12
普通猕猴 α	7.1	5.57	41.68
日本猕猴 α	7.1	5.57	41.68
小鼠 C57 α	8.5	8.50	39.75
小鼠 NB α	10.6	10.21	41.65
山羊 A α	10.6	8.96	36.26
狐猴 α*	11.3	10.45	41.46
丛猴 α*	11.3	8.67	40.67

Continued

Globin species	From ancestral eutherian mammal MMUTD†	From ancestral eutherian mammal PML	From ancestral Hb–Mb PML
Goat B alpha*	11.3	9.55	36.85
Goat II alpha	11.3	13.04	37.74
Bovine alpha*	11.3	9.16	38.08
Horse slow alpha	12.0	9.97	40.08
Horse fast alpha*	12.7	10.32	39.44
Sheep A alpha	12.7	11.56	37.61
Horse slow 24F alpha*	12.7	10.72	38.86
Horse fast 24F alpha*	13.4	10.99	39.37
Donkey alpha*	13.4	11.15	39.00
Sheep D alpha*	13.4	12.07	41.71
Pig alpha*	13.4	9.25	37.30
Rabbit alpha*	15.6	12.36	43.22
Rabbit (sub) alpha*	16.3	12.27	43.66
Sifaka alpha*	17.7	14.66	44.50
Tree shrew alpha*	17.7	12.25	43.68
Llama alpha*	19.1	11.27	40.46
Chicken alpha	—	—	49.18
Human beta	7.5	7.19	48.46
Chimp beta*	7.5	6.73	46.60
Squirrel monkey beta	7.5	8.68	50.94
Gorilla beta*	8.2	6.98	46.39
Fuscata beta*	8.2	8.06	50.21
Spider monkey beta	8.2	7.67	50.67
Tamarin beta	8.8	8.24	49.73
Mulatta beta	8.9	8.71	50.29
Rabbit beta	8.9	8.12	50.64
Human delta*	9.5	8.77	50.04
Tamarin delta	10.2	9.33	51.33
Spider monkey delta	10.2	8.54	50.81
Squirrel monkey delta	10.9	9.39	51.35
Pig beta*	14.2	11.78	48.27
Bovine A beta	16.4	12.47	48.71
Llama beta*	17.7	11.65	47.89
Bovine B beta	17.8	11.37	49.33
Sheep B beta	18.4	13.78	47.76

续表

球蛋白种类	自原始真兽次亚纲哺乳动物的MMUTD计算值†	自原始真兽次亚纲哺乳动物的父系突变长度	自祖先血红蛋白-肌红蛋白的父系突变长度
山羊 B α*	11.3	9.55	36.85
山羊 II α	11.3	13.04	37.74
牛 α*	11.3	9.16	38.08
马慢 α	12.0	9.97	40.08
马快 α*	12.7	10.32	39.44
绵羊 A α	12.7	11.56	37.61
马慢 24F α*	12.7	10.72	38.86
马快 24F α*	13.4	10.99	39.37
驴 α*	13.4	11.15	39.00
绵羊 D α*	13.4	12.07	41.71
猪 α*	13.4	9.25	37.30
兔 α*	15.6	12.36	43.22
兔（侧枝）α*	16.3	12.27	43.66
马达加斯加狐猴 α*	17.7	14.66	44.50
树鼩 α*	17.7	12.25	43.68
美洲驼 α*	19.1	11.27	40.46
鸡 α	—	—	49.18
人 β	7.5	7.19	48.46
黑猩猩 β*	7.5	6.73	46.60
松鼠猴 β	7.5	8.68	50.94
大猩猩 β*	8.2	6.98	46.39
日本猕猴 β*	8.2	8.06	50.21
蜘蛛猴 β	8.2	7.67	50.67
柽柳猴 β	8.8	8.24	49.73
普通猕猴 β	8.9	8.71	50.29
兔 β	8.9	8.12	50.64
人 δ*	9.5	8.77	50.04
柽柳猴 δ	10.2	9.33	51.33
蜘蛛猴 δ	10.2	8.54	50.81
松鼠猴 δ	10.9	9.39	51.35
猪 β*	14.2	11.78	48.27
牛 A β	16.4	12.47	48.71
美洲驼 β*	17.7	11.65	47.89
牛 B β	17.8	11.37	49.33
绵羊 B β	18.4	13.78	47.76

Continued

Globin species	From ancestral eutherian mammal MMUTD†	From ancestral eutherian mammal PML	From ancestral Hb–Mb PML
Horse beta	19.0	12.02	48.59
Goat A beta*	19.1	12.64	46.92
Sheep A beta	19.8	14.33	46.93
Bovine foetal beta	19.8	16.53	52.30
Goat C beta*	20.3	14.11	47.46
Mouse AKR beta*	20.4	13.09	49.29
Mouse Sec and C-57 Beta*	20.7	12.37	49.19
Goat A' beta*	21.2	13.23	47.46
Sheep C beta	21.7	15.15	48.58
Sheep Barb. C beta*	21.7	15.19	48.46
Sheep foetal beta*	24.2	17.03	50.50
Kangaroo-1 beta	—	—	59.68
Kangaroo-2 beta	—	—	59.84
Human gamma	—	—	54.07
Lemur beta*	—	—	53.56
Sifaka beta*	—	—	55.06
Carp alpha	—	—	50.57
Lamprey globin	—	—	50.78
Mb–horse	—	—	59.47
Mb–sperm whale	—	—	59.33
Insect CTT-3	—	—	—
Insect CTT-3 (sub)	—	—	—

* Sequence in part or wholly by composition and homology.

† Values of rabbit alpha, rabbit (sub) alpha, tree shrew alpha, mouse NB alpha and mouse C-57 alpha are directly from ancestral mammalian alpha. Values of prosimian alphas are through ancestral primate alpha node while those of catarrhine alphas are through both ancestral primate alpha node and ancestral catarrhine alpha node. Values of mouse AKR beta, mouse Sec and C-57 betas and rabbit beta are directly from ancestral mammalian beta while those of ungulate betas and primate betas are through ancestral ungulate beta node and ancestral Anthropoidea beta node, respectively.

While the patristic mutation lengths from Fig. 1 reveal that the proportion of codon positions showing mutations varied markedly among the principal branches of vertebrate globins, they do not show any especially marked variation among mammalian alpha genes, or among typical mammalian beta genes. But the patristic mutation lengths for the mammalian alpha portion of the globin tree from Fig. 2 and for the mammalian beta portion from Fig. 3 reveal that rates of evolution have indeed varied markedly both among mammalian alpha genes and among mammalian beta genes (Table 2, column 3). In both sets of mammalian genes, the most slowly evolving lines were those which led to man and

球蛋白种类	自原始真兽次亚纲哺乳动物的MMUTD计算值†	自原始真兽次亚纲哺乳动物的父系突变长度	自祖先血红蛋白-肌红蛋白的父系突变长度
马 β	19.0	12.02	48.59
山羊 A β*	19.1	12.64	46.92
绵羊 A β	19.8	14.33	46.93
牛胚胎 β	19.8	16.53	52.30
山羊 C β*	20.3	14.11	47.46
小鼠 AKR β*	20.4	13.09	49.29
小鼠 Sec 和 C-57 β*	20.7	12.37	49.19
山羊 A' β*	21.2	13.23	47.46
绵羊 C β	21.7	15.15	48.58
巴巴里绵羊 C β*	21.7	15.19	48.46
绵羊胚胎 β*	24.2	17.03	50.50
袋鼠 -1 β	—	—	59.68
袋鼠 -2 β	—	—	59.84
人 γ	—	—	54.07
狐猴 β*	—	—	53.56
马达斯加狐猴 β*	—	—	55.06
鲤鱼 α	—	—	50.57
七鳃鳗球蛋白	—	—	50.78
肌红蛋白 – 马	—	—	59.47
肌红蛋白 – 抹香鲸	—	—	59.33
昆虫 CTT-3	—	—	—
昆虫 CTT-3（侧枝）	—	—	—

* 序列已部分或全部通过组成和同源性测定。

† 兔 α、兔（侧枝）α、树鼩 α、小鼠 NB α 和小鼠 C-57 α 的值直接从原始哺乳动物 α 算起。原猴亚目 α 的值用到了原始灵长类 α 节点，而狭鼻猴 α 同时用到了原始灵长类 α 节点和原始狭鼻猴 α 节点。小鼠 AKR β、小鼠 Sec β、小鼠 C-57 β 以及兔 β 的值直接从原始哺乳动物 β 算起，而有蹄类 β 和灵长类 β 分别用到了原始有蹄类 β 节点和原始类人猿 β 节点。

虽然图 1 中的父系突变长度揭示出发生突变的编码位置比例在脊椎动物球蛋白各主分枝之间差异很大，但是在哺乳动物 α 基因或在典型哺乳动物 β 基因中，编码位置比例并没有表现出特别显著的变化。然而，图 2 球蛋白树中哺乳动物 α 部分的父系突变长度和图 3 中哺乳动物 β 部分的父系突变长度显示，哺乳动物 α 基因之间和哺乳动物 β 基因之间的进化速度确实有很大的差异（表 2，第 3 列）。在两个系列的哺乳动物基因中，进化最慢的支系是进化成为人类和其他高等灵长类的支系。在这些大的球蛋白系列中（图 1），很早之前就已分离的种类之间的突变距离，例如任

other higher primates. In the large globin series (Fig. 1) the mutation distance between very anciently separated species, such as between any alpha and any beta globin chain, would be grossly underestimated due to uncounted multiple mutations at the same nucleotide sites. Thus, differences in rates of evolution among homologous mammalian genes, which are reflected in the patristic mutation lengths shown in Figs. 2 and 3, are smoothed out in the lengths shown in Fig. 1 where the apportioning of the mutation distances between the more recently separated genes is disproportionately affected by the mutation distance comparisons to the many, very anciently separated globin genes. Kimura[61] concluded that homologous genes evolved at uniform rates because about the same number of amino-acid substitutions separate any mammalian beta from any mammalian alpha and from carp alpha. But he failed to consider that the further in the past the separation of two lineages the larger the number of multiple mutations that must have occurred at the same nucleotide sites.

To detect a larger proportion of the accumulated mutations in a gene lineage, we constructed ancestral sequences (Table 3) for branching points of the globin phylogenetic tree and, using the MMUTD program, determined the mutation distances through the consecutive ancestors to the contemporary polypeptide chains. The mutational change in codon sites from the node for ancestral carp–tetrapod haemoglobin chains to the node for ancestral chicken–mammal alphas and from the latter to the ancestral node for mammalian alpha chains was 23.9 and 9.2% respectively. In the descent of the beta-like line, the mutational change from the ancestral carp–tetrapod node to the ancestral gamma–beta node and from this node to the ancestral node for typical mammalian beta chains was 53.2 and 2.0% respectively. The further mutational change in descent of each eutherian alpha and beta line is given in column 2 of Table 2. These results show that after the alpha–beta globin gene duplication in early vertebrate history, after the ancestral separation 380 million years ago of teleosts and tetrapods, many more mutations accumulated during the descent towards mammals in the beta-like line than in the alpha line. Moreover, during eutherian phylogeny, both alpha and beta chain evolution was much slower (on the average, almost by half) in higher primates than in other mammals. Furthermore, from the ancestral carp–tetrapod node about as much mutational change accumulated up to the ancestral chicken–mammalian alpha branching point as after this point in the descending mammalian alpha line. Yet one has to go back about 280 million years ago to the early reptiles to find the most recent common ancestor of birds and mammals. Thus the evidence suggests that the descending alpha genes evolved at a more rapid rate in earlier less advanced vertebrates than in later higher vertebrates.

一 α 和任一 β 球蛋白链之间的距离，可能由于同一核苷酸位点处的未计数多重突变而被严重低估。因此，图 2 和图 3 中父系突变长度所反映出的同源哺乳动物基因间进化速度的不同，在图 1 所示的这个长度中并未体现出来，其中更后期分离的基因间突变距离的分配，不成比例地受到与许多非常远古时就已分离的球蛋白基因间突变距离相比较的影响。木村资生 [61] 认为：同源基因以一致的速度进化，因为任一哺乳动物 β 与任一哺乳动物 α 之间以及任一哺乳动物 β 与鲤鱼 α 之间的氨基酸替换数大致相等。但是他没有考虑到以下这一点：两条支系分离的时间越早，在同一核苷酸位点处发生的多重突变数目也就越多。

为了在一个基因支系中检测到更高比例的积累突变，我们构建了球蛋白系统发生树中各分枝点的祖先序列（表 3），并用 MMUTD 程序确定了各祖先基因到当代多肽链的突变距离。从鲤鱼 – 四足动物祖先血红蛋白链的节点到鸡 – 哺乳动物祖先 α 的节点，以及从后者到哺乳动物祖先 α 链节点之间的编码位点的突变变化分别是 23.9% 和 9.2%。在 β 类支系的演变中，从鲤鱼 – 四足动物祖先节点到 γ–β 祖先节点，以及从该节点到典型哺乳动物 β 链祖先节点之间的突变变化分别是 53.2% 和 2.0%。表 2 的第 2 列给出了每个真兽次亚纲 α 和 β 支系在进化过程中的进一步突变变化。这些结果显示：在早期脊椎动物史中，α–β 球蛋白基因的复制发生在 3.8 亿年前硬骨鱼和四足动物的祖先分离后；在这之后，就指向哺乳动物的进化过程而言，积累于 β 类支系中的突变数量远远高于积累于 α 支系中的突变数量。此外，在真兽次亚纲系统发生过程中，高等灵长类 α 和 β 链进化的速度远比其他哺乳动物慢（平均而言，几乎慢一半）。而且，从鲤鱼 – 四足动物祖先节点到鸡 – 哺乳动物祖先 α 分枝点间所积累的突变变化，大致与哺乳动物 α 支系在鸡 – 哺乳动物祖先 α 分枝点之后的进化过程中所积累的突变变化相等。但是我们必须回到大约 2.8 亿年前的早期爬行类中来寻找鸟类和哺乳类离现在最近的共同祖先。因此，这些证据表明：世代相传的 α 基因在早期低等脊椎动物中的进化速度要高于在后期高等脊椎动物中的进化速度。

Table 3. Probable Ancestral Residues for Vertebrate Globin Chains at Different Nodes during Descent

Residue position	11	13	14	15	16	18	19	21	22	23	24	25	27	28	29	30	31	32	34	36	38	40	42	43	44	45	46	48	50	51	52	54
β-Mammal	His	Thr	Ala	Glu	Glu	Ala	Ala	Thr	Ala	Leu	Trp	Gly	Val	Asx	—	—	Val	Asp	Val	Gly	Ala	Gly	Leu	Leu	Val	Val	Tyr	Trp	Gln	Arg	Arg	Glu
γ-β-Mammal	His	Thr	Ala	Glu	Glu	Ala	Ala	Thr	Ala	Leu	Trp	Gly	Val	Asn	—	—	Val	Asp	Val	Gly	Ala	Gly	Leu	Leu	Val	Val	Tyr	Trp	Gln	Arg	Arg	Glu
α-Mammal	—	Ser	Pro	Ala	Asp	Thr	Asn	Lys	Ala	Ala	Trp	Gly	Ile	Gly	Gly	His	Ala	Gly	Tyr	Ala	Ala	Glu	Met	Phe	Leu	Ser	Phe	Thr	Lys	Thr	Tyr	Pro
α-Chicken-Mammal	—	Ser	Ala	Ala	Asp	Ala	Asn	Lys	Ala	Ala	Trp	Ala	Ile	Gly	Gly	His	Ala	Glu	Tyr	Ala	Ala	Glu	Met	Phe	Ile	Gly	Phe	Thr	Lys	Thr	Tyr	Pro
α-β-Carp	—	Ser	Ala	Ala	Asp	Ala	Ala	Lys	Ala	Ala	Trp	Ala	Ile	Gly	Gly	His	Ala	Asp	Tyr	Gly	Ala	Gly	Met	Phe	Ile	Gly	Thr	Thr	Lys	Thr	Thr	Ala

Residue position	55	57	61	62	63	64	65	66	68	69	70	71	73	79	81	83	84	85	86	88	90	92	93	94	97	98	99	100	103	106	107	110
β-Mammal	Ser	Gly	Ser	Ala	Asx	Ala	Val	Met	Asn	Pro	Lys	Val	Ala	Leu	Asx	Phe	Ser	Asp	Gly	Asx	Leu	Asn	Leu	Lys	Thr	Phe	Ala	Gln	Glu	Cys	Asp	His
γ-β-Mammal	Ser	Gly	Ser	Ala	Ser	Ala	Val	Met	Asn	Pro	Lys	Val	Ala	Leu	Asx	Phe	Ser	Asp	Gly	Asx	Leu	Asn	Leu	Lys	Thr	Phe	Ala	Gln	Glu	Cys	Asp	His
α-Mammal	His	—	—	—	—	—	—	—	Ser	Ala	Gln	Val	Gly	Ala	Asp	Leu	Thr	Asn	Ala	Gly	Leu	Asp	Leu	Pro	Ala	Leu	Ser	Ala	Asp	Ala	His	Arg
α-Chicken-Mammal	His	—	His	—	—	—	—	—	Ser	Ala	Gln	Val	Gly	Ala	Asp	Leu	Thr	Asn	Ala	Gly	Leu	Asp	Leu	Pro	Ala	Leu	Ser	Ala	Asp	Ala	His	Arg
α-β-Carp	His	Gly	—	—	—	—	—	—	Ser	Ala	Gln	Val	Gly	Ile	Asp	Val	Ser	Asp	Ala	Gly	Leu	Asp	Leu	Glu	Ala	Leu	Ala	Ala	Glu	Ala	His	Arg

Residue position	114	117	120	121	122	123	124	125	126	128	129	131	132	133	134	135	136	138	140	142	143	144	147	148	149	151	152	153	155	156	159
β-Mammal	Glu	Arg	Gly	Asn	Val	Leu	Val	Ile	Val	Ala	His	Phe	Gly	Lys	Glu	Phe	Thr	Glx	Gln	Val	Tyr	Gln	Val	Ala	Gly	Ala	Asn	Ala	Ala	His	His
γ-β-Mammal	Glu	Arg	Gly	Asn	Val	Leu	Val	Ile	Val	Ala	His	Phe	Gly	Lys	Glu	Phe	Thr	Glx	Gln	Val	Phe	Gln	Val	Ala	Gly	Ala	Asn	Ala	Ala	His	His
α-Mammal	Val	Lys	Ser	His	Val	Leu	Leu	Val	Thr	Ala	Ala	Leu	Pro	Ala	Asp	Phe	Thr	Ala	His	Ser	Leu	Asp	Leu	Ala	Ser	Ser	Thr	Val	Thr	Ser	Arg
α-Chicken-Mammal	Val	Lys	Ser	His	Cys	Leu	Leu	Val	Thr	Ala	Ser	Leu	Pro	Ala	Glu	Phe	Thr	Glu	His	Ser	Leu	Asp	Leu	Ala	Ala	Ser	Thr	Val	Thr	His	Arg
α-β-Carp	Glu	Lys	Ser	Asn	Ala	Leu	Val	Val	Val	Ala	Ser	Leu	Pro	Ala	Glu	Phe	Thr	Glu	His	Ser	Val	Asp	Leu	Ala	Ala	Ala	Asn	Ala	Thr	Arg	Arg

Amino-acid residues of vertebrate globins are aligned so as to maximize homology by introducing the necessary gaps (refs. 14 and 15). The residue positions are numbered from 1 to 165 in order to accommodate lamprey globin. In this alignment carp alpha, tetrapod alphas, and mammalian betas begin at position 10 and end at position 159, with a gap at position 96. Carp alpha and tetrapod alphas have in addition gaps at position 11 and at position 62 through 66. Further gaps introduced are: tetrapod alphas at positions 57 and 78; mammalian betas at positions 29, 30, and 78; carp alpha at position 73. Residue positions omitted are the same as chicken[17] when aligned as described. Probable ancestral residues of mammalian alpha and beta chains at branching points within the span of eutherian phylogeny are given in the previous investigation[10]. Ancestral sequences were reconstructed by approximation after the rules described by Fitch and Margoliash[7]. In brief, an ancestral residue is selected if it gives fewer mutations in the lines of descent than any other residue which could be selected and, where more than one residue meets this criterion, distributes the mutations as equally as possible between the lines of descent.

表3. 在进化过程不同节点上的脊椎动物球蛋白链所可能含有的原始氨基酸基残基

残基位置	11	13	14	15	16	18	19	21	22	23	24	25	27	28	29	30	31	32	34	36	38	40	42	43	44	45	46	48	50	51	52	54
β-哺乳动物	组氨酸	苏氨酸	丙氨酸	谷氨酸	谷氨酸	谷氨酸	丙氨酸	苏氨酸	丙氨酸	亮氨酸	色氨酸	甘氨酸	缬氨酸	天冬氨酸	-	-	缬氨酸	天冬氨酸	缬氨酸	甘氨酸	丙氨酸	甘氨酸	亮氨酸	亮氨酸	缬氨酸	缬氨酸	酪氨酸	色氨酸	谷氨酰胺	精氨酸	精氨酸	谷氨酸
γ-β-哺乳动物	组氨酸	苏氨酸	丙氨酸	谷氨酸	谷氨酸	谷氨酸	丙氨酸	苏氨酸	丙氨酸	亮氨酸	色氨酸	甘氨酸	缬氨酸	天冬氨酸	-	-	缬氨酸	天冬氨酸	缬氨酸	甘氨酸	丙氨酸	甘氨酸	亮氨酸	亮氨酸	缬氨酸	缬氨酸	酪氨酸	色氨酸	谷氨酰胺	精氨酸	精氨酸	谷氨酸
α-哺乳动物	-	丝氨酸	脯氨酸	丙氨酸	天冬氨酸	苏氨酸	天冬酰胺	蛋氨酸	天冬氨酸	丙氨酸	色氨酸	甘氨酸	异亮氨酸	亮氨酸	甘氨酸	组氨酸	丙氨酸	天冬酰胺	酪氨酸	丙氨酸	亮氨酸	甘氨酸	亮氨酸	丙氨酸	异亮氨酸	苯丙氨酸	苯丙氨酸	苏氨酸	赖氨酸	半胱氨酸	酪氨酸	脯氨酸
α-鸡	-	丝氨酸	脯氨酸	丙氨酸	天冬氨酸	丙氨酸	天冬酰胺	赖氨酸	天冬氨酸	丙氨酸	色氨酸	丙氨酸	异亮氨酸	亮氨酸	甘氨酸	组氨酸	苏氨酸	天冬酰胺	酪氨酸	甘氨酸	亮氨酸	甘氨酸	亮氨酸	亮氨酸	苏氨酸	苯丙氨酸	丝氨酸	苏氨酸	赖氨酸	苏氨酸	酪氨酸	脯氨酸
α-β-鲤鱼	-	丝氨酸	脯氨酸	丙氨酸	天冬氨酸	丙氨酸	丙氨酸	缬氨酸	天冬酰胺	丙氨酸	赖氨酸	缬氨酸	甘氨酸	亮氨酸	甘氨酸	组氨酸	丙氨酸	天冬酰胺	甘氨酸	甘氨酸	缬氨酸	甘氨酸	亮氨酸	谷氨酸	异亮氨酸	亮氨酸	丙氨酸	苏氨酸	谷氨酸	苏氨酸	苏氨酸	丙氨酸

残基位置	55	57	61	62	63	64	65	66	68	69	70	71	73	79	81	83	84	85	86	88	90	92	93	94	97	98	99	100	103	106	107	110
β-哺乳动物	丝氨酸	甘氨酸	丝氨酸	丙氨酸	天冬氨酸或天冬酰胺	亮氨酸	缬氨酸	蛋氨酸	天冬氨酸	脯氨酸	赖氨酸	缬氨酸	丙氨酸	天冬酰胺	天冬氨酸或天冬酰胺	苯丙氨酸	丝氨酸	天冬氨酸	甘氨酸	亮氨酸	亮氨酸	天冬酰胺	亮氨酸	赖氨酸	苏氨酸	苯丙氨酸	丙氨酸	谷氨酸	谷氨酸	半胱氨酸	精氨酸	组氨酸
γ-β-哺乳动物	丝氨酸	甘氨酸	丝氨酸	丙氨酸	天冬氨酸或天冬酰胺	亮氨酸	缬氨酸	-	天冬氨酸	脯氨酸	赖氨酸	缬氨酸	丙氨酸	苯丙氨酸	天冬氨酸或天冬酰胺	苯丙氨酸	丝氨酸	天冬酰胺	甘氨酸	亮氨酸	天冬氨酸	天冬酰胺	亮氨酸	谷氨酸	苏氨酸	苯丙氨酸	丙氨酸	谷氨酸	甘氨酸	丙氨酸	精氨酸	组氨酸
α-哺乳动物	组氨酸	组氨酸	-	组氨酸	半胱氨酸	亮氨酸	-	-	-	-	-	-	-	丙氨酸	天冬氨酸	丙氨酸	丙氨酸	天冬酰胺	甘氨酸	亮氨酸	天冬氨酸	天冬酰胺	天冬氨酸	脯氨酸	丙氨酸	丝氨酸	丝氨酸	丝氨酸	苏氨酸	丙氨酸	组氨酸	精氨酸	精氨酸
α-鸡	组氨酸	组氨酸	-	组氨酸	半胱氨酸	亮氨酸	-	-	-	-	-	-	-	丙氨酸	天冬氨酸	丙氨酸	苏氨酸	天冬酰胺	甘氨酸	亮氨酸	天冬氨酸	天冬酰胺	天冬氨酸	脯氨酸	丙氨酸	丝氨酸	苏氨酸	赖氨酸	谷氨酸	丙氨酸	丙氨酸	精氨酸	精氨酸
α-β-鲤鱼	丝氨酸	甘氨酸	丝氨酸	天冬氨酸	天冬氨酸或天冬酰胺	丙氨酸	-	-	丝氨酸	丙氨酸	甘氨酸	甘氨酸	甘氨酸	异亮氨酸	天冬氨酸或天冬酰胺	丝氨酸	甘氨酸	天冬酰胺	甘氨酸	亮氨酸	天冬氨酸	天冬酰胺	甘氨酸	谷氨酸	丙氨酸	丝氨酸	天冬酰胺	谷氨酸	甘氨酸	丙氨酸	苏氨酸	精氨酸

残基位置	114	117	120	121	122	123	124	125	126	128	129	131	132	133	134	135	136	138	140	142	143	144	147	148	149	151	152	153	155	156	159
β-哺乳动物	谷氨酸	精氨酸	天冬酰胺	天冬酰胺	缬氨酸	亮氨酸	天冬酰胺	异亮氨酸	缬氨酸	丙氨酸	组氨酸	甘氨酸	赖氨酸	赖氨酸	谷氨酸	谷氨酸	谷氨酸	谷氨酰胺或谷氨酸	谷氨酸	丙氨酸	酪氨酸	谷氨酰胺	谷氨酰胺	丙氨酸	甘氨酸	丝氨酸	天冬酰胺	丙氨酸	丙氨酸	组氨酸	天冬酰胺
γ-β-哺乳动物	谷氨酸	精氨酸	丝氨酸	天冬酰胺	缬氨酸	亮氨酸	天冬酰胺	异亮氨酸	丙氨酸	苏氨酸	组氨酸	甘氨酸	谷氨酸	赖氨酸	谷氨酸	谷氨酸	苏氨酸	谷氨酸或谷氨酰胺	谷氨酸	丝氨酸	苯丙氨酸	甘氨酸	缬氨酸	丙氨酸	丝氨酸	丝氨酸	苏氨酸	苏氨酸	丝氨酸	组氨酸	丝氨酸
α-哺乳动物	缬氨酸	赖氨酸	丝氨酸	丙氨酸	半胱氨酸	亮氨酸	亮氨酸	缬氨酸	丙氨酸	丝氨酸	丙氨酸	甘氨酸	脯氨酸	丙氨酸	组氨酸	丙氨酸	丙氨酸	谷氨酸	丙氨酸	丝氨酸	酪氨酸	甘氨酸	天冬氨酸	天冬氨酸	丝氨酸	丝氨酸	苏氨酸	苏氨酸	丝氨酸	精氨酸	丝氨酸
α-鸡	缬氨酸	赖氨酸	丝氨酸	丙氨酸	半胱氨酸	亮氨酸	亮氨酸	缬氨酸	丙氨酸	丝氨酸	丙氨酸	甘氨酸	脯氨酸	丙氨酸	组氨酸	丙氨酸	丙氨酸	谷氨酸	丙氨酸	丝氨酸	苏氨酸	天冬氨酸	天冬氨酸	苏氨酸	丝氨酸	丝氨酸	苏氨酸	苏氨酸	丝氨酸	精氨酸	丝氨酸
α-β-鲤鱼	谷氨酸	赖氨酸	丝氨酸	天冬酰胺	天冬氨酸	丙氨酸	丙氨酸	缬氨酸	丙氨酸	丝氨酸	丝氨酸	丙氨酸	谷氨酸	脯氨酸	组氨酸	丙氨酸	丝氨酸	谷氨酸	谷氨酸	丝氨酸	苏氨酸	天冬氨酸	天冬氨酸	苏氨酸	丙氨酸	丝氨酸	苏氨酸	苏氨酸	丝氨酸	精氨酸	谷氨酰胺

对齐脊椎动物球蛋白的氨基酸残基的目的是为了通过引入必要的缺口以使同源性最大化（参考文献[14和15]）。残基位置按1到165编号以适应七鳃鳗球蛋白。

在这一对齐过程中，鲤鱼α，鲤鱼α和四足动物β蛋白从位置10开始，结束于位置96，缺口位于位置96。四足动物和哺乳动物β蛋白在位置57和78，哺乳动物α在位置29，30和78，鲤鱼α在位置73，的地方有缺口。引入的另一些缺口是：四足动物α在位置57和78，哺乳动物α和β链在跨度内的分枝对齐鸡球蛋白白的氨基酸残基时[17]一样。在之前的研究中，我们已经给出了哺乳动物α和β链在真兽亚纲系统发生真兽目次亚纲动物的分枝内可能出现的原始残基[10]。按非奇和马格利亚什描述的规则[11]以粗略估计值重建祖先序列。简言之，如果一个原始残基能在进化支系中比其他可能被选择的原始基带来的突变少，那么它将被选择；如果不止一个残基符合这个标准，那么就在不同的进化支系中尽可能地分配这些突变。

The patristic distance data on beta genes show that ceboid delta, bovid foetal beta, and caprine C beta initially evolved more rapidly than the genes from which they were duplicated (Fig. 3), but later in descent their rates of evolution slowed. Note (Table 1) that ceboid deltas actually diverge less from each other than ceboid betas, that sheep and bovine foetal betas diverge less from each other than sheep and bovine adult betas, and that sheep and goat C betas diverge less than sheep and goat A betas. Presumably mutations had accumulated freely at the duplicated loci until certain fortuitous mutations resulted in the emergence of new proteins with useful functions. Then natural selection not only caused these particular advantageous mutant genes to spread rapidly through the populations in which they occurred but also drastically slowed their further evolution.

Following the gamma–beta gene duplication, more mutational change occurred in the descent of human gamma than in most typical eutherian beta chains. Nevertheless amino-acid composition data[62] indicate that slightly less divergence exists between gamma chains of man and baboon than between either beta or alpha chains of these animals. Thus when sequence data become available on gamma chains of different higher primates, the pattern of decelerating evolution will probably be found again. This pattern is presented by the myoglobin genes, for the divergence between horse and sperm whale myoglobins (Fig. 1 and Table 1) is no more than that between any two alpha chains belonging to different eutherian orders; yet the overall mutational change in the descent of the myoglobin branch is larger than in the branch containing the various chains of vertebrate haemoglobin (Table 2, column 4). Ohno[63] describes early vertebrate history as a time when tetraploidization and bursts of gene duplication were occurring in our ancestors; at the later, mammalian stage specialized functions were found for pre-existing redundant genes, but the level of genome organization was such that viable tetraploidization was no longer possible. If mutations accumulate more readily in silent genes than in functional ones, this is equivalent to the hypothesis that molecular evolution decelerated during the descent of man.

In lemurs and other prosimians, foetal haemoglobin seems to be the same as adult haemoglobin[64]. But in the lineage leading to higher primates a specialized function, coding for the non-alpha chain of foetal haemoglobin, was found for the gamma locus. A further advance took place when from certain beta duplications of the early Anthropoidea functioning delta genes and a new haemoglobin type emerged in later Ceboidea and Hominoidea. The new level of organization imposed additional functional restraints, which increased the likelihood that new mutations would be detrimental, thereby slowing the further evolution of the haemoglobin genes. While the alpha and beta chains of man are among the most slowly evolved globins, those of the kangaroo and lemuroids are among the most rapidly evolved. As previously discussed, an additional selective factor, maternal isoimmunizations to foetal antigens, might have also acted to decelerate molecular evolution in the higher primates. The opportunity for such attacks would be virtually absent in kangaroo, and minimal in lemuroid primates which have epitheliochorial type placentas[65] rather than the haemochorial type of higher primates.

关于 β 基因的父系突变长度数据显示，悬猴 δ、牛胚胎 β 和羊 C β 在开始时曾比复制为它们的基因进化得更快（图 3），但是在后代中它们的进化速度变慢了。注意（表 1）：悬猴 δ 相互之间的偏离实际上比悬猴 β 相互之间的偏离少，绵羊胚胎和牛胚胎 β 比绵羊成体和牛成体 β 之间的偏离少，以及绵羊和山羊 C β 比绵羊和山羊 A β 之间的偏离少。假设突变一直在复制基因座处自由积累，直到某些偶然的突变能够产生具有实用功能的新蛋白质。而后自然选择不但使这些特定的有利突变基因在它们发生的种群内部迅速扩散，而且也极大地减缓了它们的进一步进化。

在 γ–β 基因复制之后，人类 γ 后代中发生的突变变化超过了大多数典型真兽次亚纲 β 链中发生的突变变化。虽然如此，氨基酸构成数据 [62] 显示，人类和狒狒 γ 链间存在的偏离略少于它们的 β 链或 α 链之间的偏离。因此，当可以获得各种灵长类动物的 γ 链序列数据时，或许将会再次发现减速进化的趋势。这种趋势在肌红蛋白基因中有所体现，因为马和抹香鲸肌红蛋白间的偏离（图 1 和表 1）不会高于真兽次亚纲下不同目动物的任何两种 α 链间的偏离；而肌红蛋白分枝在进化过程中的全部突变变化要大于含脊椎动物血红蛋白多种链的分枝中的突变变化（表 2，第 4 列）。大野乾 [63] 将早期脊椎动物史描述为我们祖先体内发生基因复制的四倍体化和爆发的时代；后来，哺乳动物阶段的特异化功能被发现源自于早先存在的冗余基因，但基因组组织的等级使得本来可以实现的四倍体化变得不再可能。如果突变在沉默基因中的积累速度比在功能基因中更快，这就等价于假设在人类进化过程中分子进化速度放慢。

在狐猴和其他原猴亚目动物中，胚胎血红蛋白与成体血红蛋白看似一样 [64]。但在通向更高等灵长类动物的支系中发现，编码胚胎血红蛋白非 α 链的特定功能源自于 γ 基因座。当早期类人猿亚目的功能性 δ 基因发生某些 β 复制时会导致进化的推进，从而在后来的悬猴总科和人猿总科中出现了一种新的血红蛋白类型。组织的新等级会产生附加的功能性抑制，这就增加了新突变为有害突变的可能性，从而使血红蛋白基因的进一步进化放缓。虽然人类的 α 和 β 链处于进化最缓慢的球蛋白行列，但袋鼠和狐猴的相同基因却在进化最快的球蛋白行列中。正如前面讨论的那样，一个附加选择因子，即母体和胚胎抗原不相容引起的同族免疫，可能也会使高等灵长类动物的分子进化减速。在袋鼠中发生这类攻击的可能性几乎不存在；在有上皮绒膜型胎盘而非高等灵长类中的血绒膜型胎盘的狐猴类灵长目动物 [65] 中，这种攻击的可能性也非常小。

Cladistic Relationships of Man and Other Mammals

The phylogenetic trees constructed from amino-acid sequence data not only reveal differences in relative rates of evolution among homologous genes but also provide evidence on the cladistic relationships of the animal species in which the genes occur. The branching topologies of alpha chain genes and beta chain genes depict a very close relationship, with no detectable mutational divergence, between man and chimpanzee, and between this man–chimpanzee branch and gorilla, in which the divergence is only one point mutation per chain. A beta phylogenetic tree, which includes the partially sequenced gibbon beta chain, joins gibbon to the branch leading to chimpanzee, man and gorilla, and then joins cercopithecoid (macaques) and hominoid branches[10]. Orang-utan haemoglobin chains have not been sequenced. Amino-acid composition data, however, show orang-utan diverging from the branch of African apes and man[66]. In the beta phylogenetic tree (Fig. 3), the ceboids branch away from the line leading to cercopithecoids and hominoids just before these two catarrhine groups branch apart. The phylogenetic tree of alpha genes (Fig. 2) joins the prosimians (galago together with the lemuroids, lemur and sifaka) to the line leading to higher primates, next joins the mouse branch to the base of the primate branch, and then joins the ancestral mouse–primate lineage with that of the ungulates. Both alpha and beta trees join caprines to bovines, llama and pig lines to the bovids, the horse branch with these artiodactyls, and then these ungulates with the lineage descending towards primates. Lemuroids do not produce a globin chain directly homologous to mammalian beta chains, so the phylogenetic tree of beta genes cannot provide cladistic evidence on the lemuroids. Otherwise the topology of the beta tree is similar to the alpha, except that rabbit beta joins primate betas before mouse.

Sequence data have also been obtained on mammalian fibrinopeptides A and B. They contain no more than forty amino-acid residues, all of which, with the exception of one or two invariant sites, have accepted amino-acid substitutions without harm to the function of fibrinogen. Thus these peptide sequences have been able to undergo such extensive divergent evolution that they are capable of depicting cladistic relationships among present day mammals. A matrix of mutation values for thirty-six mammalian combined A and B fibrinopeptide sequences[67-75] is given in Table 4, and the best tree of thirty alternatives tried portraying the phylogeny of these sequences is shown in Fig. 4. The APSD coefficient of this tree is 10.80 compared with 14.63 for the UWPGM tree.

人类和其他哺乳动物的进化枝关系

用氨基酸序列数据建立的系统发生树不仅揭示了同源基因间相对进化速度的不同，同时也为存在这些基因的动物物种的进化枝关系提供了证据。α 链基因和 β 链基因的分枝拓扑结构显示出在人类和黑猩猩间具有非常紧密的关系，未曾探测到两者之间存在突变偏离；人 – 黑猩猩枝同大猩猩枝之间的关系也很密切，每条链上只有一个点突变的偏离。包含部分测序的长臂猿 β 链的 β 系统发生树，将长臂猿连接到通向黑猩猩、人和大猩猩的分枝，然后与猕猴科（猕猴）分枝和人科分枝相连 [10]。目前还没有对红毛猩猩血红蛋白链进行测序。然而氨基酸组成数据显示，红毛猩猩是从非洲类人猿和人类的分枝中分离出来的 [66]。在 β 系统发生树上（图 3），悬猴分枝正好在猕猴科和人科这两个狭鼻猴组分叉前离开了通向这两科的支系。α 基因系统发生树（图 2）将原猴亚目（丛猴和狐猴科动物——狐猴和马达加斯加狐猴）连接到通向高等灵长类的支系上，其次将小鼠分枝结合到灵长类分枝的基部，然后又把小鼠 – 灵长类祖先的支系添加到有蹄类支系。α 树和 β 树都将羊支系连接到牛支系上，将美洲驼和猪支系连接到牛上，将马分枝添加到这些偶蹄类动物，然后把有蹄类添加到向灵长类进化的支系。狐猴科动物并不产生与哺乳动物 β 链直接同源的球蛋白链，所以 β 基因系统发生树不能提供关于狐猴科的进化枝证据。除了兔 β 是在小鼠前加入灵长类 β 之外，β 树的拓扑结构与 α 树类似。

关于哺乳动物血纤维蛋白肽 A 和 B 的序列数据也已得到。它们包含的氨基酸残基数不超过 40 个，在所有残基中，除了 1 或 2 个不变位点以外，其余都已接受了不损害血纤维蛋白原功能的氨基酸替代。因此，这些肽序列已经能够承受住偏离足够大的进化，以至于可以描述现今哺乳动物间的进化枝关系。表 4 给出了一个由 36 种哺乳动物的突变值构成的矩阵，这 36 种动物都兼有 A 和 B 血纤维蛋白肽序列 [67-75]，为描述这些序列系统发生进行尝试而得到的 30 个备选树图中的最佳树图如图 4 所示。该树的 APSD 系数为 10.80，与之相对比，UWPGM 树的 APSD 系数为 14.63。

Table 4. Mutation Values from Pairwise Comparisons of Mammalian Fibrinopeptide A and B Sequences

	Rabbit	Rat	Mulatta	Drill	Vervet	Gibbon-1	Gibbon-2	Man	Chimp	Horse	Mule-1	Zebra-2	Zebra-1	Donkey	Mule-2	Pig	Camel	Llama	Vicuna	Reindeer	Mule Deer	Muntjak	Sika Deer	Red Deer	Am. Elk	Pronghorn	Sheep	Goat	Bovine	Eur. Bison	Cape Buffalo	Water buffalo	Cat	Dog	Fox	Kangaroo
Rabbit	0																																			
Rat	22	0																																		
Mulatta	20	16	0																																	
Drill	18	15	6	0																																
Vervet	17	15	3	3	0																															
Gibbon-1	16	12	5	6	3	0																														
Gibbon-2	17	11	4	7	4	1	0																													
Man	18	14	5	8	5	4	3	0																												
Chimp	18	14	5	8	5	4	3	0	0																											
Horse	20	19	15	18	16	14	15	19	19	0																										
Mule-1	20	19	15	18	16	14	15	19	19	0	0																									
Zebra-2	22	22	18	19	19	17	18	22	22	8	8	0																								
Zebra-1	22	22	17	19	18	16	17	21	21	7	7	2	0																							
Donkey	24	22	18	19	19	17	18	22	22	6	6	2	2	0																						
Mule-2	24	22	18	19	19	17	18	22	22	6	6	2	2	0	0																					
Pig	24	26	19	22	19	16	17	22	22	15	15	15	14	14	14	0																				
Camel	19	21	15	19	16	12	13	17	17	14	14	14	13	14	14	13	0																			
Llama	20	20	16	20	17	13	14	18	18	15	15	15	14	15	15	12	1	0																		
Vicuna	20	20	16	20	17	13	14	18	18	15	15	15	14	15	15	12	1	0	0																	
Reindeer	21	26	15	20	18	14	15	19	19	17	17	17	16	17	17	17	14	15	15	0																
Mule Deer	21	26	15	20	18	14	15	19	19	16	16	18	17	18	18	18	12	13	13	1	0															
Muntjak	23	24	17	20	20	16	17	21	21	18	18	18	18	18	18	16	14	14	14	4	5	0														
Sika Deer	21	22	17	23	21	17	18	22	22	19	19	19	18	19	19	17	14	14	14	6	7	4	0													
Red Deer	21	23	16	22	20	18	19	21	21	20	20	20	19	20	20	18	15	15	15	7	8	5	1	0												
Am. Elk	21	23	16	22	20	18	19	21	21	20	20	20	19	20	20	18	15	15	15	7	8	5	1	0	0											
Pronghorn	19	31	22	26	25	21	22	26	26	21	21	20	22	22	22	25	20	21	21	14	15	15	16	17	17	0										
Sheep	22	26	14	21	19	14	15	20	20	14	14	16	15	16	16	19	16	17	17	11	9	12	14	15	15	18	0									
Goat	22	26	14	21	19	14	15	20	20	14	14	16	15	16	16	19	16	17	17	11	9	12	14	15	15	18	0	0								
Bovine	26	24	19	20	20	17	18	20	20	20	20	22	22	21	21	18	18	18	18	16	16	13	16	15	15	24	22	22	0							
Eur. Bison	24	22	17	19	17	14	15	17	17	19	19	20	19	19	19	17	15	15	15	13	13	12	13	12	12	22	19	19	3	0						
Cape Buffalo	23	19	12	16	14	9	10	14	14	16	16	15	14	14	14	11	12	12	12	11	11	11	12	13	13	19	16	16	5	3	0					
Water buffalo	25	23	16	21	19	14	15	19	19	18	18	20	19	19	19	17	14	15	15	13	13	14	15	16	16	20	17	17	7	6	2	0				
Cat	23	22	18	19	18	14	15	18	18	23	23	22	21	22	22	17	19	20	20	21	22	22	21	22	22	29	23	23	23	22	15	21	0			
Dog	25	23	18	26	25	22	23	25	25	22	22	20	19	18	18	23	21	22	22	23	24	25	24	25	25	27	23	23	29	27	18	25	19	0		
Fox	25	23	18	26	25	22	23	25	25	23	23	20	19	19	24	21	22	22	22	23	25	24	25	25	27	24	24	29	27	24	18	25	20	2	0	
Kangaroo	20	30	14	18	18	16	17	21	21	25	25	20	19	20	20	24	22	23	23	24	25	27	27	27	27	25	25	29	27	20	26	22	13	13	13	0

The half matrix lists minimum numbers of mutations interrelating pairs of fibrinopeptides. Numbers of shared amino-acids vary considerably in mammalian fibrinopeptides. For example, human has thirty amino-acid residues and rhesus has twenty-five residues, all the positions of which are shared by human. The mutation value for the human–rhesus pair presented in the table is obtained from the twenty-five shared amino-acid positions. Cape buffalo has thirty-six residues, only twenty-six positions of which are shared by human. Thus the mutation value for the human–Cape buffalo pair is obtained from these twenty-six shared positions. The alignments for most of the fibrinopeptide sequences can be found in ref. 14. The mutation values are converted into % mutational divergence values for constructing the phylogenetic tree in Fig. 4.

表 4. 由成对比较哺乳动物血纤维蛋白肽 A 和 B 序列得到的突变值

	兔	大鼠	普通猕猴	鬼狒	黑长尾猴	长臂猿-1	长臂猿-2	人	黑猩猩	马	骡-1	斑马-2	斑马-1	驴	骡-2	猪	骆驼	美洲驼	骆马	驯鹿	黑尾鹿	鹿	梅花鹿	赤鹿	美洲麋鹿	叉角羚	绵羊	山羊	牛	欧洲野牛	南非水牛	水牛	猫	狗	狐狸	袋鼠
兔	0																																			
大鼠	22	0																																		
普通猕猴	20	16	0																																	
鬼狒	18	15	6	0																																
黑长尾猴	17	15	3	3	0																															
长臂猿-1	16	12	5	6	3	0																														
长臂猿-2	17	11	4	7	4	1	0																													
人	18	14	5	8	5	4	3	0																												
黑猩猩	18	14	5	8	5	4	3	0	0																											
马	20	19	15	18	16	14	15	19	19	0																										
骡-1	20	19	15	18	16	14	15	19	19	0	0																									
斑马-2	22	22	18	19	19	17	18	22	22	8	8	0																								
斑马-1	22	22	18	19	18	16	17	21	21	7	7	2	0																							
驴	24	22	18	19	19	17	18	22	22	6	6	2	2	0																						
骡-2	24	22	18	19	19	17	18	22	22	6	6	2	2	0	0																					
猪	24	26	19	22	19	16	17	22	22	15	15	15	14	14	14	0																				
骆驼	19	21	15	19	16	12	13	17	17	14	14	14	13	14	14	13	0																			
美洲驼	20	20	16	20	17	13	14	18	18	15	15	14	15	15	12	13	1	0																		
骆马	20	20	16	20	17	13	14	18	18	15	15	14	15	15	12	13	1	0	0																	
驯鹿	21	26	15	20	18	14	15	19	17	17	17	17	17	14	16	15	15	15	15	0																
黑尾鹿	21	26	15	20	18	14	15	19	16	18	17	18	18	12	13	13	1	0																		
鹿	23	24	17	20	20	16	17	21	21	18	18	18	18	16	14	14	14	4	5	0																
梅花鹿	21	22	17	23	21	17	18	22	22	19	19	18	19	17	14	14	14	6	7	4	0															
赤鹿	21	23	16	22	20	18	19	21	20	20	19	20	20	18	15	15	7	8	5	1	0															
美洲麋鹿	21	23	16	22	20	18	19	21	20	20	19	20	20	18	15	15	7	8	5	1	0	0														
叉角羚	19	31	22	26	25	21	22	26	26	21	21	20	22	22	25	20	21	21	14	15	16	17	17	0												
绵羊	22	26	14	21	19	14	15	20	20	14	14	16	16	15	16	17	11	9	12	14	15	15	18	0												
山羊	22	26	14	21	19	15	20	20	14	16	16	16	17	17	11	9	12	14	15	16	0	0														
牛	26	24	19	20	20	17	18	20	20	20	22	22	21	21	18	18	18	16	16	13	16	15	15	24	22	22	0									
欧洲野牛	24	22	17	19	17	14	15	17	20	20	15	15	13	13	12	13	12	12	22	19	19	3	0													
南非水牛	23	19	12	16	14	9	10	14	14	14	14	11	12	11	11	11	11	12	13	13	16	16	5	3	0											
水牛	25	23	16	21	16	14	15	17	17	14	14	14	16	16	16	20	17	17	7	6	2	0														
猫	23	22	18	19	14	15	18	18	23	23	22	21	22	22	17	19	20	20	21	22	21	24	25	27	25	27	18	25	19	0						
狗	25	23	16	25	23	20	21	24	24	25	25	24	26	24	24	25	27	24	24	25	27	18	25	20	2	0										
狐狸	25	23	16	25	23	20	21	24	24	25	25	24	26	24	24	25	27	24	24	25	29	20	26	22	2	0										
袋鼠	20	30	14	18	18	16	17	21	21	20	20	24	24	27	27	27	25	25	29	20	26	22	13	13	0											

半矩阵列出了与各血纤维蛋白肽链配对相关的最小突变数。在哺乳动物血纤维蛋白中，共享氨基酸的数量差别非常大。例如：人有 30 个氨基酸残基，恒河猴有 25 个残基，所有这 25 个位置对于人来说都是共享的。表中出现的人 - 恒河猴配对突变值就是从这 25 个共享氨基酸位置获得的。南非水牛有 36 个残基，其中只有 26 个位置与人类共享。因此，人 - 南非水牛配对突变值就是从这 26 个共享位置获得的。大多数血纤维蛋白肽序列的比对结果可在参考文献 14 中找到。为了构建图 4 中的系统发生树，将突变值都转化为百分比形式的突变偏离值。

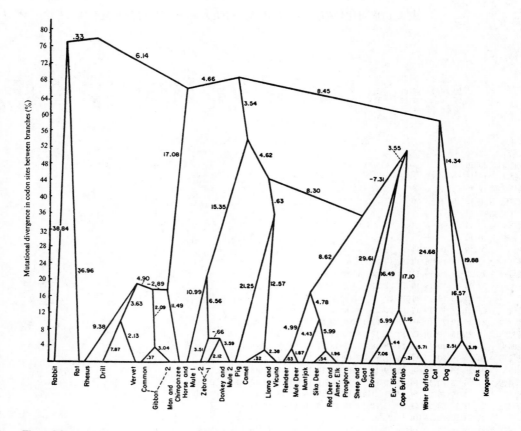

Fig. 4. Mammalian fibrinopeptide phylogenetic tree. 1, Rabbit[67,68]; 2, rat[67]; 3, *Macaca mulatta*[69]; 4, drill (*Mandrillus leucophaeus*)[70]; 5, vervet (*Cercopithecus aethiops*)[69]; 6, gibbon-1 (3 Gly–numbered from right to left)[71]; 7, gibbon-2 (3 Ser)[71]; 8, man[69]; 9, chimpanzee[72]; 10, horse[67,68]; 11, mule-1[67,68]; 12, zebra-2[73]; 13, zebra-1[73]; 14, donkey[67]; 15, mule-2[67,68]; 16, pig[67,68]; 17, camel[74,75]; 18, llama[67,68]; 19, vicuna (*Vicugna vicugna*)[74,75]; 20, reindeer (*Rangifer tarandus*)[74,75]; 21, mule deer (*Odocoileus hemionus hemionus*)[74]; 22, muntjak (*Muntiacus muntjak*)[74,75]; 23, sika deer (*Cervus nippon*)[67,68]; 24, red deer (*Cervus elaphus*)[67,68]; 25, American elk (*Cervus canadensis*)[74,75]; 26, pronghorn (*Antilocapra americana*)[74,75]; 27, sheep[67,68]; 28, goat[67,68]; 29, bovine[67,68]; 30, European bison[67,68]; 31, Cape buffalo[67,68]; 32, water buffalo[67,68]; 33, cat[67,68]; 34, dog[67,68]; 35, fox[67,68]; 36, kangaroo[73].

The branching arrangement among ungulate fibrinopeptides is essentially the same as that for ungulates in the alpha and beta globin phylogenetic trees, except that more ungulate species are represented. Pronghorn and caprines join bovines and then these bovoids join cervids (reindeer and various deers). Yet caprines and cervids on the average show less mutation distance from each other than from bovines (Table 4). Doolittle and Blombäck[76] discussed the possibility that caprines might have a more recent common ancestor with cervids than with bovines, and, indeed, the tree produced in our study by the UWPGM algorithm depicts such an ancestry relationship. Nevertheless, the best arrangements of artiodactyl branches with respect to lowering the APSD coefficient placed the caprines closer to bovines than to cervids in agreement with morphological evidence on ruminant relationships.

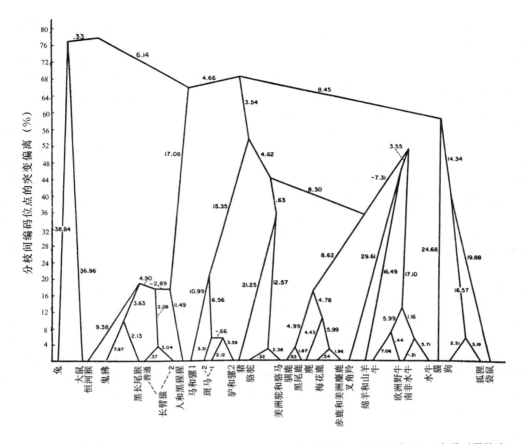

图 4. 哺乳动物血纤维蛋白肽的系统发生树。1, 兔[67,68]；2, 大鼠[67]；3, 普通猕猴[69]；4, 鬼狒（黑脸山魈)[70]；5, 黑长尾猴（非洲绿猴)[69]；6, 长臂猿–1（3 甘氨酸，编号从右到左)[71]；7, 长臂猿–2（3 丝氨酸)[71]；8, 人[69]；9, 黑猩猩[72]；10, 马[67,68]；11, 骡–1[67,68]；12, 斑马–2[73]；13, 斑马–1[73]；14, 驴[67]；15, 骡–2[67,68]；16, 猪[67,68]；17, 骆驼[74,75]；18, 美洲驼[67,68]；19, 骆马（小羊驼)[74,75]；20, 驯鹿（角鹿)[74,75]；21, 黑尾鹿（北美骡鹿)[74]；22, 麋（赤鹿)[74,75]；23, 梅花鹿（梅花鹿)[67,68]；24, 赤鹿（马鹿)[67,68]；25, 美洲麋鹿（加拿大马鹿)[74,75]；26, 叉角羚（北美羚羊)[74,75]；27, 绵羊[67,68]；28, 山羊[67,68]；29, 牛[67,68]；30, 欧洲野牛[67,68]；31, 南非水牛[67,68]；32, 水牛[67,68]；33, 猫[67,68]；34, 狗[67,68]；35, 狐狸[67,68]；36, 袋鼠[73]。

除了能代表更多的有蹄类物种以外，有蹄类血纤维蛋白肽间的分枝排列与有蹄类在 α 及 β 球蛋白系统发生树中的分枝排列基本相同。叉角羚与羊连接到牛科，然后这些牛总科动物又连到鹿科（驯鹿和各种鹿）。然而平均而言，羊和鹿相互之间的突变距离比羊和牛的突变距离小（表 4）。杜利特尔和布隆贝克[76] 讨论过以下这种可能性，即羊和鹿的共同祖先可能比羊和牛的共同祖先出现得更晚，我们在研究中用 UWPGM 算法构造的树图的确描绘出了这样一种祖先关系。尽管如此，为降低 APSD 系数，偶蹄类分枝的最佳排列使羊和牛之间的位置比羊和鹿之间的位置更接近，这与证明反刍动物间关系的形态学证据一致。

The joining of carnivores with ungulates before they join the Primates fits established ideas on mammalian phylogeny, for the Palaeocene Condylartha and Carnivora (from which the two ungulate orders, Perissodactyla and Artiodactyla, descended) are traced to late Cretaceous palaeoryctoid insectivores[77]. The marked divergence of the rabbit line from all other mammals is also in agreement with fossil data on mammalian phylogeny[77]. Although joining rat to rabbit at the apex of the tree is not in accord with the idea[77] from palaeontological evidence that rodents evolved out of the basal Primates, it may be noted that rat fibrinopeptides show less mutational divergence from primate fibrinopeptides than from those of other mammals (Table 4). Furthermore, the globin phylogenetic trees joined mouse to the base of the Primates. A finding at variance with our general knowledge of mammalian phylogeny is the grouping of kangaroo, a marsupial, with the carnivore branch. Fibrinopeptides from additional marsupials need to be sequenced, however, if we are to construct a phylogenetic tree for the relationship between marsupial and placental fibrinopeptides.

In the descent of primate fibrinopeptides, where hominoids (chimpanzee and man) and cercopithecoids (macaque, vervet, drill) branch apart, the gibbons split off as a distinct lineage from the base of the cercopithecoids. No splitting occurs in the terminal descent of man and chimpanzee: their fibrinopeptides are identical. Furthermore, the mutational divergence among the catarrhine primates is not nearly as marked as in other comparable taxonomic groups. In this connexion, the fibrinopeptides of the catarrhine primates are among the least rapidly evolving ones in the class Mammalia as revealed by the patristic mutation lengths in Fig. 4.

In addition to the amino-acid sequence data on haemoglobin chains and fibrinopeptides, there are partial sequence data on the erythrocyte enzyme carbonic anhydrase B which can be used to depict cladistic relationships among catarrhine primates[78]. Of the 133 homologous residues examined, chimpanzee and man differ at only one site, whereas orang utan differs from chimpanzee at three sites and from man at four sites. These hominoids differ from cercopithecoids (vervet, irus and rhesus macaques, and baboon) at four to six sites. Thus again the very close genetic relationship between man and chimpanzee is highlighted. The findings from the various sets of amino-acid sequence data support the conclusion drawn from extensive comparative immunodiffusion studies[79-82] on primate proteins that in the descent of the hominoids, after the early divergence of gibbon and orang utan lines, there was still a common ancestor for man, chimpanzee, and gorilla. The cladistic relationships depicted by the protein sequences support a classification of the Hominoidea which places *Gorilla* and *Pan* with *Homo* in the family Hominidae[80-82]. This agrees with the view of Darwin[83] that man originated in Africa from the same ancestral stock as chimpanzee and gorilla.

Four to five million year old fossil remains of man's immediate generic ancestor, *Australopithecus*, have recently been found in Pliocene deposits of Ethiopia[84], and fourteen million year old remains of *Ramapithecus*[86] (*Kenyapithecus*[87]), interpreted as a lineal ancestor of *Australopithecus*, date from the terminal Miocene of Kenya. Another Kenya hominoid,

在加入灵长目之前，食肉动物就已经和有蹄类动物相结合的现象符合哺乳动物系统发生学已建立的观点，因为古新世的踝节目和食肉目（有蹄类动物下的两个目——奇蹄目和偶蹄目即来自于此）可追溯到晚白垩纪的古掘猥科食虫动物[77]。兔支系与所有其他哺乳动物的显著分离也符合哺乳动物系统发生的化石证据[77]。虽然大鼠与兔在树顶处结合并不符合由古生物学证据推出的结论[77]，即啮齿类是从灵长类基部逐步进化而来，但可以发现大鼠血纤维蛋白肽同灵长类血纤维蛋白肽之间显示出的突变偏离要小于大鼠与其他哺乳动物血纤维蛋白肽之间的突变偏离（表4）。而且，球蛋白系统发生树中的小鼠是连接到了灵长类动物的基部。有一个发现与我们对哺乳动物系统发生的常识性认识不符，即将一种有袋类动物——袋鼠结合到食肉动物枝上。虽然如此，如果我们要构建一个关于有袋类和有胎盘类血纤维蛋白肽间关系的系统发生树，还需要对其他一些有袋类动物的血纤维蛋白肽进行测序。

在灵长类血纤维蛋白肽的进化中，长臂猿在人科（黑猩猩和人）和猕猴科（猕猴、黑长尾猴和鬼狒）枝分开的位置从猕猴科基部分离出来，成为一条单独的支系。在人和黑猩猩的演变终点并没有分离发生：它们的血纤维蛋白肽完全相同。而且，狭鼻猴灵长类中的突变偏离远远没有其他类似分类学组群中的那样显著。在这个系统发生树中，狭鼻猴灵长类的血纤维蛋白肽属于哺乳纲中进化速度最慢的群体之一，这一点可以从图4所列的父系突变长度中发现。

除了血红蛋白链和血纤维蛋白肽的氨基酸序列数据外，还有红细胞酶碳酸酐酶B的部分序列数据，后者可用于描述狭鼻猴灵长类间的进化枝关系[78]。在检测过的133个同源残基中，黑猩猩和人只在1个位点上有所不同，而红毛猩猩和黑猩猩有3个位点不同，和人有4个位点不同。人科和猕猴科（黑长尾猴、食蟹猕猴、恒河猴和狒狒）有4～6个位点不同。因此人和黑猩猩在遗传学上的密切关系再次凸现出来。源自多系列氨基酸序列数据中的发现证实了从对灵长类动物蛋白质的大量比较免疫扩散研究[79-82]中得到的结论：在人科动物进化过程中，人、黑猩猩和大猩猩在长臂猿支系与红毛猩猩支系发生先期分离后仍拥有共同祖先。由蛋白质序列给出的进化枝关系为人猿总科的一种分类，即把大猩猩和黑猩猩属连同人属一起放到人科[80-82]提供了证据。这和达尔文的观点[83]一致，达尔文认为：人起源于非洲，其祖先血统与黑猩猩和大猩猩的祖先血统相同。

400万到500万年前的人类直系祖先——南方古猿的化石近日在埃塞俄比亚的上新世堆积物中被发现[84]。南方古猿化石和被认为是南方古猿直系祖先的1,400万年前的腊玛古猿[86]（肯尼亚古猿[87]）的化石可追溯到肯尼亚的中新世末期。另一种

an eighteen million year old *Dryopithecus* ape, is considered an ancestor of *Gorilla* and to have even then separated from the line to *Ramapithecus* and *Homo*[88]. The hypothesis that molecular evolution decelerated in higher primates reconciles such palaeontological views with protein findings on the close genetic relationship of the African apes to man, DNA reassociation experiments[89,90] on nonrepeating polynucleotide sequences (the DNA fraction best suited for cladistic comparisons) further demonstrate the close relationship between *Pan* and *Homo*. The DNA findings emphasize the possibility that steadily increasing generation lengths may have been an important parameter[79,89,90] in slowing molecular evolution during the past sixty-five million years in the descent of man.

We thank Mr. Walter Farris for assistance, Miss Joan Bechtold and Mrs. Geraldine Fockler for drawings, and the staff of the Wayne State University Computing Center for help. This work was supported by grants from the US National Science Foundation Systematic Biology and US–Japan Cooperative Science Programs.

(**233**, 604-613; 1971)

Morris Goodman and John Barnabas: Department of Anatomy, Wayne State University School of Medicine, Detroit, Michigan 48207, and Plymouth State Home and Training School, Northville, Michigan 48167.
Genji Matsuda: Department of Biochemistry, Nagasaki University School of Medicine, Nagasaki.
G. William Moore: Institute of Statistics, Biomathematics Program, North Carolina State University, Raleigh, North Carolina 27607.

Received February 17; revised March 18, 1971.

References:

1. Ingram, V. M., *Nature*, **189**, 704 (1961).

2. Goodman, M., *Human Biol.*, **33**, 131 (1961).

3. Goodman, M., in *Classification and Human Evolution*, 203 (Aldine Press, 1963).

4. Goodman, M., in *Protides of Biological Fluids*, 70 (Elsevier, Amsterdam, 1965).

5. Kimura, M., *Nature*, **217**, 624 (1968).

6. King, J. L., and Jukes, T. H., *Science*, **164**, 788 (1969).

7. Fitch, W. M., and Margoliash, E., *Science*, **155**, 279 (1967).

8. Sokal, R., and Sneath, P. H. A., *Principles of Numerical Taxonomy*, 309 (W. H. Freeman, San Francisco, 1963).

9. Moore, G. W., thesis, Univ. North Carolina (1970).

10. Barnabas, J., Goodman, M., and Moore, G. W., *Comp. Physiol. Biochem.*, **39B**, 455 (1971).

11. Braun, V., Crichton, R. R., and Braunitzer, G., *Z. Physiol. Chem.*, **349**, 45 (1968).

12. Braunitzer, G., Buse, G., and Braig, S., *Z. Physiol. Chem.*, **350**, 1477 (1969).

13. Edmundson, A. B., *Nature*, **205**, 883 (1965).

14. Dayhoff, M. O., *Atlas of Protein Sequence and Structure*, **4** (1969).

15. Rudloff, V., Zelenik, M., and Braunitzer, G., *Z. Physiol. Chem.*, **344**, 284 (1966).

16. Hilse, K., and Braunitzer, G., *Z. Physiol. Chem.*, **349**, 433 (1968).

17. Matsuda, G., Takei, H., Wu, K. C., Mizuno, K., and Shiozawa, T., *Eighth Intern. Cong. Biochemistry*, Abstract, 4 (1970).

18. Von Ehrenstein, G., *Cold Spring Harbor Symp. Quant. Biol.*, **31**, 705 (1966).

19. Hill, R. L., unpublished data taken from *Handbook of Biochemistry* (The Chemical Rubber Company, 1968).

20. Rifkin, D. B., Hirsch, D. I., Rifkin, M. R., and Konigsberg, W., *Cold Spring Harbor Symp. Quant. Biol.*, **31**, 715 (1966).

21. Popp, R. A., *J. Mol. Biol.*, **27**, 9 (1967).

22. Matsuda, G., Maita, T., Takei, H., Ota, H., Yamaguchi, M., Miyanchi, T., and Migita, M., *J. Biochem.* (Japan), **64**, 279 (1968).

23. Zuckerkandl, E., and Schroeder, W. A., *Nature*, **192**, 984 (1961).

肯尼亚人科动物——1,800万年前的森林古猿被认为是大猩猩的祖先，而且在那个时候已经从通往腊玛古猿和人属的支系上分离出来[88]。分子进化在高等灵长类中减速的假说使古生物学观点与证明非洲类人猿和人的密切遗传学关系的蛋白质测序结果一致，在非重复多聚核苷酸序列（这种DNA片段最适合进化枝比较）上进行的DNA重组实验[89,90]进一步证明黑猩猩属和人属之间的密切关系。DNA的研究结果强化了如下的可能性：稳步增长的世代长度可能就是证明在过去6,500万年的人类起源过程中分子进化速度减慢的一个重要参数[79,89,90]。

我们要感谢沃尔特·法里斯先生的帮助，感谢琼·贝克托尔德小姐和杰拉尔丁·弗克勒夫人的制图，还要感谢韦恩州立大学计算中心团队的帮助。这项工作得到了来自美国国家科学基金会的系统生物学计划和美日合作科学计划的拨款支持。

（邓铭瑞 翻译；崔巍 审稿）

24. Rifkin, D. B., and Konigsberg, W., *Biochim. Biophys. Acta*, **104**, 457 (1965).

25. Braunitzer, G., Gehring-Mueller, R., Hilschmann, N., Hilse, K., Hobom, G., Rudloff, Y., and Wittman-Liebold, B., *Z. Physiol. Chem.*, **325**, 283 (1961).

26. Schroeder, W. A., Shelton, J. R., Shelton, J. B., and Cormick, J., *Biochemistry*, **2**, 1353 (1963).

27. Kilmartin, J. V., and Clegg, J. B., *Nature*, **213**, 269 (1967).

28. Matsuda, G., Gehring-Mueller, R., and Braunitzer, G., *Biochem. Z.*, **338**, 669 (1963).

29. Schroeder, W. A., Shelton, J. R., Shelton, J. B., Robberson, B., and Babin, D. R., *Arch. Biochem. Biophys.*, **120**, 1 (1967).

30. Huisman, T. H. J., Brandt, G., and Wilson, J. B., *J. Biol. Chem.*, **243**, 3637 (1968).

31. Huisman, T. H. J., Dozy, A. M., Wilson, J. B., Effremov, G. D., and Vaskov, B., *Biochim. Biophys. Acta*, **160**, 467 (1968).

32. Beale, D., Lehman, H., Drury, A., and Tucker, E. M., *Nature*, **209**, 1099 (1966).

33. Wilson, J. B., Brandt, G., and Huisman, T. H. J., *J. Biol. Chem.*, **243**, 3687 (1968).

34. Schroeder, W. A., Shelton, J. R., Shelton, J. B., Cormick, J., and Jones, R. T., *Biochemistry*, **2**, 992 (1963).

35. Air, G. M., and Thomson, E. O. P., *Austral. J. Biol. Sci.*, **22**, 1437 (1969).

36. Rifkin, D. B., Rifkin, M. R., and Konigsberg, W., *Proc. US Nat. Acad. Sci.*, **55**, 586 (1966).

37. Braunitzer, G., Best, J. S., Flamm, U., and Schrank, B., *Z. Physiol. Chem.*, **347**, 207 (1966).

38. Boyer, S. H., Crosby, E. F., Thurmon, T. F., Noyes, A. N., Fuller, G. F., Leslie, S. E., and Sheppard, M. K., *Science*, **116**, 1428 (1969).

39. Matsuda, G., Maita, T., Ota, H., Tachiwaka, I., Tanaka, Y., Araya, A., and Nakashima, Y., *Intern. J. Protein Res.*, **3**, 41 (1971).

40. Ingram, V. M., and Stretton, A. O. W., *Biochim. Biophys. Acta*, **63**, 20 (1962).

41. Smith, D. B., *Canad. J. Biochem.*, **46**, 825 (1968).

42. Babin, D. R., Schroeder, W. A., Shelton, J. R., Shelton, J. B., and Robberson, B., *Biochemistry*, **5**, 1297 (1966).

43. Wilson, J. B., Edwards, W. C., McDaniel, M., Dobbs, M. M., and Huisman, T. H. J., *Arch. Biochem. Biophys.*, **115**, 385 (1966).

44. Schroeder, W. A., Shelton, J. R., Shelton, J. B., Robberson, B., and Babin, D. R., *Arch. Biochem. Biophys.*, **120**, 124 (1967).

45. Huisman, T. H. J., Dasher, G. A., Moretz, W. H., Dozy, A. M., and Wilson, J. B., *Biochem. J.*, **107**, 745 (1968).

46. Boyer, S. H., Hathaway, P., Pascasio, F., Orton, C., Bordley, J., and Naughton, M. A., *Science*, **153**, 1539 (1966).

47. Huisman, T. H. J., Adams, H. R., Dimock, M. O., Edwards, W. E., and Wilson, J. B., *J. Biol. Chem.*, **242**, 2534 (1967).

48. Huber, R., Epp, O., and Formanck, H., *J. Mol. Biol.*, **42**, 59 (1969).

49. Briehl, R. W., *J. Biol. Chem.*, **238**, 2361 (1963).

50. Balani, A. S., and Barnabas, J., *Nature*, **205**, 1019 (1965).

51. Balani, A. S., Ranjekar, P. K., and Barnabas, J., *Comp. Physiol. Biochem.*, **24**, 809 (1968).

52. Huisman, T. H. J., Wilson, J. B., and Adams, H. R., *Arch. Biochem. Biophy.*, **121**, 528 (1967).

53. Ranjekar, P. K., and Barnabas, J., *Indian J. Biochem.*, **6**, 1 (1969).

54. Barnicot, N. A., and Huehns, E. R., *Nature*, **215**, 1485 (1967); Wade, P. T., Skinner, A. F., and Barnicot, N. A., *Protides in Biological Fluids*, 263 (Pergamon, London, 1970).

55. Oliver, E., and Kitchen, H., *Biochim. Biophys. Acta, Res. Commun.*, **31**, 749 (1968).

56. Hilse, K., and Popp, R. A., *Proc. US Nat. Acad. Sci.*, **61**, 930 (1968).

57. Kunkel, H. G., and Wallenius, G., *Science*, **122**, 288 (1955).

58. Kunkel, H. G., Ceppellini, R., Mueller-Eberhard, V., and Wolf, J., *J. Clin. Invest.*, **36**, 1615 (1957).

59. Huisman, T. H. J., Reynolds, C. A., Dozy, A. M., and Wilson, J. B., *J. Biol. Chem.*, **240**, 2455 (1965).

60. Hamilton, W. J., Boyd, J. D., and Mossman, H. W., *Human Embryology* (Williams and Wilkins, Baltimore, 1952).

61. Kimura, M., *Proc. US Nat. Acad. Sci.*, **63**, 1181 (1969).

62. Buettner-Janusch, J., and Buettner-Janusch, V., *Amer. J. Phys. Anthrop.*, **33**, 73 (1970).

63. Ohno, S., *Evolution by Gene Duplication* (Springer, Berlin, 1970).

64. Buettner-Janusch, J., and Hill, R. W., in *Evolving Genes and Proteins*, 167 (Academic Press, London and New York, 1965).

65. LeGros Clark, W. E., *The Antecedents of Man* (Edinburgh University Press, Edinburgh, 1959).

66. Buettner-Janusch, J., Buettner-Janusch, V., and Mason, G. A., *Arch. Biochem. Biophys.*, **133**, 164 (1969).

67. Blombäck, B., Blombäck, M., and Grondahl, N. J., *Acta Chem. Scand.*, **19**, 1789 (1965).

68. Blombäck, B., Blombäck, M., Grondahl, N. J., and Holmberg, E., *Arkiv. Kemi.*, **25**, 411 (1966).

69. Blombäck, B., Blombäck, M., Grondahl, N. J., Guthrie, C., and Hinton, M., *Acta Chem. Scand.*, **19**, 1788 (1965); Blombäck, B., Blombäck, M., and Edman, B., *Biochim. Biophys. Acta*, **115**, 371 (1966).

70. Doolittle, R. F., Glasgow, C., and Mross, G. A., *Biochim. Biophys. Acta*, **175**, 217 (1969).

71. Mross, G. A., Doolittle, R. F., and Roberts, B. F., *Science*, **170**, 468 (1970).

72. Doolittle, R. F., and Mross, G. A., *Nature*, **225**, 643 (1970).

73. Blombäck, B., and Blombäck, M., in *Chemotaxonomy and Serotaxonomy*, 3 (Academic Press, London and New York, 1968).

74. Doolittle, R. F., Schubert, D., and Schwartz, S. A., *Arch. Biochem. Biophys.*, **118**, 456 (1967).

75. Mross, G. A., and Doolittle, R. F., *Arch. Biochem. Biophys.*, **122**, 674 (1967).

76. Doolittle, R. F., and Blombäck, B., *Nature*, **202**, 147 (1964).

77. McKenna, M. C., *Ann. NY Acad. Sci.*, **167**, 217 (1969).

78. Tashian, R. E., and Stroup, S. R., *Biochem. Biophys. Res. Commun.*, **41**, 1457 (1970).

79. Goodman, M., *Human Biol.*, **34**, 104 (1962).

80. Goodman, M., *Ann. NY Acad. Sci.*, **102**, 219 (1962).

81. Goodman, M., *Human Biol.*, **35**, 377 (1963).

82. Goodman, M., *Primates in Med.*, **1**, 10 (1968).

83. Darwin, C., *The Descent of Man and Selection in Relation to Sex* (Appleton, New York, 1871).

84. Patterson, B., Behrensmeyer, A. K., and Sill, W. D., *Nature*, **226**, 918 (1970).

85. Howell, F. C., *Nature*, **223**, 1234 (1969).

86. Simons, E. L., *Nature*, **221**, 448 (1969).

87. Leakey, L. S. B., *Nature*, **213**, 155 (1967).

88. Pilbeam, D. R., *Peabody Mus. Bull. Yale*, **31** (1969).

89. Kohne, D. E., *Quart. Rev. Biophys.*, **3**, 327 (1970).

90. Kohne, D. E., Chison, J. A., and Hoyer, B. H., *Carnegie Inst. Yr Book*, **69**, 488 (1971).

Logarithmic Relationship of DDE Residues to Eggshell Thinning

L. J. Blus *et al.*

Editor's Note

Beginning in the 1960s, there was great concern among environmentalists and naturalists, particularly in the United States, about the effects of small quantities of chemicals such as pesticides in the environment. This paper by Lawrence Blus and colleagues argues that the pesticide called DDE had been responsible for a decline in the population of brown pelicans off the coast of California, producing evidence that the pesticide reduced the thickness of the shell from which young pelicans hatched. The publication of this paper caused some controversy with several scientists producing conflicting evidence, but the eventual outcome of the controversy was that DDE was banned from use in agriculture in the United States. The population of brown pelicans off the coast of California has recovered.

S HELL thinning has been recorded in eggs of the brown pelican (*Pelecanus occidentalis*) which were collected in widely separated nesting colonies[1-3], and it has been reported among numerous other species of wild birds[4-9]. The condition has been used as an indicator of population trend; thinning of 15 to 20% has been associated with declining populations of several species[9].

A cause-and-effect relationship has been established between DDE (1,1-dichloro-2,2-*bis* (*p*-chlorophenyl) ethylene) in the diet and shell thinning; the associated residues in eggs of American kestrels (*Falco sparverius*) fed DDE were comparable with those in eggs of peregrines (*Falco peregrinus*)[10] collected in the field. It is necessary to understand the quantitative relationships between residue content and shell thinning in order to evaluate the problem properly. We have studied this relationship as derived from a study of eggs of the brown pelican and we compare here these results with those reported for other species.

The questions to be explored are (1) whether a concentration-response relationship, paralleling the traditional dose-response relationship, in fact exists between DDE in eggs and the thinning of the shells, and (2) the nature of such a mathematical relationship. The amount of DDE in the egg is taken as an index to the concentration of residues in the female[11-13], the physiological processes of which determine shell thickness. DDE is the only residue considered here, because this residue consistently accounts for a significant percentage of eggshell thinning in these pelicans (our unpublished work).

Eighty eggs of brown pelicans were used in the primary analysis of the problem. Seventy eggs were collected in 1969 from twelve colonies, one in California, two in South Carolina

DDE残留量对数与蛋壳薄化的关系

布卢斯等

编者按

从 20 世纪 60 年代起，尤其是在美国，环境人士和自然主义者们就开始格外关注像杀虫剂这样的小量化学物质对环境产生的影响。这篇由劳伦斯·布卢斯及其同事撰写的文章认为，一种被称为 DDE 的杀虫剂是造成加利福尼亚海岸褐鹈鹕种群数量下降的元凶，并给出证据证明杀虫剂使得孵出小鹈鹕的蛋壳发生了薄化。这篇论文发表后引起了几位科学家之间的争论，他们给出的证据相互矛盾，但争论的最终结果是 DDE 在美国农业生产中被禁用。加利福尼亚州沿岸的褐鹈鹕种群数量得以回升。

对蛋壳薄化的报道已涉及在相距较远的几个褐鹈鹕鸟群聚集地收集的鸟蛋 [1-3]，对于许多其他野生鸟类也有过类似的报道 [4-9]。蛋壳薄化已被用于指示鸟群数量的变化趋势；有几种鸟类的数量曾在薄化达到 15%～20% 时出现下降 [9]。

人们已经确定了饲料中 DDE（1,1- 二氯 -2,2- 双（对 - 氯苯基）乙烯）含量和蛋壳薄化之间的因果关系；将用 DDE 喂养的美洲隼所生的蛋与从野地里收集的游隼蛋 [10] 相对比，两者所含的相关残留物差不多。为了对这一问题进行正确的评估，我们必须了解残留物含量与蛋壳薄化之间的定量关系。我们通过对褐鹈鹕蛋的一项研究得到了两者之间的关系，并在这里将所得结果与其他鸟类的已知结果进行比较。

需要探讨的问题有：（1）与传统的剂量 - 反应关系相类似的浓度 - 反应关系是否确实可以反映蛋中 DDE 与蛋壳薄化之间的关系，（2）这种数学关系的本质。蛋中的 DDE 含量反映了雌鸟体内的残留物浓度 [11-13]，而雌鸟的生理过程决定了蛋壳的厚度。DDE 是本文中唯一考虑的残留物，因为这种残留物一直被看作是引起鹈鹕蛋蛋壳薄化的主要因素（我们尚未发表的研究结果）。

在对这一问题进行初步分析时我们使用了 80 枚褐鹈鹕蛋。其中有 70 枚蛋是1969 年从 12 个鸟群聚集地收集的：1 个在加利福尼亚州，2 个在南卡罗来纳州，9

1011

and nine in Florida. Ten more eggs were collected from one of the South Carolina colonies in 1970. Analytical procedures for preparation, clean up, and residue analysis followed those used at the Patuxent Wildlife Research Center[14-16]. The samples were prepared and analysed by Soxhlet extraction and clean up by acetonitrile partitioning and "Florisil" column. The residues were separated and removed in four fractions from a silica gel thin layer plate. Sample fractions were analysed by electron capture chromatography on a column of 3% OV-1 on "Chromosorb W" H.P., or on a column of 3% OV-17 on "Gas Chrom Q". The DDT metabolites were confirmed on a column of 3% XE-60 on "Gas Chrom Q". Some of the samples were treated with alkali to confirm DDT (1,1,1-trichloro-2,2-*bis* (*p*-chlorophenyl) ethane). Each of the three glass columns was 1.8 m long and the outside diameter was 0.64 cm.

The average recovery of the chlorinated insecticides and their metabolites from fortified eagle tissue ranged from 75 to 112%; the recovery value for DDE was 95%[4]. The pelican egg residues were not corrected for recovery. Residues are expressed on a fresh wet weight basis. We found that certain external egg measurements were significantly correlated with the weight of the contents of fresh eggs. The resulting regression equation was used to convert weight of the contents of addled eggs to a fresh wet weight basis (unpublished work of L. F. Stickel, S. N. Wiemeyer and L. J. B.). The statistical analyses were performed after the residues were transformed to logarithms.

The percentage of eggshell thinning was measured by comparison with the pre-1947 mean thickness as computed by Anderson and Hickey[17]. These means were 0.557 mm for Florida and South Carolina eggs and 0.579 mm for California eggs. Eggshell thinning occurred in eleven of the twelve colonies where eggs were collected. In eggs from the nine Florida colonies the mean change in thickness varied from a 13% decrease to a 0.4% increase. There was a 17% decrease in shell thickness of eggs from the two South Carolina colonies, and a 35% decrease in shell thickness of eggs from the California colony.

The thinning of eggshells of the brown pelican proved to be related to the concentrations of DDE in the eggs (Fig. 1). The relationship was essentially linear ($P<0.01$) on a logarithmic residue scale. We used the following regression equation to describe this relationship:

$$\hat{Y} = b_0 - b \log_{10} X$$

where $\hat{Y}$ = % of pre-1947 eggshell thickness; b_0 = expected % of pre-1947 thickness at 1 p.p.m. of DDE; b = the regression coefficient; and $\log_{10} X$ = p.p.m. of DDE on a fresh wet weight basis.

个来自佛罗里达州；还有 10 枚蛋是 1970 年从南卡罗来纳州的一个鸟群聚集地收集的。遵照帕图克森特野生动物研究中心过去所使用的分析步骤 [14-16] 进行样品的制备、清洗和残留物分析。用索氏萃取法制备和分析样品，用乙腈分配和"硅酸镁载体"柱清洗样品。残留物从硅胶薄层板上分离下来并被分成 4 份。4 份样品采用电子俘获气相色谱法进行分析，分析是在以惠普公司的"硅烷化白色硅藻土"为担体、以 3% OV-1 为固定相的色谱柱，或者以"硅藻土型色谱载体 Q"为担体、以 3% OV-17 为固定相的色谱柱上进行的。DDT 代谢物是用以"硅藻土型色谱载体 Q"为担体、以 3% XE-60 为固定相的色谱柱进行确认的。部分样品用碱处理以确证 DDT (1,1,1– 三氯 –2,2– 双 (对 – 氯苯基) 乙烷)。3 个玻璃色谱柱的长度均为 1.8 m，外径为 0.64 cm。

在处理后的鹰组织中含氯杀虫剂及其代谢物的平均回收率为 75% ~ 112%；DDE 的回收率为 95%[4]。对鹈鹕蛋中的残留物没有进行过回收率的校正。残留物是用鲜湿重来表示的。我们发现对鸟蛋外部的某些测量结果与新鲜鸟蛋内含物的重量显著相关。用得到的回归方程可以将臭蛋内含物的重量转化成以鲜湿重为基准的结果（施蒂克尔、威迈耶和布卢斯尚未发表的研究结果）。统计分析是在将残留量取对数之后进行的。

蛋壳薄化的百分比是与安德森和希基计算的 1947 年以前的蛋壳平均厚度 [17] 相比较后得到的。佛罗里达州和南卡罗来纳州的鸟蛋蛋壳平均厚度为 0.557 mm，加利福尼亚州为 0.579 mm。在采集鸟蛋的 12 个鸟群聚集地中有 11 个发生了蛋壳薄化。在位于佛罗里达州的 9 个聚集地采集的鸟蛋中，蛋壳厚度的平均变化从下降 13% 到增加 0.4% 不等。来自南卡罗来纳州 2 个聚集地的鸟蛋蛋壳厚度出现了 17% 的下降，而加利福尼亚州的鸟蛋蛋壳厚度下降了 35%。

可以证明褐鹈鹕蛋蛋壳薄化与蛋中 DDE 浓度之间存在着关联（图 1）。当对残留量取对数时，两者之间的关系基本上是线性的（$P<0.01$）。我们使用以下的回归方程来描述这种关系：

$$\hat{Y} = b_0 - b \log_{10} X$$

式中：$\hat{Y}$= 相对于 1947 年前蛋壳厚度的百分数；b_0 = 当 DDE 含量为 1 ppm 时相对于 1947 年前蛋壳厚度的预期百分数；b = 回归系数；$\log_{10} X$ = 根据鲜湿重计算出来的、以 ppm 为单位的 DDE 含量。

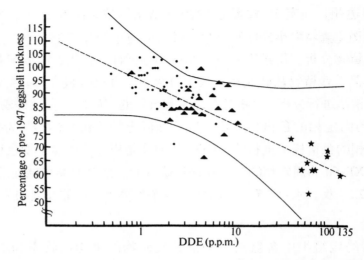

Fig. 1. Association of DDE residues in eighty brown pelican eggs from Florida (●), South Carolina (▲) and California (★) with the % of pre-1947 eggshell thickness. Solid lines represent 95% confidence limits. $\hat{Y} = 95.787 - 15.689 \log_{10} X$; $r = -0.80$ ($P < 0.01$).

The significance of the regression indicates that the shell thickness decreases in a predictable manner as the DDE concentration increases. It also means that the percentage change was greater per unit of DDE when the concentration of DDE was lower. In other words, the lower concentrations were more effective. For example, the calculated percentage of thinning per p.p.m. of DDE is 4.2 at 1 p.p.m., 3.0 at 5 p.p.m., 1.9 at 10 p.p.m., and 0.4 at 100 p.p.m.

Analysis of covariance revealed no significant differences ($P > 0.05$) among slopes of the three regression lines that were plotted using data from each of the three states from which the eggs were collected. Thus, most of the variation in eggshell thickness (64%; $P < 0.01$) may be explained by the common regression used here.

The prediction of a no-effect level is also theoretically possible, but should be approached with caution because of the scarcity of eggshell measurements in eggs with lower residues, and the hazard of making predictions of X far removed from the mean[18]. The estimated no-effect level is 0.5 p.p.m., but the validity of this estimate is questionable because of the forementioned reasons. In the eggs from Florida that contained 0.52 p.p.m. of DDE, the thickness (0.64 mm) was slightly less than 0.65 mm, the maximum pre-1947 measurement; thus, the possibility of thinning was not ruled out completely in any of the eighty eggs. Anderson et al.[4] indicated an apparent absence of a no-effect level of DDE on the eggshell thickness of the double-crested cormorant (*Phalacrocorax auritus*) and the white pelican (*Pelecanus erythrorhynchos*). The relationship of the logarithm of DDE to eggshell thinning also seems to apply to the prairie falcon (*Falco mexicanus*)[5] and the double-crested cormorant[4].

The relationship between log dose and response is often encountered and is in accord

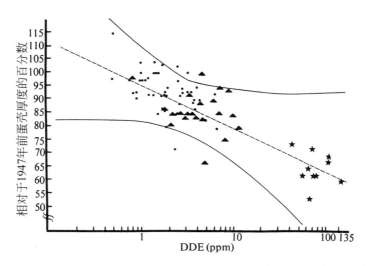

图 1. 在 80 枚来自佛罗里达州（●）、南卡罗来纳州（▲）和加利福尼亚州（★）的褐鹈鹕蛋中，DDE 残留量与相对于 1947 年前蛋壳厚度的百分数之间的关系。实线代表 95% 的置信区间。$\hat{Y} = 95.787 - 15.689 \log_{10} X$；$r = -0.80$（$P<0.01$）。

回归的显著性表明：蛋壳厚度会以一种可预计的方式随 DDE 浓度的增加而下降。这也意味着当 DDE 浓度较低时，对应于每个单位 DDE 的蛋壳厚度百分数的变化值也会较大。换句话说，浓度越低效果越明显。例如：当 DDE 浓度为 1 ppm 时，对应于每 ppm DDE 的蛋壳薄化百分数的计算值为 4.2；当浓度达到 5 ppm 时为 3.0；10 ppm 时为 1.9；100 ppm 时为 0.4。

由协方差分析结果可知：根据在 3 个州采集的鸟蛋数据绘制而成的 3 条回归线在斜率上并没有显著的差异（$P>0.05$）。因此，采用本文中的公共回归方程或许可以解释大部分的蛋壳厚度变化（64%；$P<0.01$）。

虽然预测出无作用剂量在理论上是可行的，但在实施时应小心谨慎，因为一方面我们缺少较低残留量下鸟蛋蛋壳厚度的测量数据，另一方面预测远离平均值的 X 是很冒险的 [18]。无作用剂量的估计值是 0.5 ppm；不过，由于前述原因，这个估计值的有效性是有待商榷的。在 DDE 含量为 0.52 ppm 的来自佛罗里达州的鸟蛋中，其厚度（0.64 mm）比 1947 年前的厚度测量结果的最大值 0.65 mm 只略微少一点；因此不能把这 80 枚蛋中任何一枚发生薄化的可能性完全排除掉。安德森等人 [4] 指出：DDE 对双冠鸬鹚和白鹈鹕蛋蛋壳厚度的影响显然不存在无作用剂量。DDE 含量的对数与蛋壳薄化之间的关系似乎也适用于草原隼 [5] 和双冠鸬鹚 [4]。

经常会遇到剂量对数与反应之间相关的情况，这种关系与毒理学和药理学的理

with toxicological and pharmacological theory[19-22]. The association between residue and response is poorly known.

The relationship between shell thinning and DDE residues in the eggs is particularly important in understanding the population status of the brown pelican.

The brown pelican population in South Carolina has been declining for at least 12 yr[1,23] and the number of young fledged per breeding female in 1969 and 1970 was well below the estimated number necessary to maintain a stable population (unpublished work of C. Henry). The brown pelican in California experienced reproductive failure in 1969[2-3], but the Florida population seems stable over the past 3 yr[24-25].

The brown pelican seems to be unusually susceptible to shell thinning, a 15% thinning being associated with DDE residues between 4 and 5 p.p.m. In the declining South Carolina colonies eight of the eleven eggs collected in 1969 and two of ten collected in 1970 contained DDE concentrations greater than 4 p.p.m. Thirteen of the twenty-one eggs collected in the 2 yr exceeded 15% shell thinning. In California, where reproductive failure occurred, a 35% decrease in eggshell thickness was associated with 71 p.p.m. of DDE in the egg.

In contrast, only ten of the forty-nine brown pelican eggs collected in Florida were more than 15% thinner than the pre-1947 average; and residues exceeded 4 p.p.m. in only four eggs. It seems probable, therefore, that some pelicans in Florida are adversely affected by shell thinning although the extent of this thinning is not great enough for obvious effects on the size of the populations.

In contrast to the brown pelican, the herring gull (*Larus argentatus*) showed no thinning when DDE residues were between 4 and 5 p.p.m. and only 11% thinning when residues were near 80 p.p.m[8]. The eggshell thinning response induced by DDE in the brown pelican was similar to that found in the prairie falcon[5]. The double-crested cormorant[4] seemed somewhat more resistant to thinning by DDE than these two species, but shell thinning generally occurred in cormorant eggs that contained less than 5 p.p.m. of DDE and 15% thinning was recorded in one colony when DDE egg residues averaged just under 20 p.p.m.

The concentration-effect relationship involving the logarithm of DDE and eggshell thinning seems to exist and to follow a mathematically similar pattern in different species, but to operate at different levels in different species. A level of DDE in eggs that would result in population collapse among brown pelicans would not be expected to effect an overall population change among herring gulls.

We thank the many individuals who helped us with the collection of eggs.

(**235**, 376-377; 1972)

论是一致的 [19-22]。至于残留量和反应之间的关系目前还很少有人认识到。

蛋壳薄化与蛋中 DDE 残留量之间的关系对于理解褐鹈鹕种群数量的状况尤为重要。

南卡罗来纳州的褐鹈鹕种群数量已经持续下降了至少 12 年 [1,23]，在 1969 年和 1970 年间，每只雌鸟繁殖的幼鸟数量远远达不到能够维持种群数量稳定所必需的预估值（亨利尚未发表的研究结果）。加利福尼亚州的褐鹈鹕在 1969 年出现了繁殖障碍 [2-3]，但佛罗里达州褐鹈鹕的种群数量在过去 3 年中似乎是保持稳定的 [24-25]。

褐鹈鹕似乎非常容易受到蛋壳薄化的影响，当 DDE 残留量为 4 ppm ~ 5 ppm 时，蛋壳会发生 15% 的薄化。在种群数量不断下降的南卡罗来纳州，1969 年采集的 11 枚鸟蛋中有 8 枚、1970 年采集的 10 枚鸟蛋中有 2 枚所含的 DDE 浓度超过了 4 ppm。在这两年之内收集的 21 枚鸟蛋中有 13 枚的蛋壳薄化率超过了 15%。在种群出现繁殖障碍的加利福尼亚州，蛋壳厚度下降 35% 的蛋中 DDE 残留浓度为 71 ppm。

相比之下，在佛罗里达州采集的 49 枚褐鹈鹕蛋中，只有 10 枚比 1947 年前的平均水平变薄了 15% 以上；而且只有 4 枚蛋的残留物浓度超过了 4 ppm。所以，似乎很可能达到这样的薄化程度还不足以对鸟群数量产生明显的影响，但佛罗里达州的一些鹈鹕的确受到了蛋壳薄化的不利影响。

与褐鹈鹕相对比，当 DDE 残留量在 4 ppm ~ 5 ppm 之间时，黑脊鸥并没有出现蛋壳薄化现象；只有在残留量接近 80 ppm 时才显现出 11% 的薄化 [8]。DDE 对褐鹈鹕蛋壳薄化的影响类似于草原隼 [5]。与这两个物种相比，双冠鸬鹚 [4] 似乎对 DDE 引起的蛋壳薄化有更强的抵抗力，但在 DDE 浓度小于 5 ppm 的鸬鹚蛋中往往会发生蛋壳薄化，有人曾报道在一个蛋中 DDE 平均残留量略小于 20 ppm 的鸬鹚聚集地中发现蛋壳薄化达到了 15%。

在各种不同的物种中似乎都存在着 DDE 浓度对数与蛋壳薄化之间的浓度 – 效应关系，并且遵循着相似的数学模式，但在不同物种中有不同程度的体现。导致褐鹈鹕种群数量下滑的蛋中 DDE 残留水平未必会使黑脊鸥的总体数量发生变化。

在此我们要感谢很多帮助我们采集鸟蛋的人。

（吕静 翻译；周江 审稿）

Lawrence J. Blus, Charles D. Gish, Andre A. Belisle and Richard M. Prouty: Patuxent Wildlife Research Center, Laurel, Maryland 20810.

Received October 1, 1971.

References:

1. Blus, L. J., *Bioscience*, **20**, 867 (1970).

2. Keith, J. O., Woods, jun., L. A., and Hunt, E. G., *Trans. N. Amer. Wildl. Nat. Res. Conf.*, **35**, 56 (1970).

3. Risebrough, R. W., Davis, J., and Anderson, D. W., *Oregon State Univ. Env. Health Sci. Series*, No. 1, 40 (1970).

4. Anderson, D. W., Hickey, J. J., Risebrough, R. W., Hughes, D. F., and Christensen, R. E., *Canad. Fld Nat.*, **83**, 91 (1969).

5. Fyfe, R. W., Campbell, J., Hayson, B., and Hodson, K., *Canad. Fld Nat.*, **83**, 191 (1969).

6. Ratcliffe, D. A., *J. Appl. Ecol.*, 7, 67 (1970).

7. Ratcliffe, D. A., *Nature*, **215**, 208 (1967).

8. Hickey, J. J., and Anderson, D. W., *Science*, **162**, 271 (1968).

9. Anderson, D. W., and Hickey, J. J., *Proc. Fifteenth Ornithol. Cong.* (in the press).

10. Wiemeyer, S. N., and Porter, R. D., *Nature*, **227**, 737 (1970).

11. Cummings, J. G., Eidelman, M., Turner, V., Reed, D., Zee, K. T., and Cook, R. E., *J. Assoc. Off. Agric. Chem.*, **50**, 418 (1967).

12. Cummings, J. G., Zee, K. T., Turner, V., and Quinn, F., *J. Assoc. Off. Agric. Chem.*, **49**, 354 (1966).

13. Noakes, D. N., and Benfield, C. A., *J. Sci. Food Agric.*, **16**, 393 (1965).

14. Krantz, W. C., Mulhern, B. M., Bagley, G. E., Sprunt, A., IV, Ligas, F. G., and Robertson, jun., W. B., *Pest. Monit. J.*, **4**, 136 (1970).

15. Mulhern, B. M., *J. Chromatog.*, **34**, 556 (1968).

16. Mulhern, B. M., Reichel, W. L., Locke, L. N., Lamont, T. G., Belisle, A., Cromartie, E., Bagley, G. E., and Prouty, R. M., *Pest. Monit. J.*, **4**, 141 (1970).

17. Anderson, D. W., and Hickey, J. J., *Wilson Bull.*, **82**, 14 (1970).

18. Snedecor, G. W., and Cochran, W. G., *Statistical Methods*, sixth ed. (Iowa State University Press, Ames, 1967).

19. Scholz, J., *Nature*, **207**, 870 (1965).

20. Hayes, jun., W. J., *Toxicol. Appl. Pharmacol.*, **11**, 327 (1967).

21. Kinoshita, F. K., Frawley, J. P., and DuBois, K. P., *Toxicol. Appl. Pharmacol.*, **9**, 505 (1966).

22. Ortega, P., Hayes, jun., W. J., Durham, W. F., and Mattson, A., *US Public Health Serv. Publ. Health Monograph*, No. 43, 1 (1956).

23. Beckett, T. A., III, *Chat*, **30**, 93 (1966).

24. Williams, jun., L. E., and Martin, L., *J. Florida Acad. Sci.*, **31**, 130 (1968).

25. Williams, jun., L. E., and Martin, L., *Proc. Twenty-fourth Ann. Conf. SE Assoc. Game Fish Comm.* (1970).

Disagreements on Why Brown Pelican Eggs Are Thin

W. Hazeltine

Editor's Note

After the decline of the American brown pelican population in the 1960s, Lawrence Blus suggested that DDE, a breakdown product of the pesticide DDT, was responsible for the species' thinning eggshells, and the belief became well established. Here William Hazeltine challenges the statistics and methodology of Blus, questioning his use of whole egg analysis when DDE residues are found in the yolk and are metabolised during incubation. Blus's data, he argues, show correlation not cause and effect, and he warns against calls to ban pesticides based on these "faulty" conclusions. "There is no place in science for suppressed conflicting data, or an "end justifies the means" philosophy," he says. The agricultural use of DDT was nonetheless banned in most developed countries in the 1970s and 80s.

I Find four points of disagreement with the proposal of Blus *et al.*[1,2] that DDE is the probable cause of thin eggshells in brown pelicans.

First, his Fig. 1 is based on data points of residue and shell thickness for three separate colonies composed of two subspecies. If this overall correlation is meaningful, each colony should show a similar trend in itself, which is not the case. None of the separate colonies shows a clear trend in itself.

Second, within the lines for 95% confidence limits in Fig. 1, it is possible to have a series of shell measurements parallel to the abscissa. In other words, his 95% confidence limit could include a series of eggs with residues extending from none to a maximum, with no change in shell thickness. This suggests extremely variable supporting values for the regression.

Third, whole egg analysis is inappropriate for incubated eggs because the residues are found in the yolk, and during incubation yolk contents including residues are subject to metabolic changes. I show below that DDE residues are metabolized as brown pelican eggs are incubated. It is not possible to determine the extent of incubation of Blus's eggs from the published literature, but a table was presented at the public hearing on DDT (Exhibit R-74) which shows that Blus's South Carolina and Florida eggs contained embryos; two were even "heard peeping".

Fourth, the use of Pearson's product moment correlation coefficient (r) is not an appropriate method for values which are not bi-variantly normally distributed. Using logarithms for residue levels shows that residues are not normally distributed around a

在褐鹈鹕蛋蛋壳薄化原因上的不同意见

黑兹尔坦

编者按

在 20 世纪 60 年代美国褐鹈鹕种群数量下降之后，劳伦斯·布卢斯提出：杀虫剂 DDT 的降解产物 DDE 就是造成褐鹈鹕蛋蛋壳薄化的元凶，这一观点得到了大家的普遍认可。在本文中，威廉·黑兹尔坦对布卢斯的统计数据和研究方法提出了质疑，在发现 DDE 残留存在于蛋黄中并且在孵化时还会发生代谢的情况下，他质疑布卢斯所使用的全蛋分析法。他认为，布卢斯的数据所表现出来的关系并非因果关系，他呼吁不要根据这些"错误"的结论而禁用杀虫剂。他说："科学上绝对不允许隐瞒对立数据，也不能采取'只要目的正当就可以不择手段'的处世态度。"尽管如此，在 20 世纪七八十年代，大多数发达国家仍然禁止了 DDT 在农业生产上的使用。

我对布卢斯等人 [1,2] 提出的关于 DDE 可能会引起褐鹈鹕蛋蛋壳薄化的观点有四点不同意见。

第一，他文章中的图 1 是基于三个鸟群聚集地中两个亚种的残留物和蛋壳厚度的数据点绘制而成的。如果这种整体相关性是有意义的，那么每个聚集地本身都应该表现出类似的趋势，但实际情况并非如此。没有哪个单独的聚集地表现出明确的自身趋势。

第二，在图 1 中的 95% 置信区间内，可能会有一系列平行于横坐标的蛋壳厚度测定值。换句话说，他的 95% 置信区间可以包括一系列残留量从零到最大而蛋壳厚度不变的鸟蛋。这说明回归所用的数据带有很大的不确定性。

第三，全蛋分析不适合孵化蛋，因为残留物是在蛋黄中被发现的，在孵化期间蛋黄中的物质（包括残留物）会发生代谢变化。我在下文中将证明 DDE 残留物在褐鹈鹕蛋的孵化过程中发生了代谢变化。从布卢斯已发表的文章中我们无法确定他所使用的蛋的孵化程度，但从 DDT 公开听证会上展示的一张表格（展品 R-74）中可以看出：布卢斯所使用的南卡罗来纳州鸟蛋和佛罗里达州鸟蛋中含有胚胎；甚至可以从其中的两枚蛋中"听到吱吱声"。

第四，如果不是双变量的正态分布就不适合使用皮尔逊积矩相关系数（r）。对残留物浓度取对数的结果说明：残留量并没有在某个平均值附近呈正态分布。应该

mean value. Non-parametric statistics should be used[3].

To understand that Blus's claims about pelican eggs and residues may not be correct, we need to look at some unpublished analyses provided by G. R. Arnett, director of the California Department of Fish and Game (CDFG). These findings were from eggs collected on Anacapa Island off the California coast. Four of these eggs were part of 25, collected on April 18, 1969 (ref. 4). Mr. Blus's sample of 10 was from the same collection (11 eggs are not accounted for). A sample of May 27, 1969, represents eggs taken when adults were shot off their nests on Anacapa Island by State and Federal researchers[5]. The female with the higher residue of DDE had the thicker shelled egg of the two females collected.

The data of Table 1 show the following points. 1, Lipid levels in the yolk drop nearly tenfold during incubation (26.9% to 2.8%). 2, Yolk plus embryo weight increases about threefold (13.6 to 49.7 g) during incubation. 3, Whole egg residues of DDE seem to fit a similar ten-fold level of decrease with incubation (357.5 to 29.4 p.p.m.). 4, Whole egg DDE residues in variously incubated eggs therefore should not be expected to correlate with shell thickness, even if a correlation existed in newly laid eggs.

Table 1. Anacapa Island (California) Brown Pelican Egg Data, supplied by the California Department of Fish and Game

Date collected	Weight yolk (g)	% lipid in yolk	Shell thickness (mm)	Incubated	Residues in µg/g of sample (p.p.m. whole yolk)					Calculated p,p'DDE lipid basis (p.p.m.)
					p,p'DDE	p,p'DDMU	p,p'DDD	p,p'DDT	o,p'DDT	
18/4/69	15.1	21.8	0.42	no	357.5	20.9	8.3	6.9	4.3	1,640
	38.7	6.3	0.38	yes	61.1	4.1	1.6	2.0	1.2	970
	15.3	23.7	0.37	no	204.4	20.3	11.4	10.5	5.0	860
	17.5	22.9	0.37	no	232.1	30.3	17.2	14.7	10.5	1,010
27/5/69	13.6	26.2	0.36	no	178.4	13.0	8.9	7.5	–	680
	16.8	26.9	0.34	no	183.0	13.4	9.1	8.9	–	680
	47.9	4.4	0.40	yes	55.8	2.4	1.1	1.4	–	1,270
	25.3	12.2	0.40	yes	143.4	7.4	3.0	2.9	–	1,172
	49.7	2.8	0.38	yes	29.4	3.3	2.2	1.7	–	1,045

Eggs submitted for analysis by James Keith, US Department of Interior, Bureau of Sport, Fishery and Wildlife.

Dr. E. H. Dustman (personal communication) supplied the data used to establish the points in Fig. 1 of Blus's paper[1]. These data had one obvious typographical error for Anacapa Island, which was corrected. Using Blus's data and those from Table 1, Spearman's rank values were calculated[6] for brown pelican eggs (Table 2).

使用非参数统计方法 [3]。

为了说明布卢斯对鹈鹕蛋和残留物的论述有可能是错误的，我们需要回顾一下美国加州渔猎部（CDFG）主任阿内特提供的一些尚未发表的分析结果。该研究使用的鸟蛋采集自加州海岸的阿纳卡帕岛。在全部 25 枚鸟蛋中，有 4 枚是在 1969 年 4 月 18 日采集的（参考文献 4）。布卢斯先生的鸟蛋样品中有 10 枚也是从这个地方采集的（剩余 11 枚鸟蛋未作说明）。其中一个 1969 年 5 月 27 日的样品是由州和联邦研究人员在阿纳卡帕岛将成鸟从巢中打落后取得的数枚鸟蛋中的一枚 [5]。从捉到的两只雌鸟的情况来看，DDE 残留量较高的雌鸟会产出蛋壳厚度更厚的蛋。

表 1 中的数据可以说明以下几点：1. 在孵化期间蛋黄中脂类成分的含量降低至约为孵化前含量的 1/10（从 26.9% 降低到 2.8%）；2. 在孵化期间蛋黄加胚胎的重量增加了大约 3 倍（从 13.6 g 增加到 49.7 g）；3. 在孵化期间 DDE 全蛋残留似乎降至原来的 1/10（从 357.5 ppm 降低到 29.4 ppm）；4. 因此在孵化程度不同的蛋中，DDE 全蛋残留与蛋壳厚度之间不应该存在相关性，即使相关也只能发生在刚产下的蛋中。

表 1. 由加州渔猎部提供的来自阿纳卡帕岛（加利福尼亚州）的褐鹈鹕蛋数据

采集日期	蛋黄重量 (g)	脂类成分在蛋黄中所占的%	蛋壳厚度 (mm)	是否已孵化	每 g 样品中以 μg 表示的残留物含量（ppm 全蛋黄）					脂类成分中 p,p'DDE 含量的计算值 (ppm)
					p,p'DDE	p,p'DDMU	p,p'DDD	p,p'DDT	o,p'DDT	
1969 年 4 月 18 日	15.1	21.8	0.42	否	357.5	20.9	8.3	6.9	4.3	1,640
	38.7	6.3	0.38	是	61.1	4.1	1.6	2.0	1.2	970
	15.3	23.7	0.37	否	204.4	20.3	11.4	10.5	5.0	860
	17.5	22.9	0.37	否	232.1	30.3	17.2	14.7	10.5	1,010
1969 年 5 月 27 日	13.6	26.2	0.36	否	178.4	13.0	8.9	7.5	—	680
	16.8	26.9	0.34	否	183.0	13.4	9.1	8.9	—	680
	47.9	4.4	0.40	是	55.8	2.4	1.1	1.4	—	1,270
	25.3	12.2	0.40	是	143.4	7.4	3.0	2.9	—	1,172
	49.7	2.8	0.38	是	29.4	3.3	2.2	1.7	—	1,045

用于分析的鸟蛋是由美国内政部渔业和野生动物体育局的詹姆斯·基思提供的。

达斯特曼博士（个人交流）提供了用于绘制布卢斯文章 [1] 中图 1 的数据。在这些数据中，有一个来自阿纳卡帕岛的数据存在明显的印刷错误，现在已经被纠正。由布卢斯的数据和表 1 中的数据可以计算出褐鹈鹕蛋的斯皮尔曼等级系数 [6]（表 2）。

Table 2. Spearman's Rank Values for Blus's and Arnett's Data

Whole egg DDE × shell thickness	
Blus's data, South Carolina, $n=21$, r_s	$= -0.0964$ NS
Blus's data, Anacapa Is., $n=10$, r_s	$= +0.1454$ NS (thickest shells × highest DDE)
r_s	$= +0.393$ NS (thinnest shells × highest DDE)
CDFG, Anacapa Is., $n=9$, r_s	$= +0.4771$ NS
Blus+CDFG, Anacapa Is., $n=19$, r_s	$= -0.0548$ NS
Lipid basis DDE × shell thickness	
CDFG, Anacapa Is., $n=9$, r_s	$= +0.9834$ highly significant, nearly perfect (as residues increased, shells were thicker)

From these data, I conclude that the statement of Blus *et al.*[1], "A concentration-effect relationship seems to exist between DDE in eggs and shell thinning", is correct, but not in the way Blus *et al.* intended. Whole egg residues of incubated eggs seem to be valueless in determining a cause and effect relationship. The CDFG data (Table 1) show a nearly perfect correlation of lipid DDE residues to shell thickness, and the relationship is positive. Even though thicker shells are associated with higher residues, I do not believe that DDE causes shell thickening in brown pelican eggs. The data appear to completely refute that DDE causes thinning of pelican eggs. If DDE were causally related to shell thinning, it would be correlated in every sample and other factors should be investigated to find the cause of the thin shelled eggs observed in this species.

Blus *et al.* mention peregrine falcon egg residues, suggesting that cause and effect studies were conducted with this species. Arguments for the cause of collapse in peregrine falcon populations in the Arctic may[8] suffer from the same problems as the work of Blus *et al.* Three populations of varying reproductive success are considered together, unidentified, and whole egg DDE residues are used to determine a regression coefficient (r) for residues correlated to eggshell values. There is no mention of stage of embryo development, lipid level or which of the three populations provide the points in the figure showing the regression line. There are further problems of non-uniform methods of egg content preservation used in this study. More important is evidence that the available eggs were as thin in 1952 and 1964 as they were in 1970 when the alleged collapse occurred. Scientific persecution appears to be just as viable a hypothesis as DDE or other causes for problems of reproduction failure in these northern peregrine populations.

In order to check further, the lipid residues given by Risebrough[7] for Anacapa Island eggs were evaluated by Spearman's rank (Table 3).

Table 3. Spearman's Rank Values from Risebrough's Data

Lipid basis residue × shell thickness, Anacapa Is.	
DDE; $n=65$, r_s	$= -0.4318$ highly significant
PCB; $n=65$, r_s	$= -0.1361$ NS

Risebrough gives r values for DDE as -0.5605 (Sig<0.001) and PCB as -0.2527 (Sig<0.05).

表 2. 由布卢斯的数据和阿内特的数据计算出的斯皮尔曼等级系数

全蛋中的 DDE × 蛋壳厚度	
布卢斯的数据，南卡罗来纳州，$n=21$，r_s	$= -0.0964$ 无显著性差异
布卢斯的数据，阿纳卡帕岛，$n=10$，r_s	$= +0.1454$ 无显著性差异（蛋壳厚度最大值 ×DDE 最高值）
r_s	$= +0.393$ 无显著性差异（蛋壳厚度最小值 ×DDE 最高值）
CDFG，阿纳卡帕岛，$n=9$，r_s	$= +0.4771$ 无显著性差异
布卢斯 + CDFG，阿纳卡帕岛，$n=19$，r_s	$= -0.0548$ 无显著性差异
脂类成分中的 DDE × 蛋壳厚度	
CDFG，阿纳卡帕岛，$n=9$，r_s	$= +0.9834$ 非常显著，近乎完美（蛋壳随残留物的增加而变厚）

根据这些数据，我发现布卢斯等人 [1] 关于"鸟蛋中 DDE 残留与蛋壳薄化之间似乎存在着浓度 – 效应关系"的论断是正确的，但并不是以布卢斯等人预想的方式呈现。用孵化蛋的全蛋残留数据来确定因果关系似乎是没有意义的。CDFG 的数据（表 1）表明脂类成分中 DDE 残留与蛋壳厚度之间存在着一种近乎完美的相关性，而且是正相关。尽管较厚的蛋壳与较高的残留量相关联，但我并不认为 DDE 残留会导致褐鹈鹕蛋的蛋壳变厚。这些数据彻底驳斥了 DDE 残留会使褐鹈鹕蛋蛋壳变薄的观点。如果 DDE 残留与蛋壳薄化之间存在着因果关系，那么在所有样本中都应该存在这样的关系，我们应该调查其他一些因素来找出导致该物种中出现蛋壳薄化的原因。

布卢斯等人提到了游隼蛋中的残留物，说明他们也对这个物种进行过因果关系的研究。某些人提出的有关北极地区游隼种群数量下降原因的论据 [8] 也存在与布卢斯等人的研究一样的问题。不加区分地同时考虑三个繁殖成功率不同的种群，用全蛋 DDE 残留确定残留量相对于蛋壳厚度的回归系数 (r)。没有提到胚胎发育阶段、脂类水平以及在回归线中的点到底来自于三个种群中的哪一个。进一步的问题包括没有用同样的方法来保存该项研究中所用的蛋的内容物。更重要的是：在可用于研究的鸟蛋中，1952 年和 1964 年的鸟蛋与 1970 年（也就是所谓发生种群数量下降的年份）的鸟蛋都显示出同样的蛋壳厚度。这种 DDE 假说或者其他一些用于解释北部游隼种群繁殖出现障碍的假说似乎正成为一种现实存在的科学迫害。

为了进行进一步核对，我用斯皮尔曼等级系数评估了由赖斯布拉夫 [7] 提供的有关阿纳卡帕岛鸟蛋脂类成分中残余物的数据（表 3）。

表 3. 根据赖斯布拉夫的数据得到的斯皮尔曼等级系数

脂类成分中的残留物 × 蛋壳厚度，阿纳卡帕岛	
DDE：$n=65$，r_s	$= -0.4318$ 非常显著
PCB：$n=65$，r_s	$= -0.1361$ 无显著性差异

赖斯布拉夫给出的 r 值是：对于 DDE 为 -0.5605（统计显著性 <0.001），对于 PCB（译者注：多氯联苯）为 -0.2527（统计显著性 <0.05）。

The data necessary to arrive at an understanding of pesticide residue levels, rapid residue loss rates in eggs with incubation, metabolism of lipids and other pertinent factors should have been published, along with the original contentions and conclusions. That DDE is the cause of thin brown pelican or peregrine eggs is well established in the popular press and scientific literature, but the underlying data to test the conclusion are just now becoming available and do not support such a conclusion. This is reason for concern about actions to ban pesticides based on these faulty conclusions. There is no place in science for suppressed conflicting data, or an "end justifies the means" philosophy. Scientists can be responsible agents for change only when they consider and present all the available data which bear on their conclusion.

(239, 410-411; 1972)

William Hazeltine: 26 Rosita Way, Oroville, California 95965.

Received July 10, 1972.

References:

1. Blus, L. J., Gish, C. D., Belisle, A. A., and Prouty, R. M., *Nature*, **235**, 376 (1972).

2. Blus, L. J., Heath, R. G., Gish, C. D., Belisle, A. A., and Prouty, R. M., *Bio-Science*, **21** (**24**), 1213 (1971).

3. Risebrough, R. J., Cross-examination at Public Hearing on DDT, Washington, DC, transcript pages 8473–8475 (Jan. 7, 1972).

4. Risebrough, R. W., Sibley, F. C., and Kirven, M. N., *American Birds*, **25**(1), 8 (1971).

5. Keith, J. O., Woods, L. A., and Hunt, E. G., *Trans. North American Wildlife Conference*, **35**, 56 (1970).

6. Lathrop, R. G., *Introduction to Psychological Research* (Harper and Row, London, 1969).

7. Risebrough, R. W., *6th Berkeley Symposium on Mathematical Statistics and Probability*, MS as exhibit Int. EDF 29 at Public Hearing on DDT, Washington, DC (in the press).

8. Cade, T. J., Lincer, J. L., White, C. M., Roseneau, D. G., and Swarts, L. G., *Science*, **172**, 955 (1971).

在提出新论点和结论时，应该同步发表一些能说明杀虫剂残留水平、孵化蛋中残留物快速损失速率、脂类代谢以及其他相关因素的必要数据。大众媒体和科学文献已经在公众中确立了 DDE 能引起褐鹈鹕蛋或者游隼蛋蛋壳薄化的观念，但是能检验这一结论的基础数据才刚刚发表，并且这些数据并不支持这一结论。这就是我担心人们基于这些错误结论而禁用杀虫剂的理由。科学上绝对不允许隐瞒对立数据，也不能采取"只要目的正当就可以不择手段"的处世态度。只有在考虑并提供所有支持其结论的有效数据的情况下，科学家们才能成为改变世界的可依赖动力。

（吕静 翻译；周江 审稿）

Use of "Whole Egg Residues" in Pesticide/Eggshell Studies

K. H. Lakhani

Editor's Note

A year earlier, William Hazeltine had criticized the idea that brown pelican eggshell thinning was caused by DDE, on the basis that the underlying studies relied on the inappropriate analysis of whole egg residues. DDE residues, he argued, are found in the yolk, where they are metabolised during incubation. Here K. H. Lakhani criticizes Hazeltine's methodology and argues that the original data linking eggshell thinning with DDE are likely to be "even more significant than suggested by the probability value quoted." The case for the harmful effects of DDT eventually became strong enough to motivate a ban in many countries.

HAZELTINE[1] questions the well established belief that DDE probably causes eggshell thinning in brown pelicans chiefly by finding four points of disagreement with the proposal by Blus et al.[2] that a concentration-effect relationship seems to exist between DDE in eggs and shell thickness. In their subsequent reply, Blus et al.[3] refute Hazeltine's criticisms. There is a further argument against Hazeltine's third criticism of Blus et al.'s conclusions; and the argument has an important bearing on the interpretation of analyses based on "whole egg residues".

Hazeltine expresses the view that the "whole egg residues" are valueless in pesticide/eggshell studies of incubated eggs on the basis of his assumption that the residues are metabolized during incubation. He provides no data for residues expressed on a whole egg (fresh weight) basis, and gives no acceptable evidence to show that DDE or other residues are metabolized (that is, broken down chemically), as distinct from mobilized. Even if we accept that the residues are indeed metabolized during incubation, this does not necessarily make the use of the whole egg residues inappropriate. If DDE residues are metabolized during incubation, then the whole egg residues for incubated eggs will tend to be low. Bearing in mind the thinning of eggshells by withdrawal of calcium in embryonic development during incubation, it is obvious that in the presence of DDE metabolism during incubation, the use of the whole egg residues for pesticide/eggshell studies would provide a conservative test if the correlation between the eggshell thickness and the levels of residue is asserted to be negative. Blus et al.'s "highly significant regression ($P<0.01$)" with a negative slope is then likely to be even more significant than suggested by the probability value quoted.

(**242**, 340-341; 1973)

关于在杀虫剂/蛋壳研究中使用"全蛋残留数据"

拉卡尼

编者按

一年以前，威廉·黑兹尔坦批驳了 DDE 引起褐鹈鹕蛋蛋壳薄化的观点，他的根据是：基于此的研究建立在了不恰当分析全蛋残留数据的基础之上。他指出：DDE 残留物是在蛋黄中被发现的，而蛋黄在孵化期间会发生代谢变化。在本文中，拉卡尼对黑兹尔坦的分析方法提出了批评，他认为证明蛋壳薄化与 DDE 相关的原始数据很可能"比黑兹尔坦列出的概率值更加显著"。后来，DDT 的有害效应案例严重到了促使很多国家颁布禁令的程度。

目前普遍认为 DDE 可能就是造成褐鹈鹕蛋蛋壳薄化的元凶，但黑兹尔坦[1]对这一观点表示怀疑，他尤其针对布卢斯等人[2]关于鸟蛋中 DDE 残留物与蛋壳厚度之间存在浓度–效应关系的结论提出了四点不同意见。布卢斯等人[3]在随后的回复中驳斥了黑兹尔坦的批评意见。本文将进一步反驳黑兹尔坦对布卢斯等人的结论提出的第三点批评意见；而这一见解对于解释基于"全蛋残留数据"的分析有着重要的意义。

黑兹尔坦表示，在孵化蛋的杀虫剂/蛋壳研究中使用"全蛋残留数据"是没有意义的，他的根据是残留物在孵化过程中会发生代谢。然而，他既没有提供以一枚全蛋（鲜重）为基础的残留物数据，也没有给出任何令人信服的证据来证明 DDE 或者其他残留物发生了代谢（即化学分解）而不是迁移。即使我们承认残留物在孵化过程中确实发生了代谢，也不见得不能使用全蛋残留数据。如果 DDE 残留物在孵化过程中发生了代谢，那么孵化蛋的全蛋残留数值将会非常低。别忘了在孵化期间的胚胎发育阶段会因为钙损失而造成蛋壳薄化，显然当孵化过程中确实存在 DDE 代谢时，在杀虫剂/蛋壳研究中使用全蛋残留数据就为我们提供了一种保守的方式来验证蛋壳厚度和残留物水平之间是否是负相关。因而布卢斯等人得到的斜率为负的"非常显著的回归结果（$P<0.01$）"很可能比黑兹尔坦列出的概率值更加显著。

（吕静 翻译；周江 审稿）

K. H. Lakhani: Natural Environment Research Council, The Nature Conservancy, 19-20 Belgrave Square, London SW1.

Received November 13; revised December 18, 1972.

References:
1. Hazeltine, W., *Nature*, **239**, 410 (1972).
2. Blus, L. J., Gish, C. D., Belisle, A. A., and Prouty, R. M., *Nature*, **235**, 376 (1972).
3. Blus, L. J., Gish, C. D., Belisle, A. A., and Prouty, R. M., *Nature*, **240**, 164 (1972).

DDE in Eggs and Embryos of Brown Pelicans

I. C. T. Nisbet

Editor's Note

Here Ian Nisbet criticizes William Hazeltine's preceding dismissal of the link between brown pelican eggshell thinning and the DDT metabolite, DDE. The association of eggshell thinning in birds with DDE is, he argues, "one of the best known of all environmental phenomena," and points out that Hazeltine's sample was "too small and homogeneous to demonstrate anything." The link between eggshell thinning and DDE had been shown so many times in both wild and captive species that at least one journal had complained about receiving further "verifications of phenomena already fully demonstrated." He concludes scornfully that Hazeltine's data "add nothing to previous knowledge except for his demonstration that yolks grow larger during incubation."

HAZELTINE[1] claims to have demonstrated that DDE residues are metabolized by developing embryos of brown pelicans (*Pelecanus occidentalis*). This conflicts with experimental work[2] on Japanese quail (*Coturnix coturnix*), in which incubation did not seem to affect total residue levels in eggs, except for some conversion of p,p'-DDT to p,p'-DDE.

Hazeltine's claim seems to be based on a comparison of DDE levels in the yolks of four incubated and five fresh eggs. As he made clear in the text, the column labelled "Weight yolk" in his Table 1 actually refers to the yolk plus embryo. The apparent 3.2-fold decrease in the mean concentration of DDE in "yolk" simply reflects the 2.6-fold increase in the weight of the yolk + embryo, as the embryos absorbed material from the white. In Hazeltine's sample the whole-egg residues of DDE were slightly smaller in the incubated eggs (mean 2.53 mg) than in the fresh eggs (3.62 mg), but the difference is not statistically significant and in any case this does not demonstrate metabolism of DDE. It is more simply explained by the fact that eggs with higher levels of DDE are broken more frequently during incubation, so that they are less frequently available for collection: this differential breakage has been demonstrated not only in the brown pelican[3], but also in other species[4-7]. For the same reason[3-7] samples of incubated eggs are expected to have thicker shells, on the average, than fresh eggs, as in Hazeltine's sample (means 0.390 mm and 0.372 mm, respectively).

Hazeltine also reported that eggshell thickness was positively correlated with DDE concentration in the lipids of the "yolk". But the latter is not an appropriate measure of the DDE levels in the eggs, because it increases during incubation as the egg lipids are reduced by metabolism[8] (from 3.80 g to 2.26 g in Hazeltine's sample). The most appropriate measures are the whole-egg residue or whole-egg concentration, which

褐鹈鹕蛋和胚胎中的DDE

尼斯比特

编者按

在本文中，伊恩·尼斯比特驳斥了威廉·黑兹尔坦先前提出的关于褐鹈鹕蛋蛋壳薄化与DDT代谢产物——DDE之间并不存在关联的论点。尼斯比特认为鸟类蛋壳薄化与DDE之间的关系是"所有环境现象中最为著名的现象之一"，并且指出黑兹尔坦的样本"范围太小并且均一，根本说明不了什么问题"。蛋壳薄化与DDE之间的关系已经在野生物种和圈养物种中多次被发现，以至于至少有一家杂志开始抱怨说又收到了"已完全得到证实的现象的证据"。在文章最后，他嘲讽黑兹尔坦得到的数据"除了能说明蛋黄在孵化过程中会长大以外，并没有给出任何新的认识"。

黑兹尔坦[1]声称他已经证明DDE残留物在褐鹈鹕的胚胎发育中发生了代谢。这与用日本鹌鹑得到的实验结果[2]并不一致，日本鹌鹑蛋中的残留物水平似乎并没有受到孵化过程的影响，除了有一部分 p,p'–DDT转化成 p,p'–DDE以外。

黑兹尔坦的结论似乎是根据对4枚孵化蛋蛋黄和5枚鲜蛋蛋黄中DDE水平的对比结果得到的。正如他在发表的文章中所述：表1中标有"蛋黄重量"的那一列实际上指的是蛋黄加上胚胎的重量。"蛋黄"中DDE平均浓度显著降低至原来的1/3.2，这只能说明蛋黄＋胚胎的重量增加至2.6倍，因为胚胎会从蛋白中吸收物质。在黑兹尔坦的样品中，孵化蛋的全蛋DDE残留物（平均值为2.53 mg）比鲜蛋的全蛋DDE残留物（3.62 mg）略微少一些，但是这种差别在统计学上不是特别显著，而且无论如何也不能由此证明DDE发生了代谢。用以下事实来解释会更为简单：DDE残留量较高的鸟蛋在孵化过程中更容易破碎，所以很少能收集到这样的蛋。这种易碎程度有差别的现象不仅存在于褐鹈鹕中[3]，在其他鸟类中也有类似情况[4-7]。由于同样的原因[3-7]，孵化蛋样品的蛋壳平均厚度通常会高于鲜蛋，黑兹尔坦的样品也不例外（平均厚度分别为0.390 mm和0.372 mm）。

黑兹尔坦还指出：蛋壳厚度与"蛋黄"脂类成分中的DDE浓度呈正相关。但是后者不能正确地反映出蛋中的DDE含量，因为在孵化过程中DDE含量会随着蛋中脂类的代谢分解（黑兹尔坦的样品是从3.80 g降到了2.26 g）而逐渐增加[8]。最适合的测量方式是全蛋残留量或者全蛋浓度，这两个参数可以反映雌鸟在产蛋时的

reflect the levels of DDE circulating in the female at the time of laying[9-11]. In Hazeltine's sample, the Spearman rank correlation coefficient r_s between whole-egg residue of DDE and eggshell thickness is +0.244 (not +0.477 as stated in Hazeltine's Table 2). This is not statistically significant, which is not surprising in a small sample with a very small range in eggshell thickness: but the points fall close to the regression lines of Risebrough[12] and Blus et al.[13]. As Hazeltine points out (his Table 3), in Risebrough's larger sample the correlation is negative and highly significant ($r_s = -0.4318$, $P < 0.01$).

Hazeltine also stated that non-parametric statistics should have been used by Blus et al.[13] to test the relationship between eggshell thickness and DDE residues, because these variables were "not bi-variantly normally distributed". This would be valid if the goal of the study had been simply to demonstrate association of eggshell thinning with DDE, but Blus et al.[13] were attempting to define the dose-response relation. Parametric regression techniques require only that the dependent variable be random and normally distributed about the regression line[14]. This condition was satisfied by the brown pelican eggshell data of both Risebrough[12] and Blus et al.[13], and both found a good fit to a logarithmic dose-response relation. A logarithmic relation between eggshell thickness and DDE residues in eggs has also been reported in wild peregrine falcons (*Falco peregrinus*)[4,15] and in experimental mallards (*Anas platyrhynchos*)[16]. The advantage of applying a logarithmic transformation to the DDE variable is that it is then possible to use multiple linear regression techniques to separate the effects of co-existing pollutants. This was done by both Blus et al.[17,18] and Risebrough[12], who found independently that most of the variance in eggshell thickness was explained by the log DDE and DDE variables, and no significant fraction by any other chemicals.

Hazeltine also criticized Blus et al. for combining data from brown pelicans of two different subspecies. Blus et al. corrected for the known difference between the subspecies by using as dependent variable the eggshell thickness expressed as a percentage of the pre-1947 mean for the subspecies. In any case this criticism cannot be applied to Risebrough's data, which were all drawn from Pacific Coast populations[12].

The association of eggshell thinning in birds with *p,p′*-DDE is one of the best known of all environmental phenomena[19]. It has been shown so many times in both wild and captive species[3-7,12,13,16-18] that at least one journal has complained about receiving further "verifications of phenomena already fully demonstrated"[20]. Scientific work in this area is now devoted to elucidating details such as the form of the dose-response relation and the reasons for the known interspecific differences in sensitivity. The brown pelican is one of the species in which the phenomenon has been explored most fully[3,12,13,17,18,21,22]. It is therefore somewhat odd to find another letter[1] discussing whether the association exists, based on a sample too small and homogeneous to demonstrate anything. In fact, Hazeltine's nine eggs fall exactly into the pattern of eggshell thinning known from previous work[12,13,22], and his data add nothing to previous knowledge except for his demonstration that "yolks" grow larger during incubation.

(**242**, 341; 1973)

DDE 循环水平 [9-11]。在黑兹尔坦的样品中，全蛋 DDE 残留和蛋壳厚度之间的斯皮尔曼等级相关系数 r_s 为 +0.244（而非黑兹尔坦文章中表 2 所列出的 +0.477）。这在统计学上不具有显著性，在蛋壳厚度范围非常狭小的小样本中出现这样的结果并不令人惊奇；而这些点都落在赖斯布拉夫 [12] 和布卢斯等人 [13] 的回归线附近。正如黑兹尔坦所指出的（他文章中的表 3），在赖斯布拉夫采用更大样本进行分析时，相关性呈负相关，并且非常显著（r_s = –0.4318，P < 0.01）。

黑兹尔坦还指出：布卢斯等人 [13] 应该使用非参数统计方法来检测蛋壳厚度与 DDE 残留物之间的关系，因为这些变量不是"双变量的正态分布"。如果研究目的只是为了证明蛋壳薄化与 DDE 有关，那么使用非参数统计应该没有问题，但布卢斯等人 [13] 的目标是要确定剂量–反应关系。参数回归方法仅需要因变量是随机的且在回归线附近呈正态分布 [14]。赖斯布拉夫 [12] 和布卢斯等人 [13] 的褐鹈鹕蛋壳数据都可以满足这些条件，并且他们都发现剂量对数与反应之间符合很好的拟合关系。还有人报道在野生游隼 [4,15] 和实验绿头鸭 [16] 的蛋壳厚度与 DDE 残留物之间也存在对数关系。对 DDE 变量进行对数变换的好处在于随后可以使用各种多元线性回归技术以排除共存污染物的干扰。布卢斯等人 [17,18] 和赖斯布拉夫 [12] 都是这样做的，他们各自独立地发现用 log DDE 和 DDE 变量可以解释大多数蛋壳厚度的变化，而任何其他化学物质都无法作为显著的因子。

黑兹尔坦还批评布卢斯等人混合了来自两种不同褐鹈鹕亚种的数据。布卢斯等人曾通过以下方式校正过两个亚种之间的已知差异——用现在的蛋壳厚度占 1947 年前几个亚种蛋壳厚度平均值的百分数作为因变量。这种批评无论如何不适用于赖斯布拉夫的数据，因为赖斯布拉夫的数据全部来自于太平洋沿岸的种群 [12]。

鸟蛋蛋壳薄化与 p,p'–DDE 相关是所有环境现象中最为著名的现象之一 [19]。这一现象已经在野生物种和圈养物种中多次被发现 [3-7,12,13,16-18]，以至于至少有一家杂志开始抱怨说又收到了"已完全得到证实的现象的证据"[20]。目前这一领域的科学研究集中在解释一些细节问题上，如剂量–反应关系的形式以及种间存在敏感度差异的原因。褐鹈鹕是人们对上述现象研究得最全面的物种之一 [3,12,13,17,18,21,22]。因此，当我发现有一篇快报 [1] 还在讨论这种关系是否存在时，确实感到有点奇怪，文章中所依据的样本范围太小并且均一，根本说明不了什么问题。实际上，黑兹尔坦的 9 枚鸟蛋也完全落在前面研究 [12,13,22] 得到的蛋壳薄化分布之内，他的数据除了能说明"蛋黄"在孵化过程中会长大以外，并没有给出任何新的认识。

（吕静 翻译；周江 审稿）

I. C. T. Nisbet: Massachusetts Audubon Society, Lincoln, Massachusetts 01773, and Environmental Defense Fund, 1712 N Street, Washington DC 20036.

Received November 24, 1972.

References:

1. Hazeltine, W., *Nature*, **239**, 410 (1972).

2. Cooke, A. S., *Pest. Sci.*, **2**, 144 (1971).

3. Keith, J. O., Woods, L. A., jun., and Hunt, E. G., *Proc. 35th N. Amer. Wildl. Conf.*, 56 (1970).

4. Ratcliffe, D. A., *J. Appl. Ecol.*, 7, 67 (1970).

5. Hickey, J. J., and Anderson, D. W., *Science*, **162**, 271 (1968).

6. Longcofe, J., Samson, F. B., and Whittendale, T. W., jun., *Bull. Environ. Contam. Toxicol.*, **6**, 485 (1971).

7. Switzer, B., Lewin, V., and Wolfe, F. H., MS presented as exhibit USDA-RBTL-9 at public hearings on DDT (Environmental Protection Agency, Washington DC, 1972).

8. Romanoff, A. L., and Romanoff, A. J., *The Avian Egg* (Wiley, New York, 1949).

9. Cummings, J. G., Eidelman, M., Turner, V., Reed, D., Zee, K. T., and Cook, R. E., *J. Assoc. Off. Agric. Chem.*, **50**, 418 (1967).

10. Cummings, J. G., Zee, K. T., Turner, V., and Quinn, F., *J. Assoc. Off. Agric. Chem.*, **49**, 354 (1966).

11. Noakes, D. N., and Benfield, C. A., *J. Sci. Food Agric.*, **16**, 393 (1965).

12. Risebrough, R. W., *Proc. 6th Berkeley Symposium on Mathematical Statistics and Probability* (in the press).

13. Blus, L. J., Gish, C. D., Belisle, A. A., and Prouty, R. M., *Nature*, **235**, 376 (1972).

14. Steel, R. G. D., and Torrie, J. H., *Principles and Procedures of Statistics*, 187 (McGraw-Hill, New York, 1960).

15. Cade, T. J., Lincer, J. L., White, C. M., Roseneau, D. G., and Swarts, L. G., *Science*, **172**, 955 (1971).

16. Heath, R. G., MS presented as exhibit R-128 at public hearings on DDT (Environmental Protection Agency, Washington DC, 1972).

17. Blus, L. J., Heath, R. G., Gish, C. D., Belisle, A. A., and Prouty, R. M., *BioScience*, **21**, 1213 (1971).

18. Blus, L. J., MSS presented as exhibits R-70 and R-71 at public hearings on DDT (Environmental Protection Agency, Washington DC, 1972).

19. Peakall, D. B., *Bird Study*, **18**, 47 (1971).

20. Behnke, J. A., *BioScience*, **22**, 73 (1972).

21. Schreiber, R. W., and Risebrough, R. W., *Wilson Bull.*, **80**, 119 (1972).

22. Blus, L. J., *BioScience*, **20**, 867 (1970).

Two Types of Mountain Building

J. T. Wilson and K. Burke

Editor's Note

This beautifully concise paper by geophysicists John Tuzo Wilson and Kevin Burke at the University of Toronto explains how different types of mountain features can be produced at subduction zones, where the convergence of oceanic and continental tectonic plates causes the ocean plate to bend and plunge down into the Earth's mantle. Depending on whether it is the oceanic or the continental plate that is advancing, or both, one might find volcanic mountain ranges along the continental coast (such as the Andes) or volcanic island arcs such as the Philippines. These ideas helped to establish a link between the theory of plate tectonics and the broad-scale geological features that should be expected to arise from it.

ACCORDING to plate tectonic theory subduction zones form where two plates converge. Observation shows that these zones frequently form along the margins of continental plates where they override oceanic plates with Benioff zones dipping towards the continents. We consider the motion relative to the deeper mantle of two converging plates. Neglecting lateral shear components we find three cases possible. First, continental plate may be actively advancing and overriding an oceanic plate which is stationary relative to the mantle. Second, an oceanic plate may be actively advancing and passing beneath a stationary continental plate. Third, both plates may be in motion relative to the mantle, but if so their behaviour may be nearer to one or the other of the two previous cases.

Attempts have been made to determine the absolute motions of some existing plates relative to the deeper mantle[1,2], using Wilson's[3] proposal that convective plumes rise in the mantle and are fixed in location like such common diapiric structures as saltdomes, pingos and volcanic pipes and Morgan's[4] hypothesis that these plumes drive the lithospheric plates. For the case in which a continental plate is actively advancing, the subduction zone takes the form of coastal mountains as in Chile with a marginal trench which is pushed ahead of the continent[5] (Fig. 1a, b), and for the case in which the oceanic plate is actively advancing, island arcs and trenches form off-shore as in East Asia with little disturbance of the continental coast[6] (Fig. 2a, b).

两种类型的造山运动

威尔逊，伯克

编者按

这篇短小精悍的论文出自多伦多大学地球物理学家约翰·图佐·威尔逊和凯文·伯克之手，该论文解释了不同类型的山貌是怎样在俯冲带上形成的。在俯冲带，大洋板块和大陆板块的汇聚使大洋板块发生弯曲并向下扎入地幔中。在大陆海岸附近是出现火山山脉（如安第斯山脉）还是形成像菲律宾群岛那样的火山岛弧，取决于前进的板块是大洋板块还是大陆板块，或者两者皆有。这些构想有助于我们在板块构造理论和被认为与此相关的大尺度地质特征之间建立一种联系。

根据板块构造理论，俯冲带形成于两个板块的汇聚处。观测结果表明，这些俯冲带大多形成于大陆板块的边缘。在那里，大洋板块伏于大陆板块之下，且贝尼奥夫带向大陆倾斜。本文将讨论两个汇聚板块相对于深部地幔的运动。我们发现在不考虑侧向剪切分量时，可能会出现三种情况。首先，大陆板块可能会主动向前运动并推覆到相对于地幔静止的大洋板块之上。其次，大洋板块可能会主动向前运动并俯冲到静态的大陆板块之下。第三，两个板块可能都会相对于地幔运动，如果是这样的话，它们的行为可能会更接近于前面两种情形中的一种。

人们曾试图确定一些现存板块相对于深部地幔的绝对运动[1,2]，其研究方法是利用威尔逊假设[3]（即羽状对流产生于地幔内部并且其位置固定，类似于常见的底辟构造，如盐丘、冰丘、火山喉管等）和摩根假说[4]（即这些羽状流驱动了岩石圈板块）。对于大陆板块主动前推的情况，在俯冲带处会形成海岸山脉，就像智利的情况一样，并且在大陆前部出现边缘海沟[5]（图1a，b）；如果是大洋板块主动向前推进，则会在远离海岸处形成岛弧和海沟，比如东亚地区，它们对大陆沿岸影响很小[6]（图2a，b）。

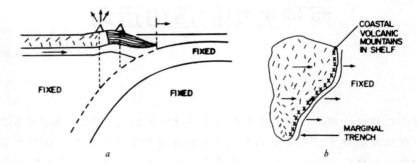

Fig. 1. *a*, Section showing continental plate advancing over an oceanic plate stationary over the mantle. The marginal trench is advancing and the shelf deposits are intruded and disturbed by volcanism arising from the Benioff zone (dashed line). *b*, Sketch plan of *a* indicating that orogeny can only affect the leading edge of the continent.

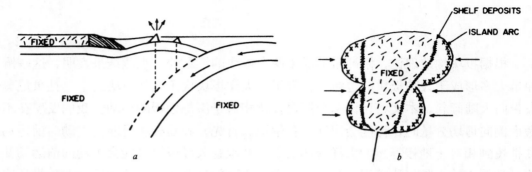

Fig. 2. *a*, Section showing oceanic plate advancing and passing beneath a continental plate stationary over the mantle. The shelf deposits are not affected by the arc volcanism which forms a separate deposit. *b*, Sketch plan of *a* indicating that more than one moving oceanic plate may approach a fixed continent and produce orogeny on several sides at the same time.

In the first case it is evident that a marginal trench and coastal mountains can only form at any one time on a single side, that is the leading edge, of an advancing continental plate (Fig. 1*b*); the Andes range appears a good example.

In the second case island arcs and trenches can form simultaneously on more than one side of a stationary continent if two or more oceanic plates are advancing towards it from different directions (Fig. 2*b*). This could explain why the Burma-Indonesia, Philippine and Taiwan-Luzon arcs have formed on three sides of the south-eastern part of Asia which we consider to be nearly stationary[1].

According to these arguments the active advance of North America over both the mantle and the Pacific Basin during the Mesozoic Era would explain why the Nevadan orogeny and the Cordillera have no counterparts on other North American coasts and took the form of a marginal trench and coastal mountains.

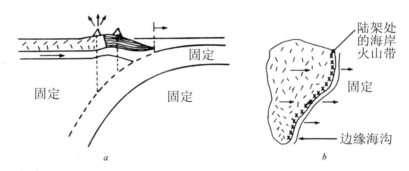

图 1. *a*，大陆板块向前推覆到相对于地幔静止的大洋板块之上的剖面。大陆边缘的海沟向前运动，并且来自贝尼奥夫带（虚线）的火山作用侵入和扰动了陆架沉积物。*b*，图 *a* 的平面示意图，表明造山运动只影响大陆的前缘。

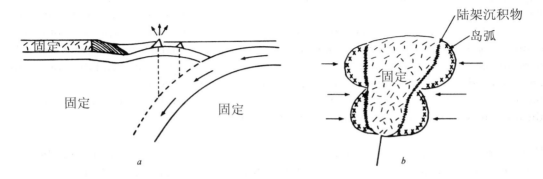

图 2. *a*，大洋板块向前推进并俯冲到相对于地幔静止的大陆板块之下的剖面。岛弧火山作用并不影响陆架沉积物，而是形成自己的沉积。*b*，图 *a* 的平面示意图，表明可能会有多个大洋板块向同一块固定大陆靠近，从而在大陆的多侧同时发生造山运动。

在第一种情况下，显然边缘海沟和海岸山脉在任何时候均只能在前进的大陆板块的一侧形成，这一侧就是其前缘（图 1*b*）。安第斯山系是一个很好的例子。

在第二种情况下，倘若有两个或两个以上的大洋板块从不同方向向静止的大陆俯冲，那么岛弧与海沟就可能同时在静止大陆的多侧边缘形成（图 2*b*）。这样就可以解释为什么缅甸–印度尼西亚、菲律宾以及台湾–吕宋岛一线的岛弧能够从三面包围被认为是近乎静止不动的东南亚大陆板块了 [1]。

根据以上论述，用覆于地幔与太平洋海盆之上的北美大陆在中生代时期的主动向前推移即可解释为什么在北美的其他沿海地区没有出现内华达造山运动和科迪勒拉山系那样的情况，以及为什么会形成边缘海沟和海岸山脉。

On the other hand, the evidence that during the Palaeozoic several orogenies developed contemporaneously on different coasts[7] suggests that at least from Devonian to Triassic times North America was approximately stationary. This is supported by palaeomagnetic evidence[8]. If North America was stationary it follows that these Palaeozoic orogenies would have taken the form of island arcs. This difference in the nature of the Palaeozoic and Mesozoic orogenies may serve to explain important distinctions in their characteristics.

Kuno[9] and Dickinson[10] have discussed the rise of volcanic activity above dipping Benioff zones. The narrow width of island arcs and of the Andes and the absence of volcanoes in marginal seas and to the East of the Andes shows that this volcanism is confined to narrow belts extending a few hundred kilometers landwards from trenches.

Where orogeny has produced marginal trenches as in the Andes, Sierra Nevada and Coast Ranges of British Columbia, this volcanism rises close to the coast. Gilluly[11] and James[12] have discussed how the sedimentary deposits of the continental shelves have been intimately involved, becoming contaminated with volcanic additions and metamorphosed into great complex batholiths. No separate island arcs existed, nor, as James remarks, any separate depositional eugeosynclinal basins. It is true that marginal trenches existed and that some have become filled, but trenches also form along island arcs and may become filled. The deposits of filled trenches which can occur in either case should be distinguished from those constituting the arcs themselves which only occur in the second case.

Where orogeny has produced island arcs the products of volcanism accumulate and become metamorphosed separately from, and without affecting, the sedimentary shelf deposits[6]. It has thus been logical to interpret the extensive and little altered fold belts of the Acadian, Appalachian, Antler, Sonoma and similar orogenies as unaltered shelf and marginal sea deposits and identify the associated, but very different, eugeosynclinal deposits such as those of Central Newfoundland, the Piedmont and the Purcel Mountains as former island arcs[13]. The forces which have folded the shelf deposits and which seem to have pushed the arcs inland still require explanation.

We now consider an oceanic plate which enters and is consumed in a subduction zone over a long period of time. There is a good chance that ultimately it will carry in another continent or a continental fragment. That this will create a series of major disturbances and ultimately close the ocean has been accepted by some as an explanation for the several pulses of orogeny in the Caledonian-Appalachian system[14-17].

These arguments suggest that during the Mesozoic the coastline of western north America between Mexico and the Yukon approximately followed the locus of Jurassic volcanic fields and Cretaceous magmatic activity through the Sierra Nevada, north-western Nevada, the Idaho Batholith and the Coast Ranges of British Columbia[18-21]. Stewart has defined a late Precambrian shore-line in this area[22]. The two are significantly separated only in Central British Columbia and in Nevada opposite the principal fold belts. It has already been suggested that these areas may be new continental additions whose union with North America caused

另一方面，有证据表明，古生代期间曾有几个造山运动同时发生于北美大陆上的不同海岸地区[7]，这说明至少在从泥盆纪到三叠纪这段时期内，北美大陆是近于静止的。这一观点在古地磁学方面也得到了证实[8]。倘若北美大陆是静止的，那么古生代造山运动就应该形成岛弧。古生代与中生代造山运动的这种差异也许可以解释它们在造山特征上的重要区别。

库诺[9]和迪金森[10]曾讨论过发生于倾斜的贝尼奥夫带之上的火山活动。结果显示：岛弧和安第斯山脉的宽度均较窄，并且边缘海地区和安第斯山脉以东均没有火山活动。这些现象说明火山作用仅限于狭窄的地带，从海沟向陆地方向只延伸了几百公里。

在造山运动形成边缘海沟的地区，如安第斯山脉、内华达山脉以及不列颠哥伦比亚海岸山系等地，火山作用一般紧邻海岸发生。陆架沉积物是如何与火山作用密切关联并与火山加积物相混染从而变质形成巨大的复杂岩基的？吉拉里[11]和詹姆斯[12]曾对此进行过研究。不存在单独的岛弧，也没有如詹姆斯所述的单独的优地槽盆地。边缘海沟确实存在，并且有的已被充填。不过，海沟也沿岛弧形成，同样也有可能被充填。无论属于哪种情况，充填海沟的沉积物可与构成岛弧本身的物质区别开来，其中岛弧只出现于第二种情况中。

在造山运动已经形成岛弧的地区，火山物质发生堆积和变质，但这种过程并不影响陆架沉积物[6]。因此，我们可以合理地将阿卡迪亚、阿巴拉契亚、安特勒和索诺马的以及由类似造山运动形成的广阔且基本未发生变质的褶皱带看作是未被改变的陆架和边缘海沉积物，并且识别出与其相关但特征迥异的优地槽沉积，如出现在纽芬兰中部、皮德蒙特高原以及珀塞尔山的岛弧区的沉积[13]。对于导致陆架沉积物发生褶皱并可能推挤岛弧的力还需研究。

现在我们来考虑进入俯冲带后长期处于消减状况的大洋板块，它很有可能最终将另一个大陆或大陆碎块携带到俯冲带。这一过程将引起一系列大的扰动，并最终导致大洋的闭合。一些学者已经接受了上述观点并利用其解释喀里多尼亚–阿巴拉契亚体系中的几个造山运动阶段[14-17]。

这些论点表明：在中生代期间，位于墨西哥和育空之间的北美大陆西部海岸线大致就是侏罗纪火山带以及白垩纪岩浆活动带，它穿过内华达山脉、内华达西北部、爱达荷岩基以及不列颠哥伦比亚海岸山系[18-21]。斯图尔特确定了该地区在前寒武纪晚期的海岸线[22]。两者明显分离的地方仅出现在不列颠哥伦比亚中部和与主褶皱带相对的内华达。已有学者指出，这些区域可能是新大陆的加积体，它们与北美大陆

uplift and folding and introduced faunal invasions[23-25].

The Mesozoic shoreline departs significantly from the present coast only in the vicinity of Oregon where an embayment is underlain by thin, possibly oceanic, crust[26] and seems to be closed by the Cascade Mountains, marking a subduction zone resembling an island arc[27,28].

One possible corollary of the proposed Palaeozoic stand-still of North America may be noted. Krenkel observed that during Tertiary time a series of basins divided by elongated swells developed on the African continent[29]. If this was due to influences from the deeper mantle upon a stationary plate, then the same explanation could apply to the development during Palaeozoic time of many basins and swells across the United States and Western Canada (for example, the Williston, Peace River and Michigan Basins).

We acknowledge support received from the National Research Council of Canada.

(**239**, 448-449; 1972)

J. Tuzo Wilson and Kevin Burke: Erindale College, University of Toronto.

Received April 20, 1971, revised August 14, 1972.

References:
1. Burke, K. C., and Wilson, J. T., *Nature* (in the press).
2. Dietz, R. S., and Holden, J. S., *J. Geophys. Res.*, **75**, 4948 (1970).
3. Wilson, J. T., *Phil. Trans. Royal Soc.*, A, **258**, 145 (1965).
4. Morgan, W. J., *Nature*, **230**, 42 (1971).
5. Orowan, E., *Phil. Trans. Roy. Soc.*, A, **258**, 284 (1965).
6. Parke, M. L., Emery, K. O., Szymankiewicz, R., and Reynolds, L. M., *Bull. AAPG*, **55**, 723 (1971).
7. Johnson, J. G., *Geol. Soc. Amer. Bull.*, **82**, 3263 (1971).
8. Collinson, D. W., and Runcorn, S. K., *Geol. Soc. Amer. Bull.*, **71**, 915 (1960).
9. Kuno, H., *Bull. Volcanol.*, **29**, 195 (1966).
10. Dickinson, W. R., *Rev. Geophys. Space Phys.*, **8**, 813 (1970).
11. Gilluly, J., *Science*, **166**, 992 (1969).
12. James, D. E., *Geol. Soc. Amer. Bull.*, **82**, 3325 (1971).
13. Higgins, M. W., *Geol. Soc. Amer. Bull.*, **83**, 989 (1972).
14. Wilson, J. T., *Nature*, **211**, 676 (1966).
15. Church, W. R., and Stevens, R. K., *J. Geophys. Res.*, **76**, 1460 (1971).
16. Bird, J. M., Dewey, J. F., and Kidd, W. S. F., *Nature Physical Science*, **231** (1971).
17. Whittington, H. B., and Hughes, C. P., *Phil. Trans. Roy. Soc.*, B, **263**, 235 (1971).
18. Kistler, R. W., Evernden, J. F., and Shaw, M. R., *Geol. Soc. Amer. Bull.*, **82**, 853 (1971).
19. Smith, J. G., McKee, E. H., Tatlock, D. B., and Marvin, R. F., *Geol. Soc. Amer. Bull.*, **82**, 2933 (1971).
20. Zietz, I., Hearn, jun., B. C., Higgins, M. W., Robinson, G. D., and Swanson, D. A., *Geol. Soc. Amer. Bull.*, **82**, 3347 (1971).
21. Souther, J. G., *Publ. Earth Physics Branch*, **42**(3), 55 (1972).

的结合造成了隆升与褶皱，并造成动物区系的侵入 [23-25]。

中生代海岸线与现今海岸线仅在俄勒冈附近明显不同。在那里，海湾下面较薄的地壳可能是洋壳 [26]，而喀斯喀特山似乎包围了整个海湾，说明这是一个类似于岛弧的俯冲带 [27,28]。

应该注意北美大陆在古生代时期是静止的这一推论也许是可能的。克伦克尔注意到，非洲大陆在第三纪（译者注：原为新生代的一个"纪"，分为老第三纪、新第三纪。新制订的地质年代表将老第三纪改称古近纪，新第三纪改为新近纪，"第三纪"不再使用。）发育了一系列被长条形隆起分割的海盆 [29]。如果这种现象是由于深处地幔对静止板块影响的结果，那么这种观点同样可用于解释美国与加拿大西部许多古生代时期的盆地和隆起的成因（例如：威利斯顿盆地、皮斯河盆地及密歇根盆地）。

感谢加拿大国家研究委员会为我们提供支持。

（齐红艳 翻译；孟庆任 审稿）

22. Stewart, J. H., *Geol. Soc. Amer. Bull.*, **83**, 1345 (1972).

23. Wilson, J. T., *Amer. Phil. Soc. Procs.*, **112**, 309 (1968).

24. Monger, J. W. H., and Ross, C. A., *Canad. J. Earth Sci.*, **8**, 259 (1971).

25. Ross, J. R., and Ingham, J. K., *Geol. Soc. Amer. Bull.*, **81**, 393 (1970).

26. Hill, D. P., *Geol. Soc. Amer. Bull.*, **83**, 1639 (1972).

27. Atwater, T., *Geol. Soc. Amer. Bull.*, **81**, 3513 (1970).

28. Silver, E. A., *Geol. Soc. Amer. Bull.*, **82**, 3491 (1971).

29. Krenkel, E., *Geologie und Bodenschatze Africas* (Verlag, Leipzig, 1957).

The Macroscopic Level of Quantum Mechanics

C. George *et al.*

Albert Einstein and other critics of quantum theory had long noted the difficulty of reconciling its description of the microscopic world—where it suggests particles often exist in a superposition of two or more states—with the existence of macroscopic objects always definite properties. Here Leon Rosenfeld and colleagues attempt to show how this inconsistency could be resolved by considering the "complementarity" of distinct modes of description at the atomic level, advocated by Niels Bohr. They argue that Bohr's view could be put into a formal framework using the density matrix of quantum statistical mechanics. This proposal, physicists later showed, did not resolve the matter, which continues to be an important foundational problem for quantum theory today.

ATOMIC theory raises the epistemological problem of harmonizing the detailed dynamical description of atomic systems given by quantum mechanics and the description of individual atomic processes and of the behaviour of matter in bulk at the level of macroscopic observation. The logical side of this problem is completely elucidated by the recognition of relationships of complementarity between the two modes of description: on the one hand, there is the complementarity expressed by the indeterminacy relations, which governs the application of the macroscopic space-time localization and momentum-energy conservation to the individual atomic processes; on the other, there is the complementarity between the account of the behaviour of a large system of atomic constituents given by quantum mechanics (and electrodynamics) and the description of the same system as a material body in terms of the concepts of macroscopic mechanics, electromagnetism and thermodynamics.

The formal side of the problem, however, which consists in establishing the consistency of the rules connecting the formalism of quantum mechanics with the concepts used in the account of macroscopic observation, still leaves scope for a presentation more in accordance with the conceptual simplicity of the actual situation. A general treatment of the quantum theory of large atomic systems which satisfies this desideratum has been given in a recent article[1]. The purpose of this note is to outline the method and the principal results.

The work pursued during the past decade by the Brussels group has clearly shown that the method best adapted to the investigation of large atomic systems is not the ergodic but the kinetic approach of statistical mechanics, applied to the limiting case of infinite systems (that is, systems of infinite degree of freedom, but such that the number of elements

宏观层次的量子力学

乔治等

编者按

量子理论对微观世界的描述认为，微观粒子常常处于两个或两个以上状态的叠加态中。阿尔伯特·爱因斯坦以及其他量子理论的批评者们很早就注意到，此一对微观世界的描述与宏观物体通常具有明确的属性这一事实之间存在着难以调和的矛盾。本文中，利昂·罗森菲尔德与其同事们试图说明这一矛盾可以通过考虑尼尔斯·玻尔所倡导的、原子层次上不同描述模式间的"互补性"来加以解决。他们认为，利用量子统计力学中的密度矩阵就可将玻尔的观点纳入一个形式的框架中。物理学家们后来指出，上述提议并没有解决这个难题，直至今日它仍然是量子理论中一个重要的基本问题。

原子理论提出了一个认识论问题——如何调和量子力学所给出的对原子系统的详细动力学描述，与在宏观观测水平上对单个原子过程以及大块物质行为的描述二者之间的关系。认识到两种描述模式之间的互补关系就可以完全阐明这一问题的逻辑性：一方面，不确定关系表达出互补性，它决定了宏观的时空局域性与动量–能量守恒可应用于单个的原子过程；另一方面，对于一个由原子组成的大系统，根据量子力学（和电动力学）计算其行为与将此系统视为材料实体按照宏观力学、电磁学以及热学的概念对其进行描述，这两者之间存在着互补性。

但是，这一问题形式上的一面，即建立能将量子力学公式与描述宏观观测所用概念联系起来的各个规律之间的一致性，仍为发展出一种与实际情况概念上的简单性更符合的表述留出了空间。我们在近期发表的一篇文章[1]中给出的用量子理论处理较大原子体系的一般性方法能满足上述急迫需求。本文旨在概述这一方法及其重要结论。

布鲁塞尔小组过去十年所从事的工作清楚地表明，最适于研究大原子系统的是曾经用于无限系统的极限情况（即具有无穷多自由度的系统，但该系统在给定相位范围内的单元是有限的）的统计力学动力学方法而不是各态遍历方法。因为这类系

within a given phase extension has a finite limit). Because such systems have essentially a continuous energy spectrum, the vexed question of "coarse graining" can be ignored and the asymptotic limit of the density operator for times very large on the atomic scale, but finite, can be directly discussed. This discussion leads to the conclusion[2] that the time evolution of the system may be split rigorously into formally independent "subdynamics", characterized, in a manner presently to be explained, by certain projection operators depending on the correlations between the constitutive elements of the system. One of these subdynamics belonging to the projector $\widetilde{\Pi}$ given by equation (7) below contains all the information about equilibrium properties and linear transport properties. We may therefore define the macroscopic level of description of quantum mechanics as the reduced description in terms of the variables of the $\widetilde{\Pi}$-subspace. That such a reduced description is at all possible results precisely from the fact that the $\widetilde{\Pi}$-subdynamics is expressed by an independent equation of evolution. The application of this analysis to the case of a measuring apparatus, initially triggered off by an interaction of atomic duration with an atomic object, shows in a surprisingly simple way that its evolution in $\widetilde{\Pi}$-space conforms to the "reduction" rule of quantum mechanics; this important conclusion follows directly from the mathematical structure of the $\widetilde{\Pi}$-subspace of the apparatus, which entails the elimination of the initial phase relations between the components of the density operator of the atomic object. Our paper contains a simple and general derivation of these remarkable results, which shows more clearly how these methods not only lead to a deeper understanding of the epistemological problems of atomic theory, but even to a significant extension of the scope of quantum mechanics.

In a superspace defined as the direct product of the Hilbert space and its dual, the density operator $\rho(t)$ appears as a supervector, varying in time according to a Liouville equation of the form

$$i\,\dot{\rho}(t) = L\rho(t)$$

The Liouville superoperator L may be expressed in terms of the Hamiltonian H of the system. For this purpose, we may use a convenient notation for the special class of "factorizable" superoperators $O \equiv M \times N$ depending on a pair of supervectors M, N according to the definition $O\rho = M\rho N$; we may then write $L = H \times 1 - 1 \times H$. Our aim being to find the long time effect of correlations, we must, to begin with, compare our system, defined by the Hamiltonian H, with a "model" system H_0, from which the interaction energy V, responsible for the correlations, is removed, in such a way that $H = H_0 + V$. The eigenstates of H_0 form a complete orthogonal basis of representation in Hilbert space, from which we construct a similar basis in superspace: the latter may be divided into two classes of supervectors, those built up of pairs of identical (or physically equivalent) eigenstates, and those built up of pairs of different eigenstates; they belong, respectively, to two orthogonal subspaces of superspace, characterized by projection superoperators P_0, P_c. Then the projections $\rho_0 = P_0\rho$ and $\rho_c = P_c\rho$ of the density supervector correspond, respectively, to the average distribution densities and the correlation amplitudes. Putting $L_{00} = P_0 L P_0$, $L_{0c} = P_0 L P_c$ and so on, we obtain for ρ_0 and ρ_c the coupled Liouville equations

统基本上具有连续能谱，所以可以忽略棘手的"粗粒化"问题。此外，关于时间的密度算符的渐近极限虽然在原子尺度上非常大，但仍然有限，可以直接讨论。讨论的结果[2]是：或许可以将系统的时间演化严格地分成形式上独立的"子动力学"部分，以目前的解释方式（也就是采用取决于系统组成元素之间关联性的特定投影算符）来表征。下文中式(7)给出的投影算符 $\tilde{\Pi}$ 的其中一个子动力学即可包含关于平衡性质和线性输运性质的所有信息。因此，我们可以将宏观层次的量子力学描述定义为基于 $\tilde{\Pi}$ 子空间变量的约化描述。这一约化描述有可能恰好是源于以下事实：$\tilde{\Pi}$ 子动力学是由一个独立的演化方程来表示的。将这种分析方法应用于一测量装置，该装置初始时通过原子寿命与原子物体之间的相互作用而触发。结果出人意料地表明：它在 $\tilde{\Pi}$ 空间中的演化遵循量子力学的"约化"规则；这一重要结论是由该装置 $\tilde{\Pi}$ 子空间的数学结构直接得出的，它消除了原子物体密度算符各分量之间的初始相位关系。在本文中我们叙述了以一种简单而通用的方式推导出上述不寻常结论的过程，由此可以更清晰地表明：这些方法如何能不仅使我们更深刻地理解原子理论中的认识论问题，甚至还能显著拓展量子力学的范围。

定义希尔伯特空间与其对偶空间的直积为超空间，其中的密度算符 $\rho(t)$ 表现为超矢量，它按照以下形式的刘维尔方程随时间变化：

$$i\dot{\rho}(t)=L\rho(t)$$

刘维尔超算符 L 可以用系统的哈密顿量 H 表示。为此，根据定义 $O\rho=M\rho N$，我们可以用简便的符号来表示取决于一对超矢量 M、N 的一类特殊的"可分解"超算符 $O\equiv M\times N$；然后，我们可以得到 $L=H\times1-1\times H$。我们的目的是要找出关联性造成的长时效应，首先我们必须将我们的由哈密顿量 H 描述的系统与由 H_0 描述的"模型"系统进行比较。在"模型"系统中，与关联性有关的相互作用能 V 被去掉，它们的关系可以由 $H=H_0+V$ 表示。H_0 的本征态在希尔伯特空间中形成了表象的一组完备正交基，据此，我们在超空间中构造一组类似的基矢；后者可以被分为两类超矢量——由成对的全等（或物理上等效的）本征态构成的超矢量和由成对的不同本征态构成的超矢量；它们分别属于超空间中的两个正交子空间，可用投影超算符 P_0 和 P_c 来表征。因此，密度超矢量的投影算符 $\rho_0=P_0\rho$ 和 $\rho_c=P_c\rho$ 分别对应于平均分布密度和关联的振幅。取 $L_{00}=P_0LP_0$，$L_{0c}=P_0LP_c$ 等等，我们可以得到关于 ρ_0 和 ρ_c 的耦合刘维尔方程：

$$i\dot{\rho}_0 = L_{00}\rho_0 + L_{0c}\rho_c, \quad i\dot{\rho}_c = L_{cc}\rho_c + L_{c0}\rho_0 \tag{1}$$

The next step is to extract from these equations the asymptotic forms $\tilde{\rho}_0(t)$, $\tilde{\rho}_c(t)$ of ρ_0 and ρ_c for large positive values of the time variable: these are expected to express our possibilities of prediction of the future evolution of the system on the macroscopic time scale.

We must here restrict the generality of the Liouville superoperator in order to characterize the class of systems which we expect to exhibit the "normal" asymptotic behaviour, that is an approach to a state of equilibrium. To this end, we observe that the time evolution of the correlation density ρ_c is essentially governed by the superoperator $T_c = \exp(-iL_{cc}t)$, depending on the part of the Liouville superoperator which acts entirely in the correlation subspace. We assume accordingly that the asymptotic effect of this superoperator $T_c(t)$ upon any regular supervector A which is not an invariant is to reduce this supervector to zero: $\lim_{t\to\infty} T_c(t)A = 0$; we express by this assumption the fading of the system's "memory" of its correlations. This condition, which may also be expressed as an analyticity condition on the Laplace transform of $T_c(t)$, has first been verified in this form by a perturbation expansion, for infinite systems in whose description there enters a "small" physical parameter such as the coupling constant or the density[3]. More recently, it has been shown that for soluble models, such as the Friedrichs model, the analyticity assumption is satisfied rigorously (that is, independently of any perturbative approach) for a large class of interactions[4]. By means of this assumption, we readily derive from the second Liouville equation (1) the following relation between the asymptotic densities:

$$\tilde{\rho}_c(t) = \int_0^\infty d\tau\, e^{-iL_{cc}\tau} (-i\, L_{c0})\, \tilde{\rho}_0(t-\tau) \tag{2}$$

It has the form of an integral equation, showing how the asymptotic correlations build up by sequences of processes starting from the average situations through which the system passes in the course of time.

We now introduce an asymptotic time evolution operator by writing $\tilde{\rho}_0(t)$ in the form

$$\tilde{\rho}_0(t) = e^{-i\theta t}\, \tilde{\rho}_0(0) \tag{3}$$

The advantage of the representation (3) is to reduce the integral equation (2) to a simple linear relation between $\tilde{\rho}_0(t)$ and $\tilde{\rho}_c(t)$ taken at the same time:

$$\tilde{\rho}_c(t) = C\tilde{\rho}_0(t), \quad C = C(\theta) = \int_0^\infty d\tau\, e^{-iL_{cc}\tau} (-iL_{c0})\, e^{i\theta\tau} \tag{4}$$

The first Liouville equation (1) then yields a functional equation for θ:

$$\theta = L_{00} + L_{0c}\, C(\theta) \tag{5}$$

which can be solved by iteration.

1052

$$i\rho_0 = L_{00}\rho_0 + L_{0c}\rho_c, \quad i\rho_c = L_{cc}\rho_c + L_{c0}\rho_0 \tag{1}$$

下一步，从这些方程中求出当时间变量取很大正值时 ρ_0 和 ρ_c 的渐近形式 $\rho_0(t)$ 和 $\rho_c(t)$：由此我们期望能够在宏观时间尺度上预见系统未来的演变。

为了表征我们期望会出现"正常"渐近行为的那一类系统，也即趋近于平衡态的系统，我们在此必须限制刘维尔超算符的通用性。为此，我们发现关联密度 ρ_c 的时间演化实质上是由超算符 $T_c = \exp(-iL_{cc}t)$ 决定的，该超算符与刘维尔超算符中在关联子空间内完全作用的那一部分有关。因此我们假定，超算符 $T_c(t)$ 对任何正则的变化超矢量 A 的渐近作用是将这个超矢量减小到零：$\lim_{t\to\infty} T_c(t)A = 0$；我们通过这个假定来表示系统对其关联性的"记忆"的衰减。这一条件也可表示为对 $T_c(t)$ 进行拉普拉斯变换的解析条件。在那些可以引入一个诸如耦合常数或密度等"小"物理参数来表示的无限系统中，利用微扰展开，人们已经首次证实该条件确实是这样的形式 [3]。最近有人指出：对于可解模型，例如弗里德里克斯模型，有一大类相互作用是严格满足解析性假定的（即独立于任何微扰方法)[4]。根据上述假设，我们很容易从刘维尔方程 (1) 中的第二个式子导出渐近密度之间的下述关系：

$$\tilde{\rho}_c(t) = \int_0^\infty d\tau\, e^{-iL_{cc}\tau} (-i L_{c0})\, \tilde{\rho}_0(t-\tau) \tag{2}$$

上式具有积分方程的形式，由此可以说明系统的渐近关系是怎样通过以系统在一段时间内的平均状态为起始的一系列过程而建立的。

现在我们通过 $\tilde{\rho}_0(t)$ 的下述表达式来引入渐近时间演化算符：

$$\tilde{\rho}_0(t) = e^{-i\theta t}\, \tilde{\rho}_0(0) \tag{3}$$

表达式 (3) 的优点是可将积分方程 (2) 简化为时间取相同值时 $\tilde{\rho}_0(t)$ 与 $\rho_c(t)$ 之间的一种简单线性关系：

$$\tilde{\rho}_c(t) = C\tilde{\rho}_0(t),\ C = C(\theta) = \int_0^\infty d\tau\, e^{-iL_{cc}\tau} (-iL_{c0})\, e^{i\theta\tau} \tag{4}$$

因此，由刘维尔方程 (1) 中的第一个式子可以得到一个关于 θ 的函数方程：

$$\theta = L_{00} + L_{0c}\, C(\theta) \tag{5}$$

该式可用迭代法求解。

The total asymptotic density $\rho = \rho_0 + \rho_c$ thus obtained has the remarkable property of being an exact solution of the Liouville equation. According to equation (4), it may be written in the form $\rho = P_a\rho$, with $P_a = P_0 + C$. It is again remarkable that this superoperator P_a has the characteristic properties of a projection operator in superspace, idempotency and "adjoint symmetry" (that is, it is such that the projection P_aA of a self-adjoint supervector A is self-adjoint). The projector P_a defines a subspace in which the asymptotic density is confined. This subspace differs from the average subspace P_0 by the adjunction of a part of the correlation subspace P_c, namely that part which is specified by the superoperator C; the latter may be interpreted as representing the building up of correlations from asymptotic average situations (we call it the superoperator of correlation creation)—it sorts out those correlation processes which have a long time effect and accordingly manifest themselves at the macroscopic level. Thus, the asymptotic density $\tilde{\rho}$ is not, as one might have expected, governed by a "kinetic equation" different from the dynamical Liouville equation: it is an exact solution of the latter, and its asymptotic character is conferred upon it by its confinement to a subspace defined by the projector P_a.

The expression for the superoperator of correlation creation C, which enters in the definition of P_a, is clearly unsymmetrical in time, and gives the projector P_a the expected bias towards a preferred direction of the time evolution. In fact, time inversion transforms P_a into a different projector $\tilde{P}_a = P_0 + D$, where the superoperator

$$D = \int_0^\infty d\tau\ e^{i\eta\tau}(-iL_{0c})\ e^{-iL_{cc}\tau}$$

is the time-inverse of C; it contains the superoperator η which is the time-inverse of θ and obeys the equation $\eta = L_{00} + DL_{c0}$ derived from equation (5) by time-inversion. In contrast to C, the superoperator D describes sequences of "destructions" of correlations leading to asymptotic average situations.

An important element is still missing in the picture: we must establish a link between the asymptotic density supervector $\tilde{\rho}(t)$ and the arbitrarily chosen dynamical density supervector $\rho(0)$ from which the time-evolution is assumed to start. This is readily supplied, however, on the basis of a further remarkable property (easily derived) of the superoperator θ and its time-inverse η:

$$P_a\theta = LP_a, \quad \eta\tilde{P}_a = \tilde{P}_aL \tag{6}$$

With the notation $N_0 = 1 + DC$, it follows from equations (6) and (3) that

$$N_0\ \tilde{\rho}_0(t) = N_0\ e^{-i\theta t}\tilde{\rho}_0(0) = e^{-i\eta t}\ N_0\ \tilde{\rho}_0(0)$$

and, on the other hand,

$$\tilde{P}_a\rho(t) = \tilde{P}_a e^{-iLt}\ \rho(0) = e^{-i\eta t}\tilde{P}_a\rho(0)$$

由此得到的总渐近密度 $\rho=\rho_0+\rho_c$ 具有不同寻常的性质——它是刘维尔方程的一个精确解。根据式 (4)，可以将其改写成 $\rho=P_a\rho$ 的形式，其中 $P_a=P_0+C$。超算符 P_a 在超空间中具有投影算符的特性、幂等性和"伴随对称性"（即，自伴超矢量 A 的投影 P_aA 也是自伴的），这些同样不同寻常。投影算符 P_a 定义了一个渐近密度有限的子空间。这个子空间与平均子空间 P_0 之间的差别在于叠加了关联子空间 P_c 的一部分，即由超算符 C 确定的那部分；可以把后者解释为代表了在渐近平均情况下的关联建立（我们称之为关联产生超算符）——它可以区分出那些具有长时效应并因此在宏观层次上有所显现的关联过程。因此，渐近密度 $\tilde{\rho}$ 并非如预期的那样，是由不同于刘维尔动力学方程的"动力学方程"决定的：它是刘维尔动力学方程的一个精确解，其渐近特性是通过被限制在由投影算符 P_a 定义的子空间中而得到的。

在 P_a 的定义中引入了由关联产生的超算符 C 的表达式，该表达式在时间上显然是非对称的，它使投影算符 P_a 向时间演化的择优方向发生了预期的偏移。实际上，时间反演将 P_a 变换成了另一个投影算符 $\tilde{P}_a=P_0+D$，其中超算符

$$D=\int_0^\infty d\tau\ e^{i\eta\tau}(-iL_{0c})\ e^{-iL_{cc}\tau}$$

是 C 的时间逆；它含有 θ 的时间逆——超算符 η，并且满足将式 (5) 进行时间反演而推导出的表达式 $\eta=L_{00}+DL_{c0}$。与 C 不同，超算符 D 描述的是导致出现渐近平均状态的关联"相消"序列。

在此图景中仍然缺少了一个重要的元素：我们必须在渐近的密度超矢量 $\tilde{\rho}(t)$ 与任意选取的动态密度超矢量 $\rho(0)$ 之间建立起联系，其中 $\rho(0)$ 被假定为时间演化的起始点。这一点很容易实现，但要以超算符 θ 及其时间逆 η 的一个更为不同寻常的性质（容易推导出）为基础：

$$P_a\theta=LP_a,\quad \eta\bar{P}_a=\bar{P}_aL \tag{6}$$

记 $N_0=1+DC$，由式 (6) 和式 (3) 可得：

$$N_0\tilde{\rho}_0(t)=N_0\ e^{-i\theta t}\tilde{\rho}_0(0)=e^{-i\eta t}\ N_0\tilde{\rho}_0(0)$$

而另一方面：

$$\bar{P}_a\rho(t)=\bar{P}_a\ e^{-iLt}\ \rho(0)=e^{-i\eta t}\ \bar{P}_a\rho(0)$$

This shows that $N_0\widetilde{\rho}_0(t)$ and $P_a\overline{\rho}(t)$ have the same time-evolution, governed by the superoperator $\exp(-i\eta t)$: we may therefore equate them at any instant and in this way fix the correspondence between the dynamical and the asymptotic density. This gives the quite fundamental relation, valid at any time,

$$\widetilde{\rho}(t) = \widetilde{\Pi}\rho(t) \text{ with } \widetilde{\Pi} = P_a N_0^{-1}\overline{P}_a \tag{7}$$

from which follows

$$\widetilde{\rho}(t) = \widetilde{\Sigma}(t)\,\rho(0) \text{ with } \widetilde{\Sigma}(t) = \widetilde{\Pi}e^{-iLt}$$

the answer to our last question, completing the theory.

The striking feature about the superoperator $\widetilde{\Pi}$ occurring in equation (7) is that it is also a projector in the extended sense defined above (which does not include the property of self-adjointness); moreover, it is time-reversal invariant: it defines a time-symmetrical subspace of the superspace in which the asymptotic part of the time-evolution, starting from any given situation, remains confined, exhibiting the features observed at the macroscopic level; whereas the irregular fluctuations occurring on the atomic time scale are contained in the complementary subspace orthogonal to the asymptotic one. That such a clean separation between the two aspects of the atomic system could be effected is an entirely unexpected property specific to the density supervector representation: it could never have been found by a study of the evolution of the system in Hilbert space, for it can only be formulated in terms of the superspace formalism.

The superoperator $\widetilde{\Pi}$ is not factorizable: one cannot ascribe any state vector to an asymptotic situation as we have defined it, but only a density supervector $\widetilde{\rho}$. In fact, as appears from equation (4), the correlation part $\widetilde{\rho}_c$ of the density ρ is directly derived from the part $\widetilde{\rho}_0$ expressing the average probability distributions of the system; owing to this remarkable structure of the projector $\widetilde{\Pi}$, the evolution in $\widetilde{\Pi}$-space may be entirely described in terms of probabilities only. In particular, the "reduction of the wave-packet" of an atomic system after its interaction with a measuring apparatus is a direct consequence of this property of the $\widetilde{\Pi}$-space description: the essential point being that the apparatus must necessarily belong to the macroscopic level of quantum mechanics, and that its behaviour must accordingly be described in terms of its $\widetilde{\Pi}$-space variables (loosely speaking, the behaviour of the apparatus has "thermodynamical" character, inasmuch as variables pertaining to thermodynamic equilibrium or near-equilibrium states all belong to $\widetilde{\Pi}$-space). Any phase relations in the initial state of the atomic system are therefore wiped out (that is, they are rejected into the orthogonal subspace): this is the only meaning of the "reduction" of the initial state of the atomic system resulting from the measurement. As to the human observer, his interaction with the apparatus is also entirely described in the $\widetilde{\Pi}$-subspace, and therefore without any influence whatsoever on whatever goes on in the orthogonal subspace.

这表明 $N_0\tilde{\rho}_0(t)$ 和 $P_a\tilde{\rho}(t)$ 的时间演化相同，均由超算符 $\exp(-i\eta t)$ 决定：因此，我们可在任意时刻令二者相等，由此得到动态密度与渐近密度之间的对应关系。这样就给出了一个非常基本的关系，并且在任意时刻均成立：

$$\tilde{\rho}(t) = \tilde{\Pi}\rho(t) \quad 式中 \quad \tilde{\Pi} = P_a N_0^{-1} \bar{P}_a \tag{7}$$

由此可得：

$$\tilde{\rho}(t) = \tilde{\sum}(t)\,\rho(0) \quad 式中 \quad \tilde{\sum}(t) = \tilde{\Pi}e^{-iLt}$$

这就是最后一个问题的答案，整个理论完成。

式 (7) 中超算符 $\tilde{\Pi}$ 的显著特征是：根据上文中的定义，它也是一个意义扩展了（不包含自伴性质）的投影算符；此外，它在时间反演后保持不变：它定义了超空间中的一个时间对称的子空间，从任意给定的状态开始，该子空间中时间演化的渐近部分保持有限，表现出了在宏观尺度上所观测到的性质；而在原子时间尺度上出现的不规则涨落则被纳入与渐近子空间正交的互补子空间中。对于密度超矢量表象而言，能够实现原子系统两个方面之间的明确分离完全是一个出乎意料的特性：在希尔伯特空间中对系统演化进行研究是不可能得到这一结果的，因为只有通过超空间的形式才能阐释它。

超算符 $\tilde{\Pi}$ 是不可分解的：除密度超矢量 $\tilde{\rho}$ 外，不能将其他任何态矢量归于我们所定义的渐近状态。事实上，由式 (4) 可以看出：密度 ρ 的关联部分 $\tilde{\rho}_c$ 是从表征系统平均几率分布的 $\tilde{\rho}_0$ 部分直接推导出来的；由于投影算符 $\tilde{\Pi}$ 的这种特殊结构，有可能仅用几率就能完全描述 $\tilde{\Pi}$ 空间中的演化。特别地，原子系统与测量装置发生相互作用之后的"波包坍缩"正是 $\tilde{\Pi}$ 空间描述的这一性质的直接结果：最关键的一点是，测量装置必须属于量子力学的宏观层次，于是它的行为必须通过它在 $\tilde{\Pi}$ 空间中的变量来描述（大体来说，因为与热力学平衡态或近平衡态有关的变量都属于 $\tilde{\Pi}$ 空间，所以测量装置的行为具有"热力学"的特征）。因此，我们可以去掉原子系统初态中的所有相位关系（即，使它们退化到正交子空间）：这就是原子系统的初态经测量后"坍缩"的唯一内涵。至于人类观测者，他与装置之间的相互作用也在 $\tilde{\Pi}$ 子空间中得到了完整的描述，因而他对正交子空间中发生的一切不会造成任何影响。

One further point should be mentioned. The theory gives us a simple criterion to decide whether the system shows the normal macroscopic behaviour described by thermodynamics. The superoperator of asymptotic time-evolution θ is closely related to a "collision superoperator" defined as the Laplace transform of the superoperator $L_{0c} T_c(\tau) L_{c0}$:

$$\Psi(z) = \int\limits_0^\infty d\tau\, L_{0c}\, T_c(\tau) L_{c0} e^{-z\tau}$$

Indeed, equation (5) may be written as a functional relation in terms of $\Psi(z)$:

$$i\theta = iL_{00} + \Psi(-i\theta) \tag{8}$$

Now, an homogeneous system (a system for which $L_{00}=0$) will obviously not exhibit any tendency towards equilibrium if the collision operator vanishes identically. Equation (8) then shows that it will exhibit an irreversible tendency towards equilibrium provided that θ itself does not vanish identically. This "condition of dissipativity" is a practical one: it can be tested in concrete cases[4] by actual computation of θ.

It is thus clear that the epistemological consistency problem raised at the beginning of this note is completely answered by the neat, clear-cut representation we obtain for the complementarity between the two levels of description of atomic phenomena. It need hardly be pointed out that the problem here discussed of the macroscopic level of quantum mechanics is just a simple illustration of a general method of representation in superspace, which actually amounts to an extension of the scope of quantum mechanics. Perhaps the most significant feature of the method is the introduction of generalized projectors, involving the replacement of self-adjointness by time-inversion invariance (which reduces to the former in the absence of dissipation, that is, for systems for which the collision operator vanishes)—a generalization which may be expected to find application to a large variety of problems.

(**240**, 25-27; 1972)

C. George and I. Prigogine: Université Libre, Brussels, and Center for Statistical Mechanics and Thermodynamics, Austin, Texas.
L. Rosenfeld: Nordita, Copenhagen.

Received January 28; revised March 20, 1972.

References:
1. George, C., Prigogine, I., and Rosenfeld, L., *Det kgl. Danske Videnskabernes Selskab, mat.-fys. Meddelelser*, **38**, 12 (1972).
2. Prigogine, I., George, C., and Henin, F., *Physica*, **45**, 418 (1969).
3. Balescu, R., and Brenig, L., *Physica*, **54**, 504 (1971).
4. Prigogine, I., *Non-Equilibrium Statistical Mechanics* (Interscience, 1962).
5. Grecos, A., and Prigogine, I., *Physica*, **59**, 77 (1972).
6. Grews, A., and Prigogine, I., *Proc. US Nat. Acad. Sci.*, **69**, 1629 (1972).

另有一点值得一提。上述理论给我们提供了一条简单的标准，用以判断系统是否表现出由热力学所描述的标准宏观行为。渐近时间演化超算符 θ 与由超算符 $L_{0c}T_c(\tau)\,L_{c0}$ 的拉普拉斯变换而定义的"碰撞超算符"之间有密切的关系：

$$\Psi(z) = \int_0^\infty d\tau\, L_{0c}\, T_c(\tau) L_{c0} e^{-z\tau}$$

实际上，式 (5) 可改写成含有 $\Psi(z)$ 的泛函关系式：

$$i\theta = iL_{00} + \Psi(-i\theta) \tag{8}$$

于是，当碰撞算符为零时，一个均匀系统（$L_{00}=0$ 的系统）显然不会有任何趋于平衡的表现。由式 (8) 可知：如果 θ 本身没有同时趋于零，则系统将不可逆地趋向平衡。这种"耗散条件"是实际存在的：在具体情况下 [4]，通过实际计算 θ 值可验证这一点。

由此可见，我们为得到对原子现象两种层次描述之间的互补性而采用的这种简洁、明晰的表象彻底解决了本文开篇处提出的认识论一致性的问题。不言自明的是，此处讨论的宏观层次量子力学问题仅仅是超空间表象这一通用方法的一个简单演示，它实际上拓展了量子力学的范畴。上述方法最为重要的特征或许是引入了广义投影算符，包含用时间反演不变性替换自伴性（对于碰撞算符为零的系统，在无耗散时前者可约化为后者）——可以预期这种推广将在大量问题中得到应用。

（沈乃澂 黄娆 翻译；李军刚 审稿）

1059

Computer Analyses of Gravitational Radiation Detector Coincidences

J. Weber

Editor's Note

Within the context of general relativity, gravitational radiation is expected to come from massive and compact objects such as neutron stars and black holes. Joseph Weber designed and built two antenna systems for detecting gravitational radiation, separated by about 1,000 km. Here he analyses signals obtained from them, and finds coincidences in detection that he interprets as evidence for gravitational waves passing through the instruments. The claim is now known to be wrong, but the paper helped to launch the field of gravitational-wave detection. Indirect evidence for gravitational radiation was later seen in observations of the orbit of a millisecond pulsar, but a direct detection remains to be achieved.

MY earlier publications[1] have reported the concept, theory, and development of an antenna to detect gravitational radiation. These antennae are well isolated from the local environment by acoustic and electromagnetic shielding but they do respond to sufficiently large local disturbances. Effects of the local environments can, however, be minimized when two detectors are used which are a considerable distance apart. For this reason coincidence experiments at 1,661 Hz were carried out with two antennae, one situated at the University of Maryland and the other 1,000 km away at the Argonne National Laboratory.

For all experiments reported here the only coincidences which were recorded were those which occurred within a predetermined time Δt.

Coincidences may be due to excitation of both detectors by a common source or to chance. It is customary to compute the chance (accidental) coincidence rate by formulating a classification scheme for the coincidences and computing the number of chance coincidences in each class. A significant excess of detected event over the chance coincidence rate for a given class establishes with a certain level of confidence that not all coincidences are due to chance.

For two years the experiments were done as follows. The outputs of the Maryland and Argonne detectors are obtained from synchronous detectors which have free running crystal reference oscillators and twin channels with the reference shifted by $\pi/2$ in one of them. The two channel outputs are squared and summed to recover the power, with a time constant of 0.5 s. The envelope of the total power output of the Argonne detector was transmitted over a telephone line to Maryland, in coded digital form, and reconverted

引力辐射探测器符合计数的计算机分析

韦伯

编者按

广义相对论认为引力辐射来自于大而重的致密物体，如中子星和黑洞。约瑟夫·韦伯设计并搭建了相距约 1,000 千米的两个天线系统来探测引力辐射。在这篇文章中，他分析了由这些天线系统得到的信号，并在探测中发现了符合事件，他认为这些符合事件是引力波穿过实验装置的证据。现在我们知道他的这种论断是错误的，但是这篇论文帮助人们开创了引力波探测的领域。之后，人们在对一个毫秒脉冲星轨道的观测中发现了引力辐射的间接证据，但直接探测还有待实现。

我已经在之前发表的文章 [1] 中陈述过探测引力辐射的天线的概念、理论和研制。这些天线通过声屏蔽和电磁屏蔽与局部环境充分隔离，但仍然会对足够大的局部扰动产生响应。不过，使用相距很远的两个探测器可以将局部环境的影响降到最低。因此我们使用两个天线在 1,661 赫兹频率上进行了符合计数实验，其中一个天线位于马里兰大学，另一个则位于 1,000 千米之外的阿贡国家实验室。

在本文报告的所有实验中，被记录的符合事件都发生在事先确定的时间间隔 Δt 中。

符合事件可能是因为一个共同的源激发两个探测器而引起的，也可能是偶然产生的。制定一个符合事件的分级方案并计算每个等级中的偶然符合数目，是计算偶然符合计数率的通常做法。对一个给定等级来说，如果探测到的符合事件明显超出该等级的偶然符合计数率，就表明在一定置信水平上，并非所有的符合计数都是偶然产生的。

两年时间的实验开展情况如下。马里兰和阿贡探测器的输出由同步探测器获得，该同步探测器装备了自由运转的晶体参考振荡器，并具有双通道，其中一个的参考相位移动了 $\pi/2$。设定时间常数为 0.5 秒，可将两个通道的输出求平方和来得到原先的功率。通过电话线将阿贡探测器的总功率输出包络以数字编码形式传递到马里兰，并在马里兰将其转换回模拟直流信号。输出信号由一个符合探测器接收。在时间间

to analogue d.c. at Maryland. The outputs are fed to a coincidence detector. If both channels cross some preset threshold from below, within the time interval Δt, a pulse is emitted to drive a recorder marker pen.

The amplitudes of the noise pulses have a Rayleigh distribution, and their shapes vary widely. Analysis is simplified if all pulses have roughly the same shape, because then one parameter, the pulse height, will suffice for their classification. To shape the pulses properly a second stage of filtering is carried out after coincidence detection. There is a small amount of additional filtering associated with the mass of the pen which records the output on a chart.

A mean solar day is chosen as the unit of time. Consider a given coincidence with power amplitudes P_A and P_B for the two channels. Let N_A and N_B represent the number of times per day that the powers P_A and P_B are equalled or exceeded, on the average. Let Δt be the maximum time between threshold crossings for the two channels in order to record a coincidence. The expected number of chance coincides with amplitudes equal to or exceeding those observed for an experiment with effective duration M days is η_{AB} with

$$\eta_{AB} = 2N_A N_B \Delta t M \tag{1}$$

To employ equation (1) we select some arbitrary numbers which may or may not be the same for channels A and B. A given class consists of all those coincidences for which N_A and N_B each are equal to or less than the arbitrarily selected numbers for them.

A second classification scheme was employed in order to determine if the difference between the observed and chance coincidences is sensitive to details of the statistical methods. Instead of requiring N_A and N_B each to remain within certain bounds for a given class, we require the product $N_A N_B$ to be equal to or less than some arbitrary number for a given class. The total number of such chance coincidences will be finite because neither N_A nor N_B can ever be less than one or greater than the total number of pulses observed for each channel. The most useful classifications are those for which N_A and N_B are less than some number N_S which is about an order greater than the numbers which characterize most of the real coincidences classified by equation (1).

A two dimensional space with N_A and N_B as coordinates is useful to calculate the number of chance coincidences $\tilde{\eta}_{AB}$ for which the product $N_A N_B$ is equal to or smaller than some constant and for which neither N_A nor N_B exceeds some maximum value N_S. $\tilde{\eta}_{AB}$ is expression (1) plus the integral under the hyperbola $N_A N_B$=constant, that is

$$\tilde{\eta}_{AB} = 2N_A N_B \Delta t M \left[1 + \ln(N_S^2 / N_A N_B)\right] \tag{2}$$

In equations (1) and (2) M is smaller than the actual number of days which the experiments run, because allowance must be made for the detector relaxation time after crossing the threshold. A new coincidence cannot occur during this time.

隔 Δt 内，如果两个通道的信号都上升至超过事先设定的阈值，就会发出一个脉冲来驱动记录仪的记号笔。

噪声脉冲的幅值符合瑞利分布，且其形状变化很大。如果所有脉冲的形状都大致相同，分析将得以简化，因为这时只需使用脉冲高度这一个参数就能够对它们进行分级。对脉冲的适当整形需要在符合计数检测后再进行第二级过滤。此外还存在少量附加滤波，它们与在图纸上记录输出的记号笔的质量有关。

选择平均太阳日作为时间单位。考虑功率幅值分别为 P_A 和 P_B 的两个通道的给定符合计数。令 N_A 和 N_B 代表每天功率值达到或者超过 P_A 和 P_B 的平均次数，Δt 代表：为了记录到一次符合计数，两个通道越过功率阈值的最大时间间隔。在有效实验时间 M 天的观测中，功率幅值达到或者超过规定值的偶然符合的预期次数 η_{AB} 为：

$$\eta_{AB} = 2N_A N_B \Delta t M \tag{1}$$

为了利用公式（1），我们任意选择了一些数值，这些数值对通道 A 和 B 来说可能相同，也可能不相同。一个给定的等级包含所有满足下述条件的符合计数，即 N_A 和 N_B 都等于或者小于那些针对它们任意选择的数值。

为了确定观测到的符合计数和偶然符合计数的差值是否对统计方法的细节敏感，我们采用了另一种分级方案。我们不限定 N_A 和 N_B 每一个都必须处在给定的等级区间中，而是要求它们的乘积 $N_A N_B$ 等于或者小于为某一给定等级设定的任意值。因为不管是 N_A 还是 N_B 都不能小于 1，也不能大于在每个通道观测到的总脉冲数量，所以这样的偶然符合的总数目是有限的。最有用的等级是那些 N_A 和 N_B 小于某个数值 N_S 的，这个 N_S 比按照公式（1）进行分级的大多数代表真正符合计数的数目约大一个数量级。

考虑一个以 N_A 和 N_B 为坐标的二维空间，它有助于计算乘积 $N_A N_B$ 等于或者小于某个常数并且 N_A 和 N_B 都不超过某个最大值 N_S 的偶然符合的数目 $\tilde{\eta}_{AB}$。$\tilde{\eta}_{AB}$ 等于公式（1）加上双曲线 $N_A N_B =$ 常数下的积分，即

$$\tilde{\eta}_{AB} = 2N_A N_B \Delta t M \, [1+\ln(N_S^2/N_A N_B)] \tag{2}$$

公式（1）和（2）中的 M 小于实验运行的实际天数，这是因为必须考虑越过阈值后探测器的弛豫时间，在这段时间内不会出现新的符合计数。

Early experiments[5,6] observed that the number of coincidences for certain values of N_A, N_B, N_AN_B substantially exceeded the accidental rate computed from equations (1) and (2). These gave about the same numbers for the difference of the observed and chance coincidences. The conclusion that positive results are obtained is based on certain assumptions—for example that the classification scheme based on amplitude alone with the successive filtering is sound. To test this, a parallel experiment was done to measure the accidental rate by inserting time delays of varying length in one channel or the other.

This time delay experiment showed a large decrease in the number of coincidences for which N_A, $N_B \leq 100$; and also those coincidences for which $N_AN_B \leq 6,000$ with $N_S \leq 1,000$ for all time delays significantly larger than Δt. There is a subjective element in the data processing, in that for each coincidence mark the leading edge of the pulse must be examined. If it increases smoothly to a peak then the peak value is the required amplitude. If there is a discontinuity in slope before reaching the peak it is concluded that the excitation which results in a threshold crossing was followed at the discontinuity by a heat bath noise excitation. The required pulse height is then only the value measured to the point of discontinuity. Sometimes the discontinuity is not well defined and a human decision is needed.

Using a magnetic tape and a computer provides an independent procedure for data processing. The human element is only involved in the program preparation. A variety of thresholds and time delays can be applied to any stretch of data. The synchronous detector output with 0.5 s filter time constant was recorded in digital form every 0.1 s with both channels on one tape. A computer program was prepared by Mr. Brian K. Reid in the following way: thresholds were set such that if both channels crossed from below within 0.5 s the computer measured the pulse heights after a second stage of 5 s time constant filtering and a third stage of filtering with 0.5 s time constant to simulate the ink recorder pen. Then the computer counted the number of times the filtered data amplitude was equalled or exceeded for the previous hour, the previous 6 h, and the given day following the schematic diagram in Fig. 2. The same procedure was repeated for time delays of 1 s, 2 s, 5 s, 10 s, 20 s and 40 s.

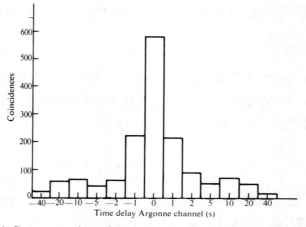

Fig. 1. Computer analyses of magnetic tapes, October 1970–February 1971.

由早期的一些实验[5,6]发现：对于特定的 N_A、N_B、N_AN_B 值，符合计数的数目大大超过了由公式（1）和（2）计算得到的偶然符合计数率。这些实验给出的符合计数观测值和偶然符合计数的差值大致相同。认为能够获得肯定性结果的结论建立在某些假设的基础之上——例如，假设单纯基于幅值然后再过滤的分级方案是合理的。为了检验这个假设，我们进行了一项对照实验，通过在一个或者另一个通道中加入不同长度的时间延迟来测量偶然符合计数率。

这个时间延迟实验显示，在时间延迟显著大于 Δt 的情况下：当 N_A、$N_B \leq 100$ 时，符合计数的数目大大降低；当 $N_AN_B \leq 6,000$ 且 $N_S \leq 1,000$ 时，符合计数的数目也大大降低。数据处理中的一个主观因素在于，标记每个符合计数时都必须检查脉冲的前沿。如果它平滑地上升到峰顶，那么这个峰值就是所需的幅值。如果在到达峰顶前的上坡中间有一个间断点，我们就认为：导致超越阈值的激发之后，在间断点处紧跟着一个热库噪声激发。这样所需的脉冲高度就只能是间断点处的值。有时候这个间断不是很明显，需要人为主观判断。

磁带和计算机的应用提供了一个独立的数据处理程序。只有在程序准备的过程中会牵涉到人为因素。可以对任何一部分数据应用不同的阈值和时间延迟。设过滤时间常数为 0.5 秒，同步探测器两个通道的输出都以数字形式每隔 0.1 秒记录到同一个磁带上。布赖恩·里德先生准备了一个计算机程序，情况如下：设定好阈值，一旦两个通道在 0.5 秒的时间范围内都上升超过阈值，计算机就会在第二级时间常数为 5 秒的过滤以及第三级时间常数为 0.5 秒的过滤之后模仿记录笔来测量脉冲高度。接下来计算机按照图 2 所示的流程计算出前 1 小时、前 6 小时以及某一天之内过滤后的数据幅值达到或者超过阈值的次数。对 1 秒、2 秒、5 秒、10 秒、20 秒和 40 秒的时间延迟，也重复运行同样的程序。

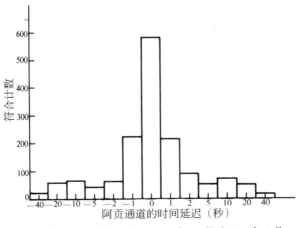

图 1. 磁带数据的计算机分析，1970 年 10 月至 1971 年 2 月。

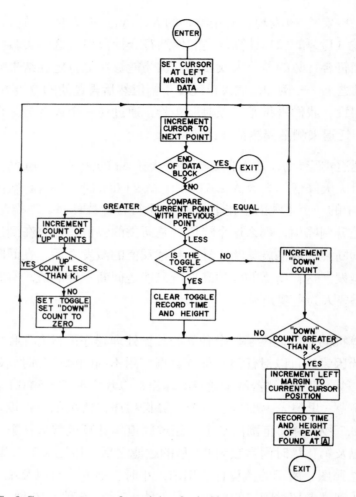

Fig. 2. Computer program for statistics of coincidences recorded on magnetic tape.

The program was inaccurate beyond 20 s delay and the bin values given in Fig. 1 for 40 s delay are much too small. A subsequent computer program has verified that there is no further decrease in the chance coincidence rate for delays exceeding 100 times the coincidence window.

The pen and ink records show pulses with relatively smooth leading edges. The greater time resolution of magnetic tape results in pulses with a certain roughness everywhere. It is therefore difficult to prepare a program which measures the pulse height to a point of discontinuity in leading edge slope. The computer defines the peak as the point where a trend of increases is followed by a trend of decreases. Detailed study of greatly expanded pulses indicates that this is a sound procedure for most of the coincidences. Because of the 5 s averaging it is expected that the pulse peak will be reached between 2 and 15 s after the threshold is crossed and only those coincidences are recorded which reach peaks within such an interval. This range of values is required because of noise and the initial

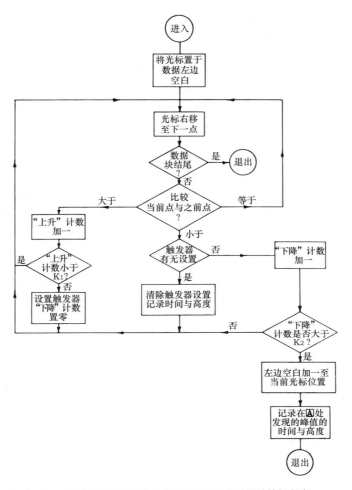

图 2. 用于对磁带上记录的符合计数进行统计的计算机程序。

    这个程序对 20 秒以上的延迟不是很精确。图 1 中 40 秒延迟的柱高的数值太小了。随后的一个计算机程序证实：对于超过符合时间窗 100 倍以上的延迟，偶然符合计数率并没有进一步的降低。

    笔墨记录的脉冲前沿比较平滑。磁带记录的时间分辨率较高，导致脉冲在各点处都有点粗糙。因此很难用一个程序去测量到前沿上坡间断点处的脉冲高度。计算机对峰顶的定义是从上升走向变为下降走向的转折点。对大大扩展的脉冲进行的详细研究显示：对绝大多数符合计数，这一定义是合理的。由于平均时间为 5 秒，一般预期在超越阈值后 2 秒到 15 秒之间达到脉冲峰顶，也只有当峰顶出现在这一区间时，符合才会被记录。规定这一数值范围是因为考虑到了噪声和滤波电路的电容器的初始充电情况。计算机也测量脉冲的面积，不过没有包括在统计分析中。

conditions of charge on the capacitors of the filter. The computer measures the area of the pulse, but this is not included in the statistical analysis.

A small fraction of the coincidences are not found by the program because no peak is found in the required interval following threshold crossing. Detailed plotting usually permits the peak to be identified within the required time after threshold crossing. Such coincidences are not included in these data in order to conserve computing time and costs.

Results are shown in Fig. 1 for all coincidences for which $N_A N_B \leq 10,000$ and $N_S \leq 1,000$. The low intensity coincidences are often counted more than once if threshold is crossed and re-crossed in the presence of noise. The histogram therefore shows about twice the real number of coincidences for the 120 day period covered by the tapes. All data of Fig. 1 came from the computer and not from human examination of printed lists.

It is significant that for delays in either channel as small as twice the coincidence interval Δt, the coincidence rate drops by a factor about 2.5. At delays of 20 s the coincidence rate is down by roughly a factor 10. These data, untouched by human hands, leave no doubt whatsoever that the gravitational radiation detectors, separated by 1,000 km, are being excited by a common source.

Before we can conclude from Fig. 1 that the source is gravitational radiation, it is essential to rule out other presently known interactions including seismic, electromagnetic, and cosmic ray effects.

The detectors are coupled to each other by the Earth and respond to sufficiently large seismic events. A number of seismometers were developed including a vertical axis accelerometer tuned to the detector frequency of 1,661 Hz, a three axis accelerometer covering frequencies near 100 Hz, and a two axis tilt meter. No significant correlations were observed between seismic activity and the coincidences.

Electromagnetic signals may enter the instrumentation through the vacuum chambers and through the cables and shields of the electronic equipment. Experiments were carried out to measure the susceptibility to electromagnetic excitation. It was found that 1,661 Hz magnetic fields of amplitude about 0.1 Gauss will excite the detector, and much larger fields at 830.5 Hz will also excite the detector. Non-linear effects are expected because the electromagnetic stress tensor is quadratic in the fields, and electromagnetic stresses can cause mechanical forces on the detector cylinders. The response is large at 1,661 Hz because the electronics has its acceptance band there and because 1,661 Hz currents in the aluminium cylinder give forces by interacting with the Earth's magnetic field.

Both laboratory sites are to some degree shielded as a result of grounded metal ceilings and structures around the apparatus. A radio receiver was employed at the Maryland site, with non-linear pre-amplifier and post-amplifier tuned to a narrow band of frequencies near 1,661 Hz. The receiver sensitivity could be adjusted to respond to fields much

由于在超越阈值后所要求的时间区间内未能发现峰顶，有一小部分符合计数没有被程序捕捉到。一般来说，通过详细的测绘可在超越阈值后所要求的时间内识别出这个峰顶。为了节约计算时间和成本，这样的符合计数没有被包括在这些数据中。

图 1 是 $N_A N_B \leq 10,000$ 且 $N_S \leq 1,000$ 的所有符合计数结果。当阈值被超越且由于噪声的存在而被再次超越时，低强度的符合经常被多次计数。因此，直方图给出的符合计数是磁带记录的 120 天内真实符合计数的两倍左右。图 1 中所有数据都来源于计算机，而不是对打印列表人工检验的结果。

值得注意的是：任一通道的时间延迟，尽管小到只有符合计数时间间隔 Δt 的两倍，也使得符合计数率下降到原来的 2/5。对 20 秒的延迟，符合计数率下降到原来的 1/10 左右。这些未经人工处理的数据毫无疑问地表明，相隔 1,000 千米的引力辐射探测器受到了同一个源的激发。

在我们根据图 1 确定这个源就是引力辐射之前，必须排除其他目前已知的干扰。这些干扰包括地震、电磁以及宇宙线的影响。

这些探测器通过地球互相耦合，会对足够大的地震事件产生响应。我们研制了许多台地震计，包括一台探测器频率被调到 1,661 赫兹的垂直轴加速度计、一台覆盖 100 赫兹左右频率的三轴加速度计以及一台二轴倾斜仪。在地震活动与符合计数之间没有发现显著的关联。

电磁信号可能会通过真空室或者电子设备的电缆及屏蔽物进入仪器。我们进行了一些实验来测量系统对电磁干扰的敏感度。结果发现强度约为 0.1 高斯的 1,661 赫兹磁场能够激发探测器。若为 830.5 赫兹，则要激发探测器所需的磁感应强度就要大得多。因为电磁应力张量是电磁场的二次型，并且电磁应力可以在探测器圆筒上产生机械力，所以这种非线性效应是可以预期的。1,661 赫兹处的响应很强是因为电子在那里有一个接收带，并且因为在铝制圆筒中 1,661 赫兹的电流通过与地磁场的相互作用而产生了力。

由于金属天花板和仪器周围的金属结构接地，两个实验站在某种程度上都是被屏蔽的。我们在马里兰站使用了一台无线电接收器，将其非线性前置放大器和后置放大器调频到 1,661 赫兹附近的窄波段。接收器的灵敏度可调，哪怕场强小到远远

smaller than those which excite the gravitational radiation detectors. Magnetic and electric dipole antennae were employed at different locations and with different orientations at various times. Local electromagnetic fields associated with air conditioning, magnetic tape recorders, and power line fluctuations limited the radio receiver sensitivity to values about three orders smaller than those to which the gravitational radiation detector responds. No significant correlations were observed with the gravitational radiation detector coincidences.

There is additional evidence that the coincidences are not due to electromagnetic or seismic interactions. The gravitational radiation detector system input temperature has been measured by a noise generator. This resulted in an accurate accounting of all significant signal sources and ruled out the possibility that any significant fraction of the input temperature is due to some background other than internal noise. If the coincidences are caused by terrestrial effects such as seismic and electromagnetic activity, these must give signals arriving simultaneously or nearly simultaneously at both sites from a region on or within the Earth. For each coincident arrival at the two locations, however, there must be many individual arrivals, and these would result in a higher system noise level than is observed. Measurements were also carried out of coincidence rates for a pair of gravitational radiation detectors at the Maryland site over a period of six months. Within limits of experimental error the one-site, two-detector coincidence rate was identical with the separated-site two-detector coincidence rate. This indicates that for the sensitivities reported here, the isolation from the local environments was adequate and that electromagnetic and seismic interactions do not cause the observed coincidences.

The separation of 1,000 km makes a cosmic ray shower explanation very unlikely. Nonetheless it was important to investigate the effect of cosmic ray charged particles. Professors N. Sanders Wall and Gaurang B. Yodh and Dr. David Ezrow instrumented one of the Maryland site gravitational radiation detectors with Čerenkov radiation counters and later with meter square plastic scintillators. They observed no significant correlations with the gravitational radiation detector coincidences[7].

A search was made for coincidences between a 1,661 Hz gravitational radiation detector and a 5,000 Hz mode of a second gravitational radiation detector, both at the Maryland site. No excess of coincidences above the chance rate was observed. Subsequent investigation showed that the 5,000 Hz mode was a bending mode and not a compressional mode. General relativity theory predicts that this bending mode should not interact with gravitational radiation. The lack of coincidences is thus evidence against a non-gravitational radiation origin for the 1,661 Hz coincidences.

Other papers have presented evidence that there is anisotropy of the observed coincidences, the maxima occurring in the direction of the galactic centre[8]. Experiments with a disk were consistent with predictions of Einstein's pure tensor theory. Small effects of the local environment can affect the anisotropy in a significant way. To average these properly at least six months of data are required. The magnetic tapes considered here

不够激发引力辐射探测器，也可以产生响应。我们在不同的位置使用磁偶极和电偶极天线，在不同的时间采用了不同的方向。与空调、磁带记录仪和电源线波动相关的局部电磁场限制了无线电接收器的灵敏度，其数值大概比引力辐射探测器响应的小 3 个数量级。在电磁干扰与引力辐射探测器符合计数之间没有观测到显著关联。

还有其他证据可以证明符合计数不是电磁或地震干扰引起的。我们曾用噪声发生器测量引力辐射探测器系统的输入温度。这样可以准确说明所有显著信号源的情况，并排除输入温度的任何主要部分来源于内噪声以外的其他背景的可能性。如果符合计数是由像地震或者电磁活动这样的地球效应引起的，那么这样的信号会同时或者几乎同时到达地表或地球内部同一区域的两个实验站。然而，对于每一个同步到达两个地点的符合事件，都应该伴随有很多单个的到达，这样就会产生高于实际观测值的系统噪声水平。我们还测量了 6 个月内马里兰站一对引力辐射探测器的符合计数率。在实验误差范围内，同一站中两个探测器的符合计数率与另一站中两个探测器的符合计数率是完全相同的。这个结果表明：在本文涉及的灵敏度范围内，与局部环境的隔离是足够好的，并且观测到的符合计数不是由电磁和地震干扰引起的。

1,000 千米的距离太远，因此不太可能用宇宙线簇射来解释符合事件。尽管如此，研究宇宙线带电粒子的影响还是很重要的。桑德斯·沃尔教授、高朗·尤德教授和戴维·埃兹罗博士在马里兰站的一个引力辐射探测器上装备了切伦科夫辐射计数器，后来又装备了米方塑料闪烁体。他们在宇宙线簇射与引力辐射探测器符合计数之间没有观测到显著的关联 [7]。

我们对同样位于马里兰站的一个 1,661 赫兹引力辐射探测器和另一个 5,000 赫兹模式引力辐射探测器之间的符合计数进行了研究。没有观测到超过偶然符合计数率的符合计数。接下来的研究表明：5,000 赫兹模式是一个弯曲模式，而不是一个压缩模式。广义相对论预言这种弯曲模式不会和引力辐射发生相互作用。两个探测器之间缺乏符合计数的事实就成为否定 1,661 赫兹下符合计数来自非引力辐射源的证据。

另有一些文章提出证据指出：观测到的符合计数具有各向异性，最大值出现在银河系中心方向 [8]。圆盘实验的结果与爱因斯坦纯张量理论的预言一致。局部环境的小作用会显著影响各向异性。为了适当地平均这些影响，最少需要 6 个月的数据。本文采用的磁带记录在时间上不连续。空白以及记录器故障使得数据不足以用来进

did not have times continuously written. Gaps and recorder failures left insufficient data for a study of the anisotropy. Visual examination of the lists of coincidences found by the computer implied that the data are consistent with the earlier anisotropy experiments based on human observer study of pen and ink recorder charts.

The present data are free of human observer bias. No assumptions are made concerning the duration of expected pulses or their shapes beyond the requirement of a fairly smooth leading edge. This is important because addition of noise will change the shape of received pulses. It is considered established beyond reasonable doubt that the gravitational radiation detectors at ends of a 1,000 km baseline are being excited by a common source as a result of interactions which are neither seismic, electromagnetic nor those of charged particles of cosmic rays.

I thank F. J. Dyson, V. Trimble, and G. R. Ringo for valuable discussions and D. J. Gretz and J. Peregrin for maintaining and operating the gravitational radiation detectors. This work was supported in part by NSF and in part by the Computer Science Center of the University of Maryland.

(**240**, 28-30; 1972)

J. Weber: Department of Physics and Astronomy, University of Maryland, College Park, Maryland.

Received April 19; revised August 4, 1972.

References:

1. Weber, J., *Phys. Rev.*, 117, 306 (1960).
2. Weber, J., in *General Relativity and Gravitational Waves*, chap. 8 (Interscience, New York, London, 1961).
3. Weber, J., in *Relativity Groups and Topology*, 875 (Gordon and Breach, New York, 1964).
4. Weber, J., *Nuovo Cim. Lett.*, Series I, 4, 653 (1971).
5. Weber, J., *Phys. Rev. Lett.*, 22, 1320 (1969).
6. Weber, J., *Phys. Rev. Lett.*, 24, 276 (1970).
7. Ezrow, D., Wall, N. S., Weber, J., and Yodh, G. B., *Phys. Rev. Lett.*, 24, 17 (1970).
8. Weber, J., *Phys. Rev. Lett.*, 25, 180 (1970).
9. Weber, J., *Nuovo Cim.*, 4B, 197 (1971).

行各向异性的研究。对计算机发现的符合事件列表进行的表观检查显示，这些数据与之前基于对笔墨记录表格进行人工观测研究而得到的各向异性实验结果一致。

现有数据没有人为观测偏差。除了要求有相当平滑的前沿之外，对预期脉冲的持续时间或其形状都没有作任何别的假设。这一点的重要性在于，噪声的加入会改变接收到的脉冲的形状。我们认为已经可以毫无疑义地接受，在 1,000 千米基线两端的引力辐射探测器是由一个共同的源激发的。这是相互作用的结果，这个作用既不是地震或电磁，也不是来自宇宙线带电粒子。

感谢戴森、特林布尔和林戈与我进行了有价值的讨论，还要感谢格雷茨和佩雷格林对引力辐射探测器的维护和操作。美国国家科学基金会和马里兰大学计算机科学中心都为这项工作提供了部分支持。

（何钧 翻译；张元仲 审稿）

Problems Still with Scrapie Agent

Editor's Note

In this leading article, *Nature* drew attention to other diseases with similarities to scrapie, notably Creutzfeld–Jacob disease. The sequel, now widely influential in agriculture, is the recognition in 1986 that a disease in British cattle called bovine spongiform encephalopathy was the cow's equivalent of scrapie. Within five years it had been established that human beings were at risk from eating infected beef, and the European trade in cattle was disrupted for several years afterwards. The cause of scrapie and the other diseases has been linked to the genetics of a protein present in all animals called the prion protein, which is surmised to be capable of existing in more than one form, at least one of which coagulates in nerve cells, leading to severe encephalitis and death.

IN working with the class of agents which cause scrapie, transmissible mink encephalopathy, kuru and Creutzfeld–Jacob disease there have been two recurrent problems. These are the difficulty of distinguishing primary from secondary events in the disease and the need to use whole-animal assays, which last many months or even years, in order to detect and titrate the infective agents.

Scrapie agent has now replicated in a cell culture line for more than 100 tissue culture passages, but without any signs of its presence, so this has not provided any basis for a quicker assay of infectivity. Equally frustrating have been the attempts to develop immune assays specific for infectivity, although Gardiner showed six years ago that scrapie tissues have increased antigenicity. The average concentration of infective units of scrapie in brain is ultimately higher than elsewhere but only reaches about the same order as the number of brain cells, and it has not been possible to purify and concentrate the agent. This is generally regarded as one reason why many workers have failed to detect a specific immune response, for the "antigen" has been a more or less crude preparation of tissues from affected hosts. Such tissues presumably contain many antigens associated with the chronic degenerative changes in the brain and, even with the infective tissues outside the central nervous system, the failure to observe tissue damage may simply reflect the insensitivity of present techniques. On the biochemical side, the inability to differentiate between the primary aspects of agent replication and the secondary tissue changes has produced a decade of studies, the results of which are mostly equivocal.

Within a month, two entirely different methods have been published which may reduce to a few days the time needed for assays in this context. It is therefore opportune to discuss their likely merits in the light of the types of difficulty which have beset work with scrapie. Carp, Licursi, Merz and Merz[1] used both multiple sclerosis and scrapie, and they report

关于瘙痒症病原体的待解决问题

编者按

这篇发表于《自然》杂志上的社论将人们的注意力吸引到了类似于瘙痒症的其他疾病，尤其是克罗伊茨费尔特－雅各布病上。继之而来的是人们在 1986 年认识到英国牛得的一种被称为牛海绵状脑病（译者注：俗称疯牛病）的疾病就相当于牛瘙痒症，这对当前的农业造成了广泛的影响。人们仅用 5 年时间就证实人类食用带有病毒的牛肉会有被感染的危险，因而欧洲的牛贸易在此后数年内遭到了重创。瘙痒症及其他疾病的病因被认为与一种存在于所有动物体内的蛋白质的遗传有关，该蛋白质被称为朊蛋白，据推测它能够以多种形式存在，其中至少有一种会凝结在神经细胞中，从而导致严重的脑炎甚至死亡。

在研究引起瘙痒症、传染性水貂脑病、库鲁病和克罗伊茨费尔特－雅各布病这一类疾病的病原体时，总会反复遇到两个难题。一个难题是很难把疾病中的原发事件和继发事件区分开；另一个难题是为了发现和滴定传染性病原体，需要使用整个动物进行分析，这种分析花费的时间长达数月甚至数年。

瘙痒症病原体在一个培养细胞系中复制，目前已经组织培养传代 100 余次，但是没有任何迹象表明它的存在，所以这种方法不能为感染性的快速检测提供任何依据。尝试开发专门用于检测感染性的免疫测定法也同样遭到了挫折，尽管加德纳在六年前就已经发现瘙痒症组织具有更强的抗原性。脑内瘙痒症感染单位的平均浓度最终会超过体内其他部位，但只能达到和脑细胞数量相近的量级，因而目前还不可能纯化和富集这些病原体。大家普遍认为这就是为什么许多研究者没有检测到特异性免疫应答的一个原因，因为"抗原"一般是受感染宿主组织的粗提物。这些组织被认为含有很多与脑内慢性退行性改变相关的抗原，即使对于中枢神经系统之外的感染性组织，未能观察到组织损伤也只能说明目前技术的灵敏度低。在生物化学方面，人们为解决无法鉴别病原体复制产生的原发因素和继发性组织改变的问题已经研究了十年，但得到的结果大多是模棱两可的。

在一个月之内，研究人员报道了两种完全不同的方法，这两种方法都能使检测瘙痒症病原体所需的时间减少到几天。因此，现在正好可以探讨一下它们对解决瘙痒症研究时所遇到的难题是否会有帮助。卡普、利库尔西、默茨和默茨[1] 同时研究

a replicating factor which is first detectable in mice by a reduction in the proportion of circulating polymorphs the day after injection with tissues from cases of multiple sclerosis. A similar effect was found to occur three days after injection with scrapie tissues. With both scrapie and multiple sclerosis tissues the effect persists at least for many months.

The other report is on page 104 of this issue of *Nature*. Field and Shenton have used a lymphocyte sensitization technique which differentiates efficiently between tissues from uninfected mice and those from mice affected by scrapie: the method involves a combined *in vivo* and *in vitro* test which takes about a week. It will be a real advance if both these reports fulfil the expectations which they will generate.

The most exciting possibilities come from the work of Carp and associates, because they may not only provide a rapid assay but may also bridge the gap between scrapie-like diseases and multiple sclerosis. The confidence of their report, with its modest claims for the assay, rests on the finding of a consistent difference between tissues from normal and affected subjects in the ability to produce the polymorph reduction. A number of different tissues were used, which came from several human, sheep and mouse sources. The authors are careful to state that the "virus" in the mouse assay may well be unrelated to the aetiology of multiple sclerosis, and in the case of scrapie they only conclude that it may be related to scrapie agent in some way, even though the assay virus seems to have some properties in common with scrapie agent. This is prudent because they have not yet produced evidence to fulfil the criteria which earlier workers with scrapie found necessary even before it was easy to work with scrapie in laboratory animals[2]. The high thermal stability of scrapie permits serial passage using boiled inocula each time: this eliminates from the inocula conventional viruses which could be producing misleading effects. Even though the polymorph assay may be specific for scrapie, multiple sclerosis and any related diseases, it is important to know if the effect comes from a non-causal secondary virus normally present in such diseases. Another conceivable possibility is that multiple sclerosis and scrapie tissues merely release a latent virus in the mice, which would not necessarily invalidate the assay though it would be less interesting: this alternative is perhaps excluded by the authors' statement that "the characteristics of the multiple sclerosis and scrapie factors that induce the decrease are similar but not identical". Their findings will need independent confirmation and may not prove to be an assay of the respective causal agents, but the prospects are that this approach will not incur problems of dealing with effects merely due to tissue damage.

In the case of the lymphocyte sensitization test it is to be hoped that the claim of Field and Shenton, that it "enables the presence of scrapie to be established within 8 days" rather than several months, will prove correct. As the evidence stands, however, this is too broad a generalization and other kinds of evidence are needed. The problem is to find a way of distinguishing between the agent and tissue damage antigens, and the authors are aware of this difficulty. The scrapie brain and spleen tissues so far tested presumably come from mice at an advanced stage of the disease, and chronic degenerative changes

了多发性硬化症和瘙痒症，他们利用在注射多发性硬化症动物组织一天后小鼠血液循环中多形核白细胞的比例降低首次在小鼠中检测到了复制因子。在注射瘙痒症组织三天后也会出现类似的效应。如果同时注射瘙痒症组织和多发性硬化症组织，则该效应至少能够持续数月。

另一篇报告发表在本期《自然》杂志的第 104 页。菲尔德和申顿用到了能有效鉴别未感染小鼠组织和感染瘙痒症小鼠组织的淋巴细胞致敏技术；该方法采用了体内体外联合实验，耗时大约一周。如果这两篇报告都能达到预期的目标，那么就将出现一项重大的突破。

最令人兴奋的可能性来自于卡普及其同事的工作，因为他们有可能不仅提供了一种快速检测的方法，而且还在瘙痒症类疾病与多发性硬化症之间建立了某种联系。这篇对检测过程进行了适度报道的报告的可信性是基于他们发现正常组织与患病组织在导致多形核白细胞减少方面所具有的差异总是保持一致。实验中使用了来自于数个人、羊和小鼠的很多种不同组织。作者很谨慎地声明在小鼠中检测到的"病毒"很可能与多发性硬化症的病因无关，而关于瘙痒症，他们只是推测它可能在某些方面与瘙痒症病原体有关，虽然检测到的病毒看似具有一些与瘙痒症病原体相同的性质。这样做是非常谨慎的，因为他们得到的证据还不符合那些早期的瘙痒症研究者在能够轻易用实验动物来研究瘙痒症之前就已经发现的必备标准 [2]。瘙痒症病原体的高度耐热性使我们在每次进行连续传代培养时都可以使用煮沸的接种物，这样就可以避免由接种物本身通常会带有的病毒所导致的误导性结果。即使多形核白细胞检测法只对瘙痒症、多发性硬化症以及其他相关疾病有效，了解清楚这种作用是否源自正常存在于这类疾病中的非致病性次要病毒也是很重要的。另一种可能性是多发性硬化症组织和瘙痒症组织在小鼠中仅仅释放了一种潜伏病毒，尽管它没那么引人注目，但也不一定就能证明这种检测法是无效的。作者的一句话也许能排除这种可能，即"引起这种减少的多发性硬化症因子和瘙痒症因子的特征虽然相似但并不相同"。卡普等人的发现还需要独立的证据去证明，而且这一效应可能并不能作为检测各自致病原的方法，但其前景在于不会造成需要排除仅由组织损伤引起的效应的麻烦。

对于淋巴细胞致敏法，菲尔德和申顿声称这一方法"能够在 8 天内诊断出瘙痒症"，而不是几个月。我们希望他们的判断将被证明是正确的。但是，从支持上述论点的论据来看，这只是一个太宽泛的概括，还需要其他类型的证据。问题在于要找到一种鉴别病原体和组织损伤抗原的方法，而且这些作者也知道解决这个问题的难度。据推测目前被检测的瘙痒症脑组织和脾组织都来源于疾病晚期的小鼠，其慢性

will have been present in the brain for many weeks. It cannot be assumed that the spleens of such animals have not been chronically exposed to any changed antigens arising in the brain. If the test is eventually shown only to detect tissue damage as an index of agent concentration it will still be useful because it is "exquisitely responsive to minor changes in antigenic determinant structure" and can evidently detect more subtle degrees of damage than can at present be quickly estimated by conventional histological means. Some of these possible secondary effects could be excluded by using it for a time sequence study of spleen in the four weeks after injection, when the concentration of the agent is rapidly increasing there but long before gross signs of damage appear in the brain, or, better, to compare the new and conventional assays using the tissue culture line developed by Haig and Clarke[3].

But even in these cases the difficulty remains because of the high sensitivity of their technique, which may be detecting antigens from unseen damage. Its value will only be established when it can be shown that there is a close correlation between the titre estimates of the conventional assay and this new one in a large range of circumstances. This range will need to include various severe physical and chemical treatments of tissue preparations, which could alter the antigenic spectrum without removing all the infectivity. If a close correlation cannot be established between the two types of assay, it will be necessary to await the purification of scrapie as an antigen.

It may therefore be premature to use the method for collateral evidence that there is more scrapie agent in neuronal than glial preparations, as is done in the accompanying communication by Narang, Shenton, Giorgi and Field (Page 106). At this stage standard evidence of infectivity titre is also needed for these two cell populations, and this would give further confidence in the use of the proposed assay. Meanwhile it is difficult to assess the significance of their electron micrographs of particles, but the detection of these in serial passages using only boiled inocula would be more impressive than other evidence.

As the lymphocyte sensitization assay takes only a few days it should be possible to deal quite quickly with some of the points raised here, even though, as Field describes elsewhere, the technique involves "a most fickle and unstable instrument which makes great demands upon the patience and endurance of the observer".—From a Correspondent.

(**240**, 71-72; 1972)

References:

1. Carp, R. I., Licursi, P. C., Merz, P. A., and Merz, G. S., *J. Exp. Med.*, **136**, 618 (1972); *Infect. Immunity*, **6**, 370 (1972).

2. Mackay, J. M. K., Smith, W., and Stamp, J. T., *Vet. Rec.*, **72**, 1002 (1960).

3. Haig, D. A., and Clarke, M. C., *Nature*, **234**, 106 (1971).

退行性改变已经在脑内存在了许多周。我们不能认为这些动物的脾脏从未长期暴露在任一产生于脑内的已改变的抗原中。如果最终发现这种方法只能检测作为病原体浓度指标的组织损伤，它仍是有用的，因为它能"对抗原决定结构的微小改变作出灵敏的反应"，而且与目前能够快速估计出损伤度的常用组织学方法相比，这种方法可以明确地检测到更精细的损伤度。采用这种方法对注射后 4 周内的脾进行时间序列研究也许能排除一些可能出现的继发反应，在 4 周之内病原体浓度会快速增加，而脑内损伤的明显症状还远未出现，或者说，与黑格和克拉克 [3] 发明的利用组织培养系的常规检测法相比，这种新方法更具优势。

然而即便如此，困难仍然存在，因为这项技术的灵敏度很高，有可能检测到不可见损伤产生的抗原。只有在能证明这种新方法的测定值在大多数情况下与用常规分析方法得到的滴度值密切相关时，其价值才能得到认可。上述过程必须包括在组织制备时所进行的各种各样严格的物理、化学处理。这些处理可能在保留感染性的同时改变了抗原谱。如果无法验证这两种检测法之间的高度相关性，那就只有等到瘙痒症组织能够作为一种抗原被纯化出来之后才能证明这种新方法的可用性了。

因此，像纳兰、申顿、乔治和菲尔德在本卷后一篇文章中（第 106 页）所做的那样，用这种方法作为协同证据来证明在神经元样本中的瘙痒症病原体比在胶质细胞样本中的更多还为时尚早。在现阶段，我们还需要这两种细胞群体的感染性滴度的标准证据，有了这个证据，我们才能更自信地使用电子显微镜检测法。同时，虽然很难评估这些微粒的电子显微照片有多大意义，但是在仅用煮沸过的接种物所获得的系列传代细胞中检测到这些微粒本身就会比其他证据的意义更重大。

因为用淋巴细胞致敏法进行检测只需几天，所以有可能很快就能解决这里提出的一些问题，尽管正如菲尔德在其他文章中所指出的：这项技术使用了"最易变化和最不稳定的检测手段，因而非常需要检测者的耐心和毅力"。——来自于一位通讯作者。

（毛晨晖 翻译；刘佳佳 审稿）

Influence of Continental Positions on Early Tertiary Climates

L. A. Frakes and E. M. Kemp

Editor's Note

This prescient paper from Lawrence Frakes and Elizabeth Kemp at Florida State University recognizes that the Earth's climate might be influenced by changes in the positions of the continents in the past. They say that different distributions of the land masses would alter circulation patterns of ocean water, thereby affecting climatically important processes such as sea surface temperature, evaporation and heat transport. The researchers consider the qualitative differences in ocean circulation during the Eocene and Oligocene epochs (30–48 million years ago). Feedback between global geological change and climate is now widely discussed in relation to climate change, for example in terms of the effects of mountain-range formation and continental ice-sheet formation.

CONTINENTS can be positioned in their earlier places on the Cainozoic globe by means of their rock magnetism; continents for which such data are lacking can be placed in their relative positions by removing the subsequently generated seafloor. On such a reconstructed globe for a particular time in the Cainozoic the distribution of palaeoclimates, as deduced from significant rock-types and fossil plants and animals, can be plotted in their true geographical relationships. Locations of the continents and subcontinents with respect to the rotational coordinate system, as well as to each other, will largely determine the prevailing climatic trends by affecting the circulation patterns in oceans and atmosphere. Here we attempt to model, in a semi-quantitative way, the climates of the Earth in the later half of the Eocene (40–48 m.y. ago) and in the early half of the Oligocene (30–37 m.y. ago), an interval of marked climatic change.

For deciphering global palaeoclimates a reconstruction must be used which positions continents with respect to the poles of the Earth's rotation, because of the strong latitude-dependence of climate. The mean palaeomagnetic pole probably approximated the position of the Earth's rotational pole throughout the Cainozoic, and deviation of the palaeomagnetic pole from the geographic pole can be treated by sampling rock intervals representing more than 10^4 yr (ref. 1). The rock magnetism data selected for use in this study consist of many samples from multiple sites, display relatively small values for α (radius of the circle of 95% confidence), and have all been a.c. magnetically cleaned. Most continents, however, can only be positioned within about 5 arc deg and the pole positions, and hence palaeolatitudinal positioning of the continents, represent a time interval of as much as 7–8 m.y., although the data were selected for geological synchroneity. Neither the geometrical nor the chronological accuracy is thus as good as in reconstructions based

大陆位置对早第三纪气候的影响

弗雷克斯，肯普

编者按

这篇由佛罗里达州立大学的劳伦斯·弗雷克斯和伊丽莎白·肯普撰写的论文颇具预见性，文中指出地球上的气候可能会因以往的大陆位置发生变化而受到影响。他们认为大陆的不同分布情况将改变海洋的环流模式，从而影响到一些对气候有重要影响的过程，如洋面温度、蒸发以及热传递过程等。这两位研究者还对始新世和渐新世时期（3,000万年~4,800万年前）海洋环流之间的差异进行了定性分析。如今，全球地质变迁与气候之间的反馈对于气候变化的影响正在被大家广为讨论，例如山脉形成和大陆冰盖形成所造成的影响。

　　根据大陆的岩石磁性，可以确定早在新生代时期大陆在地球上所处的位置；对于缺乏磁性数据的大陆，则可以通过移除后来生成的海底来确定大陆的相对位置。在对新生代中某个特殊时期的全球大陆分布进行重建的基础上，从重要的岩石类型和动植物化石进行推断，就可以用大陆间真实的地理关系绘制出古气候分布图。大陆、次大陆在旋转坐标系中的位置以及它们相互之间的位置会影响海洋和大气的环流模式，从而在很大程度上决定了盛行气候的趋势。在本文中，我们将试着用半定量的方法建立一个模型，以模拟始新世后半期（距今4,000万年~4,800万年）和渐新世前半期（距今3,000万年~3,700万年）时地球上的气候，后一时期是气候发生明显变化的时期。

　　为了解释全球的古气候，必须重建各大陆相对于地球旋转极的位置，因为纬度对气候有很大影响。在整个新生代，平均古地磁极很可能位于接近地球旋转极的位置，而古地磁极相对于地理极的偏离可用时间跨度超过1万年的岩石样本来判断（参考文献1）。本研究选用的岩石磁性数据来自于在多个地区采集到的大量样本，它们的α值（95%置信圆半径）相对较小，并且都经过了交流退磁处理。然而，虽然这些数据是按同一地质时代来选择的，但大多数大陆的定位只能精确到约5弧度以内，而极地位置以及由此确定的大陆古纬度位置所代表的时间间隔可达700万年~800万年。因此，从几何上的精度和年代上的精度来看，仅由海底扩张数据进行的重建比仅由岩石磁性数据进行的重建精度更高[2]。对于研究古气候而言，首先利用岩石磁

solely on seafloor spreading data[2]. For palaeoclimates the advantage gained in the use of rock magnetism data first, but with reliance on seafloor data as well, lies in the greater assurance that continents are primarily positioned with respect to the pole. Moreover, no assumptions are made as to the fixity of any continent, plate, oceanic ridge or pole.

In the Eocene reconstruction (Fig. 1), positioning of most continents is based on rock magnetism—as summarized by McElhinney and Wellman[3] for Australia (New South Wales shield volcanics) and Africa (Ethiopian volcanics), and by Creer[4] for western Europe (Antrim basalts), North America (Green River Formation), and Pakistan–India (post-Deccan Traps[5]).

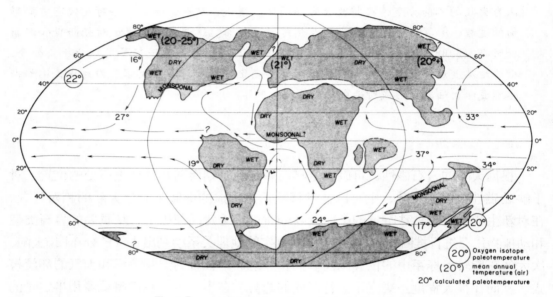

Fig. 1. Reconstruction of weather patterns in Eocene.

The positions of South America relative to Africa[6], and of Antarctica relative to Australia–New Zealand–New Guinea[7-9], are determined by reversing the seafloor spreading process to its late Eocene configuration. Seafloor data are used here because of the lack of Cainozoic rock magnetism information from South America and Antarctica. The result is a much different Earth—a very wide Indopacific Ocean (spanning about 210° at the equator), a narrow Atlantic, a south polar landmass probably connecting to South America and separated from Australia by a narrow seaway, and Pakistan–India astride the equator. By the middle of the Oligocene (Fig. 2) the equatorial Pacific had been narrowed substantially, concurrently with the widening of the Australia-Antarctic seaway[5], as a result of the northward motion of Australia–New Guinea[1]. Also, the South America–Antarctica join appears to have been interrupted by formation of the Scotia arc, though this conclusion must be tentative because the positions for Antarctica are based on seafloor spreading data alone. But this timing for formation of the arc is in accord with the post-Mesozoic, pre-20 m.y. date suggested by Dalziel and Elliot[10].

性数据然后再用海底数据进行确证的优势在于可以更准确地得到大陆原先相对于极地的位置。此外，在模型中无需假定任何大陆、板块、洋脊或极地是固定的。

在始新世的重建中（图 1），大多数大陆的位置是根据岩石磁性确定的——参见麦克尔希尼和韦尔曼[3] 对澳大利亚（新南威尔士盾形火山）和非洲（埃塞俄比亚火山）的总结，以及克里尔[4] 对欧洲西部（安特里姆玄武岩）、北美洲（格林河地层）和印度–巴基斯坦地区（后德干玄武岩[5]）的总结。

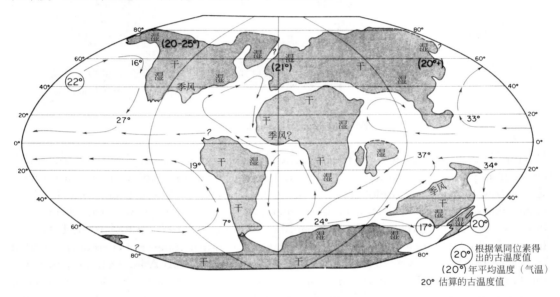

图 1. 始新世气候模式的重建

将海底扩张过程逆推至其始新世晚期的构型，从而得到了南美洲相对于非洲的位置[6] 以及南极洲相对于澳大利亚–新西兰–新几内亚[7-9] 的位置。在此处使用海底数据是因为缺少南美洲和南极洲新生代岩石的磁性信息。所得结果与现在的地球差异很大：印度–太平洋很宽（在赤道处跨越约 210 度）；大西洋很窄；南极大陆很可能连着南美洲，并且与澳大利亚之间只隔着一条狭窄的航道；印度–巴基斯坦地区横跨过赤道的两侧。到了渐新世中期（图 2），由于澳大利亚–新几内亚向北移动[1]，使得赤道太平洋明显变窄，同时使澳大利亚–南极洲的航道变宽[5]。并且，南美洲–南极洲之间的联系似乎因为斯科舍岛弧的形成而分开。不过这个结论还只是一个假设，因为在确定南极洲的位置时仅参考了海底扩张数据。不过，由此确定的该岛弧的形成时间倒是与达尔齐尔和埃利奥特提出的时间——2,000 万年以前的后中生代[10] 相一致。

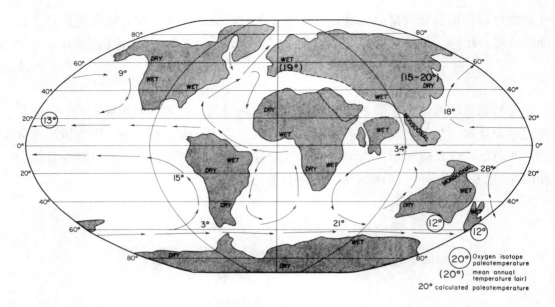

Fig. 2. Mid-Oligocene weather patterns.

Having made reconstructions for these Cainozoic intervals, we can deduce rough circulation patterns of surface currents in the world ocean, and, with less assurance, suggest resulting trends in global climates. In the late Eocene South Pacific, much of the equatorial segment of the enormous counterclockwise gyral swept westward from Peru into the area of the present Indian Ocean, before being diverted southward by Pakistan–India toward Antarctica and eventually Australia. The north equatorial current spanned at least 150 arc deg and was deflected northward by south-eastern Asia, eventually to reach the Gulf of Alaska. The interruption of the circumpolar current in the Southern Ocean by the South America–Antarctica landmass, and possibly also near New Zealand by the Macquarie Rise system[9], was also significant. The broad patterns of oceanic circulation are clear enough, except for the extent of exchange between the Atlantic and bordering water masses; we have not attempted to decipher detail, nor to include epicontinental seas.

Temperature distributions in the Eocene world ocean are poorly known but can be approximated by use of published oxygen-isotope determinations[11-13] as base values. From surface-temperature maps[14] we calculate warming rates for the equatorial currents (at present averaging about 0.1°C/deg longitude). Similarly, warming and cooling rates in meridional currents are about +0.29°C/deg latitude. These rates were applied to yield the temperature value for the Indopacific shown on Fig. 1. Mean annual temperatures for continental areas are from published analyses of fossil flora[15-17].

Circulation patterns during the early Oligocene differ in that the Indopacific is segmented, for the first time, by the northward motion of Australia–New Guinea. The Pacific consequently approximates its present equatorial width. Further, the circumpolar current encircles the globe in the Southern Ocean, and exchange between the Atlantic

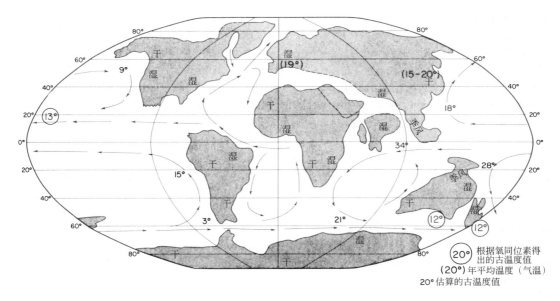

图 2. 渐新世中期的气候模式

在完成对新生代的这两段时期的重建之后，我们就可以推断出表层洋流的大体环流模式，并可以不太有把握地提出由此导致的全球气候趋势。始新世后期，南太平洋在赤道地区的大部分巨大逆时针涡旋会从秘鲁向西席卷到现在印度洋所在的位置，然后在印度−巴基斯坦地区转往南极方向，最终到达澳大利亚。赤道北部的洋流跨越了至少 150 弧度，并在东南亚地区向北偏转，最终到达阿拉斯加湾。同样值得注意的是：绕极流在南大洋地区被南美洲−南极洲大陆阻断，或者还可能在新西兰附近被麦夸里海岭系统[9]阻断。除了大西洋与其毗连水团之间的交换地带以外，大洋环流的主要模式已足够清晰了。我们还没有尝试去解释细节，也没有把陆缘海考虑进去。

我们对始新世时期全球海洋的温度分布所知甚少，但可以利用已发表的氧同位素测定结果[11-13]作为基值进行近似估算。根据表层水温图[14]，我们计算出了赤道洋流的增温率（目前的平均值约为每度经度 0.1℃）。同样，经向洋流的增温率和冷却率大约为每度纬度 +0.29℃。由这些变化率可以得到印度−太平洋的温度值，见图 1。大陆区的年平均气温来自于一些关于植物化石的已发表分析结果[15-17]。

渐新世早期各环流模式表现出的不同在于：印度−太平洋因澳大利亚−新几内亚的向北移动而首次被分隔开。于是太平洋在赤道区的宽度就和现在差不多了。此外，绕极流在南大洋区域中环绕地球运动，而大西洋与其近邻北冰洋之间的交换可能要

and the neighbouring Arctic Ocean is probably greater than in the Eocene. Sea surface temperatures have been estimated as before. It is clear that surface waters were colder than in the Eocene interval; they tend to be intermediate between the very warm temperatures of the Eocene and those of the present Pacific. Similarly, the few mean annual air temperatures for the Oligocene fall between present and Eocene values. This coincidence of meridional displacement of the continents with the evolution of colder global climates during the Cainozoic may be a cause and effect relationship.

The temperature distributions we deduce for the Palaeogene oceans suggest related distributions of evaporation and precipitation over the landmasses. Evaporation is best developed where warm segments of the oceans are in contact with relatively cold air, and precipitation occurs most readily where moist air is forced upward by convergence of surface air-masses or by the existence of orographic barriers. At present, precipitation is most abundant in the zones between the equator and 10° N, and near the frontal convergence zones between 30° and 50°. Precipitation is also concentrated along the west coasts of continents at 40° to 60° and on the east coasts at 15° to 30°. In the Eocene, abundant precipitation characterized the entire western margin of the Indopacific, and the wet belts probably extended to considerably higher latitudes than at present because surface waters in the oceans were warmer. Continental regions adjacent to and downwind from high surface-water temperatures in Fig. 1 are accordingly marked "wet". Similarly, areas bordering on and upwind from cold currents are considered to be "dry", as compared with the average conditions for that latitude. In these deductions we follow Lamb[18], who suggests that on an ice-free globe the trade wind belts would be expanded poleward at the expense of the high-latitude westerlies. Monsoonal conditions must have existed on coastal regions facing the equator and within the range of the seasonally varying intertropical convergence zone. Important warming currents such as the Gulf Stream and the Kuro Shio were already in existence.

This suggestion of warm, wet climates at high latitudes in the Palaeogene has been well documented by the distribution of fossil plants and animals and by climatically significant rock types[17]. Fossil plants from the Early Eocene London Clay are largely comparable, on a taxonomic basis, with those of the modern Indo-Malayan region[20], although Daley[21] has recently cautioned against interpretation of this fossil flora in strictly tropical terms. The small admixture of temperate elements in the flora may reflect something of the seasonal variation to be expected at relatively high latitudes. Eocene floras from the Gulf of Alaska region have been designated "subtropical or paratropical", primarily on the basis of leaf morphology[15,27]; floras similarly suggestive of warm humid climatic regimes are known from the Eocene of Hokkaido. In the southern hemisphere, palynological evidence suggests floras of "subtropical" aspect from New Zealand[23,24] and temperate forests in the Ross Sea region of Antarctica[25]. Other indicators of high-latitude warmth include reef corals in northern California, South Australia and New Zealand, and "lateritic" or bauxitic weathering profiles which form today in Köppen's "A" type climates of the tropics and wet subtropics. The latter soils are known from Eocene high mid-latitudes in Northern Ireland, the north-western United States, New Zealand, and northern Australia[26-28].

比在始新世时大。海面温度的估算方法和前面一样。很明显，表层水的温度要低于始新世时的温度；渐新世时的表层水温倾向于介于始新世时很暖的温度与目前太平洋的温度之间。同样，渐新世的年平均气温也会下降至始新世与现在的年平均气温之间。在新生代时期恰好同时出现了大陆的经向位移和全球气候变冷，这两者可能具有因果关系。

我们对早第三纪（译者注：现称古近纪）时海面温度分布情况的推断显示了大陆上蒸发和降水的相关分布。当海洋中比较温暖的部分与相对较冷的空气接触时，最容易出现蒸发；而当湿润气团因为地面气团辐合或被地形阻挡而被迫上升时，则最易发生降水。现在，降水在赤道～北纬10度之间以及30度～50度之间锋面辐合带的附近最为丰富。降水还集中在沿大陆西海岸的40度～60度之间和东海岸的15度～30度之间。在始新世，降水丰沛是整个印度-太平洋西部边缘的主要特征，而且湿润带可能会延伸到比现在高很多的纬度，因为那时的表层水温较高。因而与较高的表层水温相邻近的大陆区域以及其下风方的大陆区域，在图1中被标记为"湿"。以此类推，与同一纬度的平均条件相比，在低表层水温的周边以及其上风方的区域被认为是"干"。我们认同兰布 [18] 的推论，他认为：在无冰冻的地球上，信风带将向极地方向扩展，并影响到高纬度的西风带。季风气候必然会出现在朝向赤道的海岸区以及有季节变化的热带辐合带内部。一些重要的暖流，如墨西哥湾流和黑潮，在那时就已经存在了。

高纬地区在早第三纪时为暖湿气候这一观点已经被动植物化石的分布以及有气候指示意义的岩石类型所证明 [17]。从分类学的角度考虑，始新世早期的伦敦黏土中的植物化石与现代印度-马来半岛地区的植物 [20] 非常相似，不过最近戴利 [21] 对仅用热带术语来解释这些植物化石表示反对。植物化石中混有的少许温带成分或许反映了高纬地区可能发生过的季节变化。阿拉斯加湾地区的始新世植物群之所以被归于"亚热带或副热带"，最初就是因为参考了树叶形态方面的资料 [15,27]，在北海道地区也有一些始新世植物群能够证明气候类型为暖湿气候。在南半球，孢粉学研究结果证明新西兰的植物群具有"副热带"的特征 [23,24]，而南极洲的罗斯海地区则为温带森林 [25]。其他一些能说明高纬地区气候温暖的指标包括加利福尼亚北部、澳大利亚南部和新西兰的珊瑚礁，还有"红土"或铝矾土的风化剖面，在现今热带和湿副热带的柯本"A"型气候中就可以形成这种剖面。已经知道这种铝矾土存在于始新世时位于中高纬度的北爱尔兰、美国西北部、新西兰和澳大利亚北部 [26-28]。进一步证

Abundant high-latitude precipitation is further suggested by widespread coals of Eocene age.

An important climatic effect of the cooling of Oligocene surface waters was to restrict the high-latitude wet belts to latitudes below 60°, although atmospheric temperatures also dropped. Monsoonal regions of continents were probably restricted as well, primarily because of the motion of the continents out of the appropriate positions.

On the basis of the geological record available, the Oligocene climatic picture appears slightly cooler and drier. Evidence from fossil floras suggests a temperature decline that was dramatic in some cases[15,22], gradual in others[16,17,23,29,31]. But reef corals were able to thrive to at least 40° latitude, about 10° beyond their present range[32].

Great warmth and high precipitation in the Eocene high-latitude regions can be explained at least in part by the global temperature distributions derived from calculations based on oxygen isotope data for the oceans. Because of their prolonged residence time in equatorial regions, surface waters reaching the Antarctica–Australia and Gulf of Alaska regions were much warmer than at present—their main effect would be to warm the coastal atmosphere through the processes of evaporation (transfer of latent heat from ocean to atmosphere) and subsequent condensation (conversion of latent heat to specific heat within the atmosphere). The very warm and wet conditions which apparently characterized latitudes beyond 45° in the late Eocene were altered during the first half of the Oligocene to conditions more like the present. Simultaneously, equatorial transport in the oceanic gyrals of the Pacific was restricted, giving colder surface waters around the western Pacific and thus less efficient poleward heat transport. Colder Oligocene surface waters in high latitudes led to less evaporation and therefore to decreased precipitation and colder air temperatures. The process of poleward heat transport by the oceans operates even less effectively today, and the consequences are seen in the still lower temperatures and precipitation rates.

Feedback mechanisms arising from the existence of warm oceans may have contributed to more efffcient atmospheric transfer of heat energy away from the equatorial heat source as well, but the relative significance of these processes is difficult to quantify. Today, 20% of the total poleward heat transfer is effected by ocean currents; in the Eocene, certainly, a greater proportion would have been required. We emphasize the significance of the oceans to store and transport heat, particularly if given the proper configurations of land and sea, but this is with the recognition that other direct and indirect factors undoubtedly play a part in influencing climate[33].

This study was supported by the US National Science Foundation.

(**240**, 97-100; 1972)

明高纬地区降水丰沛的证据是，始新世时期形成的煤分布很广。

渐新世时表层水温变冷对气候的一个重要影响是把高纬度湿润带限制在了 60 度以下，不过大气温度也会同步下降。大陆的季风区可能也同样受到了限制，这主要是因为大陆移出了相应的位置。

从已有的地质记录来看，渐新世的气候状况显得有点偏冷和偏干。植物化石提供的证据表明：气温的下降在有些地区是突然的 [15,22]，而在其他地区又是渐进的 [16,17,23,29,31]。但珊瑚礁适宜生长区域的纬度至少可达 40 度，这比其现在的生长范围高了约 10 度 [32]。

由海洋氧同位素数据计算出的全球气温分布至少可以部分地解释始新世时高纬地区的温暖多雨气候。因为海水在赤道地区的停留时间加长，所以到达南极-澳大利亚和阿拉斯加湾地区的表层水要比现在暖和得多——它们造成的主要影响是通过蒸发过程（将潜热从海洋输送到大气）和随后的凝结过程（在大气中将潜热转化为显热）使沿岸大气变暖。在始新世后期，纬度 45 度以外的地区的明显特征是气候非常温暖和湿润，而到了渐新世的前半期，气候就变得更加类似于现在的情况了。同时，通过太平洋海洋涡旋来输送赤道热量也受到了限制，使得西太平洋周围的表层水变冷，因而降低了向极地方向输送热量的效率。在渐新世时，由于高纬地区的表层水温变低从而使蒸发量下降，并由此引起降水减少、气温降低。今天，海洋将热量向极地输送的效率还要更低，因而现在我们看到的是更低的温度和更少的降水。

暖海洋存在时的反馈机制可能曾使大气高效率地向外输送来自赤道热源处的热量，但是该过程的相对重要性很难量化。目前，由洋流向极地输送的热量占总量的 20%；在始新世，这个比例当然会更大一些。虽然我们强调海洋在储存和输送热量方面的重要性，特别是在陆地和海洋的位置合适的情况下，但还是会承认其他直接和间接因素也无疑能对气候产生一定程度的影响 [33]。

本研究得到了美国国家科学基金会的支持。

（蔡则怡 翻译；李三忠 审稿）

Lawrence A. Frakes and Elizabeth M. Kemp: Department of Geology, Florida State University, Tallahassee, Florida.

Received June 13, 1972.

References:

1. Creer, K. M., *J. Geophys. Res.*, **67**, 3461 (1962).

2. Jardine, N., and McKenzie, D., *Nature*, **235**, 20 (1972).

3. McElhinny, M. W., and Wellman, P., *Earth Planet. Sci. Lett.*, **6**, 198 (1969).

4. Creer, K. M., *Earth Sci. Rev.*, **6**, 369 (1970).

5. Wellman, P., and McElhinny, M. W., *Nature*, **227**, 595 (1970).

6. Dickson, G. P., Pitman, III, W. C., and Heirtzler, J. R., *J. Geophys. Res.*, **73**, 2087 (1968).

7. Weissel, J. K., and Hayes, D. E., in *Antarctic Oceanology* (edit. by Hayes, D. E.), 2 (Amer. Geophys. Union, Washington, DC, in the press).

8. Griffiths, J. R., and Varne, R., *Nature Physical Science*, **235**, 83 (1972).

9. Davies, H. L., and Smith, I. E., *Geol. Soc. Amer. Bull.*, **82**, 3299 (1971).

10. Dalziel, I. W. D., and Elliot, D. H., *Nature*, **233**, 246 (1971).

11. Dorman, F. H., *J. Geol.*, **74**, 49 (1966).

12. Devereaux, I., *NZJ. Sci.*, **10**, 988 (1967).

13. Douglas, R. G., and Savin, S. W., in *Initial Reports of the Deep Sea Drilling Project*, **6**, 1123 (1971).

14. Sverdrup, H. U., Johnson, M. W., and Fleming, H. R., *The Oceans* (Prentice Hall, New York, 1942).

15. Wolfe, J. A., and Hopkins, D. M., in *Tertiary Correlations and Climatic Changes in the Pacific*, 67 (Eleventh Pacific Sci. Congr., Tokyo, 1967).

16. Schwarzbach, M., *Z. Deutsch. Geol. Ges.*, **118**, 33 (1968).

17. Tanai, T., *J. Fac. Sci., Hokkaido Univ.*, **19**, 384 (1970).

18. Lamb, H. H., in *Descriptive Paleoclimatology* (edit. by Nairn, A. E. M.), 8 (Interscience, New York, 1961).

19. Frakes, L. A., and Kemp, E. M., in *Continental Drift, Sea Floor Spreading and Plate Tectonics—Implications for the Earth Sciences* (edit. by Tarling, D. H.) (Univ. of Newcastle upon Tyne, in the press).

20. Reid, E. M., and Chandler, M. E. J., *The Flora of the London Clay* (Brit. Mus. Nat. Hist., London, 1933).

21. Daley, B., *Palaeogeogr., Palaeoclim., Palaeoec.*, **11**, 177 (1972).

22. Wolfe, J. A., *Palaeogeogr., Palaeoclim., Palaeoec.*, **9**, 27 (1971).

23. Couper, R. A., *Palaeont. Bull.*, **32**, 1 (1960).

24. Wilson, G. J., *NZJ. Botany*, **6**, 56 (1968).

25. McIntyre, D. J., and Wilson, G. J., *NZJ. Botany*, **4**, 315 (1966).

26. Dury, G. H., *Geogr. J.*, **137**, 511 (1971).

27. Millot, G., *Geology of Clays; Weathering, Sedimentology, Geochemistry* (Springer Verlag, New York, 1970).

28. Harder, E. C., *Geol. Soc. Amer. Bull.*, **60**, 887 (1949).

29. Axelrod, D. I., and Bailey, H. P., *Palaeogr., Palaeoclim., Palaeoec.*, 6, 163 (1969).

30. Kobayashi, T., and Shikama, T., in *Descriptive Climatology* (edit. by Nairn, A. E. M.), 292 (Interscience, New York, 1961).

31. Vlasov, G. M., *Dokl. Akad. Nauk SSR*, **157**, 589 (1964).

32. Squires, D. F., *NZ Geol. Surv. Palaeont. Bull.*, **29** (1958).

33. Crowell, J. C., and Frakes, L. A., *Amer. J. Sci.*, **268**, 193 (1970).

Rapid Diagnosis of Scrapie in the Mouse

E. J. Field and B. K. Shenton

Editor's Note

Scrapie is an ancient agricultural disease of sheep whose cause was unknown until the 1990s. Here two British scientists describe a means for the rapid diagnosis of the presence of scrapie by the use of infected mice. At the time there was no tangible idea of what the infective agent might be—a virus, or perhaps even an agent lacking nucleic acid? The development of a rapid test for scrapie nevertheless enabled studies of its transmission between animals to be carried out.

RESEARCH into scrapie, an enigma of veterinary medicine which may embody principles of considerable interest for human disease, commonly involves demonstration of agent activity or its titration. A great step forward was made by Chandler[1] when he showed the disease could be produced in mice, and biological titration in these animals is currently widely employed. This takes 6–8 months. From a recent study of multiple sclerosis, with which scrapie has been linked[2], we were led into an immunological study of scrapie itself. We found that brain or spleen from a scrapie mouse when injected into a guinea-pig (adult Hartley) led to the appearance of blood lymphocytes which were more highly sensitized to scrapie brain or spleen than to normal brain or spleen.

In early experiments, guinea-pigs were inoculated intracutaneously with 0.1 ml. of 10^{-1} suspension of scrapie brain or scrapie spleen in sterile saline. Control animals were similarly injected with brain or spleen from normal mice which had been injected some weeks previously with normal brain suspension. At intervals after 5 days, 2–3 ml. of blood was removed by cardiac puncture and lymphocyte sensitization to the scrapie and normal suspensions estimated by the sensitive and highly specific macrophage electrophoretic migration (MEM) method[3]. In principle the method depends on the release by sensitized lymphocyte of a protein which slows migration of normal guinea-pig macrophages in an electric field (macrophage slowing factor (MSF)—which may be identical with macrophage inhibitory factor (MIF)). Our measurements have been carried out in a Zeiss cytopherometer and full experimental details have been given[4].

Guinea-pig blood lymphocytes were prepared by the method of Coulson and Chalmers[5], as modified by Hughes and Caspary[6], and normal guinea-pig macrophages by washing out the peritoneal cavity with heparinized Hanks solution 6–8 days after injection of sterile liquid paraffin. In order to obviate a two-way mixed lymphocyte reaction (at least for the duration of the test) the normal exudate was subjected to 100 rad γ-irradiation[3].

快速诊断小鼠瘙痒症

菲尔德，申顿

编者按

瘙痒症是在绵羊中发现的一种古老的农业病。在20世纪90年代以前，人们一直不了解瘙痒症的病因。在这篇文章中，两位英国科学家描述了一种利用感染的小鼠快速诊断瘙痒症的方法。那时，人们完全不知道其传染性病原体大概是什么样的——到底是一种病毒还是一种没有核酸的病原体。尽管如此，研制出快速检测瘙痒症的方法能使人们对瘙痒症在动物之间传播的研究得以开展下去。

瘙痒症是兽医学界的一个谜，它可能体现了人类疾病的某些关键法则，人们对瘙痒症的研究通常涉及病原体活性或其滴定方法的确定。钱德勒[1]在这方面取得了一项突破性的进展，他发现小鼠会感染这种病，因而人们目前在广泛地使用小鼠进行生物滴定。这类测试需要6到8个月。从一项与瘙痒症有关的疾病[2]——多发性硬化症的最新研究结果中受到启发，我们开始进行瘙痒症本身的免疫学研究。我们发现：患瘙痒症小鼠的脑组织或者脾组织被注射到豚鼠（成年的哈特利种）中后将导致其血液中出现一种淋巴细胞，这种淋巴细胞对瘙痒症脑或脾组织的敏感性要高于其对正常脑或脾组织的敏感性。

在早期实验中，我们给豚鼠皮内接种的是0.1 ml 用无菌生理盐水稀释10倍的瘙痒症脑或脾的悬液。同样也给对照组动物注射了正常小鼠脑或脾的悬液，而这些正常小鼠又在数周前被注射过正常动物的脑悬液。5天后，我们通过心脏穿刺得到2 ml～3 ml血，并用灵敏和高度特异的巨噬细胞电泳迁移（MEM）法估测淋巴细胞对瘙痒症悬液和正常悬液的致敏程度[3]。这种方法的基本原理是已致敏的淋巴细胞会释放出一种能减慢正常豚鼠巨噬细胞在电场中迁移速度的蛋白（巨噬细胞致缓因子（MSF）——可能与巨噬细胞抑制因子（MIF）为同一分子）。我们在测量中使用了蔡司细胞电泳测量装置，全部实验细节都已公布[4]。

豚鼠血淋巴细胞采用由库尔森和查默斯发明[5]并经过休斯和卡斯帕里改进[6]的方法获取。而正常豚鼠的巨噬细胞则是用肝素化的汉克氏平衡盐溶液从注射无菌液态石蜡6天～8天后的腹腔内冲洗出来的。为了消除双向混合淋巴细胞反应（至少是在测试期间），正常动物的渗出液要经过100拉德的γ射线照射[3]。

10^{-1} scrapie brain, scrapie spleen, normal brain and normal spleen suspensions were used as test antigen and for later testing lymphocyte sensitization. 0.5×10^6 guinea-pig blood lymphocytes were incubated for 90 min at 20°C with 0.1 ml. of a 10^{-1} suspension of scrapie mouse brain or spleen (cleared by spinning at $1,800g$ for 10 min) in the presence of 10^7 irradiated normal macrophages. Control tubes comprised lymphocytes and macrophages without antigen. The migration time of macrophages in each specimen was measured by timing ten cells (readily identified by their size and paraffin droplet content) in each direction of the potential difference so that a mean (with SD) from twenty readings could be calculated. A full protocol from one specimen is given by Caspary and Field[4]. All measurements were made "blind" and results unscrambled later. If t_c= migration time of control macrophage in the absence of antigen and t_e= migration time when antigen is present; then in general $t_e > t_c$ and $t_e - t_c/t_c \times 100$ is a measure of lymphocyte sensitization to the antigen.

The scrapie brain and spleen with which the guinea-pigs were inoculated were titred out by inoculation into groups of 6 mice at dilutions of 10^{-1} through 10^{-7}. The animals were observed for eight months and all clinical scrapie diagnoses were checked histologically.

Guinea-pigs were immunized with either scrapie or normal mouse brain and spleen, 0.1 ml. of a 10^{-1} suspension being inoculated intracutaneously in the dorsum of the right foot (Table 1a, b). The guinea-pig lymphocyte sensitization to normal brain and normal spleen is always greater when the animal has been injected with scrapie material than with normal (as pointed out by Gardiner[7] with respect to circulating antibody in rabbit experiments). Moreover, the scrapie-normal difference (when scrapie brain or spleen is used as test antigen for the lymphocytes) is greater in the guinea-pig immunized with scrapie brain than with normal brain. The difference appears to be greatest between five and thirteen days. Table 1b shows that the same is true when guinea-pigs immunized with scrapie or normal spleen are tested for cellular sensitization to scrapie and normal brain and spleen. The results with spleen are particularly interesting since this organ whilst rich in agent ($LD_{50}=10^{-4.7}$) shows no morphological change[8] so that the test antigen being used might well be the scrapie agent itself (or scrapie-altered but morphologically normal membrane).

Table 1. Demonstration of Scrapie Activity in Mouse Brain and Spleen

	a, Mouse scrapie brain injected guinea-pig 10^{-1}				b, Mouse scrapie spleen injected guinea-pig 10^{-1}			
	5 days	13 days	22 days	34 days	7 days	11 days	25 days	35 days
EF	12.0	15.3	11.1	4.7	6.6	9.2	11.3	2.2
Normal brain	11.3	12.5	10.3	3.4	3.4	8.9	7.6	0.8
Scrapie brain	16.5	17.9	14.3	5.4	10.1	14.2	12.3	2.6
Brain difference	5.2	5.4	4.0	2.0	6.7	5.3	4.7	1.8
Normal spleen	5.2	6.1	6.1	1.7	11.5	12.2	10.8	1.8
Scrapie spleen	9.6	11.1	10.4	3.5	17.4	17.9	15.3	3.9
Spleen difference	4.4	5.0	4.3	1.8	5.9	5.7	4.7	2.1

我们用稀释10倍的瘙痒症脑、瘙痒症脾、正常脑和正常脾悬液作为测试抗原，随后再用它们检测淋巴细胞的致敏程度。将0.5×10^6个豚鼠血淋巴细胞与0.1 ml稀释10倍的瘙痒症小鼠脑或者脾组织悬液（净化的方法是在相对离心力为1,800 g 下离心10分钟）以及10^7个经过照射的正常巨噬细胞的混合物在20℃下孵育90分钟。对照管内包含淋巴细胞和巨噬细胞，但没有抗原。每个样本中的巨噬细胞迁移时间都是由测量沿电势差任一方向移动的10个细胞（很容易通过它们的大小和石蜡滴的含量来鉴别）的迁移时间得到的，因而可以计算20个读数的平均值（包括标准差）。卡斯帕里和菲尔德[4]已经针对单独样品给出了完整的实验方案。所有测量均采用"盲法"，对结果的分析随后再进行。如果设t_c=无抗原组对照巨噬细胞的迁移时间，t_e=有抗原组的迁移时间；则一般会有$t_e > t_c$，而淋巴细胞对该抗原的致敏程度可以用 $\dfrac{t_e - t_c}{t_c} \times 100$ 来度量。

用于给豚鼠接种的瘙痒症脑和脾组织的滴度是通过将其稀释10倍~10^7倍后接种到6只为一组的小鼠体内得到的。我们对这些小鼠进行了为期8个月的观察，并用组织学方法检测了瘙痒症的所有临床诊断指标。

我们用患瘙痒症小鼠的脑和脾组织或者正常小鼠的脑和脾组织对豚鼠进行免疫，方法是将0.1 ml稀释10倍的悬液皮内接种到豚鼠右足的背部（表1a和1b）。相对于注射正常脑组织的豚鼠来说，那些注射瘙痒症脑组织的豚鼠，其淋巴细胞对正常脑和脾的敏感程度通常会更高一些（正如加德纳[7]在用实验研究兔子循环抗体时所指出的）。此外，用瘙痒症脑免疫的豚鼠比用正常脑免疫的豚鼠具有更显著的瘙痒症组织与正常组织之间的差异（当使用瘙痒症脑或者脾检测淋巴细胞的抗原时）。这种差异似乎在第5天~第13天之间最为明显。表1b说明当用瘙痒症脾或正常脾免疫的豚鼠被用于检测对瘙痒症脑和脾以及对正常脑和脾的细胞致敏程度时将会得出同样的结果。用脾实验的结果非常有意思，因为这种器官虽然富含病原体（半数致死量$LD_{50} = 10^{-4.7}$），却没有出现形态上的改变[8]，所以测试时使用的实验抗原很可能就是瘙痒症病原体本身（或者是虽然被瘙痒症改变但在形态上仍然正常的膜）。

表1. 小鼠脑和脾内的瘙痒症病原体活性数据

	a. 注射稀释10倍的瘙痒症小鼠脑悬液的豚鼠				b. 注射稀释10倍的瘙痒症小鼠脾悬液的豚鼠			
	5天	13天	22天	34天	7天	11天	25天	35天
EF	12.0	15.3	11.1	4.7	6.6	9.2	11.3	2.2
正常脑	11.3	12.5	10.3	3.4	3.4	8.9	7.6	0.8
瘙痒症脑	16.5	17.9	14.3	5.4	10.1	14.2	12.3	2.6
脑的差别	5.2	5.4	4.0	2.0	6.7	5.3	4.7	1.8
正常脾	5.2	6.1	6.1	1.7	11.5	12.2	10.8	1.8
瘙痒症脾	9.6	11.1	10.4	3.5	17.4	17.9	15.3	3.9
脾的差别	4.4	5.0	4.3	1.8	5.9	5.7	4.7	2.1

Continued

	Mouse normal brain injected guinea-pig				Mouse normal spleen injected guinea-pig			
	5 days	13 days	22 days	34 days	7 days	11 days	25 days	35 days
EF	12.0	13.5	9.6	3.0	6.2	8.7	8.2	2.4
Normal brain	9.9	13.7	9.4	2.5	4.0	6.2	6.9	1.5
Scrapie brain	12.1	15.5	10.3	3.2	5.7	8.2	8.4	2.4
Brain difference	2.2	1.8	0.9	1.3	1.7	2.0	1.5	0.9
Normal spleen	4.0	5.9	6.2	1.2	13.9	13.9	11.4	2.7
Scrapie spleen	6.2	7.7	7.6	2.2	14.6	15.7	13.3	3.5
Spleen difference	2.2	1.8	1.4	1.0	0.7	1.8	1.9	0.8

Adult Hartley guinea-pigs inoculated intracutaneously in the dorsum of the right foot with 0.1 ml. 10^{-1} crapie brain or spleen (titre 10^{-6}; $10^{-4.7}$ respectively) and lymphocyte sensitization to scrapie and normal brain measured at intervals by the macrophage electrophoresis method of Field and Caspary[3]. Results expressed as percentage slowing (*loc. cit.*).

In the case of inoculation with scrapie brain, however, the difference may perhaps be attributed to morphological changes (especially astrocyte increase) in the inoculated material. Having established the quantitative difference in response to scrapie as opposed to normal tissue we used this method to titre out scrapie activity.

Guinea-pigs were injected with scrapie brain at dilutions of 10^{-1} to 10^{-6} and the lymphocytes examined for sensitization to scrapie brain or spleen and normal brain or spleen at six or seven days and at seventeen or eighteen days. For comparison a similar study was made in guinea-pigs injected with normal brain (Tables 2 and 3). In the scrapie brain sensitized guinea-pig the difference in lymphocyte sensitization to scrapie as compared with normal brain is 2.5% ($P<0.01$) even at 10^{-6} original inoculum level when the guinea-pig is tested at six days but falls to 2.0% ($P =0.1-0.05$) by sixteen days. When sensitization to scrapie spleen and normal spleen in these animals is compared, the difference is significant only in guinea-pigs which have received 10^{-4} scrapie brain.

Table 2. Titration of Scrapie Activity from Mouse Brain

Antigen	Lymphocytes tested at 6 days					Lymphocytes tested at 16 days		
	10^{-1}	10^{-2}	10^{-3}	10^{-4}	10^{-6}	10^{-2}	10^{-4}	10^{-6}
	% macrophage slowing							
	Scrapie brain							
Normal mouse brain	11.3	11.0	8.1	5.7	3.7	11.1	5.9	3.9
Scrapie brain	16.5	14.1	11.7	9.6	5.2	14.7	9.9	5.9
Brain difference	5.2	3.1	3.6	3.9	2.5	3.6	4.0	2.0
Normal mouse spleen	5.2	6.1	4.7	3.9	1.7	5.9	4.7	2.9
Scrapie mouse spleen	9.6	10.8	8.1	7.4	3.2	10.1	8.1	4.4
Spleen difference	4.4	4.7	3.4	3.5	1.5	4.2	3.4	1.5
	Normal brain							
Normal mouse brain		8.9		7.1	5.9	9.6	5.5	4.4
Scrapie mouse brain		10.3		7.9	6.7	10.1	6.5	5.2
Brain difference		1.4		0.6	0.8	0.5	1.0	0.8
Normal mouse spleen		5.4		2.5	3.0	6.1	4.4	3.5

	注射正常小鼠脑悬液的豚鼠				注射正常小鼠脾悬液的豚鼠			
	5天	13天	22天	34天	7天	11天	25天	35天
EF	12.0	13.5	9.6	3.0	6.2	8.7	8.2	2.4
正常脑	9.9	13.7	9.4	2.5	4.0	6.2	6.9	1.5
瘙痒症脑	12.1	15.5	10.3	3.2	5.7	8.2	8.4	2.4
脑的差别	2.2	1.8	0.9	1.3	1.7	2.0	1.5	0.9
正常脾	4.0	5.9	6.2	1.2	13.9	13.9	11.4	2.7
瘙痒症脾	6.2	7.7	7.6	2.2	14.6	15.7	13.3	3.5
脾的差别	2.2	1.8	1.4	1.0	0.7	1.8	1.9	0.8

在成年哈特利豚鼠右足背部皮内接种 0.1 ml 稀释 10 倍的瘙痒症脑或者脾组织液（滴度分别为 10^{-6} 和 $10^{-4.7}$），然后每隔一定时间用菲尔德和卡斯帕里发明的巨噬细胞电泳迁移法 [3] 测定淋巴细胞对瘙痒症脑和正常脑的致敏程度。结果以迁移减慢的百分比表示（见上文）。

然而，在接种瘙痒症脑的实验中，其差异或许可以归因于接种物的形态变化（尤其是星形细胞的增加）。在确认对瘙痒症组织和对正常组织的反应存在量上的差异之后，我们就可以使用这种方法来测定瘙痒症病原体的活性了。

给豚鼠注射稀释10倍~10^6倍的瘙痒症脑组织，然后在第6天或第7天以及第17天或第18天检测淋巴细胞对瘙痒症脑或脾以及对正常脑或脾的致敏程度。为了便于对比，我们用注射过正常脑组织的豚鼠进行了类似的实验（表2和表3）。在瘙痒症脑致敏的豚鼠中，即便原始接种物被稀释至10^6倍，到第6天时淋巴细胞对瘙痒症脑和正常脑的致敏程度之差也可以达到2.5%（$P<0.01$），但在第16天时降到了2.0%（$P=0.1\sim0.05$）。当比较豚鼠对瘙痒症脾和正常脾的致敏程度时，只有在注射稀释至10^4倍及以下瘙痒症脑的豚鼠中才会出现明显的差别。

表2. 小鼠脑的瘙痒症病原体活性滴定

抗原	测试第6天的淋巴细胞					测试第16天的淋巴细胞		
	稀释10^1倍	稀释10^2倍	稀释10^3倍	稀释10^4倍	稀释10^6倍	稀释10^2倍	稀释10^4倍	稀释10^6倍
	巨噬细胞迁移减慢的%							
	瘙痒症脑							
正常小鼠脑	11.3	11.0	8.1	5.7	3.7	11.1	5.9	3.9
瘙痒症脑	16.5	14.1	11.7	9.6	5.2	14.7	9.9	5.9
脑的差别	5.2	3.1	3.6	3.9	2.5	5.9	4.7	2.9
正常小鼠脾	5.2	6.1	4.7	3.9	1.7	5.9	4.7	2.9
瘙痒症小鼠脾	9.6	10.8	8.1	7.4	3.2	10.1	8.1	4.4
脾的差别	4.4	4.7	3.4	3.5	1.5	4.2	3.4	1.5
	正常脑							
正常小鼠脑		8.9		7.1	5.9	9.6	5.5	4.4
瘙痒症小鼠脑		10.3		7.9	6.7	10.1	6.5	5.2
脑的差别		1.4		0.6	0.8	0.5	1.0	0.8
正常小鼠脾		5.4		2.5	3.0	6.1	4.4	3.5

Continued

	Normal brain					
Scrapie mouse spleen	6.2	3.8	4.2	7.2	5.7	4.5
Spleen difference	0.8	1.3	1.2	1.1	1.3	1.0

Guinea-pigs inoculated with scrapie mouse brain with a titre of $10^{-5.6}$. 0.1 ml. inoculated at different dilutions.

Table 3. Titration of Scrapie Activity from Mouse Spleen

Antigen	Lymphocytes tested at 7 days						Lymphocytes tested at 17 days		
	10^{-1}	10^{-2}	10^{-3}	10^{-4}	10^{-5}	10^{-6}	10^{-2}	10^{-4}	10^{-6}
	% macrophage slowing								
	Scrapie spleen								
Normal mouse brain	3.4	4.5	2.7	1.0	1.7	0	4.7	1.5	0.7
Scrapie brain	10.1	10.3	7.2	4.4	3.8	1.2	10.1	4.9	1.5
Brain difference	6.7	5.8	4.5	3.4	2.1	1.2	5.4	3.4	0.8
Normal mouse spleen	11.5	12.6	10.4	10.6	8.1	4.5	11.1	10.0	4.4
Scrapie mouse spleen	17.4	17.0	15.3	14.4	10.8	6.3	15.0	13.8	6.2
Spleen difference	5.9	4.4	4.9	3.8	2.7	1.8	3.9	3.8	1.8
	Normal spleen								
Normal mouse brain		4.5		1.5		1.0	6.4	3.0	1.8
Scrapie mouse brain		5.9		2.9		1.2	7.6	4.4	2.9
Brain difference		1.4		1.4		0.2	1.2	1.4	1.1
Normal mouse spleen		11.1		9.1		4.7	10.5	7.9	4.7
Scrapie mouse spleen		12.4		10.2		6.4	11.5	8.9	5.6
Spleen difference		1.3		1.1		1.7	0.9	1.0	0.9

Guinea-pigs inoculated with spleen suspension with a titre of 10^{-5}. 0.1 ml. inoculated at different dilutions.

Animals injected with normal brain showed no significant difference when their lymphocytes were tested with scrapie as opposed to normal brain or spleen (though in general the values with the former were higher).

Guinea-pigs were sensitized by injecting scrapie spleen at 10^{-1} to 10^{-6} and their lymphocytes tested for sensitization to scrapie brain and spleen (Table 3). A significant difference between sensitization to scrapie and normal spleen still exists at 10^{-5} ($P<0.01$) with spleen as antigen but barely with brain (2.1% difference; $P=0.05$), showing apparent scrapie antigenicity in the 10^{-5} dilution.

The titre of the scrapie brain inoculated into the test guinea-pigs was calculated to be $LD_{50}=10^{-5.6}$. We noted that 1/6 mice developed scrapie at 10^{-6} and 1/6 at 10^{-7} and the immunological test suggests that some activity is still present at 10^{-6}. The titre of spleen used for immunizing the guinea-pigs was $LD_{50}=10^{-5}$. The results of *in vivo* titration therefore agree with the *in vitro* immunological assay, and the significance of these results is two-fold. (1) Attempts to show the existence of circulating antibody and/or specific antigen in scrapie disease have not been successful[7,8]. Gardiner did show by inoculation of rabbits with scrapie and non-scrapie spleen material that the latter had increased antigenicity *in*

		正常脑				
瘙痒症小鼠脾		6.2	3.8	4.2	7.2	5.7	4.5
脾的差别		0.8	1.3	1.2	1.1	1.3	1.0

接种滴度为$10^{-5.6}$的瘙痒症小鼠脑组织的豚鼠。对每种不同的稀释度都接种0.1 ml。

表3. 小鼠脾的瘙痒症病原体活性滴定

抗原	测试第7天的淋巴细胞						测试第17天的淋巴细胞		
	稀释10^1倍	稀释10^2倍	稀释10^3倍	稀释10^4倍	稀释10^5倍	稀释10^6倍	稀释10^2倍	稀释10^4倍	稀释10^6倍
	巨噬细胞迁移减慢的%								
	瘙痒症脾								
正常小鼠脑	3.4	4.5	2.7	1.0	1.7	0	4.7	1.5	0.7
瘙痒症脑	10.1	10.3	7.2	4.4	3.8	1.2	10.1	4.9	1.5
脑的差别	6.7	5.8	4.5	3.4	2.1	1.2	5.4	3.4	0.8
正常小鼠脾	11.5	12.6	10.4	10.6	8.1	4.5	11.1	10.0	4.4
瘙痒症小鼠脾	17.4	17.0	15.3	14.4	10.8	6.3	15.0	13.8	6.2
脾的差别	5.9	4.4	4.9	3.8	2.7	1.8	3.9	3.8	1.8
	正常脾								
正常小鼠脑		4.5		1.5		1.0	6.4	3.0	1.8
瘙痒症小鼠脑		5.9		2.9		1.2	7.6	4.4	2.9
脑的差别		1.4		1.4		0.2	1.2	1.4	1.1
正常小鼠脾		11.1		9.1		4.7	10.5	7.9	4.7
瘙痒症小鼠脾		12.4		10.2		6.4	11.5	8.9	5.6
脾的差别		1.3		1.1		1.7	0.9	1.0	0.9

接种滴度为10^{-5}的瘙痒症小鼠脾组织悬液的豚鼠。对每种不同的稀释度都接种0.1 ml。

对于注射正常脑组织的动物，其淋巴细胞对瘙痒症脑或脾的致敏程度与其对正常脑或脾的致敏程度相比并无显著差异（尽管从总体情况来看前者的数值要大一些）。

给豚鼠注射稀释 10 倍 $\sim 10^6$ 倍的瘙痒症脾组织使之致敏，然后检测它们的淋巴细胞对瘙痒症脑和脾的致敏程度（表3）。在用脾作为抗原时，淋巴细胞对瘙痒症脾和正常脾的致敏程度在稀释 10^5 倍时仍存在明显的差异（$P<0.01$），但在用脑作抗原时则只有很小的差异（差异为2.1%，$P=0.05$），这说明在稀释 10^5 倍时会出现明显的瘙痒症抗原性。

对接种到实验豚鼠上的瘙痒症脑组织的滴度进行计算所得的结果是$LD_{50}=10^{-5.6}$。我们注意到在稀释10^6倍时有1/6的小鼠染上了瘙痒症，在稀释10^7倍时也会有1/6发病，免疫学实验证明在稀释10^6倍时仍存在一些活性。用于免疫豚鼠的脾组织的滴度为$LD_{50}=10^{-5}$。这样，体内滴定结果就与体外免疫学检测结果取得了一致，因而上述结果的重要性是双重的。（1）目前人们在瘙痒症患者体内寻找循环抗体和/或特异性抗原的尝试尚未取得成功[7,8]。加德纳在将瘙痒症和非瘙痒症脾组织接种到兔子中

vivo. The present work extends these very important findings in that it suggests that this is true also of lymphocyte sensitization and that the reactivity is greater against scrapie material (both brain and spleen) than against normal material. This suggests that some specific antigen—perhaps the agent itself, or specifically agent-altered material since the spleen is so potent as a testing tissue—may be active. The macrophage electrophoretic migration (MEM) method is exquisitely responsive to minor changes in antigenic determinant structure and appears to be able to distinguish between normal and scrapie tissue. It is, of course, not possible to decide whether the difference resides in the presence of a specific scrapie agent or whether we are dealing with a structural (antigenic) change induced by the agent. However, if scrapie infected brain is split into a neuronal and glial compartment by the method of Giorgi (unpublished) then, contrary to expectations based on the precocious glial hypertrophy, higher scrapie titre is associated with the neuronal rather than the glial fraction and it is in the former that particles with the size and structural characters postulated for scrapie agent have been found[9]. (2) Lymphocyte sensitization test enables the presence of scrapie to be established and titration carried out within 8 days, an important saving in time during the study of this fascinating condition. Further experiments are in progress involving the use of Freund's adjuvant to boost the responses. A full account of these experiments will be published elsewhere.

(**240**, 104-106; 1972)

E. J. Field and B. K. Shenton: Medical Research Council, Demyelinating Diseases Unit, Newcastle General Hospital, Westgate Road, Newcastle upon Tyne NE4 6BE.

Received July 25, 1972.

References:
1. Chandler, R. L., *Lancet*, ii, 1378 (1961).
2. Field, E. J., *Int. Rev. Exp. Path.*, **8**, 129 (1969).
3. Field, E. J., and Caspary, E. A., *Lancet*, ii, 1337 (1970).
4. Caspary, E. A., and Field, E. J., *Brit. Med. J.*, **2**, 613 (1971).
5. Coulson, A. S., and Chalmers, D. G., *Immunology*, **12**, 417 (1967).
6. Hughes, D., and Caspary, E. A., *Int. Arch. Allergy*, **37**, 506 (1970).
7. Gardiner, A. C., *Res. Vet. Sci.*, **7**, 190 (1966).
8. Chandler, R. L., *Vet. Rec.*, **71**, 58 (1959).
9. Narang, H. K., Shenton, B., Giorgi, P. P., and Field, E. J., *Nature*, **240**, 106 (1972).

后确实发现后者在体内的抗原性增加了。我们的研究拓展了这些非常重要的发现，因为它表明淋巴细胞的致敏也是存在的，并且对瘙痒症组织（无论是脑还是脾）的反应性要比对正常组织的强。这意味着某些特异性抗原可能是具有活性的，这些特异性抗原也许就是病原体本身，或者是特异性的病原体改变的物质，因为脾脏是一种非常有效的检测用组织。巨噬细胞电泳迁移（MEM）法对抗原决定结构的微小变化反应很敏感，应该能够辨别出正常组织和瘙痒症组织。当然，我们不可能裁断这种差异能不能归因于某种特定的瘙痒症病原体，也不能说明我们是否检测到了由病原体导致的结构（抗原性）改变。但是，如果利用乔治的方法（尚未发表）将瘙痒症感染的脑分为神经元部分和胶质细胞部分，那么与根据胶质细胞过早肥大得到的预期相反，对应于较高滴度瘙痒症病原体的并不是胶质细胞部分，而是神经元部分，也正是在神经元内人们找到了具有疑似瘙痒症病原体大小和结构特征的颗粒[9]。

（2）我们可以通过淋巴细胞致敏实验来确定瘙痒症病原体的存在，并能在8天内得到滴定的结果，这为研究这个非常吸引人的问题节省了大量的时间。我们正在进行更多的实验，其中包括用弗氏佐剂来加强反应。这些实验的完整细节将在其他论文中详述。

（毛晨晖 翻译；刘佳佳 审稿）

Scrapie Agent and Neurones

H. K. Narang *et al.*

Editor's Note

The search for the infectious agent behind scrapie and similar neurodegenerative disorders had previously focused on a non-neuronal cell type called glia, which appeared swollen in the infected brain. Here Harash Narang and colleagues provide evidence that the scrapie agent primarily targets neurons rather than glia. They see numerous tiny elongated particles inside the neurons of scrapie-infected rats brains which, they suggest, could be the elusive scrapie agent. It is now thought the infectious agent in most transmissible spongiform encephalopathies is a misshapen protein called a prion, and that whilst neurons are the prime target of damage within the brain, glia are also involved.

THE nature of the scrapie agent[1,2] is of considerable interest especially as to whether it is a virus in the strict sense, or some replicating agent devoid of nucleic acid[3,4], or indeed whether scrapie disease represents a transmissible progressive biochemical transformation of cellular membranes[5,6]. Thorough electron microscope studies have been carried out in the disease and, although a number of particles have (not unexpectedly) been described[7,8], their role in scrapie is unconfirmed, especially as none has the special features associated with virions or has the size or other characters currently attributed to the agent.

During careful search in the brain of the scrapie rat granular inclusion bodies were seen in the cytoplasm of apparently normal neurones and their axons in the sites studied; the cortex, Ammon's horn and thalamus. At high magnification these uninteresting neuronal inclusions comprised very large numbers of minute elongated particles about 60 nm long and 20 nm wide, with a dense linear core about 4 nm wide (Figs. 1 and 2). When these particles had once been recognized they were also quickly found in blocks of scrapie rat brain which had been examined years ago.

瘙痒症病原体与神经元

纳兰等

编者按

以前对瘙痒症和类似的神经退行性疾病致病因子的搜寻集中在被称为胶质细胞的非神经元细胞上，因为它在被感染的脑内会出现肿胀现象。在这篇论文中，哈拉什·纳兰及其同事提出证据证明瘙痒症病原体的主要靶标是神经元而非胶质细胞。他们在感染瘙痒症的大鼠脑神经元中发现了数量众多的细长形小颗粒，并指出这些小颗粒可能就是难于发现的瘙痒症病原体。现在人们认为：大多数传染性海绵状脑病的致病因子是一种被称为朊病毒的畸形蛋白质，虽然神经元是脑内受损害的主要靶标，但胶质细胞也会受到牵连。

瘙痒症病原体的本质[1,2]是个非常有趣的问题，尤其在于：它是一种严格意义上的病毒，还是某种没有核酸的可复制病原体[3,4]；或者，瘙痒症是否确实反映了细胞膜的一种可传染的进行性生物化学转化[5,6]。人们利用电子显微镜对该病进行了深入的研究，尽管已经对大量的颗粒进行过（意料之中的）描述[7,8]，但它们在瘙痒症中的作用尚不确定，尤其是因为所有这些颗粒都不具备与病毒相关的特征，其大小或其他特征也与目前所认为的病原体不相符合。

对患瘙痒症大鼠脑内进行仔细搜索时，在皮层、阿蒙氏角和丘脑部位看似正常的神经细胞胞质及其轴突中发现了一些颗粒状包涵体。在高倍镜下，这些不引人注目的神经元包涵体中含有数量众多的长约 60 nm、宽约 20 nm 的细长形颗粒，颗粒中有一约 4 nm 宽的致密线性核（图1和图2）。首次识别出这些颗粒之后，很快在数年前已研究过的患瘙痒症大鼠脑块中再次找到。

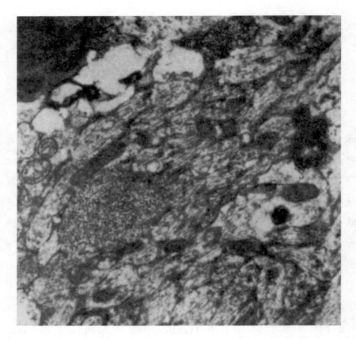

Fig. 1. Scrapie rat thalamus. Axon close to a nerve cell body showing a colony-like accumulation of small elongated particles not bounded by membrane. The neurotubular and other constituents of the axon are normal. ×20,625.

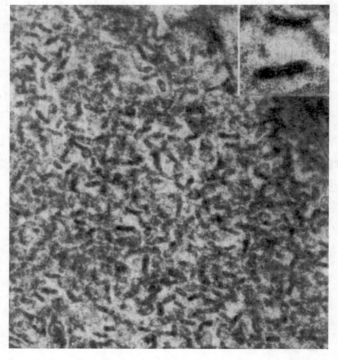

Fig. 2. High power view of colony. Note elongated particles often with dense core (see inset), about 60 nm long and 20 nm wide. The core is about 4 nm thick. Tilting and rotating the preparation confirm the discrete character of the particles. ×72,000; inset, ×208,000.

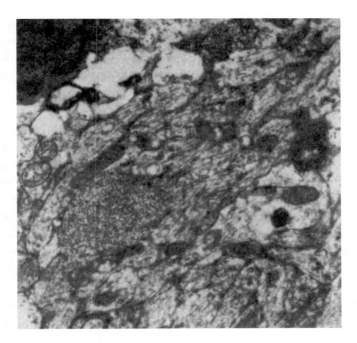

图 1. 患瘙痒症大鼠的丘脑。在靠近神经细胞体的轴突内显示无包膜细长形小颗粒的集落样聚集。轴突的神经管和其他成分都正常。放大 20,625 倍。

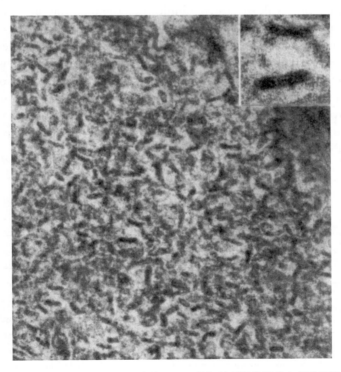

图 2. 集落的高倍图像。注意，长约 60 nm、宽约 20 nm 的细长形颗粒通常含有致密核（见右上角的小图）。核的宽度约为 4 nm。通过倾斜和旋转该样本证明这些颗粒是分离的。放大 72,000 倍；右上角小图，放大 208,000 倍。

A thorough and realistic search of comparable normal rat brain has not revealed similar particles though the vagaries of electron microscope sampling must constantly be borne in mind. The size of the particles is about that deduced from modern infectivity filtration experiments[9]. Moreover the size of central rod accords well with that of the target nucleic acid estimate made by Alper *et al.*[3,4] and by Latarjet *et al.*[10].

If the particles described are indeed scrapie agent, it is surprising to find them in neurones rather than glial cells since there is widespread agreement that the first element in the nervous system to react in the scrapie process is the astroglia[11-13] and the working assumption has been made that colonization of astroglial cells by the agent is responsible for their precocious hypertrophy. Indeed we have tended to concentrate search on glial cells, even though unusual neurological reactions may be detected early in the incubation period[14]. Simultaneously with the electron microscope findings here reported, unexpected collateral evidence has emerged that the agent may in fact proliferate in neurones rather than glial cells.

Preparations of neuronal and glial perikarya have been obtained from scrapie mouse brain using a modification (Giorgi, unpublished work) of the method of Sellinger *et al.*[15]. To these preparations we have applied the macrophage electrophoretic method of titration of scrapie agent[16] in a study of the apportionment of scrapie activity in infected brain as between neuronal and glial compartments. The method briefly consists in immunizing guinea-pigs with successive dilutions of the material under test and measuring the degree of sensitization developed by the lymphocytes to scrapie brain (or spleen) and to normal brain (or spleen) as antigen. To our surprise there was clearly more scrapie activity associated with the neurone enriched fraction than with the glial compartment (Table 1). It might well be that the scrapie agent (or process) affects, or at least reaches greater development within, neurones and that glial changes, even though they are more conspicuous, have the consequential character they are usually assigned in neuropathology. The present work illustrates the synergism of different disciplines in approaching the problem of slow infection.

Table 1. Immunological Titration of Scrapie Activity

Antigen	Neuronal compartment				Glial compartment			
	10^{-1}	10^{-2}	10^{-3}	10^{-4}	10^{-1}	10^{-2}	10^{-3}	10^{-4}
Normal mouse brain	9.1	9.9	8.5	6.7	8.6	7.7	7.1	6.9
Scrapie mouse brain	14.6	13.9	11.3	9.2	11.3	8.1	8.4	8.1
Brain difference	5.5	4.0	2.8	2.5*	2.7	0.4	1.3	1.2
Normal mouse spleen	6.0	5.9	5.7	4.9	6.2	6.2	5.6	4.4
Scrapie mouse spleen	9.7	9.4	9.1	8.2	9.1	8.2	6.9	6.5
Spleen difference	3.7	3.5	3.4	3.3	2.9	2.0	1.3	2.1

* With the degree of scatter in our readings a difference of 2.5% corresponds to $P<0.01$.

Guinea-pigs inoculated intracutaneously in right foot with 10^{-1} to 10^{-4} preparations of neurones and glial cells from mouse scrapie brain (0.1 ml. in each case; equivalent to 300 µg to 0.3 µg protein). Sensitization of the guinea-pig lymphocytes with respect to 10^{-1} scrapie brain and spleen and also to normal brain

在对正常大鼠脑内进行认真而彻底的搜寻之后并没有发现类似的颗粒，不过应该提请注意的是，电子显微镜在取样上具有难以预测性。这些颗粒的大小与由现代传染性筛选实验推断的结果大体一致[9]。此外，中心杆状体的大小与阿尔珀等人[3,4]和拉塔尔热等人[10]估计的目标核酸的尺寸非常符合。

如果所描述的颗粒确实是瘙痒症病原体，那么在神经细胞而不是胶质细胞内发现这些颗粒是很令人惊讶的，因为大家普遍认为在神经系统内对瘙痒症过程作出反应的第一个元素是星形胶质细胞[11-13]，并已假定病原体在星形胶质细胞内的定居是胶质细胞早期肥大的原因。确实，我们一直倾向于集中精力搜索胶质细胞，尽管在潜伏早期就有可能检测到不正常的神经反应[14]。现在又有一个意想不到的证据可以证明本文所报道的电子显微镜结果，即病原体实际上有可能是在神经元内而不是在胶质细胞内增殖的。

利用经改进的塞林杰等人的方法[15]（乔治，尚未发表的研究结果），从患瘙痒症小鼠脑内提取出了神经元和胶质细胞的核周体。在研究瘙痒症活性在感染脑的神经元和胶质细胞间的分配时，我们运用巨噬细胞电泳法对这些提取物进行瘙痒症病原体的滴定[16]。这个方法只需用连续稀释度的待测物免疫豚鼠，并测量淋巴细胞相对于作为抗原的瘙痒症脑（或者脾）和正常脑（或者脾）的致敏程度。令我们惊讶的是，瘙痒症病原体活性在神经元富集区要明显高于胶质细胞区（表1）。瘙痒症病原体（或者过程）可能会影响神经元，或者至少在神经元内有更显著的发展；而胶质细胞的变化，尽管更加明显，却通常是神经病理学中继发的特征。本文可以说明不同学科在解决慢性感染问题中的协同作用。

表 1. 瘙痒症病原体活性的免疫滴定分析

抗原	神经元区				胶质细胞区			
	10^{-1}	10^{-2}	10^{-3}	10^{-4}	10^{-1}	10^{-2}	10^{-3}	10^{-4}
正常小鼠脑	9.1	9.9	8.5	6.7	8.6	7.7	7.1	6.9
瘙痒症小鼠脑	14.6	13.9	11.3	9.2	11.3	8.1	8.4	8.1
脑的差别	5.5	4.0	2.8	2.5*	2.7	0.4	1.3	1.2
正常小鼠脾	6.0	5.9	5.7	4.9	6.2	6.2	5.6	4.4
瘙痒症小鼠脾	9.7	9.4	9.1	8.2	9.1	8.2	6.9	6.5
脾的差别	3.7	3.5	3.4	3.3	2.9	2.0	1.3	2.1

* 读数的离散度为：2.5%的差异，对应于$P<0.01$。
在豚鼠的右足皮内接种浓度为10^{-1}~10^{-4}的患瘙痒症小鼠脑内神经元和胶质细胞的提取物（每次 0.1 ml，相当于 300 μg ~ 0.3 μg 蛋白质）。采用巨噬细胞电泳减慢法测量豚鼠淋巴细胞相对于10^{-1}浓度的瘙痒症

and spleen is measured by the macrophage electrophoretic slowing method and expressed as percentage slowing of macrophages[17].

(**240**, 106-107; 1972)

H. K. Narang, B. Shenton, P. P. Giorgi, E. J. Field: Medical Research Council, Demyelinating Diseases Unit, Newcastle General Hospital, Westgate Road, Newcastle upon Tyne NE 4 6BE.

Received July 25, 1972.

References:

1. *Nature*, 214, 755 (1967).

2. *Lancet*, ii, 705 (1967).

3. Alper, T., Haig, D. A., and Clarke, M. C., *Biochem. Biophys. Res. Commun.*, 22, 278 (1966).

4. Alper, T., Cramp, W. A., Haig, D. A., and Clarke, M. C., *Nature*, 214, 764 (1967).

5. Gibbons, R. A., and Hunter, G. D., *Nature*, 215, 1041 (1967).

6. Hunter, G. D., in *Proc. VI Int. Congr. Neuropathol.*, 802 (Masson, Paris, 1970).

7. David-Ferreira, J. B., David-Ferreira, K. L., Gibbs, C. J., and Morris, J. A., *Proc. Soc. Exp. Biol. Med.*, 127, 313 (1968).

8. Bignami, A., and Parry, H. B., *Science*, 171, 389 (1971).

9. Hunter, G. D., *J. Infect. Dis.*, 125, 427 (1972).

10. Latarjet, R., Muel, B., Haig, D. A., Clarke, M. C., and Alper, T., *Nature*, 227, 1341 (1970).

11. Pattison, I. H., in *Slow, Latent and Temperate Virus Infections, NINDB Monograph No. 2*, 249 (1965).

12. Hadlow, W. J., discussion in *Slow, Latent and Temperate Virus Infections, NINDB Monograph No. 2*, 303 (1965).

13. Field, E. J., *Int. Rev. Exp. Pathol.*, 8 (Acad. Press, New York and Canada, 1969).

14. Savage, R. D., and Field, E. J., *Anim. Behav.*, 13, 443 (1965).

15. Sellinger, O. Z., Azcurra, J. M., Johnson, D. E., Ohlsson, W. G., and Lodin, Z., *Nature New Biology*, 230, 253 (1971).

16. Field, E. J., and Shenton, B., *Nature*, 240, 104 (1972).

17. Field, E. J., and Caspary, E. A., *Lancet*, ii, 1337 (1970).

脑和脾以及正常脑和脾的致敏程度，并用减慢的巨噬细胞百分比来表示[17]。

（毛晨晖 翻译；李素霞 审稿）

Problems of Predicting Earthquakes

T. Rikitake

Editor's Note

The questions posed here by geophysicist Tsuneji Rikitake of the University of Tokyo — how can the earthquake hazard be prevented, and is it possible to predict them? — remain unanswered and contentious today. Because of the great earthquake hazard that exists in Japan, much of the important work on their prediction has happened there. The Earthquake Research Institute, where Rikitake was based, was established in 1925, but he explains here that it had been in disarray for two years because of disputes about working conditions. It recovered and still exists, but its goal of understanding and forecasting earthquakes remains challenging. Some believe that prediction may be impossible in principle, an idea that is politically as well as scientifically controversial in Japan.

MORE than 100,000 lives were lost and about 700,000 houses were destroyed, mostly by fire, during and after the great Kanto earthquake that hit the Tokyo–Yokohama area on September 1, 1923 (Kanto is the name of the area surrounding Tokyo). This was surely the worst ever in Japan, which has long suffered from disastrous events of this kind.

Why does Japan suffer from earthquakes? How can the earthquake hazard be prevented? What causes an earthquake? Is it at all possible to forecast them? In spite of widespread interest, nobody could answer these questions properly, and Japanese politicians and government officials thus became aware of the importance of understanding basic earthquake phenomena.

This was the motivation for founding the Earthquake Research Institute (ERI), attached to the Tokyo Imperial University (now the University of Tokyo), in 1925. A number of outstanding physicists, engineers, geographers and geologists of the time were appointed to chairs at the institute, but they were almost all part-time. Gradually, however, fresh graduates in physics, seismology and geology joined them in the years that followed, thus forming a research team whose energetic work heralded a new phase in earthquake research in Japan. The first director of the institute was Y. Suyehiro, originally a professor of shipbuilding engineering.

The institute, a tiny two-storied building made of reinforced concrete, was located immediately behind the university clock tower, which became world famous in 1969 because of the fight between rioting students (*Zengakuren*) and the police. As no one then knew how to construct a building that was reasonably resistive to the most serious earthquake anticipated, the building was constructed as rigidly as possible. Two seismographs with identical characteristics were placed in the basement and on the roof,

地震预报的风波

力武常次

编者按

东京大学的地球物理学家力武常次在本文中提出了两个问题：如何才能避免地震带来的灾害？地震预报能否实现？这两个问题至今仍悬而未决并且还在争议之中。因为日本是一个地震灾害多发的国家，所以日本科学家曾开展了许多关于地震预报方面的重要研究工作。力武常次所在的地震研究所成立于1925年，但他在本文中提到：由于大家在工作条件方面存在争执，该研究所曾经历了长达两年的混乱期。后来它得以恢复并保留至今，但是人们对它致力于了解和预测地震的目标仍持怀疑态度。有些人认为，地震预报在理论上是不可能实现的，这一观点在日本政界和科学界都存在争议。

1923年9月1日发生的关东大地震（东京周边地区被称为关东）对东京－横滨地区造成了严重破坏，震时及震后共有10万余人丧生，约70万幢房屋被毁，火灾是主要原因。尽管地震灾害在日本时有发生，但这一次确实是有史以来最严重的一次。

为什么日本会经常发生地震？怎样预防地震灾害？地震产生的原因是什么？人类确实有可能预测地震吗？虽然这些问题引起了广泛关注，但没有人能给出满意的答案，于是日本的领导人和政府官员开始意识到了解地震基本现象的重要性。

正是基于这样的初衷，地震研究所（ERI）于1925年成立，设在东京帝国大学（今东京大学）。当时许多杰出的物理学家、工程师、地理学家和地质学家被委派到该研究所任职，不过几乎所有人员都是兼职。后来又有一些物理学、地震学和地质学专业的应届毕业生陆续加入其中，进而形成了一支研究队伍。经过他们的不懈努力，日本地震研究步入了一个崭新的阶段。该研究所的第一任所长是末广恭二，他原本是一位船舶工程学的教授。

研究所的办公地点是一座钢混结构的两层小楼，坐落于东京大学钟楼的后面。1969年，暴动学生（全学联）与警察之间发生的那场冲突使这座小楼闻名于世。由于当时没有人知道如何去建造一座足以抵御目前可知的最严重地震的建筑，因此只能把办公楼建造得尽可能坚固。两台性能相同的地震仪分别被放置在地下室和楼顶

and, in fact, produced exactly the same seismograms.

Only 30 to 40 people, including technicians, porters and clerks in the administrative section, worked in the institute before the Second World War. There was no sectionalism in those good old days; one could go into any laboratory and use any instrument freely, provided it was not in use. But things have changed recently because a new building about ten times as large as the original one has been built in the northernmost corner of the university campus and some 200 people are now working there. The family atmosphere has inevitably vanished from such a large community where people do not know each other very well.

Starting from Scratch

There was much to learn about earthquake phenomena in the early days of the ERI. Seismology in Japan was started off by professors who had been invited there from western countries in the years that followed 1868. After the violent Nobi earthquake of 1891, the Imperial Earthquake Investigation Committee was set up; it conducted several field studies over seismic and volcanic areas and published many useful reports. The knowledge thus accumulated was, however, descriptive rather than scientific. Accordingly, the founders of the ERI had to start by doing very elementary experiments, like measuring ground motions as well as vibrations of a building during an earthquake and examining seismic wave propagation, in the hope of achieving a comprehensive understanding of earthquake phenomena on a scientific level.

M. Ishimoto, who was the second director of the ERI for ten years, designed and constructed a then revolutionary accelerometer by means of which the acceleration of earthquake motion was first measured. He also invented a silica horizontal-pendulum tiltmeter for measuring an extremely small tilt in the Earth's surface. K. Sezawa, an eminent mathematician, set out a general solution of elastic waves in spherical polar coordinates, and his theory subsequently had many applications to problems concerned with the propagation of body and surface waves. It was fortunate for ERI, although not for the local people, that a number of large scale earthquakes took place in Japan immediately after its establishment. The staff, who promptly made observations over the earthquake area, learned much about earthquake phenomena in this way. It is of particular importance that marked land deformations were shown up by analyzing levelling and triangulation surveys carried out before and after an earthquake.

The ERI's impact during its first ten years was so remarkable that many new facts about earthquake phenomena were discovered. Probably the most flourishing period in the history of ERI was, however, the following five years in which intensive seismometric studies, electric and magnetic experiments and field studies and observations on volcanoes were undertaken respectively by T. Hagiwara, T. Nagata and T. Minakami, who were later to become leading Japanese geophysicists. Regrettably the work of the ERI had to be curtailed during the Second World War.

上，实际上由它们测得的地震图是完全相同的。

第二次世界大战以前，该研究所仅有30~40人，其中包括技术人员、杂务工和行政人员。在那个美好的年代没有本位主义，人们可以自由地进入任意一间实验室，使用任意一台仪器，只要当时没人在用。然而，近些年情况发生了变化，因为在大学校园的最北端又建成了一幢大约是原办公楼10倍大小的新建筑，目前在那里工作的人员已经达到了200人左右。在这样一个人与人之间了解不够多的大团体中，那种家庭气氛不可避免地消失了。

白 手 起 家

在地震研究所成立之初，人们对很多地震现象并不了解。日本的地震学兴起于1868年，那个时期的研究人员都是从西方国家邀请来的教授。在1891年浓尾大地震后，日本成立了皇家地震调查委员会，该组织对震区、火山区进行了多次野外考察，并发表了大量有价值的报告。然而，所收集到的内容仅是对现象的描述，科学含量不高。因此，地震研究所的创办者们不得不从最基本的实验做起，比如测定地震发生时地面的运动及建筑物的震动并检测地震波的传播等，以期从科学层面上实现对地震现象的全面了解。

地震研究所的第二任所长石本巳四雄在任10年，他设计并制造了一种新型的加速仪，人们利用这台加速仪首次测定出了地震运动的加速度。他还发明了石英水平摆倾斜仪，用于测量极微小的地表倾斜。妹泽克惟是一位杰出的数学家，他得出了球极坐标下弹性波的通解，随后他的理论被广泛应用于与体波和面波传播相关的问题中。在地震研究所成立后不久，日本就发生了多次大规模的地震，这对当地的百姓来说是一种不幸，但对于研究所却刚好相反。研究人员立即对震区进行了观测，通过这种方式积累了大量有关地震现象的资料。其中最重要的是：根据对地震前后水准测量和三角测量结果的分析，可以得到陆地发生了显著形变的结论。

在成立后的第一个10年中，地震研究所取得了令人瞩目的成绩，发现了很多与地震有关的新现象。不过，地震研究所历史上最辉煌的一段时期恐怕应该是接下来的5年，萩原尊礼、永田武和水上武分别着手进行了深入的测震学研究、电磁实验以及对火山的野外研究与观测，他们三人后来都成了日本一流的地球物理学家。遗憾的是，二战期间地震研究所的工作被迫削减。

The ERI had a tough time after the war, although some activity continued in spite of shortages of food, experimental material and so on. Nonetheless several key papers, especially on theoretical aspects of surface wave propagation, electrical conductivity distribution within the Earth and the like, were somehow published. Since the early 1950s, it has been possible to send younger members of the research staff to foreign countries. This has resulted in the internationally minded work of later years.

As Japan's economic situation improved, so the ERI came to life once again in a more modernized form. The institute now consists of the following eighteen sections, each being headed by a professor or an associate professor—theoretical seismology, earthquake mechanism, seismicity, seismometry, explosion seismology, sea-bottom seismology, crustal deformation, geomagnetism, gravity, geothermy, geodesy, tsunamis, physical volcanology, chemical volcanology, structural geology, petrology, earthquake engineering, and soil dynamics. The ERI also runs eighteen observatories, scattered all over Japan, for seismic, crustal deformation, geomagnetic and tsunami observations. Fig. 1 shows what a crustal deformation observatory looks like. In recent years, two centres—the Strong Motion Seismograph Centre and the Earthquake Prediction Observation Centre—have been attached to the institute. There are now twenty-five professors and associate professors, forty-nine research associates, eighty-eight technicians working in laboratories and workshops, and thirty-eight supporting members in the administrative sections. Of these, thirty-nine work at provincial observatories.

Fig.1. Interior of the Nokogiriyama Observatory for crustal deformation, about 60 km south of Tokyo. An observer is measuring the height of water surface of a 25 m water tube tiltmeter. A 25 m silica tube extensometer with recording systems can also be seen.

战后，地震研究所经历了一段艰难时期，不过在食品和实验材料等物质短缺的情况下，一些研究活动仍坚持了下来。研究所还设法发表了一些重要的论文，尤其是在面波传播和地球内部的电导率分布等理论研究方面。20世纪50年代早期，研究所开始可以派遣青年科研人员出国深造。这使得后来的工作能够采用国际上的先进理念。

随着日本经济条件的改善，地震研究所重获新生，并且变得更加现代化。如今，研究所共有18个研究室，每个研究室由一名教授或副教授领导，这些研究室的研究方向分别是：理论地震学、地震机制、地震活动性、地震测量学、爆炸地震学、海底地震学、地壳形变、地磁学、重力学、地热学、大地测量学、地震海啸、物理火山学、化学火山学、构造地质学、岩石学、地震工程学以及土壤动力学。地震研究所还拥有18个观测站，遍布整个日本，用于地震、地壳形变、地磁以及海啸的观测。图1所示为一个地壳形变观测站。近年来，又有两个中心挂靠到研究所下，分别是强震仪中心和地震预报监测中心。目前该所共有教授和副教授25名，助理研究员49名，分布于各实验室和车间的技术人员88名，以及管理部门的行政人员38名。其中有39人在各地的观测站工作。

图1. 位于东京以南约60千米的锯山地壳形变观测站的内景。一名观测者正在测定一根25米长的水管倾斜仪的水面高度。还可以看到一个25米长、带有记录系统的石英管伸长仪。

One of the features of the ERI is that it has on its staff people from all disciplines, namely, mathematicians, physicists, seismologists, geodetists, volcanologists, geomagneticists, geologists, chemists, architects, civil engineers and so on, all of whom are interested in earthquake phenomena. One can always find the right person to handle a particular problem properly. Interdisciplinary work is, for obvious reasons, specially encouraged.

Predicting Earthquakes

At this point, mention should be made of the earthquake prediction programme[1], a nation-wide project started in 1965, in which the ERI has been deeply involved. To predict the occurrence of large earthquakes has been one of the goals for Japanese seismologists over the years, although nothing systematic had ever been undertaken until a group of seismologists proposed a plan for earthquake prediction research in 1962.

From their experience of earthquake observations over a long period of time, Japanese seismologists got to know, albeit vaguely, what kind of work they had to undertake in order to be able to predict earthquakes. The result of group discussions was published in 1962 as the now famous report *Prediction of Earthquakes—Progress to Date and Plans for Further Development*[2], which was called the blueprint for research into the prediction of earthquakes and later came to be seem as a milestone in the research.

A long-term programme for research into the prediction of earthquakes, which followed the line of the blueprint, was actually launched in 1965 after much debate in the Science Council of Japan and the Geodetic Council, which is responsible for the coordination of geophysical observations in Japan. The Niigata earthquake in 1964 certainly seems to have accelerated the launching of the programme. In 1968, the northern part of Japan was badly shaken by the Tokachi-Oki earthquake which caused considerable damage. The importance of earthquake prediction was then argued at cabinet level, so the programme was forced to aim at actual predictions, wherever possible, rather than at the acquisition of the data necessary for earthquake prediction.

The earthquake prediction programme embraces various disciplines. First, much stress is laid on the detection of anomalous land deformation by repeating levelling and triangulation surveys. It is believed that the magnitude and time of occurrence of earthquakes can be foretold to some extent from the size of the area covered by the anomalous crustal movement—the wider the area, the larger the magnitude. The use of geodimeters employing a laser source for electro-optical measurements of long distances has recently become fashionable. Continuous observation of crustal deformation is also included in the programme; tiltmeters and strainmeters installed in a deep vault are generally used for that purpose (Fig. 1). A prototype of a standard vault for the observation of crustal deformation has been put forward as a direct result of test observations made by the ERI over a long period.

The observation of seismicity, certainly one of the most important items of the earthquake prediction programme, has also been stressed. Although relatively large earthquakes with

地震研究所的特色之一是其员工来自于各个学科，其中包括数学家、物理学家、地震学家、大地测量学家、火山学家、地磁学家、地质学家、化学家、建筑师以及土木工程师等，他们都对地震现象感兴趣。针对每一个特定的问题总能找到合适的人来妥善处理。现在跨学科研究受到了格外的鼓励，其原因也是显而易见的。

地 震 预 报

这里要介绍一下地震预报项目[1]，这个全国性的项目始于1965年，地震研究所也充分参与其中。对大地震的预报多年以来一直是日本地震学家追求的目标之一，但直到1962年才有一些地震学家提出了一项地震预报研究计划，此前一直没有人对此进行过系统的研究。

根据多年的地震观测经验，日本地震学家们开始对预报地震所需要进行的具体工作有了模糊的认识。小组讨论的结果于1962年发表，即著名的《地震预报——目前的进展和下一步的发展计划》[2]，当时该报告被大家称为地震预报研究的蓝图，后来被视为地震预报研究史上的一座里程碑。

负责全国地球物理观测协调工作的日本学术会议和大地测量会议经过多次讨论后，根据该蓝图制定了一项关于地震预报研究的长期计划，并于1965年开始正式实施。1964年的新潟地震确实在一定程度上加速了该计划的启动。1968年，日本北部发生了十胜冲地震，并造成了严重的破坏。于是地震预报的重要性上升到了内阁级别，该项目的目标也因此而被设定为对地震进行尽可能有效的预报，而不是仅仅停留于收集地震预报所需的资料。

地震预报项目涉及多个学科。首先，工作重点主要放在反复进行水准测量和三角测量以探查异常的地面形变。人们相信，地震的震级以及发生的时间在某种程度上可以通过异常的地壳运动进行预报，即覆盖面积越大，震级就越高。近年来，利用激光源进行远距离光电测定的光电测距仪得到了普遍的应用。此外，该项目还包括了对地壳形变的连续观测，为此，研究人员在一个很深的地下室中安装了倾斜仪和应变仪（图1）。这个用于观测地壳形变的标准地下室的雏形是地震研究所经过长期观测试验所取得的一项直接成果。

地震活动监测是地震预报项目中最重要的内容之一，因此也得到了高度的重视。震级大于里氏4.0级左右的较大地震是由日本气象厅（JMA）建立的台网监测

a magnitude greater than 4 or so on the Gutenberg-Richter scale are to be monitored by a network organized by the Japan Meteorological Agency (JMA), microearthquake observations have been conducted mostly by university workers. The ERI has played an important part in designing the equipment for such observations.

The earthquake prediction programme also finances studies of changes in seismic wave velocities, observations of changes in the geomagnetic field, examination of active faults and foldings, rock breaking tests in laboratories and so on.

Some 4,000 million yen (or $13 million) was allocated to the programme for the period from 1965 to 1972. Salaries, costs of constructing observatory buildings, vaults and the like are met from other sources, so that this sum of money has been earmarked solely for promoting the programme. Although the budget is much smaller than that for the Japanese space project, it is certainly a lot of money for Earth science in Japan. It should also be mentioned that about eighty staff posts were specially provided by the government for the purposes of the programme.

Leading members of the ERI have participated in the programme since its planning stage, so the institute has had a lot to do with the progress of the programme. The Earthquake Prediction Observation Centre (EPOC) was thus set up in the ERI for the purpose of processing data measured by university workers. EPOC is equipped with a high speed computer and is supposed to process data relevant to earthquake prediction, which are sent there from universities, into a form suitable for the Coordinating Committee for Earthquake Prediction (CCEP). The CCEP was set up in the Geographical Survey Institute, Ministry of Construction, in 1969 and consists of about thirty specialists from universities and government institutions; it actually functions as the headquarters for earthquake prediction. Whenever CCEP foresees the possibility of a destructive earthquake in a certain area, that area is earmarked as an area of intensified observations of a certain rank depending on the assessment of the danger. It has not as yet been possible, however, to issue a warning specifying the date and magnitude of an impending earthquake.

It was timely that the proposed earthquake prediction programme was actually tested during the 1965–67 Matsushiro earthquake swarms. Matsushiro, a small town in central Japan, experienced an incredibly large number of shocks at that time. At the most violent stage 600 shocks a day were felt, including moderately large shocks from time to time which gave rise to slight damage. The ERI carried out all sorts of observations over the Matsushiro area, and, interestingly, mobile seismic observation parties often found places where many ultra-microearthquakes were occurring. Almost without exception a fairly large shock took place in such an area after a few months. The JMA summarized the results observed by the ERI and other agencies and officially issued warnings of coming earthquakes to local inhabitants for the first time ever. Only a long-term forecast, covering a few months, and a very rough estimate of earthquake magnitude were released. The experience of Matsushiro indicates that the proposed programme for earthquake

的，而小型地震则主要由高校的研究者负责进行观测。地震研究所在监测仪器的设计方面发挥了重要的作用。

地震预报项目还为地震波波速变化的研究、地磁场变化的观测、活动断层和褶皱的考察以及岩石破裂的室内试验等提供了资金。

1965年至1972年，投入到该项目中的经费约为40亿日元（按当时汇率计算为1,300万美元）。工作人员的薪金以及用于观测的建筑物和地下室的建设等费用均来自其他渠道，因此上述经费全部用于该项目的研究工作。虽然这笔经费远远比不上日本在太空计划方面的预算，但对于日本的地球科学研究来说的确是一笔不小的数目。此外还应在此说明的是，政府为配合该项目的实施专门设置了约80个岗位。

地震研究所的领导自项目筹划阶段便参与其中，因此研究所在该项目的进展中发挥了重要作用。为处理高校研究者们监测到的数据，地震研究所特别设立了地震预报监测中心（EPOC）。该中心配备有一台高速计算机，用于将来自于各个大学的与地震预报有关的数据处理成适当的形式，然后提交给地震预报联络会（CCEP）。地震预报联络会成立于1969年，隶属日本建设省国土地理院，由来自各个大学和政府机构的约30名专家组成，它实际上就是地震预报工作的总指挥部。一旦地震预报联络会预测某地区可能会发生破坏性地震，该地区就会被划为一定级别的重点监测区，而级别的高低取决于所预测的破坏程度的大小。然而，对于即将发生的地震，目前仍无法预测出确切的发生时间和震级。

上述地震预报项目很快就在1965年~1967年发生的松代地震群中得到了实实在在的检验。松代是日本中部的一个小镇，在那段时间内这里发生的地震次数多到令人难以置信的程度。在最严重的时期，每天发生的有感地震多达600次，其中还不时夹杂着具有轻微破坏性的中强震。地震研究所利用各种手段对整个松代地区进行了观测。有趣的是，流动地震观测队经常发现一些地区正在频繁发生超微地震。而几个月之后，这些地区几乎都毫无例外地发生了较大规模的地震。日本气象厅综合了地震研究所和其他机构的观测结果，有史以来第一次通过官方途径向当地居民发布了地震预警。这只是一个长期性的预测，时间跨度达几个月，而且对震级的估计也非常粗略。松代地震的经验说明：地震预报项目的总方向是正确的，尽管还存在一

prediction is going in the right direction, although there are some defects that need to be improved at once.

Unrest in the Institute

To process the large amount of data observed over the Matsushiro area, the ERI hired many temporary staff, chiefly to analyse seismograms. About sixty non-regular members were working in the ERI at the peak of the Matsushiro activity. As it is a government agency it was not possible for the ERI to increase the number of its regular employees even in such an emergency. Many of the temporary employees did not want to leave the ERI even though work on the Matsushiro event had come to an end, and about twenty of them are still working in the ERI at the moment; every effort to appoint them as regular members has been made.

The non-regular members are less well paid than regular members, and also have no paid holidays or proper pensions and the like because they are paid on a daily basis. As there are also many non-regular members in other institutes and departments of the University of Tokyo, an organized movement requesting an improvement in labour conditions emerged. This movement was quite legitimate until a group of so-called neo-leftists intervened.

There was an unfortunate occurrence in the ERI in the summer of 1970 when a professor quarrelled with one of his non-regular members who had said in no uncertain terms that he wanted to become a regular member, no matter how much difficulty such an arrangement presented. Although I do not know exactly what happened, it seems that the non-regular employee got slightly injured for his pains. After that, the institute was attacked by activists who not only demonstrated but also forcibly locked up many professors. One of their slogans called for the expulsion from the university of the professor concerned in the business I have described. Such a crazy state of affairs was at one time stopped by police intervention, but the president of the university does not like to ask the police to stay there for long. As soon as the police deaparted, some parts of the institute were again occupied by rioters who now stay there day and night. It has been difficult for most professors in the ERI to work in their offices since then. A neighouring institute, the Microbiology Research Institute, has recently come in for similar treatments.

It is really ridiculous that such a strike should have lasted more than two years. Research associates, technicians and the like can work in the ERI quite safely, foreign visitors and professors from other universities can enter there quite freely, and all the provincial observatories of the ERI are running absolutely normally. Most ERI members, it should be emphasized, have nothing to do with the riots. The most difficult thing for people from abroad to understand is that everybody in the ERI has been fully paid in spite of the fact that some of the members declared that they would not work in an institute controlled by "shameful professors".

It is difficult to say at the moment when the trouble will end. Whether the ERI will recover

些问题需要立即加以改进。

研究所的内部风波

为了处理在松代地区观测到的大量数据，地震研究所雇用了许多临时工作人员，他们的主要工作是分析地震图。在松代地震活动的高峰时期，地震研究所内的非正式员工约有60人。这是因为该所是一个政府机构，所以即便在这样的紧急状况下，研究所也不能扩编。而许多临时雇员在松代地震活动结束后仍不愿意离开研究所，因此目前仍有约20人还在所内工作，研究所正在想尽一切办法将他们纳为正式员工。

非正式员工的报酬要低于正式员工，并且没有带薪假期和适当的津贴等待遇，因为他们是按日计酬的。东京大学的其他研究所和院系也有许多非正式员工，所以他们共同组织了一场要求改善劳动条件的运动。这场运动本来是完全合法的，但是后来却有一群所谓的新左翼分子介入其中。

1970年夏天，研究所内发生了一件不愉快的事：一位教授与其下属的一名非正式员工发生了争吵，因为该员工坚决表示，不管牵涉多少麻烦，他也要成为正式员工。虽然我不了解具体的情况，不过好像这名非正式员工在冲突中受了点轻伤。自那以后，研究所就开始遭到激进分子的攻击，他们不仅向研究所示威，还强行扣押了许多教授。他们的口号之一就是要求把上述事件中的这位教授逐出学校。在警察的干涉下，这种疯狂的事件曾一度中止，但东京大学的校长并不愿意警察长期呆在学校里。警察刚一离开，研究所中的某些地方就又被闹事者霸占，并且昼夜都不离开。从那以后，地震研究所的大多数教授想要在自己的办公室里工作都很难。最近，附近的微生物研究所也遭遇了类似的事情。

极其荒唐的是，这样的冲击居然已经持续了两年多。助理研究员和技术人员之类的普通员工可以绝对放心地在所内工作，外宾和其他大学的教授也可以非常自由地进入所内，并且地震研究所的所有地方观测站都在完全正常的状态下运行。需要强调的是，大多数地震研究所的员工并没有参与这场骚乱。尽管有些人宣称他们不会在一个由"不体面的教授"所管理的研究所工作，但地震研究所的每位工作人员都拿到了满额的工资，这一点最让海外人士无法理解。

现在很难说这场风波何时能结束。地震研究所将来能不能恢复到正常状态也还

to its normal state one day is an imponderable question. One of the root causes of the trouble is that there are practically no regulations to control working conditions within the university. It was assumed in the old days that university people were all *bona fide*. I must confess, however, that the mode of administration appropriate then cannot be applied to a modern institute with 200 or more members. The professors of the ERI, many of whom are internationally known for their scientific contributions, could well be accused of paying too little attention to administrative matters.

The promotion of earthquake research, particularly in the field of prediction, is urgent in Japan. Ever since the finding of anomalous land upheaval in an area south of Tokyo in 1969, it has been feared that Tokyo, the largest city in the world, might again be hit by a large earthquake in the near future. Intensive work over the anomalous area indicates that a considerable amount of strain energy has accumulated there since the time of the Kanto earthqwuake. The ERI would have played a most important part in conducting various observations there if it had been functioning normally. Although the ERI is doing some work in the area, taxpayers may well say that the ERI is not working properly.

An intensification of earthquake prediction programmes is now under consideration in Japan. In view of the data already gathered, it is being strongly recommended that a dense network of electro-optical distance survey devices, a real time observation network by seafloor seismographs, monitoring systems for microearthquakes by telemetering and so on should be established. It is also important to reconsider the role of various organizations. If a large, modern institute were to be founded as a result of the debate about reorganization, the present ERI would lose its *raison d'être*.

(**240**, 202-204; 1972)

T. Rikitake: Earthquake Research Institute, University of Tokyo, Tokyo.

References:

1. Rikitake, T., *Geophys. Surv.*, 1 (in the press, 1972).

2. Tsuboi, C., Wadati, K., and Hagiwara, T., *Report of the Earthquake Prediction Research Group in Japan* (Earthquake Research Institute, University of Tokyo, Tokyo, 1962).

是个未知数。引起这场风波的根本原因之一在于，大学里几乎没有能规范工作条件的任何制度。以前人们普遍认为大学里的人都是讲诚信的。然而，我不得不承认，过去很适用的管理模式不能照搬到一个拥有200多人的现代化研究所。地震研究所的教授中有很多是曾为科学作出过杰出贡献的国际知名人士，他们极有可能因为对管理事务关注太少而受到指责。

在日本，推动地震研究尤其是地震预报方面的研究是一件刻不容缓的事。自从1969年在东京南部某地区发现了地面的异常隆起以来，人们一直担心：在不久的将来，东京这座世界上最大的城市会不会再次受到大地震的冲击。人们对异常地区进行了深入研究，结果表明：自关东大地震以后，该地区已经积聚了大量的应变能。倘若地震研究所一直在正常运转的话，它一定会在对该地区进行的各项观测中发挥重要作用。虽然研究所也在该地区开展了一些工作，但在纳税人看来，地震研究所并没有起到应有的作用。

目前，日本正在考虑进一步加强地震预报项目。从已搜集到的资料来看，现在非常有必要建立一个高密度的光电测距装置网、一个利用海底地震仪而建立起的实时监测网以及一些利用遥测手段建立起的微地震监测系统等等。另外，重新衡量各地震研究组织的角色也非常重要。倘若关于重组的讨论结果是应该建立一所大规模的现代化研究所，那么现今的地震研究所就将失去存在的理由。

（齐红艳 翻译；张忠杰 审稿）

Calcium Ions and Muscle Contraction

S. Ebashi

Editor's Note

Here biologist Setsuro Ebashi from the University of Tokyo sums up what is known about the role of calcium ions in muscle contraction. In the 1940s, researchers injected calcium ions into single muscle fibres causing their contraction. Then in the 1960s, Ebashi helped demonstrate the involvement of two proteins, troponin and tropomyosin. Troponin, found on the thin actin filament, acts as the calcium receptor protein, while tropomyosin mediates the effect of calcium ions on troponin. But a closer look reveals the system to be more complex, he warns, with calcium sometimes acting as an inhibitor of inhibition. Ebashi was viewed as a pioneer of muscle research and his concept of a calcium receptor protein was later extended to other cell types.

ONE of the characteristics of muscle research in Japan is the close personal contact and willing cooperation that exists among research workers. This pleasant atmosphere was the result of the paternal leadership of Professor H. Kumagai, who in 1955 invited young muscle scientists to join a research group in which enthusiastic and heated discussions on muscle contraction could take place. The problem implicit in the title of this article had also been grappled with under these conditions.

The mechanism of such a complex biological phenomenon as muscle contraction can be examined in two different ways. One is concerned with the underlying elementary process, and the other with the regulatory mechanism through which this process comes into operation as a biological function. The elementary process of muscle contraction involves the interaction of myosin and actin in the presence of ATP (MgATP). On the other hand, the Ca ion plays an indispensable and unparalleled role in turning the interaction of myosin and actin into real function[1,2] and its place in this regulatory mechanism may correspond to that of ATP in the elementary process (Fig. 1).

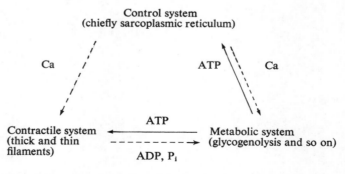

Fig. 1. Schematic representation of the functional organization of muscle.

钙离子与肌肉收缩

江桥节郎

编者按

在本文中，东京大学的生物学家江桥节郎总结了当时人们对钙离子在肌肉收缩中所起作用的认识。在20世纪40年代，研究人员发现，向单肌纤维中注射钙离子会使肌肉产生收缩。随后，江桥节郎在60年代又证明了有两种蛋白质——肌钙蛋白和原肌球蛋白也参与其中。存在于细肌丝（又称肌动蛋白丝）中的肌钙蛋白可以作为钙离子的接受蛋白，而原肌球蛋白的作用则是介导钙离子对肌钙蛋白的影响。但是他提醒大家：进一步的研究发现，该系统其实还要更复杂一些，因为钙离子有时候会表现为抑制收缩作用的抑制剂。江桥节郎被视为肌肉学研究的先驱，后来他提出的钙离子结合蛋白的概念又被拓展到其他细胞类型。

日本肌肉学研究的特色之一是，科研人员之间能保持密切的私人关系并愿意相互合作。这一良好氛围得益于熊谷洋教授所开创的家长式领导体制。在1955年，他曾邀请一批年轻肌肉学家加入到一个研究小组中去，在这个小组中大家可以就肌肉收缩问题进行热情洋溢的讨论。本文标题所隐含的问题也曾在这样的讨论中被大家激烈地争辩过。

可以用两种不同的方式来研究像肌肉收缩这么复杂的生物学现象的机理。一种关注的是这个现象背后的基本过程，另一种则关注这一过程赖以发挥生物学功能的调节机制。肌肉收缩的基本过程包括在ATP（MgATP）存在时肌球蛋白与肌动蛋白之间的相互作用。另一方面，钙离子在使肌球蛋白与肌动蛋白间相互作用转变为真正生物学功能[1,2]的过程中发挥着不可或缺的独特作用，而钙离子在肌肉收缩调节机制中的地位可以与ATP在基本过程中的地位相对应（图1）。

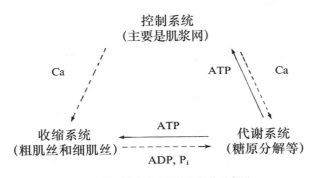

图1. 肌肉中功能性组织的示意图。

The first indication of the crucial role of the Ca ion in the contraction of living muscle came at almost the same time as the establishment of the myosin-actin-ATP system by Szent-Györgyi and his school[3] in 1941–42. Three years after the work of Heilbrunn[4] in 1940, Kamada and Kinosita[5] injected a minute quantity of Ca ions through a micropipette of diameter 2 to 5 μm into a single muscle fibre, which responded by contracting locally in a reversible manner. Unfortunately, this elegant pioneering work was not developed in war-torn Japan; in the meantime, Heilbrunn and Wiercinski[6] presented essentially the same result. These remarkable observations, however, were then ignored for more than ten years by most muscle scientists, probably because the elementary process of muscle contraction, namely the interaction of myosin, actin and ATP, does not require the presence of the Ca ion.

Establishment of the Ca Theory

The wide recognition of the part played by the Ca ion is chiefly based on several findings[1,2,7] reported between 1959 and 1961. First, it turned out that the contractile processes *in vitro* are regulated by quite low concentrations of Ca ions; 10^{-7} M Ca ion keeps the contractile system in a relaxed state, and the presence of 10^{-5} M Ca ion activates it fully. Second, the sarcoplasmic reticulum, the internal membrane system, pumps up Ca ions from the surrounding medium in the presence of ATP. The capacity and affinity of the membrane system for Ca ions are sufficient to keep the contractile system in a relaxed state.

These data allow a fairly detailed picture of the sequence of events during contraction of muscle to be built up. The action potential evoked by the transmitter derived from nerve terminals finally reaches the interior of a muscle fibre through the T-system—an extension of the sarcolemma—and exerts an effect on the terminal cistern—the swollen part of the sarcoplasmic reticulum in close contact with the T-system—to release the Ca ions accumulated there. Ca ions then reach the contractile system by simple diffusion and induce the interaction of thin filaments, chiefly composed of actin, with thick filaments made up of myosin. When the action potential dies away, Ca ions are recaptured from the contractile elements by the whole surface of the sarcoplasmic reticulum and relaxation follows. It is of considerable significance that glycogenolyses, one of the principal energy sources for contraction, is also initiated by the same concentration of Ca ions as that which activates the contractile system[8].

Troponin as the Receptive Protein

At first sight it seems strange that the Ca ion was ignored for so long after the injection experiments mentioned above. An explanation may, however, be found in the report published in 1963 that the regulatory function of the Ca ion requires a corresponding protein system different from myosin and actin[1,2,9]. (It was later shown by Kendrick-Jones *et al.*[10] that, in molluscan muscle, the Ca-receptive site is located in the myosin molecule; thus the regulation mechanism involves an interesting phylogenic problem.)

在1941年~1942年间，人们首次认识到了钙离子在活体肌肉收缩中的重要作用，这一时间与森特–哲尔吉及其追随者[3]建立肌球蛋白–肌动蛋白–ATP系统的时间几乎相同。在海尔布伦[4]1940年发表其研究结果之后三年，镰田和木下[5]利用一根直径为2 μm~5 μm的超微针头向一个单肌纤维中注射了微量的钙离子，从而引发局部的可逆收缩。遗憾的是，这一杰出的先驱性工作因为日本饱受战火摧残而未能继续下去。与此同时，海尔布伦和威尔辛斯基[6]也发表了基本相同的结果。然而，这些不同寻常的观察结果随后被大多数从事肌肉研究的科学家忽视了十多年，这可能是因为肌肉收缩的基本过程，即肌球蛋白、肌动蛋白和ATP的相互作用，并不需要钙离子的存在。

钙离子理论的建立

对钙离子所起作用的广泛重视主要基于1959年到1961年间发表的几项研究成果[1,2,7]。首先，人们发现在体外实验中，收缩过程是被极低浓度的钙离子所调控的；10^{-7} M的钙离子可使收缩系统处于松弛状态，而10^{-5} M的钙离子则可以使之完全被激活。其次，在ATP存在时，肌肉细胞的内膜系统（肌浆网）会将钙离子从周围环境中泵入。内膜系统对钙离子的吸收力和亲和性足以使收缩系统维持在松弛状态。

根据这些数据就可以获得在肌肉收缩过程中所发生的一系列事件的精细图画：从神经末梢传出的信号所引发的动作电位最终通过T管系统（肌纤维膜的延伸结构）到达肌纤维内部，并在终池（肌浆网与T管系统紧密相连的肿胀部分）发挥作用，从而使在那里蓄积的钙离子被释放出来。随后钙离子通过简单扩散到达收缩系统，并引起主要由肌动蛋白构成的细肌丝与主要由肌球蛋白构成的粗肌丝之间的相互作用。当动作电位逐渐消失时，肌浆网的整个表面就会把钙离子从收缩系统中收回，随后将再次出现松弛状态。肌肉收缩的主要能量来源之一——糖原分解也是由与激活收缩系统浓度相同的钙离子所触发的[8]，这一点非常重要。

接受钙离子的肌钙蛋白

乍一看人们似乎会感到奇怪：为什么钙离子在上文提到的注射实验之后那么久还一直被人们忽略？不过，我们也许可以从1963年发表的报告中找到对此问题的一种解释：钙离子必须通过相应的蛋白质系统才能发挥调节作用，而这种蛋白质系统并不是肌球蛋白或肌动蛋白[1,2,9]。（后来，肯德里克–琼斯等人发现[10]：在软体动物的肌肉中，接受钙离子的位点位于肌球蛋白分子的内部；因此上述调控机制就会涉及一个有趣的系统发生问题。）

This regulatory protein system, composed of tropomyosin and troponin, a new protein, is distributed along the actin filament at intervals of 38 to 39 nm (Fig. 2 and refs. 1 and 2). The function of tropomyosin, a fibrous protein about 40 nm long, was thus clarified some seventeen years after its isolation by Bailey[12] in 1946: it mediates the effect of Ca ions on troponin bound to the actin filament. (The discovery of the new protein system led to the isolation of new myofibrillar proteins like α-actinin, β-actinin and M-protein, which are involved in the structural arrangement of thin and thick filaments; these proteins, together with troponin and tropomyosin, are called "regulatory proteins"[13] by contrast with the chief contractile proteins, namely myosin and actin.)

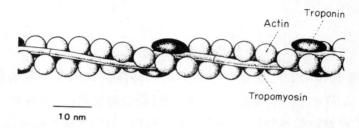

10 nm

Fig. 2. A model for the fine structure of the thin filament. One tropomyosin molecule combines with one troponin molecule and seven actin molecules. The functional integrity of this morphological unit has recently been noticed and discussed[11]. (Fig. 5 in ref. 2 as modified by I. Ohtsuki.)

It must be emphasized that the Ca ion is not a simple activator of the contractile system. In the absence of Ca ions troponin, in the presence of tropomyosin, exerts an inhibitory effect on actin filaments. When Ca ions are bound to troponin, this inhibitory action does not take place and contraction follows; thus the Ca ion behaves as an inhibitor of inhibition, or a depressor[1,2]. Substantial support for this idea has come from the work of Ishiwata and Fujime[14] in Oosawa's laboratory, which is based on the measurement of the flexibility of the actin-tropomyosin-troponin complex using quasielastic light scattering technique.

Troponin is not a single protein but a complex of three components[15,16]. One component (of molecular weight 22,000 to 23,000) can act with tropomyosin to repress the interaction of actin with myosin. The light Ca-binding component (of molecular weight 17,000 to 18,000) opposes this repressing action; this effect is scarcely influenced by Ca ions. The heavy tropomyosin-binding component (of molecular weight 38,000 to 40,000) inactivates the derepressing action of the light component in the absence of Ca ions, that is in the relaxed state, through its interaction with the light component. It thus seems that the derepressing action of Ca ions is not exerted directly on the inhibitory component, but indirectly through the interaction of the other two components[17].

The subtle structural change that takes place in the thin filament—the troponin-tropomyosin-actin complex—under the influence of Ca ions has become one of the vital problems in muscle science[18]; the answer will undoubtedly provide a crucial clue about the interaction of myosin and actin. In this way, studies on the regulatory protein systems are now closely connected with those on the elementary process.

这种蛋白质调节系统由原肌球蛋白和一种新发现的蛋白——肌钙蛋白组成，分布在肌动蛋白丝中，间距为 38 nm ~ 39 nm（图 2 和参考文献 1、2）原肌球蛋白是一种长约 40 nm 的纤维状蛋白，虽然贝利[12] 早在 1946 年就分离出了这种蛋白，但直到约 17 年以后人们才把它的功能搞清楚：它负责介导钙离子对结合在肌动蛋白丝上的肌钙蛋白的影响。（这一新蛋白质系统的发现引导人们分离出了一些新的肌原纤维蛋白，如 α– 辅肌动蛋白、β– 辅肌动蛋白和 M 蛋白，这些蛋白都与细肌丝和粗肌丝的结构排布有关，它们与肌钙蛋白和原肌球蛋白一起被称为"调节蛋白"[13]，而与主收缩蛋白——肌球蛋白和肌动蛋白是相对的。）

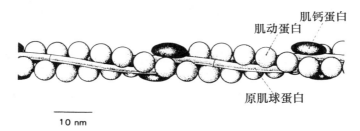

图2. 细肌丝精细结构的模型。1个原肌球蛋白分子与1个肌钙蛋白分子和7个肌动蛋白分子相结合。最近有人已经在关注和讨论这种形态单元的功能完整性[11]。（大月根据参考文献2中的图5作了修改）

必须着重指出，钙离子并不是一个简单的收缩系统激活剂。在存在原肌球蛋白但不存在钙离子的情况下，肌钙蛋白将发挥抑制肌动蛋白丝的作用。而在钙离子与肌钙蛋白结合后，就不会发生这种抑制作用了，随后出现的将是收缩过程。因而钙离子的表现就如同是抑制收缩作用的一种抑制剂[1,2]。石渡和藤明[14]在大沢实验室中的研究工作为上述想法提供了强有力的支持，他们的这一结论来源于用准弹性光散射技术对肌动蛋白－原肌球蛋白－肌钙蛋白复合物弹性的测量结果。

肌钙蛋白不是一种单一的蛋白，而是由三种成分组成的复合物[15,16]。其中有一种成分（分子量为22,000~23,000）可以和原肌球蛋白作用从而抑制肌动蛋白与肌球蛋白之间的相互作用。另一种成分是较轻的与钙结合的蛋白（分子量为17,000~18,000），其功能与上述抑制作用相反，这种作用几乎不受钙离子的影响。最后一种成分是较重的与原肌球蛋白结合的蛋白（分子量为38,000~40,000），它可以在没有钙离子存在的情况下抑制较轻成分的去抑制活性，即通过与较轻成分的相互作用使肌肉处于松弛状态。这样看来，钙离子的去抑制作用并不是直接作用于抑制成分之上，而是通过另两种成分之间的相互作用间接实现的[17]。

细肌丝内部，即肌钙蛋白－原肌球蛋白－肌动蛋白复合物，在钙离子作用下所发生的细微结构改变已成为肌肉学中的重要课题之一[18]。其结果无疑将会为肌球蛋白与肌动蛋白间相互作用的研究提供一个关键的线索。从这个角度讲，对调节蛋白系统的研究是和对基本过程的研究紧密联系在一起的。

Protein System and Living Fibres

Another remarkable contribution of Japanese scientists to the study of muscle is the so-called "skinned fibre", a muscle fibre from which the sarcolemma has been removed, which was developed by Natori[19] in 1949. This is quite a suitable material for investigating the relationship between contractile processes and the concentrations of Ca ions, and also the mechanism by which Ca is released from the sarcoplasmic reticulum. The confirmation of the role of Ca ion with the help of this kind of fibre[20] has certainly bridged the gap between the experiments on injection of Ca ions into muscle fibres and those involving extracts of the protein system. The proposal that a "Ca-induced Ca-release mechanism" is at work in the sarcoplasmic reticulum[2,21,22] is also based on experiments with skinned fibres.

(**240**, 217-218; 1972)

Setsuro Ebashi: Department of Pharmacology, Faculty of Medicine, and Department of Physics, Faculty of Science, University of Tokyo, Tokyo.

References:

1. Ebashi, S., and Endo, M., *Prog. Biophys. Mol. Biol.*, **18**, 123 (1968).

2. Ebashi, S., Endo, M., and Ohtsuki, I., *Quart. Rev. Biophys.*, **2**, 466 (1969).

3. Szent-Györgyi, A., *Studies from Institute of Medical Chemistry, University of Szeged*, 1 (1941-42); 2 (1942).

4. Heilbrunn, L. V., *Physiol. Zool.*, **13**, 88 (1940).

5. Kamada, T., and Kinosita, H., *Jap. J. Zool.*, **10**, 469 (1943).

6. Heilbrunn, L. V., and Wiercinski, F. J., *J. Cellular Comp. Physiol.*, **29**, 15 (1947).

7. Weber, A., *J. Biol. Chem.*, **234**, 2764 (1959).

8. Ozawa, E., Hosoi, K., and Ebashi, S., *J. Biochem.*, **61**, 531 (1967); Ozawa, E., *ibid.*, **71**, 321 (1972).

9. Ebashi, S., *Nature*, **200**, 1010 (1963).

10. Kendrick-Jones, J., Lehman, W., and Szent-Györgyi, A. G., *J. Mol. Biol.*, **54**, 327 (1970).

11. Bremel, R. D., and Weber, A., *Nature New Biology*, **238**, 97 (1972).

12. Bailey, K., *Nature*, **157**, 368 (1946).

13. Maruyama, K., and Ebashi, S., *The Physiology and Biochemistry of Muscle as a Food* (edit. by Briskey, E. J., Cassens, R. G., and Marsh, B. B.), **2**, 373 (Univ. of Wisconsin Press, 1970).

14. Ishiwata, S., and Fujime, S., *J. Mol. Biol.*, **68**, 511 (1972).

15. Hartshorne, D. J., and Mueller, H., *Biochem. Biophys. Res. Commun.*, **31**, 647 (1968).

16. Greazer, M. L., and Gergely, J., *J. Biol. Chem.*, **246**, 4226 (1971).

17. Ebashi, S., in *Thirty-seventh Cold Spring Harbor Symposium on Quantitative Biology* (*The Mechanism of Muscle Contraction*) (in the press).

18. Oosawa, F., Hanson, J., *et al.*, Haselgrove, J. C., and Huxley, H. E., in *Thirty-seventh Cold Spring Harbor Symposium on Quantitative Biology* (*The Mechanism of Muscle Contraction*) (in the press).

19. Natori, R., *J. Physiol. Soc. Japan* (in Japanese), **11**, 14 (1949); Natori, R., *Jikeikai Med. J.*, **1**, 119 (1954).

20. Podolsky, R. J., and Costantin, L. L., *Fed. Proc.*, **23**, 933 (1964).

21. Ford, L. E., and Podolsky, R. J., *Science*, **167**, 58 (1970).

22. Endo, M., Tanaka, M., and Ogawa, Y., *Nature*, **228**, 34 (1970).

蛋白质系统与活体纤维

日本科学家对肌肉学研究的另一个重要贡献是所谓的"脱鞘纤维"——一种去掉了肌纤维膜的肌肉纤维。"脱鞘纤维"是由名取礼二[19]于1949年开发的。这是一种非常适合于研究肌肉收缩过程与钙离子浓度关系，以及研究钙离子从肌浆网中释放的机理的材料。在脱鞘纤维的帮助下，人们明确了钙离子的功能[20]，这无疑可以使我们在向肌纤维中注射钙离子的实验和有关蛋白质系统提取物的实验之间建立起一定的关联。此外，关于"钙离子引发的钙离子释放机制"适用于肌浆网的假说[2,21,22]也是建立在脱鞘纤维的实验基础之上的。

（张锦彬 翻译；刘京国 审稿）

The Solar Spoon

F. W. W. Dilke and D. O. Gough

Editor's Note

The nuclear fusion reactions taking place in the Sun's core release photons and neutrinos. The photons take about a million years to reach the surface of the Sun, then arrive 8 minutes after that. But the neutrinos, because they interact very weakly with matter, escape from the Sun's interior almost at once. By the early 1970s it was clear that fewer neutrinos were being observed than theory predicted. F. W. W. Dilke and Douglas Gough here propose a model for the Sun in which it undergoes periodic (every few hundred million years) mixing due to convection. This would, for a period of about ten million years, lead to a lower temperature at the surface of the Sun, and fewer neutrinos coming from it. The neutrino problem has since been solved in another way: some of the neutrinos change their type on the way from the solar core to the Earth. The kind of convective instability proposed here has now almost certainly been ruled out.

SOLAR models are normally constructed by evolving for a time τ a stellar model of 1 $M_\odot$ which initially had uniform chemical composition and was situated either somewhere on the Hayashi track or on the zero age main sequence. The principal direct observational data are the present luminosity L, effective temperature T_e, upper bound to the neutrino flux F_v, and some knowledge of the chemical composition of the surface. The luminosity, effective temperature and chemical composition are essentially surface boundary conditions; the neutrino flux is an integral to which only regions very close to the center contribute. Conditions can be imposed on the past history of the Sun by the theory of stellar evolution and by the requirement that our ideas about the history of the interstellar medium are not contradicted. But there remains considerable freedom in our choice of the initial abundances by weight, Y and Z, of helium and of heavier elements; further freedom is provided by our lack of knowledge of the precise value of τ, though limits can be provided by geological evidence and by measures of certain isotope ratios in the Sun.

There may be serious errors in the microscopic physics providing the equation of state, the opacity and the nuclear reaction rates, and our understanding of the macroscopic physics describing the fluid motions within the Sun is incomplete. In particular, the mixing length formalism normally used to describe the outer convection zone is unlikely to be accurate, but even if it were the mixing length l itself remains a free parameter (or, to be more precise, free function) of the theory. Varying l causes the relatively diffuse outer layers of the model to readjust so that the heat can still be transported. This has little effect on the structure of the central regions so L is hardly affected. Broadly speaking, therefore, l determines T_e, but in practice the converse is the case: the theoretical solar model serves to calibrate the mixing length theory for use in models of other stars.

太阳的调羹

迪尔克，高夫

编者按

发生在太阳核心的核聚变反应会释放出光子和中微子。光子从太阳核心到太阳表面约需 10^6 年的时间，之后再要 8 分钟才到达地球。但中微子很快就能从太阳内部逃逸出来，因为它们与物质间的相互作用极其微弱。20 世纪 70 年代早期，观测到的太阳中微子数目比理论预测值少的事实就已经明确了。在本文中，迪尔克和道格拉斯·高夫提出了一个太阳模型，在这个模型中太阳由于对流而经历周期性（每几亿年一次）的混合。由此将导致太阳在大约 10^7 年的时期里具有较低的表面温度，并且从太阳来的中微子也会减少。后来，中微子问题从另一途径得到了解决，即某些中微子在从太阳核心到地球的途中改变了它们的类型。本文中提出的这类对流不稳定性解释现在已经基本上被排除了。

太阳模型通常是从一个初始化学组成均匀并处在林忠四郎线上或者零龄主序位置上的、质量为一个太阳质量（$M_\odot$）的恒星模型经时间 τ 的演化而构建的。主要的直接可观测数据有：当前光度 L、有效温度 T_e、中微子流量上限 F_v 以及一些表面化学组成方面的信息。光度、有效温度和化学组成实质上是在表面处的边界条件；中微子流量是一个积分，只有非常接近中心的区域才对它有贡献。我们可以根据恒星演化理论附加上一些与太阳过去历史有关的条件，但要求不能与我们关于星际介质历史的概念相抵触。即使如此，我们仍然在选择氦和更重元素的初始（按重量计的）丰度 Y 和 Z 上保有相当大的自由度；虽然地质学证据和太阳中某些同位素比可以给出一些限制，可是，由于我们对 τ 的精确值缺乏了解导致出现了进一步的自由度。

微观物理学所提供的状态方程、不透明度和核反应率可能存在严重的误差，而我们对用来描述太阳内部流体运动的宏观物理学的理解也是不全面的。尤其是，通常用于描述外对流区的混合长的方式未必准确，其实即使是混合长 l 本身也仍然只是一个理论上的自由参量（或者，更准确地说是一个自由函数）。改变 l 可以使模型相对弥散的外层重新调整从而热量仍然能被传输。这对中心区域的结构几乎没有影响，所以 L 几乎没有受到影响。因此，一般来说是 l 决定了 T_e，但在实际情况中却恰好相反：理论太阳模型被用于标定混合长理论以用于其他恒星模型。

Early measurements of F_v (ref. 1) were considerably lower than solar models predicted at the time, and now it cannot be said with confidence that any neutrinos have been detected at all (Davis, R., jun., Wolfendale, A. W., and Young, E. C. M., in preparation). This has led to a re-examination of the microphysics and the general tendency has been to depress F_v, although the latest predictions[2-4] are still greater than the experimental upper bound. It is clearly worth re-examining the macrophysics too. In particular it is normally assumed that the solar core remains unmixed because the Schwarzschild criterion for convective stability[5,6] is satisfied. Although Öpik has suggested that diffusion of material builds up a shell with high opacity around the core which eventually becomes convectively unstable and mixes[7], his rough description of the diffusion process differs considerably from the results of more sophisticated calculations[8], and if one is to believe the latter it is unlikely that the mechanism, in unmodified form, can operate in a time shorter than the age of the Sun. The possibility that there may be a strong Eckman circulation[9,10] has led to a consideration of the effect on F_v of continuous mixing in the core[11-15]. The results depend upon the timescale assumed for mixing and suggest that F_v can be reduced, but it is not clear whether the reduction is adequate. In any case it seems unlikely that sufficiently rapid Eckman circulation exists in the Sun at the present time[16]. Here we consider the stability of the solar core and find a process which may lead to intermittent mixing; indeed Fowler[17] has pointed out that such mixing may be even more efficient at reducing F_v.

Instability of the Solar Core

In the core of a main sequence star the thermonuclear generation of energy has negligible effect on the Schwarzschild criterion, because the timescale for generating energy is very much greater than the growth time of convective modes, and so is always ignored when testing for convection. But energy generation might destabilize gravity modes in much the same way as Eddington[18] thought pulsations might be driven in Cepheids. We consider a grossly oversimplified model: a plain-parallel stratified fluid layer of thickness d within which energy is being generated at a rate ε per unit mass. For the moment we assume that the only significant reactions are $p(p, \beta^+ v) D (p, \gamma)^3He$ and $^3He(^3He, 2p)^4He$ of the ppI chain which release energy at rates ε_{11} and ε_{33} respectively. Because it is unlikely that the solar core is in rapid rotation now[16] we will ignore rotation altogether, and to simplify matters still further the layer will be presumed so thin that the Boussinesq approximation can be employed to describe buoyancy driven motions[19] and gravity fluctuations will be ignored.

Because diffusion of material and momentum and the change of the H and He concentrations by nuclear burning are insignificant over the length and timescales considered in this section, the material derivatives of X and X_3, the mass fractions of H and ^3He, will be taken to be zero and viscous stresses will be neglected. In cartesian coordinates (x, y, z) with z vertical, the linearized equations can then be written

$$\rho \frac{\partial \mathbf{u}}{\partial t} = - \nabla p' + \mathbf{g} \rho' \tag{1}$$

F_v的早期测量值（参考文献 1）显著低于那时候太阳模型的预期值，但现在尚不能非常肯定地说所有中微子都被探测到了（小戴维斯、沃尔芬德尔和扬，完稿中）。这使一些人重新核查微观物理学，总的趋势是压低 F_v 值，然而最新的预测值 [2-4] 仍然高于观测值的上限。显然，重新核查宏观物理学也是一件值得做的事。尤其是，因为太阳核心满足对流稳定性的史瓦西判据 [5,6]，所以宏观物理学通常假设太阳核心保持在非混合的状态。尽管奥皮克曾经提出过：物质的扩散会围绕着核心形成一个不透明度很高的壳层，核心区最终会变得对流不稳定，并发生混合 [7]；但他对扩散过程的粗略描述与更仔细的计算得出的结果显著不同 [8]。如果我们相信详细的计算结果，那么在不经过修正的情况下，奥皮克机制不太可能在短于太阳年龄的时间内起作用。存在一个强埃克曼环流 [9,10] 的可能性使得核心的连续混合对 F_v 造成的影响成为一件值得考虑的事 [11-15]。这些结果依赖于所取的混合时标，它们表明 F_v 值可以降低，但并不清楚降低的量是否足够。无论如何，当前太阳中都不太可能存在足够快速的埃克曼环流 [16]。在本文中我们考虑了太阳核心的稳定性并且发现了一个会导致间歇性混合的过程；实际上福勒 [17] 已经指出过这种混合可能对降低 F_v 值更为有效。

太阳核心的不稳定性

在一颗主序星的核心，热核反应产能对史瓦西判据的影响可以忽略不计。这是因为产能的时标要远大于对流模式增长的时间，所以当考虑对流模式的时候通常忽略产能。但是能量产生可能会使重力模式不稳定，就像爱丁顿 [18] 认为在造父变星内部脉动有可能会被驱动一样。我们考虑一个极其简化的模型：一层简单的平行分层液体，厚度为 d，它内部每单位质量的产能率为 ε。我们暂且假设主要的核反应只有 ppI 链中的 $p(p, \beta^+\nu)D(p, \gamma)^3He$ 和 $^3He(^3He, 2p)^4He$ 反应，其产能率分别为 ε_{11} 和 ε_{33}。因为太阳核心区目前不太可能在快速旋转 [16]，所以我们将旋转一并忽略掉。为了使模型进一步简化，我们假设流体层非常薄，可以用博欣内斯克近似来描述浮力驱动运动 [19]，并且忽略重力的起伏。

由于物质和动量的扩散以及由核燃烧引起的 H 和 He 浓度的变化在本节所考虑的尺度和时标内是微不足道的，所以 X 和 X_3 的拉格朗日导数、H 和 ^3He 的质量分数都被取为零，黏滞应力也将被忽略。在笛卡尔坐标系 (x, y, z) 下，当 z 为垂直轴时，线性化方程可以被写作：

$$\rho\frac{\partial \mathbf{u}}{\partial t} = -\nabla p' + \mathbf{g}\rho' \qquad (1)$$

$$\text{div } \mathbf{u} = 0 \tag{2}$$

$$C_p\left(\frac{\partial T'}{\partial t} - \beta w\right) = \varepsilon' + \frac{K}{\rho}\nabla^2 T' \tag{3}$$

$$\frac{\partial T'}{\partial t} + w\frac{dX}{dz} = 0 \qquad \frac{\partial X'_3}{\partial t} + w\frac{dX_3}{dz} = 0 \tag{4}$$

where $\mathbf{u}$ is the fluid velocity and w its vertical component; p, ρ, T are pressure, density and temperature, K is the radiative conductivity $4acT^3/3\kappa\rho$, C_p is the specific heat at constant pressure, β is the superadiabatic temperature gradient and $\mathbf{g}$ is the gravitational acceleration. In these equations unprimed variables refer to the equilibrium state and primed variables to the perturbations. The equations must be supplemented by an equation of state; the perfect gas law for a fully ionized gas, in Boussinesq approximation, will be assumed so that

$$\frac{\rho'}{\rho} = -\frac{T'}{T} - \lambda\frac{X'}{X} \tag{5}$$

where
$$\lambda = -\left(\frac{\partial \ln\rho}{\partial \ln X}\right)_{p,T} \simeq \frac{5X}{5X+3}$$

With the help of this equation the perturbed energy generation rate is given by

$$\frac{\varepsilon'}{\varepsilon} = \eta\frac{T'}{T} + \nu\frac{X'}{X} + \nu_3\frac{X'_3}{X_3} \tag{6}$$

where

$$\eta = \frac{\varepsilon_{11}}{\varepsilon}\left(\frac{\partial \ln \varepsilon_{11}}{\partial \ln T}\right)_{\rho,X,X_3} + \frac{\varepsilon_{33}}{\varepsilon}\left(\frac{\partial \ln \varepsilon_{33}}{\partial \ln T}\right)_{\rho,X,X_3} - \left(\frac{\partial \ln \varepsilon}{\partial \ln \rho}\right)_{T,X,X_3}$$

$$\nu = \frac{\varepsilon_{11}}{\varepsilon}\left(\frac{\partial \ln \varepsilon_{11}}{\partial \ln X}\right)_{\rho,X,X_3} - \lambda\left(\frac{\partial \ln \varepsilon}{\partial \ln \rho}\right)_{T,X,X_3}$$

and
$$\nu_3 = \frac{\varepsilon_{33}}{\varepsilon}\left(\frac{\partial \ln \varepsilon_{33}}{\partial \ln X_3}\right)_{\rho,T,X}$$

As is customary in initial studies of convective instability, the simplest boundary conditions will be assumed:

$$w = 0, \, T' = 0 \text{ at } z = 0, d \tag{7}$$

After the usual manipulations[20] it can be shown that the space and time dependence of w, ρ', T', X' and X'_3 can be written in the separated form

$$e^{qwt}\, e^{i(k_xx+k_yy)}\,\sin\left(\frac{m\pi z}{d}\right)$$

where m is an integer. If $w^2 = \dfrac{k_x^2 + k_y^2}{k^2}\dfrac{|\mathbf{g}|}{d}$ where $k^2 = k_x^2+k_y^2+\left(\dfrac{m\pi}{d}\right)^2$ equations (1) to (6) imply the dispersion relation

$$\text{div } \mathbf{u} = 0 \tag{2}$$

$$C_p\left(\frac{\partial T'}{\partial t} - \beta w\right) = \varepsilon' + \frac{K}{\rho}\nabla^2 T' \tag{3}$$

$$\frac{\partial T'}{\partial t} + w\frac{dX}{dz} = 0 \qquad \frac{\partial X'_3}{\partial t} + w\frac{dX_3}{dz} = 0 \tag{4}$$

其中 $\mathbf{u}$ 为流体速度，w 是它的垂直分量；p、ρ、T 分别是压强、密度和温度，K 代表辐射传导系数 $4acT^3/3\kappa\rho$，C_p 为定压比热，β 为超绝热温度梯度，$\mathbf{g}$ 为重力加速度。在这些方程中，无撇号的变量表示平衡状态下的量，带撇号的变量表示扰动量。上述方程组还必须补充一个状态方程；在博欣内斯克近似下，可以取完全电离气体的理想气体状态方程，因而：

$$\frac{\rho'}{\rho} = -\frac{T'}{T} - \lambda\frac{X'}{X} \tag{5}$$

其中

$$\lambda = -\left(\frac{\partial \ln\rho}{\partial \ln X}\right)_{p,T} \simeq \frac{5X}{5X+3}$$

借助这一方程，扰动态下的产能率就可以表示为：

$$\frac{\varepsilon'}{\varepsilon} = \eta\frac{T'}{T} + \nu\frac{X'}{X} + \nu_3\frac{X'_3}{X_3} \tag{6}$$

其中

$$\eta = \frac{\varepsilon_{11}}{\varepsilon}\left(\frac{\partial \ln\varepsilon_{11}}{\partial \ln T}\right)_{\rho,X,X_3} + \frac{\varepsilon_{33}}{\varepsilon}\left(\frac{\partial \ln\varepsilon_{33}}{\partial \ln T}\right)_{\rho,X,X_3} - \left(\frac{\partial \ln\varepsilon}{\partial \ln\rho}\right)_{T,X,X_3}$$

$$\nu = \frac{\varepsilon_{11}}{\varepsilon}\left(\frac{\partial \ln\varepsilon_{11}}{\partial \ln X}\right)_{\rho,X,X_3} - \lambda\left(\frac{\partial \ln\varepsilon}{\partial \ln\rho}\right)_{T,X,X_3}$$

和

$$\nu_3 = \frac{\varepsilon_{33}}{\varepsilon}\left(\frac{\partial \ln\varepsilon_{33}}{\partial \ln X_3}\right)_{\rho,T,X}$$

习惯上，在开始研究对流不稳定性时，首先取最简单的边界条件：

$$\text{在 } z = 0 \text{ 和 } d \text{ 处}, \; w = 0, T' = 0 \tag{7}$$

在经过常规处理[20]之后发现，量 w、ρ'、T'、X' 和 X'_3 对空间和时间的依赖关系可以写成分离的形式：

$$e^{qwt}\, e^{i(k_x x + k_y y)}\sin\left(\frac{m\pi z}{d}\right)$$

其中 m 是一个整数。如果 $w^2 = \frac{k_x^2 + k_y^2}{k^2}\frac{|\mathbf{g}|}{d}$，式中 $k^2 = k_x^2 + k_y^2 + \left(\frac{m\pi}{d}\right)^2$，则方程（1）到（6）中含有色散关系：

$$q^3 + E\alpha q^2 + \left[\lambda \frac{d}{H_x} - (\nabla - \nabla_{ad})\frac{d}{H_p}\right]q + E\left[(\nu + \lambda\alpha)\frac{d}{H_x} + \nu_3 \frac{d}{H_3}\right] = 0 \qquad (8)$$

where H_p, H_x and H_3 are the scale heights of p, X and X_3 in the equilibrium configuration, $\alpha = \dfrac{KTk^2}{\rho\varepsilon} - \eta$ and $E = \dfrac{\varepsilon}{wC_pT}$. The superadiabatic temperature gradient β has been written as $(\nabla - \nabla_{ad})\dfrac{T}{H_p}$ where $\nabla = \dfrac{d\ln T}{d\ln p}$ and $\nabla_{ad} = \left(\dfrac{\partial \ln T}{\partial \ln p}\right)_{ad}$. Note that provided $k_x^2 + k_y^2 \ll k^2$, E is essentially the ratio of the free-fall time to the Kelvin–Helmholtz time for the core and is therefore small. Because on the main sequence the luminosity is largely balanced by the energy generated with the core, $\left(\dfrac{KT}{d}\right)d^2 \simeq \rho\varepsilon d$, where d represents the scale of the core, and the parameter $\dfrac{KTk^2}{\rho\varepsilon}$ is approximately $(kd)^2$; for the lower modes this is of order unity.

The dispersion relation (8) admits three roots. Granted that $E \ll 1$ the motion is nearly adiabatic and these roots may be written approximately:

$$q_{1,2} \simeq \pm i\left[\lambda \frac{d}{H_x} - (\nabla - \nabla_{ad})\frac{d}{H_p}\right]^{\frac{1}{2}} + \frac{1}{2}E\left[\alpha(\nabla - \nabla_{ad})H_x + \right.$$

$$\left. \left(\nu + \nu_3 \frac{H_x}{H_3}\right)H_p\right]/\left[\lambda H_p - (\nabla - \nabla_{ad})H_x\right] \qquad (9)$$

which correspond to the two g modes, and

$$q_3 \simeq -E\left(\lambda\alpha + \nu + \nu_3 \frac{H_x}{H_3}\right)H_p/\left[\lambda H_p - (\nabla - \nabla_{ad})H_x\right] \qquad (10)$$

which corresponds to the secular mode. The f and p modes have been filtered out by the Boussinesq approximation. If

$$\nabla - \nabla_{ad} > \lambda \frac{H_p}{H_x} \qquad (11)$$

the leading term of either q_1 or q_2 is real and positive, and provided this exceeds the small second term the fluid layer is unstable to direct convective motions. This criterion was obtained by Ledoux[21]. But we pointed out above that solar models are stable to even the Schwarzschild criterion: $\nabla - \nabla_{ad} < 0$, and the g modes are oscillatory. This does not, however, imply that the core is stable; if

$$\left(\nu + \nu_3 \frac{H_x}{H_3}\right)H_p > \alpha(\nabla_{ad} - \nabla)H_x \qquad (12)$$

the amplitude of the oscillations grows in a time comparable to the Kelvin–Helmholtz time for the core.

If the ^{3}He is in nuclear equilibrium with the hydrogen, $\dfrac{X_3}{3X} = \sqrt{\dfrac{\lambda_{pp}}{2\lambda_{33}}}$ where

$$q^3 + E\alpha q^2 + \left[\lambda\frac{d}{H_x} - (\nabla - \nabla_{ad})\frac{d}{H_p}\right]q + E\left[(\nu + \lambda\alpha)\frac{d}{H_x} + \nu_3\frac{d}{H_3}\right] = 0 \qquad (8)$$

其中 H_p、H_x 和 H_3 分别是平衡位形下 p、X 和 X_3 的标高，$\alpha = \frac{KTk^2}{\rho\varepsilon} - \eta$ 及 $E = \frac{\varepsilon}{wC_pT}$。超绝热温度梯度 β 被写成：$(\nabla - \nabla_{ad})\frac{T}{H_p}$，其中 $\nabla = \frac{d\ln T}{d\ln p}$ 和 $\nabla_{ad} = \left(\frac{\partial \ln T}{\partial \ln p}\right)_{ad}$。注意：如果 $k_x^2 + k_y^2 \ll k^2$，则 E 实际上是核心自由下落时间与开尔文－亥姆霍兹时间之比，因此很小。因为在主序时，核心的产能大致与光度相抵，$\left(\frac{KT}{d}\right)d^2 \simeq \rho\varepsilon d$，其中 d 代表核心的尺度，而参量 $\frac{KTk^2}{\rho\varepsilon}$ 近似等于 $(kd)^2$；对于更低的模式这个值的数量级是 1。

色散关系式（8）有 3 个根。假定 $E \ll 1$，则这一运动过程基本上是绝热的，这几个根可以被近似写成：

$$q_{1,2} \simeq \pm i\left[\lambda\frac{d}{H_x} - (\nabla - \nabla_{ad})\frac{d}{H_p}\right]^{\frac{1}{2}} + \frac{1}{2}E\Big[\alpha(\nabla - \nabla_{ad})H_x +$$

$$\left(\nu + \nu_3\frac{H_x}{H_3}\right)H_p\Big]/\left[\lambda H_p - (\nabla - \nabla_{ad})H_x\right] \qquad (9)$$

q_1、q_2 对应于两个 g 模式，和

$$q_3 \simeq -E\left(\lambda\alpha + \nu + \nu_3\frac{H_x}{H_3}\right)H_p/\left[\lambda H_p - (\nabla - \nabla_{ad})H_x\right] \qquad (10)$$

q_3 对应于长期模式。f 模式和 p 模式已经被博欣内斯克近似筛除。如果

$$\nabla - \nabla_{ad} > \lambda\frac{H_p}{H_x} \qquad (11)$$

则 q_1 或 q_2 的主项是正实数，这时只要其超过较小的第二项，流体层就是不稳定的并将导致对流运动。这一判据是由勒杜归纳得出的 [21]。但是我们在上文中指出，即使在史瓦西判据 $\nabla - \nabla_{ad} < 0$ 和 g 模式为振荡模式的情况下，太阳模型仍是稳定的。然而，假如

$$\left(\nu + \nu_3\frac{H_x}{H_3}\right)H_p > \alpha(\nabla_{ad} - \nabla)H_x \qquad (12)$$

核心区振荡幅度增长的时间与核心的开尔文－亥姆霍兹时间相当的话，则并不意味着核心是稳定的。

如果 ^{3}He 与 H 在核反应中是平衡的，则有 $\frac{X_3}{3X} = \sqrt{\frac{\lambda_{pp}}{2\lambda_{33}}}$，其中 λ_{33} 由

λ_{33} is defined in terms of the reaction rate r_{33} of the $^3\text{He}(^3\text{He},2p)^4\text{He}$ reaction by $r_{33} = \lambda_{33}\left(\dfrac{X_3}{3}\right)^2$ and λ_{pp} is defined similarly. $\dfrac{\lambda_{pp}}{\lambda_{33}}$ is a function of temperature alone, and $\dfrac{\text{d}\ln(\lambda_{pp}/\lambda_{33})}{\text{d}\ln T} \equiv -2b \approx -12$ at the centre of the Sun. Thus if the core is approximated by a polytrope of index n, $\dfrac{1}{H_3} = \dfrac{1}{H_x} + \dfrac{b}{(n+1)H_p}$ and the criterion (12) for overstability may be written

$$\frac{1}{H_x} > \frac{1}{\nu + \nu_3}\left[\alpha(\nabla_{\text{ad}} - \nabla) - \frac{b\nu_3}{n+1}\right]\frac{1}{H_p} \tag{13}$$

The analysis presented above very closely resembles the work of Defouw[22]. The thermodynamics of the overstability is identical, though the physical processes responsible for the energy source term ε are quite different. The existence of gradients in composition adds an extra term to the stability criterion: because in a hydrogen burning core $\nu > 0$, $\nu_3 > 0$, and X and X_3 do not decrease upwards, the perturbations in composition help to enhance the energy generation rate in a downward displaced fluid element relative to its surroundings and so add to the tendency towards overstability. Eddington's discussion of the overstability of spherically symmetric oscillations of Cepheids is similar, but in purely radial motion any displaced element always has the same fluid in its immediate environment and again the composition gradient does not directly enter into the stability criterion.

The existence of the composition gradients is also responsible for the secular mode whose growth rate is given by equation (10). Imagine, for example, a fluid element to experience a positive temperature fluctuation. It will rise to find a new hydrostatic equilibrium position which, because condition (11) is not satisfied, is stable on a convective timescale. Thus it will have the same pressure and density as its surroundings. But if $\text{d}X/\text{d}z > 0$, it will have a lower H abundance than its surroundings, and hence a higher temperature. Thus there will be a difference in the energy generation rate; if the increase resulting from the higher temperature, offset by thermal diffusion, exceeds the decrease resulting from the lower concentration of H and the inevitably lower concentration of ^3He, the temperature excess will be accentuated and the perturbation will grow.

An estimate of the growth rates of g modes in the Sun cannot be made by merely substituting typical values into equation (9) because the perturbations will not be confined solely to the energy generating core. Outside the core the only surviving nonadiabatic effect is the radiative damping. Auré[23] has estimated that in early type stars damping in the envelope by far exceeds the excitation (in the semiconvective zone) beneath, primarily because the amplitudes of the perturbations increase rapidly with radius. But the comparatively deep outer convection zone in the Sun makes an important difference. When $\nabla - \nabla_{\text{ad}} > 0$ radiative heat transfer tends to destabilize the oscillation, just as it does p modes[24], and in any case the amplitude then decreases with radius. Further, one might expect the interaction with the unsteady direct convective motion in this zone to destroy

^{3}He(^{3}He,2p)^{4}He 反应的反应率 r_{33} 定义为 $r_{33} = \lambda_{33}\left(\dfrac{X_3}{3}\right)^2$，$\lambda_{pp}$ 的定义与此类似。$\dfrac{\lambda_{pp}}{\lambda_{33}}$ 只是温度的函数，并且在太阳核心处有 $\dfrac{\mathrm{dln}\,(\lambda_{pp}/\lambda_{33})}{\mathrm{dln}\,T} \equiv -2b \approx -12$。因此，如果核心被近似为一个多方指数为 n 的多方球，则 $\dfrac{1}{H_3} = \dfrac{1}{H_x} + \dfrac{b}{(n+1)H_p}$ 并且超稳定性判据 （12）可以写作：

$$\frac{1}{H_x} > \frac{1}{\nu + \nu_3}\left[\alpha(\nabla_{ad} - \nabla) - \frac{b\nu_3}{n+1}\right]\frac{1}{H_p} \tag{13}$$

上述分析过程非常类似于迪佛的研究工作 [22]。尽管与能源项 ε 有关的物理过程完全不同，但超稳定性热力学是一样的。组成成分梯度的存在为稳定性判据增加了一个新的项：因为在氢燃烧的核心区 $\nu > 0$，$\nu_3 > 0$，且 X 和 X_3 不会越向上越小，组成的扰动有助于提高相对于其周围环境有向下位移的流体元的产能率，因而增加了趋于超稳定态的倾向。爱丁顿对造父变星球对称振动超稳定性的讨论与此类似，但在纯径向运动中，任何发生位移的流体元紧挨着的环境总是同样的流体，从而组分梯度也不直接进入稳定性判据。

组分梯度的存在也是造成其增长率由等式（10）给出的长期模式的原因。例如，试设想一个流体元经历温度正起伏的情况。它将上升以寻求一个新的流体静力学平衡位置。这时由于条件（11）不被满足，这个位置在对流时间尺度内是稳定的，因而流体元将具有与周围环境等同的压强和密度。但是，如果 $\mathrm{d}X/\mathrm{d}z > 0$，那么该流体元中的 H 丰度将比周围环境中的低，所以温度将比周围的高。因此，产能率就会有所不同；如果由较高温度导致的被热扩散抵消后的增长超过了由较低 H 浓度以及不可避免的较低 ^{3}He 浓度引起的降低，那么温度升高将会加剧，扰动也会增长。

不能只通过把典型值代入等式（9）来估计太阳 g 模式的增长率，因为扰动不仅仅局限于产生能量的核心。在核心外，唯一存在的非绝热效应就是辐射阻尼，奥雷 [23] 曾估计早型星包层的阻尼作用远远超过了下层（在半对流区内）的激发，这主要是因为扰动的幅度随半径增加得很快。但是，在太阳中相对较深的外对流区却存在一个重要的不同。当 $\nabla - \nabla_{ad} > 0$ 时，正如在 p 模式的情况一样 [24]，辐射热传递倾向于使振动失去稳定性，并且在任何情况下振幅都会随着半径而降低。此外，我们可以预期在此区域中与非稳定直接对流运动之间的相互作用将破坏该运动与核心内运动之间可能存在的任意相关。值得注意的是：假如辐射阻尼足以使等式（9）和（10）

whatever correlation the motion might have with the motion in the core. It is worth noting that if radiative damping is sufficient to make the effective value of α in equations (9) and (10) positive, the secular mode must be stable.

An approximate stability criterion for the Sun was derived by evaluating the work integral[25] for nonradial modes using the adiabatic eigenfunction for the fundamental g mode associated with the surface harmonic with $l=2$ published by Cowling[26] for the polytrope of index 3, and making the Boussinesq approximation in calculating the divergence of the radiative heat flux. The polytrope approximates the Sun reasonably well beneath the convection zone. In view of the more extensive analysis by, for example, Smeyers[27] of nonradial modes in other stars, one might expect the $g_1(l=2)$ oscillation to be a strong contender for the most unstable mode. Bearing in mind the discussion in the previous paragraph, the integrals were truncated at 70% of the total radius of the polytrope, the position of the base of the convection zone in the solar model considered in the next section. The analogue of criterion (13) for instability so obtained is

$$\frac{1}{H_x} > \left[(30 - \eta)(\nabla_{\mathrm{ad}} - \nabla) - \frac{\nu_3 b}{n+1}\right]\frac{1}{(\nu + \nu_3)H_p} \tag{14}$$

where now one must enter typical values. In the solar core $\nu \simeq \frac{1}{2}$, $\nu_3 \simeq 1$, $\eta \simeq 9$, $b \simeq 6$ and $\nabla_{\mathrm{ad}} - \nabla \simeq 0.1$, and the criterion becomes

$$H_x < 2.5\, H_p \tag{15}$$

The Main Sequence Evolution of the Sun

The early main sequence Sun is roughly chemically homogeneous (H_x is infinite). The core is stable and no mixing occurs, except possibly at the very beginning when X_3 is far from its equilibrium value. A spatial variation in composition builds up until criterion (14) is satisfied and the core becomes unstable to oscillatory g modes.

What happens when large amplitude motions occur? If the core is mixed until the chemical composition and specific entropy are uniform, local nuclear equilibrium is upset: in the central regions X_3 increases proportionately more than X (because $H_3 < H_x$ before mixing) and the pp chain is dominated by the temperature sensitive $^3\mathrm{He}$ burning reactions. The rate at which energy is generated close to the center is increased by the redistribution of fuel; if, for example, an equilibrium abundance of $^3\mathrm{He}$ in the inner 20% by mass is thoroughly mixed, the central abundance is increased by a factor of about 5 in a polytrope model and if the temperature were to stay constant the rate of the $^3\mathrm{He}$–$^3\mathrm{He}$ reaction would increase by a factor of 25. The consequent increased heat flux can no longer be stably transported by radiation alone, the Schwarzschild criterion for stability is violated and a mechanism to drive the motions originally postulated for mixing is thus provided. The core, though stable to infinitesimal direct convective modes, is unstable to finite amplitude convection.

中的 α 有效值为正的话，那么长期模式必然是稳定的。

太阳的一个近似稳定性判据可以通过以下方式导出：用基本 g 模式下的绝热本征函数，结合考林[26]针对指数等于 3 的多方球发表的 $l=2$ 的面调和函数计算出非径向模式下的功积分[25]，并利用博欣内斯克近似值计算热辐射流的散度。对于太阳对流区以下的区域用多方球近似是合理的。考虑到更广泛的分析，例如斯梅耳斯[27]对其他恒星在非径向模式下所作的分析，我们可以预期，$g_1(l=2)$ 振动模式将是最不稳定模式的一个可能性很大的候选者。别忘了我们在前一段中的讨论，积分在多方球总半径的 70% 处被截断，这正是在下一节我们将考虑的太阳模型中对流区基部所在的位置。因此，不稳定状态的判据（13）可以类似地表达为：

$$\frac{1}{H_x} > \left[(30-\eta)(\nabla_{ad} - \nabla) - \frac{\nu_3\, b}{n+1}\right]\frac{1}{(\nu+\nu_3)H_p} \tag{14}$$

现在需要将一些典型值代入式中。在太阳核心，$\nu \simeq \frac{1}{2}$，$\nu_3 \simeq 1$，$\eta \simeq 9$，$b \simeq 6$ 和 $\nabla_{ad} - \nabla \simeq 0.1$，因而上述判据变为：

$$H_x < 2.5\, H_p \tag{15}$$

太阳在主序阶段的演化

早期主序阶段的太阳在化学上大致是均匀的（H_x 为无穷大）。除了在非常早期 X_3 可能会远远偏离它的平衡值外，其核心是稳定的并且没有混合发生。直到满足判据（14）且核心对于振荡 g 模式变得不稳定的时候，组分在空间的变化才得以建立起来。

大幅度运动出现时会发生什么？如果在化学组成和比熵达到均衡之前，核心一直在混合，那么局域核反应平衡就会被打破：在中心区域，X_3 按比例的增长比 X 要大（因为混合之前 $H_3<H_x$），而 pp（质子－质子）链取决于对温度敏感的 ^{3}He 燃烧反应。中心区附近的产能率随着燃料的重新分配而不断增加；比如，如果在质量占 20% 的内部区域，具有平衡丰度的 ^{3}He 被彻底混合，则在多方球模型中，中心丰度会增加到原来的 5 倍左右，如果温度保持不变，那么 ^{3}He－^{3}He 反应的速率将增加到原来的 25 倍。仅仅通过辐射便不再能够稳定地传输随之增长的热流量了，史瓦西稳定性判据不再被满足，从而提供了那种一开始假设的驱动物质混合运动的机制。虽然核心对于极微小的直接对流模式来说是稳定的，但是对于有限幅度对流来说却是不稳定的。

The combination of overstability to infinitesimal disturbances and instability to finite amplitude convection has been studied in other contexts, for example, convection in a rotating layer of Boussinesq fluid[28] and thermosolutal convection[29]. It is thought that overstable oscillations first appear which ultimately grow until they are of sufficient amplitude to trigger convection. Laboratory experiments, though not conclusive, support this idea[30-32]. The combination of the subsequent persistent convective motion and diffusion finally destroys or substantially weakens the stabilizing mechanism. We note that in the circumstances considered here, although diffusion of material was ignored when deriving the linear stability criterion, it was tacitly invoked later to render the solar core chemically homogeneous.

What are the evolutionary consequences for the Sun? As a result of transporting fuel to hotter regions of the star there is a tendency for the total energy generation rate to increase. But because the Sun is thermally stable this is adequately offset by an expansion of the core, converting thermal energy into gravitational energy, reducing the temperature and density and hence the energy generation rate. The timescale for this process, the Kelvin–Helmholtz time for the core, is shorter than the Kelvin–Helmholtz time for the whole star by a factor of about ten. So the envelope, which adjusts almost immediately to stay in hydrostatic equilibrium, at first expands almost adiabatically and cools. This causes a reduction in the effective temperature and surface luminosity. Meanwhile, as the ^{3}He abundance relaxes to equilibrium the temperature sensitivity of the energy generation is reduced and the convective core disappears. The bulk of the envelope has not yet had time to adjust thermally and the central temperature still remains anomalously low. Finally, in about 10^7 yr the whole star reaches thermal equilibrium; the central temperature, effective temperature and luminosity have increased somewhat, but not to their previous values, for the Sun is now chemically less inhomogeneous than it was before mixing began and takes on an appearance similar to when it was in a less evolved state. Normal main sequence evolution without mixing follows until condition (14) is satisfied once more, and the process is repeated.

To check this argument quantitatively, we modified a stellar evolution computer program provided by B. Paczyński. The only nuclear reactions considered were those of the pp chain, using published data for cross-sections[15] and for the rate of electron capture by ^{7}Be (ref. 33).

The time which elapses between successive mixing phases is that required to build up a composition gradient sufficient to make the core overstable. This is a nuclear burning time and, taking criterion (14) literally, was found to be of the order of 10^9 yr. We emphasize that this value is not accurate because the coefficient in (14) was obtained by taking the difference between two numbers each of which was obtained from the structure of a particular g mode in a simple polytrope. We are now studying the stability of nonradial modes in a more realistic solar model. Because the Sun is now about 40% more luminous than it was when it arrived on the main sequence, evolution is occurring more rapidly. Consequently, provided the structure is not changing so much as to significantly alter the

对无限小扰动的超稳定性和对有限幅度对流的不稳定性已在其他情况下被联合研究过：比如，在旋转的博欣内斯克流体层中的对流 [28] 和热溶质对流 [29]。人们认为超稳态下的振动首先出现，它们最终会发展到具有足够的振幅以触发对流。实验室中的一些结果，虽然不具备结论性，但是支持这一想法 [30-32]。随后持续的对流运动与扩散过程相结合，最终破坏或者极大地削弱了这种稳定机制。我们注意到：在本文所讨论的情况下，尽管在推导线性稳定性判据时忽略了物质扩散，但后来还是默许用它来说明太阳核心在化学组成上的均一性。

太阳最终会演化成什么样子？由于燃料向恒星中更高温度处的输运，因而总产能率趋向于不断增加。但因为太阳是热稳定的，所以这一效应会被核心区的膨胀适当抵消，从而将热能转化为重力势能，降低温度和密度从而降低产能率。这一过程的时标，即核心的开尔文－亥姆霍兹时间，还不到整个恒星的开尔文－亥姆霍兹时间的 1/10。因此，几乎立即调节到处于流体静力学平衡的包层将首先几乎绝热地膨胀并冷却。这就导致了有效温度和表面光度的降低。同时，随着 ^{3}He 丰度逐渐通过弛豫趋于平衡，产能的温度敏感度会下降，对流核心也随之消失。而这时整个包层还没来得及进行温度上的调节，中心温度仍然维持在异常低的状态。最后，经过大约 10^7 年，整个恒星达到了热平衡；中心温度、有效温度和光度都有所上升，但是达不到它们以前的值，因为太阳此时在化学组成上的均一性比混合开始之前高，并且呈现出类似于处在更早演化阶段的状态。随后发生没有混合的正常主序演化过程，直到条件（14）再被满足，上述过程又得以重复。

为了从数值上检验这一观点，我们对帕金斯基提供的关于恒星演化的计算机程序进行了修改。只考虑 pp 链的核反应，使用已发表的截面数据 [15] 和 ^{7}Be 电子俘获率的数据（参考文献 33）。

两个相继的混合期之间经过的时间就是建立足以使核心区变成超稳定的组分梯度所需的时间。这就是核燃烧的时间，从判据（14）的表面意义上看，这一时间的数量级为 10^9 年。我们要说明的是这个值并不准确，因为判据（14）中的系数是由简单多方球中两个特殊 g 模式结构分别给出的值的差得到的。我们现在正在研究的是一个更实际太阳模型中的非径向模式的稳定性。因为太阳目前的光度大约比它刚进入主序阶段时高了 40%，所以它会更快地演化。因此，只要结构的变化不足以大到使稳定性判据发生显著的改变，那么两个相继的混合期之间的时间间隔就会缩短。

stability criterion, the period between successive mixing phases is decreasing. In the next section we argue that it is now about 2.5×10^8 yr.

To simulate the gross effects of earlier mixing a solar model was evolved for 4.45×10^9 yr with a core of mass m_c artificially mixed. Normal evolution was allowed for a further 2.5×10^8 yr, then the entropy and chemical composition of the core were instantaneously mixed and normal evolution was allowed to continue again. We found that a superadiabatic core did develop after the sudden mixing, though it did not extend to m_c. The velocity of the ensuing motion was sufficient to advect ^{7}Be away from the central region in a time somewhat shorter than the half life against electron capture. We assumed that mixing of ^{3}He and ^{7}Be occurs only in the superadiabatic region, because the amplitudes of at least the linear direct convective modes decay rapidly in the subadiabatic region surrounding the core[34], though finite amplitude motion may penetrate further[35]. It can be seen in Fig. 1 that with $m_c = 0.25\ M_\odot$ the minimum luminosity is some 5% lower than the luminosity before mixing. At this point, although much of the interior is in a relatively expanded state the radius at the photosphere is somewhat smaller than normal. The cooling of the outer envelope which results from the smaller heat input from below allows the temperature and pressure to fall and the surface layers to contract. Later, the luminosity rises as the thermal wave produced by the burst of energy generated immediately after mixing reaches the surface, and finally the star settles down with a luminosity somewhat lower and an effective temperature slightly higher than it had before mixing began.

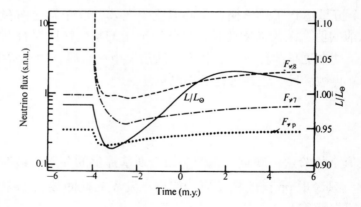

Fig. 1. Time variations of the surface luminosity of the Sun, in units of its present value, and of the neutrino fluxes $F_{\nu p}$, $F_{\nu 7}$ and $F_{\nu 8}$ measured in s.n.u. (The neutrino capture cross-sections were taken from Bahcall[36].) The first minimum in $F_{\nu 8}$ occurs soon after the convective core begins to recede, the second when the central temperature is also a minimum. Time is measured in units of m.y.

Finally, we consider the neutrino flux. The mixing of ^{3}He towards the center initially increases the rate of ^{7}Be production and the ^{7}Be neutrino flux $F_{\nu 7}$ rises. But mixing of ^{7}Be away from the centre reduces the rate of the temperature sensitive proton capture and the ^{8}B neutrino flux $F_{\nu 8}$ drops rapidly. As the central temperature subsequently falls $F_{\nu 7}$ attains a maximum and then decreases, and $F_{\nu 8}$ drops still further; temperature is the dominant

在下一节中我们将论证这个时间段的长度大致为 2.5×10^8 年。

为了模拟出更早期混合的总效应，我们让一个具有人为混合过的质量为 m_c 的核心的太阳模型演化 4.45×10^9 年。再继续进行正常的演化 2.5×10^8 年，然后核心区的熵和化学组成被迅速混合，随后再按正常演化继续进行。我们发现超绝热的核心在经过突然混合之后确实扩展了，虽然它还没有扩展到 m_c。结果产生的运动速度足以把 ^7Be 在比电子俘获的半减期更短的时间内输送出核心区。我们假设 ^3He 和 ^7Be 的混合只发生在超绝热区，因为：虽然有限幅度的运动还可以进一步穿透[35]，但至少线性直接对流模式的幅度会在核心周围的亚绝热区内迅速衰减掉[34]。从图 1 中可以看出：当 $m_c = 0.25\ M_\odot$ 时，其最低光度比混合前的光度低了大约 5%。在这一点上，尽管大部分内部区域处于相对膨胀的状态，但是其光球层的半径却比正常的要小。由于从下层传输来的热量比正常时变少导致了外包层的冷却，从而使温度和压强下降，因而表面层也将收缩。之后，由紧接着混合后立即导致的能量暴发所产生的热波到达表面，光度随之上升。最终，恒星稳定在一个光度比混合开始前略低、而有效温度比混合开始前略高的状态。

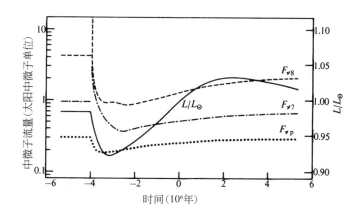

图1. 太阳表面光度的时变，以当前值为单位；以及中微子流量 $F_{\nu p}$、$F_{\nu 7}$ 和 $F_{\nu 8}$ 的时变，以太阳中微子单位为单位（中微子俘获截面取自巴考[36]）。$F_{\nu 8}$ 的首个极小值紧跟在对流核开始缩小之后出现，当中心区温度也达到极小值时出现第二个极小值。时间的单位为 10^6 年。

最后，我们来考虑中微子流量。^3He 向中心区的混合使 ^7Be 的生成率开始增加，也使 ^7Be 中微子流量 $F_{\nu 7}$ 增大。但是 ^7Be 离开中心区的混合却使对温度敏感的质子俘获率下降并使 ^8B 中微子流量 $F_{\nu 8}$ 也迅速下降。随着中心温度随后的下降，$F_{\nu 7}$ 在达到一个极大值之后也开始下降，$F_{\nu 8}$ 下降的幅度更大；温度对 pep（质子－电子－质子）

influence on the pep neutrino flux $F_{\nu p}$ which also decreases. The ^{7}Be and ^{8}B fluxes reach a minimum at the same time as the central temperature, and then gradually rise as the Sun relaxes back to thermal equilibrium. The precise details of the evolution depend on how much of the core is mixed; the model illustrated in Fig. 1 is typical. Because many of the recent improvements in the microphysics have not been included in the calculation, $F_{\nu 8}$ in Fig. 1 has been scaled by a constant factor to make its value prior to mixing similar to the latest published theoretical results. R. Rood and D. N. Schramm (private communication) report similar results. The minimum value of the total neutrino flux is of the same order as the currently quoted experimental upper bound. It appears, therefore, that if it can be demonstrated that the Sun has recently been mixed, the observed neutrino flux may no longer present a serious problem. The possibility still remains, however, that more refined measurements will lower the upper bound still further. No doubt a model can be found for which $F_{\nu 8}$ (which is very sensitive to comparatively small adjustments of the model) is negligible, but it is unlikely that the sum of $F_{\nu p}$ and $F_{\nu 7}$ can be reduced appreciably below about 0.7 s.n.u.

Solar Chronology and the Terrestrial Climate

The most recent of the Earth's major ice ages were separated by approximately 2.5×10^8 yr (ref. 37) which is of the same order as our rough estimate of the interval between successive mixing phases. The view that reductions in the solar luminosity L were responsible for the Earth's glaciations[7,38,39] is not universally accepted[37], but this is chiefly because evidence for solar luminosity variations has not been considered convincing. If major ice ages are initiated by fluctuations in L they must be a transient response, for it is believed that L has been generally increasing approximately exponentially from its zero age main sequence value of about 70% of its value today. Accepting the view[7,40] that an ice age is the equilibrium state of the climate when L is about 5% lower than its present value leads to the conclusion that the Earth was continuously glaciated until about 10^9 yr ago. It is essential to the hypothesis, therefore, that at least one of the terrestrial factors controlling the climate has a natural timescale comparable with or longer than the time taken for L to drop subsequent to the Sun being mixed. Theoretical estimates are difficult to make but there is some empirical evidence suggesting that during the Tertiary the climate underwent substantial variations on a timescale of several million years[41-44]. It seems most likely that these variations were produced either by solar variations, which would at least confirm the conclusion that the climate is strongly influenced by the Sun, or by some factor of confluence of factors intrinsic to the Earth, which would establish the existence of a sufficiently long natural timescale.

It is also necessary to ask whether the 5% drop in L is enough to produce an ice age. Theoretical discussions[7,40,45] suggest it is, but because these are deficient at least so far as they do not predict the long term stability of the climate, they cannot be relied on. The supporting empirical evidence is that the relatively short period low amplitude fluctuations in the insolation at a particular latitude arising from precession and planetary

反应产生的中微子流量 F_{vp} 起主导作用，所以 F_{vp} 也不断下降。^{7}Be 和 ^{8}B 流量与中心温度同时达到最小值，而在太阳通过弛豫回到热平衡的过程中，它们又逐渐增大。演化的精确细节取决于核心的混合程度；图 1 中给出的模型具有代表性。因为在计算中没有考虑到微观物理学的许多最新进展，所以我们在绘制图 1 时将 F_{v8} 乘上了一个常数因子，以使它在混合之前的数值接近于最新发表的理论值。鲁德和施拉姆也给出了相似的结果（个人交流）。总中微子流量的最小值与目前引用的实验值的上限在同一个数量级。因此，假如可以证明太阳在近期发生过混合，那么观测到的中微子流量也许就不再是一个严重的问题了。然而，更精密的测量仍有可能使上限值进一步降低。毫无疑问，一个 F_{v8}（其对模型中相当微小的调节十分敏感）可以忽略的模型是能够找到的，但是要使 F_{vp} 和 F_{v7} 的总和降到显著低于 0.7 太阳中微子单位则不太可能。

太阳年代学和地球气候

地球上离现在最近的两次主要冰期之间大约相隔 2.5×10^8 年（参考文献 37），这与我们对两个相继混合期之间的时间间隔的粗略估计是同一量级。太阳光度 L 的减少使地球上出现冰期的观点 [7,38,39] 并不被大家广泛接受 [37]，但这主要是由于证明太阳光度变化的证据尚不令人信服。如果说主要的冰期是由 L 的波动引起的，那么这种现象必定不会长久，因为一般认为从太阳零龄主序开始到现在，L 总是大致呈指数增长，其初始值是现在值的 70% 左右。如果接受这一观点 [7,40]，即冰期是当 L 比其现在值低大约 5% 时的一种气候上的平衡态，就可以导出直到 10^9 年以前地球一直处于冰河时期的结论。因此，下述假设是非常重要的：在控制气候的各种地球内部因素中至少有一个所具有的自然时标相当于或者长于在太阳混合之后 L 出现下降所用的时间。很难作出理论上的估计，但是一些经验上的证据表明：在第三纪时，气候经历了几百万年时间尺度上的重大变迁 [41-44]。这些变化似乎极有可能或者是由太阳变化引起的，从而至少证实了太阳会强烈影响气候；或者是由地球内在的某些因素联合形成的某个因素引起的，这要求承认存在一个充分长的自然时标。

另一个必须回答的问题是，L 下降 5% 是否足以产生冰期。虽然理论上的讨论 [7,40,45] 都支持这一点，但因为至少迄今为止它们仍是有缺陷的——它们不能预言气候的长期稳定性，所以并不可靠。一个支持此观点的经验上的证据是：已经发现在由地球运动岁差和行星摄动而引起的日射能量在某一特定纬度处的短周期低幅波动

perturbations of the Earth's motion have been correlated with the fluctuations in the extent of glaciation over the last 3×10^5 yr (refs. 46–49). Because the amplitudes of the fluctuations in the total annual insolation are typically only about 1%, one can at least say that it is not implausible that a 5% fluctuation is sufficient to bring about a major ice age.

Accepting this picture leads one to expect the beginning of the Pleistocene epoch to be located near the luminosity minimum at about 3 m.y. BP, when glaciation in midlatitudes began[50] (Fig. 1). The beginning of the depression of L, at about 4 m.y. BP, is then concomitant with the estimated onset of the Antarctic glaciation[51]. Because the beginning of the Pleistocene epoch was less than a solar Kelvin–Helmholtz time ago, the Sun is not at present in thermal equilibrium. This accounts at least in part for the discrepancy between the theoretically predicted neutrino flux and the upper bound measured by Davis and his collaborators.

After the core is mixed the Sun's evolution temporarily reverses its direction in the H–R diagram, envelope convection becomes more vigorous and presumably solar activity and the strength of the solar wind increase. The flux of high energy particles incident on the Earth and hence the production of radioactive nuclei in the atmosphere is therefore modified. One might hope that calibrating ^{14}C dating against other methods, for example, would show this, but during the comparatively short times over which this is possible other perturbing influences, such as the changes in the geomagnetic field, dominate[52]. Alternatively one might expect to unravel a direct record of the cosmic ray flux by analysing nuclear tracks in rocks, but this has not yet been possible[53].

We thank Professor N. H. Baker, Dr. A. Delany, Mr. D. C. Heggie, Professor K. H. Prendergast, Dr. D. N. Schramm, Dr. N. J. Shackleton, Professor C. T. Shaw, Professor E. A. Spiegel, Dr. N. O. Weiss, Professor A. Wolfendale, and Professor L. Woltjer for useful discussions, and Dr. J. R. Gribbin and Dr. E. Phillips for their help in rewriting the paper. We are grateful to Dr. B. Paczyński for giving us a copy of his stellar evolution program and to Dr. P. P. Eggleton for showing us how to use it. F. W. W. D. acknowledges the tenure of an SRC research studentship.

(**240**, 262-264&293-294; 1972)

F. W. W. Dilke and D. O. Gough: Institute of Theoretical Astronomy, University of Cambridge.

Received June 28; revised October 6, 1972.

References:

1. Davis, jun., R., Harmer, D. S., and Hoffman, K. C., *Phys. Rev. Lett.*, **20**, 1205 (1968).

2. Bahcall, J. N., and Ulrich, R. K., *Astrophys. J. Lett.*, **160**, L57 (1970).

3. Abraham, Z., and Iben, I., *Astrophys. J.*, **170**, 157 (1971).

4. Ezer, D., and Cameron, A. G. W., *Astrophys. Space Sci.*, **10**, 52 (1971).

5. Reye, T., *Die Wirbelstürme, Tornados und Wettersäulen* (Gesenius, Halle, 1872).

6. Schwarzschild, K., *Göttinger Nachrichten*, **1**, 41 (1906).

与过去 3×10^5 年之中冰川范围的波动之间存在关联（参考文献 46~49）。因为全年总日照能量的波动幅度通常只有大约 1%，所以我们至少可以认为 5% 的浮动足以诱发一次大的冰期的观点有一定道理。

接受这一理论框架将导致我们预期：更新世的开始时间接近于距今大约 3×10^6 年前的光度极小值时期，那时中纬度地区已开始进入冰期 [50]（图 1）。L 在距今大约 4×10^6 年前开始下降，伴随着的是预期的南极冰期的开始 [51]。由于更新世的开始时间没有达到太阳的开尔文－亥姆霍兹时间，因此太阳到现在还没有达到热平衡。这至少可以部分地解释在中微子流量理论估计值和戴维斯及其合作者测量出的上限值之间存在的差异。

在核心被混合之后，太阳的演化在赫罗图上暂时变为反向，包层对流区变得更加活跃，太阳活动性和太阳风的强度可能也会增加。因而入射到地球的高能粒子流和大气层中放射性核的生成量也发生了改变。例如，我们可以期望用定标的 ^{14}C 年龄测量与其他方法相比对来证明以上结论，但是其他扰动因素，如地磁场的变化，也可能会在较短的时间内占据主导作用 [52]。作为另一种可选择的方案，我们希望能通过分析岩石中的核径迹来解释宇宙射线流的直接记录结果，但是这种做法到目前为止还是不可能的 [53]。

感谢贝克教授、德拉尼博士、赫吉先生、普伦德加斯特教授、施拉姆博士、沙克尔顿博士、肖教授、施皮格尔教授、韦斯博士、沃尔芬德尔教授和沃尔特耶尔教授与我们进行了有益的讨论，还要感谢格里宾博士和菲利普斯博士在我们改写这篇文章时所给予的帮助。帕金斯基博士为我们提供了他的恒星演化程序的拷贝，埃格尔顿博士给我们演示了如何使用这一程序，在此也对他们表示感谢。迪尔克要感谢英国科学研究理事会一直为他提供研究生奖学金。

（孟洁 翻译；邓祖淦 于涌 审稿）

7. Öpik, E. J., *Contrib. Armagh Obs.*, No. 9 (1953).

8. Chapman, S., and Cowling, T. G., *The Mathematical Theory of Nonuniform Gases*, third edition (Cambridge University Press, 1970).

9. Howard, L. N., Moore, D., and Spiegel, E. A., *Nature*, **214**, 1297 (1967).

10. Bretherton, F. P., and Spiegel, E. A., *Astrophys. J. Lett.*, **153**, L77 (1968).

11. Ezer, D., and Cameron, A. G. W., *Astrophys. Lett.*, **1**, 177 (1968).

12. Bahcall, J. N., Bahcall, N. A., and Ulrich, R. K., *Astrophys. Lett.*, **2**, 91 (1968).

13. Iben, I., *Astrophys. J. Lett.*, **155**, L101 (1969).

14. Schatzman, E., *Astrophys. Lett.*, **3**, 139 (1969).

15. Shaviv, G., and Salpeter, E. E., *Astrophys. J.*, **165**, 171 (1971).

16. Gough, D. O., and Spiegel, E. A., *Comm. Astrophys. Space Phys.*, **4** (1972).

17. Fowler, W. A., *Nature*, **238**, 24 (1972).

18. Eddington, A. S., *The Internal Constitution of the Stars* (Cambridge University Press, 1926).

19. Spiegel, E. A., and Veronis, G., *Astrophys. J.*, **131**, 442 (1960); (correction: **135**, 655, 1962).

20. Chandrasekhar, S., *Hydrodynamic and Hydromagnetic Stability* (Oxford University Press, 1961).

21. Ledoux, P., *Astrophys. J.*, **105**, 305 (1947).

22. Defouw, R. J., *Astrophys. J.*, **160**, 659 (1970).

23. Auré, J.-L., *Astron. Astrophys.*, **11**, 345 (1971).

24. Spiegel, E. A., *Astrophys. J.*, **139**, 959 (1964).

25. Ledoux, P., and Walraven, Th., *Handbuch der Physik*, **51**, 353 (Springer, Berlin, 1958).

26. Cowling, T. G., *Mon. Not. Roy. Astron. Soc.*, **101**, 367 (1941).

27. Smeyers, P., *Bull. Soc. Roy. Sci. Liège*, **36**, 357 (1967).

28. *J.F.M.*, **5**, 401 (1959); Veronis, G., *J.F.M.*, **24**, 545 (1966).

29. Veronis, G., *J. Marine Res.*, **23**, 1 (1965).

30. Turner, J. S., *J.F.M.*, **33**, 183 (1968).

31. Shirtcliffe, T. G. L., *J.F.M.*, **35**, 677 (1969).

32. Rossby, H. T., *J.F.M.*, **36**, 309 (1969).

33. Bahcall, J. N., and Moeller, C. P., *Astrophys. J.*, **155**, 511 (1969).

34. Saslaw, W. C., and Schwarzschild, M., *Astrophys. J.*, **142**, 1468 (1965).

35. Latour, J. (reported by Spiegel, E. A.), *Ann. Rev. Astron. Astrophys.*, **10** (1972).

36. *Phys. Rev. Lett.*, **12**, 300 (1964); Bahcall, J. N., *Phys. Rev.*, **135**, B137 (1964).

37. Holmes, A., *Principles of Physical Geology* (Nelson, London, 1965).

38. Dutton, C. E., *Amer. J. Sci.*, third series, **27**, 1 (1884).

39. Öpik, E. J., *Mon. Not. Roy. Astron. Soc.*, **110**, 49 (1950).

40. Sellers, W. D., *J. Appl. Meteor.*, **8**, 392 (1969).

41. Dorman, F. H., *J. Geol.*, **74**, 49 (1966).

42. Devereux, I., *New Zealand J. Sci.*, **10**, 988 (1967).

43. Douglas, R. G., and Savin, S. M., *Initial Reports of the Deep Sea Drilling Project*, **6**, 1123 (1971).

44. Wolfe, J. A., *Palaeogeogr. Palaeoclim. Palaeoecol.*, **9**, 27 (1971).

45. Eriksson, E., *Meteor. Mon.*, **8**, 68 (1968).

46. Milankovitch, M., *Théorie Mathématique des Phénomènes Thermiques Produits par la Radiation Solaire* (Gauthier-Villars, Paris, 1920).

47. Emiliani, C., *J. Geol.*, **63**, 538 (1955).

48. van Woerkom, A. J. J., *Climatic Change* (edit. by Shapley), 147 (Harvard, Mass., 1953).

49. van den Heuvel, E. P. J., *Geophys. J. Roy. Astron. Soc.*, **11**, 323 (1966).

50. McDougall, I., and Stipp, J. J., *Nature*, **219**, 51 (1968).

51. Hays, J. D., and Opdyke, N. D., *Science*, **158**, 1001 (1967).

52. Grey, D. C., *J. Geophys. Res., Sp. Phys.*, **74**, 6333 (1969).

53. Fleischer, R. L., Price, P. B., and Walker, R. M., *Science*, **149**, 383 (1965).

Transmission of Kuru from Man to Rhesus Monkey (*Macaca mulatta*) 8½ Years after Inoculation

D. C. Gajdusek and C. J. Gibbs, jun.

Editor's Note

This paper, which focuses on the transmissible spongiform encephalopathy kuru, highlights the lengthy incubation times that can occur between exposure to the infectious agent and development of symptoms. Daniel Carleton Gajdusek and Clarence J. Gibbs focus on a rhesus monkey inoculated with a suspension of kuru-infected human brain that took 8 years to become ill. At that time, Creutzfeldt-Jakob disease (CJD), known to share many similarities with kuru, had not been shown to cause disease in old-world monkeys. But the researchers warn that none of these animals, inoculated with CJD-infected human brain suspensions, have been observed long enough to confirm this assumption.

NEUROLOGICAL disease has appeared in a female rhesus monkey (*Macaca mulatta*) following an asymptomatic incubation period of 8 years and 5 months after inoculation intracerebrally (i.c.) and intravenously (i.v.) with a 10% suspension of brain tissue from a human kuru patient. Clinical signs were remarkably similar to those observed in patients naturally affected with kuru and in sub-human primates in which the disease has been experimentally induced by inoculation of the kuru virus. Histopathological examination of the brain of this rhesus monkey has confirmed this first successful transmission of kuru to an old-world monkey. Previously the chimpanzee and four species of new-world monkeys (spider, *Ateles*; capuchin, *Cebus*; squirrel, *Saimiri*; and woolly, *Lagothrix*) have been found to be susceptible to kuru.

In August 1963, one chimpanzee (A2), 5 rhesus, 4 cynomolgus and 3 African green monkeys were inoculated i.c. (0.2 ml.) and i.v. (0.3 ml.) with a 10% suspension of brain tissue from kuru patient Enage. Thirty months after inoculation chimpanzee A2 developed experimental kuru and was killed in the terminal stages of disease 4 months after onset. During subsequent months (between 1 month and 62 months after inoculation) 1 rhesus (16L), the 4 cynomolgus and the 3 African green monkeys died of intercurrent infections without signs of neurological disease; histological examinations by light and electron microscopy revealed no pathological lesions in the central nervous system. The remaining 4 rhesus monkeys remained clinically well until January 1972 (101 months after inoculation) when one (11L) was noted to have occasional tremors and locomotor ataxia. The animal climbed with reluctance and caution and became withdrawn and docile. Her hair coat became rough and there was piloerection over the entire body. Neurological signs became progressively worse and one and a half months after onset she developed

接种8½年后库鲁病从人传染到恒河猴（猕猴）

盖杜谢克，小吉布斯

编者按

这篇文章讨论的重点是一种传染性海绵状脑病——库鲁病，文中特别强调了在接触病原体到发病之间的潜伏期可能会很长。丹尼尔·卡尔顿·盖杜谢克和克拉伦斯·吉布斯重点介绍了一只在接种人类库鲁病患者脑组织悬浮液8年后染病的恒河猴。当时，与库鲁病有很多相似之处的克罗伊茨费尔特－雅各布综合征（简称克雅氏病）尚不能使旧大陆猴致病。但研究人员提醒公众：目前人们对接种过克雅氏病患者脑悬浮液的动物的观察时间还不够长，因而不足以证明上述假设。

在雌恒河猴（猕猴）脑内和静脉内接种人类库鲁病患者的10%脑组织悬浮液，经过8年零5个月的无症状潜伏期后，恒河猴出现了神经病学疾病。临床症状与在自然感染库鲁病的患者中和在通过接种库鲁病病毒实验性诱发疾病的亚人类灵长动物中观察到的症状非常相似。用组织病理学方法对这只恒河猴的脑所作的检验已证实，库鲁病首次成功传染给了一只旧大陆猴。先前已发现黑猩猩和4种新大陆猴（蜘蛛猴，蛛猴属；僧帽猴，卷尾猴属；松鼠猴，松鼠猴属；绒毛猴，绒毛猴属）对库鲁病易感。

我们于1963年8月在1只黑猩猩（A2）、5只恒河猴、4只食蟹猴和3只非洲绿猴脑内接种（0.2 ml）和静脉内接种（0.3 ml）库鲁病患者埃纳格的10%脑组织悬浮液。接种30个月后，黑猩猩A2染上了实验性库鲁病并在该病发作后4个月进入晚期时死亡。在接种后的若干个月内(从接种后1个月到62个月)，1只恒河猴(16L)、4只食蟹猴和3只非洲绿猴死于没有神经病学疾病症状的并发性感染；用光学和电子显微镜进行组织学检查，结果显示在中枢神经系统中并无病理性损伤。其余4只恒河猴在临床上一直很健康，直到1972年1月（接种后101个月）时才发现其中有一只（11L）出现了偶尔发抖和运动性共济失调。这只猴子在攀爬时显得非常勉强和小心并且越来越孤僻和温顺。她的毛发变得粗糙并且全身都被立毛所覆盖。神经病学症状逐渐加重，她的四肢和躯体在发作后一个半月均出现了阵挛性痉挛，几乎整

clonic jerks of all four limbs and trunk and almost continuous coarse generalized tremors. Two and a half months after onset, although alert to her surroundings, she lay down on her side and had to be fed by hand. She was killed at this advanced stage of disease. At no time during clinical illness was there any fever nor were significant changes noted in haematological and serum chemistry values.

At necropsy the animal was thin with scant subcutaneous and omental fat. The brain was firm and, on cutting, a blanching of the grey matter was noted. There were no other gross pathological changes.

Preliminary histological examination of the brain by light and electron microscopy revealed extensive neuropathological lesions restricted to the grey matter. There was moderate to severe status spongiosus of the cerebral cortex and basal ganglia, most severe in the deeper layers of the cortical mantle and less extensive in the dentate nucleus of the cerebellum (Fig. 1). In all areas examined there was marked intraneuronal vacuolation, loss of neurones and astroglial proliferation and hypertrophy.

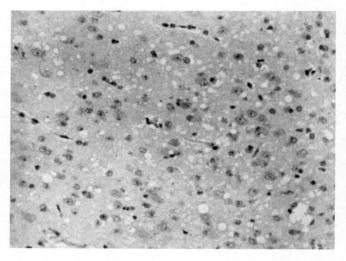

Fig. 1. Status spongiosis in the cerebral cortex of a rhesus monkey (11L) dying with kuru. In the areas of spongiform alteration there is neuronal loss and gliosis. Haematoxylin and eosin stain.

To date Creutzfeldt-Jakob disease, which resembles kuru in both the neuropathology of its cellular lesion and in many properties of its virus, has shown the same species specificity as kuru except for its failure thus far to cause disease in any of the old-world monkeys inoculated. However, none of the animals inoculated with brain suspensions from Creutzfeldt-Jakob disease has yet been observed over asymptomatic incubation periods as long as the 8.5 years required for disease to appear in this kuru-affected rhesus monkey. Rhesus monkeys inoculated with C-J disease virus 42 months ago are still under observation and remain well.

个身体都在不断地发抖。发作后两个半月时，虽然对周围环境依旧警觉，但她侧躺着不动，只能由专人喂食。这只恒河猴死于该病晚期。在临床患病期间，她既没有发过烧，也没有在血液学和血清生化指标上出现可观察到的显著变化。

在尸体剖检时发现，这个动物的皮下和网膜脂肪都很薄。脑很硬实，我们在切片时注意到灰质发生了漂白。没有出现其他的大体病理改变。

我们用光学和电子显微镜对猴子的脑进行了初步的组织学检查，结果显示广泛的神经病理学损伤仅限于灰质内。在大脑皮层和基底神经节处有中度至重度的海绵状状态，最为严重的是皮层外膜的较深层，而在小脑齿状核处则比较少（图1）。在所有检查区域中都出现了明显的神经细胞内空泡、神经元丢失及星型胶质细胞的增生与肥大。

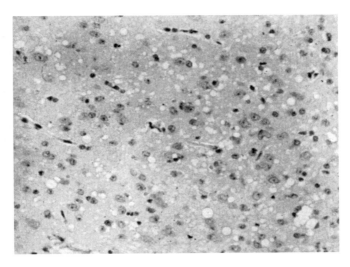

图 1. 一只将死于库鲁病的恒河猴（11L）脑皮层中的海绵状状态。在海绵状改变区域中出现了神经元丢失和神经胶质增生。苏木素和伊红染色。

迄今为止，克罗伊茨费尔特－雅各布综合征在细胞损伤的神经病理学上和病毒的许多特性上都类似于库鲁病。除了尚不能在接种的旧大陆猴中引发疾病外，该病与库鲁病有相同的种属特异性。然而，目前还没有人对接种克雅氏病患者脑悬浮液的动物无症状潜伏期的观察达到 8.5 年，8.5 年是这只感染库鲁病的恒河猴从接种到发病所需的时间。我们正在观察 42 个月前接种克雅氏病病毒的恒河猴，它们现在仍很健康。

It is of interest that the two spongiform encephalopathies of animals have been transmitted recently to old-world monkeys: scrapie to the cynomolgus monkey[1] and mink encephalopathy to the rhesus monkey[2]. In view of the rapid decrease in the incubation period of kuru in the chimpanzee and some new-world monkeys on serial passage, it seems likely that the host range may be altered by serial passage in different hosts, even perhaps on blind passages in hosts not yet demonstrated to be susceptible.

We thank Drs. Peter Rampert and Reid Heffner for electron microscopy.

(**240**, 351; 1972)

D. C. Gajdusek and C. J. Gibbs, jun.: National Institute of Neurological Diseases and Stroke, National Institutes of Health, Bethesda, Maryland.

Received June 26; revised July 31, 1972.

References:

1. Gibbs, jun., C. J., and Gajdusek, D. C., *Nature*, **236**, 73 (1972).

2. Marsh, R. F., Burger, D., Eckroade, R., ZuRhein, G. M., and Hanson, R. P., *J. Infect. Dis.*, **120**, 713 (1969).

值得关注的是，最近有两种动物海绵状脑病传染到了旧大陆猴中：羊瘙痒症传染到食蟹猴中 [1]；水貂脑病传染到恒河猴中 [2]。鉴于库鲁病在黑猩猩和一些新大陆猴中连续传代的潜伏期迅速缩短，可以猜测在不同寄主内的连续传代也许会改变寄主范围，甚至在寄主中盲传时也有可能是易感的，尽管现在没有证据能证明这一点。

感谢彼得·兰伯特博士和里德·赫夫纳博士为我们提供了电子显微镜。

（李梅 翻译；袁峥 审稿）

Inhibition of Prostaglandin Synthetase in Brain Explains the Antipyretic Activity of Paracetamol (4-Acetamidophenol)

R. J. Flower and J. R. Vane

Editor's Note

A year before this paper, British pharmacologist John Robert Vane proposed a mode of action for aspirin-like drugs, ascribing their therapeutic effects to the suppression of prostaglandin production. Here, Vane and colleague Rod Flower lend support to the theory with the demonstration that paracetamol's fever-easing ability occurs because the enzyme required to make prostaglandin is inhibited in the brain. Prostaglandins occur in most tissues and organs, so the find supported the idea that aspirin-like drugs targeting tissue-specific prostaglandin release could yield a new generation of anti-inflammatory compounds with greater specificity. It also helped explain the previously puzzling observation that paracetamol is inactive against dog spleen synthetase — tissues from different body regions show differing levels of sensitivity to aspirin-like drugs.

INHIBITION of prostaglandin biosynthesis by aspirin-like drugs[1-3] has now been confirmed in several systems[4-7]. The theory[1] that this anti-enzyme action is the basis of the clinical effects of aspirin-like drugs has recently been reviewed[8-11] in detail. One of the few anomalies was that paracetamol (4-acetamidophenol) which has no anti-inflammatory activity, but is analgesic and antipyretic[12], was inactive against dog spleen synthetase ($ID_{50}=100$ µg ml.$^{-1}$). A possible explanation for this discrepancy is that synthetase systems from different regions of the body show different sensitivities to drugs.

Prostaglandins are themselves pyrogenic[13] and occur in the central nervous system[14]. Feldberg et al.[15] found that a prostaglandin-like substance appeared in the cerebrospinal fluid (CSF) at the same time as the fever produced by intravenous injections of pyrogen. Paracetamol produced a prompt defervescence, accompanied by a reduction to normal concentrations of the prostaglandin-like substance in the CSF. It seems clear that paracetamol acts centrally as an antipyretic, and we have, therefore, investigated the effect of this drug on a prostaglandin synthetase system derived from brain.

Rabbit brain was used, but, in case the effects were due to species differences, confirmatory evidence was obtained on dog brain.

New Zealand white rabbits (or mongrel dogs) of either sex were killed by an overdose of pentobarbitone sodium given intraperitoneally or intravenously. The brain was removed as

对大脑前列腺素合成酶的抑制可以解释扑热息痛（4-乙酰氨基酚）的退热作用

弗劳尔，文

编者按

在这篇论文发表的前一年，英国药理学家约翰·罗伯特·文就已提出阿司匹林类药物的一种作用方式是通过抑制前列腺素合成而发挥疗效。在本文中，文及其同事罗德·弗劳尔对上述观点给予了支持，他们指出：扑热息痛之所以具有退热能力是因为大脑中合成前列腺素所需的酶受到了抑制。因为前列腺素存在于大多数组织和器官中，所以该发现支持了以下观点，即通过以特定组织中前列腺素释放为靶向的阿司匹林类药物可能得到一类新的特异性更强的抗炎化合物。这篇文章也有助于我们解释以前发现的一个令人困惑的现象：扑热息痛对狗脾的前列腺素合成酶无效——身体不同部位的组织对阿司匹林类药物的敏感性不同。

目前，已有多个系统的研究 [4-7] 证实，阿司匹林类药物 [1-3] 可以抑制前列腺素的生物合成。近来亦有文献 [8-11] 详细综述了有关理论 [1]，即对前列腺素合成酶的拮抗作用是阿司匹林类药物临床功效的基础。也有少数例外情况，其中之一是没有抗炎作用、但有止痛和退热作用的扑热息痛（4-乙酰氨基酚）[12] 对狗脾前列腺素合成酶无效（$ID_{50}=100\ \mu g/ml$）。出现这种不一致的原因可能是身体不同部位的合成酶系统对药物的敏感性不同。

前列腺素本身有致热作用 [13]，存在于中枢神经系统中 [14]。费尔德伯格等人 [15] 发现：当通过静脉注射热原导致发热的同时，脑脊液（CSF）中也出现了一种前列腺素样的物质。应用扑热息痛能够迅速退热，并且 CSF 中前列腺素样物质的浓度会下降至正常水平。显然，扑热息痛是作用于中枢的退热剂，因而我们研究了该药物对大脑前列腺素合成酶系统的影响。

我们应用兔脑进行研究；为了防止其效果存在种属差异，又应用狗脑进行了研究确证。

腹腔或静脉注射过量戊巴比妥钠处死任意性别的新西兰白兔（或杂种狗）。以最快的速度取出脑组织，用剪刀剪碎，再用冷的克雷布斯溶液冲洗以去除残留血液，

quickly as possible, cut into pieces with scissors, washed in cold Krebs solution to remove any residual blood, and homogenized in four times its volume of ice cold phosphate buffer (pH 7.4) for 1 min at full speed in a Waring blender. The homogenate was then centrifuged at 100,000g for 1 h to separate the soluble cytoplasmic fraction which contains an NAD$^+$-dependent prostaglandin destroying factor. After the supernatant had been discarded pellets were resuspended in phosphate buffer in the proportion (by volume) of 1:3. This suspension (1 ml.) was added to 1 ml. of the buffer containing 20 µg sodium arachidonate, 100 µg reduced glutathione and 10 µg hydroquinone. Drugs tested as inhibitors were added to the reaction mixtures in varying concentrations. Samples were incubated aerobically for 20 min at 37°C with shaking, after which time the reactions were stopped by heating the tubes in boiling water for 1 min.

Prostaglandin was routinely bioassayed using the rat fundic strip[16], but the identity of the biologically active reaction products was verified by parallel bioassay using the rat fundic strip, rat colon and chick rectum, superfused in series with Krebs solution containing antagonists[17] and by thin layer chromatography (TLC) using the AI and AII systems of Gréen and Samuelsson[18]. More than 90% of the biological activity eluted from the TLC plates corresponded to the prostaglandin E_2 standard. The potency of the inhibitors of prostaglandin synthesis was calculated from the curves plotted for % inhibition versus log concentration and expressed as the concentration (µg ml.$^{-1}$) required to produce 50% inhibition (ID_{50}) of the control synthesis. Brain homogenates were freshly prepared for every experiment.

Zero time activity of the incubation mixture was equivalent to 275±54 ng prostaglandin E_2 (mean ±s.e.). After incubation, there was an average increase in prostaglandin content of 180±31 ng ml.$^{-1}$.

Table 1 shows the ID_{50} concentrations of indomethacin, aspirin and paracetamol against the synthetase derived from rabbit brain compared with their ID_{50} values against the dog spleen enzyme which we reported earlier[6]. Aspirin had similar activities in both systems. However, indomethacin was much less active as an inhibitor of prostaglandin production in brain tissue than in spleen and paracetamol was a more potent inhibitor of brain enzyme than of spleen enzyme. In dog brain also, paracetamol had a similar relatively high potency (ID_{50}=12.5 µg ml.$^{-1}$).

Table 1. Inhibition of Prostaglandin Formation by Anti-Inflammatory Drugs

	Dog spleen synthetase ID_{50} µg ml.$^{-1}$	Rabbit brain synthetase ID_{50} µg ml.$^{-1}$
Indomethacin	0.06	1.3
Sodium aspirin	6.6	11.0
4-Acetamidophenol	100.0	14.0

There is a remarkable correlation between the clinical actions of these drugs and their

然后加入 4 倍体积冰块预冷的磷酸盐缓冲液（pH 值 7.4），用韦林氏搅切器以最高速度匀浆 1 min。随后将该匀浆以 100,000g 离心 1 h，分离出含有 NAD^+ 依赖性前列腺素破坏因子的可溶性胞质组分（译者注：NAD 是一种传递电子的辅酶，成分为烟酰胺腺嘌呤二核苷酸）。弃除上清液后，将沉淀用比例为 1:3（体积）的磷酸盐缓冲液再次悬浮。取该悬浮液（1 ml）加入到 1 ml 含 20 μg 花生四烯酸钠、100 μg 还原型谷胱甘肽和 10 μg 对苯二酚的缓冲液中。将不同浓度的待测药物加入上述反应混合液。将样品置于 37℃ 下有氧振荡孵育 20 min，随后将试管放入沸水中加热 1 min 以中止反应。

按照常规用大鼠胃底条 [16] 对前列腺素的生成量进行生物测定。但在对这些生物活性反应产物进行鉴别时采用了大鼠胃底条、大鼠结肠和小鸡直肠平行测定法，用含拮抗剂的克雷布斯溶液对它们进行连续灌流 [17]；还采用了格伦和萨穆埃尔松发明的在 AI 和 AII 系统中进行的薄层色谱法（TLC）[18]。90% 以上从 TLC 平板上洗脱的生物活性物质与前列腺素 E_2 的标准品相符。以抑制百分比对浓度的对数作图来计算前列腺素合成抑制剂的效能，效能的大小用对前列腺素合成对照组产生 50% 抑制（ID_{50}）所需的浓度（μg/ml）来表示。每次实验均使用新鲜制备的脑匀浆。

孵育混合物的零时刻活性相当于 275 ng ± 54 ng 前列腺素 E_2（均值 ± 标准误差）。孵育后，前列腺素含量平均上升了 180 ng/ml ± 31 ng/ml。

表 1 给出了消炎痛、阿司匹林和扑热息痛抑制兔脑前列腺素合成酶的 ID_{50} 浓度，以及与我们以前曾报道过的它们抑制狗脾酶 ID_{50} [6] 的比较。阿司匹林在两种系统中的活性相似。不过作为前列腺素合成的抑制剂，消炎痛在脑组织中的活性要远远低于在脾脏中的活性，而扑热息痛对脑组织中酶的抑制作用则要强于对脾脏中酶的抑制作用。扑热息痛在狗脑中同样具有相对较强的效能（ID_{50}=12.5 μg/ml）。

表 1. 抗炎药物对前列腺素合成的抑制作用

	狗脾合成酶 ID_{50} μg/ml	兔脑合成酶 ID_{50} μg/ml
消炎痛	0.06	1.3
阿司匹林钠	6.6	11.0
4-乙酰氨基酚	100.0	14.0

这些药物的临床疗效与其抑制某一种前列腺素合成酶的效能之间存在着显著的

potency against one or other of the enzymes. All three compounds are antipyretic (a central action) and all have an inhibitory effect on the brain enzyme in concentrations found in the plasma after therapeutic doses[6]. Both as antipyretics and as inhibitors of brain prostaglandin synthetase, the descending order of potency is indomethacin; aspirin; paracetamol[12,13]. Furthermore, indomethacin is about twelve times more potent than aspirin in both tests. The sensitivity of prostaglandin synthetase derived from brain tissue to paracetamol seems to occur in other species also, for Willis *et al.*[11] found that paracetamol inhibited enzymes from mouse and gerbil brain (ID_{50}=20 μg ml.$^{-1}$).

Indomethacin and aspirin are both anti-inflammatory (a peripheral action) and both are active against the spleen enzyme (a peripheral tissue) in therapeutic concentrations. The much higher potency of indomethacin as a synthetase inhibitor both in dog spleen[6] and in bull seminal vesicles[5] is also reflected against inflammation in animal models[5,19] and in man[12]. Paracetamol has no anti-inflammatory activity and is not active against the dog spleen enzyme in therapeutic concentrations.

In addition to providing further support for Vane's theory[1,8], we believe that our results illustrate the mechanism by which the clinical actions of the aspirin-like drugs are determined by the differential sensitivity of the prostaglandin synthetase systems of the "target" tissues. Thus they support the idea[1,8] that a study of prostaglandin synthetase systems from different tissues will lead to aspirin-like drugs with a greater specificity of action.

We thank Dr. J. Pike of the Upjohn Company, Kalamazoo, for his gift of prostaglandins, and the Wellcome Trust and the MRC for grants.

(**240**, 410-411; 1972)

R. J. Flower and J. R. Vane: Department of Pharmacology, Institute of Basic Medical Sciences, Royal College of Surgeons of England, Lincoln's Inn Fields, London WC2A 3PN.

Received September 14, 1972.

References:

1. Vane, J. R., *Nature New Biology*, **231**, 232 (1971).

2. Smith, J. B., and Willis, A. L., *Nature New Biology*, **231**, 235 (1971).

3. Ferreira, S. H., Moncada, S., and Vane, J. R., *Nature New Biology*, **231**, 237 (1971).

4. Smith, W. L., and Lands, W. E. M., *J. Biol. Chem.*, **246**, 6700 (1971).

5. Tomlinson, R. V., Ringold, H. J., Qureshi, M. C., and Forchielli, E., *Biochem. Biophys. Res. Comm.*, **46**, 552 (1972).

6. Flower, R., Gryglewski, R., Herbaczynska-Cedro, K., and Vane, J. R., *Nature New Biology*, **238**, 104 (1972).

7. Sykes, J. A. C., and Maddox, I. S., *Nature New Biology*, **237**, 59 (1972).

8. Vane, J. R., *Hospital Practice*, 7, 61 (1972).

9. Vane, J. R., in *Inflammation: Mechanisms and Control* (edit. by Lepow, I. H., and Ward, P. A.) (Academic Press, New York, 1972).

10. Vane, J. R., *Proc. Fifth Intern. Congr. Pharmacol.* (Karger, Basle, in the press).

11. Willis, A. L., Davison, P., Ramwell, P. W., Brocklehurst, W. E., and Smith, J. B., in *Prostaglandins in Cellular Biology* (edit. by Ramwell, P. W., and Pharriss, B. B.), 227 (Plenum Press, New York and London, 1972).

相关性。所有这三种化合物均可退热（主要作用），且在使用治疗剂量后的血浆浓度水平下对脑组织酶都有抑制作用[6]。作为退热剂和大脑前列腺素合成酶的抑制剂，以上药物的效能从高到低依次为：消炎痛、阿司匹林、扑热息痛[12,13]。此外，在两组实验中消炎痛的作用都约为阿司匹林的 12 倍。来自脑组织的前列腺素合成酶对扑热息痛的敏感性似乎在其他动物中也存在，因为威利斯等人[11]发现扑热息痛也能抑制小鼠和沙鼠脑中的酶（$ID_{50} = 20$ μg/ml）。

消炎痛和阿司匹林都有抗炎作用（次要作用），两者在治疗浓度下都具有拮抗脾酶（外周组织）的活性。消炎痛在狗脾[6]和牛精囊[5]中表现为更强的合成酶抑制剂，这种更强的效能同样体现在其对动物模型[5,19]和人体[12]的抗炎作用上。而扑热息痛没有抗炎作用，在治疗浓度下也没有抑制狗脾酶的活性。

除了能为文氏理论[1,8]提供进一步的支持以外，我们认为我们的结果还阐明了一种机制，即阿司匹林类药物的临床功效取决于其对"靶"组织前列腺素合成酶系统的敏感性差异。因此也支持了这样一个观点[1,8]，即对不同组织前列腺素合成酶系统的研究将会促使我们研发出特异性更强的阿司匹林类药物。

感谢美国卡拉马祖市普强制药公司的派克博士为我们提供了前列腺素，还要感谢英国维康信托基金会和英国医学研究理事会为我们提供资金上的援助。

（周志华 翻译；王昕 审稿）

Inhibition of Prostaglandin Synthetase in Brain Explains the Antipyretic Activity of Paracetamol (4-Acetamidophenol)

12. Woodbury, D. M., in *The Pharmacological Basis of Therapeutics* (edit. by Goodman, L. S., and Gilman, A.), fourth ed. (Macmillan, New York, 1970).

13. Milton, A. S., and Wendlandt, S., *J. Physiol.*, **207**, 76P (1970).

14. Coceani, F., and Wolfe, L. S., *Canad. J. Physiol. Pharmacol.*, **43**, 445 (1965).

15. Feldberg, W., Gupta, K. P., Milton, A. S., and Wendlandt, S., *Brit. J. Pharmacol.* (in the press).

16. Vane, J. R., *Brit. J. Pharmac. Chemother.*, **12**, 344 (1957).

17. Gilmore, N., Vane, J. R., and Wyllie, J. H., *Nature*, **218**, 1135 (1968).

18. Greén, K., and Samuelsson, B., *J. Lip. Res.*, **5**, 117 (1964).

19. Collier, H. O. J., *Adv. Pharmac. Chemother.*, **7**, 333 (1969).

对大脑前列腺素合成酶的抑制可以解释扑热息痛（4-乙酰氨基酚）的退热作用

A Possible Role for Histone in the Synthesis of DNA

H. Weintraub[*]

Editor's Note

In the 1950s, it was recognized that native DNA found in living cells is intimately associated with protein molecules called histones, but the function of these proteins was not known. This article by Harold Weintraub at the University of Pennsylvania, Philadelphia, suggested that histones regulate the synthesis of DNA. The modern view is that histone molecules are structural elements in the chromosome, and that they serve as a means of binding the double helix of DNA to a platform. It is also now know that chemical modification of the histone molecules can determine which genes in the genome are sued for the production of proteins in the living cell. Weintraub's conclusion, in other words, was only part of the story.

WHEN protein synthesis is inhibited in primitive chick erythroblasts, linear DNA synthesis continues for about 45 min, but at half the control rate[1]. The depression in DNA synthesis occurs within 25 s of the addition of cycloheximide, is readily reversible, and is manifested as a decrease by half in the gross rate of DNA chain elongation. The labelled DNA made under these conditions is covalently bound to previously synthesized DNA and associated with single stranded segments well over 10^7 molecular weight. The effects of cycloheximide on DNA synthesis are due neither to a direct action on the DNA replicase, nor to an effect on cell permeability or nucleotide metabolism mediated by decreased protein synthesis. It is also unlikely that this behaviour is a consequence of the accumulation of an inhibitor in the absence of protein synthesis[1]. All our data indicate that when the synthesis of protein is inhibited, the synthesis of DNA proceeds normally except that the rate of chain elongation is slower. This applies to each replicon in each S phase cell. Here I present evidence that the proteins, termed chain elongation proteins (CEP), involved in this fine control of DNA synthesis are histones.

Cycloheximide Resistance

It was previously shown[1] that low concentrations of cycloheximide or puromycin, although inhibiting bulk protein synthesis by as much as 30%, resulted in no inhibition of DNA synthesis. This could indicate that the synthesis of the CEP was relatively resistant to low concentrations of inhibitor, or that a pool of this protein existed within the cell. The latter possibility was unlikely since higher concentrations of inhibitor lead to a maximal effect on DNA synthesis within 25 s. The dose response curves to cycloheximide for DNA synthesis and the synthesis of various protein fractions are shown in Fig. 1. DNA synthesis was linear

* Present address: MRC Laboratory of Molecular Biology, Hills Road, Cambridge CB2 2QH, England.

组蛋白在DNA合成中的可能角色

温特劳布 *

编者按

在 20 世纪 50 年代，人们就认识到存在于活细胞中的天然 DNA 与被称为组蛋白的蛋白质分子密切相关，但是这类蛋白质的功能尚不为人所知。来自于费城宾夕法尼亚大学的哈罗德·温特劳布在本文中指出，组蛋白调控 DNA 的合成。现代的观点是：组蛋白分子是染色体中的结构组分，DNA 双螺旋就是通过它们与基体相连接的。现在人们还知道，通过对组蛋白分子的化学修饰可以确定基因组中有哪些基因参与了活细胞中蛋白质的合成。换句话说，温特劳布的结论只回答了一部分问题。

当小鸡前成红细胞中的蛋白质合成被抑制后，线性 DNA 的合成仍可以持续 45 min 左右，但合成率只有对照组的一半 [1]。DNA 的合成在加入放线菌酮后 25 s 之内就会被抑制，这种抑制作用很容易得到恢复，并且已经证明此时 DNA 链的总延伸速率下降了一半。在上述条件下形成的标记 DNA 与之前合成的 DNA 以共价键相连，并且还结合到了分子量大大超过 10^7 的单链 DNA 片段上。放线菌酮对于 DNA 合成的抑制作用既不是因为它可以直接抑制 DNA 复制酶的活性，也不是因为它能通过抑制蛋白质合成来影响细胞的通透性或核苷酸的代谢。这种现象亦不可能是在蛋白质合成停止后由某种抑制性物质的积累导致的结果 [1]。我们的所有实验数据均表明：当蛋白质合成受到抑制时，DNA 的合成仍可以正常进行，只不过链延伸的速率有所减慢。这适用于所有处于 S 期的细胞的各个复制子。我将在本文中提出证据证明，这种参与 DNA 合成过程中此类精细调控的被称作链延伸蛋白（CEP）的蛋白就是组蛋白。

放线菌酮抗性

之前的研究结果表明 [1]：虽然低浓度的放线菌酮或嘌呤霉素会使总蛋白合成量减少 30%，但它们并不影响 DNA 的合成。这也许可以说明 CEP 的合成对于低浓度的抑制剂有相当的抗性，或者在细胞内存在着一定量的 CEP 库存。后一种可能性不大，因为高浓度抑制剂可以在 25 s 之内达到对 DNA 合成的最大抑制。放线菌酮对 DNA 合成及多种蛋白质合成的量效曲线示于图 1。在至少 30 min 内，DNA 合成的抑制

---

* 现在的地址：英国剑桥医学研究理事会分子生物学实验室，希尔斯路，剑桥 CB2 2QH，英国。

for at least 30 min. The curve for DNA synthesis normalized to the maximum amount of DNA inhibition is also given. Data show that histone synthesis is relatively resistant to cycloheximide[3,4] and that the dose response curve of histones follows the normalized dose response curves for DNA synthesis. SDS-acrylamide gel analysis of the cytoplasmic fraction and the acidic nuclear protein fraction at 1, 5, and 20 μM cycloheximide detected no proteins resistant to cycloheximide using a double-label analysis. Similar experiments showed all histones to be equally affected at each cycloheximide concentration.

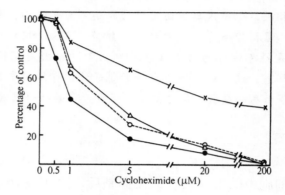

Fig. 1. Resistance of histone synthesis to cycloheximide. Four day old erythroblasts were incubated *in vitro*[1] in L-leucine-4, 5-³H (20 μCi ml.⁻¹; 35 Ci mM⁻¹) or ³H-methyl-TdR (20 μCi ml.⁻¹; 15 Ci mM⁻¹) for 30 min in the presence and absence of the stated concentrations of cycloheximide. The various protein fractions were then isolated[2] from cells labelled with leucine. Briefly, nuclei were obtained from washed cells using 0.5% "Nonidet" in RSB (0.01 M NaCl; 0.01 M Tris-HCl, *p*H 7.4; 0.003 M MgCl₂). Histone (O--O) was extracted twice from washed nuclei using 200 volumes of 0.25 M H₂SO₄. The residual proteins were termed the acidic nuclear proteins (●—●). DNA(×—×), added to the cytoplasmic fraction, sedimented and extracted with acid, failed to show any bound histone-like protein. The incorporation is expressed as a percentage of that incorporated by control cells either by an internally controlled double-label analysis[2] or by direct measurements. Incorporation of ³H-TdR into TCA precipitable material was measured directly[1]. "Normalized DNA" (△—△) represents the amount of inhibition by cycloheximide as a percentage of the maximum amount achieved at 200 μM (68% inhibition). All isotopes were obtained from New England Nuclear Corporation; all analogues and inhibitors, from Sigma Corporation. Radioactive incorporation was measured using a "Beckman LS-200 Liquid Scintillation Counter".

The Effects of Amino-Acid Analogues

Compared to other proteins, histones are unusual in that they contain no tryptophan, little tyrosine, but much arginine. It is shown in Table 1 that DNA synthesis is (*a*) resistant to high concentrations of the tryptophan analogues, methyl-tryptophan and beta indole acrylic acid, (*b*) only slightly sensitive to high concentrations of the tyrosine analogues, methyl-tyrosine and iodo-tyrosine, and, (*c*) extremely sensitive to low does of the arginine analogue, canavanine. Also that the tryptophan and tyrosine analogues can interfere with the metabolism of their corresponding amino-acids as equimolar concentrations can markedly depress uptake of labelled amino-acid into TCA precipitable material. Addition of cycloheximide with canavanine results in only a light potentiation. This indicates that

率与放线菌酮的浓度呈线性关系。本文还给出了归一化为最大 DNA 合成抑制量的 DNA 合成曲线。这些数据表明：组蛋白的合成对于放线菌酮具有相当大的抗性 [3,4]，并且组蛋白的量效曲线与对 DNA 合成进行归一化后的量效曲线是一致的。在放线菌酮浓度为 1 μM、5 μM 和 20 μM 时对细胞质组分以及酸性核蛋白组分进行十二烷基硫酸钠（SDS）– 丙烯酰胺凝胶电泳分析的结果显示：通过双标记分析可以得到，这些蛋白质中没有哪个蛋白质的合成对放线菌酮有抗性。类似的实验表明：在各种放线菌酮浓度下，所有组蛋白都受到相同程度的影响。

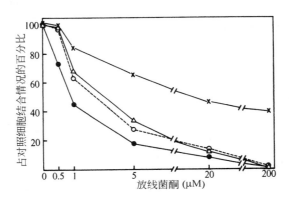

图 1. 组蛋白合成对放线菌酮的抗性。将第 4 天的鸡成红细胞在体外 [1] 与 L– 亮氨酸 –4,5–³H（20 μCi/ml，35 Ci/mM）或 ³H– 甲基胸腺嘧啶脱氧核苷（20 μCi/ml，15 Ci/mM）一起孵育 30 min，有一组不加入放线菌酮，另外几组中放线菌酮的浓度如图所示。然后从亮氨酸标记的细胞中分离出各种蛋白质组分 [2]。简言之就是用含 0.5%“诺乃洗涤剂”的网织红细胞标准缓冲液（0.01 M NaCl；0.01 M Tris-HCl，pH 值 7.4；0.003 M MgCl₂）从冲洗后的细胞中分离细胞核组分。用 200 倍体积的 0.25 M H₂SO₄ 从冲洗后的细胞核中抽提 2 次以得到组蛋白（○—○）。残留的蛋白质被称为酸性核蛋白（●—●）。将 DNA（×—×）加入到细胞质组分中，然后在酸性条件下进行沉淀和抽提，并未发现其结合了类似组蛋白的蛋白。通过内参双标记分析法 [2] 或直接测定法用占对照细胞掺入情况的百分比来表征掺入率。三氯乙酸（TCA）沉淀物中 ³H– 胸腺嘧啶脱氧核苷的掺入率是通过直接测定得到的 [1]。“归一化的 DNA”（△—△）代表放线菌酮的抑制率占放线菌酮在浓度为 200 μM 时所获得的最大抑制率（68%）的百分比。所有放射性同位素均来自新英格兰核公司，所有氨基酸类似物和抑制剂均来自西格马公司。利用“贝克曼公司的 LS-200 液闪计数器”来测量放射性的掺入。

氨基酸类似物的作用

与其他蛋白质相比，组蛋白的特殊性在于它不含色氨酸，只含很少量的酪氨酸，但含有大量的精氨酸。表 1 说明 DNA 的合成：（a）耐受高浓度的色氨酸类似物——甲基 – 色氨酸以及 β– 吲哚丙烯酸；（b）对高浓度的酪氨酸类似物——甲基 – 酪氨酸和碘代酪氨酸只表现出轻度的敏感；（c）对低剂量的精氨酸类似物——刀豆氨酸极度敏感。此外，色氨酸和酪氨酸类似物可以干扰与它们对应的两种氨基酸的代谢，因为当摩尔浓度相等时，在 TCA 沉淀物中这两种放射性标记的氨基酸含量明显下降。同时加入放线菌酮和刀豆氨酸只能起到轻微的强化作用。这表明上述两种药物可能

both drugs are probably affecting the same step in DNA synthesis, made more likely by the observation (not shown) that the kinetics of inhibition by canavanine mimic those of cycloheximide. In canavanine, ^{3}H-leucine incorporation is decreased by 10%. (Fig. 1 shows that a comparable amount of inhibition by cycloheximide has no effect on DNA synthesis.) This might indicate that canavanine affects DNA synthesis by inhibiting the synthesis of a specific class of proteins, rather than producing altered proteins of a specific class.

Table 1. Effect of Amino-Acid Analogues on the Synthesis of DNA

Treatment	Amino-acid ratio[4] (histone to nuclear acidic)*	Ratio of analogue to amino-acid†	% Inhibition of ^{3}H-TdR incorporation	Ratio of analogue to amino-acid†	% Inhibition of labelled amino-acid uptake‡
C-^{3}H-tryptophan	0	100:1	0	1:1	22%
3β-Indole acrylic acid	0	100:1	0	1:1	24%
3-Iodo-L-tyrosine	0.09	100:1	22%	1:1	25%
O-C-^{3}H-L-tyrosine	0.09	100:1	24%	1:1	26%
plus cyclo.			56%		
Cyclo. alone			53%		
L-Canavanine	1.83	1:1	62%		
plus cyclo.			68%		
Cyclo. alone			58%		

Cells were treated with the analogues and labelled concurrently with ^{3}H-TdR for 30 min.

* Ratio of amino-acid in histone to that in nuclear acidic protein for the amino-acid corresponding to the given analogue. Incorporation of ^{3}H-TdR was measured as a percentage of an untreated control culture.

† Ratio of analogue to amino-acid in the medium.

‡ A 1:1 ratio of analogue to amino-acid was tested for its effect on the incorporation of labelled amino-acid for 30 min into TCA precipitable material. L-tryptophan-^{3}H(G) (3 Ci mM^{-1}) was at 5 μCi ml.$^{-1}$ and L-Tyrosine-3,5-^{3}H (25 μCi mM^{-1}) was at 10 μCi ml.$^{-1}$. In all cases background was obtained from a sample taken at time zero. To test for effects of the analogues at levels other than protein synthesis, cycloheximide (20 μM) was added alone and together with the analogue and the degree of inhibition monitored.

Actinomycin Resistance

Fig. 2a shows the dose response for DNA synthesis and the synthesis of the various protein fractions after a 90 min pre-incubation with actinomycin D[5-7]. Both histone and DNA synthesis are again comparatively resistant to low concentrations of inhibitor, both follow curves compatible with those obtained using cycloheximide. Fig. 2b gives the time course for the inhibition of histone, DNA, and RNA synthesis. After a lag of about 30 min, both histone and DNA synthesis decrease to a constant rate. Aside from this lag period the kinetics for both DNA and histone synthesis are similar to those obtained from cultures inhibited with sub-maximal doses of cycloheximide (5 μM). In actinomycin at 2.5 μg ml.$^{-1}$, RNA synthesis is about 18% of controls and constant by 5 min. If actinomycin had been affecting DNA synthesis directly, presumable by binding to the DNA, it might have been expected that DNA and RNA inhibition follow the same time course. This is clearly not the case. Additional experiments have shown that pre-incubation with actinomycin

影响了 DNA 合成中的同一步骤，观察到（未显示）刀豆氨酸的抑制动力学曲线类似于放线菌酮的抑制动力学曲线更加大了这种可能性。当加入刀豆氨酸时，³H– 亮氨酸的掺入率减少了 10%。（图 1 说明：在放线菌酮对蛋白质合成造成相当大的抑制时，DNA 的合成并没有受到影响。）这可能表明刀豆氨酸是通过抑制某种特殊类型蛋白质的合成而不是通过产生变性的特殊类型蛋白质来影响 DNA 的合成的。

表 1. 氨基酸类似物对 DNA 合成的影响

处理方式	氨基酸比例 [4]（组蛋白与细胞核酸性蛋白之比）*	氨基酸类似物与氨基酸之比 †	对掺入 ³H– 胸腺嘧啶脱氧核苷的抑制率 %	氨基酸类似物与氨基酸之比 †	对结合放射性标记氨基酸的抑制率 %‡
C–³H– 色氨酸	0	100:1	0	1:1	22%
3β– 吲哚丙烯酸	0	100:1	0	1:1	24%
3– 碘 –L– 酪氨酸	0.09	100:1	22%	1:1	25%
O–C–³H–L– 酪氨酸	0.09	100:1	24%	1:1	26%
加放线菌酮			56%		
只有放线菌酮			53%		
L– 刀豆氨酸	1.83	1:1	62%		
加放线菌酮			68%		
只有放线菌酮			58%		

在用氨基酸类似物处理细胞时，同时使用 ³H– 胸腺嘧啶脱氧核苷标记细胞 30 min。

* 组蛋白中对应于给定类似物的氨基酸与细胞核酸性蛋白质中对应于给定类似物的氨基酸之间的比例。

用相当于未经处理的对照培养物的百分比来表示 ³H– 胸腺嘧啶脱氧核苷的掺入率。

† 培养基中氨基酸类似物与相应氨基酸之间的比例。

‡ 使用比例为 1:1 的氨基酸类似物与氨基酸来检验其对标记氨基酸掺入 30 min 后造成的影响。

L– 色氨酸 –³H(G) (3 Ci/mM) 的浓度为 5 μCi/ml；L– 酪氨酸 –3,5–³H (25 μCi/mM) 的浓度为 10 μCi/ml。在所有实验中均以零时刻的样品作为本底。为测试氨基酸类似物对除蛋白质合成以外的其他过程的影响，采用单独加入放线菌酮（20 μM）以及将其与氨基酸类似物一起加入的方法并对 DNA 合成的抑制率进行检测。

放线菌素抗性

用放线菌素 D 预孵育 90 min 后，DNA 合成及多种蛋白质合成的量效曲线如图 2a 所示 [5-7]。组蛋白和 DNA 合成又一次对低浓度抑制剂表现出相当程度的抗性，两者都与用放线菌酮得到的曲线相吻合。对组蛋白、DNA 以及 RNA 合成的抑制随时间变化的曲线如图 2b 所示，在滞后大约 30 min 之后，组蛋白和 DNA 合成都降至一个恒定的水平。除了都存在这种滞后期以外，DNA 合成和组蛋白合成的动力学曲线均类似于用次最大量（5 μM）放线菌酮抑制培养物时得到的结果。当放线菌素的浓度为 2.5 μg/ml 时，细胞中 RNA 的合成量约为对照组的 18%，并且在 5 min 后就能达到这种抑制效果。如果放线菌素直接影响 DNA 合成，假如是通过与 DNA 结合，那么其对 DNA 和 RNA 合成的抑制作用就应该遵循相同的时间进程。显然实际情况

(2.5 µg ml.⁻¹) fails to add to the inhibition of DNA synthesis caused by cycloheximide. This supports the idea that both actinomycin and cycloheximide are affecting the same protein species. Although it is possible that both drugs are inhibiting the synthesis of an RNA species necessary for chain elongation, it becomes somewhat less likely since in both cases bulk RNA synthesis follows a different time and dose dependence than DNA synthesis.

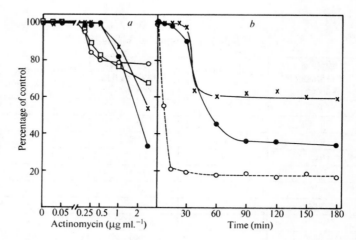

Fig. 2. *a*, Resistance of histone synthesis to low concentrations of actinomycin D. After 90 min incubation in actinomycin D at the stated concentrations, the cells were labelled with ³H-leucine (20 µCi ml.⁻¹) for 30 min; the various protein fractions isolated; and the incorporation compared to control cells, either directly, or using double-label methods. ●—●, Histone; ×—×, DNA; □—□, nuclear acidic proteins; ○—○, haemoglobin. *b*, Kinetics of incorporation after 2.5 µg ml.⁻¹ actinomycin D. Incorporation of ³H-TdR (10 µg ml.⁻¹), ³H-5-uridine (10 µCi ml.⁻¹ 20 Ci mM⁻¹), and ³H-leucine (20 µCi ml.⁻¹) into histone was measured as a rate percentage of controls after addition of actinomycin D (2.5 µg ml.⁻¹). ×—×, ³H-TdR; ●—●, ³H-leucine in histone; ○--○, ³H-U.

Relation to DNA Synthesis

It was previously shown[1] that after release of FUdR blockage of DNA synthesis, there is a lag in the onset of inhibition of DNA synthesis by cycloheximide. The lag period increased with increasing exposure to FUdR, but the length of the lag was extremely short compared to the length of exposure, for example, 10 h in FUdR resulted in a lag time of about 20 min. The lag period was interpreted as indicating the accumulation of a pool of chain elongation protein. The disparity between the exposure to FUdR and the length of the lag could indicate either of two processes; (*a*) chain elongation protein is rapidly synthesized and partially degraded, or (*b*) the synthesis of chain elongation protein is coupled to the synthesis of DNA, but the coupling is leaky.

Synthesis of nuclear histone is sensitive to inhibition by cytosine arabinoside[6,7] as shown in Fig. 3. A similar curve is obtained for FUdR. At high levels of DNA inhibiton, histone synthesis is not completely inhibited; thus histone synthesis is coupled to DNA synthesis in these cells in a leaky fashion. Acrylamide gel analysis has demonstrated that although the synthesis of all histone species is inhibited, the slightly lysine-rich histones are somewhat

并非如此。另有一些实验表明，用放线菌素（2.5 μg/ml）对细胞进行预孵育并不能增加放线菌酮对 DNA 合成的抑制作用。这说明放线菌素和放线菌酮影响的是同一类蛋白质。尽管这两种药物都有可能会抑制链延伸所必需的某一种 RNA 的合成，不过这种情况比它们共同影响 DNA 合成的可能性略低一些，因为这两种抑制剂对大部分 RNA 合成的抑制时间—剂量曲线并不相同。

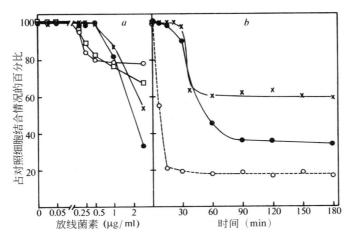

图 2. a, 组蛋白合成对低浓度放线菌素 D 的抗性。使用如图所示的各种浓度的放线菌素 D 孵育细胞 90 min 后，再用 ³H– 亮氨酸（20 μCi/ml）标记 30 min；然后分离不同的蛋白质组分，并用直接测定法或双标记法比较实验细胞和对照细胞的掺入率。●—● 为组蛋白；×—× 为 DNA；□—□ 为细胞核酸性蛋白；○—○ 为血红蛋白。b, 加入 2.5 μg/ml 放线菌素 D 之后的掺入动力学曲线。加入放线菌素 D（2.5 μg/ml）之后，分别用占对照组的百分比来表示 ³H– 胸腺嘧啶脱氧核苷（10 μCi/ml）、³H–5– 尿嘧啶核苷（10 μCi/ml, 20 Ci/mM）和结合组蛋白的 ³H– 亮氨酸（20 μCi/ml）的掺入率。×—× 为 ³H– 胸腺嘧啶脱氧核苷；●—● 为组蛋白中的 ³H– 亮氨酸；○ --- ○ 为 ³H–5– 尿嘧啶核苷。

与 DNA 合成的关系

此前已证明 [1]：在用 5– 氟尿嘧啶脱氧核苷（FUdR）来抑制 DNA 的合成后，放线菌酮对 DNA 合成的抑制作用在起始阶段有一个滞后。滞后期会随着 FUdR 处理时间的增加而延长，但滞后期的长度与处理时间相比是非常短的，例如，用 FUdR 处理 10 h 只会导致 20 min 左右的滞后。对于这个滞后期，人们认为其表明了细胞内存在 CEP 的聚集。FUdR 处理时间与滞后期长度之间的差异很大表明下列两种机制中的一种在起作用：(a) 链延伸蛋白被快速合成，且有一部分发生了降解；或 (b) 链延伸蛋白的合成与 DNA 的合成同步，不过这种同步是有缺陷的。

如图 3 所示，细胞核组蛋白的合成对阿糖胞苷的抑制作用很敏感 [6,7]。由 FUdR 也可以得到类似的抑制曲线。当 DNA 的合成被显著抑制时，组蛋白的合成并没有被完全抑制；因此，在这些细胞中，组蛋白的合成与 DNA 的合成并不是完全同步的。由丙烯酰胺凝胶分析结果可知：尽管各类组蛋白的合成都受到了抑制，但赖氨

more sensitive[8]. Attempts to detect other proteins, cytoplasmic and nuclear acidic, which follow either of the two criteria listed above have not yet been successful.

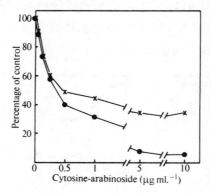

Fig. 3. Leaky coupling of histone synthesis to DNA synthesis. After 90 min in the stated concentrations of cytosine arabinoside, control and treated cells were labelled with ^{3}H-TdR (20 μCi ml.${}^{-1}$) and ^{3}H-leucine (25 μCi ml.${}^{-1}$) for 30 min. The inhibition of DNA (●—●) and histone (×—×) synthesis as a function of dose was measured as described in Fig. 2.

Given these results, it is possible to ask if CEP participates in the same step of chain elongation as deoxynucleotide addition. Two possibilities can be schematized as follows:

$$(1)\ \text{XTP} + \text{DNA} \xrightarrow{\text{CEP + replicase}} \text{DNA–XMP}$$

$$(2)\ \text{XTP} + \text{DNA} + \text{replicase} \longrightarrow \text{XMP–DNA–replicase} \xrightarrow{\text{CEP}} \text{XMP–DNA–CEP} + \text{replicase}$$

If TTP is made rate-limiting with FUdR such that the overall rate of precursor incorporation is some 10–30% of controls, then, given the results described in the previous paragraph, the synthesis of the CEP would also be inhibited. If deoxynucleotide addition and the CEP share the same step (1), then an initial inhibition of DNA synthesis should eventually lead to a subsequent inhibition of DNA synthesis because the concentration of two participants (TTP and CEP) of a multi-molecular reaction would then be decreased. Moreover, this process is auto-catalytic and the rate of DNA synthesis should gradually drift toward 50% of the control rate. This is the amount of DNA synthesis not dependent on concurrent protein synthesis. On the other hand, if deoxynucleotide addition and CEP participate in two separate reactions (2), the initial amount of inhibition should be stable, and a drift toward 50% inhibition should not be observed. If CEP is histone, Fig. 3 shows that both steps of the overall reaction depicted in (2) are inhibited to about the same extent. Either one becomes rate limiting and no secondary decreases in the overall reaction rate will occur. Experiments designed to distinguish between these two possibilities favour the second mechanism. With either FUdR or cytosine arabinoside it was found that various low levels of inhibition were stable over at least 3–4 h. These

1176

酸含量略多的组蛋白会更敏感一些 [8]。迄今为止试图检测出其他两种蛋白——胞质蛋白和细胞核酸性蛋白是否也符合上述两个标准之一的尝试并没有取得成功。

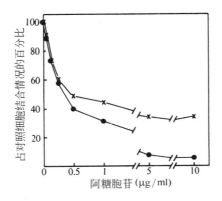

图 3. 组蛋白合成与 DNA 合成的不完全同步性。在用如图所示浓度的阿糖胞苷处理细胞 90 min 之后，将对照细胞和实验细胞用 ³H– 胸腺嘧啶脱氧核苷（20 μCi/ml）和 ³H– 亮氨酸（25 μCi/ml）标记 30 min. 采用图 2 中所描述的方法来测量 DNA（●—●）合成以及组蛋白（×—×）合成的抑制率与剂量之间的关系。

从这些结果分析，很可能产生这样的疑问：CEP 是否参与了与脱氧核苷酸插入相同的链延伸步骤。下面用反应式列出了两种可能机制：

$$(1)\ \text{XTP + DNA} \xrightarrow{\text{CEP + 复制酶}} \text{DNA–XMP}$$

$$(2)\ \text{XTP + DNA + 复制酶} \longrightarrow \text{XMP–DNA– 复制酶} \xrightarrow{\text{CEP}} \text{XMP–DNA–CEP + 复制酶}$$

如果胸腺嘧啶核苷三磷酸（TTP）在 FUdR 的作用下反应速率受限，因而前体掺入的总速率约为对照组的 10% ～ 30%，那么根据上一段中所描述的结果，CEP 的合成也会受到抑制。如果脱氧核苷酸插入和 CEP 是在同一步中的话（反应式 1），那么 DNA 合成一旦受到抑制将最终导致随后的 DNA 合成过程被抑制，因为在多分子反应中两种反应物（TTP 和 CEP）的浓度都会不断下降。此外，这一过程是自动催化的，DNA 的合成率应该会逐渐降低至对照组的 50%。这就是不依赖于同步蛋白质合成的 DNA 合成的量。另一方面，如果脱氧核苷酸插入与 CEP 参与的是两个不同的反应（反应式 2），那么起始抑制率应该是一个恒定值，而且也观察不到抑制率向 50% 漂移。如果 CEP 就是组蛋白，则图 3 表明反应式（2）中所描述的总反应中的两个步骤将受到程度大致相同的抑制。这两个步骤都不是限速步骤，并且总反应速率也不会出现继发性降低。为鉴别这两种可能性而设计的实验倾向于支持第二种机制。不管加入的是 FUdR 还是阿糖胞苷，在至少 3 h ～ 4 h 内，抑制率都维持在较低

experiments measured the incorporation of ^{3}H-deoxyadenosine into alkali stable, TCA precipitable material, a high concentration (10 µg ml.[-1]) of deoxyadenosine in the medium was used to diminish effects from small fluctuations in the internal pool size. The acid soluble pool was monitored for all time points, and the precipitable incorporation adjusted accordingly. Similar conclusions could be derived from analogous experiments using labelled thymidine and deoxycytidine. I conclude that the process of DNA chain elongation *in vivo* is separable into at least two steps and that the step sensitive to decreased levels of CEP is different from that responsible for nucleotide addition.

A Presumptive Replication Complex

Pulse labelled DNA in erythroblasts displays characteristics which are similar to those described in HeLa cells[9,10]. Nascent DNA is preferentially extracted in either phenol or chloroform-isoamyl alcohol and also sediments to the top of a CsCl gradient. This behaviour, which probably indicates the association of nascent DNA with a low density, hydrophobic material, is, for erythroblasts, resistant to former treatment with pronase SPS, high salt, RNAase, or periodate, but sensitive to shear, sonication, alpha-amylase and phospholipase C (Sigma). "STS" gels have demonstrated contaminants in both of these last two enzyme preparations. It would be premature, therefore, to define the complexing agent in terms of either phospholipid or polysaccharide on the basis of these enzyme sentitivities. When pure DNA is incubated with either of these enzymes neither a loss in TCA precipitable counts per min nor a decrease in molecular weight in alkaline sucrose gradients could be detected. Because denatured DNA is preferentially extracted with chloroform[11], and as pulse-labelled DNA might be partially denatured, reconstruction experiments were done in which labelled, denatured DNA was added to nuclei before treatment. These experiments showed that although the labelled, denatured DNA was preferentially extracted with chloroform, it sedimented to a higher density than native DNA on CsCl and that both of these characteristics were unaffectled by shear, alpha-amylase, phospholipase C, or sonication and denaturation. It is therefore unlikely that the behaviour of pulse-labelled DNA in erythroblasts results only from some single-stranded property. Most evidence indicates that pulse-labelled DNA is associated with some nuclear structure which confers certain physical properties on it.

Fig. 4*a* shows the percentage of water soluble counts (counts not extracted with phenol) after a pulse of ^{3}H-TdR (5 min) plotted as a function of the chase time in cold medium. Graphs are given for chases in the presence and absence of cycloheximide. Addition of the drug during the pulse period makes little difference. Care was taken to expose the DNA to the same amount of shear for each point. Better separation of the complex is obtained if, instead of extracting the DNA, it is sedimented to equilibrium on CsCl (4*b*). The kinetics displayed in Fig. 4*a* and *b* are consistent with the model proposed by Friedman and Mueller[9] where the extractability of pulse-labelled DNA is a function of the distance of that DNA from an extractable replication complex. The differing behaviour of cycloheximide treated cells is then explained by a slower rate of DNA chain elongation during the chase period. Recent findings make it unlikely that this complex is associated with the nuclear membrane[11].

水平。利用这些实验可以检测 ^{3}H– 脱氧腺苷掺入到碱性条件下稳定且 TCA 可沉淀的物质中的比例，在培养基中加入高浓度（10 μg/ml）的脱氧腺苷以消除因内部积存量微小波动而造成的影响。我们在各个时间点都监测了酸溶性库存，沉淀中放射性标记的含量会随之变化。由使用放射性标记的胸腺嘧啶脱氧核苷和脱氧胞苷的类似实验也可以得到相近的结论。我认为 DNA 链在体内的延伸过程至少可以分为两个步骤，并且对 CEP 浓度下降敏感的步骤与插入核苷酸的步骤是两个不同的步骤。

一个假定的复制复合物

成红细胞中的脉冲标记 DNA 呈现出与 HeLa 细胞（译者注：是指源自一名美国妇女的子宫颈癌细胞的细胞。这名美国妇女名叫 Henrietta Lacks，于 1951 年死于癌症）中脉冲标记 DNA 相似的性质 [9,10]。新生成的 DNA 更容易被苯酚或者氯仿 – 异戊醇抽提，并且会沉于 CsCl 密度梯度的顶部。这一现象可能说明新生成的 DNA 结合了一种低密度且疏水的物质。在成红细胞中，这一现象对于链霉蛋白酶 SPS、高盐环境、RNA 酶或高碘酸盐的前期处理都不敏感，却对剪切力、超声、α– 淀粉酶和磷脂酶 C（西格马公司）的作用敏感。"STS"凝胶实验已证明在后两种酶制剂中都有污染物存在。因此，根据对这些酶的敏感性，目前还不能确定上述复杂现象到底是由磷脂引起的还是由多糖引起的。当用这两种酶中的任意一种与纯 DNA 一起孵育时，并没有发现 TCA 沉淀计数出现下降，也没有检测到碱性蔗糖梯度中的分子量减小。由于变性的 DNA 更容易被氯仿抽提出来 [11]，而脉冲标记的 DNA 也可能会发生部分变性，因此我们重新设计了实验：在处理细胞之前，将已做好标记的变性 DNA 加入到细胞核中。这些实验表明：尽管那些带有标记的变性 DNA 更容易被氯仿抽提出来，但是在 CsCl 密度梯度离心中，它会沉降在密度高于天然 DNA 的位置上，并且这两种性质都不受剪切力、α– 淀粉酶、磷脂酶 C 或者超声和变性处理的影响。因此，成红细胞中脉冲标记 DNA 的特性不太可能仅由一些单链 DNA 的性质所导致。大多数证据表明，脉冲标记的 DNA 是与某种细胞核结构结合在一起的，而赋予它特定物理性质的正是这些核结构。

图 4a 描绘了经 ^{3}H– 胸腺嘧啶脱氧核苷脉冲处理（5 min）后水溶性组分（即不能被苯酚抽提的组分）中放射性计数的百分比随着在冷媒中追踪时间的变化而改变的趋势。图中分别给出了存在或不存在放线菌酮时的追踪结果。在脉冲期间加入这种药物对实验结果几乎没有什么影响。小心操作以使 DNA 在每个时间点都受到相同的剪切力。如果用 CsCl 密度梯度离心法来代替抽提 DNA 的方法，就可以更好地分离 DNA 复合物（图 4b）。图 4a 和 4b 中的动力学曲线与弗里德曼和米勒 [9] 提出的模型一致。在他们的模型中，脉冲标记 DNA 的可抽提性随着该 DNA 与某种可抽提复制复合物之间的差距而改变。细胞在放线菌酮作用下所表现出来的不同行为可以用在追踪期间内 DNA 链延伸的速率降低来解释。最近的研究结果表明这一复合物不太可能与细胞核膜结合 [11]。

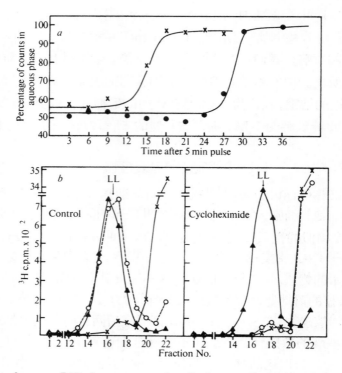

Fig. 4. Chasing of nascent DNA from a presumed replication complex in the presence and absence of cycloheximide (50 μM). Cells were pulsed for 5 min with ³H-TdR (50 μCi mi.⁻¹) and chased for increasing periods of time in the presence or absence of cycloheximide. *a*, The isolated nuclei in RSB were treated with SDS to 0.1%. An equal volume of phenol was added and the suspension mixed on a "Vortex" for 30 s. After centrifugation in a bench centrifuge, the water phase was removed and precipitated with TCA (10%) and carrier and then counted. ×—×, Control; ●—●, cycloheximide. *b*, The SDS treated nuclei were sedimented to equilibrium on CsCl¹ after a 30 s agitation on a "Vortex" mixer. Elimination of SDS fails to affect either the extraction or the sedimentation results. LL, Native DNA. ×—×, 5′ pulse; ○--○, 10′ chase; ▲—▲, 40′ chase.

Histones Remove Nascent DNA from the Replication Complex

The effect of added whole calf thymus histone (Sigma) on the extractability of nascent DNA is shown in Fig. 5. Cells were pulsed for 10 min with ³H-TdR and nuclei isolated in RSB these nuclei do not incorporate ³H-TTP. The nuclei were then suspended in increasing concentrations of histone, albumin, or haemoglobin and incubated at 37°C for 30 min. SDS was then added to 0.1% and the DNA extracted with chloroform-isoamyl alcohol. Depending on the experiment, 5 to 50 μg ml.⁻¹ of histone could protect over 90% of the nascent DNA from extraction. This protection was inhibited by 2 M NaCl before boiling the histone solution (5 min) and by exogenous DNA; haemoglobin and albumin were ineffective. Treatment of nuclei with histone before SDS solubilization also removes nascent DNA from the complex that sediments to the top of a CsCl gradient (Fig. 5, inset). High histone concentrations consistently inhibit the reaction with the replication complex. When used in high concentrations protamine and cytochrome c have activity in this assay. Both are about 20% as effective as either whole histone or the lysine-rich histones

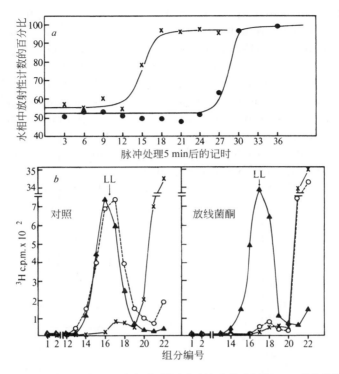

图 4. 分别在放线菌酮存在（50 μM）和不存在时对假定复制复合物中新生 DNA 的追踪结果。用 ³H− 胸腺嘧啶脱氧核苷（50 μCi/ml）脉冲处理细胞 5 min，然后在存在或不存在放线菌酮时追踪放射性标记物随时间推移的变化。a，用网织红细胞标准缓冲液分离细胞核，然后加入 SDS 使其浓度达到 0.1%。加入等体积的苯酚，悬浮液在一台"涡旋"振荡器上混合 30 s。用台式离心机离心后，吸取水相并用 TCA（10%）及载体进行沉淀并计数。×—× 为对照组，●—● 为加入放线菌酮的实验组。b，将经 SDS 处理的细胞核在一台"涡旋"振荡器上振荡 30 s，然后用 CsCl 密度梯度离心[1]，去除 SDS 的过程并未影响抽提或沉淀的结果。LL 为天然 DNA，×—× 为脉冲 5 min 的结果；○—○ 为追踪 10 min 的结果；▲—▲ 为追踪 40 min 的结果。

组蛋白可以去除复制复合物中新生的 DNA

加入小牛胸腺全组蛋白（西格玛公司）后对新生 DNA 的可抽提性产生的效果如图 5 所示。使用 ³H− 胸腺嘧啶脱氧核苷脉冲标记细胞 10 min，随后用网织红细胞标准缓冲液分离细胞核，这些细胞核中不含有 ³H-TTP。随后将细胞核悬浮于浓度逐渐升高的组蛋白、白蛋白或血红蛋白的溶液中，并在 37℃ 下孵育 30 min。加入 SDS 使其最终浓度达到 0.1%，随后用氯仿 – 异戊醇抽提 DNA。根据不同的实验，加入浓度为 5 μg/ml ～ 50 μg/ml 的组蛋白即可保护抽提物中 90% 以上的新生 DNA。加入 2 M NaCl 然后煮沸组蛋白溶液（5 min）或者加入外源性 DNA 都可以抑制组蛋白的这种保护作用；而加入血红蛋白或白蛋白是无效的。在加入 SDS 增溶之前使用组蛋白处理细胞核也会把新生 DNA 从处于某个 CsCl 密度梯度顶层的复合物中去除（图 5 中的小插图）。高浓度的组蛋白通常会抑制与复制复合物的反应。在上述实验中，高浓度的精蛋白和细胞色素 c 都是有活性的。两者活性都只有低分子浓度全组

when used at low molecular concentrations. Spermine, spermidine, and putrescine at concentrations up to 10^{-3} M fail to dissociate the complex and also fail to relieve the cycloheximide inhibition of DNA synthesis in the intact cell. The effective concentration of histone in these experiments is about the same as that in the cell, although this is a difficult comparison since most cellular histone is bound to DNA. Preliminary results indicate that over 50% of the exogenous histone becomes sequestered in nuclei during the course of experiments similar to those in Fig. 5, and that this histone can protect the nascent DNA from degradation by pancreatic DNAase. Similar experiments to be presented in more detail at a later date have shown that compared to chase DNA, pulse DNA is relatively resistant to DNAase and that this resistance is destroyed by an α amylase preparation that has no effect on the digestion of chase DNA by DNAase.

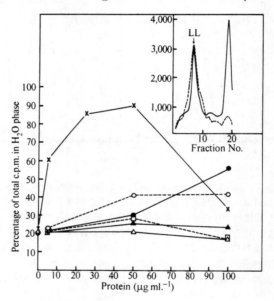

Fig. 5. Removal of nascent DNA from a replication complex by histone. After a 10 min ³H-TdR (25 μCi ml.⁻¹) treatment, nuclei were isolated from cells and incubated in RSB at 37°C for 30 min in the stated concentrations of protein under the indicated conditions. Nuclei were then treated with SDS and extracted with chloroform-isoamyl alcohol as described in Fig. 4a for phenol extraction. The percentage of the total incorporated counts associated with the water phase was then determined. In representative experiments, all of the extracted counts could be recovered in the non-aqueous phase. Control experiments showed that the extractability of nascent DNA from nuclei lysed in high salt was not dependent on the presence of SDS and that added single-stranded DNA remained at the interphase despite the prior addition of histone. ×—×, Histone; O--O, heat denatured histone; ●—●, histone and 25 μg DNA; ▲—▲, histone and 2 M salt; △—△, haemoglobin; □--□, BSA. Inset shows the sedimentation behaviour on CsCl of nascent DNA derived from untreated nuclei and nuclei treated with 25 μg ml.⁻¹ of histone. By lowering the CsCl concentration compared to that shown in Fig. 4b, the complex is seen to move into the gradient. In all experiments, nuclei were at a concentration of about 10⁷ ml.⁻¹. SDS gel electrophoresis showed that the histone preparation contained one minor and one major contaminant (%). The preparation also contained no exonuclease activity; endonuclease activity was not monitored. —, Control; ---, histone, LL, native DNA.

I conclude that *in vitro* the proper concentration of whole calf thymus histone can remove

蛋白或富含赖氨酸组蛋白作用时的 20% 左右。浓度高至 10^{-3} M 的精胺、亚精胺和腐胺并不能引起复制复合物的解离，也不能降低放线菌酮对完整细胞中 DNA 合成的抑制作用。组蛋白在上述实验中发挥作用的有效浓度与它们在细胞中的浓度大致相等，但因为细胞中的组蛋白大多与 DNA 结合在一起，所以很难进行比较。初步结果显示：在类似于图 5 的实验中，超过 50% 的外源性组蛋白会出现在细胞核组分中，而且这类组蛋白可以保护新生 DNA 不被胰腺 DNA 酶所降解。近期之内我将更详细报告一些类似实验，它们可以说明脉冲 DNA 比追踪 DNA 更能抵抗 DNA 酶的作用，并且 α– 淀粉酶会破坏脉冲 DNA 的这种抵抗能力，但却不影响 DNA 酶对追踪 DNA 的降解。

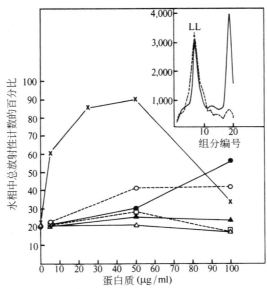

图 5. 用组蛋白去除复制复合物中新生的 DNA。在用 ³H– 胸腺嘧啶脱氧核苷（25 μCi/ml）脉冲标记细胞 10 min 后，将细胞核从细胞中分离出来，并在 37℃ 及指定条件下用含所示浓度蛋白质的网织红细胞标准缓冲液孵育 30 min。反应结束后，用 SDS 处理细胞核，并用氯仿 – 异戊醇溶液抽提 DNA，采用的方法类似于图 4a 中所述的苯酚抽提法。随后测定水相中总放射性计数所占的百分比。在这些有代表性的实验中，所有抽提物的放射性计数都能在非水相中复原。对照实验表明：在高盐条件下，从细胞核中抽提出来的新生 DNA 的量与是否存在 SDS 无关；并且，不管事先是否加入过组蛋白，外源加入的单链 DNA 都维持在水相和有机相的交界处。×—× 为组蛋白，○—○ 为经加热变性后的组蛋白，●—● 为组蛋白及 25 μg DNA，▲—▲ 为组蛋白及 2 M NaCl，△—△ 为血红蛋白，□—□ 为牛血清白蛋白。图中小插图显示的是从未经处理或经 25 μg/ml 组蛋白处理的细胞核中抽提出来的新生 DNA 在 CsCl 密度梯度离心实验中的沉淀行为。通过使用比图 4b 中更低的 CsCl 浓度，可以观察到复制复合物溶入了浓度梯度。在所有这些实验中，细胞核的浓度都约为每 ml 10⁷ 个。SDS 凝胶电泳实验结果显示，实验中所使用的组蛋白制剂含有一种含量较少和一种含量较多的污染物（%）。这种制剂也不具有核酸外切酶的活性；核酸内切酶的活性未检测。— 为对照组，--- 为添加组蛋白的实验组，LL 为天然 DNA。

我的结论是：在体外，适当浓度的小牛胸腺全组蛋白可以去除复制复合物中新

nascent DNA from a replication complex. How this activity might relate to DNA synthesis in the intact cell remains to be seen. Other basic proteins have activity in this assay but the histones are much more active at lower molar concentrations. Results with the replication complex are consistent with a previous conclusion that the CEP acts at a step other than nucleotide addition. They are also related to recent data showing that (1) histone stimulates Qβ replicase *in vitro*; (2) bacteria grown in the presence of canavanine accumulate or fail to remove their DNA from complex[13]; and (3) φX capsid proteins are required for φX DNA synthesis[13].

Probable Role of Histones

None of the experiments that I have presented proves that the histones are the DNA chain elongation proteins, although five independent experiments *in vivo* and *in vitro* make this notion likely. Final proof would be the demonstration that the proper concentration histone increases the rate of chain elongation in a cell-free system to that observed *in vivo* and that newly-made histone is located at the growing point of replication in intact cells.

There are several other reasons why the histones are a reasonable candidate for the chain elongation protein. First, they are found in the nucleus bound to the DNA. Second consistent with the rapidity of inhibition of DNA synthesis by cycloheximide, they are usually not found in any detectable free pool. Third, given the preceding observations it follows that the chain elongation protein must move rapidly from its presumed site of synthesis on cytoplasmic ribosomes to the growing point. It is at least questionable whether diffusion can account for the rapidity of this interaction which must involve recognition as well as transport. The electrostatic forces between the newly polymerized DNA phosphates and the basic histones might facilitate this process. Fourth, there are some 3,000 growing points in the average S phase cell[1]. Inhibiton of DNA synthesis by cycloheximide probably occurs within 10 s. The rapidity of inhibition, the linear kinetics after inhibition, and the fact that low levels of cycloheximide give low levels of DNA inhibition indicate that the CEP is probably used stoichiometrically. As our previous experiments showed that all replicons were affected, it follows that at least 20,000 CEPs must be synthesized by the cell per minute in order to sustain the normal rate of replicon growth. These cells make about 40,000 histone molecules per minute[2]; no other protein in the cell, apart from haemoglobin, even approaches this synthetic rate.

The most intriguing feature of the inhibitory effects of cycloheximide on DNA synthesis is that about 50% of the DNA can be replicated. Persistence of this activity can be explained if histone from pre-replicative chromatin acts as a reservoir of histone at the growing point. In conjunction with newly synthesized histone, the reaction of this recycled histone with nascent DNA and the replication complex allows the growing fork to move ahead at the normal rate. In the absence of newly synthesized histone, the rate of chain elongation is slower, but not zero since recycled histone can still be used.

Because all known polymerases have the inherent property to elongate nascent chains, the proposed requirements for histones in this process most probably reflects some higher

生的 DNA。组蛋白的这一功能如何才能与完整细胞中的 DNA 合成相关联还有待于进一步的研究。其他一些碱性蛋白在这个实验中同样具有活性，不过在摩尔浓度更低的条件下，组蛋白比它们的活性高很多。由复制复合物得到的结果与之前认为 CEP 在不同于核苷酸插入的步骤发挥作用的结论一致。这些结果也与最近得到的以下实验数据相吻合：（1）在体外实验中，组蛋白可以激活 Qβ 复制酶；（2）在含有刀豆氨酸的环境中生长的细菌会聚集在一起，或者未能使它们的 DNA 与复制复合物分离 [13]；（3）φX DNA 的合成需要 φX 衣壳蛋白的参与 [13]。

组蛋白的可能角色

尽管有 5 个独立的体内和体外实验表明组蛋白有可能就是 DNA 链延伸蛋白，但是我在文中介绍过的所有实验都不能证明这一点。最关键的证据在于：要证明在无细胞系统中，适当浓度的组蛋白可以使 DNA 链延伸的速率增加至细胞内链延伸的速率；并且还需要证明在完整细胞中，新合成的组蛋白分布于 DNA 复制的生长点。

还有其他几条理由可以说明为什么组蛋白是链延伸蛋白的合理候选者。首先，它们位于细胞核中，并且与 DNA 结合。其二，组蛋白很少以游离形式存在，这与放线菌酮能迅速抑制 DNA 的合成相一致。第三，由前面的观测结果可以推出，链延伸蛋白必须能够从它可能被合成的位置——胞质内的核糖体迅速移动到 DNA 合成的生长点。人们至少会对用扩散来解释这种包括识别和运输过程在内的相互作用的快速性表示怀疑。新聚合的 DNA 上磷酸基团与碱性组蛋白之间的静电力可能有利于这种快速移动。第四，在 S 期细胞中，平均会有大概 3,000 个生长点 [1]。放线菌酮对 DNA 合成的抑制很可能在 10 s 之内就能实现。抑制的迅速形成、抑制后得到的线性动力学关系以及低浓度放线菌酮对 DNA 合成的抑制水平也低都说明，CEP 有可能是按量分配的。由于我们之前的实验已经证明所有的复制子都会受到影响，因此为了维持复制子增长的正常速度，细胞每分钟必须合成至少 20,000 个 CEP。这些细胞每分钟大约可以合成 40,000 个组蛋白分子 [2]，除血红蛋白以外，细胞中还没有哪种蛋白能达到这样的合成速度。

放线菌酮对 DNA 合成的抑制作用的最有趣特征是大约 50% 的 DNA 可以被复制。如果复制前染色质中的组蛋白可以源源不断地为复制生长点提供组蛋白，那么这种活性的持续存在就可以得到解释。这种被循环利用的组蛋白与新合成的组蛋白一起与新生 DNA 及复制复合物发生反应，使得复制叉能够以正常的速度向前推移。当不存在新合成的组蛋白时，链延伸速率有所减慢，但不会为 0，因为还能使用可循环利用的组蛋白。

由于所有已知的聚合酶都具有延长新生 DNA 链的固有特性，因此 DNA 合成过程对组蛋白的需要很可能反映的是更高级的机制，在这种机制中，新 DNA 的合成

order mechanism by which a synthesis of new DNA is coupled to the generation of a very defined and inviolable chromosomal structure.

I thank H. Holtzer, J. Flaks, and A. Kozinski for their help and criticisms. This work was supported by grants from the National Institutes of Health, the United States Public Health Service, and the Helen Hay Whitney Foundation.

(**240**, 449-453; 1972)

Harold Weintraub: Department of Anatomy, University of Pennsylvania, Philadelphia, Pennsylvania 19104.

Received June 12; revised October 12, 1972.

References:

1. Weintraub, H., and Holtzer, H., *J. Mol. Biol.*, **65**, 13 (1972).
2. Weintraub, H., Campbell, G., and Holtzer, H., *J. Mol. Biol.* (in the press).
3. Spalding, J., Kajiwara, K., and Mueller, G. C., *Proc. US Nat. Acad. Sci.*, **56**, 1535 (1966).
4. Malpoix, P., Zampetti, F., and Fievez, M., *Biochim. Biophys. Acta*, **182**, 214 (1969).
5. Freedman, M. L., Honig, G. R., and Rabinovitz, M., *Exp. Cell Res.*, **44**, 263 (1966).
6. Borun, T. W., Scharff, M. D., and Robbins, E., *Proc. US Nat. Acad. Sci.*, **58**, 1977 (1967).
7. Mueller, G. C., and Kajiwara, K., *Biochim. Biophys. Acta*, **119**, 557 (1966).
8. Sadgopal, S., and Bonner, J., *Biochim. Biophys. Acta*, **186**, 349 (1969).
9. Friedman, D. L., and Mueller, G. C., *Biochim. Biophys. Acta*, **174**, 253 (1969).
10. Pearson, G. D., and Hanawalt, P. C., *J. Mol. Biol.*, **62**, 65 (1971).
11. Fakan, S., Turner, G., Pagana, J., and Hancock, R., *Proc. US Nat. Acad. Sci.*, **69**, 2300 (1972).
12. Kuo, C. H., and August, J. T., *Nature*, **237**, 105 (1972).
13. Schachtele, C. F., Anderson, D. L., and Rogers, P., *J. Mol. Biol.*, **49**, 255 (1970).
14. Iwaya, M., and Denhardt, D. T., *J. Mol. Biol.*, **57**, 159 (1971).

与一种固定不变的染色体结构的生成相关联。

感谢霍尔泽、弗拉克斯和科津斯基对我的帮助及批评。这项工作的资金来自于美国国立卫生研究院、美国公共卫生署和海伦·海·惠特尼基金会。

（张锦彬 翻译；孙军 审稿）

Biochemical Evidence for the Bidirectional Replication of DNA in *Escherichia coli*

W. G. McKenna and M. Masters

Editor's Note

Whereas vertebrate DNA is linear and packaged into multiple different chromosomes, the DNA of *Escherichia coli* is circular and housed within a single chromosome. This bacterial DNA replicates sequentially from a fixed point, and here W. G. McKenna and Millicent Masters present biochemical evidence suggesting that replication takes place simultaneously in both directions from the point of origin. The premise was corroborated by David Prescott and Peter Kuempel, who published autoradiographs of bidirectional bacterial DNA replication around the same time. The phenomenon of bidirectional DNA replication is now well accepted, and the process is known to proceed in three stages: initiation, elongation and termination, regulated by a complex and efficient set of catalytically active proteins.

THE chromosome of *Escherichia coli* is a single circular DNA molecule which replicates sequentially[1-3] from a fixed origin[4-14,15]. Although it was initially thought that replication proceeds in a unique direction, Masters and Broda[16] and subsequently Bird *et al.*[17] and Hohlfeld and Vielmetter[18] have presented genetic evidence that replication takes place simultaneously in both directions from the origin. We here present confirmatory biochemical evidence that this is so. Since this manuscript was submitted, Prescott and Kuempel[19] have published autoradiographs of bidirectional replication of DNA.

Bidirectional Replication of DNA

We adapted to *E. coli* the method with which Weintraub[20] demonstrated that DNA replication in developing chick erythroblasts is bidirectional rather than unidirectional. The technique allows one to analyse the way in which the segments of DNA made immediately after initiation of replication are synthesized.

Cells of a thymine-requiring mutant of *E. coli* are allowed to initiate DNA replication synchronously with the thymine analogue bromouracil (BU) present in place of thymine. BU is then rapidly replaced by ³H-thymine and replication allowed to proceed for a much longer period. The DNA is extracted avoiding degradation of the daughter DNA and divided into two aliquots, one of which is subjected to ultraviolet light to degrade the sections of DNA containing BU, as low doses of ultraviolet light lead to specific breakdown of the sugar-phosphate backbone of DNA adjacent to incorporated BU residues[21]. The newly synthesized radioactive DNA strand segments are separated from the parental DNA strands and analysed with respect to molecular weight, in an alkaline sucrose gradient.

大肠杆菌DNA双向复制的生物化学证据

麦克纳，马斯特斯

编者按

脊椎动物的 DNA 都是线性的且被组装到多条不同的染色体中，而大肠杆菌的 DNA 却是环状的且全部位于一条染色体中。大肠杆菌 DNA 的复制从一个固定位点开始连续进行，在本文中麦克纳和米莉森特·马斯特斯提出生物化学证据证明其复制是从起始点开始朝两个方向同时进行的。大约在同一时间，戴维·普雷斯科特和彼得·金佩尔发表了细菌 DNA 双向复制的放射自显影照片，从而证实了上述假设。目前，DNA 双向复制的现象已经被人们广为接受，该过程分三步进行：起始、延伸和终止，这些步骤都受到一套复杂而高效的、有催化活性的蛋白质的调节。

大肠杆菌的染色体是一个单一的环状 DNA 分子，其连续复制[1-3] 始于一个固定的起始点[4-14,15]。尽管起初认为其复制是沿单一方向进行的，但马斯特斯、布罗达[16] 和随后的伯德等人[17] 以及霍尔菲尔德、菲尔梅特[18] 提出的遗传学证据表明复制是从起始点开始沿两个方向同时发生的。在本文中，我们用确凿的生物化学证据证明事实确实如此。在这篇文章的手稿提交之后，普雷斯科特和金佩尔[19] 随即发表了DNA 双向复制的放射自显影照片。

DNA 的双向复制

我们将温特劳布[20] 证实发育过程中小鸡成红细胞的 DNA 复制是双向而不是单向时所用的方法应用于大肠杆菌。这项技术能帮助我们分析在复制刚刚开始时形成的 DNA 片段是如何被合成的。

我们用胸腺嘧啶类似物——溴尿嘧啶（BU）取代胸腺嘧啶以使需胸腺嘧啶的大肠杆菌突变株细胞进行 DNA 同步复制。随后迅速用 ^{3}H– 胸腺嘧啶代替 BU，并且使复制过程延续更长的时间。在保证子代 DNA 不发生降解的前提下将 DNA 抽提出来并分为两等份，其中一份用紫外线照射以降解 DNA 中含有 BU 的部分，因为小剂量紫外线照射即可导致 DNA 上与掺入的 BU 残基相邻的糖－磷酸骨架发生特异性的断裂[21]。将这些新合成的具有放射活性的 DNA 片段从亲代 DNA 链中分离出来并在碱性蔗糖梯度中对分子量进行分析。

As Fig. 1 shows, if replication is unidirectional (*A*), BU will be at one end only of each single-stranded segment. As the duration of BU uptake is small compared with that of ^{3}H-thymine, treatment with ultraviolet will make little difference to the size of segments as compared with the untreated control; both should form homogeneous bands in the same region of the sucrose gradient. By contrast, if replication is bidirectional (Fig. 1*B*), the bromouracil should be located in the middle of each segment, so that treatment with ultraviolet light breaks the segments in two and their molecular weight is approximately halved (see below) as compared with the control. In this case irradiated and unirradiated DNA will appear as separate bands on the sucrose gradient.

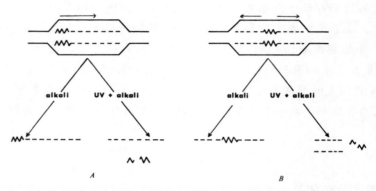

Fig. 1. Diagrammatic representation of the predicted behaviour of unidirectionally (*A*) as opposed to bidirectionally (*B*) replicating origin DNA after the following treatment. Synchronized cells are pulse for 15 s with 5-bromouraci (⁓⁓BU-DNA) and then with ^{3}H-thymine for 100 s (- - -, ^{3}H-DNA; ———, unlabelled DNA). Lysates of cultures are either irradiated with ultraviolet light, or left unirradiated, and centrifuged on alkaline sucrose gradients.

Initiation of DNA replication was synchronized in cells of *E. coli* B/r (Thy⁻, Leu⁻, His⁻, Cys⁻, Xyl⁻), growing with a generation time of 40 min on a minimal salts medium, by allowing them to terminate current rounds of DNA replication while preventing the initiation of new ones, by withholding required amino acids. Thymine was then removed from the medium and amino acids returned to allow synthesis of the proteins required for initiation of replication. Replication was then initiated synchronously by adding BU, which, after 15 s, was replaced with ^{3}H-thymine for 100 s. Replication was then stopped, DNA extracted, irradiated if required and centrifuged. Fig. 2 shows the difference in sedimentation behaviour of the irradiated and unirradiated extracts: there is a clear shift in molecular weight of the newly synthesized DNA after exposure to ultraviolet. From the positions of the peaks in a series of experiments we have determined[22] that the ratio of the molecular weights of the untreated to ultraviolet-treated DNA segments is 2.6±0.3. This agrees well with the predicted ratio of 2.32 calculated by assuming that all BU moieties will have been removed from the irradiated DNA segments leaving only the thymine-containing DNA. (The fact that increasing the exposure to ultraviolet twenty-fold leads to no further reduction in molecular weight (data not shown) supports this assumption.) The BU incorporated in this experiment therefore behaves as if it were incorporated into the middle of a DNA fragment, as in Fig. 1*B*, and not as if it were incorporated at its end (Fig. 1*A*).

如图 1 所示，如果复制是单向的(A)，那么 BU 将只会出现在每个单链片段的一端。因为摄取 BU 的时间比摄取 ³H– 胸腺嘧啶的时间短，所以经过紫外线处理与没有接受过处理的对照物在片段大小上几乎没有什么差异；两者均会在蔗糖梯度的同一区域中形成类似的条带。反之，如果复制是双向的（图 1B），那么溴尿嘧啶就应该位于每个片段的中间，因而用紫外线处理会使片段一分为二，它们的分子量约为对照物的一半（参见下文）。在这种情况下，照射过和没有照射过的 DNA 将在蔗糖梯度中表现为两条分离的条带。

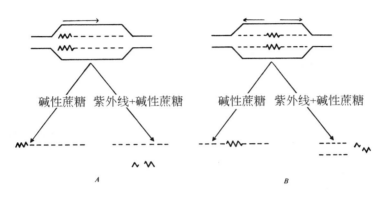

图 1. 经过下述处理后 DNA 在起始点发生单向复制（A）与发生双向复制（B）的预期结果对比示意图。同步化的细胞先用 5– 溴尿嘧啶处理 15 秒（∼∼BU–DNA），接着用 ³H– 胸腺嘧啶处理 100 秒（- - -，³H–DNA；——，未标记的 DNA）。培养物的裂解液或者被紫外线照射，或者不被紫外线照射，随后都用碱性蔗糖梯度法离心分离。

在大肠杆菌 B/r（Thy⁻、Leu⁻、His⁻、Cys⁻、Xyl⁻）的细胞内进行 DNA 复制起始同步化处理，该菌在低盐培养基中每 40 分钟繁殖一代，通过撤除所必需的氨基酸可以使它们结束当前的 DNA 复制循环，同时防止下一代复制的开始。然后从培养基中移除胸腺嘧啶，重新供给氨基酸以便能够合成启动复制所需的蛋白质。随后加入 BU 启动同步复制，15 秒之后用 ³H– 胸腺嘧啶取代 BU 再处理 100 秒。复制随即终止，然后提取 DNA，根据要求选择是否进行紫外线照射，最后离心。图 2 显示出接受照射和未接受照射的提取物在沉降行为上的不同：新合成的 DNA 在接受紫外线照射后出现了分子量上的明显变化。根据一系列实验中的波峰位置，我们断定 [22] 未经处理的与经紫外线处理的 DNA 片段的分子量之比为 2.6 ± 0.3。这与由假定所有 BU 部分均从照射过的 DNA 片段中被移去只剩下含胸腺嘧啶的 DNA 而计算出来的预期比率 2.32 非常吻合。（将紫外线的照射时间延长 20 倍并未使分子量持续下降（数据未给出），这一事实证实了上述假设。）因此，在这个实验中 BU 的掺入位置好像是一个 DNA 片段的中间，如图 1B 所示，而不太像是结合在了它的末端（图 1A）。

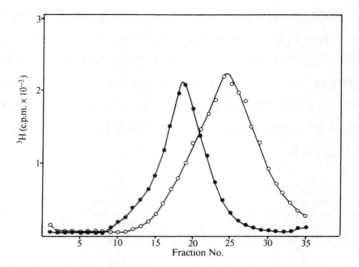

Fig. 2. Centrifugation of irradiated (○—○) and unirradiated (●—●) DNA in which initiation was allowed to take place in bromouracil. 50 ml. cultures at densities of 5×10^8 cells ml.$^{-1}$ were synchronized with regard to DNA replication by 100 min of amino acid starvation followed by thymine starvation for one mass doubling time[25]. The cells were collected on "Millipore 47 mm HA" membrane filters and washed with prewarmed buffer. The cells were pulsed for 15 s on the filter with 5-bromouracil (10 µg ml.$^{-1}$) and washed with prewarmed buffer. Finally the cells were suspended in 10 ml. M9-glucose + aa + thymine (1 µg ml.$^{-1}$) + ^{3}H-thymine (20 µCi µg^{-1}). The cells were vigorously aerated for 100 s. DNA replication was stopped and the cells lysed (Fig. 3). In this case 0.2 ml. samples of the crude lysates were exposed to ultraviolet if required (dose 3×10^5 erg) and layered on 5 ml. linear 5–20% alkaline sucrose gradients (0.1 M NaOH, 0.9 M NaCl) for centrifugation in a "Beckman L2-65B" centrifuge using an SW50.1 rotor at 20,000 r.p.m. for 12 h. Ten drop fractions were collected on "Whatman 3 MM" paper filters, washed in 5% ice cold TCA followed by 80% ethanol. The samples were counted in PPO-POPOP scintillant (Fig. 3).

By using a mouse satellite DNA fraction of known molecular weight as a standard we calculate that the newly synthesized, ^{3}H-labelled single-stranded DNA fragments have a molecular weight of 2×10^7. Assuming that the *E. coli* chromosome has a molecular weight of 1–2×10^9 and requires approximately 40 min for its synthesis this is about the size of the piece that we would have expected to have been synthesized during the 2 min period of the experiment. The fact that both the irradiated and unirradiated DNAs are homogeneous and of the size predicted, strongly supports the idea that BU is incorporated into the middle of daughter strands of DNA whose replication is bidirectional, and not into a fragment of DNA arising in one of the ways set out below.

BU Found Only in Daughter DNA

The results obtained above, that BU present during the initiation of replication is incorporated internally into a DNA fragment, could have been generated in ways other than that set out in Fig. 1*B*. According to the model presented there, BU is flanked by ^{3}H-thymine labelled daughter DNA. By contrast, a number of other models predict that ^{3}H-thymine would appear only to one side of the BU; the stretch of DNA on the other

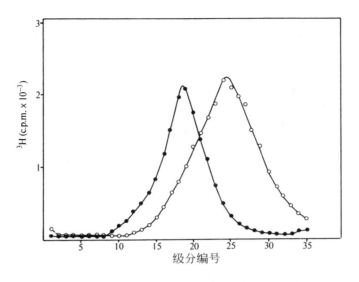

图 2. 复制起始于溴尿嘧啶的照射 DNA（○—○）和未照射 DNA（●—●）的离心结果。对于密度为
5×10⁸ 个细胞 / 毫升的 50 毫升培养物，通过 100 分钟氨基酸缺乏以及随后长达分裂增殖一倍所需
时间的胸腺嘧啶缺乏，来实现 DNA 复制同步化[25]。将这些细胞收集于"密理博 47 毫米 HA"滤膜上，
并用预热的缓冲剂洗涤。在滤膜上将细胞用 5- 溴尿嘧啶（10 微克 / 毫升）处理 15 秒，然后用预
热的缓冲剂洗涤。最后将这些细胞悬浮于 10 毫升 M9- 葡萄糖 + 氨基酸 + 胸腺嘧啶（1 微克 / 毫升）
+ ³H- 胸腺嘧啶（20 微居里 / 微克）中。对这些细胞剧烈通气达 100 秒。随后终止 DNA 的复制并
裂解细胞（图 3）。此时，0.2 毫升的粗裂解样品可根据需要选择用紫外线照射（剂量为 3×10⁵ 尔格）
或者不用紫外线照射，然后使其在 5 毫升 5% ~ 20% 线性梯度碱性蔗糖溶液（0.1 摩尔 / 升 NaOH，
0.9 摩尔 / 升 NaCl）中分层，方法是在转子为 SW50.1 的"贝克曼 L2-65B"型离心机中以 20,000 转 / 分
的转速离心分离 12 小时。10 滴分离出来的级分被收集于"沃特曼 3 MM"滤纸上，先用 5% 冷
TCA 后用 80% 乙醇溶液冲洗。样品用 PPO-POPOP 闪烁体计数（图 3）。

利用分子量已知的小鼠卫星 DNA 组分作为标准，我们计算出了新合成的、
³H- 标记的单链 DNA 片段的分子量为 2×10⁷。假设大肠杆菌染色体的分子量是
1×10⁹ ~ 2×10⁹，并且假设其合成过程需要 40 分钟左右，则得到的产物大小与我们
预期 2 分钟实验中能够合成出来的大小大致相等。照射过的和未照射过的 DNA 都
很均一且大小与预期一致的事实充分证实了这一观点，即 BU 被掺入到了双向复制
DNA 的子链中间，而非被掺入到由下文中所列举的任意一种方式形成的 DNA 片段中。

BU 仅在子代 DNA 中出现

上文中得到的结果，即在复制起始阶段存在的 BU 被掺入到了 DNA 片段中间，
也可能是由与图 1B 所示有所不同的方式产生的。根据上文中提出的模型，³H- 胸腺
嘧啶标记的子代 DNA 应位于 BU 的两侧。与之相反，另有很多模型预言 ³H- 胸腺嘧
啶只可能出现在 BU 的一侧；在 BU 另一侧的 DNA 链将包含未标记的胸腺嘧啶。然

side of the BU would contain unlabelled thymine. It should be noted, however, that for this to take place a series of coincidences would be required to explain the observed sizes and homogeneity of the fragments described above.

The first way in which this could come about would be if parental DNA were used to prime daughter DNA replication, as in rolling circle[23,24], and some other[25] models of DNA replication. According to these models daughter and parental DNA[16] are covalently linked and so first the BU and then the ^{3}H-thymine would be incorporated in continuation of high molecular weight parental DNA. If this DNA were to fragment during extraction so as to yield pieces of 2×10^7 molecular weight, some of these pieces could be expected to contain BU sequences flanked by parental and daughter DNA which could behave as described above.

If termination of rounds of chromosome replication did not occur during the synchronization treatment, but only after BU and labelled thymine had been added to the medium, linkage between parental and daughter DNA would also be found. Although Stein and Hanawalt[26] and Kuempel (submitted for publication) failed to detect linkage between parental and daughter DNA in *E. coli* 15T⁻, we thought it essential also to exclude such linkage in B/r under the conditions of our experiment.

Another source of error could be the retention of an internal pool of thymine after termination of rounds of replication or some leakiness in the thymine requirement of the strain used in these experiments. Initiation of synthesis could then occur during the thymine starvation period and the BU, when added, incorporated in continuation of a previously synthesized piece of DNA. If the amount of synthesis occurring before the addition of BU were approximately equal to that which occurs during the later pulse of ^{3}H-thymine, pieces could be generated which would behave as described above, and unidirectional synthesis mistaken for bidirectional.

We therefore excluded these possibilities by performing an experiment which showed that BU used to initiate replication is not added to a previously synthesized piece of DNA. Bacteria were grown for three generations in a medium containing ^{14}C-thymine to totally label parental DNA. The required amino acids were removed and the cells allowed to terminate rounds of replication in ^{14}C-thymine. After termination thymine was removed, amino acids re-added and incubation continued until all cells were ready to initiate replication. ^{3}H-bromouracil was then added to the medium and replication allowed to continue for 100 s. The DNA was then isolated and the strands separated and centrifuged on caesium chloride gradients (Fig. 3). The parental ^{14}C-containing DNA is of light density; daughter DNA which is fully substituted with ^{3}H-BU is of heavy density. Any DNA stretches which contained both parental and daughter DNA, or BU added to a fragment synthesized during thymine starvation from a retained internal pool, would be doubly labelled and of a density intermediate between that of the thymine containing parental and the BU containing daughter DNA. Fragments synthesized by addition of BU to the unlabelled DNA which could be made during thymine starvation by a leaky mutant

而，应该指出的是：如果 [3]H– 胸腺嘧啶仅出现在 BU 的一侧，那么就需要用一系列巧合事件来解释上述观察到的分子量大小及 DNA 片段的均一性。

造成这种情况的第一个可能原因是：如果亲代 DNA 被用于引发子代 DNA 的复制，如在滚环 [23,24] 和其他一些 [25]DNA 复制模型中那样。根据这些模型，子代和亲代 DNA[16] 是以共价键相连的，所以 BU 将首先被掺入到高分子量亲代 DNA 连续体中，然后才是 [3]H– 胸腺嘧啶。如果这个 DNA 在抽提的过程中断裂，就会产生分子量为 2×10^7 的碎片，其中一部分碎片可能会含有两侧分别是亲代和子代 DNA 的 BU 序列，在这种情况下也会出现上文所描述的现象。

如果在同步化处理的时候，染色体复制循环并未终止，而只有当把 BU 和标记的胸腺嘧啶加入到培养基之后循环才终止，那么我们也会发现亲代和子代 DNA 之间存在连接。尽管斯坦和哈纳沃特 [26] 以及金佩尔（已提交出版）都未能在大肠杆菌 15T⁻ 中检测到亲代和子代 DNA 之间的连接，但我们认为在我们的实验条件下排除大肠杆菌 B/r 中存在这种连接也是必要的。

另一个造成判断失误的原因可能是：在复制循环终止后仍存在一个内部的胸腺嘧啶代谢池，或者实验中所用菌株的胸腺嘧啶需求存在渗漏。合成的启动可能会发生在胸腺嘧啶缺乏阶段，随后一旦加入 BU，BU 就会掺入到早期合成的 DNA 片段连续体中。如果在加入 BU 以前的合成量近似等于后期与 [3]H– 胸腺嘧啶孵育合成的量，那么就会产生上文中所描述的碎片，这时单向合成就会被错误判断成双向合成。

因此，我们要进行一项实验来排除上述可能性，由这个实验可以说明用于启动复制的 BU 并没有掺入到先前合成的 DNA 片段上。细菌在含有 [14]C– 胸腺嘧啶的培养基中生长三代就可以将亲代 DNA 全部标记。撤除所需的氨基酸，细胞就会在 [14]C– 胸腺嘧啶中终止复制循环。终止之后移除胸腺嘧啶，再次加入氨基酸，继续培养直到所有细胞准备好开始复制。然后，将 [3]H– 溴尿嘧啶添加到培养基中，并使复制过程持续 100 秒。随后提取 DNA，解链成单链，并用 CsCl 密度梯度法离心（图 3）。含有 [14]C 的亲代 DNA 是低密度的；完全被 ^{3}H–BU 取代的子代 DNA 是高密度的。任何同时包含亲代 DNA 和子代 DNA 的链，或者包含 BU 掺入到在缺少胸腺嘧啶时从内部残留代谢池中合成的 DNA 片段上的链，都将被双重标记，且其密度介于含有胸腺嘧啶的亲代 DNA 和含有 BU 的子代 DNA 的密度之间。在缺乏胸腺嘧啶时渗漏的突变体可以利用重新合成的胸腺嘧啶生成未标记的 DNA，在这种 DNA 上掺入 BU 所合成的片段也具有杂合的密度，但不会被双重标记。

using thymine synthesized *de novo* would also be of hybrid density but would not be doubly labelled.

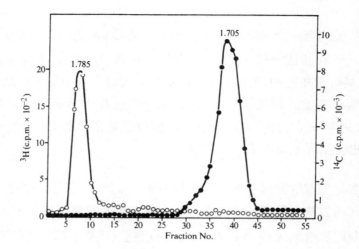

Fig. 3. Separation of daughter and parental DNA on CsCl gradients. *E. coli* B/r (L6) was grown in M9 medium + 0.2% glucose + 10 μg ml.$^{-1}$ thymine, 20 μg ml.$^{-1}$ each of leucine, histidine and cysteine (aa) with rotary shaking at 37°C. The cells were labelled with ^{14}C-thymine (10^{-2} μCi μg^{-1}) for 3 generations and synchronized by 100 min aa starvation followed by thymine starvation for 1 mass doubling time. The cells were washed with prewarmed buffer and resuspended in M9-glucose + aa + 10 μg ml.$^{-1}$ bromouracil + 2 μCi μg^{-1} ^{3}H-bromouracil for 100 s and vigorously aerated. DNA replication was stopped in 50 ml. aliquots (5×10^{8} cells ml.$^{-1}$) by pouring the cells with crushed ice into buffer B[28]. After washing twice in 1×SSC the cells were suspended in 2 ml. 0.1×SSC+10^{-3} M EDTA and lysed with 1% Na dodecyl sulphate (SDS)+pronase 1 mg ml.$^{-1}$ (ref. 29). The DNA lysate was extracted twice with an excess volume of 88% phenol—12% meta-cresol—0.1% 8-hydroxy-quinoline followed by gentle shaking in 24:1 mixture of chloroform:octanol to remove the SDS. The DNA was denatured and centrifuged according to the procedure of Stein and Hanawalt[26] except that we used "BDH Analar" grade CsCl and diluted the DNA in 10^{-3} M EDTA. Ten drop fractions were collected into ice cold 5% TCA and counted on "Whatman" GF/C filters in PPO-POPOP scintillant in a "Packard Tricarb" liquid scintillation counter. ◯, ^{3}H; ●, ^{14}C.

DNA stretches of intermediate density are clearly identifiable when thymine is replaced by BU in the middle of the replicative cycle of *E. coli*[27]. Fig. 3 gives the data we have obtained from our experiment. No doubly labelled DNA or DNA of intermediate density can be seen. The ^{14}C-DNA bands at 1.705 g cm^{-3} and the ^{3}H-DNA at 1.785 g cm^{-3}. Assuming that the change in density is proportional to the change in molecular weight these densities are what would be expected on the hypothesis that daughter DNA is fully substituted with BU and neither contains, nor is linked to, light DNA containing thymine. It should be noted that this experiment does not eliminate the possibility that daughter DNA is linked to parental DNA for a period of less than 100 s. Because, however, this is shorter than the labelling period used in the experiment reported above, we conclude that linkage between daughter and parental DNA or between daughter DNA synthesized before and after the addition of BU cannot explain the results in Fig. 2.

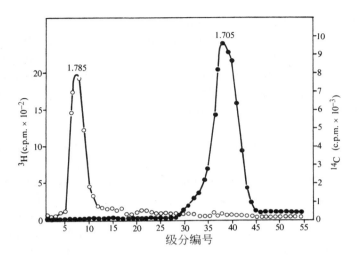

图 3. 用 CsCl 密度梯度离心法分离子代 DNA 和亲代 DNA。大肠杆菌 B/r (L6) 在 M9 培养基 +0.2% 葡萄糖 +10 微克 / 毫升胸腺嘧啶及浓度均为 20 微克 / 毫升的亮氨酸、组氨酸和半胱氨酸（氨基酸）中生长，37℃ 旋转振荡培养。细胞用 ¹⁴C– 胸腺嘧啶（10⁻² 微居里 / 微克）标记三代，通过 100 分钟氨基酸缺乏以及随后长达分裂增殖一倍所需时间的胸腺嘧啶缺乏而达到同步化。细胞用预热的缓冲液冲洗，然后重悬于 M9– 葡萄糖 ＋ 氨基酸 +10 微克 / 毫升溴尿嘧啶 +2 微居里 / 微克 ³H–溴尿嘧啶中 100 秒并剧烈通气。将细胞和碎冰加进缓冲剂 B 中以便终止 50 毫升等分试样（5 × 10⁸ 个细胞 / 毫升）中的 DNA 复制 [28]。细胞用 1 × SSC（译者注：氯化钠 – 柠檬酸钠缓冲液）洗涤两次，然后悬浮于 2 毫升 0.1 × SSC + 10⁻³ 摩尔 / 升 EDTA 中，最后在 1% 十二烷基硫酸钠（SDS）＋1 毫克 / 毫升链霉蛋白酶中裂解（参考文献 29）。用过量的 88% 苯酚—12% 间甲酚—0.1% 8– 羟基喹啉对 DNA 裂解物进行两次抽提，然后在氯仿 : 辛醇为 24:1 的混合物中轻轻振荡以除去 SDS。利用斯坦和哈纳沃特的方法 [26] 使 DNA 变性并离心，不同之处是我们使用了"英国药品所的分析纯"CsCl，并将 DNA 在 10⁻³ 摩尔 / 升的 EDTA 中稀释。10 滴分离出来的级分被收集到冷的 5% TCA 中，在"沃特曼 GF/C"滤膜上通过"帕卡德公司三汽化器"型液体闪烁计数仪中的 PPO–POPOP 闪烁体进行计数。○，³H；●，¹⁴C。

当在大肠杆菌复制周期之中用 BU 取代胸腺嘧啶时，可以清楚地辨认出中间密度的 DNA 链 [27]。图 3 中给出的数据来自于我们的实验结果。并未发现双重标记的 DNA 或者中间密度的 DNA。¹⁴C–DNA 条带位于 1.705 克 / 立方厘米处，³H–DNA 条带位于 1.785 克 / 立方厘米处。假设密度变化与分子量变化成正比，则上述密度就可以通过以下假设推导出来，即子代 DNA 完全被 BU 置换，其中既不包括含胸腺嘧啶的低密度 DNA，也不会与之相连接。应该指出的是，这个实验并不能排除子代 DNA 在一个少于 100 秒的时间段内与亲代 DNA 相连接的可能性。然而，因为这比上述实验中所用的标记时间更短，所以我们认为：用子代 DNA 与亲代 DNA 之间的连接，或者用在加入 BU 之前和之后合成的子代 DNA 之间的连接，都不能解释图 2 中的结果。

Another possible source of error is that BU continues to be incorporated into DNA for some time after it has been replaced in the medium by ³H-thymine. If BU were simply to compete with thymine for incorporation the result would be stretches of DNA containing both bases which would be expected, on irradiation, to yield many pieces of small size rather than pieces half the size of the initial fragment (Fig. 2). If, however, the BU continued to be incorporated for an appropriate interval to the exclusion of thymine and if replication were unidirectional, pieces could be generated which could be halved in size by the removal of a large number of BU moieties from one end. This could result in our mistaking unidirectional replication for bidirectional.

To eliminate this possibility, initiation was synchronized as described above, replication initiated in BU for 15 s and then the BU replaced with ³H-thymine. Samples were taken at 10 s intervals and the rate of incorporation of the ³H-thymine determined. As can be seen (Fig. 4) the thymine is incorporated linearly for at least 8 min after a lag of no more than 10 s indicating that it is not competing for incorporation with a large internal pool of BU. We therefore conclude that the reduction in molecular weight caused by irradiation of the extracted DNA fragments is not a result of their being composed, to a large extent, of bromouracil.

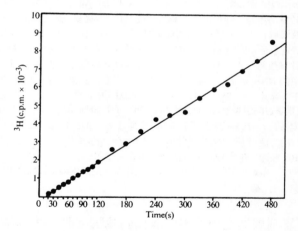

Fig. 4. Thymine incorporation after initiation of replication in BU. Cells were synchronized, labelled with BU and resuspended in ³H-thymine as described in the legend to Fig. 2. Samples are taken every 10 s for 2 min and then every 30 s for another 6 min into ice cold 7% TCA. TCA precipitates are collected on "Millipore" filters and counted as described above.

Rolling Circle Model Excluded

Our experiments demonstrate that when cells initiate replication in BU and are subsequently transferred to a medium containing thymine, the BU behaves as if it were contained in the middle of a DNA fragment. As this fragment does not contain any DNA synthesized before the addition of the BU, the BU must be flanked on both sides by ³H-thymine-containing DNA made after it had been incorporated. This result is consistent only with bidirectional DNA replication of the sort described in Fig. 1*B*, in which each daughter strand elongates in both directions from the origin of replication.

还有一个造成判断失误的原因可能是：在 BU 被培养基中的 [3]H– 胸腺嘧啶取代之后，它仍能在一段时间内继续掺入到 DNA 中。如果 BU 与胸腺嘧啶在合成中仅仅是竞争关系，那么结果将是：包含这两种可能碱基的 DNA 链在照射下会产生许多小碎片而不是恰好等于最初片段一半大小的碎片（图 2）。然而，如果 BU 继续被掺入一定的时间以排除胸腺嘧啶，并且如果复制是单向的，那么从一端去除大量的 BU 部分就有可能产生大小减半的碎片。这会使我们将单向复制误解为双向复制。

为了排除这种可能性，如上文所述采用起始同步化处理，在 BU 中启动复制 15 秒后即用 [3]H– 胸腺嘧啶取代 BU。每隔 10 秒取一次样，并由此计算 [3]H– 胸腺嘧啶的掺入率。可以看出（图 4）：胸腺嘧啶在滞后不超过 10 秒后一直保持线性掺入，时间长达 8 分钟以上，这说明它与某个大的内部 BU 代谢池之间不存在竞争关系。因此，我们可以得出如下结论：由照射提取出的 DNA 片段所产生的分子量下降并不是因为它们含有大量的溴尿嘧啶。

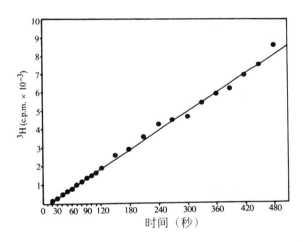

图 4. 在 BU 中启动复制后胸腺嘧啶的掺入情况。按照图 2 注的描述对细胞进行同步化、BU 标记并使其重悬于 [3]H– 胸腺嘧啶中。在开始的 2 分钟内，每 10 秒取样一次；随后的 6 分钟即改成每 30 秒取样一次。样品被放入冷的 7% TCA 中。用"密理博"滤膜收集 TCA 的沉淀物，并按照前述方法进行计数。

排除滚环模型

我们的实验证明：如果细胞在 BU 中启动复制，然后再被转移到含胸腺嘧啶的培养基中，那么 BU 的掺入位置就很像是在一个 DNA 片段的中间。因为这个片段并不包含加入 BU 前合成的 DNA，所以 BU 的两侧一定是在它被掺入之后形成的含 [3]H– 胸腺嘧啶的 DNA。这一结果只能与图 1B 中所描述的双向复制方式相吻合，其中每个子链均从复制起始点开始向两个方向延伸。

The absence of any linkage between parental and daughter DNA excludes rolling circle and related mechanisms, either uni- or bidirectional, from a role in the vegetative replication of the *E. coli* chromosome.

We thank Miss Mora McCallum for instruction in centrifugation techniques and for the gift of ^{32}P mouse satellite DNA, Professor J. M. Mitchison and Dr. W. H. Wain for advice on uptake experiments. Professor W. Hayes, Drs. J. Gross and J. Scaife for help with revision of the manuscript, and Dr. W. D. Donachie for helpful discussion and encouragement.

(**240**, 536-539; 1972)

W. G. McKenna and Millicent Masters: MRC Molecular Genetics Unit, Department of Molecular Biology, University of Edinburgh, Mayfield Road, Edinburgh 9.

Received August 14; revised October 12, 1972.

References:

1. Cairns, J., *J. Mol. Biol.*, **6**, 208 (1963).

2. Meselson, M., and Stahl, F. W., *Proc. US Nat. Acad. Sci.*, **44**, 671 (1958).

3. Lark, K. G., Repko, T., and Hoffman, E. J., *Biochim. Biophys. Acta*, **76**, 9 (1963).

4. Caro, L. C., and Berg, C. M., *J. Mol. Biol.*, **45**, 325 (1969).

5. Berg, C. M., and Caro, L. C., *J. Mol. Biol.*, **29**, 419 (1967).

6. Donachie, W. D., and Masters, M., *Genet. Res.*, **8**, 119 (1966).

7. Donachie, W. D., and Masters, M., in *The Cell Cycle: Gene-Enzyme Interactions* (edit. by Padilla, Whitson and Cameron), 37 (Academic Press, New York and London, 1969).

8. Masters, M., *Proc. US Nat. Acad. Sci.*, **65**, 601 (1970).

9. Helmstetter, C., *J. Bacteriol.*, **95**, 1634 (1968).

10. Pato, M. L., and Glaser, D., *Proc. US Nat. Acad. Sci.*, **60**, 1268 (1968).

11. Abe, M., and Tomizawa, J., *Proc. US Nat. Acad. Sci.*, **58**, 1911 (1967).

12. Cerdá-Olmedo, E., Hanawalt, P. C., and Guerola, N., *J. Mol. Biol.*, **33**, 705 (1968).

13. Wolf, B., Newman, A., and Glaser, D., *J. Mol. Biol.*, **32**, 611 (1968).

14. Ward, C. B., and Glaser, D. A., *Proc. US Nat. Acad. Sci.*, **62**, 881 (1969).

15. Yahara, I., *J. Mol. Biol.*, **57**, 373 (1971).

16. Masters, M., and Broda, P., *Nature New Biology*, **232**, 137 (1971).

17. Bird, R. E., Louarn, J., Martuscelli, J., and Caro, L. G., *J. Mol. Biol.*, **70**, 549 (1972).

18. Hohlfeld, R., and Vielmetter, W. (in the press).

19. Prescott, D. M., and Kuempel, P. L., *Proc. US Nat. Acad. Sci.*, **69**, 2842 (1972).

20. Weintraub, H., *Nature New Biology*, **236**, 195 (1972).

21. Hotz, G., and Wolser, R., *Photochem. Photobiol.*, **12**, 207 (1970).

22. Studier, F. W., *J. Mol. Biol.*, **11**, 373 (1965).

23. Gilbert, W., and Dressler, D., *Cold Spring Harbor Symp. Quant. Biol.*, **33**, 473 (1968).

24. Watson, J. D., in *Molecular Biology of the Gene*, 291 (W. A. Benjamin, Inc., New York, 1970).

25. Yoshikawa, H., *Proc. US Nat. Acad. Sci.*, **58**, 312 (1967).

26. Stein, G. H., and Hanawalt, P. C., *J. Mol. Biol.*, **64**, 393 (1972).

27. Pettijohn, D. E., and Hanawalt, P. C., *J. Mol. Biol.*, **8**, 170 (1964).

28. Oishi, M., *Proc. US Nat. Acad. Sci.*, **60**, 329 (1968).

29. Thomas, jun., C. A., Berns, K., and Kelly, jun., T. J., in *Procedures in Nucleic Acid Research* (edit. by Cantoni and Davies), 535 (Harper and Row, New York, 1966).

因为亲代 DNA 与子代 DNA 之间不存在任何连接，所以滚环以及与滚环相关的其他机制，不管是单向复制还是双向复制，都不能用于解释大肠杆菌染色体的无性复制。

感谢莫拉·麦卡勒姆小姐在离心技术方面为我们提供指导并将 ^{32}P 标记的小鼠卫星 DNA 赠送给我们，感谢米奇森教授及韦恩博士对摄取实验提出了一些建议。感谢海斯教授、格罗斯博士和斯凯夫博士帮助我们修订手稿，感谢多纳基博士和我们进行了有益的讨论而且还鼓励我们。

（董培智 翻译；孙军 审稿）

Appendix: Index by Subject
附录：学科分类目录

Physics
物理学

Chemistry
化学

Biology
生物学

Astronomy
天文学

Geoscience
地球科学